S0-FQZ-886

Oravas

Lectures on the History of Technology and Engineering I

Gunhard Æ. Oravas

Lectures on the History of Technology and Engineering

Volume I

2004
Georg Olms Verlag
Hildesheim · Zürich · New York

The publication of this work has been made possible
by a subvention from the Department of Civil Engineering
of McMaster University, Hamilton, Ontario, Canada.

Bibliografische Information Der Deutschen Bibliothek

Die Deutsche Bibliothek verzeichnet diese Publikation
in der Deutschen Nationalbibliografie; detaillierte bibliografische Daten
sind im Internet über *http://dnb.ddb.de* abrufbar.

Bibliographic information published by Die Deutsche Bibliothek

Die Deutsche Bibliothek lists this publication in the
Deutsche Nationalbibliografie; detailed bibliographic data
are available in the Internet at *http://dnb.ddb.de*.

ISO 9706

www.olms.de

Printed in Germany
Gedruckt auf säurefreiem und alterungsbeständigem Papier
Herstellung: WS Druck Werner Schaubruch, Bodenheim
ISBN 3-487-11744-4

Dedicated to the memory of
Virve Oravas

Table of Contents

PREFACE AND ACKNOWLEDGEMENTS

This panoramic overview of the history of technology and engineering began in the mid-1930's after the author purchased in an antiquarian bookstore the pioneering historical treatise of Curt Merckel (1858-1921), < The Engineering Technics in Antiquity > (***Die Ingenieurtechnik im Altertum***), Berlin, 1899, primarily for the purpose of refining his knowledge of German technical language. Merckel's book had an overwhelming influence on the author and inspired him as a Gymnasium student to search for other similar historical works on technological topics which were still available in such bookstores at the time. Soon the author discovered < History of Technology since the Middle of Eighteenth Century > (***Geschichte der Technologie seit der Mitte des achtzehnten Jahrhunderts***) of Karl Karmarsch (1803-1879) published in Munich in 1872, and a selection of historically annotated works on mechanics, technology and engineering by Dr. Moritz Christian Rühlmann (1811-1896) beginning with his pioneering treatise, < Lectures on History of Technical Mechanics and Theoretical Study of Machinery. First Part: Technical Mechanics > (***Vorträge über Geschichte der Technischen Mechanik und Theoretische Maschinenlehre. Erster Theil: Technische Mechanik***), Leipzig, 1885. By that time the author had become quite 'addicted' to the study of history of technology and engineering for its own sake as a cultural hobby to such an extent, that it had a tendency to assume precedence even over his formal school work. Moreover, he had become firmly convinced that all the studies of topics which are of keen personal interest have to be self-directed. In order to study the history of technical mechanics of Rühlmann it soon became manifest to the author that any competent student of Rühlmann's excellent historically annotated books on mechanics and technology had to master of the history of infinitesimal analysis besides geometry and algebra, a necessity which motivated the author to devote himself to an intensive autodidactic study of the history of the pertinent mathematical disciplines. Among a number of available books on the history of mathematics in English and in German language, the author found several works of Heinrich Wieleitner (1874-1931), particularly his lucid treatise in two volumes,<The Birth of Modern Mathematics, Historical and Fundamental>(***Die Geburt der Modernen Mathematik, Historisches und Grundsätzliches***), Karlsruhe, 1924/1925, most appropriate for his self-directed study because these 2 volumes significantly facilitated author's independent enquiry into the history of mathematics and its fundamentals, thereby making his critical mastery of the pertinent mathematical knowledge quite expeditious and convenient. The author found the fundamental contributions on the early history of mechanics based on original sources in the works of Emil Wohlwill (1835-1912),one of the leading 19th century connoisseurs of the early history of mechanics whose pathbreaking studies have been strangely neglected by Galileo scholars of the 20th century, of considerable help for his further study of mechanics. Then he had the good fortune to discover the admirable treatises of Pierre-Marie-Maurice Duhem (1861-1916): <The Evolution of Mechanics> (***L'evolution de la méqanique***), Paris, 1905 [the first English language translation of which the author as editor-in-chief of Sijthoff & Noordhoff was privileged to publish in 1980], and < The Origins of Statics > (***Origines de la statique***) in two volumes, Paris, 1905/1906, on the development of mechanics and on the history of mediæval science which profoundly impressed the author and notably influenced the course of his studies. This major pathbreaking work, a historical masterpiece written by the ingenious French theoretical physicist Pierre Duhem which was responsible for launching the long-neglected study of the history of mediæval science, was published by Kluwer Academic Publishers in its first English language translation only in 1991!

The author next undertook an exhaustive study of the history of technology as presented in a long series of remarkable works on various technical topics by Franz Maria Feldhaus (1874-1959), and in the book of Hermann Diels (1848-1922), < Ancient Technics, Seven Lectures > (***Antike Technik, Sieben Vorträge***), Leipzig, 1920. After having attained a considerable background knowledge of adequate sophistication in mechanics, technology and engineering, author felt sufficiently confident to undertake not only a critical study of all the pertinent literature about the history of mechanics, technology and engineering, but also a critical examination of available original sources which were of particular personal interest to him. It came as a considerable surprise to the author that in some instances he had reasons to differ from the opinions presented in such general historical works particularly after the author had an opportunity to examine the original sources. In the course of more than fifty years of critical surveying of the pertinent historical literature the author was able to accumulate what seemed to him a great store of knowledge for which he owes an indispensable intellectual debt to all the writers on the history of technology, engineering, mechanics and mathematics even when the author occasionally thought that he had good reasons to disagree to a certain extent with some of their conclusions however minor since their investigations were still of considerable benefit to the author's own critical perspective and appreciation of the subject. Insofar as there is a large number of technical subjects which were incorporated into the author's study of the history of technology and engineering, he had to approach each topic with the critical frame of mind of an avid student of the subject who is willing to learn from any well-informed writer without surrendering his critical acumen with respect to professional judgements of any writer since such judgements, whether made by a recognised expert or a competent professional, are customarily scarcely more than personal opinions depending to some extent upon the scientific taste and cultural preference of the writer.

In ancient technology and engineering the author is substantially indebted to archaeologists Robert Koldewey, William Mathew Flinders Petrie, Arthur John Evans, Charles Leonard Woolley, and Thorkild Jacobsen whose archaeological works the author had the privilege to examine over a period of many decades. The author also recognises that he reaped essential scholarly benefits from his studies of the works of Samuel Smiles, Thomas Heath, Edmund Hoppe, Wilhelm Schmidt, Roberto Marcolongo, Aurel Stodola, Antonio Favaro, Arturo Ucceli, Paul Stäckel, Hans Schimank, Albert Neuburger, Lynn Thorndike, Aage G. Drachmann, Maurice Daumas, Jean Gimpel, Bertrand Gille, William B. Parsons, Erwin Panofsky, Alexander P. Gest, Robert J. Forbes, Eduard J. Dijksterhuis, Edmund Whittaker, Sigvard Strandh, Anneliese Maier, Alistair C. Crombie, Marshall Clagett, William A. Wallace, George Sarton, David E. Smith, Joachim O. Fleckenstein, Fritz Stüssi, Charles H. Gibbs-Smith, Terry S. Reynolds, L. Sprague de Camp, Lionel Thomas C. Rolt, Derek J. De Solla Price, and many others too numerous to mention.

The author is profoundly grateful for the personal help given to him over many decades on subjects ranging across the wide spectrum of topics, even on ***corpus imaginum***, by Max Born, Dirk J. Struik, Arpad Nadai, Richard Southwell, James Kip Finch, Bern Diebner, Friedrich Klemm, Gerald Holton, Ivor B. Hart, Richard S. Kirby, Lynne White Jr., Gustavo Colonnetti, Mario Bunge, Eduardo Torroja, Hans Straub, Ludwig Föppl, Hermann J. Oberth, Alfred Lotze, Edwin B.Wilson, George Polya, Joseph E. Hofmann, Louis M. Milne-Thomson, Cornelius Lanczos, Richard Courant, Kurt O. Friedrichs, Herman H. Goldstine, Pierre Gauja, Charles S. Whitney, and Rudolf Friedrich. Author feels particularly indebted for the most magnanimous and invaluable help given to him by the late Professor Max Born (1882-1970),about the life and works of all the famous and unforgettable scientists and mathematicians, including himself, who were active at the University of Göttingen before and after the First World War.

Above all else, the author owes an enormous intellectual debt to the late Professor Clifford Ambrose Truesdell (1919-1999), a gifted linguist and in a true sense of the word a self-educated connoisseur of the mathematical and conceptual foundations of mechanics, continuum mechanics and thermodynamics, who since 1959 most generously helped the author with his strikingly unique insights, profound learning and critical knowledge drawn from his own original historical researches abounding with new discoveries, particularly in the history of theoretical mechanics of the 18th century of which he was a connoisseur beyond comparison very much like Duhem had been the unrivalled connoisseur of the mediæval science. Although both Duhem and Truesdell were by far the best scientifically qualified historians of science, they regarded themselves as 'amateur' rather than professional historians because they were primarily creative theoretical scientists and mathematicians, which is the very reason why their historical insights into the development of science were so penetrating, original and invaluable. In general, the author has learnt more about the foundations of mechanics and applied mathematics from Dr.Truesdell, Josiah Willard Gibbs (1839-1903), and Duhem than from anybody else. Duhem admired Gibbs' ingenious and profound insight into science, and worked diligently from 1901 to 1906 in his effort to relate rational thermodynamics to Gibbs' rational theory of thermostatics. Duhem attempted to develop rational thermodynamics of continua such as viscous fluids and elastic solids by taking the deformable body as the typical thermodynamic system which is subject to heat conduction and internal friction, because the physical processes such bodies undergo are generally irreversible.

Gibbs, an unsalaried honorary professor of mathematical physics at Yale University who never taught undergraduates, told the doctoral student and his mathematical collaborator Edwin Bidwell Wilson (1879-1964) that during all the years of his teaching [from 1871 to 1903] among the less than one hundred students who had taken Gibbs' advanced graduate courses only about half a dozen students including Wilson had sufficient knowledge in mathematics and physics to follow Gibbs' lectures with complete competence. Professor Wilson gave the author his invaluable personal impressions of Gibbs as a self-made physicist and mathematician. Gibbs, a man of genius whom his contemporary prominent Scottish physicist William Thomson (1824-1907) [later known as Lord Kelvin] called publicly the greatest man of science of his generation, was the American counterpart to his ingenious contemporary Scottish physicist James Clerk Maxwell (1831-1879)who was the first important scientist to recognise the genius of Gibbs and appreciate Gibbs' peerless researches. Maxwell, the German mathematician and physicist Hermann Ludwig Ferdinand von Helmholtz (1821-1894), and Gibbs were the foremost mathematical physicists of the 19^{th}century. Gibbs, who studied the phenomenon of 'change' theoretically, had to find the fundamental theoretical measure in the condition of a substance, which would predict whether or not, a chemical or physical change of state would take place in the substance. He wrote several profoundly original and pathbreaking works in theoretical physics such as his magnificent masterpiece on the phenomenological theory of the equilibrium of heterogeneous substances in which he established true minimal principles for thermostatic equilibrium of fluids, fluid mixtures, and elastic solids. Gibbs' memoir on heterogeneous systems in physics created the pure statics of the effects of temperature and heat, the so-called 'thermostatics' [a modern terminology first used in the 1960's] although Gibbs himself called it 'thermodynamics', a seminal theory which not only synthetises many different disciplines in physics and chemistry with meticulous logic and high standard of deductive mathematical rigour, but also ranks as a far-reaching, comprehensive and an all-inclusive scientific achievement of the first order.

Gibbs' electrochemical theory, chemical potential and thermochemical equilibrium in thermostatics explained the catalytic action and the electrolytic processes which were of great practical importance to the burgeoning electrochemical industry. Gibbs' revolutionary Phase Rule established the conditions which had to hold for a number of physicochemical compounds to exist together in equilibrium in their different phases: solid, liquid or gaseous. It was soon recognised to be the most important single equation since Newton's equation of universal gravitation. His theory of thermostatic equilibrium of heterogeneous substances rationalised many aspects of physics and chemistry, and created the theoretical foundation of physical chemistry as a new branch of science. Gibbs' ingenious Phase Rule occupying only 4 pages in his monograph was responsible, in the next 50 years, for more than 11,000 pages of scientific investigations devoted to the Phase Rule and its application to mineralogy, mining of salt, petrology, metallurgy, physiology, and virtually every other field of science. Gibbs' work explained the action of volcanoes, electrolytic action of storage batteries, physiological processes in blood, photosynthesis and chemical affinity. Modern methods of industrial chemistry are essentially based upon Gibbs' work. It provided a scientific guide to the metallurgical production of new alloys and to the effects of heat treatment on the properties of metals. It made possible the scientific interpretation of the intricate phenomena of solid solutions, clarified the scientific constitution of Portland cement as well as standardised its method of industrial production. In general, the Phase Rule has been of inestimable value in many manufacturing processes of heavy industry such as the manufacture of fertilisers, petroleum fuels, tungsten filaments, cloth, paper and thousands of other articles. Even Gibbs himself would have been utterly amazed about the immense scope of practical applications of his remarkable physical theories, and the numerous rediscoveries of scientific results after his death which were already explicitly or implicitly present in his unprecedented theoretical researches. In half a century after his death the Nobel prize was awarded 4 times for work based directly on some aspect of Gibbs' results. His is the one scientific work of the 19th century which accommodated quite naturally the quantum hypothesis, and still stands without any fundamental modification.

In Gibbs' peerless masterpiece of rational thermostatics [rather than thermodynamics], the variational criteria of equilibrium [including its stabilities and instabilities] which almost exclusively refer to virtual changes rather than thermodynamic processes, are imposed for the thermostatic equilibrium of heterogeneous substantive systems. In 1901,Gibbs published another of his peerless masterpieces, < The Elementary Principles in Statistical Mechanics developed with Especial Reference to the Rational Foundation of Thermodynamics >, a work of extraordinary abstraction that was also far in advance of his contemporaries like his monograph on the thermostatic equilibrium of heterogeneous mixtures. He redefined his thermostatics from a new point of view in which he treated thermal behaviour on a statistical basis. Gibbs sought to find a rational foundation for thermodynamics in his statistical treatment of the motions of a system of point-masses which made classical mechanics into statistical mechanics, a work distinguished with a very high standard of deductive rigour.

Since author's opinions of Gibbs' contribution in rational thermodynamics [properly speaking, thermostatics] to a certain extent differed from some opinions of other writers, it left the author occasionally somewhat perplexed.

Gibbs, moreover, wrote impressive memoirs in pure and applied mathematics such as his method of presenting geometric algebra as a system of vectorial algebra, particularly his geometrically based direct vectorial method of tensor [Gibbs called it polyadic] analysis in the multilinear algebra and analysis which is directly apprehensible by visual examination because of the geometrical structure of the tensor as a multidirected quantity in directed space, and has proven to be a powerful mathematical method in modern continuum mechanics that can be readily learnt and mastered by engineers and physicists. Author taught Gibbs' direct method of tensor analysis in a modified form to suit the modern trend in continuum mechanics to doctoral students in engineering and physics for many years, and his admiration of Gibbs as a prototypical autodidact in his unique geometrically and visually motivated methods of theoretical physics and mathematics was almost boundless. Professor Truesdell, as the author discovered to his great satisfaction, had a very high opinion of Gibbs as a brilliant mathematical physicist with habitually clear and profound insight into science, and he once told the author: "Gibbs suitably generalised is supreme everywhere," which not only gratified the author but also vindicated his own critical appreciation of theoretical mechanics and applied mathematics. Only twice in the author's long scholarly intercourse with Professor Truesdell was the author able to render some modest help to him concerning the origin of the Moment of Momentum Principle and the origin of a particular variational method of derivation of the complete set of spatial compatibility conditions in elasticity by means of stresses, but despite the rather minor nature of this help it meant a great deal to the author. Author always thought of himself as an engineer 'inspired' by the exceptional scholarly spirit of Dr.Truesdell, an intellectual giant with an immense scope of profound learning who was, moreover, a proficient linguist in ancient as well as in modern languages, and one of the best writers of incisive American vernacular reminiscent of the great master of American idiom, Henry Louis Mencken (1880-1956).

Author received indispensable assistance from many libraries, museums, institutes and archives over many decades which was essential to his historical research in technology, engineering, science and mathematics: Deutsches Museum in Munich, Germany; Niedersächsische Staats- und Universitätsbibliothek Göttingen in Göttingen, Germany; Daimler-Benz Aerospace in Munich, Germany; Institution of Civil Engineers in London, England; Institution of Mechanical Engineers in London, England; Institution of Electrical Engineers in London, England; Science Museum in South Kensington, England; Center for Technology and Society, University of Trondheim in Trondheim, Norway; Ernst Heinkel Archives in Stuttgart, Germany; MTU Motoren- und Turbinen Union in Munich, Germany; Deutsche Forschungsanstalt für Luft- und Raumfahrt, Zentralbibliothek in Göttingen, Germany; Bibliothek, Technische Hochschule Dresden [now Technische Universität Dresden] in Dresden, Germany; The Royal Society in London, England; Archives of King's College, University of London in London, England; Gonville and Caius College in Cambridge, England; Institute of Physics in London, England; Lund University Library in Lund, Sweden; Kungliga Tekniska Högskolans Bibliothek in Stockholm, Sweden; Tekniska Museet in Stockholm, Sweden; Library, University of Tartu [Dorpat] in Tartu, Estonia; Institut de France, Académie des Sciences in Paris, France; Bibliotheca Nazionale Centrale Vittorio Emanuele II in Rome, Italy; Università degli Studi in Padova, Italy; Butler Library at Columbia University in the City of New York, U.S.A.; Library of Technological University in Copenhagen, Denmark; Universitetsbibliothek in Oslo, Norway; Library of Swiss Federal Institute of Technology in Zurich, Switzerland; Österreichische Nationalbibliothek in Vienna, Austria; Historical Collection at the University of Amsterdam in Amsterdam,The Netherlands; Philips International B.V. in Eindhoven, The Netherlands; Institut de Mécanique, Université de Liège in Liège, Belgium; Bell Telephone Laboratories in Schenectady, N.Y.,U.S.A.; Center for the History of Electrical Engineering at Rudgers University in New Brunswick, N.J., U.S.A.; Cornell University Library in Ithaca, N.Y., U.S.A.; Archive, Institute of Electrical and Electronics Engineers, in New York City, N.Y., U.S.A.; A.T.&T. Archives, in Warren, N.J., U.S.A.; Bibliothèque Nationale et Universitaire de Strasbourg, France; Section Sciences, Université Louis Pasteur in Strasbourg, France; and Osaka University Library in Osaka, Japan.

These lectures were not restricted to be solely introductory in exposition for the sake of undergraduate students as the discussions of some topics in several Chapters were carried to a higher intellectual level so that graduate and doctoral students could also find something in the lectures that may appeal to their particular intellectual taste. Each Chapter of these lectures was written relatively independent of the other Chapters so that they could be studied quite independently of other Chapters in the book, which was the general intention of the author when he began to write this history. Topics on which the author had done more extensive historical research of his own such as the Chapters on Ancient Greece, Italian Engineering, Mediæval Technology, Baroque Technology, Age of French Engineering, Birth of Electrical Sciences, Turbines as Heat Engines, Electronics in Space, and Electric and Electronic Transmission of Vision were composed to touch a more advanced intellectual level, but an undergraduate student still has the option of stopping short before reaching the higher level without affecting his general appreciation of the topic. Most college educated readers whose scholastic background includes the introductory physics course can study the lectures without having any particular difficulty in obtaining an overview of the subject matter under discussion.

Soon after the author began to teach history of technology and engineering to university students he was surprised to discover that many of his students were deplorably ill-informed, or even blissfully ignorant, of the intellectual and scientific legacy of ancient Greeks to the Western civilisation since ancient Greece is the very cradle of Western science and scientific technology. For this reason the author was motivated to provide the Chapters on technology and engineering in antiquity with the historical background of the particular ancient people. Since he further discovered that instruction of the mediæval history in general, and mediæval contributions to science, technology and engineering in particular, was quite inadequate in high schools, the author wrote this Chapter according to his own critical appreciation of the mediæval contributions to science, technology and engineering. For this reason the Chapters on the fundamental revolutionary intellectual legacy of the ancient Greeks and on the revolutionary mediæval technology and theoretical mechanics are the most extensive accounts in this book. For the sake of contextual balance, the author also decided to provide some pertinent historical background to other topics of the lectures in which he was substantially assisted by his wife.

Many different abridged versions of these lectures were taught by the author over the past decades. Author is much indebted to his daughter, Dr. Monica Oravas for collaborating in the final version of the manuscript and preparing the Index. Author is also indebted to his late wife Virve Oravas, a connoisseur of the history of mediæval age, Renaissance and 19th century, for her indispensable collaboration in editing and polishing the historical background accounts of these particular periods. Author is very grateful to his friend and colleague Dr. Stan Pietruszczak for the latter's most generous assistance, advice and devoted support over many years that substantially contributed to the successful completion of this manuscript. Author has also benefited from the dedicated efforts of his colleague Dr. Robert Drysdale which made the publication of author's manuscript feasible. Moreover, the author wishes to express his admiration for Mrs. Janet Nurnberg who most heroically prepared the 'almost countless' emendated, altered and abridged versions of his lectures over the span of many years. Finally, the author had the good fortune to receive the resolute support for the publication of his manuscript in the distinguished series: ***Geschichte der Naturwissenschaften, Mathematik und Technik*** (*History of Natural Sciences, Mathematics and Technics*) of the Georg Olms Verlag from Dr. Peter Guyot, Lektorat of Georg Olms Verlag, as well as his valuable editorial advice and expert formatting of the manuscript for publication. Author is particularly beholden to Dr. Georg Olms for his steadfast interest and personal involvement in promoting the publication of author's manuscript by the Georg Olms Verlag.

The author assumes personal responsibility for any mistakes found in this book which contains a massive amount of information collected over a very long period of time, therefore, making it unlikely that it is entirely free of errors.

Gunhard Æ. Oravas
Hamilton, Ontario, Canada

Prolegomenon

Engineering as a profession is difficult to define in an inclusive way. The prominent English engineer, Thomas Tredgold (1788-1829), defined engineering as "... the art of utilising the forces of nature for the use and convenience of man." Many other definitions of engineering have been given such as: "Engineering is the method of systematic modification of the physical environment for human ends." Engineering has always been limited by nature since material changes are always narrowly confined by what are popularly called 'natural laws'. It is within such limits that men over countless centuries have spent their efforts to create machines and instruments in order to reduce or even eliminate their manual labour. The primary test of any technology is its efficacy to process available materials into amenities of life. Then the next question which can be posed is: Who is an engineer ? The most demanding qualifications for the engineer were stated by the famous Roman engineer, Marcus Vitruvius Pollio, about 30 B.C.. In ancient Rome an engineer was called ***architectus*** [chief technician]. Vitruvius gave the following qualifications that are essential to an ***architectus***:

"The ***architectus*** should be equipped with knowledge of many branches of study and varied kinds of learning, for it is by his judgement that all work done by the other arts is put to test. This knowledge is the child of practice and theory. Practice is the continuous and regular exercise of employment where manual work is done with any necessary material according to the design of a drawing. Theory, on the other hand, is the ability to demonstrate and explain the productions of dexterity on the principles of proportion.

It follows, therefore, that ***architecti*** who have aimed at acquiring manual skill without scholarship have never been able to reach a position of authority to correspond to their pains, whilst those who relied only upon theories and scholarship were obviously hunting the shadow, not the substance. But those who have a thorough knowledge of both, like men armed at all points, have attained their objective sooner and carried authority with them.

In all matters, but particularly in engineering, there are these two points: the thing signified, and that which gives it its significance. That which is signified is the subject of which we may be speaking; and that which gives significance is a demonstration on scientific principles. It appears, then, that one who professes himself an ***architectus*** should be well versed in both directions. He ought, therefore, to be both naturally gifted and amenable to instruction. Neither natural ability without instruction nor instruction without natural ability can make the perfect professional.

Let him be educated, skilful with the pencil, instructed in geometry, know much history, have followed the philosophers with attention, understand music, have some knowledge of medicine, know the opinions of the jurists, and be acquainted with astronomy and the theory of the heavens.

The reasons for all this are as follows:

"An ***architectus*** ought to be an educated man so as to leave a more lasting impression in his treatises. Secondly, he must have a knowledge of drawing so that he can readily make sketches to show the appearance of the work which he proposes. Geometry, also, is of much assistance in engineering, and in particular it teaches us the use of the ruler and compass, by which we acquire special readiness in making plans for buildings in their grounds, and rightly apply the square, the level, and the plummet. By means of optics, again, the light in buildings can be drawn from fixed quarters of the sky. It is true that it is by means of arithmetic that the total cost of building is calculated and measures are computed, but difficult questions involving symmetry are solved by means of geometrical theories and methods. A wide knowledge of history is requisite because, among the ornamental parts of the design work of an ***architectus***, there are many underlying ideas the employment of which he should be able to explain to enquirers.

As for philosophy, it makes an ***architectus*** highminded and not self-assuming, but rather renders him courteous, just, and honest without avariciousness. This is very important, for no work can be rightly done without honesty and incorruptibility. Let him not be grasping nor have his mind preoccupied with the idea of receiving perquisites, but let him with dignity keep up his position by cherishing a good reputation. These are among the precepts of philosophy. Furthermore, philosophy treats of physics where a more careful knowledge is required because the problems which come under this are numerous and of very different kinds; as, for example, in the case of the conduction of water. For at intake and at curves, and at places where it is raised to a level, currents of air naturally form in one way or another; and nobody who has not learnt the fundamental principles of physics from philosophy will be able to provide against the damage which they do. So the reader of Ktesibios or Archimedes and the other writers of treatises of the same class will not be able to appreciate them unless he has been trained in these subjects by the philosophers.

Music, also, the ***architectus*** ought to understand so that he may have knowledge of the canonical and the mathematical theory, and besides be able to tune ***ballistae***, ***catapultae***, and ***scorpiones*** [military missile-throwing machines operating by tensioned elastic skeins] to the proper key. For to the right and left in the beams are the holes in the frames through which the strings of twisted sinew are stretched by means of windlasses and bars, and these strings must not be clamped and made fast until they give the same correct note to the ear of the skilled workman. For the arms thrust through those stretched strings must, on being released, strike their blow together at the same moment; but if they are not in unison, they will prevent the course of projectiles from being straight.

The ***architectus*** should also have a knowledge of the study of medicine on account of the question of climates, air, the healthiness and unhealthiness of sites, and the use of different waters. And as for principles of law, he should know those which are necessary in the case of buildings having party walls, with regards to water dripping from the eaves, and also laws about drains, windows, and water supply. And other things of this sort should be known to ***architectus***, so that, before they begin upon buildings, they may be careful not to leave disputed points for the householders to settle after the works are finished, and so that in drawing up contracts the interests of both the employer and the contractor may be wisely safeguarded. For if a contract is skilfully drawn, each party may obtain a release from the other party without disadvantage. From astronomy we find the east, the west, the south, and the north, as well as the theory of the heavens, the equinox, the solstice, and the course of stars. If one has no knowledge of these matters, he will not be able to have any comprehension of the theory of Sundials [for the measurement of time].

Consequently, since this study is so vast in extent, embellished and enriched as it is with many different kinds of learning, I think that men have no right to profess themselves ***architectus*** hastily, without having climbed from boyhood the steps of these studies and thus, nursed by the knowledge of many arts and sciences, having reached the heights of the holy ground of engineering.

But perhaps to the inexperienced it will seem a marvel that human nature can comprehend such a great number of studies and keep them in the memory. Still, the observation that all studies have a common bond of union and intercourse with one another, will lead to the belief that this can easily be realised. For a liberal education forms, as it were, a single body made up of these disciplines. Those, therefore, who from tender years receive instruction in the various forms of learning, recognise the same stamp on all the arts, and in intercourse between all studies, and so they more readily comprehend them all. This is what led one of the ancient ***architecti***, Pytheos, the celebrated builder of the temple Minerva at Priene, to say in his Commentaries that an ***architectus*** ought to be able to accomplish much more in all the arts and sciences than the men who, by their own particular kinds of work [specialisation] and practice of it, have brought each a single subject to the highest perfection. But this is in point of fact not realised.

For an ***architectus*** ought not to be, and cannot be such a philologian as was Aristarchos, though not illiterate; nor a musician like Aristoxenos, though not absolutely ignorant of music; nor a painter like Apelles, though not unskilled in drawing; nor a sculptor such as Myron or Polykleitos, though not unacquainted with the plastic arts; nor again a physician like Hippokrates, though not ignorant of medicine; nor in other sciences need he excel in each, though he should not be unskilled in them. For, in the midst of all this great variety of subjects, an individual cannot attain to perfection in each, because it is scarcely in his power to take in and comprehend the general theories of them.

Still it is not ***architecti*** alone that cannot in all matters reach perfection, but even men who individually practice specialties in the arts do not all attain to the highest point of merit. Therefore, if among artists working each in a single field not all, but only a few in the entire generation acquire fame, and that with difficulty, how can an ***architectus***, who has to be skilful in many arts, accomplish not merely the feat – in itself a great marvel – of being deficient in none of them, but also that of surpassing all those artists who have devoted themselves with unremitting industry to single fields?

It appears, then, that Pytheos made a mistake by not observing that the arts are each composed of two things, the actual work and the theory of it. One of these, the doing of the work, is proper to men trained in the individual subject, whilst the other, the theory, is common to all scholars ... But the actual undertaking of works which are brought to perfection by the hand and its manipulation is the function of those who have been especially trained to deal with a single art. It appears, therefore, that he [***architectus***] has done enough and to spare who in each subject possesses a fairly good knowledge of those parts, with their principles, which are indispensable for engineering, so that if he is required to pass judgement and to express approval in the case of those things or arts, he may not be found wanting. As for men upon whom nature has bestowed so much ingenuity, acuteness, and memory that they are able to have a thorough knowledge of geometry, astronomy, music, and the other arts, they go beyond the functions of ***architecti*** and become pure ***mathematikoi*** [men of science], ... Such men, however, are rarely found, but there have been such at times; for example, Aristarchos of Samos, Philolaos and Archytas of Taras, Apollonios of Perge, Eratosthenes of Kyrene, and among the Syracusans Archimedes and Skopinas, who through mathematics and natural philosophy discovered, expounded, and left for posterity many things in connexion with mechanics and with Sundials."

Vitruvius, in his discussion of what an engineer ought to be, expresses the ancient belief that history ought to teach. In this course, an effort is made to teach about the history and philosophy of technology and engineering beginning with Sumerians about 3500 B.C. and ending in modern times. The importance of such knowledge to engineers was quite well expressed by Vitruvius. There is a well-known adage, which states: "Facts speak for themselves." Unfortunately this statement is incorrect: facts (unless definitions are meant by the word 'facts') do not speak for themselves, ideas and theories do, because, as the Latin word ***facere*** (meaning 'to make') implies, the so-called 'facts' are man-made. Therefore 'facts' must be interpreted in terms of 'ideas', since 'ideas' make 'facts' for behind every 'fact' lurks an 'idea' or 'theory'. This is certainly true in history, and, therefore, it is incumbent on any person who studies history to interpret the so-called 'historical facts'. The author of these notes has made every effort to give as precise information as he could on the so-called 'facts', but the interpretations of these 'facts' are entirely his own. Interpretation depends on opinion, and opinions depend upon the ideas that a person believes to be valid.

However, opinions are man-made because ideas are man-made, and since man is neither omniscient nor omnipotent, his opinions may not be the best opinions fitting the facts, or they may even be altogether erroneous. Therefore, it is incumbent on any professional person to be skeptical about opinions; and that includes science, which is nothing more than a particular kind of opinion, experimentally supportable opinion, but nevertheless still an opinion. Opinions of individuals are expressions of their personal culture which are moulded by personal experience and intellect. Therefore, it is important for students to exercise skepticism at all times by not accepting any opinion expressed in this course of lectures, or elsewhere, on their face value. Only if in your opinion it seems reasonable from your present point of view, the opinion should be provisionally accepted, yet it should always be kept in mind that at any time you may have good enough reason to change your mind about it. A person in possession of uncritically acquired learning is indoctrinated. Authentic knowledge is always personal knowledge, that is, critical knowledge which an individual as a person has acquired by means of an intense critical examination which is an entirely personal effort. Indoctrinated knowledge, in the words of an English writer, is a "load of learned lumber ignorantly acquired by a bookful blockhead." Therefore, indoctrinated knowledge which is not critically acquired does not make an engineer into a learned professional as defined by Vitruvius, but rather into a technician in need of a master 'who really knows'. Already an ancient Ionian philosopher and poet Xenophanes of Kolophon (6thcentury B.C.) pointed out in his poetic masterpiece,< About Nature > (***Peri Physeos***), that man's knowledge is really a 'web of guesses', something like the truth, that there is no absolute certainty in knowledge and, therefore, man can only be confident about his opinions, but never 'absolutely certain'; and that man could never know with absolute certainty if he is in possession of the 'absolute truth'.

In judging history, it is absolutely essential that an individual should be able to discern, to discriminate, to classify, to evaluate and to judge. To do all this, and to decide on the merits of any historical achievement requires a definite cultural [that is, moral, ethical, philosophical, and intellectual] point of view. To have a cultural point of view, means to have a cultural bias, something that is almost daily being vilified out of popular ***ignorantia*** as 'chauvinistic prejudice'. Critical judgement of historical events is not possible for any person without a cultural viewpoint, that is, without cultural bias. Moreover, cultural bias is a changeable quality, since neglect to refine one's personal cultural viewpoint should not be a characteristic of a person in a learned profession.

Correct ideas about engineering cannot be obtained if the knowledge of engineering is limited only to the 'gossip of the moment'. Therefore, an engineer ought to be at least knowledgeable about the history of his profession, if not more. Technology, in general, is a historical phenomenon which can be adequately understood only within its particular historical context. An engineer, who meets the Vitruvian requirements for a learned professional, recognises no master but himself, or herself. It is professionally not too unrealistic to expect an engineer to reflect certain qualities of a tragic ancient Greek hero who struggled unrelentingly all throughout his life for personal excellence and, yet, in the end he was predestined to fail and perish, because man is mortal as gods are not. Therefore, the mortal Greek heroes were to be admired for their deeds, but not worshipped as if they were immortal gods. In the same spirit an engineer as a professional person should not revere men, however 'great' their deeds, but only respect them for their individual achievements which are worthy of admiration by their fellow men, for the simple reason that there are no 'great or extraordinary men', but rather 'ordinary' men who on a rare occasion get hold of an 'extraordinary idea' in the pursuit of which they manage to do 'extraordinary' deeds. To worship other men for their deeds means to degrade oneself, and a learned engineer worthy of his profession has to have self-esteem as was implied by Vitruvius. For this reason, an engineer should never appeal to prestige, and use ***argumentum ad verecundiam*** in support of his engineering judgements. The prerequisite of self-esteem is a difficult virtue called self-respect, which is not the same as self-satisfaction, and still less as self-conceit. The very source of self-respect is found in worthy personal accomplishments achieved through hard work and dedication to the pursuit of personal excellence done to the best of one's ability which, it ought to be noted, lies within the power of every individual. In the world of ancient Greeks the way to self-respect could be expressed in the following dictum: Any task worth doing is only worth doing as well as one can for one's own sake. Therefore, self-respect requires self-confidence, and self-confidence requires self-reliance. Contrary to the clarion propaganda of modern autocratic educracies, self-esteem of any individual does not come from 'feeling good' about oneself in one's lethargic state of mediocrity which resists all striving towards personal excellence whilst insisting that everybody else be restrained to remain arrested also in a state of mediocrity so that one's factitious self-esteem not be exposed as the humbug it is by the personal excellence of others.

History of engineering and technology is as enlightening and profoundly humanising as the study of great literature, for it bridges the gap separating engineering from humanities. For this reason, history of engineering has an important humanistic and cultural purpose. Therefore, engineers have as their primary responsibility to understand themselves and their profession as engineers who are active within the bounds of their civilisation, an understanding which can only be obtained through historical study of engineering and technology, and to impart that understanding to the rest of the people in the society whom the engineer serves in his, or her professional capacity for there is no learning so proper for the direction of the life of a professional person as history. Julius Hardegg, a German Grave, expressed the value of historical knowledge in the following words: "If you know the old, the new will become clear to you." French biologist and bacteriologist, Louis Pasteur (1822-1895) reminded the students at the University of Edinburgh: "... remember the past and look to the future," like Janus, the two-faced chief god of Romans whose one face looked forwards and the other looked backwards, in order to become creditable members of a learned profession. An engineer cannot fulfil this social responsibility unless he knows the place of his profession in history and in his civilisation, for which purpose he must also study the epistemological roots of his noble profession. For the sake of material progress in society, it is necessary to raise the interest of laymen, who lack talent for technology, in engineering. They should not remain strangers to this subject, because their understanding and support is a necessary ingredient in the progress of engineering in society. The diversity and proliferation of technologies in modern times lead to dissipation of laymen's interest in technology, and it is the responsibility of engineers and technologists to prevent this from happening. If it does happen, it is not the fault of technology but rather that of man. Since technology has a tendency to replace human skills with mechanical skills built into machines, without which material progress in modern civilisation is not possible, this also has to be explained to the laymen as an essential step in the material progress of the civilisation in a manner clearly understandable to them. Such an explanation can only be given within the historical context. History of engineering and technology is not a trivial matter to be dispensed in the superficial manner of the < Reader's Digest >, an attitude which can only be construed as an insult to this noble and learned profession that was poignantly expressed by the English statesman and man of letters who claimed that 'knowledge is power', Francis Bacon (1561-1626): "Epitomes are the moths and corruption of learning." No one can acquire a satisfactory and sound knowledge of the history of technology and engineering by merely attending a course of lectures such as this, because it rather requires that a lifelong interest be taken in it by the student as a personal cultural habit. Therefore, these lecture notes on the history of technology and engineering are primarily meant to be read again and again by the student at his or her leisure after entering the engineering profession. This humanistic interest in the history of engineering should persist as a professional habit for the balance of the professional life of every engineer in order to satisfy the requirements of a learned profession as Vitruvius expected.

Engineering as Learned Profession

Proper engineering is a learned profession, which means a liberal profession. A learned profession has an extensive body of systematic knowledge with a theoretical foundation, a rigorous and wide-reaching academic discipline with its intellectually defined methods of application. For this reason a learned professional person is a liberally educated individual who is professionally independent. Professional independence means that the professional service or opinion given by the learned person in any profession is in no way being dictated by the client or the employer. Professional service as such essentially depends upon professional judgement, and when such judgement is dictated by others, then such service ceases to be professional. The independence of professional judgement is not a privilege of a professional engineer, but rather an absolute professional responsibility because without it the engineer is reduced from a learned professional to a mere technician who is in perpetual need of a master. Lacking such professional independence, the engineer is actually working under conditions of servility, a condition which was the main reason why the ancient classical Greeks had such a low opinion of engineering and technology as a practical art. For ancient Romans the word ***servus***, meant a 'slave'.

It is disappointing to observe that the contemporary engineer has not been granted the kind of independence of professional judgement which is a prerequisite for a genuine learned profession. Surprisingly, the contemporary engineers do not command as much professional responsibility and freedom of professional judgement as did the engineers in the middle of the 19th century. It appears that more and more engineers lose their independent professional status by becoming technocrats, that is, technological bureaucrats in the service of the State, who are at the beck and call of self-serving modern politicians who are inclined to impose servile conditions on the State-employed technocrats. The politicians, rather than the engineers as the employees of the State, dictate the judgements to technocrats, judgements which ought to be professional but, instead, are purely political by serving political ends, and, thus, are basically disingenuous. The opportunistic nature of such political judgements, masquerading as responsible professional judgements, reflects the sorry moral character of the politician and his cohort, the career bureaucrat, and the crude and vulgar process by means of which these politically motivated people obtain their positions. Since the politicians, and the State bureaucrats, hold power over the subsistence of the engineer as an employee of the State, they control the engineer as a professional. The American statesman and former military aid and confidential secretary to General George Washington, Alexander Hamilton (1755-1804), described this servile state of man rather precisely: "Power over a man's subsistence is power over his will." Therefore, the opportunistic politicians and State bureaucrats who hold power over the subsistence of the engineer in the service of the State, hold power over his professional will unless the engineer employed by the State has the courage of his professional convictions. Frequently a pusillanimous technocrat excuses the failure of his professional nerve in the deferment of his professional integrity by deluding himself that it is for the 'public good'. Yet having learnt through bitter experience that professional dissent is dangerous, the engineer's subservience and compliance to the dictates of his political bosses is a great multiplier of professional evil because professional truth is no longer being served. And truth deferred is truth interred. But the truth will ultimately still triumph regardless of the professional distortions, or deliberate falsifications manufactured by the politician in collaboration with his subservient technocrat, for as was once remarked by the famous Roman statesman, orator, lawyer and man of letters, Marcus Tullius Cicero (106-43 B.C.): "You have the will, Sir, but not the skill to lie." At the same time the timid technocrat has suffered a professional loss of the most serious kind for he has failed to live up to the spirit of fortitude of the dignified person so well expressed in the poem < Invictus > by William Ernest Henley (1849-1903):

"It matters not how straight the gate
How charged with punishment the scroll,
I am the master of my fate,
I am the captain of my soul."

It is worth repeating a modern form of an ancient Greek truism: in professional life authentic heroism which is not rooted in brute force is the will to be oneself, something that requires a great deal of intellectual, moral, and spiritual fortitude.

A timorous surrender of professional independence by a professional person illustrates the poignant dictum of John Bosco: "The power of evil lives on the cowardice of good men." It seems that even in professional life only the brave have integrity to their principles, because cowardice in professional matters implies lack of integrity. The meaning of integrity was clearly stated by William Shakespeare (1564-1616): "Above all, to thine own self be true." Integrity is the accurate reflexion in word and deed of whatever one's highest conscience dictates as right: the best truth possible for the individual at the time. Of course, integrity itself does not assure humility, or any other virtue in man, but humility can no more be practised by those not graced with integrity; and without integrity no other professional virtues are possible since integrity is the very foundation of all human virtues.

Humility in the professional context has nothing whatsoever to do with being a meek milksop to be pushed about by his fellow men: it implies that one has the right estimate of oneself and men in general as finite creatures in the infinite universe. Humility as a professional virtue is difficult to acquire since it takes an enormous amount of honest, realistic self-scrutiny in order to grasp one's infinitesimal perception of the infinite intelligence required to comprehend the whole world as it is. Individuals who are ignorant of such philosophical understanding tend to become arrogant after they have grasped only a mere smattering of the boundless knowledge it takes to understand the world. Ignorance leads men to arrogance, and such unwarranted arrogance, which ancient Greeks called ***hubris***, captivates the soul of men and makes them cast their eyes downwards to pay heed only to inferiors and their commonplace accomplishments, instead of upwards to get a glimpse of superiors and professional excellence in their achievements. The real tragedy of such philosophically ignorant men is that they do not know that they are ignorant because their overwhelming ignorance has blinded them. Arrogant men do not engage in honest, critical self-examination, and, therefore, they remain ignorant of self-knowledge. In consequence of such lack of self-knowledge, the arrogant person is not aware of his professional shortcomings, and consequently he is incapable of self-improvement. Since every competent professional man who values perfection learns the ways of excellence only from the admirable precedents achieved by his superiors, arrogance will lead a haughty man into a state of intellectual stagnation and professional decay without recourse. In an ideal sense a professional man should be what Aristotle called a 'good man' whose emotions and reasons are perfectly harmonised. In the words of Aristotle: "A good man is not a man without feelings, but a man with self-disciplined feelings; not a man with atrophied emotions but with strong emotions directed towards the right objectives. Man should not be regarded as a battleground between reason and emotion. Rather his emotions, through training in the imaginary world of literature and art should be brought by habituation to a harmonious cooperation with reason."

In a professional atmosphere corroded by arrogance and lack of integrity to highminded principles, the love of free spirit of enquiry and freedom gives way to care about authority. Men lacking honour mask their behaviour with fine-sounding words. Old love of serious argument is debased into ingenious dispute, which makes despicable acts appear as excellent deeds. The venerable admiration for intellectual prowess degenerates into respect for craftiness consisting of the ability to advance a cause by whatever means available. This is the way the first critical historian, Thoukydeides of Athens (c.460-c.400 B.C.), whose treatise set an enduring standard for the objective study of history, saw the basic moral issues in Athens during the Peloponnesian War from 431 B.C. to 404 B.C. between Athens and Sparta. In such morally and intellectually corrupted atmosphere, as Thoukydeides stressed, even words were given new meanings: "To fit in with the change of events, words, too, had to change their usual meanings. What used to be described as a thoughtless act of aggression was now regarded as courage which was to be expected in a party member; to think of the future and wait was merely another way of saying that one was a coward; any idea of moderation was just an attempt to disguise one's unmanly character; ability to understand a question from all sides meant that one was totally unfit for action. Fanatical enthusiasm was the mark of a real man."

In his opinion such a deplorable condition comes about in a society when men have lost their 'simple way of looking at things which is a mark of a noble nature', without a trace of vulgarity, self-interest, duplicity, and ostentation. Intelligence properly used must be directed by a high moral sense: love of honour, desire to excel within the bounds of honour, generosity; and as the ancient Athenian statesman and leader Perikles (495-429 B.C.) said: "... the refusal to fall below a certain standard". Moreover, Thoukydeides stated in his histories that an overwhelming confidence is likely to lead to serious and even disastrous mistakes in judgement. Although Thoukydeides was writing about what happened to ancient Athenian society under war conditions, his arguments are still apposite to the modern technological society today.

Any profession is a learned profession if it has intellectual content. The content of a learned profession such as engineering is an integrated synthesis of sciences, engineering as a practical art, and humanities such as philosophy, history, languages and fine arts. A professional man is not moulded into a cultivated man if he is coerced against his own will to study subjects in which he himself is not the least interested, and which he utterly fails to integrate into his personal knowledge owing to a lack of genuine personal interest. A genuinely cultured professional man realises that it is in his own self-interest to learn and integrate these subjects in order to provide contextual background for his own professional knowledge. It is professionally useful to him to study the historical and epistemological foundation of his profession, and thereby discover the intimate connexion of his field of specialisation with other fields of specialisation by virtue that it has a past and performs an important social function on which the future of his specialisation largely depends. History of technology and engineering serves as the very means to cut everything down to its proper size. In this way the professional person gradually discovers that history, philosophy and other disciplines of humanities are not altogether extraneous to his or her profession, and by such a realisation and knowledge he or she gradually becomes a cultivated professional person, a person qualified to be in a learned profession such as engineering.

Professional man who neglects the contextual aspects of his intellectual learning will not become a cultivated person because he remains culturally ignorant of the relation which exists between his own professional field and other intellectual and professional fields. In Western civilisation a cultured man is a person who has harmonised through mental integration his perceptual, intellectual and contextual knowledge. A person who neglects such integration and improvement of his personal knowledge is not really a professional person but rather a gadgeteer who mistakes means for ends. The acquisition of the ennobling, lifelong habit of self-improvement should be the cardinal objective of every professional person, for good personal habits are decisive for the attainment of excellent professional virtues. The popular ancient Greek notion expressed by the English poet, political satirist and critic, John Dryden (1631-1700), in his precise adage: "We first make our habits, and then our habits make us," has a ring of truth to it.

A truly learned professional man must be a critical thinker who will not become a prisoner of inconsistent ideas because he is able to correct, systematise and enrich the hypotheses that are involved in his work: he will not mistake what is postulated for what is deduced; he will be explicit in his hypotheses underlying his theories and conscious actions; he will develop a habit of systematic ordering of his ideas and strive for consistency and clarity in his work; he will not be dogmatic for he demands from himself cogency and evidence in his work; he will not mistake means for ends, instrument for substance, and computation for mathematical theory [to mistake computation in a scientific discipline for the critical mastery of the conceptual, i.e., the theoretical structure of this discipline is the most prominent professional fallacy of the computer age]; he will respect professional achievements but will not revere them for there is no perfection nor infallibility in any works of man; he will not long be satisfied with his own works but search relentlessly for some valid criticism of it or objection to it however minor; and, finally, he should have the prudence to forgive, but never to forget the professional shortcomings and failures of his professional colleagues.

Therefore, a learned professional man must be highly discriminating, particularly about his own works, whilst he recognises no authority apart from his own autonomous mind. The general lack of discriminative, critical intellect in people was well expressed by the famous motion picture director, Reuben Mamoulian (1897-1987): "... too frequently people tend to confuse novelty with originality, fad with achievement, slogans with principles" – all of which signifies a failure in the critical acumen of man, something an individual as a member of any learned profession cannot afford. A learned professional person as a critical thinker is characterised by firmness in knowledge, by self-confidence, by moral certainty, and through all this, by personal dignity. A man must first of all have genuine self-respect before he can ever learn to respect the rights of other men, for only then is he really fit for social relationships with other men such as he has to have in a learned profession. Hence, a professional man has to become first an independent individual before he can develop sound professional relationships with other men. The mind of a critically thinking professional man has, potentially, an inexhaustible supply of ingenuity, and in any enquiry he pursues his thoughts relentlessly. Even when puzzled, he never feels helpless because he is confident of his ability to prevail over any professional problem. This self-confidence comes from his habitual self-reliance on critical personal knowledge. In the opinion of some perceptive ancient Greek thinkers, self-reliance occupies a central place in the chain of personal qualities leading to personal worth: A man has personal worth only if he has self-esteem, and self-esteem only if he has self-respect, and self-respect only if he has self-confidence, and self-confidence only if he is self-reliant, and self-reliance only if he is self-responsible.

It not only takes a great amount of intellectual, moral and spiritual fortitude to be oneself, but it also requires the development of personal beliefs, ideas, convictions, and ideals through individual exercise of willpower. The highest ideals of man ought to be so lofty that they should remain forever beyond his immediate grasp, a principle which was fancifully expressed by the English poet Robert Browning (1812-1889): "A man's reach must exceed his grasp, or what's a heaven for."

In building personal knowledge, man must seek critical knowledge rather than imagination. Cognitive knowledge fosters imagination by supplying its source: critical understanding of the individual man. Imagination is a useful faculty of the professional man for the rearrangement of the available elements of reality, but not for escaping reality because imagination divorced from reality constitutes a professional nightmare. The development of imagination is, therefore, a byproduct of seeking critical knowledge, and it is a highly personal, private concern which, if pursued with vigour, ultimately gives man a sense of his own individuality and personal creativity. In this particular sense every critically thinking person is self-educated, and, thus, self-made. It is true that man is not God for he did not create himself, nor did he establish the conditions of his being; but within these set bounds men and women do 'make themselves' by cultivating their human nature. The famous Irish political philosopher, orator, and Parliamentarian, Edmund Burke (1729-1797), made the following keen observation on man: "That wonderful structure, Man, whose prerogative it is to be in a great degree a creature of his own working, and who, when made as he ought to be made, is destined to hold no trivial place in the creation."

Marcus Tullius Cicero saw the task confronting each individual man: "Every individual must do everything in his power to develop the higher faculties that distinguish man from animals." It was Cicero who compared the education of man's mind to the cultivation of the fields in agriculture, and he stressed the importance of such cultivation to the survival of man as follows: "Cultivation to the mind is as necessary as food is to the body." It was the famous German man of letters, scientist and statesman, Johann Wolfgang Goethe (1749-1832) who, by following Cicero, named intellectual learning 'culture'. Unfortunately, the anthropologists have degraded the term 'culture' to mean the 'way of life' which was not its original meaning. In the language of the anthropologists even a primitive, illiterate barbarian has 'culture'. In the Ciceronian sense, a learned professional man, at all times, must make a great effort to excel, that is, to surpass himself in his present intellectual and cultural state. Therefore, a member of a learned profession, being an exceptional person with a superior and restless mind, should never be self-satisfied. The well-known Irish man of letters, Oliver Goldsmith (1728-1774) expressed the superior, or the 'great' mind in the following way: "The little mind which loves itself will write and think with the vulgar; but the great mind will be bravely eccentric, and scorn the beaten path," and further, "These little things are great to little men." Goldsmith implied with these statements that the 'great' mind refuses to conform to the vulgar, an attitude which requires a great deal of determination, individuality, and a strong personal will. Such a person recognises no authority save his own, and he does not seek approval for his own unique ways from his fellow men. The American philosopher and psychologist, William James (1842-1910), expressed the native dignity of an individual in the following words: "Native distinction needs no official stamp, and should disdain to ask for one ... ."

The capacity for critical thinking must be developed by the individual himself because it is an intensely personal internal faculty of man which is not externally accessible. Moreover, there are no easy shortcuts to the creation of personal critical faculty. It is quite fundamental to human nature that an individual should form ideas by himself for himself. It is possible, of course, that the environment and other people may exercise a certain influence on the individual but no one can completely determine the ideas and values which the individual will ultimately adopt and maintain throughout his life. The development of all the aspects of an individual's personality may be called his or her general education. A large part of a person's general education besides the direct experience of daily life involves cultural education which for efficient intellectual acquisition normally requires a formal course of studies and competent guidance called teaching.

The only thing that a competent teacher can accomplish is to introduce the novice into a learned intellectual discipline by showing the student the best way to proceed so that the student does not have to retrace all the byroads and dead-ends of the groping past whilst he learns the new discipline. In higher studies the student primarily learns from his teacher, who should be a master of the discipline, a method of thinking in the discipline, but very little else. The rest is up to the personal intellectual effort of the student who literally must make himself, or herself, a master of the subject by autodidactic study. As mentioned earlier, a teacher can do no more than to demonstrate a competent method of thinking, unless the student is being indoctrinated in the subject matter, in which case the student is engaged in uncritical acquisition of knowledge that is not only useless but also professionally dangerous to his or her fellow men who have to rely on the competence of his or her judgement, for an indoctrinated person does not know that he or she does not understand. The English poet, Alexander Pope (1688-1744) expressed the danger of indoctrination characterised by shallow learning rather brilliantly:

"A little learning is a dangerous thing;
Drink deep, or taste not the Pierian Spring:
There shallow draughts intoxicate the brain,
And drinking largely sobers us again..."

Indoctrinated knowledge, as the poet said, apart of being shallow, is a "load of learned lumber ignorantly acquired by a bookful blockhead." In other words, indoctrinated knowledge acquired without a critical faculty is a form of pernicious ignorance, about which Goethe had the following to say: "Nothing is more terrible than ignorance in action." In professional engineering ignorance in action can be deadly. "To be ignorant of one's ignorance is the malady of ignorance," said Amos Bronson Alcott, for there is far more mystery in the universe for a learned person than for an ignorant one. A cunning professional ***ignoramus***, as Goethe so well expressed, may make a sort of a name for himself by skilful conduct and artificial means, but if the internal quality of critical learning and noble character be wanting, all is vanity which will not last.

It is not uncommon in public life to encounter intellectuals in official positions who are arrogant and puffed up with a sense of self-importance. Such intellectuals tend to believe that what they think is the reality, and when they occupy influential positions they are an ever-present danger to their society. A genuinely learned and critically thinking intellectual can be confident, but never absolutely certain, of his opinions, for already ancient Greeks recognised that absolute certainty lies beyond the reach of any man regardless how competent and confident he may be. Unwarranted arrogant pride, called ***hubris*** by ancient Greeks, is the opposite of professional humility which recognises the all too finite limits of the power of any man. ***Hubris*** usually takes possession of an individual who lacks critical faculties and is, therefore, ignorant and haughty in spirit. Such insolent pride sprouts and grows from the ignorance of a person who thinks he knows it all, but ***nemesis***, which is always close at hand, is the price one has to pay for one's ***hubris*** manifested in excessive personal haughtiness and self-exaltation. A professional man puffed up by unwarranted self-importance and arrogance is unwilling to learn from his fellow professionals because he thinks erroneously that he knows it all, which is contrary to the surprisingly frank opinion of the pompous late Italian Renaissance man of science Galileo Galilei (A.D.1564-1642): "No man is so ignorant that something cannot be learnt from him."

A genuine professional education, in its profoundest sense, is an experience in humility, because the more one learns, the more conscious one becomes of one's ignorance. As one acquires more and more knowledge, one's scope of ignorance seems to grow at a far greater rate than one's knowledge. Goethe expressed the basic difference between knowledge and art as follows: "Work of art is complete, perfect in itself, whereas knowledge knows no bounds." The genuine humility of anyone engaged in serious study is the growing awareness of how much there is to learn. This personal sense of humility when facing the immenseness of the unknown, recognises the paltry finiteness and fallibility of one's own mind. This feeling of humility has nothing whatever to do with other men and relative standards; it is merely an honest assessment of reality and human nature. It should not be confused with the pretentious, and ostentatious 'humility' on public display, which is actually a veiled arrogance of the self-proclaimed meek well expressed by the self-contradictory slogan: "I am proud to be humble."

Professional education should not consist of stuffing more and more information into a student's mind, but rather of providing the student with intellectual inspiration for learning under his or her own intellectual power, a profound idea which was well expressed by a distinguished ancient Greek scholar and biographer, Ploutarchos of Chaironeia (A.D. c.46-c.120): "The mind is not a vessel to be filled, but a fire to be kindled." As motivation for the great personal effort required in self-education, he emphasised the ennobling personal value learning gives to the individual: "Of all our qualities, learning alone is immortal and divine." Ploutarchos was emphasising with these statements that learning, like virtue, is its own reward. For this very reason so well expressed by Ploutarchos, lectures in any intellectual discipline should teach students a method of thinking in the subject: how to frame a problem and how to solve it, but not to bury the mind of the student who wants to master the discipline intellectually with an avalanche of the so-called 'facts'. The brilliant

German mathematician, David Hilbert (1862-1943), emphasised the importance of the formulation of problems in exact sciences : "A perfect formulation of a problem is already half of its solution," a judgement that is certainly true in engineering practice. A learned professional engineer, who adheres to these tenets, promises little but delivers much in his professional responsibilities, because he is secure in his professional knowledge. It is important for him to know his own professional ability, but only an unmindful man deceives himself by using a relative standard in such assessment which consists of comparing his own professional strengths with unrelated professional weaknesses of others in order to make a favourable professional assessment of self.

A genuinely learned professional assesses his personal professional accomplishments against absolute cultural standards extracted from the history of his culture. A personal professional accomplishment means a professionally created 'personal value' of an individual which his fellow men, assuming they are free to act in their own self-interest, want to acquire for what they consider is its worth to them. Such a free choice for professional services requires a free society in which individuals can make their choices without being subjected to external coercion by the State or by pressure groups of various kinds. If such freedom exists in the society, then the so-called 'competition' is only a byproduct of the freedom of the professional man to pursue personal excellence in creating 'personal values', such as professional competence, the services of which his fellow-citizens, if they are free to act in the pursuit of their self-interest, want to acquire for a price because it is of personal interest for them to do so. In any such voluntary exchange both parties, the professional man who sells his service and the client who buys this service, have personally profited from this voluntary mutual arrangement. For this very reason, it is in the self-interest of the professional man to devote himself to a singleminded pursuit of personal excellence in creating 'personal values'. This is an effort of professional self-improvement gauged against absolute cultural standards which is done for one's own sake, and not for the sake of competition with other men that is necessarily based on a relative standard. It is important to recognise that the professional or any other kind of self-improvement is a selfish motive, a natural inducement born from self-interest – a noble and honourable motive that is unfairly denounced today as being wicked, ignoble and dishonourable because it is based on the belief in the personal merit of self as an individual. In the direct pursuit of relative standards, the professional man is concerned only with the difference in professional merit which exists between him and his fellow professionals, a viewpoint that makes every fellow professional into a personal threat, or even a personal enemy. This view of one's profession makes the professional field of action into a theater of civil war rather than a place of peaceful competition, a view that is quite alien to a society of free men.

Human reason is a weak and paltry power of man as long as he is not completely free to think, to speak and to pursue his own interests. The slightest compulsion or external reward, or penalty leads to an appearance of a defect in its ratiocination that is more detrimental to man's intellect than any error of fact or deliberate prejudice. Since man's intellect is imperfect it is always subject to error, but compulsion in its cultivation tends to strangle learning at its very source.

The celebrated theoretical physicist and natural philosopher, Albert Einstein (1879-1955), made a significant statement about the most prominent shortcoming of contemporary education, its 'built-in compulsion': "It is, in fact, nothing short of a miracle that the modern methods of instruction have not yet entirely strangled the holy curiosity of enquiry; for this delicate little plant, aside from stimulation, stands mainly in need of freedom; without this it goes to wrack and ruin without fail. It is a very grave mistake to think that the enjoyment of seeing and searching can be promoted by means of coercion and a sense of duty. To the contrary, I believe that it would be possible to rob even a healthy beast of prey of its voraciousness if it were possible, with the aid of a whip, to force the beast to devour continuously, even when he is not hungry, particularly if the food, handed out under such coercion, were to be selected accordingly."

Creativity by command, or learning as a duty is a fundamental fallacy and an imperious delusion of tyranny. The coercive approach to education is based on the mistaken belief that noble ends can be reached by ignoble means; unfortunately the truth of the matter is, as was already well expressed by the American essayist, poet and philosopher, Ralph Waldo Emerson (1803-1882), that the ends already preexist in the means: ignoble means can only lead to ignoble ends. The essential characteristic of a genuine education, as was stressed by Einstein, is freedom, for human nature transcends nature by its gift of the freedom of choice. The eminent Greek natural philosopher and astronomer Klaudios Ptolemaios (2nd century A.D.) emphasised the importance of freedom in intellectual pursuits: "He who is to follow philosophy must be a free man in mind." The ancient Greek natural philosopher Demokritos of Abdera (c.470-380 B.C.), the first 'hardboiled' scientific mind to invade the commonplace of culture, regarded free speech to be the external sign of freedom: "Freedom of speech is the sign of freedom; but the danger lies in discerning the right occasion."

Freedom implies autonomy and self-discipline which require self-imposed burden of self-responsibility from the individual. Authorities in their customary devotion to control the thoughts and actions of the individual in the society promise to remove this 'burden' of self-determination from the shoulders of the individual man and make him 'free' of self-responsibility. Authorities do not like individual men to be independent because such men are self-reliant and tend to think for themselves regardless of the prevailing 'official opinions' and 'taboos', and because they are not servile and compliant to commands, they pose a subtle threat to any authority bent on oppression. Any self-respecting professional man is self-reliant because it is in his self-interest to do so, for no man's security is any greater than his own self-reliance.

American economist, philosopher, and historian, Murray Rothbart (1926-1995), explained the issue of personal freedom that is essential to professional education as follows: "Each individual ... is the owner of himself, the ruler of his own person. Preservation of this self-ownership is essential for the proper development and wellbeing of man. The human rights of the person are, in effect, a recognition of each man's inalienable property right from which stems his right to the material goods that he has produced. A man's right to personal freedom then is his property right in himself." The property right of an individual includes the personal intellectual values created by the individual in himself or herself through an intense effort to acquire personal worth. Ideas and innovations belong also to such intellectual values which as personal property are protected by patent laws that grant the inventor monopoly for his invention over a limited period of time. The right to own such personal property is essential, for as the Italo-American philosopher George Santayana (1863-1952) so poignantly stated: "The man who is not permitted to own is owned." For this very reason the property right is the most important right of an individual for in the absence of such right the individual in effect is reduced to a serf, or even a slave, since then all his other rights remain mere floating abstractions devoid of any real meaning. The denial of property right, which includes the right of self-defence, to an individual by the laws of the State is the first sign of impending oppression, because the State in its ultimate reality is 'force'. Creation of unique personal values by an individual requires a unique personality, and a unique personality needs freedom for its full development, which is one of the major arguments for free society. Invention as a unique and deliberate personal act is a distinct achievement of a free individual which depends upon the untrammelled imagination of a unique person, and not merely upon blind luck. The Serbo-American physicist, Michael Idvorsky Pupin (1858-1935), who was a successful inventor himself, had this to say about luck: "Inventions are sometimes ascribed to luck, but that the best luck is to have a good head on one's shoulders." The celebrated French chemist and bacteriologist, Louis Pasteur (1822-1895) placed the role of luck in invention into its proper perspective, when he said: "Chance favours only the mind which is prepared." Invention is based on discovery, and in the words of the Hungarian scientist, Albert Szent-Györgi: "Discovery consists of seeing what everybody has seen but thinking what nobody has thought." This statement was foreshadowed by one made by the German philosopher, Arthur Schopenhauer (1788-1860) more than a century earlier: "Talent is hitting a mark ordinary man cannot reach; genius is noticing a point which others cannot even see." An apothegm of the English man of letters, Thomas Carlyle (1795-1881) equated genius merely with man's ability to persevere: "Genius only means an infinite capacity for taking pains," a favourite saying of those who lack native genius. This mistaken notion was somewhat improved by Thomas Alva Edison (1847-1931), a plodding genius, in an interview about 1895: "Genius is one percent inspiration and ninety-nine percent perspiration." Genius was much more soundly described by the English poet and satirist John Dryden in 1694:

"Time, place and action may with pain be wrought.
But genius must be born,
and never can be taught,"

and by the English poet Alexander Pope in 1711:

"One science only will one genius fit,
So vast is art, so narrow human wit."

The prepared mind mentioned by Pasteur is necessarily a practical mind, but practical training of a mind without sufficient theoretical background has proven to be impractical. The prominent Austrian physicist, Ludwig Boltzmann (1844-1906) put this thought into a pithy statement: "Practice is best served by a good theory," whereas Leonardo da Vinci (1452-1519), the universal man of Renaissance, referred to the importance of practice to theory: "Theory without practice is powerless." The celebrated German philosopher Immanuel Kant (1724-1804) in his discussion of facts and theories which lurk behind facts, wrote: "Concepts without factual content are empty; sense data without concepts are blind ... The understanding cannot see. The senses cannot think. By their union only can knowledge be produced." This statement of Kant is usually briefly paraphrased in a succinct sentence: "Theories without facts are empty, facts without theories are blind." Modern scientific education of the professional engineer attempts to take the intimate connexion which exists between theories and practical facts into account wherever possible. Yet the innovation based upon both cannot be created nor scientific progress organised according to a predetermined plan, because both are unpredictable creations of unique personalities.

Professional learning when imparted in professional education at its best is not ineffable but rather expressible, not private but public, and it transmits knowledge by precise and concise communication. Professional knowledge is systematic knowledge – it is not an aggregate of disconnected fragments of information without context, but rather a logically constituted system of ideas characterised by a particular fundamental yet rejectable set of hypotheses meant to correspond to a certain class of facts. Such a hypothetical deductive system of logically related ideas is called a 'theory' [to ancient Greeks, ***theoreo*** meant to 'behold']. The foundation of such a theory is a set of principles rather than a set of so-called 'facts' which are actually created by theories. The systematic nature of scientific theory, implying that it is founded, ordered and internally consistent in terms of logic, is what makes it rational. Logic as an instrument of thinking rests on the distinction between things and their mental pictures known as 'mental constructs', and its domain is the conceptual world of the mind, whilst its purpose is to handle concepts. Any science of man is based on his fundamental belief that nature is understandable by man, since otherwise he would not spend any effort in its pursuit.

It should be recognised that a picture is only an abstract likeness, and not a duplicate. Any scientific theory can be compared to an abstract likeness with respect to certain, but not all, aspects of nature. The famous German theoretical physicist, mathematician and physiologist, Hermann Ludwig Ferdinand von Helmholtz defined theory as a mathematical abstraction of nature: "A theory can be no more than a mathematical model for nature." A mathematical model is not a duplicate but rather a representation of a limited aspect of a physical phenomenon in nature as an idealisation of nature, and if it were not, it would be as complex and intricate as nature itself and, therefore, quite worthless as a theory that should help man to understand nature. Theory as an abstract 'likeness' of phenomenon can represent different 'approximations' of nature similar to a portraiture in fine art which can range from a portrait in oil to a caricature in ink, and yet each of these portraitures represents the likeness of a person by capturing some characteristics of the individual depicted with different degrees of 'exactness'. A scientific theory is only 'approximate' with respect to some aspect of nature, yet its mathematical, that is, its formal logical structure ought to be exact so that rigorous deductions from the particular mathematical model can be made as a test of the model. For this reason a modern professional engineer ought to be proficient in contemporary methods of mathematics which are used as formal logical tools of thinking in engineering sciences.

Ancient Greeks had discovered that chaos did not exist in nature, which at least in principle is intelligible, but rather in the mind of man. Intellectual discipline and conceptual knowledge that man is capable of creating by disciplined thinking, helps man to harmonise the underlying intelligibility of nature by organising it conceptually and, thus, to understand it by means of his theory consisting of conceptual models which in engineering science is expressed in some mathematical form as described above. Learning implies acquisition of knowledge by arduous, conscious, fully focussed mental attention and observation, and its subsequent development through intense mental practice is what makes this knowledge instantly available in its particular context, a mental process which makes learning subconsciously automatic and habitual so that the conscious mind is liberated to pursue new and more complex knowledge. This very act of forming, integrating and using concepts is a volitionally directed process which has to be learnt through intense practice. This mental process, or consciously realised mental potential, as an ability of man depends upon the mental method by which man acquires and organises his knowledge. This mental process, as mentioned earlier, is called ' reasoning' and its method of integrating thought in the form of mental constructs is called 'logic'. This particular mental process is a cognitive habit of dealing with the content of the mind that affects the cognitive content of the mind itself which, in turn, affects the mental process in any further improvement of the content of the mind. The popular claim that man can learn how to learn without cognitive content is no more than the cant of ignorant simpletons.

Since man's mind is bombarded virtually night-and-day with perceptual impressions from the external world, the chaos of perceptions in the mind increases unless the conceptual mind keeps abreast of the perceptual mind. This cognitive development of man's mind consists of an unending automatisation of cognitive knowledge constituting man's intellectual learning. Since man can only reach conceptual understanding through basic knowledge processed by reason, and gain self-confidence by clearly differentiating between his own consciousness and the outside world, he will realise that the purpose of his conceptual consciousness is to understand his perceptions of the outside world. Therefore, man must learn to discern, to discriminate, to identify, to categorise, to conceptualise and to integrate knowledge in his conceptual mind to develop the self-confidence necessary to reconcile the internal world of his mind with the external phenomenological world. If a man fails to do so, then instead of being self-confident he is rather caught between the chaos within and without him. It is quite clear from the foregoing discussion that the capacity for critical thinking must be developed by the individual himself or herself, and that there are no shortcuts to the development of a personal critical faculty required for critical thinking.

Hence, it is manifest that if an individual man is to develop himself as a human being, his reason and intellect must be active, and they must work to transform the perceptions of reality given by his senses. Man can only fulfil himself and his human nature, and his personality, by purposive action upon the world. All the works of a civilisation have been developed from such purposive actions of men, and this is the field in which the actions of engineers and technologists have had a decisive influence. All technological actions of man in his society reflect certain value concepts which, in turn, depend upon the system of cultural values of the civilisation to which this society belongs.

Professional learning as critical knowledge is, in a sense, the experience of man mentally processed to transcend experience. In such a mental process, thought is abstracted from concrete particulars to create concepts known as mental constructs. In this way experience itself represents a form of knowledge which Immanuel Kant expressed thus: "Experience is itself a species of knowledge which involves understanding." A learned person always strives towards comprehensiveness, that is, contextual knowledge, which provides him with a critical and continuous cultural perspective, absence of narrow-mindedness, and awareness of the boundaries of his knowledge. Such a learned person finds personal satisfaction in enquiry and in dissent, and he tends to be in a certain perpetual conflict with himself because of his insistence on critical examination of all his own works.

Professional learning is contextual for its past and its future depend to a great extent upon other fields of learning, mainly humanities and philosophy, intellectual disciplines which, therefore, are not at all external to engineering profession. A professional person, such as an engineer, should be a learned person whose learning should be based upon free enquiry. In modern professions specialisation is a necessary evil, for if it were to be eliminated no professional person could develop his professional mastery to its maximum competence. This modern need for narrow specialisation militates against the broad, general education required by a cultured professional person, a contradiction presenting an educational dilemma for the engineering profession.

In academic education of engineers the drive to specialise has turned some disciplines of engineering into virtual branches of mathematical or computer sciences by taking the educational path of least resistance: it is easier to acquire knowledge than to apply it. The discovery of new physical facts is the primary preoccupation of scientists, but the successful application of these facts is the practical art of engineers. Scientific knowledge and technological know-how are by no means identical, for no result of scientific research by itself is a sufficient basis for definite technological application. If too much emphasis is placed on discovering the facts and too little to apply such facts, then engineering will suffer, for all the science in the world cannot make a machine function as it should without the practical art and craftsman's skill of the engineer who makes the machine. It must be emphasised that it is in the technological design where the engineer primarily exercises his practical art, since good design depends upon a successful combination of scientific knowledge and practical engineering. In modern engineering education the engineering student is required to absorb an ever-increasing volume of theoretical and scientific knowledge to qualify for any specialised branch of engineering, a requirement which leaves precious little time for adequate practical training in engineering, and for a satisfactory amalgamation of practice with theory whilst being aware of the research, design, managerial, maintenance, and sales aspects of engineering. Moreover, the ever-increasing mass of information which is being crammed into the engineering curriculum leaves the engineering student virtually no time for reflexion which is necessary for the mastery of any intellectual discipline. As a result of this 'curriculum-stuffing', the engineering student is kept far too busy to be able to master intellectually the fundamentals of any discipline he studies. The fact of the matter is that an engineer should never be kept too busy with the accumulation of information in order that he be able to learn to understand the ideas behind all this information. Engineering schools should not be reduced to mere computerised information mills.

In recent times the tendency to emphasise the purely material aspect of academic engineering education has come to predominate the educational process of engineers. When the British pioneer of aeronautical and automotive engineering, Frederick Lanchester (1868-1946), after inspecting a well-known research laboratory, tersely observed: "... too much apparatus, not enough brains," he implied by this statement that it is men rather than apparatus and buildings that produce progress in engineering. Thinking of his own experience, Lanchester recognised that it is man's fallible mind which can purge an engineering theory and design of some, but not all, possible errors. In engineering, practice is the true educator, and difficulty is the best school of intellectual and professional discipline since difficulty is the engineer's most valuable adversary. In the19thand previous centuries technological inventions were more or less the work of gifted amateurs who had little specific and detailed scientific knowledge since technology at that time was rather closely related to everyday experience. Beginning with chemical industries at the close of the 19th century, contemporary technologies, being based to a large extent upon science, have become almost entirely technical fields for experts. But even today, many professional engineers on account of their lack of sound intellectual background in engineering want rules which they can follow so that they can create technology without the need of cultivated personal talent. Ever since classical antiquity most learned men thought that talent has to be cultivated to make it effective. The ancient Greek natural philosopher, Demokritos of Abdera, who had written: "Neither art nor science can be conquered if one is not willing to learn, and the noble things of life one learns only through hard work for without it one cannot even learn how to read or write, or to be a musician or an athlete," also asserted: "No one is likely to prevail by native qualities alone." The ancient Greek historian Thoukydeides expressed the opinion: "Even an untutored person could succeed if only his intelligence were powerful enough." Yet, he thought that untutored display of genius is quite rare.

The tendency towards narrow specialisation in engineering in modern times is presenting a clear and present danger to the civilisation. Scientists have created a large number of potent chemicals, and the very industrial processes where they are used are creating poisons deleterious to the wellbeing of man which are released into life-supporting air and water of the Earth, and mixed into food stuff frequently in an indiscriminate, ignorant, irresponsible and authoritarian manner. Any engineer who is applying such potent poisons in his work, bears an awesome responsibility for his professional acts. In order to exercise his enormous professional responsibility, the engineer has to be a person of a broad cultural perspective for without such intellectual background he is quite incapable of deciding whether his professional acts will benefit his society by serving the long-term interests of his civilisation. Therefore, only by becoming much more than a specialist can an engineer become an adequate specialist in his own engineering discipline. Moreover, such a cultivated engineer can only then act according to his best moral and professional judgement if he is professionally independent, that is, if he is not servile to the short-range commercial or political interests of his employer. It is a well-known in history that professional obsequiousness, pusillanimity and lack of integrity are the very springs of professional misconduct and abuse. Every professional engineer, therefore, must necessarily seek to be a highly principled professional individual who believes like the ancient Greek scholar Aristotle (384-322 B.C.) that: "Man has a right to exist for his own sake," and who accepts the motto of individualism: "Never aspire to be a leader, and never become a follower."

Currently, the population of Western civilisation is being poisoned by thousands of quite potent and life-threatening chemicals produced and promoted by industrial scientists who are rather deficient in culture, and used by technologically and culturally unsophisticated common people, from the serflike farmers to the comatose urban dwellers, in an indiscriminate manner. The reason for such uncritical and mindless use of poisons by people at large can be explained the way Thomas Edison did: "Five percent of the people think; ten percent of the people think they think; and the other eighty-five percent would rather die than think." Perhaps the motivation behind this curious lack of critical thinking on the part of the mass-man stems from the popular notion which was poignantly expressed by the American man of letters, Carl Sandburg (1878-1967): "One man is as good as any other man, if not a little better."

Computers and Engineering

In the contemporary scene, as was discussed above, many scientists and engineers are really competent only in a rather minuscule area of their specialisation and, therefore, they do not have a broad cultural perspective. For this reason many of them are easily misled by current fashions and can become addicted to popular fads mistakenly believed to be genuine achievements. One of the principal contemporary fads is promoted by cyberneticists and manufacturers of the hardware of computers. The cyberneticists have proudly claimed that computers are 'giant brains which can think'. Is this startling claim which assigns self-consciousness and animate qualities to inanimate machines really true? In the philosophical sense, this claim represents a revival of 'animism' of the neolithic man: a belief of the primitive man who sought comprehensive knowledge by assuming that the world is made of animate, irreducible entities like man himself. Therefore, the cyberneticist's view of the computer as a 'thinker' is a revival of the age-old principle of knowledge devised by the primitive neolithic man. In modern context it contains two philosophical fallacies: the behaviourist fallacy which maintains that things are precisely what they appear to be; and the pragmatist fallacy which maintains that only results and what works count. Of course, behaviourists and pragmatists are intellectual 'reductionists' who attempt to explain everything by the simple phrase: "It is nothing but...!"

What is the reality behind this fantastic claim? Thinking is a spiritual activity of man which transcends his material state. Machines as such constitute matter intelligently organised by man with the help of his technology. Such mechanical artifacts of man regardless of their complex nature operate only by material objects and never with ideal, abstract objects such as exist in man's thoughts.

What are calculators? Calculators, whether analogue or digital, are machines devised and constructed by man to carry out physical operations based on physical principles on physical objects which only man can imagine to represent ideal, abstract objects such as numbers. These material objects, like turns of the cogwheels or electric pulses, can be correlated by man's imagination to ideal, abstract objects such as numbers, and the physical operation of the machine itself can thus be correlated to computation, although the physical operation of the machine is not rational. For this reason, the computing machines do not perform abstract mathematical operations but rather physical operations conceptually coordinated by man to abstract mathematical operations. In other words, calculating machines represent some abstract mental functions of man at the technological level, but certainly not at the abstract level of thought. Therefore, the cyberneticist has confused theory with computation, resemblance with identity, and form with content.

The digital computers are essentially counting machines at the physical level which do not 'add' pure numbers but rather 'accumulate' physical objects. Machines can record the number of turns of cogwheels in mechanical calculators and the electric impulses in electronic digital computers – but only as 'finite' physical operations. Digital computers can only deal with the mental correlates of finite numbers 'one' and 'zero' and, therefore, 'natural finite numbers', but 'irrational numbers', 'infinity' and 'limits', the very foundation of the abstract science of mathematics, are completely beyond the power of digital computers. In any use of the computer, logic is surrendered to 'computation routines', because the computer is only a mechanical computing device, and that is all it is. It is basically a sophisticated version of an artifact like the pencil. A computation routine is only a method of computing, and the art of computation is only a small, mechanical part of mathematical science. People who believe that digital computers do mathematical work think erroneously that the art of computation is equivalent to performing abstract mathematics in thought. It is a serious mistake of understanding, for computers being inanimate and lacking consciousness are unaware what they are doing, very much unlike a mathematician who is aware that he is working on a mathematical problem and, therefore, it cannot deal with nonautomatic type of knowledge, nor abstract, new, nonreductive ideal objects which have no empirical counterparts. In matters of logic, being aware of the mathematical structure, and capable of rigorous error estimates at each stage of computation by qualitative methods of mathematics, metaphorically stated the digital computer is 'a blind and brainless brute'. It cannot create infinite methods, the basis of mathematics, nor demonstrate their validity. Only abstract mathematical thinking can guide and check numerical work and prove that they are correct, something that lies completely beyond the abilities of a computer as a machine because it cannot set its own intellectual standard. The digital computer is worthless without the coding of input and the decoding of output of the machine by man. The computer algorithms have to be invented by man because the computer cannot 'think', and, moreover, no amount of numerical work done by the computer by proxy is able to bring critical understanding of the structure of a mathematical problem. Computer can only supply numerical details of a problem the structure of which must already be understood by mathematicians. A mathematical structure consists of clear mathematical concepts joined together by logical inferences. It is possible for a computer by means of its physical operation to deal with that part of literal algebra and calculus which can be reduced by man to finite arithmetic routines, and conceptually coordinated to the physical operation of the machine.

These intellectual merits of the designer of the computer are fallaciously attributed to the inanimate computer by computer addicts and merchants in their cant: "Computers think!"– a naive sensational slogan representing the popular contemporary myth.

Johann Kepler (1571-1630), a man of extraordinary intellectual brilliance, had already discovered this kind of behaviouristic and pragmatic fallacy in the thinking of his contemporaries:

"My intention is to show that the heavenly machine is not a kind of divine, live being, but a kind of clockwork (and he who believes that a clock has a soul, attributes the maker's glory to his work), insofar as nearly all the manifold motions are caused by a most simple, magnetic and material force, just as all motions of the clock are caused by a simple weight. And I also show how these physical causes are to be given numerical and geometrical expressions."

This concise statement of Kepler demonstrates that his insight into man and his works was far superior to the naive contention of modern cyberneticists and computer addicts.

In reality, these calculating machines cannot even remotely be compared to their human designers because as Kepler implied they are particular physical systems technologically created by their designers to serve man. To say that 'computers think' is only a metaphorical way of speaking which falls short of conceptual precision for self-perfectability, the hallmark of a thinking man, is absent in machines since they cannot 'learn by themselves for themselves'. Without the intervention of man with his distinct abstractive power, digital computers are no more than a heap of scrap metal. Therefore, in conclusion, all the foregoing arguments can be expressed by the following concise statement:

Machines do not think, and cannot think, because thinking is a transcendental spiritual activity, and spirit is quite alien to inert matter.

Civilisation, Technology and Engineering

Civilisation represents a buffer between man's nature and his natural environment. When animals are incapable of adapting their physical selves to changes in their environment, their species perishes. When men fail to adapt to the change in their physical environment, only their civilisation perishes, but the species does not.

Civilisation is the way and the means by which a society in search of "a good life for man," according to Aristotle, makes man increasingly a master of his physical and social environment. Civilisation represents the means of living whilst its culture represents the principles and values of living. In a way, civilisation is what men use and what they have, whilst culture is how they use it, and what they have made of it. The conduct and occupations of people in their leisure, when they are free from the compulsion of daily labour and unavoidable duties and are able to follow their own personal desires and natural bent, reveals the true state of their civilisation since it is then that men express their personal tastes which is the measure of their inner culture. Civilisation, evidently, depends upon the native ability of man to improve his lot on this Earth. Man has freedom to change conditions of his existence, but this freedom has definite limits. Within these limits of freedom man erects his civilisation as a man-made nature upon nature, for civilisation is a purely human phenomenon. The limits of man's capabilities accrue from the limits of human nature: man is neither omnipotent nor omniscient.

Technological inventions of men made in the pursuit of utility require standardisation, mass-production and haste which, ultimately, may lead men to begin to idolise the cult of ugliness. Such a rapid technological advance of civilisation tends to clash with the culture of the civilisation by defying it. This kind of precipitous and uncontrolled change within the civilisation brings about an internal conflict between the civilisation and its culture, a condition which is the prominent characteristic of modern age when the civilisation seems to run far ahead of its culture. The more complex and elaborate the civilisation becomes, owing to its rapid technological advancement, the more internally precarious it becomes. The present crisis in the Western civilisation which has demoralised the people and significantly barbarised Western culture is partly due to the disruption created by the rapidly changing scientific technology which is outrunning its cultural foundation to such an extent as almost losing contact with it. It is also partly due to the anticultural influences of the regnant totalitarian political doctrines, such as Marxist socialism, which deny the individual man the right to exist for his own sake by warring against the autonomous and independent individual in an all-out effort to create a master-serf society in which the individuals are forged into 'selfless' servile instruments of the autocratic political elite by means of the high technology created by the very same oppressed individuals. It is incumbent upon every individual citizen of a free society to treat the means of living which are instruments of his civilisation as his servants, and not his masters. Men should see to it that their civilisation should not stand apart from their culture, and be unrelated to their personalities. Men must resist the tendency to become servile to their own means owing to their own ill-advised reverence for the purely 'practical' ends. The 'age of machines' liberated men from mechanical tasks, but they themselves tend to become cogs in the great machine of their own creation if their culture does not keep abreast of their rapidly changing civilisation.

Man is not omnipotent because he cannot change his conditions of existence by fiat. Inasmuch as man lacks the power to render his conditions fully satisfactory, he must act by resorting to appropriate means available to him to render his conditions more satisfactory than they were before he acted. Ideas determine what are to be considered more, or less, satisfactory conditions for the existence of man, and what means are to be used to bring the improved conditions about. If inappropriate means are chosen, instead of chosen ends, a disaster may result. Therefore, competent knowledge about the world is essential to man if he wants to achieve desired results by his purposive acts. It follows that correct ideas are of cardinal importance to the wellbeing of man and his civilisation. In this sense ideas are the very essence of any civilisation, for a civilisation is a product of realised ideas of men.

What man thinks of himself by-and-large determines how far he can go as a creator, and how much he can do as a man. As Aristotle stated: "Man wonders and wants to know." This desire of the individual man to know, and the wonder he hopes to satisfy, account for some of the spiritual energy and motivation behind all the changes that constitute the progress of a civilisation. Civilisation is the consequence of the seeking of individuals in the society to realise their personal potentialities in order to satisfy their inner drives and desires.

It is self-evident that ideas must be evaluated for their soundness, for unsound ideas may undermine a civilisation and bring about its collapse. The system of spiritual, æsthetic, and intellectual ideas prevalent among the society of a civilisation constitutes the culture of this civilisation, and the culture of the civilisation is the engine of all creative human efforts. A society is a community of individuals who as individuals believe in certain common fundamental principles and have certain common aspirations, and who strive as individuals towards the main common ideals. Without a voluntary belief in common fundamental principles on the part of the individuals of a society, instead of a society they constitute a mere crowd, or worse, a mob. It is no exaggeration to say that the genuine history of a civilisation is the history of its ideas, and ideas are not an invariable stock, since every idea originates in the mind of an individual at a definite time and place.

It is evident that civilisation is a product of human effort, since it is an achievement of men eager to fight the natural forces adverse to their wellbeing. Such human effort requires 'human action', and human action requires sound knowledge of nature, as well as of human nature. Goethe emphasised the importance of human action in the life of man in the following way: "Nature knows no pause in progress and development, and attaches her curse to all inaction ... Nature understands no jesting. She is always true, always serious, always severe; she is always right, and the errors and faults are always those of man. A man incapable of appreciating her she despises, and only to the apt, the pure and the true, does she resign herself and reveal her secrets." The salient characteristic feature of man is his power to act: man is a ***homo agens*** – an acting human, and if man wants to survive, and make his life more agreeable he must act and develop natural sciences as hypothetico-deductive systems of ideas, and use them as guides in a singleminded pursuit of technological improvements of his civilisation. Man must accomplish all of this by human action, which is a conscious effort of man to create more satisfactory conditions for his life. Yet man pays a price for every one of his achievements, and he must possess the foresight and knowledge to evaluate whether the improvements his actions bring about are worth the price he has to pay for achieving them. For a man to act means to strive after ends: to choose a goal and to resort to appropriate means in order to attain this goal. If a man wants to succeed in his act, he must proceed according to methods that are in harmony with the structure of the world about which his perception provides him with some, but not all information. The information that perception does not provide, man has to invent and develop as intellectual knowledge. Both inventiveness and invention require a refusal on the part of the individual to conform to common opinion which, in turn, requires individuality, that is, independence of the mind and a strong personal will. As a rule, inventiveness requires individual thought that deviates from the common opinion. For this reason a creative man cannot be a faceless conformist in his own society. It is not uncommon that a man with a new idea is considered by his fellow men to be a crank until his idea succeeds, as was poignantly expressed by the American humorist and writer, Mark Twain (1835-1910).

Every man, whether important or unimportant, lives and acts within the framework of his historical circumstances, and his ideas are strongly influenced by his time and his place. Every man's contribution is necessarily embedded in the sequence of historical events, and is conditioned to a great extent by the achievements of preceding generations and, consequently, his ideas represent only a chapter in the historical development of ideas. Yet, if a man adds something new and unheard of to the treasure of thoughts of his culture, then, in this sense, he may be called creative. A true innovator accomplishes what other people believe to be unfeasible, or even unthinkable. In any civilisation there exists a gaping chasm between the capabilities of a creative man of native ingenuity and the routine-bound dull crowd. If the civilisation is to advance, and to flourish, the freedom of the creative man to think and to act should be scrupulously safeguarded, since only in personal freedom is he able, because of his extraordinary individual ability, to be productive and to work with profit, that is, to create the surplus called capital. For if the creative and productive man is left at the capricious mercy of the routine-bound common men, he as an individual will be ruthlessly oppressed by the mass-men and, as a consequence, his creativity will be suppressed. The so-called commonsense, which requires foresight, is rather uncommon among the common men, and, therefore, the common men have a tendency to deny by force the uncommon man, a man of native ingenuity and enterprise, his God-given right to be himself, that is, to be at his imaginative and creative best. They prohibit him from excelling, from fully realising his personal worth. This coerced retardation and stunting of the creative individual by the mass of conformist-minded men is brought about by the inability of the common crowd to understand, and to appreciate, the true value of the extraordinary ideas of a man of genius in the long run to their, and his, civilisation, and, also, by the common man's almost congenital envy of any other man who is more capable, energetic and enterprising than he. If it were left to the crude instincts of the crowd no new invention would survive, because the invention at once will meet the most strenuous opposition from workers whom the invention threatens to replace, and from other people of the society who cannot perceive that this invention in the long-run would make life easier for all. In such historical cases of mob violence the prototypes of the invented machines were usually destroyed, and the inventors terrorised, assaulted, and sometimes even killed. Under such circumstances, no improvements of man's life in a civilisation are possible and, consequently, men are forced to live a 'hand-to-mouth' life of unremitting toil which permits no opportunity for leisure that is necessary for the life of the mind. And the life of the mind, as mentioned above, is the very source of culture, which in turn is the very foundation of the civilisation. For these reasons, freedom of thought and action of the individual has always been an important precondition of a society which has a flourishing and rapidly improving civilisation.

The emergence of civilisation is made possible by the enterprise and creativity of the individuals within the society. Moreover, the rise of the civilisation as a material creation of man is a technological achievement which to a great extent is an accomplishment of technologists and engineers, and technology and engineering, in turn, is to a great extent a material manifestation of the culture of a society. Therefore, civilisation is the practical material realisation of the culture of the people who have created and are maintaining that culture. In order to be really human, man has to have technology by means of which he can raise himself above his crude natural existence. Such technological achievements challenge nature because they transcend nature and, therefore, are quite alien to nature as it exists.

Civilisation requires a great deal of voluntary cooperation between the individuals in the society, its efficient organisation and, in particular, a division of labour in order that the civilisation can function efficiently and flourish. The appropriate form of organisation of technological processes consists of specialisation, division of labour, and mechanisms of economic exchange.

Man's civilisation is his social heritage which is passed down from one generation to another, in an improved form if possible, as a particular kind of cultural patrimony. Civilisation as it exists has not been produced by some specific human foresight and planning, but is rather a natural outcome of the countless actions of economically minded, ambitious, individual men.

Civilisation at its best is adaptive because it is capable of change, and persistent because it will not change without a compelling cause, whether internal or external. When a civilisation is adaptive to itself, it is integrative: different parts of the civilisation harmonise with one another by mutual adaptation. A genuine civilisation always exhibits a basic cultural cohesion in its inner harmony. Despite the fact that civilisation is persistent, no civilisation is eternal, for change seems to be the eternal rule of life. Any political and technological establishment of men, such as a civilisation, tends to become set in its ways and, as a result, will in the end tend to collapse under an excess of its own basic ways of life which have become petrified because an excessive amount of concern with the security, regulations, standards, and formalities has dulled the keen spirit of enterprise of its people.

The social aspects of a civilisation consist of customs, subtle emotional relationships, a complex of personalities, and customary individual behaviours and manners, all of which constitute the traditions of the society. In the course of time these traditions become so 'natural' that people no longer are explicitly conscious of them, because traditions by that time have become part of their way of life. Since acceptable social conduct is an important tradition in civilised life, therefore, the maintenance of social decorum in professional relationships is an essential part of civilisation. Thomas Jefferson (1743-1826), a self-educated engineer, architect and scientist, recognised the cardinal virtue of such decorum in civilisation when he thought that the very means of civilisation is eighty percent good conduct, and good conduct is ninety percent good manners.

Men, as individuals, have always provided all the ideas and inventions on which the progress of civilisation vitally depends. These civilisations have been the most successful which have provided for their people freedom for independent thought and action, and more ample opportunities for voluntary cooperation, since only individual men can create values in their personal pursuits to improve themselves and, if possible, to excel. If there is freedom for men to market their personally created values in a voluntary exchange of values with other men, then peaceful competition develops as a byproduct of creating individual values; and, as a consequence, the individual and his civilisation will profit by it. An innovator, who does not depend upon current ideas to create his personal values, must necessarily be a nonconformist to his own age. A new idea makes discovery possible, and discovery leads to invention. An engineer at his best is inventive, and he carries out his constructive work in his civilisation in a strict relation to, and in concord with other individuals of his society. Engineer was born, when man first specialised in some mastery of his physical environment through practical art. To an engineer as an enterprising individual, liberty in the society of his civilisation is the great means for the attainment of all his professional ends. Therefore, preservation of the free society is an essential condition for the attainment of all the professional goals of an engineer. An autonomous man who loves his liberty in a free society never sacrifices himself for any heteronomous purpose dictated by others, which is the norm in a totalitarian society where any individual is a mere 'property' and 'selfless tool' of the State to be sacrificed for any purpose of the State, and he is willing to take any risk to save his personal values that he cherishes, above all his personal freedom. For the sake of his personal freedom, an autonomous man who loves his liberty is even willing to risk his life to defend the society which guarantees him this liberty. His personal freedom is his foremost personal value that he deems worth saving at all cost for his own sake, regardless of the personal risks he has to take to defend it under the aegis of free man's right to self-defence. Even if he ultimately may lose his life in self-defence, it is never self-sacrifice. Quite to the contrary, in his self-defence fraught with great hazard, a free and autonomous man fights with all his might to defend his life in an all-out effort to protect his most important personal value, his personal freedom and his own self. An autonomous free man with personal worth and self-respect, unlike the primitive man in the ancient Near East for whom men were no better than sacrificial animals to be slaughtered on the altar to pacify their gods, never sacrifices himself for anything or anybody, although he may voluntarily risk his life in his effort to save somebody who is of great personal value to him.

The great Austrian economist, philosopher and historian, Ludwig von Mises (1881-1973), expressed the essential conditions of an enterprising individual such as a professional engineer in a free, contractual society of the Western civilisation: "Liberty and freedom are the conditions of man within a contractual society. Peaceful social cooperation under a system of private ownership of the means of production means that within the range of the market the individual is not bound to obey and to serve an overlord. As far as he gives and serves other people, he does so of his own accord in order to be rewarded and served by the receivers. He exchanges goods and services, he does not do compulsory labour and does not pay tribute. He is certainly not independent. He depends upon the other members of society. But this dependence is mutual. The buyer depends on the seller, and the seller on the buyer."

History is a chronicle of human action, recording chronologically all the changes in the civilisation. Historical studies are beneficial to an engineer or a technologist because by knowing history he can understand better his importance to his civilisation and his social responsibilities. History will clearly demonstrate to the engineer or technologist that the art of engineering and technology is a cultural patrimony of the past ages of a civilisation, and make him realise that he can see farther, and understand his professional mission better than his predecessors only because he can base his work on their achievements – an insight well expressed by an ancient Roman, Didacus Stella (A.D. 39-65):

"A dwarf standing on the shoulders of a giant may see farther than the giant himself."

Every historical age has its own character which distinguishes it from other historical periods. History never returns to its previous state - it does not repeat itself. Accomplishments of engineering and technology in any age exhibit the social, mental, political, economic, and technical capabilities of the civilisation of this age, and, therefore, serve to convey a rather reliable information on the spirit of the people of any age. Some societies were very inventive, such as the Sumerian and the classical Western civilisation, whereas some civilisations, such as that of ancient Egypt, were very uninventive and, as a consequence, became culturally stagnant – and the natural native intellect declines in a stagnant cultural atmosphere. Engineering and technology offer men means of intelligent action and understanding, and a reliable method to guide them in the building of their civilisation because it is directed by historically disciplined reason – and not merely by raw emotion as is frequently the case with great historical movements.

Man of the Paleolithic Age lived a 'parasitic' life of hunting and food gathering, which constituted the first socially organised activity of men. In the Neolithic Age man became a food producer and thereby established an agricultural civilisation, which soon led to further refinement of the civilisation. Agriculture created a need for a calendar so that man could plant and raise food efficiently which, in turn, gradually led man to astronomical studies and, thus, to science. The incipient agricultural civilisation also required a variety of tools of cultivation, which led to extensive technological developments. Agriculture, furthermore, required the creation of irrigation and land division, which needed men with special skills of construction, planning and surveying – a professional craftsman now called the 'civil engineer'.

The Stone Age passed into the Copper Age about 4500 B.C., and the smelting of copper required craftsmen who had very special knowledge about metals – the copper smiths, or metallurgical technologists.

The subsequent development of commerce between communities with surplus production necessitated the building of means of communication between the communities, such as canals and graded tracks, which engineers had to provide. Commerce also required means of efficient and readily available transportation which led to the construction of boats and carts requiring technologist such as shipwrights and wainrights, and a method of accounting, which led to the development of ***writing*** and ***mathematics*** – the two major intellectual inventions of man.

Scientific Technology and Civilisation

Technology has been the great means of building a civilisation; yet, when improperly used, it can become a serious threat to civilised life. Science and technology promise to make man from the 'maker of tools' (***homo faber***) into the 'maker of worlds'; yet, at the same time, this promise also threatens to destroy the world man knows. The technology in modern times has become so intricate as almost to defy description, let alone understanding; and there are an extraordinary number, variety and complexity of factors that take part in technology and are, in turn, influenced by it: economic and legal systems, social values and political institutions, philosophical views and religious beliefs, and scientific and practical knowledge. Therefore, technology has to be considered as a system: a collection of interrelated and intercommunicating disciplines and activities. Technology, considered only as applied science which is unrelated to the moral and philosophical principles of the society, threatens to destroy man and his social environment by destroying man's social and natural environment through artificially induced social dislocation and environmental pollution which makes a healthy civilised life impossible.

Science and technology, moreover, tend to destroy the realm of inner freedom of the individual man through which the individual experiences his personal autonomy by controlling both the conditions of his personal existence and his creativity. Only a free man can be a complete individual and, therefore, completely human. Science and engineering have created the technological instruments for the exercise of totalitarian control over the freedom of the individual, and the consequent suppression of his individual freedom, the very source of the high order technology that has made this suppression possible, will destroy the civilisation which produced this technology because force and coercion cannot control human energy, it can only arrest the use of it. All the power in the world cannot make a better world if it is implemented by means of coercion and subjugation of the individual creativity. Only the legal safeguards and, particularly, the moral and cultural traditions of the liberty of the individual stand in the way of such totalitarian control of the individual by means of technology. Therefore, the correct moral application of technology, which is in harmony with the Western tradition of individual freedom for thought and action, is essential for the freedom of the creative individual and, thus, for the continuation of the Western civilisation. Accordingly, it is paramount that technology not be divorced from the moral imagination of the people of the Western civilisation for science and technology without conscience is the ruin of man's soul as well as his body.

Technology has to be understood both in itself, and in its role in, its impact on, and its relationship with cultural values, institutions, knowledge, beliefs, individuals, and the society of the civilisation itself. A sound civilisation is characterised by its capacity for self-generated changes that emanate from the social tensions created by the effects of technology. Therefore, a viable civilisation cannot have a stable, complete, and static balance of these relationships unless the society is small and decaying, that is, unless it is rather primitive.

CHAPTER I

SUMER: Cradle of Civilisation - Genesis of Writing, Mathematics, Technology and Engineering

Mesopotamia was a hydraulic civilisation, which technically means that it was essentially an engineering and technological achievement. The ancient Greek word '***mesopotamos***' literally meant 'between the rivers', in this case referring to the two rivers called the Tigris and the Euphrates, from which comes the name 'Mesopotamia'. In this land between the two rivers, the Tigris, a fierce river, and the Euphrates, a more sluggish river, the sources of both are situated in the Zagros mountains in Armenia, rise without advance warning. The Tigris, which is confined within high banks for most of its course, rises first in the beginning of March, and the Euphrates follows a week or so later. If the two rivers rise simultaneously, extensive flooding results. The rising of these two ancient rivers is created by the melting of snow in the Zagros mountains in the spring, and the resulting inundation of the two rivers makes the two rivers to overflow their banks. The Tigris is a swift river and it carries twice as much water as the Euphrates, which occasionally runs dry during the hot summer season and, for this reason, the Tigris is much more difficult to control for irrigation purposes than the Euphrates. At the time of the inundation the tides in the Persian Gulf could rise 9 feet (2.7m) above its normal level and bank up the two rivers. The two Mesopotamian rivers are subjected to very heavy and sudden floods that can inundate the entire delta area of the two rivers, an alluvium which makes up the lowlands of Mesopotamia. The Euphrates river is confined within its banks along its course past the ancient city ***Idda*** [now, Hit] where the best known natural wells of bitumen were situated, to the contemporary Ramadi, which is the first location where the flood waters of Euphrates could escape its river valley during the inundation into the ***Habbania*** depression of about 50½ square miles (146 square kilometers) and into the deeper Lake ***Agu Dibis*** depression of about 480 square miles (1,200 square kilometers). These two depressions provided a basin for the excessive floods of the Euphrates in ancient times and, thereby, permitted a safe cultivation of the whole lower Euphrates valley. The Euphrates river is still quite violent with a current of about 5 miles (8 km) an hour at ***Carchemish***, but in its lower regions its gradient diminishes appreciably, and the current of the river becomes more sluggish. These two rivers, but particularly the Euphrates, carry an enormous amount of silt, estimated at about 500 million tons a year – about five times the amount of silt carried by the relatively tame Nile river. Since the two rivers flow between the hills of marl which contain salt and gypsum, the silt carried by the two rivers contains great quantities of salt and gypsum that are deleterious to agriculture. The Tigris river flows in a deeply cut bed, and the normal level of its waters for most of its course lies below the surrounding countryside which makes it useless as a source of irrigation. The large quantities of silt carried by the Euphrates, which settles on the river-bed, has raised the Euphrates river in the course of time above the surrounding plains and, therefore, it can be tapped as a source for the irrigation of the alluvial plain. For these reasons, the Euphrates river makes agriculture possible in the region, the climate of which is extremely dry, and the soil of which is windswept, arid, and unproductive. Moreover, there are virtually no trees to supply timber in this land. The climate of Mesopotamia is more severe than in Egypt, as it is exposed to greater extremes of both heat and cold. The existing difference in the levels of these two rivers makes gravitational irrigation system possible since the Euphrates, which lies above the alluvial plain, can be used as the source and the Tigris, which lies below the alluvial plain, as a sink of irrigation waters. The Mesopotamian plain has an average seawards slope of 1-to-26,000, about half of that of the Nile river. Therefore, the difficulty in the Mesopotamian agriculture was not only the irrigation, but also the drainage of the superfluous water and silt, which tended to form stagnant pools and swamps, and if left to evaporate in the sun, the alkaline compounds and the salt present in the silt of the irrigation water would in time impregnate the soil and make it barren. For this reason, drainage was, and is, as important as irrigation in Mesopotamia.

The Tigris and the Euphrates are in spate between the late spring and the early summer, that is from April to early June, which is the worst time for agriculture. By April the winter-sown crops are well advanced and the summer crops are in. If the sudden rise of waters would flood the fields at this time to a height of 2 to 3 feet (0.6 to 0.9m) of water all hopes for a harvest would be dashed, and after the flood waters will have dried it would be too late for a fresh sowing. Therefore, in Mesopotamia all the fields had to be protected against flooding in order to make agriculture possible, because under natural conditions the land of Mesopotamia was unpromising and doomed to desolation. All this was changed by the people who came down south from the north, and populated this land, and turned it into a rich region by means of their ingenuity and gargantuan effort. These people, who are now called Sumerians, brought with them the greatest gifts of man: supreme native intelligence, fierce vigour, enormous capacity for work, venturesome spirit, and prodigious creative energy.

The earliest inhabitants of this region were the Ubaidians, who invented the method of perennial irrigation by protecting their villages and farmlands against flooding with dykes. Ubaidians apparently were Elamite farmers, who were Caucasians, and who had migrated to the alluvial plain from Elam and became mixed with some nomadic Semites. The Ubaidians founded the first cities in this area, such as ***Eridu***, ***Uruk***, ***Ur***, ***Nippur*** and ***Kish***. The 'Great Flood', which occurred sometime between 4500 B.C. and 4200 B.C., drowned the entire delta region, and apparently killed most of the Ubaidian population. ***Ur***, which was located on a high mount, seems to have survived this natural catastrophe.

After the 'Great Flood', about 4200 B.C., a new group of immigrants who apparently belonged to the Turko-Tartar tribes invaded the lower Mesopotamia from the Caucasian mountains. They brought with them technology of metallurgy and, more importantly, they introduced the wheel to civilisation. These Asianic people, probably Tartar tribes, established themselves at ***Uruk*** in the delta, and because of it they are called the ***Uruk*** people. The ***Uruk*** people spoke an agglutinative Asianic vernacular that is known as Sumerian language, and they were the ones who invented writing about 3500 B.C. in the late ***Uruk*** period. The ***Uruk*** people apparently had invented the wheel, a major invention of man, and the potter's wheel, and constructed of mud-brick the first known building with free-standing columns in their city ***Uruk***.

About 3200 B.C., a new invasion took place when the so-called 'Jamdat Nasr' people who came from the northeast gradually conquered the Ubaidian-Uruk civilisation. These invaders appear to have been as talented as the ***Uruk*** people, and they apparently mixed with the previous population through interbreeding. They established their city ***Jamdat Nasr***, near the city ***Kish***, but their government was overthrown by the older population about 3000 B.C.. In the subsequent rise of the early Dynastic period of Sumer, the so-called 'Sumerian Civilisation' was properly formed and the amalgam of the three groups of people appeared now as a common stock, called the Sumerians, who spoke a kind of agglutinative vernacular, somewhat akin to the Tartar, the Saami, the Estonian, the Finnish and the Hungarian vernacular but having no recognisable affiliation to any other known language. For instance, more than a thousand words in the old Estonian vernacular, a language belonging to the Uro-Altaic language branch, can be made through relatively minor modifications quite similar to Sumerian words. It appears that the ***Uruk*** people who spoke the newly formed Sumerian language constituted substantially the so-called 'Sumerian people'.

Sumerians solved the vexing problems of the two rivers by developing a sophisticated perennial irrigation system, which protects the agricultural land against inundation, by building an integrated system of earthen structures consisting of dams, dykes, canals, ditches, and trenches, to control the flood and to store flood waters in the basins. Their hydraulic structures permitted the conduction of water over the fields at the right time for planting and over the proper period of time so that not too much of the salt carried by the water was absorbed in the ground. The dykes had to be carefully maintained and incessantly inspected for erosion or crumbling in order to avoid a disaster, for all earthen structures made of the alluvial soil are friable. The transverse canals were excavated from the rivers to conduct water to the farming areas, and they were supplemented by feeder canals which supplied a network of ditches enclosing the fields. The farming lands were watered to a height of a few inches (about 5 cm) by breaking the crest of the irrigation ditch but the land was not permitted to soak up all the water which was saliferous by draining off the surplus water at the proper time. In the Sumerian irrigation system each village was responsible for the maintenance of their part of the dykes.

Sumerians turned this desolate and arid land by means of their method of perennial irrigation into a highly fertile region capable of two or three harvests per year, where one bushel sown per acre (0.405 hectares) could yield as much as 30 bushels in the harvest. The maintenance of this land demanded an enormous amount of labour for the perennial irrigation farming was a dawn-to-dusk operation. Since the perennial irrigation system is a dam-controlled irrigation system, Sumerians built many such dams into the banks of their rivers, but never across the rivers because their engineering art was not sufficiently advanced for this type of construction. At the same time the entire irrigation system was very precarious, and it required relentless and careful attention. All embankments made of soft alluvial soil had to be carefully protected against erosion by reed-matting. Since the canals and ditches silt up very fast, and the levees and the barrages erode rapidly in Mesopotamia, they had to be perpetually dredged, fortified and raised. These responsibilities became more-and-more demanding and extensive as time passed because the city-States of Sumer grew in size, and as a result legitimate conflicts arose between the governments of the neighbouring city-States concerning the water-rights, which often led to open warfare. The very words 'rivals' and 'rivalry' have originated in reference to holders of water-rights.

The courses of the two rivers of Mesopotamia in ancient times were much closer to each other than they were much later in the Neo-Babylonian period, when the rivers had changed their courses and were spread farther apart than in the days of the Sumerian civilisation. Therefore, transverse canals extracting water from the rivers did not have to be as long in the Sumerian period as they were later. These canals depended at their heads on great barrages and on river weirs, the effective operation of which required an immense amount of labour.

The lands bordering the Tigris river which were too high for the river waters to reach had to be irrigated by swapes (***shadufs***) balanced by counterweights. Water was lifted by swapes over the high banks of the river into specially constructed canals. Since it is possible to lift about 212 cubic feet (6 cubic meters) of water in an hour with the swape, three people working with a shaduf could irrigate about half an acre a day. Swapes are still in use in modern Egypt.

Sumerians and the Rise of Civilisation

Sumerians founded the civilisation of man, and their civilising influence spread into the far corners of the world over many millennia : to India, to China, and to Europe.

Sumerians created the first organised city-State: an organised large-scale government as a formal State with formal laws under the guidance of a bureaucratic administration charged to run this large community according to organised thought. Sumerians believed that their city-State was an extension of the cosmic order, which had been created out of primæval chaos by *Enlil*, their god of air and storm who was the head of the Sumerian pantheon. In Sumerian myths the chief god *Enlil* created the universal laws (***me***) which in their opinion governed all existence. These divine laws governed everything and everybody in the universe, and as a consequence everything in the world acted in accordance with these divine rules which numbered more than a hundred: one ***me*** for each aspect of the world. *Enlil*'s divine laws not only guided the world but also other gods. They believed that when *Enlil* descended to the underworld, after arranging for the irrigation of the land of the two rivers by giving strict rules for agriculture as well as for the regulation of life, he entrusted the implementation of these laws to *Enki*, the god of sweet waters, as his executor. All these religious beliefs gave the Sumerians a profound conviction in the existence of order underlying both nature and human nature which together with their native ingenuity made Sumerians the most ingenious organisers and inventors of all ages: they systematised their large-scale business with standard weights, measures and timekeeping, and based their business operations on detailed records and accounting, and on institutions of credit.

Sumerians marshalled the first organised armies consisting of phalanxes for the battles of their wars, which they conducted according to war strategy and battle tactics. They planned and executed extensive public works in which the early Sumerians created the first monumental buildings, and with it the first decorative art; they created the first literature ranging from tales to the proverbs to the epics; they devised the first formally organised learning and founded the first scribal school (***edubba***).

Sumerians established the first known moral code by setting up ideals such as righteousness, truthfulness, justice, compassion, and mercy for the individual man. The primitive men who had no morality merely lived by the morale of the group. Primitive man's amoral behaviour was essentially governed by kinship and tribal custom bound by taboos, which fostered in man an attitude of uncritical compliance and unawareness of the self. Primitive man thought only of his relationship with gods, with nature, and with tribal customs. Morality, which is a personal attribute, never had any part in the primitive man's behaviour. In a Sumerian city-State, however, an individual man for the first time was obliged to think of his relationship with another man, since the right conduct of an individual man became a matter of his own conscious choice and personal responsibility. One consequence of this responsibility was that man was compelled to think about his self. The establishment of a general moral code was the Sumerian solution to the problem of the right conduct for a man who has been removed from his amoral tribal existence. Thus Sumerians established the first known formal laws, and they secured their justice by the dint of the law and moral persuasion.

Sumerians thought that the divine forces which exercise control over the universe consist of a cosmic pantheon: *Anu*, the highest of the gods, was the god of heavens who dominated the visible universe; *Enlil*, who presided over the region between heaven and Earth, was the lord of the wind and the storms who exercised lordship over the various city gods from his sanctuary in the city ***Nippur***; *Enki* was the god of the Earth. This divine trinity represented the primary cosmic gods. A secondary divine trinity consisted of the gods of the celestial bodies which govern the Earthly life by their light: *Nannar*, the Moon god; *Utu*, the Sun god; and *Inanna*, the god of the morning star Venus who also stood for the Mother Earth. Sumerians explained natural phenomena by mythical and religious stories, because they believed that everything they accomplished had its source in *Enki*, and that every natural occurrence was determined by *Enlil*'s laws of nature and by the arbitrary whims of the gods. Sumerians were the first civilised people to humanise gods in the likeness of humans. Sumerian gods had human figures, sexes and families and possessed human emotions, although their loves and hates were much more violent. The Sumerian gods only differed from men by their virtue of being immortal and possessing awesome divine powers. Beneath the gods, Sumerians believed in the existence of a realm of demons. Demons were the wicked and restless spirits of the dead who lived in tombs, in darkness, and in deserts whence they brought terror and torment upon mankind. Although Sumerians did accede to the existence of a few good demons, they regarded most of the demons to be thoroughly wicked and malicious. Sumerians believed that the demons could be overcome only by means of incantations and magic practised by the priesthood, an art consisting of many formulae that represented true learning to Sumerians. Therefore, Sumerians believed that man had no effective influence on the events in this world and on the course of human life, and that the main task of man in the defence of himself was to discover by divination, also practised as true learning by the priesthood, the rules of *Enlil* which guided the phenomena as well as the will of the gods.

The Sumerians believed that the nature was animated by the will of the gods whom they considered to be amoral beings, and that the wellbeing of any community depended entirely upon the goodwill of the patron deity of the city-State. The answer of Sumerians to all natural phenomena was: '*Enki* did it'. They claimed *Enki* to be 'the ear and mind of all the lands'. Sumerians observed that justice frequently did not prevail in nature which led them to the conclusion that the divine will is inscrutable to man as the Sumerian prototype of the story of Job reveals. Sumerians came to the conclusion that there are insolvable problems and unfathomable mysteries for man in this world, and that man's only means of survival was to worship the gods, and to obey and to submit to the inevitable in his life on Earth. They were convinced that man was born to be the slave of the gods who nominally owned everything on Earth, and that man had to devote all his efforts to the service of the gods. Sumerian city-State was theoretically, but not in practice, owned and ruled by a patron god, whose temple was the seat of its administration and whose service was the object of its enterprise. Writing was first invented by the Sumerians for the practical purpose of keeping gods' accounts.

Early Sumerian cities in the Ubaidian period seem to have enjoyed considerable political and economic freedom. They had a word for freedom (***amargi***), a theory of equality under the law, and a popular assembly. When 'kings descended from heaven' in the city-State ***Kish*** after the 'Great Flood', there still remained an appreciable social sector of free and private enterprise in the Sumerian society. The independent merchant-entrepreneurs of Sumer organised far-reaching trade, which in ancient Egypt was conducted as a stagnant bureaucratic operation by the pharaoh's officials. Smaller city-States of Sumer had a steward, called ***ensi***, who was an 'overseer', a 'caretaker', or a 'governor'. Larger city-States in addition to ***ensi***, also had a king whom Sumerians called the 'great man' (***lugal***), who had an overriding authority as a servant of the patron god of the city, or group of cities, over both the ***ensies*** and the high priests. The position of the king in theory, and in early period also in practice, was only temporary because when the gods gave the 'proper sign' it was his duty to retire or to let himself to be removed. Before 2800 B.C. there existed political life in the Sumerian cities, because there existed public affairs since kings were elected by a popularly elected bicameral assembly of free citizens consisting of an upper house of elders and a lower house of arm-bearing men. The king held office only during an emergency, usually a war, but he was completely dependent on the assembly's consent, and was never allowed to rule as military dictator or tyrant. These may have been very ancient traditions which the early Sumerians brought south from the European steppes and Caucasian mountains. After 2800 B.C., the self-ruling city-States in Sumer disappeared together with most of the real political life. Thenceforth, the government of the city-State became essentially the affair of the ruler. According to the legend, the first site of absolute kingship in Sumer was the city-State of ***Kish***. Thenceforward the rulers remained the chief overseers of public works. The reappearance of genuine political life in civilisation came much later with the ascendance of the Indo-Europeans, who came from the plains and steppes of Europe, and who had traditions similar to those of the early Sumerians but whose philosophy of life was entirely different from that of the Sumerians.

Sumerians developed the first mature and sophisticated religion [in Latin, ***res***-thing, affair; ***ligare***-to bind together] with a pantheon of gods and goddesses, and an intricate system of religious symbolism. In Sumerian view the conditions of the hereafter were the exact counterparts to the conditions on Earth. Sumerian cities were subjected to frequent attacks by the fierce warriors from the Caucasian mountains and by the wild Semitic desert nomads, whereas Egypt, because of its favourable topography, was relatively safe from foreign invasions during this period. The almost indefensible state of the Mesopotamian cities, and the precarious and unpredictable conditions of the two rivers which gave Sumerians much anxiety, fostered a deep sense of insecurity and inadequacy in Sumerians that expressed itself in their pessimistic view of life, a view which was in sharp contrast to the naive, optimistic view of life of the ancient Egyptians in the period of the Ancient Kingdom.

Each of the Sumerian city-States was centered around a holy precinct [in Greek, ***temenos***], which contained the temple of the patron god of the city who was at first called the 'king of the city', and was ruled by a high priest or king. The ***temenos***, which contained a large number of shrines, storehouses, courtyards and dwellings for the temple personnel, was dominated by the ***ziggurat*** [Assyrian word for 'peak'], a triple-staged and terraced structure topped by a sanctuary of the patron god. These temples were built on mounds because they were thought to be the 'bond between heaven and Earth'. The ziggurat was a later development of the high-staged tower structures the Sumerians had built in their earlier period as artificial mounds as a look-out for gods and the approaching flood, and it remained the very pillar of the Sumerian culture. Sumerian cities had bazaars, restaurants and taverns, and in their public squares they staged wrestling competitions, games of chance, as well as recitations by professional bards.

However, whatever the Sumerians accomplished in their civilisation was always in the name of the gods, and never in the name of men because, as mentioned above, they thought the source of every action and achievement of man to be the god *Enki*, who had the amazing ability 'to budget the accounts of the universe'. To this extent man was not quite conscious of his own powers as a creator, neither did he become conscious of himself as a creator of his own world in any other Eastern civilisation. Their assessment of man was graphically expressed in one Sumerian poem: 'Mere man, his days are numbered – whatever he may do, he is but wind '.

The ancient Sumerians had a natural passion for law and justice which arose from their competitive and individualistic temperament and, their passionate regard for private property. They were keenly conscious of their personal rights and resented any encroachment upon these rights, whether by their equals, by their superiors, or even by their king. This is the basic reason why Sumerians compiled highly refined law codes, for they tried to avoid misunderstandings, misrepresentations and arbitrariness.

About 2350 B.C. the people of the city-State ***Lagash*** rose in rebellion, overthrew the corrupt dynasty of Lagash and chose a new leader, Urukagina. Urukagina, who ruled for a decade, established 'freedom (***amargi***)' for its people by proclaiming the first laws designed to safeguard the rights of ordinary citizens. All tax collectors were abolished, because his laws protected widows and the poor from the avaricious government tax collectors. The idea of freedom provoked great excitement among the Sumerians, as frequent references to it in the extant Sumerian writings testify. However, Urukagina's legal reforms were not set down as a formal code of law.

The first formal Law Code in history was given by the King Ur-Nammu of the third dynasty of the city-State ***Ur*** about 2125 B.C., after Ur-Nammu had defeated the neighbouring city-State ***Lagash*** on the battle field and killed the King of Lagash. He established a United Kingdom and called himself: 'King of Sumer and Akkad', although the third dynasty of ***Ur*** had already assumed the title: 'King of the four quarters of the Earth', a claim for the rulership over the known world. Ur-Nammu inaugurated the so-called 'golden age' of Sumer, during which period Sumerian culture reached its zenith. In his comprehensive law code which contained about 300 concisely written laws in more than 3,600 lines of cuneiform. Ur-Nammu introduced a humane approach to the law by requiring that the 'punishment fit the crime'.

About 1850 B.C., an even more formal law code was established by King Lipit-Ishtar of the city-State ***Isin***. It had a prologue declaring its objectives as 'establishing justice in Sumer ... according to the word of *Enlil*', the laws themselves, and an epilogue stating that the State was set up by the king for the 'wellbeing' of the Sumerian people. The records of various judgements of law cases (***ditillas***) were filed in chronological order for later reference. The kings who ruled over many Sumerian city-States were, in principle, responsible for the laws they made. In practice, however, the local ruler (***ensi)*** of each city-State was responsible for the enforcement of the law and the judges he had appointed. More than a century later, during the Semitic hegemony of Mesopotamia, the Amorite King Hammurabi of ***Babylon*** issued his well-known Hammurabi Law Code, which was derived from the Sumerian Law Code.

Sumerians were venturesome merchant-entrepreneurs, and their 60-foot sailing galleys with two banks of oars plied the Mediterranean, the Persian and the Arabian gulf, and sailed as far as India, Somaliland and Ethiopia in their trading enterprises. Sumerians built sailing ships probably before the Egyptians built theirs.

Sumerians have left a permanent imprint on all civilisations, but particularly on the Occidental civilisation, since the Sumerian culture has left the Western man a spiritual legacy of the basic conflicts between reason and faith, hope and despair, freedom and authority, progress and stagnation, and conquest and defeat.

Since the modern civilisation is essentially a descendant of the pioneering civilisation created by the Sumerians, it is culturally important to the contemporary man to be knowledgeable of the enormous importance of Sumerians to the modern civilisation.

Sumerians: 4000 B.C. - 1800 B.C.

The city ***Eridu*** [now, Abu Shahrain] existed long before the 'Great Flood' and may have been founded about 5000 B.C. This city is located at the southern edge of the Mesopotamian alluvium bordering at the Arabian desert. ***Eridu*** was the first of the five cities of the Ubaidians which existed before the 'Great Flood', and it was the center of worship of the river god *Enki*, the god of sweet water. ***Eridu*** was served by the canals from the Euphrates and it was the first significant Sumerian city which had the first typically Mesopotamian temple with the cella (sanctuary) containing an altar placed in a niche and an offering table. Later Sumerian temples had a tripartite plan with subsidiary rooms on either side of the cella. ***Eridu*** was the only city of Sumer in which a variety of stones, a building material available only at the border of the Arabian desert, were used in building. It also had one of the first large royal palaces which was separate from the religious precinct.

By 3500 B.C. the early Sumerians, the ***Uruk*** people, were in complete control of the Mesopotamian civilisation, and they appear to have been the inventors of the wheel, and to have tamed the wild ass, called 'onager'. It is reasonable to assume that the ***Uruk*** people had accomplished this feat already before they came to Mesopotamia from the north. Sumerians at first used four-wheeled carts with fixed axles. The pivoted axle, which facilitates turning of carts, was introduced much later, probably about 1500 B.C.. The ***Uruk*** people also invented the seeder-plough which mechanised agriculture, and made planting crops a more efficient agricultural operation. In this period the potter's wheel was in wide use among ***Uruk*** people in an inchoate mass-production of pottery, and wedge-shaped bricks were used to line wells and to build the first crude arches.

About 3500 B.C. in a northern city of early Sumer, ***Tepe-Gawra*** [located about 10 miles northwest of ***Nineveh*** near the confluence of the Tigris and the Upper Zab river], the city streets which radiated from the central plaza were paved with stones and were provided with public drains whereas the subsidiary streets were unpaved. The temples of ***Tepe-Gawra*** were the first monumental buildings constructed by man. They were mud-brick structures which incorporated the first known wall paintings and simple wall reliefs made of mud-plaster.

By 3500 B.C. the early Sumerians, the ***Uruk*** people, had made the greatest intellectual invention of man: they had invented an essentially pictographic type of writing which consisted of symbols representing things and a few additional symbols for various meanings. At that time ***Uruk*** [Biblical ***Erech***, now Warka] was by far the largest Sumerian city, which by 2900 B.C. had reached a city perimeter of about 6 miles (9 km.). Approximately ⅓ of the area of the city ***Uruk*** was covered by the temple precinct (***temenos***). This city had established the scribal school (***edubba***) in which a written vocabulary of some 2000 different pictographic signs were taught to the Sumerian students. A remarkable building in ***Uruk*** was the 'Pillar Temple', also called the 'Red Temple', which is the first known building with free-standing columns. This new style of building had two rows of massive mud-brick columns of 8½-foot (2.6 m) diameter. The surfaces of these columns were made firm by hard cones of fired clay, or of stone, hammered into the huge columns in a pattern which simulated the trunk of the palm tree.

The earliest documented large canal built by Sumerians was constructed about 3000 B.C. by Entemanna, governor (***ensi***) of the city-State ***Lagash***. The Entemanna Canal connected the Tigris with the Euphrates near the 46th meridian in the vicinity of ***Lagash*** where the distance between the two rivers was the narrowest, from 10 to 15 miles (16 to 24 km). About this time an arched drain was constructed in the holy city-State ***Nippur*** [now, Nuffar], the sanctuary of the chief god *Enlil* of Sumer.

About 2800 B.C. the Sumerians invented the cuneiform writing which was a mixture of ideographic and phonetico-syllabic writing containing unpronounced determinatives. By 2500 B.C. it had become a flexible, entirely phonetic system which could express anything a man might say or think. It was based upon a rebus principle which associated symbols with sounds rather than meanings. This momentous event marks the beginning of the historical age of man. The cuneiform syllabary was later reduced to about 700 signs.

About this time Sumerians also invented the positional numeration, the place-value notation and a symbol equivalent to the decimal point in arithmetic, which had both a base of 10 and a base of 60. By that time, kings were already in complete control of the city-State governments, and artisans worked in guildlike organisations.

By 2600 B.C., the first hymns and epics had been written, headed by the heroic epic of Gilgamesh [the Sumerian Herakles]. Gilgamesh was an early King of ***Uruk***, who had won hegemony over other Sumerian city-States in the twenty-seventh century B.C..

In 2450 B.C., the archivists in the city-State ***Lagash*** became the first historiographers by describing the first known diplomatic treaty made between the city-States ***Lagash*** and ***Umma***.

About 2400 B.C. Sumer was conquered for the first time by foreigners. Akkadians, members of a wild Semitic tribe from the Arabian desert, had been infiltrating into the northern part of Mesopotamia for centuries, and they had settled in large numbers in the northern Sumerian cities. Many Semites had risen to eminent positions in some of these Sumerian cities, and one of them, a Semite who later called himself '***Sargon***', usurped power in the city of ***Kish***. ***Sargon***, which meant 'the true king', established the first known empire stretching from the Mediterranean almost as far as to India. ***Sargon***'s strategy of conquest established the basic purpose of any empire-builder: conquest for plunder, and for natural resources. The ancient man believed that wealth in this world is a fixed quantity, since they believed that man could not create wealth, which in their view was rather created by the gods and remained the same for all time. Therefore, if a man wanted to obtain more wealth, he had to take it from somebody else.

Sargon followed a nationalistic policy by appointing only fellow Semites to important functionary positions in his Empire of Sumer and Akkad. He built a new capital city ***Akkad***, [also known as ***Agade***] of his Empire somewhere near the contemporary city ***Baghdad*** located at the confluence of the Tigris and its tributary, the Diyala.

A large mass of fierce warriors called Gutians, or Gutii, swept down into Mesopotamia from the Zagros mountains and smashed the Sumero-Akkadian Empire of ***Sargon*** about 2300 B.C.. They razed his capital ***Akkad*** down to the ground in their savage attack which was so devastating and destructive that to this day the ruins of the ancient city ***Akkad*** have not been discovered. Gutians dominated the Sumero-Akkadian city-States over a hundred years, from about 2300 to 2200 B.C. About 2200 B.C., after Mesopotamia had been liberated from the Gutian domination, Gudea, the priest-governor (***patesi***) of the city-State ***Lagash***, brought the Sumerian culture to its highest intellectual level, for he himself was a leading scholar as well as a builder-engineer (***batu***). There exists a small green diorite statue of Gudea which depicts him sitting with a scaled plan for the reconstruction of the temple of the patron god *Ningirsu*, drawing instruments and a scale in his lap. This is the oldest extant evidence of construction plans drawn to scale. The first extant drawings of technical nature stem from this period of Sumerian revival. The priest-governor Gudea was deified after his death by the people of ***Lagash*** on account of his great piety.

In the period from 2200 B.C. to 2000 B.C., the palace of the king in the provincial city-State ***Eshnunna*** [now Tell Asmar, at the confluence of the rivers Tigris and Diyala], had a throne room and the beginning of a processional road, a paved path running from the throne room diagonally across the open courtyard. This palace was furnished with an elaborate sanitary system: lavatories and bathrooms located along the outside wall discharged their effluent directly into a large vaulted main sewer that ran the entire length of the street. All bathrooms had floors and walls made of bitumen-covered bricks. All lavatories had raised stone pedestals, and some had shaped bitumen seats. Drains were made of baked bricks joined and lined with bitumen, and provided with inspection chambers pierced with inspection holes for drain rods to facilitate the cleaning of the drains at principal junctions. The main sewer which had a height of 3feet 4 inches (1 m) was made of burnt bricks, and was covered by a circular vault made of wedge-shaped burnt bricks. All in all, the palace had assumed by that time a distinctive character as a building, and its sanitary system was a masterpiece of construction.

In 2100 B.C., the last dynasty of ***Ur*** brought the engineering skills of Sumerians to its highest perfection. Their engineers used roughly cut limestone masonry as well as rubble-and-brick masonry, they built true arches and barrel vaults in stone, in sun-dried mud-brick, and in kiln-fired brick. Corbelled vaulting and corbelled domes were built, and pendentives in the form of spherical triangles were constructed to support domed roofs of rectangular buildings.

Sumerian monumental building reached its peak in ***Ur***, and the most spectacular of these buildings were the ziggurats, or staged towers as artificial mounds. King Ur-Nammu of ***Ur***, rebuilt the great triple-staged ziggurat tower of ***Ur***, the first stage of which is still extant. It was a 3-stage structure which had a shrine for the Moon god *Nanner*, the patron god of the city ***Ur***, on top of the third stage. The base of the lower stage of this ziggurat is 236 by 177 feet (72 by 54 m), and the thickness of the battered revetment with panelled recesses is 8 feet. The total height of the 3-stage structure was 80 feet (24.4 m). The walls of the lower stage have both a horizontal curvature and a vertical entasis [perhaps to compensate for optical distortion, an architectural device later used in the design of Parthenon on the Akropolis in Athens by the ancient Greek ***architekton*** Iktinos]: the horizontal curvature is 1:125, the vertical entasis is 1:100.

Sumerians built their shrine on top of a mound as an artificial 'mountain'. The stepped structure of the ziggurat is made necessary by the inherent limit of the strength of the mud-brick which can fail under its own weight. The interior of the ziggurat was filled with mud-brick to prevent shrinkage and uneven settlement of the entire structure. The brickwork of the ziggurat was interlaced with layers of reed matting in every fifth course of bricks to distribute pressure and render the structure more cohesive. The bricks were laid in bitumen mastic. Tough twisted reed cables at right angles to one another running in bitumen mastic joints from face to face of the structure tied the entire structure together. The outside revetment walls were made of reddish-brown burnt brick masonry with bituminous mastic joints, and provided with drains at regular 3 feet 11 inches (1.2 m) intervals along the height of the wall. The reddish brown colour of these brick walls has hitherto defied explanation. It is possible that special clay was imported for the making of bricks in the exterior walls.

Bitumen is a heavy fraction of naphta (Babylonian term, ***naptu***). The chief sources of bitumen were the natural wells near the ancient city ***Iddu*** [now Hit] at the Euphrates river. The bitumen was readily obtained from the natural seepage of these wells, and it was relatively free of adulterants. Mastic was made of bitumen by melting and mixing bitumen with fillers consisting of sand and such fibrous materials as straw, but also of loam and lime. Mastic, the fibrous matter of which amounted to about 15% of the mixture, was used by Sumerian engineers as mortar, and it had such excellent strength that in time it became stronger than the burnt brick itself. Moreover, the bituminous mastic gave excellent waterproofing to the structures. The kiln-fired bricks of the Sumerians were rather porous because they were baked under relatively low heat, usually below 932°F (500°C).

King Shulgi, a son of Ur-Nammu, was one of the most brilliant rulers of ancient Mesopotamia. He was a sage, diplomat, warrior, builder, and lavish patron of arts. Shulgi governed over a realm which he stretched by conquest from the Mediterranean Sea to Persia, an Empire as large as that of ***Sargon***. Sumerian kings had always maintained a good system of graded roads, but Shulgi was particularly active in extending and improving the network of graded roads. Shulgi, himself, liked to travel extensively by roads, and he took personal pride in the improvement of the road system which had been built under his rule. He introduced a series of landscaped road houses for travellers, places where the weary voyagers could rest and receive the necessary assistance. This innovation of Shulgi later led to the establishment of postal roads.

By 2000 B.C. Sumerians had invented the pulley, an important labour-saving device. By that time it had become a general practice to provide open drains in the cities for surface water removal, and underground drains to keep the soil under the foundations of buildings dry to minimise foundation settlements – a construction practice still in use today.

Another group of Arab nomads, called Amorites, seized a small town, later called ***Babylon***, at the Euphrates and held it from 1813 B.C. to 1515 B.C. Their sixth King Hammurabi, who ruled from 1711 B.C. to 1669 B.C., made the city of ***Babylon*** the master of the entire Mesopotamia but only after 30 years of intense warfare with the Elamites. Hammurabi, who called himself the 'god of kings', is known for his Law Code that consisted of the Sumerian Law Code supplemented with many additional regulations mostly about the construction and operation of dams and canals. Under Hammurabi's rule, extensive irrigation works were carried out. It appears that during his rule the first dam was built across a major river, the Tigris, about 15 miles (24 km) north of the confluence of the Tigris and its tributary, the Adheim river, which changed the course of the Tigris. The Tigris river returned to his old course after this dam, now called the 'Nimrud Dam', failed about 1200 B.C..

About 1750 B.C. in the palace of the Aramaean kings in the city-State ***Mari***, a rich Semitic trade center located by an important caravan route at the Euphrates north of the Arabian desert, there existed extensive sanitary installations. The royal bathrooms were provided with ceramic bathtubs, one for the cold and one for the warm water, which had to be emptied by baling. The palace itself was a large complex of structures covering seven acres and consisting of open courtyards and 300 rooms which were beautifully decorated with wall paintings. The palace of ***Mari*** which was a grand example of a combined abode and administrative center of a Mesopotamian ruler incorporated a palace school for the children of the palace officials. The palace complex of ***Mari*** which had a size of 656 by 397 feet (200 by 121 meters), was razed to the ground sometime before 1703 B.C. by the Amorite King of ***Babylon***, Hammurabi, in his campaign to create the Babylonian Empire. Recently more than 20,000 clay tablet documents were unearthed jn the archives of the destroyed palace of ***Mari*** which have given invaluable information on this period of Mesopotamian history.

By 1200 B.C. when ***Sumer*** and ***Babylon*** were under the domination of the Indo-European warriors Kassites whose hegemony lasted from 1560 B.C. to 910 B.C., an all important invention was already in general use: a water-raising treadmill, which substitutes rectilinear motion for a continuous rotary motion, as some extant clay tablet documents testify.

Founding of Schools and Formal Education

Sumerians founded formal education as well as the formal teaching institution called the 'tablet house (in Sumerian, ***edubba***)' which was conducted with harsh discipline imposed by cane. In contrast to most modern schools where pupils are coerced by the State to serve time, Sumerian scribal schools were not run like penitentiaries : their pupils attended voluntarily from 6 years to 18 years of age. School studies took 11 hours a day every day, but for 6 free days every month and 3 holidays with required attendance in religious festivals. Sumerian students studied writing, and liberal arts from the literature in which gods were glorified, heroes exalted, and kings extolled in various epics. They also studied singing, conducting a choir, and playing various musical instruments such as the harp, the lute and the flute. Mathematics was taught for application such as calculating areas, volumes, reciprocals, squares, square roots, cubes and cube roots, and compound interest. In arithmetic Sumerians not only had devised the positional numeration and place-value notation based on 60, but also the decimal system based on 10 and a symbol equivalent to the decimal point, all of which they taught in their scribal schools. Moreover, Sumerians not only handled negative numbers, fractions, and division, but also proved themselves to be quite capable algebraists. Sumerian arithmetic had become by 2000 B.C. a quite sophisticated rhetorical algebra in which quadratic equations were solved by a method resembling the method of substitution in a general formula and by completing the square, and even some cubic and biquadratic equations were solved with the help of elaborate numerical tables.

In the period from 2200 to 2000 B.C., Sumerians knew how to measure areas of rectangles, and of right and isosceles triangles. They also had some practical knowledge of the so-called 'Pythagorean theorem', and they knew that the angle inscribed in the semicircle is a right angle. They also were able to calculate the volumes of rectangular parallelepipeds, of right circular cylinders, of frustrums of cones, and of square pyramids. Their formula for the volume V of the frustrum of a square pyramid with side b at the top, side a at the bottom, and height h, can be given by modern algebra as follows :

$$V = h\{[(a + b)/2]^2 + (1/3)\,[(a - b)/2]^2\} .$$

Sumerians prepared multiplication tables, tables for squares, cubes, square-roots and cube-roots of numbers to facilitate practical computation, and the solution of quadratic and cubic equations in algebra.

Engineering was taught in Sumerian schools by specialists: drawing of maps and plans of structures for the construction of public buildings, calculation of the number of bricks needed to build a wall, the volume of dirt required to build a ramp, the volume of excavation for a canal, and similar practical problems.

Sumerians were the first to invent the Lunar Calendar, in which each month had 29 or 30 days and began on the evening of the new moon. An extra month was inserted at regular intervals to make up a solar year. Their astronomy was remarkably sophisticated.

Since in Sumer virtually any natural occurrence was treated as an omen, divination was also taught in Sumerian schools: the art of reading the will of the gods, and of predicting the future. Many manuals of omens were sold on the open market. In this connexion, astronomy, and astrology were studied, since Sumerians believed that heavenly bodies were divine and, therefore, they sought to foretell the divine will also from the motions of heavenly bodies. Even medicine was taught in Sumerian schools.

In Sumerian schools oral examinations were given in individual subjects, and final examinations were held before an assembly of schoolmasters in the courtyard of the school. The students who failed their examinations and became the so-called 'drop-outs' from Sumerian scribal schools, usually established themselves as public letter writers. Sumerian scribes educated in their scribal schools were the first known professionals: teachers, administrators, lawyers, priests, secretaries, physicians and engineers.

Mesopotamian Chronology:

4500 B.C.- 4200 B.C.	The 'Great Flood' kills most autochthonous inhabitants, called Ubaidians.
4000 B.C.	Turko-Tartar tribes with their bronze technology invade Mesopotamia from the Caucasian mountains after the 'Great Flood'. These Asianic people, together with the remnants of Ubaidians, and some Semitic invaders from the Arabian desert become the Sumerians. Revolutionary technological invention of the wheel.
3500 B.C.	Revolutionary intellectual invention of writing and mathematics by Sumerians.
	Semitic Hegemony **:**
c.2400 B.C.- 2300 B.C.	Empire of Sumer and Akkad. Semitic overthrow of the Sumerian city-States by the Akkadian usurper ***Sargon***. Rise of imperialism: conquest for wealth and natural resources. The first known empire.
	Indo-European Hegemony **:**
2300 B.C.- 2200 B.C.	Indo-European Gutians, known as Gutii, conquer Akkad and part of Sumer.

	Sumerian Recovery :
c.2200 B.C.	Priest-governor Gudea of ***Lagash*** and rebirth of high Sumerian culture.
c.2150 B.C.-1900 B.C.	Third Dynasty of ***Ur*** and the zenith of Sumerian culture and engineering. First construction of far-reaching road system.
	Semitic Hegemony :
c.1900 B.C.-1600 B.C.	***Babylon*** - Semitic Amorites rule Sumer and Akkad.
c.1711 B.C.-1669 B.C.	Reign of Hammurabi: extensive hydraulic engineering, and the first dam across a major river, the Tigris.
	Indo-European Hegemony :
c.1600 B.C.	Hittites conquer ***Babylon***.
c.1560 B.C.- 910 B.C.	Kassites rule ***Babylon***.
c.910 B.C.- 612 B.C.	Assyrians rule ***Babylon***. Construction of extensive military road system.
	Semitic Hegemony :
c.606 B.C.- 538 B.C.	***Neo-Babylon*** – Semitic Chaldeans rule ***Babylon***. King Nebuchadrezzar II and extensive hydraulic engineering.
	Indo-European Hegemony :
c.600 B.C.	***Zarathushtra***: intellectual monotheism ministered by dual philosophy and freewill of man.
539 B.C.	Persian King Cyrus conquers ***Neo-Babylon***. Persian Empire. First large-scale highway construction.
330 B.C.	Alexandros III of Macedon conquers Persian Empire.

CHAPTER II

ANCIENT EGYPT: Monumental Engineering

Topographically, the entire country of Egypt is a forbidding barren desert. Only the narrow Nile river valley, a green belt of arable land which varies from a mile width to an average of 13 miles (20.9 km) to the maximum of 150 miles (241.4 km) in the delta, is fertile and inhabitable – and this valley is only fit for human occupation because of the Nile river. This fact was clearly recognised by Egyptian priests who told the ancient Greek historian Herodotos in the 5th century B.C.: "Egypt is a gift of the river ." This narrow inhabitable region bordering the Nile river was virtually isolated from the rest of the ancient world by the Libyan desert in the West, by the cataracts and the Nubian desert in the South, by the Arabian desert to the East and by the Mediterranean Sea in the North.

The Nile river is one of the most predictable major rivers in the world. It inundates virtually on schedule from the end of July to the end of October – just in time for planting of the winter crops. The Nile river, very generously, signals the coming of its inundation by first turning green with the scum of the tropical vegetation that floats down the river from the mountains of Central Africa as a result of the heavy tropical rains that precipitate in these mountain ranges. The subsequent inundation of the Nile carries with it about one hundred million tons of rich tropical silt from the mountains – just the right amount to obviate the great labour of removing the excess silt which was necessary in Mesopotamia. The nature of the inundation of the Nile was ideal for the 'basin irrigation system', which yields generally one harvest per year, and this is the irrigation system that was developed by the ancient Egyptians. The normal depth of inundation above the river bed along the 60-mile (973.6 km) length of the Nile river was about 48 feet (14.6 m) at the Elephantine Island, 41½ feet (12.6 m) at Edfu, 27½ feet (8.4 m) at Memphis, and 10½ feet (3.2 m) in the delta region. The river bed of the Nile has been raised some 20 feet (6.1 m) over the span of 5,000 years as a result of the silt deposited by the countless inundations of the Nile river.

Emergence of Ancient Egyptian Nation

About 3500 B.C. the upper Nile Valley was invaded by the Falcon Clan, the worshippers of ***Horus***, who came from the Red Sea through the ***Rohanu*** Depression (now called Wadi Hammamat) to the Nile valley near the city ***Qebti*** (in Greek, Koptos), and conquered the autochthonous inhabitants of the valley. They were probably the seafaring copper traders who brought with them the superior copper technology of Sumer. By 3100 B.C. the Falcon Clan had conquered also the delta area and, thereby, had united the entire Nile valley into one single nation, an accomplishment that was facilitated by the geographical isolation of the region and by the dependence of life on the

Nile river. The two archaic kingdoms of the Nile – the Upper Egypt, the narrow valley of the Nile, and the Lower Egypt, the delta region of the Nile – were united under the legendary King Mena (the name probably refers to three kings of the first dynasty: Scorpion, Narmer and Aha, during whose rules the unification of Egypt took place), who established the new capital city ***Men-nofer*** (in Greek, Memphis) at the boundary of the two former archaic kingdoms. The capital was also known as ***He-kuptah***, the 'Land of Khem', a term which referred to the black fertile silt. The capital city was surrounded by a great white wall, the so-called 'White Wall of Memphis' which at first probably consisted of mud-brick masonry coated with white gypsum plaster but was later replaced by white limestone masonry.

The ancient Egyptians were the first people in history to create a powerful centralised political institution called the 'national State' through this unification. Ancient Egypt became the first monolithic managerial State under a central authoritarian government headed by an autocratic god-king which was administered by an all-pervasive and all-powerful bureaucracy. The efficiency of the Egyptian bureaucracy made statism built about the totalitarian despotism of the Pharaoh, who ruled on Earth as the falcon-god ***Horus***, and later also as the son of the Sun-god ***Re*** (or ***Ra***), possible. The god-king who had divine dominion on Earth owned everything in Egypt in principle, and at first also in fact, and he was worshipped by the people as a god among other gods. Only the Pharaoh had creative command (***he***), perception or understanding (***sia***), of the divine order of creation out of primordial chaos (***ma-hat***). The divine harmony of the world (***ma-hat***) built into it by the gods at the creation of the world, represented the will of the gods, and man had the responsibility to live in harmony with this divinely established universal order. In their opinion man sinned if he failed to do so. Since the Pharaoh, whom common Egyptians believed to be a god, was also indistinguishable from the State, therefore, the State was regarded as an extension of the divine despotic cosmic order on Earth. The common Egyptians believed the Pharaoh to be the great intermediary between men and other gods. People venerated the Pharaoh in their everyday practice of worshipping the State by being absolutely submissive and subservient to the rules and edicts issued by the ubiquitous State bureaucracy. The sacred Egyptian monarchy discouraged the growth of spirituality and intellectual freedom by identifying the cause of religion with the cause of the State. In later times, government bureaucrats boasted: 'It is the scribe who imposes taxes . . . who commands the whole country' and, 'There is nothing like being a scribe, for the scribe gets all that is upon the Earth.' Pharaohs ruled through a formidable and all-powerful bureaucracy, a hierarchy headed by a vizier, trained in the palace school. Ancient Egypt represented a monolithic managerial State of high order of organisation built about the State-planned economy in a striking anticipation of the modern totalitarian collectivist-State. Government bureaucrats worked in the ancient Egypt, as they still do today, to sanctify the status quo of the State.

In the basic ancient Egyptian outlook of life, only the Pharaoh worshipped other gods on behalf of his subjects and he alone did everything creative. In war, the official Egyptian propaganda depicted the Pharaoh defeating the enemy singlehanded despite the fact that thousands of Egyptian soldiers might have been slaughtered in the battle by the enemy. No individual achievements were possible in the Egyptian form of autocratic statism, since every deed was interpreted to be an accomplishment of the dictatorial Pharaoh. Only upon the Pharaoh depended the condition of the country and the progress of the society. When the Pharaoh prospered so did everything and everybody else, since the ancient Egyptians believed that all collective benefits were transmitted to the people through the Pharaoh. This ancient idea is still very much alive and prospering in modern statist countries where the political ideologues have assumed the Pharaonic mantle.

Pharaoh, like any other statist tyrant, was not inclined to honour vigorous independence of spirit: conformity to his opinions and submission to his will was what he promoted. Commoners, such as engineers, were able to rise to important positions far above their status in ancient Egypt, but they could rise only with Pharaoh's favour, a favour most certainly acquired through servility and obsequiousness.

Religion permeated the total existence of an ancient Egyptian from cradle to grave. Every minute detail of his life, and the life about him, was to an ancient Egyptian a specific calculated act of the gods, and his dictatorial Pharaoh was one of the gods. The ancient Egyptians, like all ancient people, were steeped in the neolithic belief of animism, which instilled them with reverence of the wonders and powers of nature. This reverence of nature led them to the deification of nature, and to the worship of animals, both wild and tame. The ancient Egyptians worshipped beasts because they were in awe of their fierce, mysterious powers, and they treated such animals as if they were better than humans. Such animals were sacred to the ancient Egyptians, and any man who deliberately killed such a sacred animal was promptly executed. Fortunately, the ancient Egyptians did not extend their worship to inanimate objects, which made material progress in the ancient Egyptian civilisation possible. It is mainly for this reason that all the Egyptian gods in the pre-dynastic (or archaic) time had animal forms. The first Egyptian anthropomorphic god was the god of the crafts, Ptah, who appeared first in Memphis during the Old Kingdom.

The ancient Egyptian sought eternity by considering afterlife to be a continuation of life on Earth. Therefore, an ancient Egyptian made his life on Earth a preparation for afterlife and immortality. The preservation of his hollowed-out dead body which had to serve as a hull for his eternal soul at the resurrection was an important aspect of his concept of the eternal life. Therefore, the ancient Egyptian men of means devoted their temporal life to the building of their tombs which were to house their mummies and last an eternity. All of their temporal buildings, such as palaces and dwelling, were not built to last, in contrast to their tombs and temples. Even in their art and sculpture, the ancient Egyptians wanted to capture the eternal essence of the subject, and, for this reason, the Egyptian human figures are lifeless and devoid of secular character, vitality, human emotion, and motion. This attitude to life led the ancient Egyptians to the stereotyped art, the canons of which were essentially established during the Old Kingdom.

In ancient Egypt nobody had inviolable rights to land and property, or equal rights – such rights were not defined by law in Egypt as they were in Sumer. Nominally, it was the dictatorial Pharaoh who owned the whole land. Justice to the ancient Egyptians meant conformity to the divine order (***ma-hat***), whereas injustice meant violation of it which brought personal dishonour. Evil seems to have meant to ancient Egyptians failure to live up to the ***ma-hat***. Any rebel against the autocratic and dictatorial Pharaoh would have been accused to be a man who had ceased to live in harmony with the divine order of the world by attempting to substitute chaos for order.

It is apparent from this brief description that although the ancient Egyptians were at first influenced by the Sumerian culture, within a few centuries they had developed a civilisation which was quite distinct from the Sumerian civilisation. This fact implies that the ancient Egyptians were capable of originality, particularly during the Archaic and Old Kingdom periods. Only during the Middle Kingdom the idea that a change is a departure from the established divine harmony of the universe (***ma-hat***) began to ossify into a dogma.

Chief Divisions of Egyptian History :

1. 2700 B.C.-2134 B.C. – The 'Old Kingdom'
2. 2050 B.C.-1800 B.C. – The 'Middle Kingdom'
3. 1570 B.C.-1090 B.C. – The 'New Kingdom'

Egyptian Engineering

The basin irrigation system developed by the ancient Egyptians consisted of checkerboard patterns of basins which were formed by earth embankments running parallel to the banks of the Nile river and by dykes crossing at right angles to the embankments. This checkerboard of basins consisted of fields varying in size from a few thousand square feet to 40,000 acres. The auxiliary canals, enclosed by dykes when necessary, conducted water from the upper regions of the river which were not reached by the natural inundation. Then water was conducted by means of sluices into one basin at a time, and after the upper field had been allowed to soak in a sufficient amount of the silt-carrying water, the water was conducted by means of sluices into the next lower basin by gravity flow, and so on, until the water had returned to the subsided river. The marginal basins above this canal were irrigated by water-lifting devices such as the ***shaduf*** (*swape*).

The alluvial silt of the Nile around the turn of this century had the following constituents in percentage: organic material 15, phosphates 2, calcium 2, magnesium 1, potash 2, sodium 1, clays 21, sand 55, carbonates and other particulates 2.

Since one acre (0.405 hectare) of cultivated land can adequately support the life of one man, and the arable land area of Egypt is about 11,500 square miles (29,790 square kilometers), then an eight million population would give a population density of 695 people per square mile (269 people per square kilometer). In comparison, Belgium, the most densely populated country in Europe and the nearest in size to ancient Egypt, has a population of more than 6 million on an area of 11,370 square miles (29,448 square kilometers), giving a population density of 563 people per square mile (203 people per square kilometer).

In any hydraulic civilisation, such as Egypt, the sound engineering condition of the irrigation structures is of cardinal importance to the welfare of its inhabitants. For this very reason the primary duty of the ***nomarchs*** (district governors) of ancient Egypt was the maintenance of dykes and canals in their ***nomes*** (districts), because dykes are easily undermined by erosion and seepage which makes them friable, and canals rapidly silt up or are blown full of desert sands. During the inundation period of the Nile river the dykes had to be patrolled around the clock to detect any signs of inchoate seepage or cracks due to the saturation of the mud embankments. The district irrigation administration included cadastral surveyors and tax inspectors whose duty it was to determine, and to check the boundary markers after each inundation, since the precise location of boundary markers was necessary for Pharaoh's taxation purpose. By 3100 B.C., in the time of the pre-dynastic kings of the Scorpian Clan, the administration of irrigation and the 'breaching of the dykes' ceremony had already become a formal public affair.

The ancient Egyptians pioneered in building with megalithic masonry, as various grades of stone, such as limestone, sandstone, granite, quartz, alabaster, and various igneous rocks such as diorite, prophyry and basalt were available at the bluffs and local outcrops all along the Nile valley. Hard granite was available at ***Swenet*** (now Aswan) and at the ***Rohanu*** Depression (now Wadi Hammamat), alabaster was available at ***Hat-Nub*** (near Asyut, on the Eastern bank of the Nile), and basalt, one of the hardest rocks, was quarried at the ***Fayum*** Depression.

Not only did the ancient Egyptians use the trabeatic stone construction, *i.e.*, the column-and-lintel stone construction, but also the corbelled (or false) arch and true arch construction. The true arches were constructed with centering in stone structures, and without centering in ring-vaulting of brick structures. Stones and bricks were laid in mortar which was generally made of clay, crushed limestone chips and sand, although gypsum and stone chips were occasionally employed. The addition of pottery shards further strengthened the mortar. It appears that the ancient Egyptians did not use mortar as a cohesive binder in joints but rather as a lubricant and filler of joints. Gypsum concrete was poured as a fluid mixture over floors and foundation trenches. Mud-brick was a mixture of mud, water, and chaff or sand, which was dried in the sun. Elaborate interlocking brick-moulds were developed for the construction of true arches and ribbed vaults.

The earliest Egyptians built dwellings of slender wood frame, or skeletal construction. The timber available in Egypt provided only small beams in the form of acacia and palm logs for floors, whereas the walls and roofs of these houses were made of reed, lotus and papyrus clusters. The walls of houses were also made of wattle daubed with mud and dried in the sun, but such dwellings had to be continually repaired.

In larger and more permanent buildings ancient Egyptians began to build in mud mixed with chaff, which was rammed between forms. The forms were removed as soon as the mud had hardened into solid walls. Such mud-walls had to be thick to support the weight of the roof and the wall itself. Since there is a definite limit to the self-weight a mud-wall can support, such walls had to be tapered 4-to-1. In the later development of such wall construction, mud-brick masonry was used in the construction of battered walls. Fuel having been scarce in the Near East in general, only such inferior fuels as chaff, brushwood, and dung were available. The use of fired, or baked bricks in construction was limited to important buildings such as palaces, temples and tombs. Such buildings were finished with faience and gold inlays, and they had imported cedar wood doors and panels, and were usually decorated with painted stucco. Stucco consisted of a thin layer of fine plaster or cement laid over stone and wood alike as a base for painting. Painted stucco was even used as pavements in palaces, certainly during the New Kingdom. Thick square tiles of terracotta were used in paving around drains during the Middle Kingdom. Walls and floors that were subject to dampness were usually lined with stone slabs. Good quality timber, such as cedar, or sycamore logs which were not available in Egypt had to be imported from Palestine.

Quarrying of smaller stone blocks was accomplished by chiselling a series of slots in the rock with bronze chisels and then splitting the rock by driving wooden wedges into the slots and wetting them. Stone megaliths were pounded out of the parent rock with dolerite (a very hard igneous rock of greenish colour) balls 5 to 12 inches (12.7 to 30.5 cm) in diameter. The megalith was separated from the parent rock by pounding trenches around, and galleries underneath it. There still exists a 137-foot (41.8 m) long obelisk weighing some 1,168 tons in the Aswan quarry, which was left unfinished about 1500 B.C. because a crack was discovered in it. This obelisk was separated from its parent granite rock by 300-foot (91.4 m) long and 2½-foot (0.76 m) wide trenches which were made by pounding. If it would have been finished, the trenches would have been 14 feet (4.27 m) deep, and it would have been tunnelled underneath by a series of galleries. If a gang of 400 men toiled 12 hours each day, this megalith would have been quarried in 15 months.

Egyptian engineers used three labour-saving devices: the inclined plane, the lever, and the roller. Pulleys and screws were unknown to ancient Egyptian engineers, who were called 'chiefs of works'. The ancient Egyptian engineer was above all a master-planner and an efficient executor, who organised and directed some of the largest work forces of all ages. The labour forces consisted of forced-labour gangs, the so-called ***'corvees'***. The peasants were coerced into these compulsory labour gangs during the inundation period when they were relatively idle, and their forced labour was counted as payment of their taxes imposed by the ubiquitous bureaucracy of the Pharaoh. Cane or knout was the standard equipment of the construction taskmasters who ran these construction gangs.

Egyptian history in engineering can be conveniently divided into four periods:

Archaic or Pre-dynastic Period **:**
[from c.3100 B.C. to 2700 B.C.]
Age of Mastaba Tombs and the First Masonry Dam.

Old Kingdom:
[from c.2700 B.C. to 2134 B.C.]
Age of Pyramids and Naval Construction.

First Intermediate Period:
[from c.2134 B.C. to 2050 B.C.]
Civil Wars and Moral Awakening.

Middle Kingdom:
[from c.2050 B.C. to 1800 B.C.]
Age of Irrigation and Monumental Engineering

Second Intermediate Period:
[from c.1800 B.C. to 1570 B.C.]
Hyksos Occupation.

New Kingdom:
[from c.1570 B.C. to 1090 B.C.]
Age of Towering Obelisks, Colossal Buildings and Gigantic Statues.

Archaic Period: ***Mastaba Tombs and First Masonry Dam***
[From c.3100 B.C. to 2700 B.C.]

During the first dynasty, from about 3100 B.C. to 2900 B.C.,the Mastaba tombs of the kings (***mastaba*** in Arabic, bench) were roofed with sun-dried brick vaults constructed without centering. The earliest Egyptian hieroglyphs stem from this period. These archaic tombs resembled the mud-brick benches built by Egyptian peasants.

At the close of the second dynasty, from c.2900 B.C.-2700 B.C., King Kha-Sek-Hem, the last king of the Archaic Period, had his royal engineer-builder, Ken-Nofer, construct a stone-lined burial chamber in his Mastaba tomb, in which the stone had no structural function.

All throughout the Archaic Period, mines in Mount Sinai, Palestine, were worked by the Egyptians for turquoise and pottery glazing material.

At this time the first known large masonry dam was constructed in a valley, now called Wadi Garrawe, near the present Helwan located about 20 miles (32.2 km) southeast of Cairo, to catch about 20 million cubic feet (0.57 million cubic meters) of rain water near an alabaster quarry. The catchment area for the stored water was about 72 square miles (186.5 square km). The dam consisted of double walls, each 78 feet (23.8 m) in thickness at the base, which were separated by a 118-foot (40 m) gap filled with 60,000 tons of gravel and debris from the valley. The two walls of the dam were made of 30,000 cubic yards (22,937 cubic meters) of fitted limestone masonry. This dam had no cut-off trench to anchor the base of the dam into the ground, and the stepped-back external faces of the two walls were not water-tight since no mortar was used to render the dam cohesive. The width of the dam was 348 feet (106 m) on top and 265 feet (80.8 m) along the floor of the valley, and the height was 37 feet (11.3 m). The total thickness of the dam on top was 200 feet (61 m). It appears that the very first great flash flood after the completion of the dam spilled over the dam and caused it to collapse from erosion and internal pressure of water. The abutments of this most ancient dam are still extant since only some 150 feet (45.7 m) of the central portion of this dam was washed away by the flood. Arabs who conquered the land of ancient Egyptians thousands of years later called this dam the ***Sadd el-Kafara***, the Dam of the Pagans.

Old Kingdom: ***Age of Pyramids***
[from c.2700 B.C. to 2134 B.C.]

The ancient Egyptian society under the Old Kingdom was worldly, materialistic, and optimistic. In this period the Pharaoh's rule relied mainly on his divine power as a god on earth. The dominant morality of the Pyramid Age was well expressed by a contemporary inscription: 'Live today for you are gone tomorrow'.

About 2686 B.C., the royal engineer-builder Im-Hotep, who was also the vizier of Pharaoh Djoser, or Zoser (meaning 'most sacred one') [in Greek, Tosorthos] and apparently the son of Ken-Nofer, constructed in Sakkara the first known dressed stone structure, the so-called 'Stepped Pyramid'. Ancient Greeks called these structures ***pyramis,*** a term obtained from the Egyptian ***pyremas*** meaning 'height'. The Stepped Pyramid was an experimental structure based on the mastaba tomb of the Archaic Period. It has a maze of underground tunnels and chambers unmatched by any later pyramid, and consists of 6 uneven steps with faces having a batter of 2-to-7. The base of the stepped pyramid is 350 by 200 feet (106.7 by 61 m) and its height is 200 feet (61 m, or 18 stories). The pyramid is located in an enclosure of the size 912 by 1,790 feet (278 by 545.6 m) that is lined with a 35-foot (10.7 m) high wall, which apparently imitated the 'White Wall of Memphis'. This wall had 14 bastions, each of which incorporated a false door in stone. The single entrance was located in a broader bastion near the southern end of the eastern wall. The complex of buildings located within the enclosure consists of a mortuary temple, a chapel, a dummy structure of the palace of the Pharaoh, and the building used in the 'Jubilee ceremony' (***heb-sed)*** of the Pharaoh in Memphis. All these structures appear to have been built in duplicate and most of these buildings were built solid, or nearly so, or filled with earth and debris.

Im-Hotep, the engineer of the Stepped Pyramid, was also a renowned sage, physician and high priest. He wrote the first known book of proverbs, and the first known medical treatise. He was deified and became the god of healing about a thousand years later. Im-Hotep remained the most revered engineer-sage in ancient Egypt, and only one other engineer was ever considered to be remotely comparable in importance to Im-Hotep. It is fair to say that dressed stone masonry construction appeared virtually as a refined practical art from the hands of Im-Hotep, because little improvement of his method of construction could be made over the millennia.

About 2650 B.C., Pharaoh Sen-Feru (meaning 'bringer of beauty') [in Greek, Snefru] built a pyramid at Meydum which still had a mastaba-like stepped structure, but was encased by a smooth facing of limestone. This pyramid collapsed, leaving only the central core intact. Sen-Feru built two more pyramids at ***Dahshur*:** the so-called 'Bent Pyramid', the best-preserved pyramid, was the first tomb of the pharaoh Sen-Feru planned from the very beginning to be a true pyramid until progressive instability problems compelled the builder to reduce the weight of the upper part of the pyramid by reducing its slope after reaching a critical height in its construction. The base of this pyramid is 620 by 620 feet (189 by 189 meters), and its height is 336 feet (102.4 m). The Northern Pyramid which had no construction problems is the first true pyramid. Its base has the size 719 by 719 feet (219.2 by 219.2 meters), and its height is 342⅓ feet (104.2 m). Sen-Feru's pyramids together contain about 9 million tons of rock - an incredible amount of building material.

By about 3000 B.C., Egyptians became builders of a large number of sailing ships. In Pharaoh Sen-Feru's reign, the first known fleet of sailing ships, 60 in number, was constructed. He used a fleet of 40 ships to import cedar logs from the city of Byblos in Palestine. The oldest extant shipping documents stem from this period.

The Egyptian ship had no keel, and the hull of the ship was a dowelled patchwork to which were later added ribs and thwarts, and possibly a reinforcing member along the bottom. The entire ship was held together by a giant truss consisting of a manila rope as thick as a man's waist which ran from the stem to the stern of the ship and was spanned by a few vertical members supported against the rigid deck. The ship's cargo had to be carried on the deck because the hull of the Egyptian ship was far too weak to support any load. The mast of the Egyptian ship was a splayed bipod which pivoted about its base on the deck and could be lowered when the ship was in the harbour. These ships were not worthy of the open sea and, therefore, they had to be confined to voyages along the coastline.

About 2600 B.C. Pharaoh Khufu [in Greek, Cheops], son of Sen-Feru, ordered his engineer Khufu-Onekh to build a pyramid at Giza that is the largest such structure ever erected. Its base is 750 by 750 feet (228.6 by 228.6 meters) and its height is 481 feet (146.6 meters, or 43 storeys) consisting of 206 courses of limestone blocks. The average weight of the stone blocks in this pyramid is 1.5 tons with the maximum of 2.4 tons. The huge limestone slabs over the mortuary chamber of the Pharaoh weigh about 15 tons each. The construction of this pyramid was remarkably careful: the mistake between two diagonal corners in levelling is half an inch, alignment error is 5 minutes, and the mistake in side lengths is almost 8 inches (17.8 cm). The average joint in this pyramid is 1/50-th of an inch (0.051 cm) whereas the smallest joints are 1/200-th of an inch (0.0127 cm). Khufu's pyramid was the tallest structure in the world until the 'Eiffel Tower' was built in A.D. 1889.

About 2560 B.C. Pharaoh Khaf-Re (meaning 'appearing like the Sun god Re') [in Greek, Chephren], son of Khufu, built the second largest pyramid in Giza, the dimensions of which are 707¾ by 707¾ feet (215.7 by 215.7 meters) in base, and 447 feet (136.2 m) in height. Khaf-Re's pyramid still has some finishing encasement stones left at the top. It was formerly thought that Khaf-Re erected his gigantic sphinx (meaning 'strangler' in Greek) having a lion's body and a human head, probably in his own likeness, to the west of his pyramid, but recent research indicates that at least a part of the giant sphinx may be much older than the large pyramids. The size of this gigantic statue carved out of a rock outcropping and completed with stone block masonry is 240 feet (73.1 m) in length, 66 feet (20.1 m) or six storeys in height, and 13 ⅔ feet (4.2 m) in width. An open-air temple was located between the front paws of the sphinx. Khaf-Re's mortuary temple had functional square columns and random ashlar masonry walls made of squared stones cut to fit rather than laid in courses.

The third, and the smallest pyramid at Giza which has the base dimensions of 356½ by 356½ feet (108.7 by 108.7 meters) and the height of 204 feet (62.2 m) was constructed by the order of Men-Kau-Re (in Greek, Mykerinos), son of Khaf-Re. Many stone blocks in the wall of this pyramid complex weigh as much as 220 tons. The lower courses of this pyramid were constructed of much harder granite stone blocks than limestone blocks.

About 2500 B.C., Pharaoh Sahu-Re, grandson of Men-Kau-Re, built his pyramid complex near the modern village Abu Sir, which was distinguished by an unprecedented engineering and artistic magnificence. It contained 2½ acres of limestone reliefs as wall decorations. The mortuary temple had an elaborate drainage system consisting of about 1,300 feet (396 m) of copper piping, the first known metal drain piping system, which was provided with lead plugs. The roof of the temple had limestone drainage troughs and limestone gargoyle-spouts in the form of lion's head.

Sahu-Re established the first naval power known, and he dispatched his fleet of warships to raid the Palestine city-States in the first known naval campaign. During this period the Egyptians invented a wheeled scaling-ladder as a siege-craft which was used in their raids into the Libyan desert.

In about 2300 B.C., the royal engineer Nek-Hebu built a mortuary temple for the Pharaoh Pepi I, and also dug two canals. Uni, an official under the Pharaohs Pepi I and Teti II, superintendent of the irrigated lands and engineer for Pharaoh Me-Re-Ne-Re, son of Pepi I, had a boat built of acacian wood 103 feet (31 m) long and 51½ feet (15.6 m) wide in 17 days to transport an alabaster table to Memphis. He excavated five canals through granite in a single year in the first cataract near the Island of Elephantine at ***Swe-net*** (in Greek Syene, now Aswan), about 500 miles (800 km) south of Memphis, for the safe and rapid passage of Pharaoh's patrol boats to Nubia where ancient Egypt had rich gold mines. These canals, the first canals cut in the cataracts, were so well constructed that they lasted for six centuries without any need for maintenance or improvement.

Already near the close of the Old Kingdom, there existed in ancient Egypt a fairly extensive and effective basin irrigation system. In construction during the Old Kingdom limestone lintels were used in Egyptian trabeatic construction, but these fissual lintels could safely span only about 9 feet (2.7 m).

There existed an important ancient Egyptian school of crafts in the temple of the creator god Ptah in Memphis, the high priest of which bore the title 'chief of craftsmen'. In this way a great amount of craft tradition of high quality was created and transmitted to new generations. The high priests of Ptah were often the foremost Egyptian engineers and master-craftsmen of their time.

At the close of the Old Kingdom, the cult of the Sun god Re (or Ra) gained ascendancy, and its priesthood was granted privileges which, however, undermined the supreme authority of the Pharaoh. Since all men were officially considered to be slaves of the god-king in the Old Kingdom, the Egyptian society was not yet rigidly stratified along the class lines, and as a result ambitious individuals of humble origin could rise to positions of importance and power in the State bureaucracy by demonstrating their skill and prudence.

Vizier Ipu-wer complained to the last Pharaoh of the Old Kingdom, the centenarian Pepi II, a period when the central power of the State was rapidly crumbling: "Nobles are in lamentation whilst poor men have joy. Serfs have become the owners of serfs."

In this period Egyptians invented the papyrus, ink and reed pen, which were immeasurably more convenient for writing than the clay tablet and stylus used in Sumer. The papyrus was produced by splitting the soft core of a river reed into thin strips which were then laid crosswise and pounded into a sheet of yellow paper and rubbed smooth by rounded stones. Ink was made of a mixture of water, a little vegetable gum and soot from blackened cooking pots. The pen was made of reed cut to a point. In writing Egyptians developed a system of 24 consonantal signs, but they never fully realised the great advantage of this system of writing, and thus they never established a true alphabet. The scribes of the city Ugarit in Palestine borrowed the Egyptian consonantal system about 1300 B.C. and established the first strictly consonantal alphabet.

In ancient Egypt the day was divided into 24 hours, and each hour was divided into 60 minutes. A system of metric weights was in general commercial use.

First Intermediate Period

[from c. 2134 B.C. to 2050 B.C.]

Collapse of the central Pharaonic power, and the rise of the power of the feudal lords that brought about civil wars, marked the First Intermediate Period. Since the unity of the country was thereby broken, the national state disintegrated into petty States in which social classes were overturned. This was a creative period in ancient Egyptian history which gave rise to higher moral principles, and to democratic ideals both in religion and in justice. The dead were presumed to face the Last Judgement, and to earn life everlasting by good conduct in this life. Even the Pharaoh was to be judged. For the first time in Egyptian history Pharaoh was treated as a fallible human being. On a tombstone from about 2100 B.C. there is engraved a significant inscription: 'A man's virtue is his monument, forgotten is the man of evil repute'. A Coffin Text from about 2000 B.C. states that the Sun-god Re proclaims that 'all men are created equal' and that the annual floods of the Nile have been brought about 'so that the poor man might have rights therein like the great'. This period of unrest gave the ancient Egyptians a sense of dissatisfaction and disquiet, and an urge to quest for novelty. The new literature which appeared in this period not only sought to instruct but also to entertain: the ballad of Sinu-He, the tale of the 'Shipwrecked Sailor'(the origin of 'Sinbad the Sailor'), the lamentations of scribe Ne-fer-ti and sage Ipu-wer, and several lyrical works appeared for the first time.

In this period, the Pharaoh Akh-toy IV of Herakleopolis, who ruled over a very limited domain of Egypt and was known as 'doer of evil to the people of Egypt' , dug a 50-mile (80 km) long canal from Herakleopolis to the old capital Memphis, the longest canal in existence anywhere in the world in its time.

Middle Kingdom: ***Age of Large-Scale Irrigation***

[from c.2050 B.C. to 1800 B.C.]

Pharaoh Mentu-Hotep II (2060 B.C.-2010 B.C.) of Thebes, who was a general, reunited the fragmented ancient Egypt under the so-called Theban dynasty. It was an age of immense irrigation projects and large scale public works which led to large scale food production. A concerted effort was made in this period to use all the land capable of cultivation, a task made feasible by the availability of a national system of irrigation. In the past canals had been built primarily for military purposes, whereas now they were built mainly for irrigation and transportation purposes. The Middle Kingdom, when Pharaoh's power depended mainly on his military power and on the collaboration and support of the nomarchs, was not only a period of national rebirth and intellectual advance, but also the 'golden age' of Egyptian literature as well.

Pharaoh Mentu-Hotep II (meaning 'Mentu is content') advanced construction as well as sculpture in the revolutionary design of his mortuary temple at Deir el-Bahri opposite the modern city Luxor (Arabic name, Al Ucqor) on the west bank of the Nile river. This dramatically new design must have depended heavily on the taste of this particular Pharaoh since only a Pharaoh had the authority to change the stereotype design traditions. This temple incorporated many building innovations: a terrace with colonnades and an access ramp, a ¼ mile (0.4 km) long causeway, and a solid pyramid filled with rubble and supported on a high podium. The pyramid which had a size of 70 by 70 feet (21.3 by 21.3 meters) at the base and 70 feet (21.3 m) in height contained the Pharaoh's cenotaph and tomb.

After the death of this Pharaoh less capable rulers followed and the country fell again into widespread disorder and civil war. During this period a battering ram with a portable rawhide as the protective covering was in use for breaching the defensive walls of enemy fortresses in the civil wars waged by various nomarchs contending for political supremacy.

By 1990 B.C., ancient Egypt was again made a unified and strong national State under the usurper Amen-Em-Het I [in Greek, Ammenemes] who ruled from 1991 B.C. to 1962 B.C. and who had been the vizier of Pharaoh Mentu-Hotep IV, a weak ruler. He established the XII dynasty and moved the capital from Thebes to ***Ithet-Tawny*** (Usht) near Memphis. His successors Sen-Usert I [in Greek, Sesostris], Amen-Em-Het II, Sen-Usert II, Sen-Usert III, and Amen-Em-Het III were all vigorous military rulers who carried out one of the largest reclamation projects of all ages in the ***Fayum*** Depression.

Pharaoh Sen-Usert I (meaning 'man of power'), who ruled from 1970 B.C. to 1936 B.C. began the construction of the so-called 'Pharaoh Ship Canal' to connect the Red Sea with the Tanitic branch of the Nile and, thus, with the Mediterranean Sea. It seems that this canal was engineered by the Royal builder Sen-Usert-Ankh, a priest of Ptah who was the dean of the college of craftsmen and scribes. It appears that Pharaoh Sen-Usert I did not finish the Pharaoh Ship Canal because he believed that the Red Sea was higher than the Nile river, and therefore might flood the sweet Nile water with saline sea water if connected by a canal. In this period the first known Egyptian vaults and arches, including some pointed arches, were constructed. This Pharaoh and subsequent rulers built many fortresses beyond the first and the second cataract to protect Egyptian gold mines, as well as Egyptian trading and raiding posts.

Pharaoh Sen-Usert III (1878 B.C.-1843 B.C.), the great Egyptian canal builder, reopened and extended the ***Mer-Ne-Re*** canal in the first cataract. The length of this canal was 260 feet (79 m), its width was 35 feet (10.7 m), and the depth was 26 feet (7.9 m). He was the Pharaoh who is most likely to have finished the excavation of the Pharaoh Ship Canal. This canal evidently followed a dried-up bed of an old branch river, the Goshen Depression now called Wadi Tumilat, which had naturally connected the Nile river with Red Sea, thousands of years ago. It seems that the Pharaoh Ship Canal was operational only during the inundation period, and for the rest of the year it served as an irrigation canal. It had a length of 120 miles (193 km), a width of 150 feet (45.7 m), and a depth of 16 feet (4.9 m). This canal ran from ***Bu-Past*** to ***Patumos*** along an old dried-up river bed in the Goshen Depression. The Pharaoh Ship Canal was a military as well as an economic necessity because it connected the Tanitic branch of the Nile river to the Red Sea, which in those days ran into the Bitter and the Timsah Lake, and allowed Egypt to maintain commercial fleets both in the Mediterranean and in the Red Sea.

A barrage was built across the Hawara channel to lower the water level in the ***Fayum*** Depression, a large marshy oasis west of the Nile river and south of Memphis, in order to reclaim some 16,800 acres (6,800 hectares) of land around the ***Fayum*** Depression for agriculture. This immense project was completed by the next Pharaoh, Amen-Em-Het III who embarked upon a monumental construction programme during his rule which lasted from 1842 B.C. to 1797 B.C.

The Bahr el-Yusuf, the branch river to the Nile, was extended by a supply canal, called ***Mi-War***, with the width of 300 feet (91.4 m) and the length of about 5,000 feet (1,524 m) into the Lake ***Moeris*** in order to carry the flood waters of the Nile river into this artificial lake which had a 400-mile (644 km) shoreline. A complex system of dykes, flood control gates, canals, and bridges over the canals were built to direct the flow of the lake water back into the irrigation system in the ***Fayum*** Depression at will. Water ran into this immense catchment basin for 6 months of a year, and out of it for the next 6 months. It was the first and only perennial irrigation system built in ancient Egypt.

Amen-Em-Het III erected an enormous building near the artificial Lake ***Moeris*** which served not only as his mortuary temple but also as a center of religious cults of the ***nomes*** and administration of justice, and, most importantly, as a national center of administration of irrigation. This enormous building covered an area of 980 by 890 feet (298.7 by 271.3 meters) and it consisted of about 3,000 rooms, half of them in the underground hypogeum. There were 12 separate courtyards, one for each nome, and innumerable small courts. The hypogeum was hewn out of the rock and connected by a honeycomb of galleries. This building contained such a complicated network of passages and rooms that, according to the ancient Greek historian Herodotos (484 B.C.-c.425 B.C.), a guide was required to find one's way out of this complicated maze of rooms. The ancient Greeks called this gigantic ancient Egyptian building, a true monument to bureaucracy, the 'Labyrinth' (***La-Po-Runt***), and it was a much more complicated structure than the well-known, elaborate Palace of Knossos in Crete, the famous Labyrinth in Greek mythology. This colossal building was located in the nome where crocodiles were worshipped, and it lay near the city ***She-Det*** (in Greek, Krokodilopolis). The hypogeum of the Labyrinth was mainly reserved for the mummies of the sacred crocodiles, whereas the mummy of the Pharaoh was located in the pyramid attached to the north side of the Labyrinth building.

Amen-Em-Het III built a series of 'nilometers' from the Elephantine Island to the Island of Rhoda (near contemporary Cairo), with the southern-most 'nilometer' being built in the fort of ***Semna*** located south of the second cataract. A relay of runners carried the message from one station to another until it reached the Labyrinth for evaluation. The speed of travel of these messengers was about 11 miles (17 km) an hour. Ultimately there were altogether 20 'nilometers' along the Nile river.

In this period the Egyptian State monopoly operated about 100 gold mines, which produced about 60 pounds (27 kg) of gold per year. Pharaoh Sen-Usert III, but particularly the Pharaoh Amen-Em-Het III, carried out imperialistic ventures into Palestine with the intent of reducing the local kings to vassalage, and controlling their politics with appointed Egyptian commissioners. This was an entirely new foreign policy for Egypt, which ultimately led ancient Egypt into outright imperialism, since the earlier Pharaohs had only carried out occasional raids into neighbouring countries for the purpose of booty. Amen-Em-Het III, in contrast, intended to gain permanent lordship over Palestine. As a result of this policy, Egypt was no longer isolated, and became exposed to foreign influences which ultimately brought it into conflict with other imperial States.

Second Intermediate Period: *Hyksos Occupation of Egypt*

[from c.1800 B.C. to 1570 B.C.]

As a first repercussion from the imperial ventures of Egypt, the Nile valley was invaded by the Asiatic horsemen, called 'Hyksos' (in ancient Egyptian, ***hikau khasut*** - rulers of foreign countries), who conquered the Lower Egypt because they had the horse and the chariot, scale armour, composite bow and efficient bronze weapons, all of which the Egyptians lacked. About 1700 B.C., during the Hyksos occupation, the well-known 'Joseph Well', located near Cairo, was sunk about

300 feet (91.4 m) through the solid rock. The upper part of the well had a cross-section of 18 by 24 feet (5.5 by 7.3 meters) and a depth of 165 feet (50.3 m). A pathway led down to the bottom of the well where mules operated an endless chain of buckets by means of a whim and, thereby, raised water 130 feet (39.6 m) up a small shaft.

New Kingdom: ***Age of Obelisks***
[from c.1570 B.C. to 1090 B.C.]

In the New Kingdom, the Egyptians became intentionally imperialistic in an attempt to discourage foreign invasions. In this period the Egyptian army and bureaucracy became predominantly foreign in their constitution, and for the first time the Egyptian ruler was called 'Pharaoh' (in Egyptian ***par-o*** meant the 'big house'). Common Egyptians of the New Kingdom became slavishly resigned to their condition and devoted to the ideal of 'silence'.

In the New Kingdom the Pharaohs built towering obelisks, gigantic temples, massive pylons, colossal statues, immense forecourts, opulent palaces and ponderous hypostyle halls. The new monumental scale construction led to new engineering problems, particularly to foundation problems. As construction methods deteriorated the foundation failures became frequent. In the Obelisk Age the Egyptian engineers began to use sandstone lintels which could safely span 25 feet (7.6 m).

In the reign of Tuth-Mose I (meaning 'child of god Tuth'), father of Queen Hat-Shep-Sut, engineer Anna transported two 93-foot (28.3 m) obelisks down the Nile river from the Aswan quarries on a boat of his design, which was 200 feet (61 m) long and 69 feet (21 m) wide.

One of the outstanding engineers of ancient Egypt was Ineni, known as the 'efficient Ineni', who worked for Pharaohs Amen-Hotep I [in Greek, Amenophis], Tuth-Mose I, II and III, Queen Hat-Shep-Sut, and Pharaoh Tuth-Mose III. He is the first known temple architect-engineer. Ineni built two pylons for Tuth-Mose I, the first 175 feet (53 m) wide and the second 250 feet (76 m) wide, and erected in front of the new gateway two granite obelisks. About 1527 B.C., Ineni built a boat, which was 207 feet (63.1 m) in length and 69 feet (21 m) in width to transport the two great obelisks of red granite, 64 feet (19.5 m) high and weighing 143 tons, from ***Swe-Net*** (present Aswan) down the Nile river. Obelisks capped by gold tips were monuments to the sun god Amen-Re. Ineni, for his time, was the 'chief of all works' for Amen-Re temple complex in ***Karnak***, where he spent much of his time supervising its construction. Ineni is also the engineer who built the first known rock-cut tomb for the Pharaoh, a tradition that lasted beyond the rule of Tuth-Ankh-Amen.

Sen-Mut was a younger contemporary of Ineni, but he far excelled the older man in social importance, for he became not only the chief of public works but also the chief advisor to Queen Hat-Shep-Sut (meaning 'foremost of noble ladies') (died 1482 B.C.), a daughter of Tuth-Mose I who became a wife of Tuth-Mose II and the first important woman in history by usurping power whilst she was the regent for the boy-Pharaoh Tuth-Mose III. Sen-Mut built Queen Hat-Shep-Sut's funerary temple in Deir El-Bahri, the finest functional structure in ancient Egypt inspired by the funerary temple complex of Mentu-Hotep II located next to the Queen's temple. This building had terraces, porticoes with polygonal columns, and walls with beautiful sunken reliefs, and it harmonised perfectly with the striations of the limestone cliffs in its background. Sen-Mut also erected for Queen Hat-Shep-Sut two 97 ½-foot (30 m) obelisks, the tallest up to that time, in front of the Queen's pylon in the temple complex of Amen-Re in ***Karnak***. He brought the two giant obelisks, weighed about 323 tons each, down the Nile river from the Aswan quarry in 27 galleys propelled by 900 oarsmen. In the erection of one of these obelisks, Sen-Mut made a mistake by missing the anchoring holes in the supporting plinth which left this obelisk not perfectly vertical. One of these obelisks is still standing, although it is the earliest extant obelisk. Queen Hat-Shep-Sut undertook an extensive domestic building programme to restore what had been neglected during the Hyksos occupation of Egypt as well as a commercial exploration of Somaliland, and African and Arabian coasts in general.

In this period the Pharaoh Ship Canal was re-dredged and improved for rapid transit of the warships of Pharaoh Tuth-Mose III, who disposed his aunt Queen Hat-Shep-Sut and became the greatest warrior king of Egypt. Syphon was used for the first time during his reign. The 105-foot (32 m) obelisk of Tuth-Mose III in ***Karnak***, now located in Rome, was the tallest obelisk erected in ancient Egypt.

The great builder of the new Kingdom was Pharaoh Amen-Hotep III (meaning 'Amen is content') who ruled from 1402 B.C. to 1364 B.C. and fought few battles. He launched a vast building programme consisting of the construction of opulent palaces, colossal statues and expansive funerary and cult temples throughout ancient Egypt. His chief engineer was Amen-Hotep son of Hapu, who planned and directed this vast building enterprise and who acquired such fame for his practical wisdom that he may have been deified in his own lifetime. Subsequent ages considered him almost an equal of Im-Hotep, which was the highest Egyptian honour accorded to an engineer. He was given permission by the Pharaoh to construct for himself a mortuary temple of almost royal proportions at Thebes. He was also given a statue in the temple of Amen, which was an extraordinary recognition for a person not of royal blood.

Amen-Hotep III built the Temple at Luxor near Thebes, which was later extended by Pharaoh Ra-Meses II, who added a large forecourt with pylons and a number of colossal statues of himself. Amen-Hotep III, who was later known as the 'Greek Memnon', planned to construct a grand hypostyle hall in this temple but he was only able to complete the twin colonnades of bell-shaped columns that are 42 feet (12.8 m) high. He did build a mortuary temple, later called the 'Memnonium', on the west bank of the Nile river at Thebes, but nothing has survived of this grand structure apart of the twin colossal statues of the Pharaoh originally 68 feet (20.7 m) high and weighing 700 tons each, which were standing at the entrance of the building in place of the obelisks. These two statues are known since classical antiquity as the Colossi of the mythical Memnon, son of Eos of Aurora, who fell in the Trojan War at Troy (Greek, ***Ilion***). These two giant statues, the inspiration for which was the Great Sphinx, were the first gigantic statues ever built. The rock material for the 2 colossi were brought down the Nile river in 8 ships specially constructed by Amen-Hotep, son of Hapu. Amen-Hotep III built a huge artificial lake of the size 1.25 by 0.60 miles (2 by 1 km) at his palace near Thebes, which also served as a harbour, but neither the palace nor the lake have survived the ravages of time. In the reign of Amen-Hotep III, Egypt reached its economic peak which was so prosperous that even the fellaheen of this period had better living quarters than the Arab peasant of modern times.

Amen-Hotep III had a son, Amen-Hotep IV, who ruled from 1375 B.C. to 1358 B.C. and who became the first great religious rebel and heretic in history. The son changed his name to Akhen-Aten (meaning, servant of Aten), and became the great religious reformer by making every effort to eliminate all other gods except the single god Aten represented by the life-giving disk of the Sun, who was a loving father of all men in Akhen-Aten's new universal monotheism. Akhen-Aten ordered his engineer Bek to build a new capital city Akhet-Aten (meaning, the 'Horizon of Aten') for him at the contemporary Tell el-Amarna. His religious revolution, now called the 'Amarna Revolution', lasted only about 20 years and it ultimately failed, but some of its influence was transmitted to Hebrews who lived in Egypt and through Hittites to the Persian religious philosopher Zarathushtra (in Greek, Zoroaster). Akhen-Aten's favourite epithet was, 'Living in Truth', for Atenism was essentially a 'truth movement'. Even the ancient Egyptian art became quite naturalistic, or 'truthful', in the Amarna Period.

Pharaoh Seti I and his son Ra-Meses II, who were both very capable generals and ruled from 1293 B.C. to 1223 B.C., became engaged in the construction of the largest temple complex ever built by man, the temple complex of the Sun-god Amen-Re (or Amon-Ra) in ***Karnak***. The final form of the Temple of Amen-Re was a cumulative creation of a series of Pharaohs from Sen-Usert I to the Macedonian Queen Cleopatra VII of Egypt. The temple complex of Amen-Re has 6 pairs of pylons added by successive Pharaohs (from Tuth-Mose I about 1500 B.C. to the Ptolemaic Pharaohs ending with Queen Cleopatra VII about 30 B.C.) and various courts, obelisks, and halls leading to the sanctuary of the god Amen-Re built by Tuth-Mose I. The extension added by Seti I [in Greek, Sethos] and Ra-Meses II [in Greek, Ramses] took the form of the huge Hypostyle Hall, one of the largest halls every built, which had the size of 338 by 1,220 feet (103 by 372 meters) incorporating 134 colossal columns in 16 rows. The central nave is 79 feet (24 m) high, and its 12 columns, which are constructed of large cylindrical stone drums, have the diameter of 11 ⅔ feet (3.6 m), and the height of 69 feet (21 m). The lintels weigh about 70 tons each. The 122 smaller columns in the aisles have the height of 42½ feet (12.8 m) and the diameter of 8¾ feet (2.7 m).

Ra-Meses II was as great a builder as Amen-Hotep III, and certainly the greatest erector of giant statues of himself. He built more gigantic statues of himself than all the previous Pharaohs taken together.

The Royal engineer Hatey was in charge of the erection of the gigantic columns in the Hypostyle Hall, of which, as Hatey himself wrote, he was very proud, although his foundation engineering was of poor quality for many of these giant columns practically rest on beds of pebbles and because they tended to settle excessively, some of the columns collapsed in a severe flood of A.D. 1889. The pylons, in contrast, have 10-foot deep foundations in clayey soil. The clerestory lighting of the Hypostyle Hall was provided by a higher central nave, a system that was more fully developed in the later Roman Basilicas and Gothic Cathedrals for which this Hall served as a model.

Bekhen-Khonsu, high priest of Amen and chief engineer of the Pharaoh Ra-Meses II (who restored the Egyptian Empire and undertook to complete the temple at Luxor), erected several obelisks of Amen-Re, and he was responsible for further construction of the Hypostyle Hall. He gave the temple of Luxor its final shape by adding 2 obelisks, 6 colossal statues of Ra-Meses II, a pylon and a forecourt. A unique feature of the columns in the forecourt of the temple at Luxor is that each of them has an entasis. One obelisk built by Bekhen-Khonsu, which is 74 feet (22.5 m) tall and weighs 254 tons, was removed to Paris in A.D. 1836, and stands now in the ***Place de Concorde***. The other obelisk is 82 feet (25 m) tall and still stands in front of the pylon and the remains of the colossal statues of Ra-Messes II where it was originally erected.

Egyptian engineers in the New Kingdom built rather poor foundations, and they did not recognise the differential settlement between adjacent foundations, which were subjected to heavy and light loads. In Deir el-Bahri, which has a firm soil of broken rock, the depth of the foundation was usually a layer of stones 20 inches (50.8 cm) or less thick. Low brick walls were often built directly on sand without any trench.

There exists a plan of the tomb of Ra-Meses IV, dating from the period between 1164 B.C. and 1157 B.C., which is a 1:28 scale drawing in ink and colour wash on papyrus. It compares well with a modern sketch-plan, and the drawing itself agrees with the actual built tomb except in certain minor details. Egyptian engineers drew their plans on reticulated papyrus, and they made scale models of their buildings.

The first known strike of workers took place in 1170 B.C. in ancient Egypt. The Pharaoh fell two months arrears of payments and supplies to the construction workers at the Necropolis in Thebes which incited the workers to go on strike, that ultimately led to systematic tomb robberies.

Egyptian Engineers

Ancient Egyptians venerated usage because they were an extremely pragmatic and materialistic people who esteemed the useful as the good. This practical habit of thought made the Egyptians honour the efficient man. The ability to transmit orders effectively, and to do it efficiently, was the primary and most important requisite of a 'chief of works'. The Egyptian master-builder had to be a personification of practical intelligence and sagacity, because they were respected for their practical wisdom, and not for their originality nor professional taste. Taste, æsthetics and creative originality were not the criteria of ability in the practice of ancient Egyptian engineering profession, a profession which by the Royal command was dedicated to the perpetuation of tradition. This practical attitude towards engineering at first gave the ancient Egyptians such efficient and original methods of construction that were possible in the time of the Old Kingdom when no rigid traditions yet existed. However, later, particularly in the period of the New Kingdom, any change was thought to be a breach of traditions and, therefore, of the divine order of harmony (or ***ma-hat***), and the traditions were essentially the stereotype habits adopted during the Old Kingdom. Such a petrified mental attitude of the ancient Egyptian engineers led inescapably to professional stagnation.

The ancient Egyptian engineers, being pure empiricists, lacked scientific curiosity and were, therefore, quite satisfied to know 'how' without ever caring 'why' anything worked as it did. As a result of this purely pragmatic mentality of the ancient Egyptian engineer, the early technological progress made in the Old Kingdom came to a grinding halt in the New Kingdom. It is for this reason that most of the canons of ancient Egyptian engineering methods were established in the Old Kingdom, and they soon became as stereotyped as Egyptian art.

Therefore, a successful ancient Egyptian engineer had to be a technocrat, who was an efficient planner, organiser and administrator, but most importantly, who always followed orders of his superiors faithfully and without question. In other words, an ancient Egyptian engineer had to be a technically competent, obsequious bureaucrat corresponding very much to a modern technocrat. This type of an engineer has made a rather triumphant return to prominence in contemporary socialist States.

What did Egyptian engineers think of their own profession and their own work? Here are a few samples of their opinions of themselves:

Engineer Nekhebu, who was the master-builder for Pharaoh Pepi I, boasted of his many virtues and asserted that he never hit a workman hard enough to knock him down.

Meri, who constructed for Pharaoh Sen-Usert I a mortuary temple in Lisht, said:
'I myself rejoiced and my heart was glad at that which I had executed.'... 'I was a zealous servant, great in character, amiable in love.' He was very proud of the height of the columns and the great pylons 'towering heavenwards'.

The 'efficient' Ineni (or, Anena):
'I became great beyond words'; 'I did no wrong whatever'; 'I continued powerful in peace and met with no misfortune'; 'I was a foreman of foremen'; 'I never blasphemed scared things'; 'My years were spent in gladness'; 'I was the revered dignitary, the overseer of the granary of Amen, the scribe, Ineni, triumphant'. It is quite clear that Ineni took special pride in fulfilling faithfully his professional duties.

Sen-Mut, Ineni's younger contemporary:
'I was the greatest of the great in the whole land – one to whom judges listened and whose very silence was eloquent'; '... secure in favour and given audience alone'; '... there was nothing from the beginning of time which I did not know'. Sen-Mut had acquired extraordinary bureaucratic powers without holding one of the customarily required four highest offices in the land: the High Priest of Amen in ***Karnak***, the Vizier for Upper Egypt, the Vizier for Lower Egypt, and the Viceroy for Ethiopia ('Pharaoh's son of Kush'), positions which had gradually become restricted to a few trusted families and, therefore, made hereditary.
Sen-Mut held the following offices:
Hereditary Prince and Count, Seal-bearer of the Pharaoh of Lower Egypt, Sole Companion, Steward of Amen; Overseer of the Fields, the Garden, the Cows, the Serfs, the Peasant-farmers, and the Granaries of Amen; Chief Prophet of Amen; Prophet of Amen's Sacred Barque; Chief Prophet of Montu in Hermonthis; Spokesman of the Shrine of Geb; Headman of the House of the Official; Steward of the Pharaoh; Overseer of the Royal Residence; Controller of Every Divine Craft; Steward of the Princess Neferu-Re; Controller of all Construction Work of the Pharaoh in ***Karnak***, Hermonthis, Deir el-Bahri, the Temple of Mut at ***Karnak***, and of Luxor; and 'a superior of superiors, an overseer of overseers of construction works'. Evidently Sen-Mut was a technocrat ***extraordinaire***!
The revered Amen-Hotep, son of Hapu, in reference to his own structures:
'They were wonderful for size and height, and they will last as long as the heaven'. This statement emphasises that monumentality and the enduring quality of structures in engineering works was the purpose of the foremost Egyptian engineers.

History has shown that in ancient Egypt an engineer could rise from modest circumstances to social prominence, something that proved impossible in Mesopotamia. However, under the Egyptian Empire in the New Kingdom foreigners became influential in such professional classes as majordomos, mercenary soldiers, and engineers. A class-cleavage developed as a result of this situation between the rulers, the professional classes and the common Egyptians. It no longer was possible for an ordinary Egyptian engineer to move up in his social status, because foreigners had gradually taken command of his profession.

Pharaoh Ship Canal

The 'Pharaoh Ship Canal', the excavation of which began under the rule of Pharaoh Sen-Usert I, remained in service over a period of 1,200 years with few interruptions until about 525 B.C. By the time the Assyrian King Esar-Haddon conquered Egypt in 670 B.C., the desert winds had sanded up the natural connexion between the Bitter Lakes and the Red Sea.

About 608 B.C., Egyptian prince Nikau (Necho) II of ***Sais*** tried to excavate a new canal from Lake Timsah to the Tanitic branch of the Nile river but he eventually abandoned the project after more than 100,000 workers had perished during its construction. Nikau's canal was100 feet (30.5 m) wide, 40 feet (12.2 m) deep, and it had a length of 37 miles (59.5 km) before the digging of the canal was abandoned.

During the period from 525 B.C. to 485 B.C., the Persian King Darios I, who had conquered Egypt about 525 B.C., dredged and extended the Pharaoh Ship Canal by excavating a canal between the Bitter Lakes and the Red Sea in order to restore this natural connexion which by his time had been closed by the shifting desert sands. Since the Nile river changes its level, it was necessary to introduce sluice works, dams and also locks between the Nile river and the Bitter Lakes. Darios sent a fleet of 24 ships through the extended Pharaoh Ship Canal in the opening ceremony of this seaway which made large scale sea trade between Egypt, Persia and India possible.

From 283 to 246 B.C., the Macedonian King of Egypt, Ptolemaios Philadelphos (Ptolemy II), built some new water-gates and a cofferdam at the Bitter Lakes to make the Pharaoh Ship Canal wide enough for two triremes to pass each other in the canal. The journey of a ship from ***Bupastos*** to ***Arsinoe*** (now Suez) took about 4 days.

The Roman Emperor Traianus (in English, Trajan), who ruled from A.D. 98 to A.D.117, maintained and improved the Pharaoh Ship Canal when the Romans had dominion over Egypt. After the departure of the Romans the Pharaoh Ship Canal, as well as Lake ***Moeris***, fell into disuse and disrepair, and both were completely neglected after the fourth century A.D., the result of which was that the Pharaoh Ship Canal gradually silted up and Lake ***Moeris*** evaporated. In the 7th century A.D. when Egypt was under the dominion of Islam, the Pharaoh Ship Canal was finally abandoned by the Muslims because it was no longer needed either for conquest or for trade which now moved overland in caravans and, therefore, the canal was gradually buried by the shifting sands of the desert.

Suez Canal:

The modern Suez Canal without locks was a long trench through the sand which was built after the plans of the Austrian engineer Alois Negrelli (1799-1858) under the direction of the French ***entrepreneur*** Ferdinand Lesseps (1805-1894) from 1859 to November 17,1869 when the canal was ceremonially opened.

In 1879, 10 years after the successful completion of the Suez Canal, Lesseps was prepared to undertake in Central America the construction of the Panama Canal, an extremely difficult engineering project because this canal that connects the Atlantic with the Pacific Ocean had to incorporate many locks [Lesseps believed locks were unnecessary!]and pass through an extremely difficult territory with severe climate. This engineering enterprise of Lesseps, that was poorly planned and improperly executed, became a colossal engineering failure, and an international financial scandal in which Lesseps himself was convicted of bribery. In 1907, Americans undertook this enormously difficult engineering project, and succeeded to construct the Panama Canal with exemplary efficiency and engineering know-how in 7 years under the direction of the American engineer George Washington Goethal (1838-1928). On August 15, 1914, the first ship passed through the Panama Canal on his way from the Atlantic to the Pacific Ocean.

Egyptian Roads

The most impressive ancient Egyptian '<u>roads</u>' were the immense causeways constructed during the Pyramid Age as roads of access to the pyramids from the Nile river. The heretical and individualistic Pharaoh Akhen-Aten was the only Pharaoh to build an elaborate system of military patrol roads around his new capital city Akhet-Aten.

A stone paved ceremonial road is known to have existed between the temples of Bast and Thoth at the holy city ***Bu-Past***. It was about 400 feet (121.9 m) wide and nearly ½ mile (0.8 km) long. This ceremonial road ran straight through the marketplace of ***Bu-Past***, and it was lined with lofty trees. Pharaoh Ra-Meses III built another holy road which is known to have been lined with flowers at his new city ***Per-Ra-Meses*** in the delta. Otherwise, every ***nome***, or district, in ancient Egypt had market squares which were paved with flagstones.

CHAPTER III

INDO-EUROPEANS: Men of Action and Engineering

The Indo-Europeans, who appear to have been indigenous to the Baltic region and the flatlands of Europe, suddenly entered the stage of history at the end of the third millennium B.C. with their horses, chariots, swords, and with the might and main of the conqueror.

The Indo-Europeans spread with an unprecedented speed and drive for conquest from their homeland in all directions over the flatlands of the known world: to the Atlantic Ocean in Western Europe, to the Mediterranean and the Mediterranean Islands, to Anatolia, to the Iranian plateau, to Ural Mountains and even as far as to India. By the middle of the second millennium B.C. the Indo-Europeans were dominant over a large portion of the known world, from Europe to India, hence the name Indo-Europeans. They possessed a significant technological advantage over other people they vanquished by having domesticated the horse, the most important mobile source of power available to man, by having expert knowledge of metallurgy, and by making fine wagons and chariots. Although the Indo-Europeans were first of all pastoral people who preferred cattle raising, they were also skilled farmers. They were the first mobile people in history who were free to move with their chariots when and where their spirit moved them.

Indo-Europeans were free to think for themselves as individuals, and, therefore, they had great aptitude for learning from others. They had a natural penchant for lofty thoughts and soaring imagination about freedom in the image of their sky-god ***Djaus*** [or ***Zeus*** in Greek, or ***Deus*** in Latin], who did not grovel in the murky cave like the Earth Mother, but rather soared freely like an eagle in the boundless sky where there is light instead of darkness, and freedom to roam.

The Indo-Europeans had a culture with pastoral elements, a patriarchal social system with strong emphasis on personal honour, personal struggle, competitiveness, ambition, and heroism - and, above all else, rationalism. The Indo-European was born a man of action who had a dynamic character and a restless spirit.

Indo-Europeans tended to celebrate not so much the success of the hero, as his unconquerable spirit that made him superior to his fate – a fate commonly tragic as befits a realistic man who is always aware of his mortality. Consequently, the Indo-European did not live in fear of gods, like the Oriental man, but instead he asserted his own personal power and his own virtue by refusing to submit tamely to the forces of nature or to the will of other men. Therefore, the Indo-European did not believe in the impotence of the individual man but rather had confidence in the vigour and dignity of his spirit. This awareness of the personal virtue of the individual man, and other personal attributes of the Indo-European made their mission of conquest possible.

History to Indo-Europeans was an affair of men, and not an affair of the gods as the ancient Oriental people believed. Oriental people considered man to be a born slave of the gods, as well as of the kings whom they thought to be divinely appointed agents of the gods and, therefore, man's role was to recognise his worthlessness as an individual, and to submit himself to the will of the patron god and, of the king [and, therefore, of the State] in his submissive resignation. In this Oriental resignation of man, prostration in the dust was the only proper place for him. In the imagination of the ancient Orientals, man was hopelessly ignorant, and his gods remained forever inscrutable to him. For the Semites such as Hebrews, man was no better than a miserable worm only fit to crawl in the dust.

In an ancient Babylonian text: "Man is dumb; he knows nothing. Mankind, everyone that exists – what does he know? Whether he is committing sin or doing good he does not even know."

The Hebraic Job, in contrast to his original Sumerian prototype, repented forever in 'dust and ashes' for having dared to question the motives of God. Consequently, everything the ancient Oriental man ever accomplished was always in the name of the gods, never in the name of man.

This mental attitude of the Oriental stood in sharp contrast to the frame of mind of the Indo-European, who was a defiant individual recognising sovereignty over his own person by no one but himself. The Indo-European was a vigorous, hardy, and physically and mentally active man who had the courage of a warrior. He was not submissive as an individual, but obeyed voluntarily his chieftain, who was elected by a council of elders and an assembly of freemen, and whose authority was limited by the same bodies, out of loyalty rather than out of docility. In other words, the Indo-European chieftain was a ***primus inter pares*** who was subject to the same laws as everybody else. Moreover, to the Indo-European the law was valid only if it existed first in the practice of the people. Hence, they did not easily tolerate oppression of their people by the dint of law : a group or a council could not capriciously impose an arbitrary law of their own choosing on people, if the people already did not practice it in their daily life by virtue of their common beliefs.

The rationalism of the Indo-Europeans was fundamental in their habits of thinking, a notable feature of which was the determined effort they made to find explanations of natural events in terms that are understandable to man's conscious mind. This effort impelled the Indo-Europeans to find a cause for every event in an explanation consisting of a logical sequence of thought constructed by reason. Intrinsic in this way of thinking was the assumption that man possesses an independent faculty of reason which is distinct from his general faculty of thinking.

The Oriental people, such as the ancient Semites, also thought, but they never felt any need to consider reasoning a distinct faculty of man, since the ancient Orientals recognised no separate existence of independent rational thought and, therefore, they did not distinguish between science and myth because the Oriental mind was a natural 'myth-making mind'. A myth to the ancient man was a fabulous story that explained an eternally continuing event. The ancient Oriental regarded the universe as animate and endowed with an intelligence and will like his own. Hence, to him, cosmic or natural events represented an encounter of two kinds of wills, the result of which was a myth. For instance, if a river did not behave as it ought to have behaved, then the forces that control the river, the river gods, but not the river itself, were considered to be angry at man for some misdeed man had committed. Since they believed that man cannot understand this because he is ignorant, and that he cannot do anything about it because he is impotent, they concluded that he can only appease the river gods by utter submission and sacrifice.

The myth-making character of the ancient Oriental did not mean that he was unable to think rationally, but rather that he never felt any need to distinguish reason as an independent mental faculty of man. The ancient Orientals, such as the ancient Semites, were not analytically minded, because they were not explicitly aware of reason. Therefore, they did not seek logical explanations for recurrent events that would have been understandable to man's conscious mind, but rather explained the events by an inscrutable mythological fable in which imagination and fancy, which were undisciplined by reason, shrouded the intellect of man. The ancient Orientals, by virtue of accepting the idea of man's ignorance and impotence and, therefore, of man's unimportance, led lives of quiet desperation and complete submission to the will of the gods and of their rulers, who were thought to be the arbiters between men and gods if not gods themselves.

The rationalism in the thinking of Indo-Europeans led them to a polarised view of life, and to the acceptance of two-valued logic in rational explanation which, in turn, led to the principle of contradiction. In consequence of this dualism in their rational thinking, the Indo-Europeans created the modern intellectual process by turning from the mythological to the logical attitude of the mind towards the external world.

The polarised thinking of the Indo-Europeans created rigorous distinctions between man and god, man and nature, male and female, individual and group, past and future, right and wrong, truth and falsehood, life and death, and so on. The very grammar of the Indo-European language is a reflexion of these fine polar distinctions made in their rational thinking: categories of gender, sharp distinction of person and number, great emphasis on chronological tense, which, in its turn, had a strong logical and classifying influence on their thought processes. Owing to their rational turn of the mind, the Indo-Europeans had a natural tendency for analysis. Therefore, they developed a highly inflected objective language which had a complex of particles, auxiliaries, subordinating syntax, and an extensive vocabulary of abstract nouns.

In contrast, the ancient Semitic languages did not possess the particles, the auxiliaries, the array of tenses, and the elaborate subordinating syntax which makes a wide variety of logical and temporal relationships explicit, and provides for the continuity of thought. For instance, the Hebrew syntax is atomistic, the reader himself must supply the relationships. It has only the past and the future tense, and, consequently, it must use an awkward participal phrase to express the present. Moreover, thought in a Semitic language does not proceed step-by-step, nor is it detached or objective. Its disconnectedness and its love of holding imagery makes Semitic writing lyrical rather than rational, concrete rather than abstract, and sublime rather than elegant. Moreover, Semitic languages possess few abstract nouns.

In the view of the Indo-Europeans, the Earth and the Sky, and the whole world had been created for the benefit of man, and not for the benefit of the gods as the Oriental people thought. Man had to take diligent care of the Earth by continuing the work of creation in tilling the soil, raising domestic animals, and being productive. They believed that the wellbeing of man was dependent upon doing all this with strenuous effort, unrelenting hard work, and heroic struggle.

A high sense of honour, personal integrity and fearlessness were the most important characteristics of Indo-Europeans for they considered man to be a noble creature of the Sky-god. One of the most important principles they lived by was to speak the truth, since this implied respect for facts, that is, for things as they really are, for reality. Some of the most important ideals the Indo-Europeans struggled to achieve were to develop an unyielding will, to have unshakeable integrity, to keep contract, to be upright, to have probity, to be kind, to show mercy, to give alms to the needy, and to live with dignity. They thought that to have to swear an oath to act or to speak the truth was an indignity for a man of his noble stock – his word should suffice. An agreement was concluded with a handshake, which was considered as good as the bond of blood.

Indo-Europeans saw the horse as a noble and most valuable animal whom they treated with great respect, kindness and care. Indo-Europeans considered dogs to be the most loyal companions of man. They loved and respected dogs, and even to strike a dog was a crime subject to public reprobation and retribution. The affection of the Indo-Europeans for useful domestic animals has been cherished by the Western man throughout history as a noble Western tradition.

The ancient Semites, such as Chaldeans, Akkadians, Amurru, Aramaeans and Phoenicians, in contrast, were extremely pragmatic, myth-minded, unimaginative, matter-of-fact, unartistic, cruel, hard-headed, yet shrewd, practical and businesslike. They were not outstanding creators, artists or inventors, but rather capable international brokers, clever merchants, and skilful organisers. In the absence of conscious reasoning, they tended to become fanatical under duress – an attitude that Indo-Europeans despised as being undignified. Indo-Europeans regarded fanaticism an irrational state of mind of man which disregards self-interest and deliberate risks taken in the pursuit of it.

The first Indo-Europeans who became important in history were the Hittites, also called the Hatti. Hittites had great talent for organised government, and they were the first outstanding military engineers. Hittites appeared on the historical stage about 2000 B.C. and became extremely powerful and influential about 1500 B.C.. They conquered the Hurrians, a group of warlike Caucasians from the region of modern Armenia who appeared on the scene with their war chariots drawn by horses somewhat earlier than Hittites. Hurrians, also known as Hurri, established the Mitanni State in the northern region of Mesopotamia. Hurrians after their submission by the Hittites became the important intermediaries between the Sumerian culture and the Indo-European invaders of the Mesopotamia, such as the Hittites. Hurrians were a musical folk, who have left the oldest extant piece of written music after Sumerians, dating from about 1800 B.C., which is the very origin of Western music. Hittites, who ultimately conquered the Mitanni State, founded the first efficiently organised imperial State which employed rational diplomacy and written pacts in dealing with their enemies.

Although there were many other powerful Indo-European groups, such as Kassites, Mycenaeans (also called Achaeans), Terremareans, Aryans, Gutians (also called Gutii), Medes, Persians, Scythians, Dorians, Parthians, Phrygians, Thracians, Celts, Cimmerians, Samartians, Lydians and later Greeks, Latins, Germans, and Norsemen known as Vikings, the most important of these early Indo-European people were Hittites, Persians, Greeks, and Latins also known as Romans. Even the ancient Assyrians were mostly a group of Caucasians mixed with other local inhabitants, such as Semitic Amurru, but they spoke a Semitic tongue and entertained an Oriental outlook of life. Although Kassites were probably the Indo-Europeans who brought the horse to Mesopotamia, the Hittites were the first who quickly adopted the horse from the Hurrians, and promptly developed new war tactics and strategies involving chariotry which centuries later was adopted by the Assyrians in the conduct of their bloodthirsty wars in the Assyrian ascendancy to an important military and imperial power. The outstanding horsemen of antiquity were the Medes who bred the first large horses that man could ride.

Hittites and Persians, after subjugating other ancient Oriental people, were influenced by the Oriental thought and, as a consequence, they themselves became somewhat orientalised. Persian kings soon acquired the absolute power of Oriental potentates, which tended to corrupt the holders of such power.

The ancient Greeks were passionate believers in Indo-European principles in general, and rationalism in particular. The rationalistic and individualistic tendencies of the Indo-European people had been intensified by the weakening of their social and tribal beliefs, and the ancient Greeks among the ancient Indo-Europeans were the leading promoters of rationalism and individualism, because they were the first characteristically Western men.

Since the modern Western civilisation, its science and technology is deeply rooted in the traditions of the Indo-European rational thought, it is worthwhile for a Western man to know something about the ancient cultural legacy of the European civilisation.

Hittites: ***Fortification Engineering***

[from c.2000 B.C. to 1200 B.C.]

Hittites, also known as Hatti, were the Indo-Europeans who came to Anatolia [Asia Minor] from the plains and steppes of Europe. They had great talent for political and military organisations, and, therefore, they were skilled masters of both the defensive and offensive military arts. Hittites gradually conquered the autochthonous inhabitants of Anatolia since they were as skilled in negotiations and diplomacy as in warfare, and established a far-reaching tributary Hittite Empire founded on written pacts. Apart from their military and political talent, Hittites made several fundamental contributions to law, literature, history, technology and engineering of the Western civilisation.

Hittites attempted to harmonise respect for gods with an equal respect for the rights of the individual. They introduced a legal code which was unique in the ancient world because it had a character of a democratic law which established and preserved a balance between the rights of the individual and his duties to the State. In the Hittite law there was a conscious striving for justice to the individual under full consideration of motives, extenuating circumstances, and the presence or lack of premeditation. Hittite justice administered by their courts punctiliously observed due process of law. Hittite court not only considered testimony and weighed evidence, but it went to incredible pains to ascertain all the facts of the case under consideration. The general principle of Hittite justice was proper restitution rather than State-imposed retribution. For instance, in the case of premeditated murder, the family of the victim decided whether to accept compensation or to decree death penalty. All the people, Hittites as well as foreigners and even slaves, were treated alike by the Hittite law. Command of the Hittite King to his military judges was: "Do not make the better case the worse, or the worse case the better. Do what is just!" These basic Indo-European tenets of justice were later indirectly carried over to Ionian Greeks, and they ultimately reappeared in the Roman law and, in this manner, indirectly influenced the modern law in the West. In their efforts to establish just and objective laws, Hittites successfully amalgamated individualistic and Oriental thoughts.

Hittites, being Indo-Europeans, had a natural sense for order and a belief in cause-and-effect. They became the first people in history who were capable of historical inference, since this requires an abiding belief in cause-and-effect, and the ability for reasoned argument. Sumerians who came before Hittites were also able to sense order, for they had their lists of kings, however they were incapable of historical inference since they considered man unable to influence his own fate. Therefore, in the outlook of the ancient Orientals there was no historical development of human society and civilisation. In contrast, Hittites, believed that man does influence his own life through his actions, because they thought man to be a purposive creature who acted to influence the conduct of his life through the power of his will. Therefore, Hittites did not assume that man was only a creature of reaction and a mere toy to the gods.

Royal annals of Hittite were the first straightforward national histories which were expounded as reasoned narratives, and which had a definite literary style. Hittite scribes were the earliest known self-conscious authors who attached their names to their writings, thereby showing a modern spirit of authorship. In these annals Hittite kings used reasoned arguments to explain their political actions that was revolutionary for its time.

Another important cultural progress is apparent in the autobiography of the Hittite King Hattusilis III. In his biography, this King gives a reasoned defence of his conduct in which he recognised the truth, and even the unjustified acts that he had committed in his usurpation of power as a servant of his people and his god. This Hittite King showed great respect for the law and expressed his sense of responsibility to his people by explaining his historical actions, an unprecedented attitude among ancient men, which characterises the basic rational beliefs of the Indo-Europeans.

Hittites organised their Empire on a feudal basis by granting local autonomy to their subject people, by showing general tolerance and full respect for foreign gods and alien customs, and by seeking to win their loyalty through equitable treatment. Hittites originated and developed the international treaty as a written contract between different countries, which has remained the backbone of the Western civilisation ever since.

Moreover, Hittites are also of great importance to the Western literature because they improved the cuneiform writing and created new literary genres which they raised to the highest cultural refinement hitherto achieved. In Hittite epics the divine hero conquers the forces of evil and slays the dragon; in their lyrical poetry there are hymns and prayers. The Hittite version of the Sumerian epic of Gilgamesh, which was greatly improved by the Hittite writers, was ultimately transmitted to Ionia where it influenced the first great Greek poet ***Homeros*** (in English, Homer) in the his epic of ***Odyssey***. The funeral of Proklos and Hektor in Homer's ***Iliad*** [about the Trojan War] resembles the cremation ceremony of a Hittite monarch. The fundamental theme of the Hittite mythology, a great deal of it being original, is struggle: good against evil, dynasty against dynasty, everyman against vicissitues of life and fate, and so on, expressing the venerable tradition of the Indo-European dualism. All Hittite deities were like humans : they had as many faults as they had virtues! Moreover, Hittite literature is the first ancient literature to exhibit a sense of humour. Hittite mythology had an influence on the Greek mythology through the Mycenaean and Ionian Greeks, and the Hittite's rationalism indirectly influenced the emergence of natural philosophy in the Ionian city, Miletos, about 600 B.C.. In this way, the Hittites have had a lasting influence, indirect though it was, on Western science.

Hittites have also left a permanent legacy in technology: they were the first people to introduce iron metallurgy to civilisation about 1300 B.C., thereby ushering in the Age of Iron which lasted until about A.D. 1850. They engineered the first sound military fortifications, which were ingeniously adapted to local topological conditions. Hittites were the first competent specialists in fortification engineering who built the first soundly constructed structures with deep foundations of stone-masonry. Their most influential engineering achievements were their fortifications, which were planned with supreme technical competence and sophistication, and remarkable engineering ingenuity. The uncanny ability of Hittites to use the terrain to its maximum defensive advantage, and the monumental character of their fortifications has been seldom equalled or surpassed.

Hittites built the first large fortified city of the antiquity, their capital city ***Hattusas***, which was located in the bend of the Marassantiya (modern, Halys) river. ***Hattusas*** had a size of about 1⅓ by 1 mile (2.1 by 1.6 km) and occupied about 400 acres. Its double defensive walls were about 4 miles (6.4 km) long and were lined with stone-paved glacis at the low parts of the city fortress. The inside defensive wall was about 15 feet (4.6m) thick and 50 feet (15.2m) high, defensive towers were 50 by 39 feet (15.2 by 11.6 meters) in plan and 60 feet (18.3m) high and were spaced alternately at 100 feet (30.5m) and at 50 feet (15.2m) intervals. The outer defensive wall was set about 20 feet (6.1m) in front of the inner defensive wall, and it had a thickness of about 5 feet (1.5m) and a height of about 15 to 20 feet (4.6 to 6.1m). Both defensive walls were topped by battlements. The walls and towers were of casement construction in which the cross-walls tied together the double curtain walls and the compartments so created were filled with rubble. Hittite engineers were the first engineers in history who built deep and massive stone foundations for their structures. They used the Indo-Germanic cyclopean limestone masonry without mortar, with many stones cut to fit. The stone foundation of the city wall had a 15-foot (4.6m) high socle above the ground on which the superstructure made of mud-brick and reinforced with timber framing to resist Earth tremors rested. The timber baulks of the framing were anchored into the limestone socle with wooden dowels. The massive defensive wall at the knoll spanned a deep chasm, which was about 28 feet (8.5m) wide, in a corbelled stone arch, the first massive false arch in history.

The city-wall had parabolic gateways, 10 feet (3m) wide and 15 feet (4.6m) high, which were flanked by two rectangular defensive towers and two stone orthostats carved in the image of lions. Nine narrow corbel-vaulted stone postern tunnels [underground sally tunnels] of approximately 230 feet (70.1m) in length and slanting towards the outside were constructed under the paved ramparts at the low vulnerable parts of the fortified city to afford an attack against the besieging enemy. These tunnels were not camouflaged.

Hattusas had finely dressed stone-paved ramparts and courtyards. The city streets were from 10 to 13 feet (3 to 4m) wide and paved with finely dressed stones and provided with drains. It had one of the first systems of public utilities in which earthenware pipes carried potable water. ***Hattusas*** had the first known paved processional boulevard which skirted the city and was lined by temples. The Hittite temple complex occupied some 5 acres (2 hectares), and incorporated numerous, deep, square windows in the outside walls which were probably covered with oiled skins to admit light. The palace of the Hittite king had a 2-column porch entrance with 2 square flanking towers, known as the 'Hittite portico', and an audience hall which was 105-foot square (32m square) with timber columns supporting the timber roof. Hittites built staircases in their buildings with one or two parallel flights.

Hittite army had a corp of military engineers, the first rationally organised engineering body in the world. Hittite military engineers not only introduced the 'battering ram' as a siege craft, which they first used in their siege of the city ***Ursu***, but also designed the 'mountain' (***agger***) serving as an access ramp for the 'battering ram' to the defensive wall of the enemy's fortification.

Minoans: *Naval and Civil Engineering*

[from c.2000 B.C. to 1400 B.C.]

The first European civilisation, the Minoan civilisation on the Island of Creta (modern Crete), had the political form of a thalassocracy under the Minoan sea-kings. Minoans, a physically lean and graceful people who loved nature and its scenery, were people of a non-Semitic race. Minoan sea-kings built the first known fleets which were capable of sailing the open seas, since Minoans were the first expert naval engineers of antiquity. The Mycenaeans, also called Achaeans [Helladic Greeks of the Trojan War fame], and Phoenicians learnt their shipbuilding and seamanship from the Minoans, who had trading posts all along the eastern Mediterranean coastline. Minoan civilisation apparently owed much to the Egyptian civilisation. In religion, Minoans were more Oriental in their thoughts than the Hittites, and like the Egyptians, they preached a wild form of animism patronised by a bull-like nature god. It is reasonable to assume that the ferocious and aggressive nature of the bull-god influenced the wild behaviour of the apparently quite secular Minoans. Minoans, unlike the Hittites, had no sense of history since they left no historical records, no literature, no names, and no dates despite the fact that they did have their own writing, the so-called 'Linear A', which hitherto no one has been able to decypher. Therefore, Minoans were intellectually inferior to Hittites. On the other hand, they were remarkably innovative artists, who emphasised nature in their art. In their way of life Minoans were a talented, luxury loving and quite sophisticated people of their time.

Minoan palaces in ***Knossos***, ***Phaistos*** and ***Mallia*** , but particularly the largest palace in ***Knossos***, known to ancient Greeks as the 'Labyrinth', derived both their style and construction from the Hittite prototypes in Anatolia. Since the word ***labrys*** meant double-ax which was a religious symbol of holiness to the Minoans, the word ***'labyrinth'*** identified the palace of ***Knossos*** as the house of the double-ax, a holy place. Minoan decorative art of their buildings shows some Egyptian influence. The Minoan palaces were the industrial-military-administrative-religious complexes of the Minoan sea-kings who probably were also the high priests of their religion, a cult based on the worship of the ***Minotaur***, a nature god with bull's head on human body. Apparently their religious ceremony not only involved bull-baiting and bull-leaping, a dangerous acrobatic practice which took place in an arena representing the first such structure constructed for spectators anywhere in the world, but also for primitive human sacrifice. Minoans engaged in such sports as boxing. The entire country on the Island of Creta was run by the palace economy, since arts and crafts appear to have been practiced there. The palace-complex itself was run by an intricate bureaucracy who had established an efficient distribution system of production.

The largest Minoan palace located in ***Knossos*** had 5 storeys and spread over 6 acres (2.43 hectares). It was an extremely elaborate building containing a great maze of apartments, corridors, lightwells, colonnades and staircases. Minoan houses were the first buildings in the ancient world in which windows formed an integral part of the building design. Minoan windows were covered with louvers, grilles, oiled skins, or cloths. Hittites had already built deep square windows in their temple complexes in ***Hattusas***, and in their other buildings, but it was not the dominating feature of their building design. The Minoan palace had its principal rooms not on the ground floor as was customary in the Near East, but on the first floor, which made the main staircase the central feature of the Minoan building. The construction of the palace structure in ***Knossos*** resembled that of the Hittites: walls were reinforced with a timber framework, and the free-standing cypress columns tapering downwards, a unique feature in the Minoan construction, were used in colonnades and in open stairwells. This type of building construction and design, led to the European building style in much later ages.

In the later Minoan palaces, there existed domestic luxuries which were unmatched in the palaces in Egypt or the Near East. The palace of ***Knossos*** had remarkable domestic hydraulics consisting of running water and hub-and-spigot type water pipes of terracotta laced together by thongs or ropes, flushed toilets, and bathrooms with 2 bathtubs, something that remained unequalled in Europe until long after A.D. 1800. The bridge leading to the palace of ***Knossos*** had stone piers and a timber superstructure.

The Minoan sea-kings built the first known paved road system: a net of highways crossing the island from ***Knossos*** and ***Phaistos*** to the ports at the gulf of Mesara near ***Gortyna*** and ***Komo*** on the southern coast of the Island of Creta, the busy docks of which were engaged in trade with Egypt and the Near East. This road, which had steep gradients, crossed mountains 5,000 feet (1,524m) high. The road surface consisted of basalt flagstones laid in a thin clay mortar bed, which in turn was laid on stones bound by plaster. The flagstones covered the central 4½ feet (1.4m) of the road, the two strips 3½ feet (1.1m) wide on both sides of the flagstone pavement were surfaced with limestone rammed into clay, pebbles and potsherds. The entire road was slightly cambered and drained on both sides with stone drains. Limestone walls, 15 feet (4.6m) high, which lined both sides of the road, were constructed for shade and, possibly, for safety. It is reasonable to assume that these roads may have been patrolled. The Minoan roads were as good as the Roman roads built many centuries later in Creta when the island was under the Roman rule.

Minoans were one of the best, if not the very best, metalworkers, pottery makers and fresco painters of the ancient world. They exported wine, oil, textiles and such timber as cypress and pine. Egypt traded with Minoans as early as 2000 B.C.. Since Minoans were prominent producers of wine, they tried to improve its technology. It appears that the beam-press was first invented in Creta about 1800 B.C. to squash grapes.

Although the Minoan sea-kings in earlier times may have engaged in piracy and marauding, their palaces had no military defences. Their merchant navy, however, was well armed. The Minoan civilisation came to a sudden end, when the Helladic Greeks, the Mycenaeans [also known as Achaeans] conquered the island about 1400 B.C. long after an enormous earthquake and volcanic eruption in 1628 B.C. blew apart the small Island of Thira [modern Santorini] inhabited by a Minoan colony, and covered the Island of Creta, which is only about 70 miles (129 km) south of the Island of Thira, with volcanic trass consisting of a fine pumice dust called ***tephra***. The giant seismic sea-wave, now called '***tsunamis***', created by the immense volcanic eruption apparently swept over the northern coast of the Island of Creta and devastated everything in its wake. Soon after the Minoans disappeared from history without a trace.

Assyrians: *Systematic Large Scale Military and Hydraulic Engineering*
[from c.1100 B.C. to 612 B.C.]

Assyrians were a mixed race consisting predominantly of white Caucasians, Subarians, or even of Hurri, who had interbred with Amurru Semites. They entertained the ancient Oriental outlook and spoke a Semitic dialect called the Akkadian. This racial mixture apparently produced men of inborn ferocity and native cruelty who took fiendish pleasure in torture and terror. Assyrian kings were intelligent, sadistic monsters who proudly depicted mass atrocities in giant bas-reliefs covering miles of dados in their palaces. The Assyrian State was a centralised autocratic military despotism which commanded a vast aggressive military force using the method of mass terror and psychology of fear. Despite this repulsive and grisly aspect of their character, the Assyrians were quite talented and enterprising engineers. In earlier, more peaceful times, about 2000 B.C., Assyrians had been peaceful traders of the Near East, and had demonstrated their great ability to learn and exploit foreign skills, and to utilise foreign resources in their own industry, technology and art. Assyrians proved to be extraordinarily resourceful in mastering, developing and extending the practical art of engineering of the Hittites, Amorite Babylonians, and the Caucasian mountaineers, and armed with all this knowledge and expertise they undertook vast engineering projects and carried them out with ingenuity, efficiency and unprecedented speed. Assyrians, out of sheer military necessity, became not only the developers of military arts, but also mechanical and civil engineering. Their engineers built armoured wagons, siege towers, rams, and extensive networks of graded military roads. They not only were the first known masterbuilders of aqueducts, and brick, wooden and pontoon bridges, but also masters of the Hittite's fortification engineering, which they improved with hydraulic defences. In their ability to learn and exploit foreign skills and resources, the Romans very much resembled the Assyrians.

About 1100 B.C., the Assyrian King Tiglath-Pileser I (Akkadian name, ***Tukulti-Pal-Esarra***), who ruled from 1115 B.C. to 1102 B.C., organised and trained the Assyrian army into a formidable force of conquest which relied on the principle of terror. He introduced specialisations in his army and instituted a corps of military engineers (***ummani***), which they organised after the Hittite prototype. Ultimately the Assyrian army was composed of groups of military specialists in every branch of warfare, such as cavalry, chariotry, bowmen, lancers, shield bearers, execution and deportation squads, a fierce infantry, and a corps of military engineers with specialisations in sapping, bridge engineering, communication and transport engineering, and building of military equipment. Assyrians learnt their horsemanship, chariotry and cavalry tactics from the expert Indo-European horsemen, the Mitanni and the Medes, and because of this newly founded mobility of the Assyrian army, the availability of a network of roads that made rapid transport of Assyrian troops and military equipment possible became of vital importance to the Assyrian military juggernaut. This king was responsible for supplying his army with iron weapons, the first large army in history to be so equipped. He also mechanised his army with siege-machinery, which made the Assyrian army the first systematically mechanised army in the history of warfare. The Assyrian military engineers developed the Hittite battering-ram into a formidable siege-engine consisting of a towering siege belfry as tall as the defensive wall operated on wheels, and a massive battering-ram encased in a protective armour. On account of the mechanised warfare conducted by the Assyrians, canals alone could not provide the great mobility required by the conquering Assyrian army, and the rapid means of transport necessary for the punitive expeditions of the Assyrian army to quell many local revolts. Out of the necessity for rapid means of communication, the Assyrians became the first systematic builders of extensive networks of graded military roads. These military roads were provided with fortified stations and messenger relays for the quick royal messenger service. For expeditious transportation, the Assyrians followed the example of the Sumerian King Shulgi of ***Ur***, who had built in Sumer a system of roads with rest stations as early as 2100 B.C..

Tiglath-Pileser I, who founded the New Assyrian Empire, made ***Assur*** [or ***Ashur***] the seat of the chief Assyrian god *Assur*, his capital city. This city had been an ancient military and commercial outpost of Sumer, both under the Akkadian rule of Sargon I, and under the rule of Sumerian dynasty of ***Ur.*** By 1800 B.C. a Semitic-speaking tribe of Assyrians led by the chieftain Shamsi-Adad had made ***Assur*** their independent capital. The deity *Assur* became the patron god of the new Assyrian Kingdom, and the city of ***Assur*** became the religious capital and trading center of Assyria.

The city of ***Assur*** occupied an area of from 60 to 85 hectares (hectare = 10^4 square meters), and it had a population of about 20,000 inhabitants. This city had almost a right triangle shape of about 2,100-yard (1,920 m) base and 1,467-yard (1,341 m) height, and it was located on the Western bank of the Tigris river with a moat encircling the city on its eastern side. The enormous new and old palaces, and the temples of the gods *Assur*, *Sin* and *Shamash*, *Anu* and *Adad*, and *Ishtar* (the goddess of love and victory) were located on the northern end of this fortified city. There were 3 paved processional roads in Assur. The processional road at the temple of Sin and Shamash had 2-foot deep ruts cut into the roadway for the passage of the chariots of the deities. The finest surviving processional road in ***Assur*** which led to the temple of *Ishtar* was laid on the foundation of burnt brick and supported on loose stone and gravel. It was paved with limestone flags with carved ruts for the wheels of the chariot carrying the goddess *Ishtar*. The dual temple of *Anu* and *Adid* had twin ziggurats with temples stretching between them. Assyrians also worshipped the god of writing called *Nabu* in a particular temple built for this god. The main reason for the worship of the god of writing was that the Amorite Babylonians as well as Assyrians believed that the written word shaped man's destiny: death came to a man when a divine scribe etched his name into a mythical Book of Fate. Ancient Egyptians had entertained similar views on writing. There were also two gigantic palaces in ***Assur*** of which one was mainly used for administrative purposes since Assyrians created the first administrative Empire, in contrast to the Hittite's tributary Empire.

About 879 B.C., the Assyrian King Assur-Nasir-Pal II, who ruled from 884 B.C. to 859 B.C. and initiated the systematic large-scale Assyrian war expeditions for plunder, rebuilt an old city, founded by king Shalmaneser I about 1250 B.C., into a magnificent new capital ***Kalhu*** [biblical ***Kalakh***; modern, Nimrud] which covered some 642 acres (260 hectares) and was located at the confluence of the Tigris and its tributary, the Upper Zab river, about 19 miles (30.6) south of the present city Mosul. ***Kalhu*** was laid out in a vast rectangle of 1¼ by 1¼ mile (2 by 2 km), and surrounded by mud-brick ramparts and by the Tigris river on the southern side of the city. This walled city had 4 fortified gates and its defensive city wall had a perimeter of about 6 miles (9.7 km).

Kalhu was supplied with water by tunnels cut through the rock of the intervening hills which led to open canals in the valleys.

A 100-foot (30.5 m) deep well was sunk at ***Kalhu*** to provide an ample supply of drinking water for the inhabitants of the city. ***Kalhu*** was also provided with a system of sewers having corbelled vaults. For the purpose of water supply, Assur-Nasir-Pal II had an enormous dam erected near ***Kalhu***, that was built of large ashlar masonry in which the stone blocks were clamped with iron cramps set in lead. He also had a 7-mile (11.3 km) long canal dug from the Upper Zab river to ***Kalhu*** to irrigate the lands about ***Kalhu***.

Most of the citadel of the city ***Kalhu***, which covered an area of 1,800 by 2,050 feet (548.6 by 624.8 meters) was occupied by the palace and the temples, the largest of which was dedicated to *Nabu*, the god of writing. He built a sumptuous palace, a citadel of the size 1,800 by 1,050 feet (548.6 by 320 meters), the hypogeum of which had vaulted ceilings. By that time, the Assyrian engineers were already master-builders of vaults and arches, both pointed and circular, and they built them on a vast scale. This new palace had rooms panelled in cedar, cypress, juniper, ebony, pistachio and tamarisk woods, and in polychrome glazed ornamental brick. The throne was inlaid with silver and gold, and the throne room was roofed by a giant barrel vault. The palace also had an archive which was discovered in the middle of the 19th century A.D.. In this palace, for the first time, stone dados consisting of 9-foot (2.7m) high plinths placed on edge and carved in low relief sculpture depicting scenes of war and pursuit as well as domestic activities, were used as a continuous frieze. Assur-Nasir-Pal's palace provided the traditional plan for the later Assyrian palaces. In 879 B.C., King Assur-Nasir-Pal II, upon the completion of his sumptuous palace threw a 10–day feast for 63,000 people which included the 47,000 labourers transported from the conquered territories to work in building his capital city ***Kalhu***.

Assur-Nasir-Pal II was a typical fiendish King of the Assyrians which can be learnt from his statement: "All chiefs who had revolted I flayed, with their skins I covered the pillar, some in the midst I walled up, others on stakes I impaled, still others I arranged around the pillar of stakes ..." Other equally monstrous Assyrian kings proudly declared: "I burnt 3,000 captives with fire ..."; "From their hostile mouths I have torn their tongues ..."; "The monuments which I have erected are made of human corpses from which I have cut the heads and limbs ..." Some of their kings took great pleasure in personally gouging out the eyes of hundreds of their prisoners who were tethered to the king with rings through their noses and mouths. Such grisly scenes were proudly depicted in huge wall reliefs lining the rooms in the king's palace.

Assyrian kings, like all tyrants, aggrandised themselves with grandiose buildings. All palaces of Assyrian kings were enormous citadels, and their sumptuousness and monumentality had the intended psychological function to awe the common man with the irresistible power and resplendent glory of the warrior-king of Assyria and, thereby, to make the man in the street feel insignificant and unimportant. In all Assyrian cities, palaces took distinct precedence over religious buildings.

Assyrian King Shalmaneser III, who ruled from 859 B.C. to 824 B.C., built a fortress outside the citadel of ***Kalhu*** as an administrative capital: it served as a palace, as barracks, as an arsenal and storehouse. His fortress incorporated a Hittite portico with a Sumerian arch as a novel monumental feature of the building. It is known that his engineers built a pontoon bridge of boats at the present Tell Balawat.

The Assyrian King Tiglath-Pileser II, who ruled from 744 B.C. to 727 B.C., regenerated the Assyrian Empire by conquering the long-resisting Aramaean city and citadel ***Damascus*** in 732 B.C., by reducing Israel to a grateful puppet state, as well as by instituting the Assyrian practice of mass deportations which his successors made into a normal Assyrian military practice, a practice that intensified the need for the availability of an extensive network of military roads. It was Tiglath-Pileser III who established a system of messenger relay stations along the Assyrian road network, an inchoate postal road system, which availed him of ready and immediate communications with all parts of his administrative Empire. Tiglath-Pileser III established by such means the largest empire known up to his time.

The usurper King, Sargon II (in Akkadian, ***Sharrukin***), who ruled from 721 B.C. to 705 B.C., built in a desert of stones his palace-city, ***Dur-Sharrukin*** (meaning 'Home of ***Sharrukin***', now modern Khorsabad) 11 miles (17.7 km) in the hills northeast of ***Nineveh***. It is one of the first known cities which was built on modern principles of town planning. ***Dur-Sharrukin*** had a size of more than a mile (1.8 km) square occupying about 741 acres (300 hectares), and it was oriented diagonally to compass points in order to provide shade. It had 7 city gates and was built on a gridiron pattern similar to modern planned towns. Sargon II made ***Dur-Sharrukin*** the new capital of Assyria, although the city of ***Assur*** still remained the religious capital of Assyria until the very end of the Assyrian Empire, just as ***Nippur*** had remained the religious capital of Sumer. ***Dur-Sharrukin*** incorporated an enormous palace citadel built on a high mud-brick platform which was faced with stone masonry and was as high as the city wall. The palace district occupied about 23 acres (9.3 hectares), partly inside and partly outside of the walled city. The city walls were 20 feet (6.1 m) thick and consisted of brick masonry built on stone foundations. The citadel walls which had 150 defensive towers were 80 feet (24.4 m) thick. The palace had 14 courts, and 87 major rooms, a library, storerooms, stables and a harem. Sargon II imported 15,200 cedar logs from Palestine for the beams of the palace, and the walls of the palace were decorated by a mile–long (1.6 km) dato of stone orthostats with bas-reliefs, and by polychromatic glazed bricks. It took 6 ships to transport the imported colossal statues decorating his palace. The palace entrance was a monumental Hittite portico containing a large Sumerian arch, which was supported by 2 winged human-headed bulls, called '***lamassa***'. The rainwater of the palace was drained by terracotta tiles. In sharp contrast to the general sumptuousness of the palace, Sargon's private apartment was of Spartan austerity. The ziggurat of the citadel had a base of 148 by 148 feet (45.1 by 45.1 meters), and a height of 148 feet (45.1 m). It had 7 stories, one for each planet, and a 6 foot (1.8 m) wide winding ramp, an Assyrian invention, that led to the top of the ziggurat. The arsenal of ***Dur-Sharrukin*** still contained about 200 tons of iron weapons, when it was excavated in modern times. One of the best preserved ancient paved roads runs from ***Dur-Sharrukin*** to ***Nineveh***. It had a system of fortified messenger relay stations placed at 2 hours travel for royal communication, where written itineraries were provided for the use of the traveller. ***Dur-Sharrukin*** was built within 20 years but it was never finished for it was abandoned by Sargon's son, Sennacherib, after Sargon II was killed in battle.

About 714 B.C., Sargon II had discovered during his campaigns in the Zagros mountains the sloping tunnel aqueducts (***qanaats*** in Arabic) which brought pure water from the underground springs in the hills to the valleys below without being subjected to pollution or evaporation. The qanaats were pioneered by the Caucasian miners, who drove vertical shafts at intervals from 65 to 165 feet (19.8 to 50.3 m) to the watertable, and then excavated a tunnel between the two shafts by following the watertable. Inclined shafts, or adits, were driven down to the tunnel to provide ready access to wells. A typical qanaat could deliver as much as 100,000 gallons (378,540 liters) of water in 24 hours. Sargon II destroyed all the qanaats he could find in the Zagros mountains, and brought the qanaat technology to Assyria by importing every Caucasian miner he was able to capture. In the same campaign Sargon II encountered many pontoon bridges which indicates that by his time such bridges were in general use.

Sennacherib (in Akkadian, ***Sin-Akh-Eriba***), who ruled between 705 B.C. and 686 B.C., was both an engineer and King who liked vegetation and rivers, and disliked the desert. Therefore, he abandoned ***Dur-Sharrukin*** after his father's death and moved the capital to ***Nineveh***, an old city located at the confluence of the Tigris and its tributary, the Tebitu [modern Khosr], a place where the Tigris became navigable. Sennacherib completely rebuilt this old city and made it intentionally into the largest fortified city in the world, a grander city than the Chaldean ***Babylon*** which he had militarily subdued.

He enclosed ***Nineveh*** by double defensive walls, which ran a full circuit of about 8 miles (12.9 km) around the city, and in his effort to emulate and improve on the Hittite method of fortification he provided the city also with hydraulic defences. ***Nineveh*** which occupied an area of about 1,800 acres (729 hectares) had an irregular quadrangular shape with the longest side having a length of about 3 miles (4.8 km) and the shorter side of about 1 mile (1.6 km). Sennacherib changed the existing irregular streets of ***Nineveh*** into a gridiron pattern and paved the main streets with stone and the side streets with gravel. Inside the city he built a citadel and his Southwest palace, in his own words, a 'Palace without Rival', which occupied about 5 acres (2 hectares) and was surrounded by ramparts containing battlements and fortified gates. The beams of the palace were made of imported cedar, sandalwood, ebony and pistachio wood, and the dadoes of the 71 palace halls were covered with 2-mile (3.2 km)-long alabaster bas-reliefs depicting war pursuits and other activities of the King. His palace had a less massive design than that of his father in ***Dur-Sharrukin***, but like his father, Sargon II, he also used the Hittite portico with monumental Sumerian arches as the central feature of his palace. He housed a library in his palace which contained all available official and literary records. Nearby his palace, Sennacherib constructed the 'House of Tribute', a vast marble storehouse for looted wealth. These monumental buildings were outfitted with unprecedented sumptuousness.

The oldest known bridge constructed of brick had been built about 1800 B.C. by the Elamite King Adda-Pakshu in ***Susa***, Elam, at the time when the first Amorite dynasty governed in ***Babylon***. About 700 B.C., Sennacherib built in ***Nineveh*** the second known brick bridge, probably a corbelled arch bridge which spanned the Tebitu river and led from the palace gate to the city. In ***Nineveh*** a number of pontoon bridges were constructed across the Tebitu, a river which divided the city into two parts. The city walls were also surrounded by ramparts with battlements and fortified gates. A wide moat lined the city wall at the northern, eastern and southern sides, whereas the Tigris river flanked the city walls at the western side. Sennacherib built brick wharves with stone block parapets to prevent the Tigris river from flooding the city. The inner city wall was over 90 feet (27.4 m) high and from 30 to 50 feet (9.1 to 15.2 m) thick. It consisted of two shells of burnt brick masonry with the space between the two shells filled with rubble. The outer wall, being more than 80 feet (24.4m) high and having 15 gates and 1,500 evenly spaced defensive towers, was made of brick and faced with stone. The inner curtain wall and the palace were completed by 703 B.C., after a record two year building effort. The outer wall was constructed from 694 B.C. to 690 B.C., but the extra ramparts on the vulnerable eastern side of the city were never completely finished. Sennacherib was a lover of trees, shrubs and vegetation, and, therefore, he surrounded the palace with parks and lined the outer city wall with a broad belt of orchards. He planted trees along the main streets of the city and even introduced the 'wool-bearing' cotton trees imported from India.

It was important to provide potable water for the large population of ***Nineveh***, estimated to have been at its peak at least 230,000 inhabitants, and to supply massive quantities of water for irrigation and hydraulic defences of the city. He sunk deep wells to provide the drinking water, which was a relatively easy task, but the irrigation problem was an extremely difficult civil engineering project, and by taking personal charge of the solution of it, Sennacherib proved himself to be one of the most capable and inventive executive engineers of antiquity.

Since the level of the Tigris river is low, he decided to use the Tebitu river as the source of water supply for ***Nineveh***. He dammed up the Tebitu river near the village Kisiri, about 10 miles (16.1 km) north of ***Nineveh***, and canalised it by dyking both of its banks, thereby raising the water level of the Tebitu sufficiently high in the canalised part of the river to permit gravity irrigation of the plains around ***Nineveh***. But already by the time the palace and the inner curtain wall of the city were finished in 703 B.C., new supplies of water were required. He dug a new canal to the northwest where he tapped another stream to augment the flow of the Tebitu.

In 700 B.C., when still more water was required, he located three smaller rivers near the towns ***Sulu***, ***Shinbaniba*** and ***Dur-Ishtar***, which were located about 13 miles (21 km) northeast of ***Nineveh*** in the Musri mountains and again he diverted these 3 rivers into the Tebitu to increase the flow of the river. In connexion with the diversion of these rivers, he had to construct two dams below the point where the Musri canal joined the Tebitu. Both dams were made of roughly shaped blocks of limestone, sandstone and other stones, all bound by mortar. The upper dam was more than 4½ feet (1.4 m) high and its thickness varied from 8½ feet (2.6 m) at one end to 9½ feet (2.9 m) at the other. This dam was 340 feet (103.6 m) long with the first 90 feet (27.4 m) being at right angles to the river and the remaining 250 feet (76.2 m) being parallel to the river bank. The upstream face of the dam was vertical, whereas the downstream face was made in stepped masonry consisting of five courses of stone to reduce erosion. Headworks of the canal were located on the northeastern bank.

The second dam was located 1,200 feet (365.8 m) downstream and had an overall length of 750 feet (228.6 m). It ran about 600 feet (182.9 m) along the northeastern bank before it crossed diagonally the river. The upstream face of the dam was vertical whereas the downstream face was stepped at both ends of the dam, but in the central section both faces were stepped. The height of the dam was 9 ½ feet (2.9 m), and its cross-section was not uniform. Both dams discharged water over their crests as part of the flow of the Tebitu river was diverted into the canals at both dams and the rest of the flow was spilled over the crest of the dam. These 2 dams, which are still extant, have their particular shapes apparently to provide the best anchoring for the dams at their bases and also the longest crests for spilling the water over the dams as a engineering method to reduce erosion. These dams created a large catchment basin, the water of which was carried to the city in canals. Sennacherib built a municipal canebrake northeast of ***Nineveh*** to take care of the overflow during the high water season. The large marsh created by the overflow, he used as a wild game reserve and a sugar-cane plantation. Sennacherib completed the Musri irrigation system in 694 B.C..

However, as early as 690 B.C., still more water was needed and he had to go 30 miles (48.3 km) northeast of ***Nineveh*** to an entirely new source, the Atrush [also called Putpullia; modern, Gomel] river at the foot of the Tas Mountain. He tapped the Atrush at the Bavian hills where the river flows in a deep gorge and built an oblique weir across it to guide water into the canal. At about 985 feet (300.2 m) downstream from the weir he built another dam of 39-foot (11.9 m) length across the river, and conducted the water by a tunnel through the dam to the rest of the canal downstream. The flow of water was controlled by wooden sluice gates provided at the downstream end of the tunnel. The width of the canal at the Bavian was about 20 feet (6.1 m). The Bavian canal had a length of more than 50 miles (80.5 km), and it was contained within two dykes from the Bavian hills to the Tebitu river at ***Kalatah***, where it emptied into the Tebitu river. At the same time four additional streams were diverted into the Bavian canal near the town ***Shifsirin*** where the Bavian canal was widened to 66 feet (20.1 m). The average gradient of the canal is 1– to – 800, and it was a remarkable achievement in surveying to determine the proper elevation at which the Atrush river had to be tapped to obtain such an excellent gradient for this 50-mile (80.5 km) long canal.

The Bavian canal had to cross a small tributary to the Tebitu river at a place now known as Jerwan. It appears that Sennacherib is the inventor of the aqueduct bridge which crosses this small stream over five arches. This stone aqueduct had 5 pointed corbelled arches each spanning 8 feet (2.4 m), which were supported by massive 10-foot (3.1 m) thick piers with water-breakers. The entire length of the aqueduct is about 920 feet (280.4 m), but the bridge itself has a length of 90 feet (27.4 m). The height of the aqueduct varies from 23 to 30 feet (7 to 9.1 m), and its width is 66 feet (20.1 m) inside and 84 feet (25.6 m) outside. The parapets of the water channel were about 5 feet (1.5 m) high and 9 feet (2.7 m) thick. The aqueduct was buttressed at approximately 50 feet (15.2 m) intervals. The structure of the aqueduct contained more than 2 million stone blocks of about 20 by 20 by 20 inches (50 by 50 by 50 cm) in size. They were laid in a 16 inch (40.6 cm) bed of lime concrete (1 part lime, 2 parts sand, 4 parts limestone aggregate), which in turn was poured on a one inch (2.5 cm) thick bed of mastic (25% to 35% bitumen, 15% fibres, the rest fillers). The paving stones were laid at a slope of 1– to – 80.

Sennacherib in his canal opening speech said the following: "By Assur, my great god, I swear that with these few men I dug the canal, and in a year and three months I completed it."

As Sennacherib claimed, this particular canal was built in a record time of 15 months. In this way, Sennacherib had been able to build a new irrigation system with 14 canals within 4 years. He had supplied ***Nineveh*** with 18 fresh water canals, all built within 13 years, from 703 B.C. to 690 B.C., a truly remarkable engineering achievement even by modern standards.

Sennacherib also built an extensive water supply system for the city ***Arbila*** [now Erbil] by diverting several different sources of water into a single river, the Bastara. He constructed a dam across the river about 12 miles (19.3 km) north of Arbila to feed the canal system through an underground sloping tunnel conduit for water, which was 9 feet (2.7 m) wide, except at the intake where it was wider. The tunnel entrance in the river-bed was faced with ashlar masonry on the floor, walls and ceiling, and it was relatively narrow to regulate the flow in the canal with wooden sluices. This tunnel conduit of water, or qanaat, was nearly 12 miles (19.3 km) long and able to supply daily 250,000 gallons (946,350 liters) of fresh water to the temple of Ishtar in ***Arbila***. The shafts of the tunnel were sunk at about 138 feet (42.1 m) intervals.

In 689 B.C. Sennacherib, a fierce Assyrian King, used his engineering prowess to quell the Chaldean revolt in ***Babylon***. He razed the city of ***Babylon*** to the ground by cutting canals through the city and then damming up the Euphrates river, and breaching the dam after the water level behind the dam had reached high enough. The huge flood wave, thus released, swept everything in its path leaving ***Babylon*** in ruins in its wake.

Siloam Tunnel

About 700 B.C., when Sennacherib and his fierce Assyrian army was threatening the Kingdom of Judah with a siege, the Hebraic king Hezekiah who ruled from c.715 B.C. to 687 B.C. had a tunnel cut through the Ophel hill to provide a protected access to the mountain spring which supplied fresh water to the Siloam Pools within the fortified city of ***Jerusalem***. This tunnel has a cross-section of 2⅓ by 5 ⅔ feet (0.7 by 1.7 m) and a length of 1,749 feet (533.1 m), and it was excavated through limestone rock simultaneously from its two ends, one end being at the Gihon Well and the other at the Siloam Pool. In a straight line that tunnel would have had a length of 1,098 feet (334.7 m), and a very steep gradient of 1-to-105, since the level difference between the well and the pool was 7 feet (2.1 m). But the miners for some reason were unable to maintain a straight line, which resulted in the tunnel that wound like a serpent through the Ophel hill. When the two mining parties finally met, this serpentine tunnel had a length of 1,749 feet (533.1 m), which, fortunately, gave a much more suitable gradient of 1-to-235 to the tunnel. This tunnel was excavated without a survey, and the cutting was done with chisels and picks.

Marib Dam in Sab'a

About 750 B.C., a huge and renowned Rahab dam was built in the valley of the river Dhana in the Balak Mountain near ***Marib*** city in ***Sab'a*** [Biblical ***Sheba***] to catch the sudden floods caused by the rainfall in the mountains. It was located in the southeastern corner of the Arabian peninsula, in the present Yemen. It was an earthen dam with a triangular cross-section that had a crest height of about 13¼ feet (4 m) and a length of 2,000 feet (610 m). This dam had a sizeable spillway which was essential in order not to spill excessive flood waters over the crest of the dam because the spilled water would have rapidly eroded its earthen structure. For this reason, the dam was not built across the narrowest point in the river valley but rather about 400 feet (122 m) or so further down the valley to leave a space between the dam and the rocky cliff through which the excess flood waters could escape northwards over the northern spillway cut into the rock. The intake of the canal which took the flood waters to the city that lay 3 miles (4.8 km) to the east, was also located at the northern end of the dam. At the southern end of the dam there were no sluices or canals, because at this time there was no need to irrigate the southern bank of the valley, which was rather remote from the ***Marib*** city. No traces of this early dam have survived.

About 500 B.C. the ***Marib*** dam was increased to a height of 23 feet (7 m) and its triangular cross-section with both of its faces sloping at 45 degrees. The water face was covered with stone slabs set in mortar to make the dam water tight and to resist the erosive effect of the wave action of the impounded water. The new dam had a new spillway with 5 canals which were adequate to protect the higher dam against flooding spills. The new dam supplied irrigation water also to the southern side of the valley by means of a 16½-foot (5 m) wide channel cut through the rock at the southern end of the dam. Sluice gates made of a series of logs placed in grooves controlled the flow in the channel.

The ***Marib*** dam was heightened to increase the irrigated land area, because the ***Marib*** kingdom had grown in size and power since the old dam was built, making the expansion of the arable land mandatory. The dam protected the top soil from erosion and provided year-round irrigation for a large area near the capital city ***Marib*** which made this region into a rich garden. ***Sab'a*** was a rich center for spices and it had a virtual monopoly on the spice trade at the time, because the Sabans were more efficient than anybody else in the spice trade. Ancient ***Sab'a*** in its own time was generally known as the land of incense and spices.

The second major reconstruction doubled the dam's height and led to elaborate waterworks at both ends of the new earthen barrier, which was now 46 feet (14 m) high. At the northern end, the spillway was raised by 16½ feet (5 m) and water flowed away from the dam along 5 spillway channels. Irrigation water was drawn off through 2 masonry sluices in the upstream side of a masonry tank. The inside of the tank was used as a settling pond, implying that the silting of the irrigation canals had become a problem. The water flowed from the settling tank along a paved channel of 3,820-foot (1,000 m) length, to a distribution tank which was tapped by 14 separate irrigation canals. The southern sluices were also rebuilt and extended. The floor of the channel was raised by 11½ feet (3.5 m) and masonry walls were constructed to contain the flow. The masonry construction of this dam was of very high quality, and its carefully cut and fitted blocks were joined by lead dowels rather than bound by mortar.

The third reconstruction appears to have been the work of Himyarites, who ruled ***Sab'a*** from 115 B.C. on, in a period when ***Sab'a*** was already in its decline as the center of spice and incense trade.

The dam finally failed in a flash flood in A.D. 575, as a result of general neglect after having been in service nearly a thousand years.

Neo-Babylon: ***Large Scale Hydraulic Works***
[from 625 B.C. to 539 B.C.]

Indo-European horsemen Medes under their king Cyaxares who ruled from 625 B.C. to 585 B.C., captured ***Assur***. Then the Medes, Scythians and General Nabopolassar (***Nabu-Apal-Usur***), of the Kaldu tribe of Semites, who ruled ***Babylon*** from 625 B.C. to 585 B.C., attacked ***Nineveh***, which fell in 612 B.C. after a siege of 2 years. The city of ***Nineveh*** was left a vast heap of rubble never to rise again. Subsequently, Nabopolassar usurped the throne of ***Babylon***, and he and his son Nebuchadrezzar (***Nabu-Kudurri-Usur***) II, who ruled from 604 B.C. to 561 B.C., rebuilt ***Babylon*** and made it the greatest monumental fortified city of antiquity until the time of Romans. This city was rebuilt according to a general master-plan. The Neo-Babylonian, or Chaldean method of engineering was prominently influenced by the Assyrian engineering.

The inner city of ***Babylon*** (***Bab-Ilu*** meant, the 'Gate of God') representing a distorted rectangle of about 2 miles (3.2 km) by 3 miles (4.8 km) which occupied an area of about 1,000 acres (405 hectares) was enclosed by a double curtain wall of brick masonry. The inner curtain wall made of sun-baked brick was about 115 feet (35.1 m) high and 23 feet (7 m) thick, its towers had the size of 28 feet by 28 feet (8.5 m by 8.5 m) in plan and were spaced at 144-foot (43.9 m) intervals. The outer curtain wall made of burnt brick was about 75 feet (22.9 m) high and 20 to 25 feet (6.1 to 7.6 m) thick, and spaced at 39 feet (11.9 m) from the inner wall. Every 5th course of the brick masonry of the outer curtain wall was reinforced with reed-matting. A 5½-mile (8.9 km) long navigable moat encircled the defensive city wall, the top of which was wide enough for a chariot to turn around.

The Euphrates river ran through the city of ***Babylon*** dividing it into two parts: the eastern part was the old city, and the western part, the new city. The eastern part was walled-in along the bank of the Euphrates with the burnt brick wall which also acted as a dam against the high water, but the western part of the city had no wall along the Euphrates river.

The defensive city wall was intercepted by 9 fortified gates, all faced with blue glazed bricks decorated with yellow and white reliefs of dragons and lions. The Ishtar Gate of ***Babylon***, the remains of which were dismantled and reassembled in the Berlin Museum about A.D. 1900, was the most fortified gate ever built by man in antiquity. A system of major boulevards, which intersected approximately at right angles, led to the fortified city gates which were made of timber and sheathed with copper. The hinges and bearings of the city gates were made of bronze. Out of the 50 main streets, 25 ran parallel and 25 at right angles to the Euphrates river. A 65-foot (19.8 m) wide boulevard ran the whole length of the inner curtain wall. An 80-foot (24.4 m) wide Processional Way called ***Aibu-Shabu*** of 2½-mile (4 km) length ran from the Summer Palace, located in the northernmost tip of the walled-in greater city, past the Ishtar Gate to the southern end of the old city. It had a multilayered brick foundation set in mastic and was finished with 3 to 4-foot square (0.90 or 1.2 m square) limestone flags having bevelled joints laid in mastic, and inlays of coloured marble and sea shells. The Processional Way rose 40 feet (12.2 m) above the street level at the Ishtar Gate to reach the level of the high platform of the palace-citadel.

In the enclosed holy precinct of the old city (***temenos)*** stood ***Etemenanki***, the loftiest ziggurat ever built . This ziggurat had an Assyrian spiral ramp and consisted of 7 stages associated with the 7 known planets. The base of the ziggurat was about 300 feet square (91.4 m square), and its height was also about 300 feet (91.4 m).

Nebuchadrezzar II constructed an outer city wall around the eastern part of the greater city that formed a large right-angle triangle with the sides 1.8 miles (2.9 km) in the northeasterly direction and 2½ miles (4 km) in the northwesterly direction. This outer-city wall protected part of the greater city which was intended for the refuge of the inhabitants living in the unprotected countryside in the time of war. The northern apex of this outer enclosure at the Euphrates river was the location of the Summer Palace of the King. The outer-city wall extended the city's perimeter to 11.2 miles (18 km).

In the northern part of the inner city, next to the Ishtar Gate, was the palace-citadel standing on a high burnt-brick platform which covered 28 acres (11.3 hectares). It was a huge complex of palaces, garrison building, administrative building, vast throne room of the size 170 by 56 feet (51.8 by 17.1 m) decorated with polychrome glazed bricks, and the celebrated 'Hanging Gardens', all arranged around five enormous courtyards. The elevated roof garden, the so-called 'Hanging Gardens' occupying an area of roughly 900 by 600 feet (274.3 by 182.9 m), was supported on 14 tiers of heavy stone vaults with hollow piers. The roof of this renowned garden consisting of lofty stepped terraces which were waterproofed by layers of asphalt and sheet lead, and covered with a thick layer of soil in which grew rich tropical verdure. It appears that endless chain buckets operated by a whim or a treadmill supplied water from a well for the irrigation of the vegetation on the elevated roof garden. West of the 'Hanging Gardens' at the Euphrates river, lay the monumental fortress, the Southern Citadel, enclosed by its 70-foot (21.3 m) thick brick walls. The houses of the old city had 2, 3, and even 4 stories, which made this ancient city a densely populated metropolis.

The greater city of ***Babylon*** was surrounded by a belt of suburbs and a network of canals. The entire population of the larger city may have been as numerous as 400,000 inhabitants. Nabopolassar and his son Nebuchadrezzar II, built the first known bridge (***Bibil-Chigill***) in brick and stone that crossed one of the major rivers of the world, the Euphrates, which connected the old city on the eastern bank with the new city on the western bank of this river inside the city of ***Babylon***. This bridge was more than 384 feet (117 m) long, the clear span between its piers was 29½ feet (9 m), and the size of the piers was 29½ by almost 69 feet (9 by 21 meters). The bridge had 7 evenly placed piers, which had the cross-sectional shape of the waterline of a boat, and they were constructed of brick masonry laid in asphalt mortar. The piers were capped by ashlar stone masonry clamped by iron cramps set in lead. The superstructure of the bridge was constructed of imported timber. Rectangular baulks of cypress and cedar spanned between the 7 piers and supported 18-foot (5.5 m) long logs as transverse beams on which, in turn, rested the roadway of stone slabs. The bridge over the Euphrates river was a 'draw-bridge' because the 2 central spans were nightly removed as a protective measure against surprise attack by Babylonian enemies .

There were several timber bridges made of mulberry and cedar woods in ***Babylon*** which spanned the 42½ feet (13 m) wide canal, ***Libil-Chegalla,*** that ran diagonally through the old city.

Hydraulic Works

Nebuchadrezzar II constructed a 76-mile (122 km) long dam, the so-called 'Median Wall', 70 miles (112.7 km) northwest of ***Babylon***, near the city ***Sippar***, which joined the banks of the Tigris and the Euphrates. It made a marsh out of the land directly north of it, and created a huge reservoir lake on which waves rose as high as on the sea. This lake had a perimeter of about 40 miles (64.4 km), and it was about 75 feet (23 m) deep. The 'Median Wall' was an earth-filled dam lined with burnt bricks set in asphalt. A similar dam must have existed south of the city of ***Babylon***. These huge reservoirs provided ***Babylon*** with massive hydraulic defences.

A navigable canal, ***Nar-Malka***, up to 50 miles (64.4 to 80.5 km) in length, was built to join the Tigris with the Euphrates river north of ***Sippar***. A large navigable canal, ***Nar-Wan***, built near the city of Opis [ancient ***Eshnunna***] running parallel to the Tigris and joining its tributaries, the Adem and the Diyala, had a length of 200 miles (322 km), a width of 450 feet (137.2 m), and a depth of 30 feet (9.1 m).

To reduce the danger of inundation of the Euphrates in the spring, and to improve the marshland at the mouth of the Euphrates, Nebuchadrezzar II built the large navigable ***Pallakopas*** canal which branched out of the Euphrates river south of the city of ***Nippur*** and terminated at ***Diritotis***, a city built by Nebuchadrezzar II at the Persian Gulf. This canal, which ran through many lakes, had a length of 250 miles (402 km) and was navigable like the ***Nar-Malka*** and the ***Nar-Wan*** canal. In the Neo-Babylonian time the major rivers of Mesopotamia were no longer navigable for large ships, a condition that made the construction of navigable canals necessary. When the Euphrates river started to subside in November, the ***Pallakopas*** canal had to be closed. The barricading of the canal required the work of a huge labour force of about 100,000 men for a period of several months.

The massively fortified ***Neo-Babylon*** was virtually an impregnable city, yet the Persian King Cyrus conquered it in 539 B.C. with the greatest of ease because of internal dissentions among the populace of ***Babylon***. The Persian army merely had to walk through the massive fortified gates of ***Babylon***, left open by Babylonian traitors, to invade the city where they encountered trivial organised resistance.

CHAPTER IV

ANCIENT PERSIA: Imperial Engineering

Persians like all other Indo-Europeans believed in dualism : life is a conflict between good and evil, and for that reason life for the ancient Persians was a struggle – a warfare. The educational ideal of the Persians was the manly quality: to ride a horse, to draw a bow, and to speak the truth. To speak the truth meant to a Persian to have respect for facts and events of the world as they really are, and to live strenuously meant to fight for righteous life.

The Persian religious philosopher Zarathushtra Spitama (in Greek, Zoroaster the White) overthrew the magical religion of the Magi in the seventh century B.C. by preaching an intellectual and ethical monotheism which was rooted in the philosophy of dualism and based exclusively on personal morality. Zarathushtra preached the aristocratic morality of the Indo-Europeans at its best by preaching it in the name of the Wise Lord (***Ahura Mazda***, later ***Ormuzd***), the God of truth, wisdom, justice, purity, goodness, and light. According to Zarathushtra, the Wise Lord as the creator of the world is not omnipotent since he is engaged in a perpetual battle with the powers of darkness, evil, treachery, ignorance, injustice, mendacity and corruption marshalled by the Spirit of Darkness (***Angra Maynu***, later ***Ahriman***), the Personification of Evil.

Zoroastrianism was a highly ethical religion fit to command the voluntary faith and allegiance of individuals rather than to demand blind devotion to organised religious cults of the State. Zarathushtra's religion was concerned with the polarity of life, manifested in good and evil, which affords answers to the inscrutability of life. According to Zarathushtra, man has 'freewill' and it is man's responsibility as a free agent within his limits of free choice to fight in the battle of life between good and evil on the side of ***Ahura Mazda*** , the Wise Lord, against ***Angra Maynu,*** the Evil Spirit. Man fights for the goodness at the side of the Wise Lord through his voluntary acts: by speaking the truth; by being clean and not defiling the sacred elements of fire, Earth and water; by conquering the desert; by planting trees; by digging wells; by increasing bodily comforts; by working diligently and profitably in tilling the soil to continue the work of creation of the Wise Lord; by being kind to useful animals; by keeping contract; by being just; by teaching wisdom to ignorants; by doing to others what one would wish others to do to oneself; and by being merciful. In the venerable Indo-European tradition, Zarathushtra praised agriculture above commerce: "Whoever cultivates the corn cultivates righteousness." In his religious doctrine Zarathushtra introduced the important 'principle of voluntarism' into the daily conduct of life of every individual man. Voluntarism and individual liberty are the two fundamental principles of Western culture which represent the principal ideas of the civilised and morally upright life.

According to Zarathushtra the sin that damns a man is his freedom to choose to fight in the battle of life at the side of the Evil Spirit (***Angra Maynu***) through his willingness to practice mendacity, sloth, gluttony, arrogance, treachery, dishonesty, illwill and ignorance. Zarathushtra asserted that the Wise Lord (***Ahura Mazda***) shall win the battle of life for righteousness, since Evil has no foresight because it has no respect for the past and, therefore, cannot understand the present, and consequentially is unable to foresee the future – Evil lives only for the profit of the moment. These rather profound insights are of cardinal importance to man in the conduct of his affairs. Therefore, according to Zarathushtra, goodwill and goodness ultimately will triumph over illwill and Evil, which made Zoroastrianism an optimistic religious doctrine.

After the death of man, according to Zarathushtra, there comes the Judgement Day when man's good deeds and bad deeds are counted in the Book of Life. If man's good deeds predominate, he goes to the blessed garden, or blessed meadow (***paradaiso***) and beatitude with the Wise Lord (***Ahura Mazda***). If man's bad deeds predominate, he goes to infernal agony with the Evil Spirit (***Angra Maynu***). Hence an individual man in Zoroastrian religion had to earn his afterlife by a strenuous and active moral life on Earth, and not by passive obedience and ritual appeasement, nor by any means of miracle and mystery. Above all, man had to speak the truth – a virtue for which the ancient Persians won a widespread and well-deserved reputation. Very importantly, Zarathushtra maintained that the Wise Lord (***Ahura Mazda***) is not tangible to man's senses because He transcends man's direct experience, and He requires from men not external ritual correctness, but rather internal personal morality as an individual.

The basic command of Zarathushtranism, or Zoroastrianism, as a highly individualistic religious doctrine having no rituals or external organisation, was: "Good thoughts, good words, good deeds (***humata, hukhta, hvarshta***)." In his ethical monotheistic religious doctrine, Zarathushtra separated the divine from the natural and the human and, thereby, he rose above the religious myths of other ancient people who either deified nature and mortal human beings, or humanised immortal gods. He excluded the particular religious element that is usually the first to succumb to pagan practices of rituals by omitting the formal worship of the Wise Lord (***Ahura Mazda***).

The significant contribution of Zarathushtra's religious doctrine was to give man a clear purpose and incentive in life by linking human life with the cosmic struggle between good and evil, a struggle which according to Zarathushtra would have a positive denouement, and in which man participates through his voluntary acts. In the great Indo-European tradition Zarathushtra's religious conception assumed the power of logic of ***Ahura Mazda*** to be active in His universe, an important idea that gave man his sense of mission in life, a mission that depends upon his own free choice, as well as a theory of history which comprised the idea of progress. Zarathushtra's dual gospel made human history understandable and meaningful to man and, thereby, satisfied the innate rational disposition of the Indo-European mind. In contrast, all people who were not Indo-European, such as Sumerians, ancient Semites and ancient Egyptians, believed that gods ruled history and that the misfortunes of men were arbitrary and fortuitous, or the result of offences committed by men against gods who always remained inscrutable to men.

Although Zoroastrian religious doctrine did give the ancient Persians an independent spirit, yet politically they enjoyed no freedom. Zoroastrianism, a dynamic religious doctrine of cosmic scope, was the first monotheistic and intellectual religion with profound personal morality, and challenging appeal to the individual, qualities which made it tower above other somnolent faiths of the Orient. It affected the religious views of Hebrews in Babylonian captivity, and much later influenced the practical homilies of Jesus of Nazareth as well as the Christian religious dogma in which the Personification of the Evil Spirit became the Devil. By founding these superb religious and ethical ideals, Zarathushtra, in effect, had created the ideals for the archetypical Western man.

Long after Zarathushtra's violent death, the Magi restored certain components of their old idolatrous polytheism with its magical accessories that included some misinterpreted elements of the Zoroastrian religion, which they reintroduced with an insistence upon doctrinal and ritual purity. Later Zoroastrians began to expect the coming of the 'Redeemer' (***Sayoshant***), who would redeem all men from the power of the Evil Spirit.

The Persian Empire was established by King Cyrus (in Persian, ***Kurush***), who ruled from 557 B.C. to 529 B.C., and whose Zoroastrian beliefs gave him the spiritual drive to embark upon his mission to bring a new order to the world which will be better than the venerable past. In his mission to help the Wise Lord win the Holy War against the Evil Spirit and bring more light to the world, Cyrus exercised spiritual tolerance as an enlightened self-interest. Even if political liberty was lacking in the Persian Empire, but so was the monstrous cruelty of the Assyrians and the Chaldeans. Yet it must be understood, that everything built under the Persian 'King of kings', just like under the Assyrian kings, was meant to create in the common-man a feeling of awe and reverence for the mighty ruler of the Empire. Engineering, architecture, and art were completely subordinated to the creation of an impression of the irresistible power of the mighty ruler of the Persian Empire. Therefore, all imperial buildings of the ancient Persians had few personal comforts, since they were built as showplaces of impressive monuments to the overwhelming power of the Persian ruler.

King Cyrus instituted a corps of military engineers in his Persian army by following the example of the Assyrian army. Since Cyrus was a Zoroastrian, he appeared on the historical scene as a self-proclaimed liberator of people from the powers of the Evil Spirit by leading them to the Wise Lord and, thereby, carrying out the mission of Zarathushtra in bringing more 'light' to the world. Since the Persian soldiers had to be a hardy breed of men who were physically well-conditioned by martial sports, Persians were the first people to develop martial athletics into physical culture. Cyrus expressed a fundamental view of the Indo-Europeans when he said: "Soft lands breed soft men." In the opinion of ancient Persians only agriculture and warfare were the truly respectable occupations for a vigorous and dignified Indo-European of Persian stock.

In 539 B.C., Cyrus conquered Babylon of the Chaldeans. Subsequently he subdued the Lydian Empire by defeating the armies of the fabulously rich King Kroisos (in Latin, ***Croesus***) in Anatolia, and vanquished Palestine in a remarkably brief campaign. His son, Cambyses (in Persian, ***Kambujia***), conquered Egypt in 525 B.C., after the death of Cyrus.

After the death of Cambyses, Darios (in Persian, ***Darayavahush***), a cousin of Cambyses, became the King, and he ruled the Persian Empire from 521 B.C. to 485 B.C.. Darios was also a Zoroastrian like Cyrus, as well as the best athletic soldier among all the contenders to the throne of the Persian Empire.

Darios defined his creed of man in these words, "Says, Darios, the King: by the favour of ***Ahura-Mazda*** I am such a sort that I am the friend of right, I am not a friend of wrong; it is not my desire that the weak man should have wrong done to him by the mighty, nor is it my desire that the mighty man should have wrong done to him by the weak. What is right, that is my desire ... I am not hot-tempered. What things developed in my anger, I hold firmly under control by my will-power." These sound principles of Darios are being grossly violated today.

These were basic Zoroastrian principles, and Darios intended to carry these truths to all parts of the world. Darios, through his own personal example, lived up to his principles better than any previous ruler in history. He made a concerted effort to improve the economic conditions and the standard of living of all countries in the Persian Empire in sharp contrast to previous empires which had followed the imperialistic idea of Sargon I, the ferocious Akkadian King, who conquered other countries for the explicit purpose of plunder and exploitation. Darios imported new domestic animals, and new plants to countries which lacked them, and his engineers constructed numerous qanaats for efficient irrigation all over the Persian Empire. Darios ran the Persian Empire like a big commercial Empire which was soundly based on financial operations and private banking. He recognised that rectitude and justice are the only stable and sound foundations of the society in the Persian Empire.

Darios adopted the monetary system of King Kroisos of Lydia, a country in Anatolia conquered by Cyrus, who had issued both gold and silver coins as a standard medium of exchange. He also standardised the weights and measures throughout the Persian Empire which further facilitated transactions in trade. Private banks in the Persian Empire offered loans, accepted deposits, and invested in various enterprises such as canals, housing, farmland, livestock and maritime trade. They improved on the Assyrian administrative system in the management of both the military and the civilian affairs, introduced the Aramaic language [a Semitic tongue spoken by Jesus of Nazareth] as the official administrative language of the Persian Empire, all of which served to unify the commercial activities and the wealth of the Empire into a comprehensive and efficient economy.

The great Persian legacy to the West is liberalism in governing and intellectualism in religion. But power corrupts and soon the Oriental influence began to make itself felt and already Darios' son, Xerxes (in Persian, ***Khshayarsha***), who ruled from 485 B.C. to 465 B.C., became appreciably orientalised and as a consequence he gradually relinquished his father's Indo-European principles and Zoroastrian beliefs, except for the purpose of external appearances. Xerxes soon adopted the Oriental methods of pure exploitation, and indulged in the cruelties of an Oriental despot.

In 512 B.C. Darios led a campaign against the Scythians in an effort to subdue these fierce horsemen of the steppes, and to cut off the timber and grain supplies to the ancient Greeks in Greece proper, another group of recalcitrant European people whom he intended to subjugate next. Darios lost about 80,000 men in the scorched-Earth method of warfare conducted by the Scythians which was disastrous to the Persian army. In this military campaign the Greek engineer Mandroklos of Samos (*floruit* c. 514 B.C.) built a ½ mile (0.8 km) long pontoon bridge over the Bosporus Strait for the crossing of Darios' army, for which he was richly rewarded by Darios. Another pontoon bridge was subsequently slung over the Danube River in the same campaign probably also by Ionian Greeks under the direction of the Greek engineer Mandroklos of Samos.

In 490 B.C., Greeks from democratic Athens defeated a large army of Darios on the Marathon Plain in Greece, and thereby arrested the Persian penetration into Europe. In 480 B.C., after the death of Darios, his son Xerxes organised an army of about 500,000 men to invade and conquer the recalcitrant Greeks in Europe, but it rapidly became an ill-fated military campaign for the Persians.

Xerxes ordered the Greek scientist-engineer, Harpales, head of the Ionian scientific school in Tenedos (a school founded by Thales of Miletos, the first scientist), to build 2 pontoon bridges, both over 1¼ mile (2 km) in length, across the Hellespont (now, Dardanelles) Strait for the crossing of the large Persian army consisting of a motley of foreign troops. At first the 2 bridges were built by the Egyptian and the Phoenician engineers, but a storm destroyed both of these pontoon bridges. Xerxes promptly ordered the engineers of the bridges to be decapitated and the sea scourged in retaliation for defying the 'King of kings'. In his pontoon bridges, Harpales used 674, '50-oar galleys (***pintekonters***)', 360 in one bridge and 314 in the other, each galley heavily anchored at the prow and the stern, and spaced from 9 to 11 feet (2.7 to 3.4 m) apart. The galleys were lashed together with heavy flaxen ropes, weighing 50 pounds (23 kg) per foot, and tightened by wooden winches; the deck was made of thick planks attached to the ropes and covered with brushwood, straw matting and compacted dirt. A wooden palisade was built along both sides of the roadway to calm the horses. All the building material for these bridges was prepared at the Ionian city of Abydos, in the vicinity of which the 2 bridges were built.

In the same Persian campaign, the Persian military engineers Artachaies (in Persian, ***Artahaya***), who was an 8-foot (2.4 m) giant and the tallest man in Persia, and Bubares (in Persian, ***Bubaranda***), excavated a 1½-mile (2.4 km) long canal through the Isthmus of the Mount Athos to let Xerxes' Persian fleet pass in safety through that part of the treacherous sea which had destroyed Darios' fleet in 490 B.C.. This canal, which interconnected a sequence of ponds, was from 60 to 90 feet (18.3 to 27.4 m) wide, its deepest cutting was about 60 feet (18.3 m) below the surface of the ground, and the highest rise of the canal above the sea level was about 50 feet (15.2 m). It is not definitely known whether the Persian fleet actually used this canal on its passage to Greece.

King Darios, and his grandson Artaxerxes (in Persian, ***Artakh-Shatra***), built the palace-city ***Persepolis*** founded by King Cambyses. It had a complex of buildings, among which the most prominent building was 'The Grand Audience Hall' (***Apadana***) which had a square ground plan of 250-foot (76.2 m) side dimension, a cedar roof supported on 36 columns, 65 feet (19.8 m) high and 7 feet (2.1 m) in diameter, and 20-foot (6.1 m) thick walls.Another important building in this complex was the Throne Room, known as the 'Hall of Hundred Columns', which had a 225-foot (68.6 m) square ground plan and a flat cedar roof supported on 100 slender columns 37-feet (11.3 m) tall. This building enclosed by double walls was designed in the style of the Egyptian Hypostyle Hall distinguished with the novel slenderness of its columns.

King Darios was a tireless road builder, and he tried to make his roads safe for travel. In highway construction the Persian engineers followed the Assyrian road-building methods. Darios first built the Royal Postal Road from ***Susa*** to ***Ecbatana***, which had a length of 200 miles (322 km). Then the main Royal Postal Road was built from ***Susa*** in Elam, all the way to ***Sardeis*** in Lydia, and finally to ***Ephesos*** in Ionia. It had a total length of 1,677 miles (2,699 km), and its surface was paved at least near important landmarks. Later this road was continued from ***Susa*** through ***Persepolis*** to Bactria, and from there all the way to India. The Persian Royal Postal Road from ***Susa*** to ***Sardeis*** cut the travel time from 3 months to less than 2 weeks, to a known record of 9 days. The paved road built from ***Susa*** to ***Babylon*** took less than 2 days to travel. The known travelling speed of the Royal Persian messenger was about 100 miles (160.9 km) a day. The Persian Royal Postal Road was provided with postal stations. In the mountains the postal stations were spaced about 12 miles (19 km) apart. In general, the Persian Postal Road followed the most efficient topological route. Persians kings also established a system of optical telegraph in their Empire.

Darios placed great importance on maritime trade, the first Empire to do so, and he engaged in a far-reaching global trade on a larger scale and over longer distances than any previous empire.

The Persian Empire had a large fleet of merchant ships that displaced from 200 to 500 tons which enabled the Persians to carry their trade to Africa, to India, to Ceylon, and to the western and the northern Europe. Persians themselves were not known as particularly able seamen and, therefore, they used other conquered people skilled in seamanship, usually Phoenicians, to man their ships. Their sailors were strictly graded according to their skills. Persians, like Assyrians and Chaldeans before them, also utilised foreign technology and craftsmen to do much of their engineering and production of manufactured goods. Ionian Greeks occupied a prominent place in the Persian engineering by being employed in the construction of important structures in the Persian Empire since already by that time the ancient Greeks were the most prominent engineers in the world, because the Ionian Greeks had introduced rational procedures into their methods of engineering.

Riddle of Sumerian Cuneiform Writing

Modern scholars could not read the ancient Sumerian writing because they did not know the meaning of the symbols in cuneiform script, and, therefore, could not decypher the writing. The puzzle of cuneiform script was solved by an athletic young English officer Henry Creswicke Rawlinson (1810-1895), who served in the army of the East India Company, first in India and then in Persia, and later occupied various British governmental posts in other parts of Asia. In 1835 Rawlinson discovered the Behistun Rock on the Iranian plain of the Zagros Mountains which had a 40-foot (12 m) long monumental trilingual inscription carved in bas-relief in 521 B.C. in commemoration of the military victories of Darios. It is the longest trilingual cuneiform inscription in existence. The cuneiform inscription of Darios was in 3 ancient languages: Old Persian, Babylonian, and Elamite; and it had been made inaccessible by having been carved into a vertical cliff high above the plain. Rawlinson, who was an athlete and also a linguistic scholar, realised that the trilingual cuneiform inscription of Darios provided the key to the decypherment of the 3 ancient languages used in the inscription. He exploited all his athletic skills to climb the steep cliff to copy the inscription carved into it, which took altogether 2 years.

Rawlinson succeeded to decypher the huge cuneiform inscription of Darios in 3 ancient languages, Old Persian, Babylonian and Elamite, that was carved into the Behistun Rock which towered over the Iranian plain in Zagros Mountains. By 1847 he had completed the translation of the Old Persian, and by 1851 he had discovered the meanings of 200 signs in Babylonian cuneiform script which finally enabled European scholars to read thousands of cuneiform tablets which had been discovered in Mesopotamia. The decypherment of the cuneiform script by the ingenious Rawlinson served to augment the knowledge of European scholars of ancient languages and, therefore, also of ancient history.

CHAPTER V

ANCIENT GREEKS: Natural Philosophy, Birthplace of Mathematical and Mechanical Sciences

[from c.700 B.C. to 338 B.C.]

Ancient Greeks, or Hellenes were men who incorporated in themselves the northern brawn with the eastern wit. They were an energetic, restless, and high-spirited, martial people who seem to have been a race of born thinkers, and who took the empirical knowledge of the Orient and made it into the theoretical science of the Occident. The remarkable ability of the ancient Greeks to improve anything they had borrowed from other people was confidently expressed by Plato (his Greek nickname, ***Platon***) (429-348 B.C.): "Whatever the Greeks take over from foreigners, they transform it by making it something finer." Ancient Greeks were able to supply new content and new meaning to anything they borrowed because they had an unerring instinct for assimilating information that was worth having, and rejecting the rest. They were remarkably inventive because they had a speculative genius which is unrivalled in history. For instance, they invented the first true alphabet in 732 B.C. by adding vowels to the Phoenician alphabet of 22 consonants, which promoted refinement in narrative intellectual writing.

Ancient Greeks, though being Indo-Europeans like Persians, had a revolutionary temper when compared to any other ancient people. Other ancient people had discovered the gods as supernatural creatures worthy of awe and fear, whereas the ancient Greeks discovered man as a natural creature worthy of admiration and respect. This discovery was succinctly expressed by Sophokles of Kolonos (c.496-406 B.C.), a poet, dramaturge, military leader, and the quintessential ancient Greek: "The world is full of wonders, but nothing is more wonderful than man." ... "Many a mighty creature lives, but none mightier than man."

Protagoras of Abdera (c.485-c.411 B.C.), the first and the most successful itinerant professional teacher known as Sophist (***sophistes***), the founder of the pragmatic philosophy and the author of the first Greek grammar, expressed this view of man in another way: "Man is the measure of all things, of things that are what they are, and of things that are not what they are not." Protagoras has the dubious historical distinction of being the first author whose books were burnt in the central public square (in Greek, ***agora***) of Athens (Greek name, ***Athenai***) for their blasphemous content after his conviction in 411 B.C. for impiety. It is historically the first well known case of book burning in public. Protagoras escaped his punishment by fleeing Athens in the nick of time, but he perished in the shipwreck during his flight.

The ancient Greeks not only embraced but also revolutionised their Indo-European heritage in their ardent and abiding belief in individual excellence, personal honour, competitiveness, heroic struggle in the conduct of life and, above all else, rationalism. The Greek contribution to these basic

Indo-European beliefs was original, fundamental and decisive for the Western civilisation. According to their cultural outlook, the ancient Greeks admired not so much the ultimate success of the heroic individual as his unconquerable spirit that makes him superior to his fate – a fate which they recognised is tragic for man is mortal and, therefore, ultimately he has to succumb to his fate, but not without a relentless lifelong struggle in resisting the forces of fate. In this martial spirit, the ancient Greeks asserted their own personal power, and their own personal virtue by steadfastly refusing to submit tamely to the forces of nature, or to the will of other men. In their Homeric way of thinking, a short glorious life was preferable to a long inglorious one.

Ancient Greeks, as was typical of the Indo-Europeans, were hardy and vigorous men who loved action and who had the courage of warriors. Among all the Indo-European people, the ancient Greeks had the most brilliant and versatile imagination, a keen thirst for knowledge, and an innate desire and willpower for personal independence, which made them feel completely free to think for themselves. The native soaring imagination of the ancient Greeks endowed them with a remarkable aptitude for learning from others, and for independent thought and invention. No other people in history have been as imaginative and intellectually creative as the ancient Greeks and yet, as a direct consequence of their belief in rationalism, the Greeks endeavoured to keep their mind clear of reckless fantasies. If rationalism in general had been the proclivity of the thinking habits of the Indo-Europeans, with ancient Greeks it became a popular passion. They were the foremost, and certainly the most consistent advocates of rationalism among all the Indo-European people, and it was the ancient Greeks who made the first systematic effort to try to explain natural phenomena in rational terms that was understandable to the conscious mind of man. The ancient Greek scholar first of all sought to know and to understand the primordial substance of matter and the world as a rational whole. They cleaved to the polarised conception of life of the Indo-Europeans, and were the pioneer creators and promoters of the two-valued logic which they successfully developed into a formal intellectual discipline. More than this, ancient Greeks created the modern intellectual process of the mind: explanation of phenomena based on logical sequences of thought that are rationally conceived through a search for natural causes and effects.

Ancient Greeks, by creating the modern intellectual method of reasoning, provided man with the theoretical foundation for rational thought and, therefore, with the essential means for the acquisition of critically processed intellectual knowledge.

Aristotle (his real name, ***Aristoteles***) (384-322 B.C.), who defined good life as a life ruled by standards of excellence with sufficient resources to achieve it, pointed out that a basic desire of man is his want to know, and enquiry is born out of his fundamental curiosity and wonder: "To learn gives the liveliest of pleasure, not only to philosophers, but to men in general." Sokrates of Athens (469-399 B.C.), a stonemason and former apprentice sculptor, assessed the value of enquiry in man's life as follows: "A life without enquiry is not worth living," since enquiry implies freedom for critical acquisition of knowledge, and according to Aischylos of Eleusis (525-456 B.C.), the premier poet and dramaturge of ancient Athens, there is a personal price to be paid for acquiring knowledge: "Suffering is the price of learning (***pathei mathos***)."

The integrity of the mind of a man to the ancient Greeks was sacred: the mind of an individual Greek was his inner sanctum not to be violated by other men. The mind of a man represented to the ancient Greeks the foremost in thoughts, and thoughts are diversified by man and formed into critical knowledge and wisdom. Since every man has an individual mind, there existed much faith in the individual in ancient Greek society, which is why ancient Greeks had an unshakeable faith in the worth of the individual and they tried at all cost to be themselves. They realised that the will to be oneself demands authentic heroism from the individual man, for he must successfully resist the tyrannising social forces which always tend to violate the dignity and integrity of man as an individual by attempting to coerce him into vulgar conformity, a condition of complaisance which they thought is characteristic of a slave rather than a freedom-loving individual. They readily recognised that refusal of any man to conform requires from him individuality and exceptionally strong willpower. The ancient Greek poet of the 7th century B.C., Archilochos of the island of Paros, who is the author of the oldest surviving personal poetry, gave this idea an hedonistic flavour: "No man would enjoy very many delights who heeds the censure of the people."

The ancient Greeks thought that a man should be respected only for his own demonstrated virtues, and to them man's virtues were his own personal creations. In the words of the famous Ionian Greek, Homer (his real name, ***Homeros***) of Smyrna, 8th century B.C., the first great Greek poet: "... there is no greater honour for man than what he has achieved through his own efforts and by his own hands," a statement expressing the time-honoured Greek ideal of personal virtue, called ***arete***. Homeric heroes, such as Achilles, fought for their own personal glory, and not for the glory of their city or their king.

In the opinion of ancient Greeks an individual man who fails to develop all his native gifts to the fullest because he spends all his energies trying to change other people to his liking, fails himself. Such an 'improver' of the people has a tendency for impertinent interference with other people's affairs which does not concern his person, and because of his minding other people's business he tends to leave his own personal business, most of all his own self-improvement, unattended. Such a person who assumes the role of a 'friend of humanity' and who stops at nothing to 'help to improve' other people has forgotten that friendship is a mutual affection, and that one-sided imposition of 'friendship' is an inexcusable act of urban aggression and social tyranny denying freedom of self-determination to one's fellow citizens. Since to think and to decide what another individual ought to do is fascinating and self-flattering, it can be self-servingly regarded as public-spirited by the individual who indulges in 'improving and uplifting' other people. However, the real motives behind such apparently 'benevolent' intrusions into the affairs of other people are often not so noble as they seem: to direct other people's lives gratifies a number of human weaknesses in such a 'friend of humanity', to plan what other people ought to do gives such a 'do-gooder' a sense of self-importance and a feeling of superiority over fellow-citizens. Evidently, Sokrates had understood well the true character of such reformers presenting themselves as 'friends of humanity', and his advice to them was succinct: "Let him who would improve the world first improve himself – and thus serve the eternity," to which he added: "The wise man, above all, will cultivate his own garden." Sokrates implied with this terse advice that every individual man in the society has only one principal social responsibility: to mind his own business, and to take care of his own self.

Another service of Homer to the ancient Greek thought was his humanisation of the immortal Greek gods after the example of the Hittite gods. The Greek gods of Homeric Olympian Pantheon were, like the Hittite gods, far too human to be all-powerful, so much so that no major phenomenon or catastrophe of nature, could be adequately explained as an act of the Greek gods.

The heroic ideal of the ancient Helladic Greeks as expressed by Homer expected a man to exert himself at all times, and to make the most of his opportunities, often indeed, to create his own opportunities. This outlook was well expressed by Sophokles: "Leave no stone unturned." The heroic ideal of the Helladic Greeks was later democratised by the Hellenic Greeks living in the ***polis*** (also ***poleis***), the Hellenic city-State. They sought for a moral equivalent of the heroic ideal also in actions other than war, and they found it in their ideal of the all-round personal excellence.

The heroic ideal emphasised personal honour for honour is what morality cannot always be: an incentive to vigorous action in any field of endeavour. The ultimate test of honour, as the ancient Greeks saw it, was human dignity: anything that lowers human dignity was dishonourable, anything that enhances it was honourable. An undignified exhibition of any man in his degraded state in public was obscenity to the ancient Greeks, whereas in the modern world in a striking contrast such degrading events take place virtually daily, often promoted and encouraged by emotionally excited public approbation. In the opinion of ancient Greeks, the last court of appeal on the question of honour was the individual's own feelings, and according to Aristotle: "Honour is the prize appointed for the noblest deeds." Therefore, an ancient Greek who sought honour and dignity, sought fame in the praise of his fellow citizens for his personal achievements. The democratised heroic posture of the Hellenic Greeks accorded an unexpectedly prominent place to the intelligence of man.

Xenophanes of Kolophon, in Ionia, (c.570-c.475 B.C.), philosopher and poet, asseverated that wisdom (***sophia***) is superior to brute force and physical skill (***arete***). He preached of a single God, being all eye, all ear, all intellect, and governing everything by the power of His mind without any extraneous effort. In his conception God resembled man neither in form nor in understanding, very much like the God of light and wisdom of the Persian religious philosopher Zarathushtra. Xenophanes left his native city at the age of 25 after the Persians had conquered it, and he ultimately helped to found a Greek city-State Elea in Italy. He is probably the intellectual founder of the Eleatic school of philosophy. The views of Xenophanes were influential in raising man's intellect to a high place of honour in the culture of the ancient Greeks. Consequently the Greeks admired intelligence, whether practical or theoretical, and thought that they surpassed other foreign people, the so-called barbarians (***barbaroi***), because the Greeks pursued a higher virtue: intelligent action. However, they did have qualms about the uninhibited exercise of intelligence and, therefore, they insisted that intelligence be balanced by other qualities of character through self-discipline. In the opinion of most of the ancient Greeks, self-discipline was the only discipline worth having for its own sake since any other kind of discipline was a bald exercise of tyranny .

Ancient Greeks thought that if a man relies mainly on his intelligence, that is, on his native cleverness alone, he was likely to frustrate even his own ends by being too cunning for his own good because, thereby, he was prone not to comprehend much that even an ordinary man understands. A distinguishing feature of the ideal Greek character was the willpower for self-restraint and moderation, the 'golden mean' being its ideal manifestation. The ancient Greeks felt in themselves a compelling power of natural gifts which they thought came from the gods, and they believed it was their personal responsibility to make the most of it in their lives by pursuing excellence in all things which led to rational and desirable ends. They tried to make the most of their natural gifts in order to be worthy of their human nature. They were eager to be as much like their gods as possible, yet they realised that mortal human beings should not attempt to do this in excess, lest they imagined that they were immortal gods themselves. They believed that it was the task of mortal human beings to make proper moderate use of what gods had provided for men which led them to the ideal of moderation. The eminent 6th century B.C. poet, sage, reformer and political leader (***archon***), Solon of Athens (c.640-c.560 B.C.), expressed this thought in his concise motto: "Nothing too much (***meden agan***)," which remained a leading Greek maxim. This explicitly stated ideal suggests that the ancient Greeks were not by their nature inclined to subject themselves to self-restraint because they were high-spirited, easily excitable, eristic, impulsive and imaginative, qualities of character which were probably responsible for their remarkable creativity that is unequalled in the history of man. Ancient Greeks considered anything carried to excess to undermine the very spirit of a man with personal worth and self-respect.

Solon's contemporary in Ionia, Thales of Miletos, (c.625-c.548 B.C.), the first known scientist and one of the Seven Wise Men of Hellas (***hoi hepta sophoi***), gave the leading maxim of ancient Greeks as thinkers: "Know thyself (***gnothi sauton***)," because he believed that: "The most difficult thing in life is to know thyself." "Know thyself" remained a cherished motto of the ideal Hellenic character, because it was believed that if a self-confident man really knew himself and his human limitations, he himself would curb his ambitions and his personal pride through self-discipline. All this requires critical self-examination, which is the hallmark of a critical thinker.

Thales, furthermore, advised that men can live a virtuous life only by never doing themselves what they blame in others.

The Seven Sages of ***Hellas***, a distinguished group of seven men which besides Thales included Solon of Athens, Pittakos of Mytilene, Chilon of Lakedaimon, Periandros of Korinthos, Kleobulos of Rhodos, and Bias of Priene.

Pittakos of Mytilene stated: "Seize the opportunity (***kairon gnothi***)." Chilon of Lakedaimon declared: "Suretyship, then ruin." The mottos of Thales of Miletos, Solon of Athens, Pittakos of Mytilene, and Chilon of Lakedaimon were later inscribed in letters of gold in the vestibule wall of the temple of the god of prophesy, Apollo, in the panhellenic religious center Delphi which was the seat of the oracle of Apollo.

Bias of Priene is known to have said: "Most men are wicked," whereas Periandros of Korinthos declared: "Practice does everything." Thales is said to have been proclaimed a 'wise man' (***sophistes***) by the oracle of Delphi in 582 B.C.. Apparently these seven men were called wise on account of their shrewd moral sayings (***gnomai***) and political sagacity but not because of their wisdom in science. Among the Seven Wise Men only Thales was a scientist and Solon an amateur astronomer, whereas the rest of the seven men were all clever politicians.

In regards to moderation, the ancient Greeks showed little tolerance to any marked departure from the Greek tradition of austerity because they believed that wealth tends to breed self-indulgence. They realised, of course, that wealth was indispensable for a good life since it affords leisure which is necessary for the pursuit of philosophy and art, but they also recognised that wealth offers great dangers to any man who possesses it. The poetess Sappho of the island of Lesbos (6th century B.C.) expressed briefly her concern about wealth: "...wealth without virtue is not a harmless neighbour"; and the 8th century B.C. speculative pastoral poet Hesiod (his real name, ***Hesiodos***) of Kyme, Ionia, expressed in his great poem < Theogony > (***Theogonis***) this basic concern of the ancient Greeks in stern words: "Wealth is the very life of wretched men." The celebrated Solon of Athens gave his opinion of the influence of wealth in the following statement: "Riches know no limit ... How hard to see the hidden measure of intelligence, which alone holds the limits of things." Anaximandros of Miletos (c.611-c.546 B.C.), Ionian scholar and statesman, expressed his reservation about wealth and its corruptive influence on men in these words: "Men are tempted to gain riches by unjust acts; they snatch from one another and they steal, not sparing sacred or public property; not guarding themselves against the dread foundation of justice who silently notes what's done, what was before, and comes in time to exact unfailing vengeance." Herakleitos of Ephesos (c.540-c.475 B.C.), the sombre and cynical philosopher of the 6th century B.C., expressed his opinion of wealth with his usual sarcasm: "May you have lots of wealth, men of Ephesos, so that you may be punished for your evil ways."

All these adverse Hellenic judgements refer to the thin line that exists between prosperity and disaster, and connect disaster with ill-advised ***hubris*** manifesting itself in unbridled arrogant pride which induces a man to step over due limits of propriety. Alkaios of Mytilene on the island of Lesbos, an older contemporary of Sappho, an aristocrat, a notable poet and a member of one of the first Greek city-States to coin money, proclaimed: "Man is money," thereby probably implying that money tends to usurp the integrity, honesty and personal worth of man. Sophokles expressed it this way: "Of all the evils thriving in the world, money is the worst. Money drives men from home, plunders great cities, perverts the honest mind to shameful practice, godlessness, and crime." A contemporary of Plato and the head of a rival school to Plato's Academy, Isokrates of Athens (436-338 B.C.), who was a famous rhetorician and the main creator of rhetoric as a distinct science and the 'grand style' of prose as well, said that men who have obtained great wealth cannot rest content, but are driven to risk what they already have by reaching after more riches. Perikles (c.495-c.429 B.C.), the illustrious Athenian statesman and leader who had been tutored by Anaxagoras of Klazomenai and Protagoras of Abdera, expressed the general Athenian attitude about wealth: "Wealth we employ as an opportunity for action rather than as a subject for boasting; and with us it is not a shame for a man to acknowledge poverty, but the greater shame is for him not to do his utmost to avoid it."

Compelled by their traditional sense of austerity and suspicion of wealth, no vast engineering projects were ever undertaken by the ancient Greeks, since they had definite views on the proportion of things relative to the individual man, who, so many of them thought, was the measure of all things. Sophokles stated his views on this topic in the following sentence: "Nothing that is vast enters into the life of mortals without a curse." In the opinion of the ancient Greeks, anything in life that becomes vast and disproportionate relative to man, particularly institutions and enterprises, ultimately becomes a curse instead of a blessing to the man of personal worth and dignity.

By calling foreigners 'barbarians' (***barbaros***, means strange, ignorant), the ancient Greeks paid tribute to the Greek heroic ideal, to their rationality, to their civility, to their highly refined language capable of expressing lofty thoughts, and to their cultural traditions inspired by the liberty of the individual.

The ancient Greeks, but particularly the Ionians and the Athenians, heeded law and valued order, whilst at the same time they despised corruption and oppression, and had a great passion for the liberty of the individual. Perikles expressed the Hellenic credo in a brief statement: "We are free and tolerant in our private lives, but in public affairs we keep to the law." In their own cultural tradition, the ancient Greeks valued most highly their personal liberty, and what they deplored in alien people the most was the tendency to behave below the level of free and self-responsible men. In the opinion of the ancient Greeks, the barbarian being without liberty, has at best the morality of a slave, and as such he might all too easily indulge in acts of violence fit only for brutes. They believed that even an ordinary man who has personal liberty is capable of extraordinary accomplishments.

In the opinion of most ancient Greeks, only a free and autonomous man, an individual who is self-organised, tends to perceive the truth, whereas the institutionalised heteronomous man who is compelled to conform by others tends to pervert the truth. Mainly for this reason, ancient Greeks shunned formal institutions of the State, or other political organisations that produced institutionalised heteronomous men whom they regarded decidedly inferior to the self-organised autonomous men.

The ancient Greeks were able to combine rather generous personal rights of the individual with a strong sense of personal responsibility for his city-State, to which the ancient Greek owed all his personal rights, because the ancient Greeks, unlike the Anglo-Saxons, the Teutons and the Norsemen, did not properly recognise inalienable rights of the individual. In fact, such words as 'individual', 'self, and 'ego' did not exist in ancient Greek language. The ideal of individualism of ancient Greeks was first recognised in Ionia, whence it spread to various other Greek colonies in the southern Italian peninsula called the Greater Greece (***he megale Hellas***, which Romans called ***magna Græcia***), and finally to Athens (***Athenai)*** in Greece itself.

The ancient Greeks did not consider the individual man as an entity entirely apart from the city-State, the ***polis***. The ***polis*** as a political commonwealth did not constitute a particular form of government: its essential principle was rule by law, by the public consent, in the public interest. It was much more than a modern State – it was people itself. It was virtually coextensive with the society embracing their moral, religious, cultural, social as well as their political interests – in other words, it was like one big family, or a clan.

As stated above, in ancient Greece, or ***Hellas*** as the Greeks themselves called their country, the citizen of the ***polis*** had no inalienable rights since all his liberties were considered privileges endowed by his membership in a community, the ***polis***, and none were based on his status as a human being. The 'unwritten laws', or religious responsibilities, were equally binding on all citizens as pious men of the ***polis***. Written, or not, the law had precedence over the rights of the individual in ***Hellas*** since all the liberties of a citizen were derived from the society and, therefore, revocable by the community. For this reason, ostracism or political exile of a citizen of a Greek ***polis*** was almost as dreadful as death. In ancient Greece there existed no concept of privacy, no proper place for a private individual (***idiotes***) who had a private conscience: in Hellas conscience had to be public rather than private. In fact, there was no such word as 'conscience' in the ancient Greek language.

The ancient Greeks believed that ***polis*** was the essential means of any Greek to enjoy freedom, justice, security, and a good life – and to being a Hellene instead of a barbarian. Thales emphasised the typical male chauvinist sentiment of the ancient Greeks when he counted his blessings: "For these three blessings I am grateful to Fortune: that I was born human and not a brute, a man and not a woman, a Greek and not a barbarian." It was through the ***polis*** that the ancient Greek sought to develop his distinctive individuality: a man achieved his particular excellence by participating naturally, freely, and completely in the life of the ***polis***, since public duty to the ancient Greeks was plain commonsense, rather than an abstract idealism. Poet Simoneides (c.556-c.468 B.C.) of the island of Keos expressed this idea in one brief sentence: "The city-State is the teacher of man." Perikles in his well-known boast about Athens (***Athenai***) said: "Our city is an education to Greece." Aristotle stated that in a well-governed ***polis*** the virtue of a good man, and that of a citizen are the same.

Greeks called a private man who was so devoted to his private life that he lacked any interest in public affairs an ***idiotes*** (***idios*** meant private, one's own), a private person who minds only his own business. Perikles expressed the typical ancient Greek opinion of the 'private man' as follows: "And you will find united in the same person an interest at once in private and in public affairs, and in others of us who give attention briefly to business, you will find no lack of insight into political matters. ...We do not say that a man who takes no interest in politics is a man who minds his own business, we say that he has no business here at all."

In the Greek ***polis*** the citizen had complete freedom of speech not circumscribed by any libel laws or strict respect for the truth, because the ancient Greeks were not subservient like the ancient Orientals, who accepted the autocratic State and the absence of freedom of speech and political freedom the same way they accepted the weather- with complete resignation. Perikles expressed the characteristic Greek attitude about political freedom, when he said: "... trusting less in system and policy than to the native spirit of our citizens. ... Each single one of our citizens in all his manifold aspects of life is able to show himself the rightful owner and lord of his own person and do this, moreover, with exceptional grace and versatility." The ancient Greeks, wisely it seems, did not trust power to anyone out of their sight. They believed that the essential attributes of any individual man cannot be delegated, and that all important functions of a citizen must be fulfilled in person, a sensible civic virtue which is still the best exercise of civic responsibility in modern society.

The ancient Greeks readily recognised that dissent is the native mental attitude of a critically thinking man, and that his ability to dissent is the very mark of his freedom. In the opinion of the ancient Greeks dissent was a result of originality, and originality was the mark of independence of mind, and independence of mind, originality and, therefore, dissent were to them the very means of progress in a free society. The ancient Greeks realised that in science and technology, like in society, there is no substitute for the independence of mind, and they readily recognised that dissent must be socially safeguarded by freedom in the society: *free enquiry*, *free thought*, and *free speech*. According to the ancient Greeks, freedom requires tolerance which should be due to the respect for the dignity of the individual man as a thinker rather than due to indifference. Since science and technology by their very nature confront the creation of one thinking man with that of another, these creations cannot survive without mutual tolerance that is due to the respect the citizen of a ***polis*** has for the dignity of the individual man, and for his fundamental right to his personal opinion. Aristotle expressed this exemplary attitude in his own work: "If those who study this subject form any opinion contrary to that we have stated, we must indeed respect both parties, but be guided by the more accurate."

The ancient Greeks had observed that in ancient Oriental societies which were governed by formal behavioural prescriptions in which even to contradict somebody might be considered a personal affront, no vital science such as natural philosophy or viable practical art such as technology were possible. Therefore, they defended with passionate zeal the freedom of dissent in their own society as the very lifeline of the thinking person. The ancient Greek civilisation cherished the principle of harmony yet, actually, it was torn by internal strife which, however, may have served to promote excellence in the achievements of the ancient Greeks in their civilisation.

Many ancient Greeks believed passionately in the personal worth of the individual man. They recognised that personal worth cannot exist without self-esteem, that self-esteem cannot exist without self-respect, that self-respect cannot exist without self-confidence, that self-confidence cannot exist without self-reliance, and that self-reliance cannot exist without self-responsibility. They regarded supreme self-confidence of the individual to be the basic condition of his personal creativity, and self-reliance the very source of his heroic attitude. In the opinion of the ancient Greeks, personal worth of the individual depends solely upon worthy personal accomplishments. It was their view that every man to be worthy of his human nature has to dedicate himself to worthy toil in creating something superb and entirely new, and to make the most of all of his natural gifts by striving for an all-round excellence. Two millennia later, in the Italian Renaissance period, a man of such all-round excellence, that is, a 'complete man', was called a 'universal man' (***uomo universale***). Since Greek gods represented the very source of power to ancient Greeks they respected every kind of power which is demonstrated not only in war, athletics, and art but also in thought, because they had equal respect for mental and physical prowess. For this reason, they believed that an ideal life of a Greek citizen in ***polis*** is spent in the pursuit of excellence in all things since a 'complete man' is acting equally in all worthy pursuits. If an ancient Greek succeeded in any of these endeavours, then he was making full use of his divinely provided gifts and, therefore, was approaching the gods as nearly as possible. Ancient Greeks believed that man was a god-like creature of integration: an individual had a personal responsibility to integrate all his personal knowledge into a comprehensive and critical cultural perspective. Aristotle believed that the very state of man's happiness depends upon the exercise of all his "vital powers along the lines of excellence." Therefore, an ancient Greek tried to keep his body as fit as his mind, and to make the most of his mind and his body in order to excel and to acquire personal worth. The achievement of personal worth required a man to excel, and to excel to ancient Greeks meant that a man had to surpass himself, that is, to surpass his present self. Aristotle expressed this Hellenic ideal in a succinct statement: "We must, so far as we can, make ourselves immortal." Since only the gods are immortal, Aristotle urged his fellow Greeks to achieve their life after death through exceptional personal achievements that transcend the mortal condition of men, and in this manner approach gods as much as possible. He contended that man becomes immortal primarily through his thoughts, thus for all the ancient Greeks *fame* was the important goal of life. In science, fine arts and poetry, a man excelled when he surpassed himself, or as the famous Roman lawyer, orator, statesman and a man of letters, Marcus Tullius Cicero (106-43 B.C.), said: "When man would become most like the divine." Sokrates expressed his particular opinion on this matter when he said: "The fewer our wants the nearer we resemble the gods." For the ancient Greek living in the ***polis***, the principal goal of any citizen was to achieve through vigorous toil in a zealous singleminded pursuit of personal excellence his best personal accomplishments which necessarily required him to use all his native god-given gifts.

It was the mathematician and mystic Pythagoras who established the 4 cardinal virtues of man as his standard of excellence: *courage, temperance, justice* and *wisdom*. If a man practised all 4 virtues he could do no more. In the opinion of the ancient Greeks, *temperance* was a matter of style: doing everything without public display, vulgarity, and arrogance. Thus in the Hellenic world, *temperance* was an essential component of good manners, whereas *justice* was a moral quality succinctly expressed by lyric poet Simoneides of Keos: "Rendering to every man his due." The polymath Demokritos of Abdera (c.470-c.380 B.C.) expressed the importance of justice and courage in the following way: "By understanding and knowledge of just action a man becomes both brave and right-minded." Sokrates believed that courage is a form of knowledge, whereas Plato fancied that the highest form of courage is the will to resist seductions of pleasure without yielding. It was recognised by the ancient Greeks that the 4 virtues: *courage, justice, temperance* and *wisdom*, were so closely related in any self-responsible individual that they were ultimately indistinguishable, and that together they stood for a balanced and self-disciplined person. They regarded unbridled arrogance (***hubris***) to be the most grievous mistake a man can commit, since it makes balance and harmony in the self impossible.

Both Pythagoras and Aristotle believed that the highest kind of life is dedicated to the pursuit of the truth which they regarded to be comparable to the contemplative activity of the gods. The pursuit of the truth was considered by both of these prominent ancient Greeks good in itself. The three basic principles of right living in ancient Greece were: the true, the good, and the beautiful (***to alethes, to agathon, kai to kalon***).

In the classical Greek culture, reason and beauty were not separable: anything beautiful had to be also reasonable, and they believed that mathematics as the art of the mind united both. In the opinion of ancient Greeks, beauty as the supreme end was beyond price, and the true was the good.

They seemed to possess a native intuition for truth as well as for beauty. They believed that everything man does or says should have grace and beauty. The cultural legacy left by the ancient Greeks to the Western man is the ideal standard of the beautiful and the statement of the true, as well as the form of their intellectual investigation. In æsthetics, the motto of the ancient Greeks can be succinctly expressed: 'Less is more', meaning that simplicity is æsthetically more pleasing than complexity. Beauty to the ancient Greeks consisted in the harmony of proper proportions based on a mathematical theory of proportions – first proposed by the Pythagoreans. Therefore, in ***Hellas***, the existence of certain mathematically precise proportions as an ideal guaranteed them æsthetic perfection, which is why the ancient Greek art is an intellectual art. Perikles justified the Greek passion for beauty and intellectual culture as follows: "Our love of what is beautiful does not lead us to extravagance, and our love of the things of the mind does not make us effeminate." Concerning physical beauty, ancient Greeks had different philosophical opinions on pulchritude: Sokrates, an ugly man, regarded beauty as "a shortlived tyranny," whereas Aristotle, a physically handicapped man, considered it to be "a gift of the gods."

The Greek mind developed a versatility that has never been equalled, a mental power of dealing with abstract thought, and an interest in philosophical questions that is as remote from the practical interests of society today as it was in the preceding ages. One of the most unique contributions of the ancient Greeks is the establishment of the theoretical foundation for the conscious thought of man, and a firm belief in its generalisation. The task of the Greek philosopher was not only to understand, but also to explain himself and his world in philosophical terms. The main task of ancient Greek science was a formal and systematic exposition of scientific knowledge. They invented hypothetico-deductive reasoning and theory; drama as literature; philosophy with its complete abstract vocabulary, both political and moral; rhetoric, or the art of logical argument; grammar, or the science of language; history as a critical intellectual discipline; formal logic; mathematical science and deductive logical proof; geography; biology; botany; zoology; geology, art as a cultural discipline; science of mechanics, scientific engineering, theoretical astronomy, and a number of other intellectual disciplines. They not only created a strictly exact method of thinking for the purpose of arriving at logically impeccable and precise results from fundamental principles called hypotheses by means of deductive reasoning, but also alternative methods of reasoning by induction and by analogy. Moreover, ancient Greeks applied reason to a variety of other basic concerns of man such as politics, justice, education, ethics as well as æsthetics, and demonstrated its power to produce knowledge which lies beyond the immediate experience of man.

The technological creed of the ancient Greeks was expressed by the poet Amphion: "... by technical art (***techne***) we conquer where by nature we are overcome." ***Techne*** consisted in knowing how and when to use rightly a power (***dynamis***) which acts as an artificial force of nature.

In conclusion, if Zarathushtra was the ancient Persian forerunner of the Western man, then the ancient Greeks were the first archetypical Western men, who from 600 B.C. to 300 B.C. created a spectacular and unprecedented development in arts and sciences which is unmatched in the history of man.

A contemporary Western professional person should still find the thoughts of his or her precursors, the ancient Greeks, of great value if he or she is to understand better his or her place and responsibilities in his or her own civilisation. An intimate knowledge of the ancient Greek thought provides an irreplaceable and invaluable cultural perspective for a contemporary professional person in the Occident.

Rise of Science as Natural Philosophy and Theoretical Mathematics

Despite the contradictions and much that was left unexplained by the traditional myths, it represented at least one way of thinking about natural events which satisfied most ancient people who believed that gods were at work everywhere, and that a revealed knowledge of gods 'explained' most physical phenomena. Therefore, myths are the discarded popular science of long ago.

However, some Indo-European people, particularly the Ionian Greeks, were not satisfied with mythical explanations of natural phenomena which were not rational, and as a result of their dissatisfaction a new critical spirit arose among Ionian Greeks who aspired to understand worldly things more accurately by intellectual means. Therefore, they attempted to explain the natural phenomena on rational basis by trying to discover principles hidden behind the phenomena of nature rather than to regard such phenomena to be the results of the inexplicable caprice of gods as depicted in their myths. This new intellectual and critical spirit of man was an inevitable outcome of the spiritual drive of the highly intelligent and curious people such as the Ionian Greeks, and of the stimulating social and political changes which took place in their world. The hereditary monarchies of ancient Greeks were gradually being replaced by enterprising merchants as the new ruling class who turned their main attention to foreign trade, and foreign trade in turn brought Ionian Greeks face-to-face with a wide range of practical problems requiring applied knowledge and technology. Construction, metal working, and sculpture presented many problems which required technical solutions, and far-reaching maritime trade was in urgent need of precise geography and astronomy to make navigation safe and efficient. Popular athletics and medical treatment of physical illnesses made more precise knowledge about the human body necessary.

These new developments and practical problems led the Ionian Greeks to fundamental enquiries about the physical world, enquiries which belonged to 3 main scientific disciplines with a considerable overlap between them: mathematics, natural philosophy, and natural science. Natural philosophy (***physis***) dealt mostly with the nature of material things, whilst natural science was essentially medical science. Already the primitive neolithic man had made attempts to develop a crude but general conception of nature by assuming that all things are made of irreducible 'elements' like man himself: that is, everything is made of a spiritual part and a bodily part in which the bodily part is controlled by the spiritual part. This kind of anthropomorphic conception of nature was, perhaps not surprisingly, revived again in an intellectually more sophisticated, elaborate and systematic form by the ancient Greeks.

Although a great deal of the thinking of ancient Greeks about nature can be called visionary, it was based on the concept of building a universal intellectual system of thought about nature. They had already realised that contemplation alone cannot lead to any cognition beyond mere definition, and that in order to transcend definition, the ancient Ionian Greeks came to recognise that it was necessary to invent general hypotheses by assuming that certain statements are valid. These hypothetical statements, now called postulates, represent assumptions of general nature which are accepted on the basis of their plausibility. However, these fundamental postulates had to satisfy certain conditions beyond their plausibility : they had to be mutually independent and logically non-contradictory, and as few in number as possible.

The raw materials for their conceptual thought were the accidental sense impressions which the mind of man abstracts into mental constructs by making them the building blocks of his ideas that are further processed by the mind into a more universal system of thought, called 'critical knowledge'. This kind of method of thinking of the ancient Ionian Greeks, the so-called 'scientific method', became the model of thinking in exact sciences. The scientific method of ancient Greeks consisted of a certain set of general fundamental postulates which were accepted as valid because of their plausibility or on the basis of some gross measurements, and combined into a logically constructed system of thought from which certain logical inferences called 'lemmas' or 'theorems' were deduced. The so-called 'reality', as ancient Greeks had already recognised, is actually a conglomeration of mentally processed sense-impressions of man. The concepts, ideas, and theories man invents are meant to reconcile man's physical reality as perceived by his senses with the rationalised reality as conceived by his mind. The ancient Greeks considered sense-perceptions to be mere fleeting and distorted images of the actual world, which in its divine purity could not be perceived by man's senses but can only be fully comprehended by man's mind. They believed that only the mind is capable of discovering the actual fundamental reality which is perceived by the senses only in a distorted, crude and approximate form. This basic belief not only dominated their natural philosophy, but also their art. The most famous ancient Greek sculptors left out many details and individual particulars of their models which they considered unnecessary in their efforts to restore the beauty of the human form to its highest ideal of which the human body as seen by the Greek artists was only an imperfect material manifestation. Ancient Greek mathematicians had a similar attitude in geometry.

Thus, the Ionian Greeks soon came to recognise that proper reasoning should proceed according to general principles and, therefore, they began to explain the world in natural terms for rational purposes by rejecting the supernatural explanation of phenomena for mythical purposes, thereby establishing the rational explanation of natural phenomena. They maintained that natural phenomena are not products of random or arbitrary influences but rather results of the underlying regularity in nature which is governed by definite sequences of cause-and-effect. This kind of approach to natural phenomena embraced the concept of general science rather than empirical rules, and it was the creation of Ionian Greeks. They sought critical understanding of the true nature of things based upon their belief that the world is rational, homogeneous, and accessible to human enquiry.

Thales of Miletos-First Greek Astronomer, Mathematician and Natural Philosopher:

About 600 B.C., Greek Ionia, where political power had been assumed by merchants interested in the promotion of technology for their trade which made manual labour a respectable occupation, was at the crossroads of civilisations and engaged in far-reaching trade with other civilisations. The new scientific spirit of the Ionian Greeks was kindled by their technological experience in the workshops supplying various merchandise for their commerce. The first known exponent of this new scientific spirit was Thales of Miletos, a natural philosopher, mathematician, astronomer, businessman and military engineer, who founded the first known scientific school in Tenedos, Ionia, a small island near the mouth of Hellespont where he probably died. Thales, who was of Greek, Karian and Phoenician stock, posed the following fundamental logical question: 'If one substance can be changed into another substance, such as wood changed into ashes, or water into steam, or ore into metal, what then is the actual nature of the substance?' For instance, is it the ore or is it the metal, or is it, in fact, some other stuff ? He wondered whether it is possible in principle to change any one substance into any other substance. If this be possible, then any substance is merely another aspect of one fundamental stuff. Thales answered this question in affirmative to bring order into the seemingly chaotic world of matter. It remained for him only to determine what is this basic stuff, or 'element' as it was much later called in Roman times, and he decided in favour of 'water' as the prime matter, since water did change into vapour and then seemingly becoming air when it evaporated into the atmosphere, and then reappearing from air as rain in an apparent cyclic substantive change. Therefore, Thales recognised that water occurs in nature in 3 different states: solid, liquid and gaseous. This kind of theory of matter is now called 'monomaterialism'.

His answer to the fundamental question about the true nature of matter was a bold scientific generalisation, and not just a mere guesswork, because it represented a physical hypothesis expressed in logical terms and based upon empirical observations. Thales postulated the substantial unity of nature by reducing the manifold appearances in nature to be governed by a 'single first principle' (***arche***), based upon his belief in the stability of such a natural 'law'. The science of Thales, as well as of other later Milesian scientists, was drawn from the technological experience of their age, because they had become aware of the need to examine critically the theories of physical nature in the light of their practical experience. The Milesian natural philosopher-scientist thought that practical technological experience gives man the clue for the understanding of operations in nature since they did not distinguish the Ionian science, which to them was a way of doing something practical by means of industrial techniques, from technology. In this sense, the technological workshops in Miletos served the pioneer Milesian scientists as their scientific laboratories.

This brief statement of Thales heralded the beginning of the emancipation of man's mind from myths, for the emancipated mind asserts its own power of reason and intellectual self-discipline. It introduced a new critical spirit into man's conception of physical nature which matched the critical attitude of Ionian Greeks in their political philosophy based upon free debate.

Thales had realised that general intellectual methods are more valuable than particular solutions, because general methods imply general principles and theorems. He founded the intellectual process of abstraction which transformed geometry from a set of empirical rules into a logical mathematical structure. In his efforts to abstract geometry, Thales became the first mathematician to conceive the need for geometric propositions on which was built by the method of deductive reasoning the logically articulated geometry, the so-called 'Greek geometry'. He revolutionised mathematics by introducing the notion of logical proof into mathematical thinking. By establishing mathematics as a deductive intellectual science, Thales drew attention to the possibility of deducing less obvious theorems and lemmas from more readily accepted premises, and he himself reputedly gave a number of proofs in geometry: the circle is bisected by any of its diameters; angles at the base of an isosceles (***isos***-equal+ ***skelos***-leg) triangle are equal; the opposite angles formed by 2 intersecting lines are equal; 2 triangles are congruent if they have 2 angles and a side of one respectively equal to the corresponding parts of the other triangle, and an angle inscribed in a semicircle is a right angle. Thales founded logically rigorous geometry on the abstract principles of congruence or a real equivalence and similitude. He pioneered the geometric method of navigation on open seas by the stars, determined the distances of ships from land by triangulation, and wrote a book on nautical astronomy. Thales was challenged by the Egyptian priests to determine the height of the largest pyramid in Egypt which Thales accomplished by means of its shadow on the ground and the principle of similar triangles, in which his concept of proportion was an important advance in the field of algebra, since the treatment of ratio, proportion, and the number theory may properly be taken as a whole. As Egyptian priests asked Thales to find the '***pyremes***' (meaning 'height' in Egyptian) of the Khufu pyramid, Thales probably coined the Greek term

pyramis from the Egyptian ***pyremes*** as the name for such unique structures, which became the modern term 'pyramid'.

Thales taught that the Earth is a sphere the surface of which is divided into 5 zones, and that Moonlight is the reflection of Sunlight. He also gave the correct explanation of the eclipse of the Moon. He was the first to make a celestial globe which was solid in construction, and the first to study the physical effects of electricity and magnetism. All these facts based on observations demonstrate that Thales was not only a speculative natural philosopher. The monomaterial constitution of all substances as proposed by Thales was readily accepted by other younger Ionian natural philosophers who only differed in their choice of the fundamental material, or stuff.

Anaximandros of Miletos, Natural Law and Theory of Evolution:

Anaximandros (in English, Anaximander) of Miletos, a fellow citizen and companion (***polites kai etairos***) of Thales, was an inventor, geographer, philosopher, engineer and leader of a Milesian colony at the Black Sea. He, like Thales, had broad interests. Since it was difficult to explain how water as the primary stuff could become its opposite, fire (which to ancient Greeks was also a substance), because these 2 substances seemed to be mutually destructive, Anaximandros thought that the primary stuff of which things are made cannot be a specific substance perceived by man, but rather something quite different from the sensible substances. This subtle, intangible and fundamental stuff he called the 'unbounded' or 'undefined' (***apeiron***). He postulated it to be indestructible and potentially present everywhere, and its eternal state of circular motion he assumed to be responsible for generating opposing qualities in nature through a process of separation of opposites which results in imbalances. Therefore, the world of Anaximandros arose out of the boundless and returned into it in a perpetual closed-cycle process. Anaximandros is the first natural philosopher to extend explicitly the notion of man-made civil law (***nomos***) regulating the behaviour of inhabitants in the city-State (***polis***) by analogy to the 'natural law' controlling physical processes in nature. Thus Anaximandros extended the idea of law from the Ionian political philosophy by analogy to natural philosophy, thereby lending physical nature certain anthropomorphic qualities. Moreover, he also introduced the principle of sufficient reason: "If we can assign no specific boundary, we had better assume there is none."

In his natural philosophy, Anaximandros seems to have distinguished between the concepts of infinity and boundlessness for he assumed time to be infinite, but space to be boundless yet finite. He proposed the first mechanical model for the heavenly bodies by assuming the Earth to be a disklike body suspended in space and surrounded by an ocean and by great Solar, Lunar, and stellar anchor rings. This cosmological model of Anaximandros was a system of an engineer. He hypothesised the world to be in an eternal state of circular motion which to him was the very source of universal power. He discovered the inclination of the ecliptic, and originated the theory of organic evolution by observing young sharks and other marine life near the Ionian coast. He wrote the first treatise on natural philosophy < On Nature > (***Peri Physeos***), the first scientific work written in prose, which unfortunately is no longer extant. Moreover, he is responsible for preparing the first map of the world, a gigantic undertaking for a single man, to help commerce and, particularly, commercial navigation. Anaximandros invented a simple astrolabe based on stereographic projection for the measurement of celestial angles, the ***gnomon*** constructed on a shadow-catcher (***skiotheron***) which showed the solstices and equinoxes, and Sundials (***horoskopeia***) with hour-lines and transverse lines indicating the course of the shadow-point at the solstices and equinoxes. All these astronomical instruments were manufactured in his workshop. Although Thales was the first theoretical mathematician, he never wrote a treatise on his mathematical and physical theories. It was Anaximandros who wrote the first textbook on mathematics.

Anaximenes of Miletos, Condensation and Rarefaction as Process of Change:

After the pioneering scientific speculations of Anaximandros, the question of the particular nature of the primary matter was raised again by Anaximenes of Miletos (c.585-c.525 B.C.), a younger contemporary of Anaximandros. Anaximenes was dissatisfied with the intangible ***apeiron***, the unlimited and undifferentiated primary stuff of Anaximandros, and he substituted for it 'air' (***aer, pneuma***), a physically more tangible yet still a rather subtle matter which seemed to be potentially everywhere. He postulated 'air' to be changeable into other substances such as 'water', and then 'earth' by condensation (***pyknosis***), and then back again into 'air' by rarefaction (***manosis***) in a cyclic process. Anaximenes boldly stated: "We come into existence by efflux (***ekpoia***) from 'air'." He also thought that the process of rarefaction (rather than condensation) creates heat. Anaximenes assumed the Earth and planets to float in a space filled with air, and the heavens to be spherical. He was the first person to differentiate between the planets and the stars, and to assume the stars to be fixed to rotating spheres – an idea used later by the Pythagoreans in their cosmology and by Eudoxos of Knidos in the first mathematical theory of astronomy. He also recognised that the Moon shines by the reflexion of the Sunlight.

Xenophanes of Kolophon, First Geologist and Palaeontologist:

The wandering Ionian natural philosopher Xenophanes of Kolophon (c.570-c.475 B.C.) in his famous poetic work < About Nature > (***Peri Physeos***), rejected the traditional archaic belief that truth is given to man by God in divine revelation by insisting that man has the responsibility to discover the truth through his own efforts: "The God did not reveal to men all things from the beginning, but men through their own search find in the course of time that which is better. Let these be taken as fancies, something like the truth." Xenophanes, established his ideal method of enquiry: the pursuit of truth by enquiry. Xenophanes correctly pointed out that man's knowledge is really a web of guesses, that there is no absolute certainty in knowledge, and that man could never know if he is in possession of the absolute truth even if he had it in his grasp. Therefore, according to Xenophanes, man can be confident about his opinions but never absolutely certain. Xenophanes, himself, lived up to his own ideal by becoming the first geologist and palaeontologist in a piece of excellent scientific enquiry on how the Earth had once been under the sea, a theory he corroborated with the empirical evidence of the existence of marine fossils on the hills and mountains of Malta, Paros and Syracuse.

Xenophanes was the only ancient Greek philosopher who believed in one God whom he considered to be beyond man's direct perception. In his opinion, polytheism and the legends told about the gods were mere human inventions. God was accessible to man through reason only, and since God is also a moral force, men should pray to God to obtain the ideal of justice. His basic dogma was the unity of the world, a world in which all things are directed without effort by the power of God's reason. In this particular view he might have been influenced by the late Zoroastrianism which may have been still present in Ionia. He found the gods of Homer and Hesiod immoral and absurd. He also stated: " God is the cause of motion."

Xenophanes of Kolophon, who was probably responsible for the rise of the Eleatic school of philosophy and logic, had the opinion that all things are made of earth as the fundamental stuff rather than of air. Although the 4 Ionian natural philosophers Thales, Anaximandros, Anaximenes, and Xenophanes, differed in their choice of the primary stuff, they all accepted the concept of monomaterialism, which implied that everything in this world is made of the same homogeneous fundamental stuff that is ostensibly capable of transformation without the intermediation of gods. They had developed their science from their contemporary technological experience in Ionia, and it was based upon their belief that natural events are not miracles brought about by the inscrutable gods. In this manner the Ionian natural philosophers attempted to discover the reality lurking behind the appearance of natural phenomena.

Pythagoras of Samos and Rise of Mathematical Physics:

Pythagoras of Samos (c.580-c. 497 B.C.) was a pupil of Perekydes of Syros who was one of the first writers of prose, and the introducer of the doctrine of metempsychosis which was adopted by Pythagoras as a means to immortality. Pythagoras was a mystical natural philosopher who was probably influenced by Zoroastrianism, as well as a mathematician and scientist. He was apparently had to flee his native island of Samos to escape the rule of the tyrant Polykrates, and for a period of time he settled in Miletos where he apparently studied with Thales, and probably also with Anaximandros. He then travelled to Syria, to Egypt, and to Babylon where he studied geometry, astronomy and music. He returned to Samos, but soon left for Delos, then the island of Kreta (modern Crete), then Greece proper and finally settled in the rich colonial city Kroton in southern

Italy, a city known for its famous medical school. He was responsible for carrying the natural philosophy of the Ionians to the Greek world in southern Italian peninsula (***he megale Hellas***, later known by Romans as ***magna Graecia***). About 530 B.C. he established a school in Kroton, and a secret learned society called the Pythagorean Brotherhood that was mostly composed of wealthy and influential citizens of Kroton, and which has served ever since as a model for all private Western professional societies. The students in his school were divided into two groups: auditors (***aukosmatikoi***) and members of his society (***mathematikoi***). All members, called mathematicians, had to pass through a probationary period as auditors. He was the first to use the term 'mathematics' (***mathemata*** – all knowledge of human experience acquired through any methodical investigation by human reason) in its modern sense. Both men and women were admitted on equal terms which was unusual in the ancient Greek world since only Etruscan women enjoyed freedom comparable to that of Etruscan men. Pythagoras was given to Orphic moral mysticism, and he affected to possess powers of divination. Moreover, he was a man with a remarkable degree of personal magnetism who always wore pants as well as a turban, which remained the traditional headgear of the leader of the Pythagorean society.

Pythagorean learned society was almost monastic in the strictness of its discipline. The most rigid of its rules were the rule of secrecy and the rule that no member should have proprietary rights to any discovery. All discoveries were formally credited to Pythagoras by the statement: 'he said it (***antos epha***)'. All knowledge was to be monopolised and kept a secret, since Pythagoras considered it undesirable that common people should have access to the recondite mysteries of science and philosophy. This secrecy was both a professional principle and an early form of copyright, as well as an early example of professional unionism.

Pythagoras explicitly recognised education as learning to think for oneself under the guidance of a teacher, who merely shows the way. He taught by word of mouth (***viva voce***) 4 liberal arts: arithmetic, geometry, harmonics (music) and astronomy, which constituted the liberal education given in his school. The general principles of the Pythagorean learned society were that contemplation is more blessed than action, that the world of senses is less real than the world of the mind, that introspection is more valuable a method of enquiry than observation, and that practical occupations are unworthy of the elite. Pythagoras saw in mystical religion an instrument of moral reform, and in music and herbs the very means for purging the soul and the body respectively. He believed that the most effective purification of the soul is produced by the disinterested pursuit of knowledge, and thought that the human soul communicates with the divine soul through thinking and, therefore, thinking to him was a divine rather than a human activity. The highest form of life, according to Pythagoras, was the theoretical life (***bios theoretikos***). He associated love for science with sanctity, and for mathematics with the soul of man. He claimed that science is valuable irrespective of its usefulness because it is the best form of contemplation and understanding. The idea of individual freedom and the concept of the self-reliant man, which became an enduring theme of ancient Greeks, was first taken up in the Pythagorean society.

Unfortunately for the Pythagoreans, their society also professed an aristocratic and elitist political philosophy to change the world of man for the better through political action, which was the main reason why the Pythagoreans were driven out of Kroton in a plebeian revolt about 510 B.C. and were forced to seek refuge in the city-State Taras which remained the main center of Pythagoreanism. Pythagoras himself as an old man fled to Metapontion where he died about 497 B.C..

Pythagoras made the singular physical discovery, a landmark in physical science and the very origin of mathematical physics, when he found experimentally that the concordant intervals of the musical scale can be exactly given in arithmetical terms as numerical ratios. He invented the monochord, a musical instrument with one string put under constant tension by a suspended weight, and discovered in an experiment with the monochord the relation that exists between the length of the vibrating musical string and the emitted note. In the scale of C where the 8 notes, CDEFGABC, constitute an interval called an octave (***diapason***), the string when halved emits a note an octave higher, when reduced to ⅔ of its length emits a note higher by an interval CG, called a fifth (***diapente***), and when reduced to ¾ of its length emits a note higher by an interval CF, called a fourth (***diatesson***). Thus, he discovered the dependence of fixed, musical intervals common to all Greek musical scales upon simple numerical ratios of whole numbers: *octave* upon 2 to 1, *fifth* upon 3 to 2, and *fourth* upon 4 to 3. The whole numbers which occur in these musical ratios are *1*,*2*, *3* and *4*, the sum of which is *10* that Pythagoras named the 'perfect number'. This striking discovery in his study of music led Pythagoras to a bold generalisation: The nature of things in this world is numerical. Thus a new theory of the physical world, a mathematical theory, was born. The scientific study of musical scales of Pythagoras is the first known work of mathematical physics.

Pythagoras gave his students the relation:

$$1 : \frac{1}{2} = \left(1 - \frac{2}{3}\right) : \left(\frac{2}{3} - \frac{1}{2}\right)$$

which was later given the name 'harmonic proportion'. The theory of harmonic progression was developed from this relation.

He was the first to use the term 'cosmos' (in Greek ***kosmos*** meant order, harmony) in reference to a well-ordered and harmonious universe which is accessible to human understanding. In contrast to Ionian scientists who believed harmony underlying the universe to be accessible through observation and experiment as in the method of modern science, Pythagoras taught that the mathematical laws of nature can be discovered solely by pure thought. He assumed the celestial movements to be circular and uniform, an æsthetic postulate on his part, because he considered the circle to represent the 'perfect geometric form'. He had an idea of the limited and the unlimited, and from the latter he took his concept of time, space and motion.

Pythagoras believed that the way to true knowledge was to free oneself from the impermanence of the senses, and to try to recover through contemplation the knowledge of the eternal concepts, ideas and forms which in his opinion were present in the soul of man. This mystical belief was later adopted by Sokrates and his disciple Plato.

In his arithmogeometry, that is, in his arithmetical geometry, Pythagoras assumed that all material objects were made up of points as units of existence in combinations corresponding to various geometric figures. In this theoretical method, he associated, or confused, geometric points with ultimate material particles. Pythagoras was struck by the realisation that quite different physical phenomena can, nevertheless, exhibit similar mathematical properties, which led him to believe that mathematical properties must be the essence of 'all' physical phenomena. Motivated by this belief, he made a bold generalisation from his discovery of numerical ratios in music by assuming it to govern 'all' physical phenomena. For this reason, Pythagoras assumed the whole world to be a mathematical pattern, which behaved according to mathematical proportions, that is, particularly numerical ratios. Therefore, Pythagoras sought to base science on fundamental mathematical principles which allowed an examination of its theorems in abstraction from matter by means of pure intellect. In his natural philosophy, Pythagoras had replaced the Ionian mechanical model of the universe by a mathematical model in which the world that was in a state of harmony, a concept also taken over from music, was built from mathematical points having magnitude. This viewpoint of Pythagoras influenced other ancient Greek philosophers to search everywhere in nature for laws amenable to mathematical formulation, a world which Pythagoras thought to be cyclically repetitive: "... that events recur in certain cycles and nothing is ever absolutely new." The ultimate motto of Pythagoreans was: "All is number." Pythagoras knew that the Earth was spherical probably by noticing the curved shadow of the Earth on the Moon during the eclipse, and by recognising that ships disappear beyond the horizon after leaving the harbours.

He was the first mathematician to give a mathematical definition when he defined a 'point' (***semeion***) as 'unity having position'. He had a devout attitude towards geometry, the function of which he believed was to draw men away from the sensible and, therefore, away from perishable and temporal towards the intelligible and, therefore, towards the nonperishable and eternal. In Pythagorean geometry 'crooked' was associated with dishonesty, and 'straight' was associated with honesty, words which are still used today with the same meaning.

Later Pythagoreans introduced the kinematic method of geometry to supplement the geometry based upon the construction by ruler and compass. Since Pythagorean mathematics consisted of both the discrete and the continuous, the Pythagorean schools taught theories of continuous quantities consisting of geometry and astronomy, and theories of discrete quantities consisting of arithmetic and harmonics [music], in which arithmetic and geometry were considered pure disciplines, and astronomy and harmonics applied disciplines. At first, Pythagoreans were content to comprehend natural sciences by means of both arithmetic and geometry, but later they tried to reduce everything to a theory of numbers which they considered to be more fundamental than geometry. Pythagoras established a sort of arithmetic geometry in which figurate numbers were associated with various geometric forms: *a one* - a point or a monad; a line - *a two* or a dyad; a surface - *a three* or a triad; a solid - *a four* or a tetrad. However, his points had bulk, his lines breadth, and his surfaces thickness, and his solids volume, therefore, he thought that 1, 2, 3, and 4 was the stuff of which the world was made: "Numbers constitute the entire heaven." This mystical number theory of Pythagoras was more than mathematics, it was also physics, since he associated numbers with things and he made them the very basis of creation. He saw number as the very cause of form and every other quality of things. His mystical way of thinking about numbers obviously did not discriminate between things and the associated concepts, but it did emphasise the importance of mathematics to science.

Pythagoreans invented the method of application of areas which consisted of dividing a line of length a into 2 parts x and $(a-x)$ such that the rectangle contained by the whole line and one of the parts is equal to the square on the other part which can be expressed in modern algebra :

$$ax = (a-x)^2 ,$$

or

$$x^2-3ax + a^2 = 0 .$$

The base of the constructed figure could be shorter (***elleipsis***), equal (***parabole***), or longer (***hyperbole***) than the length of the given line. The solution of this problem was a geometric equivalent of solving a quadratic equation in modern algebra. It was later used to great advantage by other ancient Greek mathematicians.

Alkmaion of Kroton and Geocentric Astronomy:

Alkmaion of Kroton (born c. 500 B.C.), a pupil of Pythagoras, was probably the first person to propose that planets have circular and uniform movements about the stationary Earth. He was also an eminent physician who founded the famous medical school in Kroton, and the first person known to have conducted dissections of human bodies. He discovered the existence of the optic nerve, and the canal connecting the ear and mouth which was rediscovered 2 thousand years later by the Italian anatomist Bartholommeo Eustachio (A.D. 1520-1574). He distinguished arteries from veins, and correctly identified the brain as the center of intellectual activity that was adopted by Demokritos of Abdera but not by Aristotle of Stageira.

Philolaos of Kroton and Spherical Universe:

Philolaos of Kroton (c.480-c.389 B.C.), a contemporary of Sokrates and the most eminent Pythagorean after Pythagoras himself, proposed a rather sophisticated astronomical model by rejecting the geocentric theory of Alkmaion and replacing it by a spherical and bounded universe. At the center of this spherical universe was a sacred fire of goddess Hestia representing the very engine of the universe. About this fiery center rotated 10 heavenly bodies because 10 was the perfect number according to Pythagoras. Since only 9 heavenly bodies were visible to man, Philolaos invented the anti-Earth (***antichthon***) which was the first heavenly body rotating round the center and following the Earth in such a manner that it shaded the central fire from the Earth. The other bodies also rotating about the central fire were the Moon, the Sun and the 5 planets, and finally the fixed stars. All heavenly bodies including the stars he thought to be fixed to invisible spheres rotating about the central fire. This model roughly explained the motions of the planets, but not the retrograde motions which were probably unknown at the time, and the previously known eclipses. It also contained the so-called doctrine of the harmony of the spheres which by analogy related planetary distances to musical intervals given by mathematical ratios, which assigned velocities to the heavenly spheres according to their distances from the center of the universe. The velocities of the spheres in their opinion create powerful tones, the pitch of which they thought to depend upon these velocities that all together produced the heavenly harmony. It is the first known theory in which the Earth moved through space. It appears that Philolaos was the first Pythagorean to commit the Pythagorean doctrines to writing. Since the assumption of the invisible central fire and the invisible anti-Earth led to obvious contradictions, it was not surprising that the anti-Earth was soon united with the Earth to form a hollow sphere which surrounded the central fire and that such a composite Earth had to rotate about its own axis. This modified planetary system of Philolaos was proposed by 2 Pythagoreans from Syracuse, Hiketas and Ekphantos. Then it became necessary not to regard the Sun as a reflector of the light from the central fire but rather as a light-emitting burning sphere itself, and the Moonlight became the reflected Sunlight.

Pythagoras' theory that a line can be made up of a finite number of points, however, broke down when it was discovered that the ratio of the diagonal to the side of a square could not be expressed in terms of an exact number of units but rather by a number $\sqrt{2}$ which was 'irrational' to Pythagoreans. Pythagorean Hippasos of Metapontion, according to legend, was the first member to betray the secrecy of the society, most likely by divulging to outside friends the Pythagorean secret that the square root of number 2 is irrational, a discovery which was probably made about 450 B.C. by Hippasos himself. The law of proportions of similar triangles had been one of the most basic mathematical tools of geometric proof for Pythagoreans, perhaps in the proof of the

Pythagorean theorem itself. The law of proportionality of geometric figures required that the corresponding lengths of the sides of the triangular figures be geometrically 'commensurable', which presumed the existence of a common unit of measurement that goes a whole number of times into both lengths being compared. The discovery of the 'incommensurable' lengths in geometry made the use of the method of similar triangles in mathematical proofs in general unacceptable thereby invalidating all deductions based on this method. Therefore, the discovery of the irrational number, which in its geometric interpretation implied incommensurability (since Pythagoras had identified numbers with geometry in his arithmogeometry), created a logical crisis in the foundation of Greek mathematics. Moreover, this discovery also overthrew the Pythagorean physical doctrine which held that all phenomena in the universe can be expressed by relations of whole numbers. This crisis in the foundations of Greek mathematics was finally resolved in 370 B.C. by Eudoxos of Knidos, an exceptionally brilliant mathematician of antiquity.

The Milesian natural philosophers had taken it for granted that the world of perception undergoes changes which are not illusions, but soon some philosophers began to question the trustworthiness of man's senses, whilst others questioned the reliability of man's reason. Do the appearances of change as perceived by man correspond to the underlying physical reality? Is the so-called commonsense a completely reliable guide to man? In order to examine these fundamental questions critically, the ancient Greeks had to study epistemology, the foundation of knowledge, as well as the means of knowledge, that is: 'how does man know that he knows'. The first ancient Greek philosophers who posed such questions were Herakleitos and Parmenides.

Herakleitos of Ephesos and Universal Law of Change:

Herakleitos of Ephesos, Ionia, united the Ionian monomaterialism with Pythagorean idea of harmony. His thoughts on natural philosophy were contained in his great book < On the Whole> (***Peri tu pantos***) which he wrote in an intentionally obscure style as possible before 484 B.C. and deposited in the Temple of Artemis (***Artemiseion***). On account of his obscurant literary style, he was called Herakleitos 'the Dark One' (***ho skoteinos***). Herakleitos came to the conclusion that reality is forever changing and, therefore, unstable. He, thus, came to consider the change in substance itself as fundamental to nature, and since everything including change was considered substantial, he thought 'fire', being the least consistent and most readily changeable of all substances known to the Ionian Greeks, to be the 'primary stuff'. Therefore, according to Herakleitos the 'changing phenomena' itself is the essence of nature: everything flows (***panta rhei***), that is, everything is a flux, a process like energy in motion.

Herakleitos thought strife to be the motive principle behind the process of change and the very source of the world: "Strife is the father of all things (***polemos patir panton***)." The changes produced by strife were 'transformations according to a measure which had definite bounds', thus implying that any change is confined within certain limits which provides the balance between interacting things. Yet, according to him, there exists an underlying 'harmony of the opposites', a Pythagorean principle, in strife. He advanced the idea that strife is the principle that keeps the world alive. Behind the strife between the opposites according to the measure, there lies a 'hidden harmony' which is not apparent to man, because "nature loves to hide (***physis kryptesthai philei***)." Therefore, Herakleitos recognised the existence of the universal law (***nomos***) which governs the 'scope of all changes' in the natural world.

He warned against the belief that the entire corpus of man's knowledge is obtained by senses: "Eyes and ears are bad witnesses if the mind cannot interpret what they say," meaning that evidence of the senses has to be processed by the mind with great care. He also warned that: "Learning of many things does not teach understanding ...." Moreover, Herakleitos made an astute observation about man that is worthy of the attention of any man: "Character is man's destiny." He made another profound observation about human nature and human affairs when he wrote: "Though it changes, it stands still (***metaballon anapauetai***)," which was expressed in A.D. 1849 in the well-known popular form by the French entertainer Alphonse Karr (A.D. 1808-1890): "The more things change, the more they remain the same (***Plus ça change, plus c'est la même chose***)."

Herakleitos was invited by Darios, the King of Persia, to come to Persian court and give the 'King of kings' explanations of the book ***Peri tu pantos*** which Darios found difficult to understand, but Herakleitos declined the invitation.

Parmenides of Elea and Rigorous Deductive Logic:

Parmenides of Elea (born c.540 B.C.), was much admired throughout the Greek world for the constitution he wrote for the city-State Elea. He made important contributions to geometry by classifying geometric figures, and to astronomy by identifying the morning and the evening star as one and the same planet. He also marked out on the globe the 5 zones into which it is divided by the tropics and the arctic circle. He was the first Pythagorean to teach the sphericity of the Earth, that the rest of celestial bodies rotate on hollow spherical shells about the Earth and that the Moon shines by reflected light.

He wrote a cryptic and oracular style poem < On Nature > (***Peri physeos***) which was the first philosophical text in the modern sense by revealing the power of thought, the power of logical implication, which he had invented, and the law of contradiction which had been devised earlier. He was the first to insist that any theory in natural philosophy devised by man must above all be logically consistent. He was primarily concerned with finding the truth behind physical appearances by intellectual means using logically rigorous arguments, and not by the senses which he considered unreliable.

In the opinion of Parmenides: "Thinking and Being are the same thing," which is why he believed in the power of reason. His reasoning was based on the dual ontological notion of Being and Non-Being, in which Being meant existence: 'What is' exists, and 'What is not' cannot exist. In other words, what is inconceivable is impossible. Therefore, the Void (***kenon***) as a Non-Being cannot exist. Parmenides is the founder of the Eleatic school of logic which had a great influence on ancient Greek thought.

He demonstrated that there is something fundamentally wrong with the Ionian rationalistic concept of monomaterialism as the identity persisting through change be it 'water', 'air', 'earth' or 'fire' because such a single, homogeneous substance actually makes the change impossible since it could do nothing but remain single and homogeneous unless the change involves coming into being of something out of nothing, which is impossible. He asserted that it was more reasonable to assume that creation as producing something out of nothing, and destruction as producing nothing out of something, were impossible. He concluded that by applying strict logic to monomaterialism, change is only an illusion, and that the world must really be a solid homogenous sphere.

Parmenides reached this paradoxical conclusion which contradicts experience by rigorous deductive logic when applied to the premise of monomaterialism. Xenophanes, his teacher, had been the first to profess the concept of unity 'the One', but Xenophanes declared that 'the One' is God. It appears that in ***sensu stricto*** it was Parmenides who marks the real beginning of the discipline of deductive logic and rational philosophy. The formal natural philosophy of Parmenides, which has been called 'transcendental monism', in the modern context represents a type of linguistic metaphysics. Parmenides called his own theory of natural philosophy an 'opinion' (***doxa***) because it could not be rigorously proven. From the discussion above it is obvious that Parmenides, who asserted that the world does not change, and Herakleitos, who maintained that the world is nothing but change, represent the two extreme opposite views among the ancient Greek thinkers, who were not strictly scientific in their concerns in the modern sense, because they were ultimately interested in the constitution of the cosmos and its laws of nature.

Zenon of Elea and Infinite Processes:

Zenon of Elea (in English, Zeno) (*floruit* c.450 B.C.), a colleague and disciple of Parmenides, defended Parmenides' adverse opinion of Pythagorean idea that space is a set of discrete points and also demonstrated the logical absurdity of the idea that space and time are continuous and infinitely divisible. He constructed several logical arguments dealing with the basic concepts of the One and the Unchangeable, the very foundations of the Eleatic philosophy, and with the fundamental nature of infinite processes involving 'the One' and 'the infinitely Many'. These ingenious logical arguments, popularly known as Zeno's Paradoxes, made it quite apparent that the contemporary concepts of the 'Many' and the 'motion as change of place' were obscure and led ultimately to logical contradictions.

Particularly ingenious were Zenon's arguments in which he showed that summing up an infinity of finite quantities leads to a sum which grows beyond all limits, thereby raising the fundamental issue of convergence and the logical definition of the limit of an infinite process. Zenon's Paradox of Achilles and the Tortoise mathematically involved, for the first time in history, an infinitely decreasing geometric series. He also asked: "How is it possible for a point to pass through an infinite number of positions in a finite time?" Although Zenon was not a mathematician, his arguments concerning the problem of infinitesimals, the infinitely small, the infinitely large, infinite processes and continuity were fatal to these ideas as they were used by Greek mathematicians of the period. Zenon's dialectics began with the premise of his opponent which he then reduced to absurdity by a logical method called 'reduction to absurdity' (***reductio ad absurdum***)', a method of logic devised by Pythagoreans and already used by Parmenides. However, Zenon was the first logician who made systematic use of the ***reductio ad absurdum***. In this way he was able to demonstrate by strict logic that motion is impossible under the assumption of infinite subdivisibility of space and time, and that motion is also impossible if the opposite assumption is made that the subdivisibility of space and time terminates in indivisibles, an assumption made by Pythagoras when he regarded a line to be made up of a definite number of indivisible units as points. These logical paradoxes so clearly demonstrated by Zenon exposed the serious logical difficulties that beset the limiting processes used in ancient Greek mathematics. The effectiveness of Zenon's well-known arguments discouraged the use of the notion of infinitesimal and infinite in the works of ancient Greek mathematicians and, therefore, the idea of the infinite, and even the potentially infinite was altogether banished from the ancient Greek science. Thenceforth, the ancient Greek mathematicians made no further use of magnitudes increasing or decreasing ***ad infinitum*** but rather limited themselves to the consideration of only finite magnitudes which could be made as great or as small as desired.

The indirect influence of the dialectic philosophers such as Zenon, was to increase the logical rigour in mathematical arguments and, thereby, to increase the logical rigour of ancient Greek mathematics. Moreover, Zenon's celebrated paradoxes, which he formulated in his famous debates, also had an influence on natural philosophy as far as the logic of infinite divisibility of space as a continuum as well as the infinite multiplicity of space as a point-continuum were concerned. His arguments raised the difficult but important logical question: How to reconcile the idea of space as an arithmetic, or point-continuum as assumed by Pythagoreans, with space as a geometric continuum that is infinitely divisible as assumed by most ancient Greek mathematicians? Apparently, Zenon did not present his paradoxes to deny reality but rather to refute the logically inconsistent theories about reality. Zenon himself came to a tragic end: apparently, he was a fierce defender of political liberty against a tyrant, who then accused him of treason and tortured him to death.

Melissos of Samos and Conservation of Matter:

Another Eleatic philosopher of note and a contemporary of Zenon, Melissos of Samos, who is known to have been the commander of the Samian forces which defeated an Athenian fleet in a sea battle fought in 441 B.C. near the island of Samos, in his efforts to defend Parmenides' denial of the existence of void realised that then it is not possible to speak of the world as a finite sphere because that would imply that there is something outside of it. Since the void as a Non-Being is ruled out by Eleatic philosophy, Melissos concluded by cleaving to the materialistic view rather than to Parmenides' formal view of the One that the universe has to be regarded as infinite in all directions. Now if there are many things instead of the One Sphere as Parmenides had formally concluded, then each of these things must itself be like the One Sphere of Parmenides. Since nothing can come into being or pass away, the only logically tenable theory which maintains that there are 'Many' rather than 'One' is obtained by breaking the 'One Sphere' of Parmenides into infinitely many little spheres. In this materialistic theory Melissos implied the principle of conservation of matter in the infinite universe, something that had been already tacitly assumed by Empedokles of Akragas, a contemporary Greek philosopher from Sicily. Therefore, things were 'one' in the strictly formal sense of Parmenides and 'infinitely many' in the strictly materialistic sense of Melissos. The amended Eleatic theory of Melissos of Samos inspired Leukippos of Miletos, who was probably a pupil of Zenon, to propose the atomic theory of matter in his attempt to reconcile the concept of 'One' with the concept of 'Many'.

Empedokles of Akragas, Polymaterialism and Principle of Definite Proportions:

The logical criticism of the Eleatic philosophers not only dealt a death blow to the Pythagorean theory of the world as a point-continuum, but it also called into question the monomaterialism of the Ionian philosophers. The first to attempt to meet this challenge was Empedokles of Akragas, Sicily (c.500-c.430 B.C.), apparently a member of a noble family who became an eminent physician of his time, philosopher, scientist, poet, sage, miracle worker and the founder of the Sicilian school of medicine. He travelled throughout Sicily and Peloponnesos teaching and performing miraculous cures. Some people believed him to be a demigod, others a charlatan.

Empedokles, as a physician, correctly assumed that the heart was the center of the blood vessel system and, therefore, the seat of life.

Empedokles proposed a theory of polymaterialism consisting of the 4 substances proposed by the Ionian philosophers: 'water', 'air', 'fire' and 'earth', in an effort to reconcile the immovable One of Parmenides with the changes observed in the material world.

Empedokles followed the Eleatics by considering his 4 elements: 'water', 'air', 'fire' and 'earth', to be eternal and unchanging in themselves, yet capable of combining in different proportions under the influence of 2 opposite types of substantial forces: attraction and repulsion, which he poetically called 'love' (***philotes***) and 'hate' (***neikos***), to produce all things experienced in the material world. Hence, according to Empedokles a certain number of divisions of a body reaches these 4 irreducible constitutive elements, which he said are the 'roots of all things' (***rhizomata panton***), each of which was itself permanent and unchanging. Another important idea introduced by Empedokles was the principle of fixed proportions: different substances are formed by the 4 basic elements when combined in different, but definite proportions. The idea of proportions was not new; it had been used earlier by Pythagoreans in their theory of music. Empedokles, himself, being a physician specified definite proportions to some substances such as flesh, bones, and blood. Empedokles' principle of definite proportions after more than 2 millennia emerged as the celebrated law of definite, or fixed proportions in chemical compounds proposed in A.D. 1799 by the French chemist Joseph Louis Proust (A.D. 1754-1826). Empedokles' theory of the 4 elements which were chemically impure substances is the very first step towards the conception of chemical elements – it represents the first great guiding principle of chemistry. He was the first to introduce the concept of force in the form of dual opposite forces into physical theory, although in his theory these forces themselves had to be substantial. Therefore, in the theory of Empedokles, the Herakleitean changes in the things of the world were produced by these dual forces of nature whilst the total quantity of matter in such changes remained conserved. The principle of conservation of matter in chemical processes was revived by Robert Boyle (A.D. 1627-1691) in A.D. 1661, and Antoine Laurent Lavoisier (A.D. 1743-1794) in A.D. 1775.

Empedokles assumed that Beings are mortal, but their origins are eternal. Human beings, according to him, are produced by the chance aggregation of separate components owing to attraction and only those that have the fittest combinations of elements will ultimately survive, constituting the first statement of the principle of the survival of the fittest. Thus Empedokles, like Anaximandros before him, anticipated the idea of evolution by natural selection.

Empedokles was, moreover, a keen observer and a capable experimenter. He demonstrated by a simple but ingenious experiment with a water vessel (***klepsydra***) that the visually imperceptible air had a perceptible effect on the physical world which he expressed in his own words: "... nature works by unseen bodies." He thus proved the corporeality of the invisible air, which was an important step towards the atomic theory of matter. He called 'air' as substance, ***aither***. He recognised that light takes time to travel [first empirically proved in A.D.1676 by the Danish astronomer Øle Christensen Rømer (A.D. 1644-1710) 21 centuries later], that Moon's light is indirect, and he understood the true cause of Solar eclipse. He believed the Moon to be twice as far from the Sun as from the Earth. The Earth, he thought, is held in place by the rapidly rotating heavens "as the water remains in a goblet which is swung quickly round in a circle," thus insinuating the existence of the centripetal pull acting on the Earth.

Empedokles was the first to use in his speculations the dialectic type arguments consisting of thesis, antithesis, and synthesis. Empedokles was also the first to carry out environmental engineering projects: he drained marshy lands and changed courses of some rivers in his attempt to drive pestilence [malaria] out of the city Selinous and his own city Akragas in Sicily at his own expense. These are the first known instances of collaboration between the medical and the engineering art to improve the environmental conditions for man. It is possible that Empedokles knew that malaria was carried by 'small animals', as was stated much later by the most learned Roman, Marcus Terentius Varro (116-27 B.C.) who is not known to have carried out investigations of his own on this matter. For this important service to the city the citizens of Selinous struck a medal in his honour. Empedokles had a large cutting made in the hill near his home city, Akragas, at his own expense to improve the circulation of air in the city. About 480 B.C., engineer Phaiax had constructed an elaborate system of water mains and tanks to supply the citizens of Akragas with fresh water from the sources nearby.

Empedokles wrote 3 influential poetic works: < On Nature > (***Peri physeos***) in 3 books, < The Purification > (***Katharmoi***), and a poem on medicine (***iatrikos***) containing religious, cosmological, medical and biological ideas, and his doctrine of natural philosophy.

The poems of Empedokles were later imitated by the noted Roman poet who was the foremost promoter of atomism and materialism, Titus Lucretius Carus (c.98-55 B.C.), popularly known as Lucretius, in his celebrated and influential poem < On the Nature of Things > (***De rerum natura***). He was the first author known to express the idea of progress, but only in morality, in contrast to all other ancient Greek and Roman authors who remained cleaved to the idea of a 'golden age' at the beginning of man followed by a gradual decadence, and to give the first clear statement of the 'law of the three ages': Stone, Bronze, and Iron.

Anaxagoras of Klazomenai and Centrifugal Force:

The last Ionian natural philosopher, Anaxagoras of Klazomenai (c.500-428 B.C.),was a son of a wealthy man and a disciple of Anaximenes of Miletos. When Anaxagoras was about 40 years of age he went to Athens where he taught natural philosophy and mathematics nearly 30 years. Among his pupils were some of the most prominent men of his time: Perikles, dramaturge Euripides, historian Thoukideides, Empedokles, and probably also Sokrates. Anaxagoras was very successful as a teacher, and his book < On Nature > (***Peri Physeos***) which was sold for a few drachmas at the temple called ***Hephasteion*** near the central square (***agora***) in Athens became a bestseller. He was imprisoned about 434 B.C. on the charge of having been a Persian sympathiser in his youth, and was tried and banished for impiety in expressing his opinion that the heavenly bodies were not divine, but rather large flaming rocks, thereby, as was charged, "frittering away the deities into unnecessary causes and blind forces." These charges were probably trumped up by the political enemies of his friend Perikles, who under the influence of his Ionian mistress Aspasia, another pupil of Anaxagoras, attempted to bring the more tolerant Ionian way of life to Athens and, thus, make the city more democratic. Some Athenians apparently had tried to ridicule Anaxagoras by giving him the nickname 'the Mind (***ho nous***)', yet his erudite teaching and impressive personality had exerted important influence on the Athenian life, and during his stay in the city, Athens had become the leading philosophical center of the ancient Greek world. Evidently natural philosophy had spread from Ionia first to Greek colonies in southern Italian peninsula (***he megale Hellas***) and only then to Athens and, thus, to Greece proper.

Anaxagoras was released from prison, probably with the help of Perikles, and settled in the city-State Lampsakos where he taught until his death a few years later. In contrast to the hostile treatment he had received in Athens, the day of his death in Lampsakos was commemorated by a holiday.

Anaxagoras proposed his natural philosophy which represented a particular compromise between the Ionian monomaterialism and Pythagorean pluralism by hypothesising that the entire universe and all of its parts, however small, are homogeneous in constitution and differ only in size and arrangement of its constitutive parts. He abandoned the idea that changes in the universe are caused by the natural physical properties of the matter itself. He also denied the possibility of stuff coming into being or passing from existence in the universe. In his opinion the formation of things is due to composition (***symmisgesthai***) and decomposition (***diakrinesthai***) of countless 'seeds' (***spermata***) representing a physical change directed by an external active organising power, ***nous***, meaning intelligence, or mind, or will, or reason. In his view things differ according to how these minuscule seeds group themselves under the organising power, ***nous***, into the position they ultimately occupy in the things formed. This view of Anaxagoras represented the discovery of the importance of form (***eidos***), that is, the importance of constitutive arrangement of component parts of things in nature. Thus, according to Anaxagoras anything divided up into its smallest parts does not yield the 'roots' (or elements) of Empedokles but rather the 'seeds'. His theory, called

panspermia, implied that everything contains seeds of everything else. In contrast to Empedokles, the seeds are neither elements nor atoms, but instead infinitely divisible parts which do not lose their character. The mind (***nous***) is not clearly defined by Anaxagoras: it could be interpreted to be either a physical or a spiritual force. However, in his opinion, it is the ruling principle of the universe: "Reason (***nous***) rules the world." He insisted on the infinite divisibility of matter: cutting things into smaller and smaller pieces does not produce a different material, which agrees with the notion of Parmenides that 'What is' cannot in anyway cease to be, or become what it is not. Anaxagoras' idea of infinite divisibility turned out to be inappropriate for matter, but eminently applicable to space. Anaxagoras wrote: "... in everything there is a portion of everything except ***nous***, and there are some things in which there is also ***nous***." ***Nous***, the external intelligence or rational will, is his active principle or force which replaced Empedokles' dual forces inherent in the matter, and it is ***nous*** which sets things into motion. Possession of ***nous*** sets apart the animate from the inanimate. Anaxagoras seems to have struggled to make ***nous*** an insubstantial agent or power, and to conceive of empty space, but apparently in this effort he did not entirely succeed. Since his theory was widely adopted, it influenced the ancient Greek mind to turn towards metaphysics rather than towards physics. Anaxagoras made a basic contribution to biology by proposing his principle, still current, that perception is a sensation which depends upon contrasts. He made new advances in the accurate knowledge of anatomy by dissecting animals and obtaining insight into the physiology of the brain.

In the study of planetary motion in his cosmogony, Anaxagoras introduced the concept of centrifugal force when he wrote: "... the Sun and Moon and all the stars are flaming rocks which are carried round by the revolution of the ***aither***" in an apparent analogy with a whirling sling. Anaxagoras taught that the Moon and the stars are all 'heavy' and would fall on the Earth if they were not prevented from doing so by the centrifugal force imposed on them by their rotation about the Earth, a concept revived again in A.D. 1609 by Johann Kepler (A.D. 1571-1630) with respect to the Moon and then again by Isaac Newton (A.D. 1642-1727). Anaxagoras, and not Demokritos of Abdera, was the first to state that the Milky Way is the light of many stars. Moreover, Anaxagoras also recognised that air is 'heavy' and, therefore, has weight.

During his imprisonment in Athens, Anaxagoras solved the problem of the quadrature of the circle by means of a geometric construction, but it is not known whether he regarded his solution to be an approximation. He came to the conclusion that in the small there does not exist the 'smallest' but merely the 'smaller', and that in the large there does not exist the 'largest' but merely the 'larger'. It appears that in the mathematical investigations of Anaxagoras lies the very beginning of systematic mathematical science.

The painter Agatharchos of Samos (born c.490 B.C.), who designed stage sets for the tragedies of the premier Athenian dramaturge Aischylos of Athens performed at the festival of

Dyonysios in Athens, was the first to use perspective on a large scale in his scenography (***skenographia***) in order to create illusions of space on a plane. He wrote a technical commentary on his method of scenography on a plane which gave an impression of depth. Then Anaxagoras wrote a tractate on the geometry of perspective (***aktinographia***) in which he solved the perspective problem in the art of scenography by introducing the vanishing point of perspective with a point of sight, and making systematic use of the perspective rays. His interest in the geometric design of stage scenery had been aroused by his pupil, the dramaturge Euripides. Demokritos, who was influenced by Anaxagoras, also wrote a memoir on the geometrical theory of perspective. Although the foreshortening was perfectly understood by Agatharchos, Anaxagoras and Demokritos, the linear perspective always remained partial, even as late as during the Mediæval Age. Instead of one vanishing point to which all parallel receding lines converge, several vanishing points were used with different points of sight so that the space in the picture was never presented as unity, that is, it was never viewed from the single point of sight.

The artist Apollodoros (*floruit* c. 430-400 B.C), who was called the 'shadow painter' because he imitated in his paintings form by shading and colour (called ***skiagraphia***). He was the first painter to give his painted figures the appearance of reality by using linear perspective and shadows, and mixed colours instead of pure colours which were his primary inventions in painting.

Leukippos of Miletos, Atoms and Infinite Void:

A student of Zenon, Leukippos of Miletos, (a contemporary of Empedokles and Anaxagoras, born about 490 B.C.) finally proposed a theory of matter which represented a compromise between the One and the Many, and has lasted in a more sophisticated form till modern times. Leukippos postulated the real existence of an infinite number of atoms which he called 'seeds,' and the infinite void (***kenon***) or space. All atoms (***atomos*** - indivisible) shared with the spheres of Melissos the property that they were solid, rigid, indivisible, indestructible, and so small that they were invisible like the air of Anaximenes. He regarded the void divisible without limit, but, the division of material ultimately terminated in material indivisibles, the atoms. Atoms, which among themselves differed only in their geometric shape (***schema***), were all of the same composition like the 'seeds' of Anaxagoras, and in a state of motion in empty space, the void. In Leukippos' opinion, the ever-changing aspect of the world as stressed by Herakleitos arises from the rearrangement of the atoms, which are in a perpetual state of motion in space. Leukippos set down his ideas in his lost treatise, < Macrocosmos > (***Megas diakosmos***). The atomic theory of matter devised by Leukippos made the primary stuff that things are made of not directly sensible, but rather inferentially accessible to man by his sensory perception. One of the aims of the atomist Leukippos was to seek to overcome the Eleatic criticism which denied the existence of movement, by assigning to the infinite void which contained an infinite number of invisible atoms in an eternal state of motion, a real existence, or Being.

Demokritos of Abdera and Atomic Theory:

The atomic theory of Leukippos was developed into a consistent and comprehensive system by his pupil Demokritos of Abdera, who was an important intellectual figure in ancient Greek world as well as a world traveler and author in all intellectual and literary disciplines of his time, and the inventor of the word 'atom'. In fact, Demokritos can be considered to have been the first encyclopædist of ancient times which is why he was nicknamed the 'Wise Man' (***sophistes***). In the atomic theory of matter Leukippos and Demokritos resorted to the earlier views of Anaximandros by postulating the existence of a more fundamental substance, yet, at the same time, they were able to meet the Eleatic criticism by following the notion of Melissos in incorporating into the atomic theory of matter the concept of changeless, indivisible material particles, the atoms, which are infinite in number and in an eternal state of motion within the infinite empty space. This theory of matter represented the only viable compromise between the commonsense and the logical criticism of Eleatics of the earlier monistic material doctrines of the Milesian natural philosophers. In addition, the atomic theory of matter conformed to the logical structure of causal explanation. It was Leukippos who first announced the law of causality, or the rule of cause-and-effect in nature, which asserts that every natural event has a natural cause, in the following words: "Nothing happens at random, everything happens out of reason (***logos***) and necessity (***ananke***)." The law of causality in particular was carefully upheld by the ancient Greek physicians in whose medical profession the scientific theory and medical practice could never be completely separated. Since according to atomists, man experiences the world in a variety of ways, but never directly as atoms themselves, atomic theory of matter gave rise to the distinction between primary and secondary qualities of matter. In his analysis Demokritos applied his own scientific method which was adequate for his purposes, and by using Anaxagoras' idea of forms he postulated that the atoms (***atomoi***) were distinguished from one another solely by their form (***eidos***), and by their varying subtlety. Demokritos assumed that since all atoms have weight the larger atoms fall faster than the smaller ones, and thus the larger atoms will catch up with the smaller atoms, collide with them and cause the required deflexion from the original direction of their movement. Therefore, owing to the deflexion the atoms move in whirlwinds and unite in various ways by attaching mechanically to one another in order to produce things He presumed that there are many worlds: some in the process of formation, some in the state of actual existence, and still others in the process of disintegration. He maintained that material properties are dependent upon the form and on the degree of subtlety of the atoms constituting the material. Everything in this world, even the soul of man, according to

Demokritos, is composed of atoms. Thus, in his more developed view motion became primarily local motion (***phora***), and the location (***topos***) of the atoms was accomplished by introducing the 'void', a traditional Non-Being in Eleatic philosophy, as a necessary Being, the Spatial Being, containing atoms. This atom-space concept did mitigate the Eleatic problem of Being and Non-Being, but it did not completely resolve it, although it was the last attempt in antiquity to eliminate this question within the compass of Parmenides' concept of Entity. The atomic theory of Demokritos represents the first formal attempt to establish a comprehensive theory of materialism encompassing all aspects of nature including human nature: "Nothing exists but atoms and void." Demokritos, an approximate contemporary of Sokrates, was the last pre-Sokratic philosopher, who still followed the tradition of the Ionian philosophers by being concerned with the Eleatic philosophy of Being and with physical world in which he proposed astoundingly modern ideas.

Demokritos proposed his materialist doctrine of perception which assumed that any object emits a sort of spectre in the form of a subtle image (***eidolon***) which consists of finer atoms that penetrate the sense organ to give the mind a replica of this object. His doctrine, which was sensationalist in principle, taught that all knowledge consists of such mental images.

Demokritos established a school in Abdera where he taught his physical science and all the other subjects in which he excelled.

The atomic theory of matter after Demokritos was saved from oblivion by the Greek philosopher Epikouros of Samos (342-268 B.C.) who established his famous school in Athens where his well-known doctrine of living for nonhedonistic pleasure was taught. The Roman poet Titus Lucretius Carus, popularly known as Lucretius, the last eminent promoter of materialism and Epikourian atomic theory in antiquity stated in his poem < On the Nature of Things > (***De rerum natura***): "So the atoms in spite of their unequal masses, must move in empty space with equal velocities," a strikingly modern idea which differed from that of Demokritos. He had in his poem also the simplest statement of the doctrine of conservation of matter and momentum. The didactic poem of Lucretius was intended not merely to teach but also to convert.

Summary

The development of physical theory among ancient Greeks was based on materialism. Thales advanced the rationalistic idea of monomaterialism in his hypothesis that all things are made of one basic stuff, 'water'. His friend and pupil, Anaximandros assumed it to be a subtler stuff, called ***apeiron***, which is not directly apparent to man. Anaximandros' pupil, Anaximenes considered the basic stuff to be 'air' which is also subtle but more tangible to man than ***apeiron***. Pythagoras assumed the world to be made of 'numbers' which had physical existence and were subject to the laws of harmony. Herakleitos took from Anaximandros the theory of strife acting within the ***apeiron*** to form material objects, and from Pythagoras the idea of harmony by maintaining that the world is essentially a process, a state of flux, where changes take place according to a set of measures or proportions, which makes harmony to underlie what superficially looks like strife. The basic stuff for Herakleitos was 'fire' which represented this highly combustible state of change. Parmenides gave a completely opposite view. He accepted monomaterialism and by applying strict logic, he came to the conclusion that nothing moves: the world is a uniform solid sphere. Parmenides concluded: "Being is, Non-Being is not." In other words, if all things are made of some basic stuff, there cannot be a thing called empty space, or what is not. This then was the logical conclusion of the basic-stuff theory, the monist theory. Parmenides' criticism convincingly demonstrated that monomaterialism as a logical theory of materialism will not work. It clearly indicated that the notion of empty space was necessary to allow motion. Empedokles tried to respond to Parmenides' logical criticism by introducing 4 basic stuffs: 'water', 'air', 'fire' and 'earth' which combine and separate by means of the material principle of attraction and repulsion, but the mere multiplication of basic stuff did not really help the fundamental problem. Anaxagoras improved somewhat the situation by introducing infinite divisibility which, however, does not apply to matter, but is an acceptable property of space. Finally Leukippos and, particularly, Demokritos introduced the atomic theory, by adopting Parmenides' basic stuff but breaking up his solid sphere into small parts as suggested by Melissos, and letting these small, invisible, indivisible parts called 'atoms' have various geometric shapes. Borrowing from Herakleitos the theory of perpetual motion, Leukippos and Demokritos explained all changes in this world to be the result of motions of an infinite number of changeless atoms in infinite empty void, a space which they assumed to exist. In their atomic theory the qualities of things were due to the geometry of atoms themselves and their geometric arrangement, since all their atoms were made of the same basic stuff.

In conclusion of the discussion of the pre-Sokratic natural philosophy it is important to point out that the ancient Greek scientists from Thales to Anaxagoras were not so badly misguided in their scientific speculation as modern man may think. If 'air', 'water', 'earth' and 'fire' were considered from the modern viewpoint to represent respectively gases, liquids, solids and energy, then the viewpoint of Anaximenes is not so strange when it is realised that gases can be condensed into liquids if cooled, and to solids if cooled further. The modern concept of energy as an agent and product of chemical changes stands in surprising correspondence with the basic idea of Herakleitos about 'fire'.

Greek Engineering

The Ionian Greeks had an entirely new attitude towards the inventor and the engineer. They considered the engineer to be a benefactor (***evergetes***) of the society and, therefore, technology was a respectable occupation for a man in Ionia. Ancient Greeks who lived next to the barbarians almost venerated engineers, technologists and inventors as popular heroes because they realised that the engineer, the technologist and the inventor were responsible for creating the material essentials of the Greek civilisation.

Diolkos:

In the period from 625 B.C. to 585 B.C., one of the oldest structures in the ancient Greek World, a giant slipway (***diolkos***) for hauling vessels across the Isthmus of Korinthos was constructed to obviate a 450-mile sea voyage for cargo vessels round the Peloponnesian Peninsula. This slipway was 4 miles (6.4 km) long and part of it was paved to 15-foot (4.6 m) width. It had 2 parallel ruts 5 feet (1.5 m) apart in which ran the wheels of the wagon that carried the vessel. On curves the ruts were replaced by low walls to keep the wagons from slipping. The slipway terminated in a causeway that ran into the sea. This slipway represents one of the early instances of a primitive railway. It appears that the ***diolkos*** was built during the rule of Periandros, the tyrant of the city-State Korinthos.

Anacharsis of Scythia, Barbarian Inventor and Philosopher :

About 594 B.C., one of the first well-known inventors in Greece was a Scythian called Anacharsis, who was a disciple and a close friend of the famous Greek statesman Solon of Athens and represented the prototype of a barbarian philosopher. Despite the fact that Anacharsis was a barbarian prince from Scythia [Scythians were ancient warlike nomatic Iranian tribe from Russian steppes], he is the first well-known Greek inventor who for some time resided in Athens. Anacharsis is credited with the invention of the improved potter's wheel which probably consisted of a raised wheelhead and an elevated seat for the potter placed in a position that enabled the potter to rotate the potter's wheel by kicking a disk attached to the axle of the wheel just above the floor. He also invented the grapple-armed anchor which did not drag, bellows with a clapper valve, and an improved lathe. Anacharsis appraised his Greek experience in his letter to King Kroisos (in English, Croesus) of Lydia as follows: "I have no need of money; it is enough for me to return to the Scythians a better man." After his return to Scythia, Anacharsis was killed by his own brother Saulios, King of the Scythians, who shot him dead with an arrow whilst hunting the wild game, probably because Anacharsis tried to introduce Greek customs, mythology, education and Eleusian religious mysteries into Scythian society which was resented by Scythians.

Theodoros of Samos, Casting of Life-Size Bronze Statues and Temple of Artemis in Ephesos:

Theodoros of Samos (*flourished* c.560 B.C.) was renowned as an architectural engineer (***architekton***), sculptor, goldsmith, engraver, and inventor of improved tools: the lathe, the key, the set-square, the level(***diabetes***), and other instruments used in technological practice. He was a skilled engraver of gems who developed a new way of polishing gems; the next comparable fundamental improvement came 2 thousand years later. Theodoros was also an expert metallurgist, a bronze- and brass-founder, who together with his brother Telekles, a sculptor, and his father Rhoikos of Samos, the architectural engineer (***architekton***) who built the Labyrinth in Lemnos, succeeded in improving the Egyptian method of casting life-size bronze statues in two or more parts which were joined together with rivets and reinforced by an iron supporting armature, thereby making ancient Greeks the leaders in the art of bronze (copper and tin alloy) metallurgy in antiquity. The hardest bronze contained about 12% percent tin. Theodoros and his brother Telekles were known to have each sculpted half of a large bronze statue of Apollo (in Greek, ***Apollon***), the Greek god of intellect and prophecy, for the Temple of Apollo. The two sculpted parts were joined together with rivets in a perfect fit to form the huge statue of Apollo. Rhoikos of Samos, and his sons Theodoros and Telekles had studied bronze casting methods in Egypt. Theodoros made brass by the cementation method by using copper, charcoal, and zinc ore called 'calamine' since metallic zinc was virtually unknown in antiquity.

The first modern, and for its time, the largest Greek building constructed between 575 B.C. and 560 B.C., was the Temple of Hera, the queen of the Olympian gods, on the island of Samos. The Temple of Hera, called ***Heraion***, which had a rectangular plan of 171 by 311 feet (52 by 95 m), was built on marshy ground by Rhoikos and his son Theodoros. The temple was surrounded by a double row of 132 limestone columns. The Dorian column, the thickness of which varied depending upon its particular location, was made of a vertical stack of soft-limestone drums the plane faces of which were turned smooth by rubbing on a lathe invented by Theodoros. In 530 B.C. the temple's wooden roof supported by timber architraves was struck by lightning and set ablaze which razed the building down to the ground. Theodoros wrote a commentary on his method of construction of the Temple of Hera, the first known architectural engineering treatise in history which, unfortunately, is lost.

In 550 B.C., the versatile Theodoros of Samos was engaged as the ***architekton*** to undertake the construction of a large temple for the worship of Artemis, called the ***Artemiseion***, in Ephesos, a prosperous commercial Ionian harbour city in Lydia which was the center of the wealthy cult of the Asiatic nature goddess whom Ionian Greeks identified with Artemis, the Greek goddess of wildlife and hunting. This sacred building site was unfortunately a swamp, and its marshy ground in its natural state was unable to provide adequate stable support for the foundations of a massive building such as the large Temple of Artemis. Since Theodoros had previous experience with this type of foundation problem in his engineering practice on the island of Samos, it may have been the compelling reason for hiring him to build the Temple of Artemis in Ephesos that was intended to be even a larger building than the Temple of Hera in Samos. The Temple of Artemis, which had a ground-plan of 180 by 377 feet (55 by 115 m), had to be built on a soft and unstable swampy ground. Theodoros surmounted the marshy foundation problem of the Temple of Artemis by laying a cedarwood raft covered with sheepskins on a bed of clay spread over the marshy ground upon which he built the stylobate of limestone that supported the columns of the huge temple. It was the earliest known raft-foundation of any building and the success of Theodoros' solution of the foundation problem is demonstrated by the negligible settlement of his raft-foundation on the swampy ground over the many centuries of its existence despite the fact that it had to support later even the more massive and grandiose 4th century Temple of Artemis built by the Macedonian ***architekton*** Deinokrates of Rhodos as the replacement for the original temple that was burnt down in 356 B.C., the very night when Alexandros III was born in Macedon, by a youthful pyromaniac Herostratos of Ephesos in his desperate attempt to obtain immortality by this sacrilegious arson. The worshipers of goddess Artemis believed that the nature goddess was absent from her temple in the night of the arson because she was attending the birth of Alexandros who was destined to become world famous as the incomparable military genius and empire-builder Alexandros III (alias Alexander the Great). It appears that the grown-up Alexandros believed the myth of goddess Artemis attending his birth, because he helped to pay for the rebuilding of the burnt down Temple Artemis as soon as he had obtained supreme power through his military conquests.

As far as is known Theodoros did no further work on the Temple of Artemis after the construction of its raft-foundation. It appears that Theodoros of Samos was not responsible for the final design of the huge Temple of Artemis in Ephesos which introduced the new architectural style in temple building. The roof of this temple was supported by columns of a novel architectural design, the so-called Ionian columns, the proportions of which were based on the proportions of the slender female figure, and not on the proportions of the male figure which had been the basis for column proportions of the traditional Dorian style. The Ionian column had the thickness-to-height proportion of one-to-eight, the architectural design of which was based on the proportion of the size of the footprint of a slender female figure to her height, in contrast to the proportion of 1-to-6 used in the Dorian column, the architectural design of which was based on the proportion of the size of the footprint of a male figure to his height. The capital of the Ionian column had the form of a scroll overhanging the column in two spiral volutes in an imitation of the curly locks of hair of women, and the decorative fluting in the Ionian column imitated the drapery of the garment of a married Ionian woman. The fabulously wealthy King Kroisos of Lydia lavishly financed the building of the Temple of Artemis, in particular the decorative art of the temple such as the relief carvings on the lower part of the Ionian columns, pediments and friezes, in gratitude for the generous financial credit the priests of the wealthy cult of Artemis had granted to Kroisos in the past. It established the ancient Greek tradition of associating architecture with the plastic art of sculpture and mural painting. All ancient Greek marble statues were brightly painted to look lifelike, in contrast to the modern marble statues which are left unpainted in their natural corpselike pallor.

Chersiphron and Metagenes of Knossos, and Construction Method of Temple of Artemis:

The design of the Temple of Artemis in a completely new architectural style was probably the work of the Greek ***architekton*** from the island of Kreta (modern Crete), Chersiphron of Knossos, who had extensive knowledge of temple architecture obtained from his studies of the design and construction of Egyptian temples. Chersiphron was engaged to render assistance to Theodoros in the execution of the huge temple project, but it seems that Chersiphron was not only responsible for the final architectural design but also for the building of the Temple of Artemis after the construction of the raft-foundation of the temple had been completed. In his method of construction of the temple, Chersiphron devised an ingenious means of moving the huge marble columns 7 miles (11 km) over the soft and swampy soil from the quarry to the building site of the Temple of Artemis. He fitted the roughly hewn marble columns with a wooden frame and pivots, harnessed oxen to it and then transported the marble columns like huge lawn-rollers over the treacherously soft ground to the building site. Chersiphron's son, Metagenes, who was his father's assistant, adopted his father's method of transportation of marble columns to the transportation of huge rectangular marble architraves of the temple which had lengths up to 29.53 feet (9 m) and weighed up to 40 tons. Chersiphron of Knossos was also known for the first structural use of hydraulic cement by mixing pulverised trass from the Island of Thira [now Santorini, a Minoan island which exploded in a violent volcanic eruption about 1628 B.C.] with lime. This volcanic ash, called trass, is now known as the 'Santorini earth'.

The Temple of Artemis had 127 columns of 41-foot (12 m) height, and up to 6-feet (1.8 m) in thickness depending upon the location of the column. The temple was lined on three sides with a double row of columns, whereas the front of the temple had a triple row of columns the lower parts of which were sculptured in relief. The columns, except the ones in front of the temple, were carved from a single block of marble. The entire structure, which incorporated a wooden staircase, was built of expensive white marble and it took 50 years to complete the building. Chersiphron died before the construction of the huge Temple of Artemis was finished. His son Metagenes, ***architekton*** Demetrios of Ephesos and ***architekton*** Paionios of Miletos ultimately finished the temple.

Chersiphron and his son Metagenes had found time in their busy architectural engineering practice to write a detailed commentary on the design and construction of temples in which their methods of construction were described. Their treatise on the art of architectural engineering of temple buildings remained in use for 5 centuries.

Glaukos of Chios and Welding of Iron:

About this time Glaukos of Chios invented an improved method of welding iron (***sideru kollesis***) in metal work: joining one piece of iron to another by heating the 2 pieces of iron to red heat and then hammering them into fusion on the anvil. Ancient Greeks learnt to produce brass by 'cementation' of copper bars through a process of heating them in a bed of charcoal and powdered zinc ore. It appears likely that this process of smelting was originated in the Anatolian mountains in the first millennium B.C..

Eupalinos and Water Supply System of Samos:

About 525 B.C., Eupalinos of Megara, the first European mining engineer known by name, built a water supply system on the island of Samos, to serve the fortified city of Samos. He drove a tunnel, which contained a water conduit, through a limestone mountain, now known as Mount Kastro, that is 886 feet (270 m) high, without the benefit of vertical shafts. The length of the tunnel is 3,291 feet (1003.09 m), the width 5½ feet (1.68 m), and the height over 6 feet (1.83 m). Near the village of Agiades, at the well end of the tunnel, he excavated a triangular reservoir in which 14 columns supported the earth-covered roof. Elsewhere along the qanaat there were 11 and 22 vertical shafts sunk from the ground level to the water tunnel. Eupalinos made some surveying errors in the layout of his tunnel axis: alignment error was 20 feet (6.10 m) and grade error was 3 feet (0.91 m). It was the first surveyed tunnel ever driven through the mountain without intervening shafts, a method used 2,400 years later to drive 3 long railroad tunnels through the Alps in Europe.

The trench for the water pipe varied from 3 feet (0.91 m) at the intake of the tunnel to 31 feet (9.45 m) deep at the outlet of the tunnel, which produced a grade of 1–to–180, that is, much too steep for water conduction. It would have been better for Eupalinos to lay the pipeline in the bottom of the tunnel after the breakthrough had been corrected since it had a grade of 1-to-570 which is much more suitable and close to the later good Roman grade practice of 1-to-600. The tunnel was joined by qanaats at its northern and southern portals respectively. The northern qanaat, driven from 22 shafts along the ravine of a small winding stream, was 2,790 feet (850.4 m) long and ended in the northern portal of the tunnel; the southern qanaat was driven from 11 shafts. Eupalinos' tunnel is the oldest and best preserved classical engineering structure still extant.

One of the earliest known vaults constructed by ancient Greeks was on the island of Samos. It supported a heavy stone wall near the sea. Other circular arches have been found in the city walls of the city-State of Knidos. The city of Samos had the first and the most substantial harbour structure of ancient Greeks. It had a stout breakwater, or jetty, that was more than 900 feet (274.32 m) long and scaled a depth of 120 feet (36.57 m).

Hippodamos of Miletos and City Planning:

Sometime after 493 B.C., Themistokles, the new leader of Athens, invited Hippodamos of Miletos, an eccentric Pythagorean ***architekton*** and a fop who is the founder of modern functional city-planning, to plan the city of Peiraieus, located about 6 miles (9.7 km) from Athens, as the outport of Athens. Hippodamos had fled his native city about 494 B.C., after the Miletian revolt failed against Persian domination in 494 B.C.. Hippodamos planned the city on a gridiron scheme in which the physical city plan is integrated with the city's political, physical and social functions into a harmonious whole. Previously gridiron-type towns had been built in Mesopotamia, at the Indus river and in Egypt, but they were not functionally planned. Hippodamos' main innovation was the concept of a master-plan for the city which integrated the physical, social, hygienic and æsthetic factors of the city life into a geometric plan. He had developed a political and physical theory of an integrated and functional city in which the market place (***agora***) was the functional, that is, the political and social hub of the city. In the physical planning of the city, Hippodamos consistently applied geometric principles.

Hippodamos had the old Peiraieus port fortified with walls, and connected to Athens (in Greek, ***Athenai***) with defensive walls. These walls were so hastily constructed that their foundations contained even old tombstones. The superstructures of the northern Peraic wall and the southern Phaleronic wall which enclosed the Bay of Phaleron were made of clay tiles. Athenian government granted Hippodamos a house in Peiraieus where he did his planning, and where he lived until 443 B.C..

Hippodamos apparently worked intermittently on the planning of Peiraieus over a few decades, during which period the Greeks had to defeat two Persian invasions, in 490 B.C. and 480 B.C.. After the decisive defeat of the Persian King Xerxes in 479 B.C., Hippodamos spent a number of years replanning his native city Miletos which had suffered partial destruction in the war with Persia.

In 443 B.C., Hippodamos published a utopian tract on a perfect city-State based on an ideal constitution, in which he proposed means to protect the inventor's right. His ideal city was a garden-city composed of 10,000 citizens who were divided into three classes : artisans, husbandmen and armed defenders of the city-State. The land was also divided into three parts: sacred, public and private lands. Laws were similarly divided into three classes, that is, into 3 subjects of lawsuits: insult, injury, and homicide. By virtue of this tract, which is now lost, Hippodamos became the important forerunner of Plato in political theory. Apparently, Hippodamos left Peiraieus in 443 B.C.

to plan the model city Thurii, a new colonial city of Athens at the Gulf of Taras in southern Italy, and possibly other Greek cities as well.

Akropolis of Athens and Its Builders

Kallikrates, Iktinos, Mnesikles and Pheidias:

From 460 B.C. to 456 B.C., the new leader of Athens, Kimon, a successful general, assigned ***architekton*** Kallikrates to build 2 long defensive walls, the so-called 'Long Walls' about 654 feet (199.34 m) apart, from Athens to Peiraieus over a distance of about 6 miles (9.7 km). The Long Walls were from10 to 12 feet (3.05 to 3.66 m) thick and filled with earth and rubble. These walls were fortified with 20 by 20 feet (6.1 by 6.1 m) towers spaced from 160 feet to 198 feet (48.77 to 60.35 m) apart.

In 440 B.C. Perikles, the new leader of Athens, replaced Kallikrates in 450 B.C. with Iktinos as the ***architekton***, whose chief assistant was Karpion, to be in charge of building 'the city on top of the hill' in Athens called the '***Akropolis***'. Iktinos designed the ***Parthenon*** (meaning, maiden's chamber), a temple of the maiden goddess Athena, which had a floor-plan of 101 by 228 feet (30.78 m by 69.49 m). In the building of Parthenon he used clever architectural devices to correct optical illusions: entasis of the columns which lean slightly inwards, battered walls, thicker corner columns, and horizontal entasis of the stylobate all of which were in a subtle architectural harmony. The method of Theodoros of Samos was used in preparing the cylindrical sections of the columns by turning the column drums on a lathe to a perfect fit through rubbing action. Since this structure projected over the knoll on the southern side, it had to be supported by a 40-foot (12.2 m) retaining wall as a substructure.

The structure of Parthenon was erected from 447 B.C. to 438 B.C., but the sculptor Pheidias of Athens (490-432 B.C.),one of the greatest sculptors of all time whom Perikles had made responsible for the general direction and design of all the artistic enterprise on the ***Akropolis***, decorated it until 432 B.C.. Pheidias cast a 30-foot (9 m) giant bronze statue of ***Athena Polias*** (that is, Athena of the City),later called ***Athena Promachos*** (that is, Athena, the Foremost Fighter), which he erected about a 100 feet (30.5 m) to the left of the Parthenon. Athena's statue, the ***Palladion,*** was supposed to protect the city that possessed it. Pheidias spent 5 years in creating the colossal 40-foot (12.2 m) statue of ***Athena Parthenos*** (that is, Athena the Maiden) which he erected in the main sacred hall of the Parthenon. The gigantic statue of Athena had a skin of ivory, an ivory image of Medusa on her breast, glistening jewel eyes, a golden helmet crowned with griffons, armour and garment of pure gold all attached to a wooden core. In her right hand was a golden statuette of Nike, or Victory, a spear leaning on her left shoulder, and her left hand holding the shield on which was not only a coiled snake with shining eyes of precious stones, but also the facial images of Pheidias himself and Perikles cleverly carved into the reliefs of two warriors on the shield. Parthenon had two halls: the main sacred hall and the secondary treasure hall. In the main sacred hall stood the enormous statue of Athena. In the treasure hall were housed all the other treasures of the temple which included the silver-footed throne of the Persian King Xerxes from which he had watched in 480 B.C. the disastrous defeat of the Persian fleet in the Sea Battle of Salamis. Athena, or Pallas Athena, was one of the most important Olympian deities who had many responsibilities: she was the goddess of war, industry and arts, the protectress of civilised life, the defender of righteous causes, the goddess of wisdom, and the patroness of Athens.

Moreover, Pheidias was also responsible for creating the 45-foot (13.7 m) high gigantic statue of the chief god Zeus sitting on his throne in the Temple of Zeus at Olympia. The colossal statue of Zeus had ivory skin, eyes of sparkling jewels, golden garments, and he held in his right hand the golden statuette of Nike, or Victory, and the golden sceptre in his left hand. It took Pheidias 7 years to create the gigantic statue of Zeus.

The religious power of Pheidias' gigantic statue of the maiden goddess Athena did not manifest itself in any magical spell it cast, but rather in the mesmerising effect of her superhuman beauty and dignity that created a new conception of the divine. The serene and restrained Attic school of sculpture as represented by Pheidias was founded by sculptor Ageladas of Argos who had 3 famous apprentice sculptors from Athens: Pheidias, Myron, and Polykleitos. Polykleitos worked out in his treatise on sculpture a canon of sculpture, a mathematical system of proportions for the human figure which proportioned all individual parts of the human body to one another in a definition of human beauty.

When Pheidias returned to Athens he was accused by Perikles' political enemies of stealing some of the gold for the statue of Athena, which Pheidias was able to disprove by weighing all the removable gold plates used in the Athena's statue. Then he was accused of having committed the sacrilege of carving facial images of himself and Perikles upon the figures of 2 warriors on the shield of goddess Athena. Pheidias was reportedly thrown into prison where he soon died.

Parthenon of Iktinos was a larger reconstruction of the first partially constructed Parthenon built by Kallikrates, who had been appointed ***architekton*** by Kimon (died 450 B.C.), the predecessor and a bitter rival of Perikles.

From 429 B.C. to 426 B.C., after the death of Perikles when Kimon's aristocratic party had resumed control of Athens under the new leadership of Kleon, Kallikrates built the small Temple of Athena-Nike on the Akropolis, which was dedicated to the 'Wingless Victory'.

From 420 B.C. to 393 B.C. Mnesikles erected Propylaia, the Ceremonial Gateway to Akropolis, which was built in two different architectural styles: Mnesikles designed the exterior of this building in Doric style but the interior in Ionic style. This structure incorporated wrought-iron beams of square cross-section encased in 6-foot (1.83 m) long cantilever marble lintels, which supported 6½ ton loads. These beams had a safety factor of about 4.

In 421 B.C. and from 409 B.C. to 406 B.C., Mnesikles also built the Temple of Poseidon called ***Erechtheion*** on the Akropolis as a replacement for the old temple which the Persians had burnt to the ground in 480 B.C.. An iron beam encased in lead reinforced the underside of a stone lintel spanning a lower floor doorway of ***Erechtheion***. Therefore, it can be concluded that the ancient Greeks had discovered the iron reinforcement, and the brittle nature of stone in tension, in their novel composite construction of beams. The structures on the Akropolis have a perfection of workmanship which has remained unsurpassed till this very day.

Kallikrates, the ***architekton*** appointed by Kimon, was contracted to build in 443 B.C. the third blank middle defensive wall of the Long Walls to Peiraieus, which ran parallel to the Peraic Wall and was about 60 feet (18.3m) high. Kallikrates as the general contractor sublet the work to 10 subcontractors. The old southern wall, the so-called Phaleronic Wall, was allowed to decay since it was realised that an enemy could easily land in the Bay of Phaleron.

There were other known cases of beams reinforced with iron bars in Greek structures. The foundations of the Theban treasury in Delphi were reinforced by horizontal iron bars of 3½ by 4 inch (8.9 by 10.2 cm) cross-section and 41-foot (12.50 m) length. Iktinos encased U-shaped iron bars within the hollow marble beams to support the ceiling of the temple at Bassaia. The temple at Akragas in Sicily, had wrought-iron beams of 5 by 12 inches (12.7 by 30.5 cm) cross-section encased in the architraves to span half of the 15-foot (4.57 m) distance between column capitals in order to distribute a concentrated load over half the span of the beam. Both Iktinos and Kallikrates wrote commentaries on their method of temple construction which are no longer extant.

Ancient Greeks and Banausoi:

After the Persian wars, the social structure of ancient Greece became gradually similar to that of the Orient. Soon all industrial enterprises in Greece were based on slave labour. Philosophers, such as Plato and Aristotle, gave reasons for the justification of slavery in their writings. In contrast to Ionia about 600 B.C. where technologist and engineers were venerated, the thinking of the ancient Greeks about industry over a century and a half, had arrived at the viewpoint that technology was a filthy and inferior business fit only for slaves, and that no intelligent man with self-respect would bother himself about it. Except for the commercially conscious Korinthians, the leaders of Greek society had gradually come to a low opinion about the ***banausoi***, the men who worked for living. They had developed a general bias against the dignity of labour and technology. Even bankers, businessmen, and most physicians were considered ***banausoi***. Thus disdain for the practical arts gradually came to dominate the ancient Greek world. The famous Greek historian Herodotos of Halikarnassos (c.490/480-c.424 B.C.), who in 443 B.C. settled in Thurii in Italy, wrote that Greeks had accepted the low ranking of craftsmen from the Egyptians and "almost all foreigners," and that "the feeling against handicraft is least strong in Korinthos." Aristotle went as far as to state that it was in poor taste even to discuss most ***banausic*** professions. He thought that ***banausoi*** could not fulfil civic duties because their energies were consumed by lowly affairs. Therefore, he regarded ***banausic*** activities unworthy of a free man, yet he admired mechanical tops made by ***banausoi*** :

> "The lower sort are by nature slaves, and it is better for them as for all inferiors that they should be under the rule of a master . ... The slave shares in his master's life, the artisan is less closely connected with him, and only attains excellence in proportion as he becomes a slave. The meaner sort of mechanic has a special and separate slavery . ... No man can live the life of virtue who is living the life of a mechanic or labourer . ... In the oligarchies, no labourer can ever be a citizen."

Plato wrote in his dialogue < Gorgias >, after pointing out the great value of the engineer in preserving cities from attack: "Still, you despise him and his craft, you call him machine-builder (***mechanopoios***) only by way of insult and you would not want to give your daughter to his son nor yourself to marry his."

Although Xenophon of Athens, the famous general, historian, a skilled man of letters and master of Attic prose, remarked in reference to craftsmanship: "Without love for the object no worker can succeed." He expressed the views of the ancient Greeks devoted to outdoor living, when he wrote:

> "What are called mechanical arts carry a social stigma and are rightly dishonoured in our cities. ... The ***banausic*** trades spoil the bodies of workers and foremen who are forced to sit still and work indoors. They often spend the whole day at the fire. The debilitation of the body is accompanied by a serious weakening of the mind. Moreover, the ***banausic*** occupations leave no spare time for services to one's friends or to the city. Thus the ***banausoi*** are considered unreliable friends and poor defenders of their country. ... ***banausic*** activities are held in complete disdain in the Greek cities."

Ploutarchos of Chaironeia (c.50-c.120 A.D.), a famous Greek biographer and scholar, expressed surprise that a person from his prominent social class can find pleasure in the works of art, yet despise their maker as a mere craftsman: "It does not of necessity follow that if the work delights you with its grace, the one who wrought it is worthy of esteem."

Loukian, an apprentice to a sculptor, lamented his ***banausic*** status as a stonecutter in the following words: "You'll be obscure, earning a small wage, a man of low esteem, classed as worthless by public opinion, not courted by friends, feared by enemies, or envied by your fellow citizens, but just a common worker, a craftsman, a face in the crowd, one who makes his living with his hands."

It appears that it was not so much the manual work itself that was despised by the ancient Greeks, but rather the loss of freedom when under the control of a master or employer and the stigma of the servile, dependent state of the ***banausoi*** that was associated with it. Although Aristotle contended that every man of creative gifts "loves the work of his hands," all manual labour was seen as essentially servile, making the craftsman virtually into an animate instrument of work, or a tool. Aristotle stated that when a flute is made by the craftsman, it is the musician who commands and the craftsman who obeys. Thus, the consumer is the sole judge of the purpose of the craft processes, not the craftsman. In the opinion of Aristotle, the craftsman is not really inventing his product but merely trying to imitate a form which already exists in the consumer's mind. Therefore, he concluded, the consumer is really the creator, the master, whilst the craftsman is merely the means to an end, an intermediary. The ancient Greeks had come to accept the preconceived idea that the ***banausoi*** are restricted to their particular trades, and that every trade has its own intrinsic limits determined by the form that it serves, thereby violating the Greek ideal of all-round excellence. Therefore, the ancient Greeks were not able to conceive the use of technology as a means of social progress. For this reason, members of the ancient Greek upper class criticised and frequently attacked technology, applied science, and even medicine.

A Hippokratic treatise, < On the Technical Art > (***Peri techne***) attacked the attackers of science because the author was aware that all the other ***technai*** and sciences are also threatened, and he expected their representatives as craftsmen to defend themselves. It bore witness to how difficult was the task of a craftsman who aspired to be a scientist to vindicate his professional status in the Hellenic society. Yet it seems to have been quite in order for a member of the upper social class in ancient Greek society to engage in engineering in its unmistakably creative form such as in planning, engineering design, and direction of construction. Iktinos, far from being despised for his practical engineering activities, was a close confidant of Perikles and belonged to the most eminent intellectual circle of Perikles, whereas Kallikrates had belonged to that of Kimon.

Development of Mathematics as Exact Science

After the Second Persian War in 480 B.C. which ended in a complete military triumph of Athens, Athens became a great naval power and a wealthy commercial center. The new prosperity of its citizens afforded them leisure for taking an active part in politics which required from them an easy facility to speak well and effectively not only in the ecclesia but also in public disputes. Therefore, it became important for every citizen to acquire the necessary knowledge and skill of debate. This new situation gave rise to a new phase of philosophy in which attention was turned from the study of nature to the study of man thereby making man the central concern of philosophical thought. A similar concern about man and human nature was also shown by the great dramaturges of Athens: Aischylos, Sophokles and Euripides, who placed ethical and moral questions to the fore in their tragedies.

In this new cultural atmosphere, the former aristocratic ideal, the 'perfect gentleman' (***kalos kagathos***): the well-formed heroic individual of personal virtue (***arete***) who is endowed with a handsome personality, remarkable natural talent, high principle and admirable achievements, was replaced by a new democratic ideal, the 'perfect citizen' (***poleites***): the clever man, the man with ***nous*** who always knows what to say and what to do to succeed in life, and to whom high principle and truth no longer mattered.

Sophists:

A new class of experts, the Sophists, rose to meet the challenge of teaching the requisite knowledge, the art of oratory and the skill of debate. Anaxagoras and his fellow philosophers had always been independent and disinterested enquirers of the truth which they taught in free discussions without monetary compensation. The Sophists, in contrast, emerged as professional itinerant teachers who dispensed 'practical wisdom' for monetary remuneration. They instructed the well-to-do citizens, usually young men, for high fees, and travelled from city to city. Sophists made extravagant claims of being able to teach everything and anything as well as its opposite. They believed that morality and wisdom could be taught theoretically, that the basis of morality was 'subjective' and to be found within one's own intellectual and moral being, and that it is based on reason and not on custom and tradition as in the past.

The Sophist movement was a public movement addressed to the citizen and it had some political tendency. They were orators and rhetoricians, and basically educators who gave 'formal instruction' (***paideia***) worthy of the name of formal schooling. Their success was considerable, and they had great influence on the Greek life in general. Many of the Sophists became important personalities as well as wealthy, and some of them were extremely intelligent. A few Sophists were also very capable mathematicians. They taught mathematics and astronomy, but most of all the art of language, logic, grammar and rhetoric. Their major concern was to 'speak well' (***eu legein***), to express an 'opinion' (***doxa***) in a convincing manner regardless of the truth. Trial by mass-juries put a premium on the art of effective speech in order to sway the audience, which made effective oratory the high road to personal success. Therefore, Sophists deliberately studied the function of words, and the techniques of using them in their development of speechmaking or writing as a conscious art. They were responsible for the first conscious cultivation of prose style. Most of the important Sophists had learnt their rhetorical skills from Korax and Tisias of Sicily, who had founded the principles of rhetoric as the art of persuasion. The early Ionian philosophers and their successors had been mostly concerned with physical nature and mathematics in their scientific speculations, but their theories did not help to understand man and human affairs which were of major interests to Sophists. Therefore, in the face of various conflicting theories of physical nature formulated by Ionian natural philosophers, Sophists declared that truth is not obtainable by man, and all that counts is 'useful opinion', a viewpoint contrary to the old Greek belief expressed well by the poet Pindar (c.522-443 B.C.): "Custom is king of all." They acknowledged the existence of a variety of customs, each useful and valid in its own particular circumstance, and denied the existence of any truth independent of men and their various ways. Therefore, the Sophists boasted to teach practical wisdom consisting of how to succeed in practical life, particularly in political affairs. The most famous Sophist, Protagoras of Abdera, a pupil of Demokritos who became wealthy from the income accrued from the high fees he charged for his lectures, an equivalent of 1,000 dollars for a course, said that "man is the measure of all things," by which he probably implied that every man's view of the world is true to himself. It meant then that there is really no valid reason to look for universal truth independent of man, because man is involved in human affairs regardless of his likes and dislikes, and all that matters is whether his views are useful to him. Under such circumstances, so Protagoras thought, it is pointless to regard one man's view truer than another's, it is only sensible to regard it 'better'. Protagoras was the first to teach practical logic, and to insist that there are two opposing sides to each question, and he was the first to argue on both sides of the question. These views of Protagoras expressed well the relative standard used by Sophists. Therefore, the Sophists boasted to teach practical wisdom to their students which justified their nickname 'wisdom mongers'. Perikles, who attended the lectures of Protagoras in Athens, commissioned Protagoras to draw up the constitution for Thurii, the panhellenic colony of Athens in the southern Italian peninsula, which was settled in 443 B.C..

The Sophist teaching was regarded as immoral by the ordinary Greeks because it exalted the individual by giving him full freedom and scope of personal development distinct from, and above his life as a citizen. From the viewpoint of modern thought it was a necessary destruction of the old which cleared the ground and laid the foundation for the new. The intent of Sophists to teach young men to think, speak, and act was altogether not an entirely unworthy motive.

Sophists understood that since this world is made by man for himself, technology and engineering will be important to him. Therefore, they were the first to emphasise the importance of all crafts and to speak of material progress. They presented themselves as specialists in various crafts in which each specialty had its own principles and methods. Intellectual specialists made their appearance for the first time. Applied sciences became fashionable such as town planning by Hippodamos, social contracts by Lykophron, and psychoanalysis by Antiphon. The most famous

Sophists besides Protagoras were: Hippias of Elis, Antiphon of Rhamnos, Gorgias of Leontini (c.485-385 B.C.), Prodikos of Chios, Euthydemos and Thrasimachos of Chalkedon, all of whom were teaching in Athens sometime between 440 B.C. and 400 B.C..The most important Sophists were Protagoras and Gorgias, who was a pupil of Empedokles. Protagoras as a Sophist was more of a philosopher and practical logician, whereas Gorgias already exhibited all the derogatory and arrogant characteristics of the typical Sophist of evil repute. Gorgias claimed that what is 'likely' is more worth while than what is 'true', and boasted that he can make small things look great and ***vice-versa***. Gorgias criticised natural philosophers of his time for their belief in the perceived reality in their discourse about reality which he showed to be a naive materialism. Gorgias pointed out that what they actually communicated to one another was their own discourse about reality which may or may not be the true reality. In other words, Gorgias pointed out that the natural philosophy of the physicists was nothing more than 'nominalism', a philosophy which he founded.

In linguistic art, Protagoras, an accomplished speaker, made the beginning in grammatical analysis of speech by distinguishing between the tenses of verbs and classifying the basic forms of speech. Grammatical functions in language were discovered as soon as Protagoras attempted a logical analysis of the sentences in the practical logic which he taught. Prodikos differentiated between synonyms, and Gorgias enriched prose with poetical words and phrases, and developed rhetorical devices, which he called 'figures of speech', such as antithesis, balanced rhythm and assonance. Already Ionian Greeks had become aware of grammar in the 6th century B.C., by paying close attention to declension of nouns as well as having established a doctrine of cases. In the 5th century B.C. philosophers began to study linguistics in which all aspects of the speech such as letters, syllables, words, rhythms and style became the object of careful examination. Later Aristotle, the Stoics and the Epikourians continued the work of linguistic analysis but it was made completely systematic only in the Hellenistic time by the Alexandrian linguists at the Museum. In the strict sense, the first true grammarians were Aristophanes of Byzantion and Aristarchos of Samotrake at the Museum. The earliest surviving textbook on Greek grammar is by Dionysios of Thrax who was a scholar at the Museum in Alexandria before his expulsion about 146 B.C.. His grammar defined such parts of speech as noun, verb, participle, article, pronoun, preposition, adverb and conjunction.

Mathematical Problems of Sophists:

The Sophists organised the intellectual disciplines such as grammar, rhetoric, dialectic, the structure of reason and language, and mathematical sciences into a body of learning which formed the cultural background of a cultivated man. This basic educational ideal which was reorganised into ***trivium*** and ***quadrivium*** during the mediæval times lasted well into the Renaissance Age. In geometry the Pythagoreans in Italy seem to have neglected the study of the circle for its basic mathematical properties, which is surprising, since Pythagoras considered the circle to be a perfect geometric figure. The study of the circle was taken up by the Sophists and nearly all the mathematics produced by the Sophists concentrated upon their efforts to solve 3 problems:

(1) 'Trisection of a given angle'.

(2) 'Duplication of the cube' – the so-called 'Delian problem': to find the side x of a cube the volume of which is double of the given cube with side a, which in modern algebraic notation is given by: $x^3 = 2a^3$.

(3) 'Squaring the circle': to find a square, the area of which is equal to the area of a given circle.

The earliest known attempt to solve one of the 3 problems of the Sophist was made by Anaxagoras when he tried to square the circle during his imprisonment in Athens, but this work has not survived.

The first solution of the trisection of a given angle problem was achieved about 430 B.C. by Hippias of Elis (born c. 460 B.C.), a prominent Sophist, a leading polymath and polytechnician of his time. Hippias, a fair forerunner of the 'universal man', was an arrogant and vain man so typical of many Sophists, who boasted that he earned twice as much money as any other Sophist, and claimed to be not only an expert in all intellectual fields but also in all handicrafts. Nevertheless, he was an accomplished mathematician with a remarkable memory, and he succeeded in solving the trisection of an acute angle α by means of a higher order curve, the trisectrix (***tetragonizousa***), that could not be constructed by the ruler and compass but had to be drawn point by point:

$$y/a = \alpha/(\pi/2),$$

which as a modern function can be expressed in terms of Cartesian coordinates as a transcendental curve:

$$y = x \tan(\pi y/2a).$$

This curve can be constructed kinematically as follows: If the top side of a square of length a descends with uniform speed until it coincides with the bottom side and if at the same time the vertical side of length a pivots as a radial line about the point of intersection of the same vertical side and the bottom side with a uniform angular velocity such that the top side and the radial line reach the bottom side at the same time, then the locus of their intersection represents the curve which trisects the angle α. It is a kinematic method in geometry. It was later demonstrated that the curve of Hippias not only solves the trisection problem and the multisection problem of an acute angle, but also the quadrature of the circle problem, on account of which it is now called the 'quadratrix'.

By the time Hippias solved the problem of trisection of a given angle, geometry had become a completely abstract discipline of thought dealing with properties of purely conceptual entities such as points, straight lines, circles, angles and other geometric entities which only had a conceptual existence. Geometry had assumed a purely formal character after Oinopides of Chios (c.500-

430 B.C.), an astronomer, claimed that all valid geometric proofs must be based solely on the properties of the straight line and the circle, and that all geometric constructions must be made only by the use of 2 mathematical instruments: the ruler and the compass. Unfortunately the requirement of Oinopides created a number of insoluble problems in geometry which have no exact solutions by means of a straight line and circle alone, among which were the 3 problems of the Sophists. Hippias' higher order geometric curve, the trisectrix, that solved the trisection problem was the first example of a solution which could not be constructed by a ruler and a compass, since a straight edge and compass can be used only to solve problems involving equations of first and second degree, but not equations of third degree nor transcendental equations which define the curve of Hippias. A geometric solution by ruler and compass means algebraically that the operations involved can be reducible to the 4 basic operations of arithmetic and to the taking of square roots.

Hippokrates of Chios and Method of Geometric Reduction:

One of the best mathematicians of the Hellenic era was Hippokrates of Chios (born c. 470 B.C.), a former merchant who turned to teaching mathematics for monetary compensation like the Sophists after pirates robbed him of his ship and cargo which left him penniless and stranded in Athens. Hippokrates wrote the first known textbook on geometry, the first <Elements of Geometry> (***Stoicheia***). In fact, the mathematical proofs of Hippokrates are the first extant reasoned geometric proofs available to the posterity. He used letters in his geometric figures and, as far as is known, he was the first mathematician to use in his treatise the method of analysis, but without formal explicitness. In this comprehensive textbook, Hippokrates tried to comprise the whole of geometry of his day into a single connected logical structure of propositions, which was a substantial contribution to the axiomatics of geometry, and which made him a forerunner of Leon (c. 370 B.C.), Theudios of Magnesia (c.340 B.C.), and Eukleides of Athens (in English, Euclid) who taught in Alexandria, Egypt, all of whom wrote treatises on the elements of geometry. He became very skilled in the use of the Pythagorean theory of proportions and in the treatment of transformation of areas. He was able to convert a rectangle having sides a and b into a square by finding the 'mean proportional', or 'geometric mean', between a and b, a method which Pythagoreans had developed. About 440 B.C., Hippokrates made 2 major contributions to mathematics in his efforts to solve 2 problems of the Sophists: the 'duplication of the cube' and the 'squaring the circle'. In his failed attempt to solve the 'duplication of the cube' problem he invented the method of geometric reduction (***apagoge***) whereby a 3-dimensional problem is reduced to a 2-dimensional problem in which the solution of the latter gives also the solution of the former. He generalised the transformation of areas problem by inserting between 2 given magnitudes a and b two 'mean proportionals' x and y such that the continued proportion:

$$a/x = x/y = y/b$$

holds. He recognised that his reduced problem is equivalent to the 'duplication of the cube' problem if $b = 2a$. In this brilliant approach, Hippokrates demonstrated his clear mastery of the compound ratios derived from numbers and its intuitive application to geometric lines. In modern symbolic algebra, the 'duplication of the cube' problem is to determine x such that $x^3 = 2a^3$. He attempted to solve it geometrically by his reduction method consisting of finding 2 mean proportionals x and y in a continued proportion between a and $2a$:

$$a/x = x/y = y/2a$$

since then,

$$x^2 = ay, y^2 = 2ax$$

and thus,

$$x^4 = 2a^3x \;\therefore\; x^3 = 2a^3 .$$

Of course, Hippokrates tried to solve this problem by a strict geometric construction, which is a great deal more difficult than solving it by means of modern symbolic algebra. In his method of reduction, Hippokrates arrived at 2 line segments, one twice as long as the other, from which the 2 mean proportionals could be found. However, he did not succeed in devising a geometric construction for finding these 2 mean proportionals.

Hippokrates obviously knew that the duplication of the square problem involved a single mean proportional x :

$$a/x = x/2a ,$$

which in terms of modern symbolic algebra gives the required relation :

$$x^2 = 2a^2 .$$

Hippokrates was also unable to solve the 'squaring the circle' problem, but in this class of problems he became the first mathematician to succeed in squaring a curvilinear figure in his solution of the problem of 'squaring the lune (***meniskos***)': 'the area of the triangle equals the area of its lune'. He also demonstrated that the areas of 2 circles are to each other as the ratio of their corresponding diameters squared :

$$A_1 / A_2 \propto d_1^2 / d_2^2 ,$$

which implies that a certain factor [that is ,π] is the same for all circles, a result perhaps obtained by considering the circle as a limiting form of a regular polygon. It seems that in the solution of these problems Hippokrates made systematic use of Anaxagoras' idea concerning the infinitely small and the infinitely large, when he attempted to approximate the circle from below with a limiting regular polygon – an early example of the method of 'exhausting' the difference between a figure and its approximation, but there is no definite evidence that this is what Hippokrates actually did. However, there is definite evidence that Antiphon used this method of approximation in the squaring of the circle problem.

Antiphon and Method of 'Squaring the Circle':

About 430 B.C., mathematician Antiphon of Athens, a Sophist and a contemporary of Hippokrates and Sokrates, introduced in his attempt to solve the 'squaring the circle' problem an approximate method resembling modern calculus into geometry. Antiphon inscribed an equilateral triangle (or a square) in the circle, and then by erecting isosceles triangles with their vertices lying on the circumference of the circle on the sides of the inscribed polygonal figure, and by continuing this process long enough he claimed to obtain an inscribed polygon with a vast number of sides, which coincides with the circumference of the circle because the straight and the curved lines are ultimately reducible to the same indivisible element by successive divisions, and, therefore, he concluded that the ultimate polygon with a vast number of sides, will in this type of 'indivisible limit' coincide almost precisely with the circle. In this assumption he relied on the 'geometric atom' concept of Demokritos of Abdera. Since a square can be constructed which is equal in area to any polygon, a square can be found the area of which is equal to the area of the last polygon with vast number of sides inscribed. Antiphon's method which lies at the basis of modern calculus was not accepted by the Greek mathematicians, because the idea that a polygon can coincide in this type of limit with a circle would have forced the ancient Greeks to reject their fundamental notion that geometric magnitudes such as lines, surfaces and volumes, are continuous and infinitely divisible.

A generation later Bryson of Herakleia extended Antiphon's method by introducing both the inscribed and the circumscribed polygon to the circle in the problem of 'squaring the circle'. He did not claim to obtain coincidence between the circle and the polygon of vast number of sides, but rather assumed that the area of the circle is equal to the area of the intermediate polygon drawn between the circumscribed and the inscribed polygon, two polygons which are approaching the circle as its upper and lower bounds when the number of sides of these polygons is being continually doubled by bisection. Then the areas of the inscribed and circumscribed polygons differ so little that the polygon intermediate in area to the two bounding polygons must be equal to the area of the circle which is also intermediate in area to the two bounding polygons. Antiphon's method as used by Bryson escaped the problem of infinity or the indivisible limit concept.

The idea of Antiphon implied the limit concept, and he and Bryson were the first ancient Greeks to anticipate this modern idea of calculus, which consists of enclosing a required quantity such as the area of the circle between two other quantities which can be calculated, and which can be shown to approach each other indefinitely. This method can be adjusted to exclude the limit concept, by demonstrating that the difference between the value of the area and the approaching approximation of the value of the area can be 'exhausted' (in Latin, ***exhaurire***, used by Gregoire De Saint-Vincent in A.D.1647), and made 'as small as desired', thereby obviating the numerical limit concept. His method, called the 'method of exhaustion' since A.D.1647, represents a crude anticipation of the modern (δ -ϵ) method, which was soon introduced with all its mathematical rigour by the ingenious mathematician of the Hellenic Age, Eudoxos of Knidos, who ranks with Archimedes of Syracuse (287-212 B.C.) as the two foremost mathematicians of all time.

Natural Philosophy as Natural Science

Rise of Science of Mechanics:

In the Hellenic Ionia, natural philosophy and religion were not in conflict, but after a lapse of a century and a half, by the time of the Peloponnesian War in Greece proper, which lasted from 431 B.C. to 404 B.C., there already existed a real conflict between science and religion. The man in the street of any ancient Greek city, but particularly in Athens, felt that the scientists were undermining and destroying all or most of the religious comforts in the life of ***polis*** and, thereby, were destroying the very meaning of the city life itself. There was a good deal of truth in this opinion, since the life of the ***polis*** depended mainly on the religious cults of the city. By that time, natural philosophy had already split into 2 almost distinct branches: mathematics (***mathesis***) and physical science (***physis***). Thenceforth, mathematics was developed at a greatly accelerated pace and became increasingly more abstract, sophisticated and logically rigorous.

Sokrates of Athens and Dialectical Philosophy of Ethics:

Sokrates of Athens (470-399 B.C.), an ugly ("as ugly as a mask of Seilenos") and frowzy stonecutter who in his youth had been an apprentice to his father Sophroniskos, a sculptor, became primarily a moral philosopher in his old age. Sokrates had studied natural philosophy with Anaxagoras but he soon found that the scientific speculations of the Ionian natural philosophers and their successors about physical nature did not help men to understand themselves. Moreover, the Sophists had pointed out the failure of the speculative method of science to find the true knowledge about nature which, so they had concluded, was beyond the powers of man, and consequently unimportant. What really mattered according to the Sophists is sound practice according to 'useful opinion' (***doxa***). Sokrates had met Parmenides and Zenon of Elea at the Panathenaic festival in Athens about 444 B.C. when he was still a young man, and in his discussion about natural philosophy he had been given a thorough dialectical thrashing by the two gifted Eleatic logicians. After this chastening experience, Sokrates relinquished his speculations about physical nature and devoted himself thenceforth to his studies of human nature, particularly ethics which he regarded as the philosophy of morality and logic. In his new attitude towards natural philosophy, Sokrates made a concession to mathematics: "Understanding of mathematics is necessary for a sound grasp of ethics." Although Sokrates came to the conclusion that man's knowledge is minute when compared to the infinite vastness of the unknown, he rejected the pessimistic view of the Sophists that true knowledge lies completely beyond the grasp of men, and he considered the 'useful opinion' of the Sophists quite inadequate for a sound conduct of moral life. Unfortunately, Sokrates, by becoming interested only in ethics and the moral behaviour of man, indirectly downgraded the importance of natural philosophy. The method he used in his ethics was dialectics consisting of the pursuit of truth by means of questions and answers that was basically the geometric method of mathematicians which starts from a basic premise and leads by logical deduction to a definite consequence. In other words, he sought truth in the accounts of things, and logic was involved in how we talk about things. Dialectics philosophically is the process of forming notions from conceptions, whereas psychologically it is the process of forming concepts from percepts, but logically it is the resolution of species from genus or the reverse, and scientifically it is the process of inducing general principles from the multiplicity of phenomena.

The main purpose of his moral philosophy was to teach men self-criticism since ancient Greeks were disdainful of other people and usually had a grand opinion of themselves. He warned men not to be bedazzled by their own excellence or wisdom, but rather make themselves to realise that all men are frail human beings subject to human failings. Like the Sophists, Sokrates was a semanticist and he warned people against using 'big' or abstract words, the meaning of which they did not fully comprehend. His philosophical method was not to instruct, but rather to lead men to discover what he thought they already knew, and he treated philosophy as a way of life, which was the great Pythagorean tradition. He had adopted the Pythagorean theory of 'forms' which contained all eternal prototypes arranged in a hierarchy, and applied it to the theory of knowledge. Sokrates held that knowledge can be had only of 'forms', but of their counterparts in the material world men can have only opinion (***doxa***).

Sokrates was a formidable deflator of the pompous and the arrogant when he cornered some self-declared expert with an inflated ego, frequently a Sophist, and by questioning such an expert about his special skills Sokrates often proved the pretentious expert to be quite ignorant of his claimed speciality through his own answers. Sokrates himself was wont of saying with a touch of irony that his own knowledge exceeded that of other men only because he knew his own ignorance. Although Sokrates viewed the Sophists as men who teach how to make the worse appear to be the better, he did share their interest in questioning the traditional ethics of the Greek society thereby casting doubt on established conventions just like the Sophists were doing. Although he downplayed his own importance by comparing himself to a social gadfly, his clever and ironic dialectics frequently led to personal ridicule of his adversaries which made him many enemies, and ultimately cost him his life. Sokrates had already observed that a wise man cannot succeed, at least, "not in the land of his birth," an opinion expressed again some 4 centuries later when Jesus of Nazareth, who hailed from the Hellenistic region of Palestine, noted that, "a prophet is not without honour, save in his own country."

In the opinion of Sokrates, sound growth of knowledge requires moral purity, truthfulness, individual self-discipline and rational scepticism, and he confined his own studies to the moral virtues of man. Virtue he equated with knowledge and, therefore, he thought that virtue can be taught. Sokrates as a philosopher of morals and ethics was the precursor of the Cynics, the Cyrenaics and the Stoics, ethical philosophers who appeared during the years of the decline of Athens and the rise of Macedonian power. His lack of concern for the material goods was shared by the Cynics, a philosophical movement founded by Antisthenes of Athens (c.445-after 371B.C.), a disciple of Gorgias of Leontini and Sokrates, and his interest in the virtue as the greatest good was shared by the Stoics, a movement founded by Zenon of Kition, Kypros, (c. 340-265 B.C.) who was a former Cynic and a wealthy merchant. Aristippos of Kyrene (c. 435-c.356 B.C.), a pupil of Protagoras and the least congenial disciple of Sokrates who founded the Cyrenaic school of philosophy, shared Sokrates' idea of inner freedom and independence in his hedonistic Cyrenaic philosophy, but unlike Sokrates he denied social responsibility, showed his indifference to reason, and regarded wisdom as enjoyment of pleasure and avoidance of pain. The most celebrated disciple of Sokrates, however, was Plato.

Sokrates, being inspired by the Eleatic logicians, employed the method of hypothesis and deduction as a framework for all logical arguments. To lay the groundwork on which the argument is to be built, a supposition or hypothesis is introduced and from this hypothesis are deduced the logical consequences which, then, are checked against the facts. If the consequences of the hypothesis tally with the facts of the phenomenon, then the hypothesis 'saves the appearance of the phenomenon' (***sozein ta phainomena***). If, however, the facts do not correspond to the logical deductions, then this hypothesis is to be rejected and another hypothesis is to be sought. In this method the hypothesis itself remains unproven. This scientific method was revived with improvements by the English Scholar Robert Grosseteste (A.D.c.1168-1253) in the Mediæval Age.

The Eleatic philosophers, who were the pioneer masters of logical argument, had already used the method of logical argument from hypothesis in their critique of the Ionian natural philosophy. The new feature in the Sokratic hypothetico-deductive method was the notion of saving the appearance of the phenomena: to explain the observed facts of a phenomenon by a hypothesis. According to Aristotle, it was Sokrates who is mainly responsible for the actual founding of both the inductive method and the method of universal concept formulation [universal definitions] which have to do with the foundation of science. Sokrates himself did not regard his universal definitions as separable from things and, therefore, he did not distinguish between universals and definitions, but this separation was done later by his successors, particularly Plato who called this class of objects 'ideas'. Sokrates was not the first to think of universal definitions, for already Demokritos had briefly touched it in his study of heat and cold, and Pythagoras had discussed the definition of a few concepts in his theory of numbers.

Demokritos of Abdera, Atoms and Method of 'Geometric Atom':

Demokritos of Abdera, a pupil of Leukippos of Miletos and Anaxagoras of Klazomenai, who systematised the atomic doctrine as discussed ***supra*** and made the first formal attempts to create materialism, was a polymath (***pentathlos***) since according to Aristotle he wrote treatises on all intellectual subjects of his time, 73 books in all, none of which have survived. It is known that Demokritos wrote the following tracts among the many: < On Number >, < On Geometry >, < On Tangencies >, < On Mappings >, < On Irrationals >, < On the Pythagoreans >, < On the World Order> , and < On Ethics >, in all of which he employed a literary style of exposition. He asserted that the reality underlying the constantly changing diversity of the physical world was expressible in terms of mathematics and that the happenings in this world were strictly determined by mathematical laws. Demokritos, under the influence of Leukippos, became an atomist by interpreting reality mechanically in terms of atoms and void (***koinon***) to which he assigned a certain quality of 'Being' that made it a space. He maintained that "nothing exists but atoms and the void," and he proceeded to distinguish between things as they really were and as they appeared to men. In the opinion of the atomists, the world really consists of just atoms in motion, and he supposed, like Leukippos of Miletos before him, that bodies fall with equal speed in empty space. In the atomic theory Demokritos proposed the so-called 'inertia principle'. He drew on the analogy to the alphabet when he explained how atoms make up all material objects like letters (***stoicheia***) make up words which are more than the sum of their letters. According to Demokritos, men experience the moving atoms in a variety of ways which makes it necessary to distinguish between primary and secondary qualities: shape, size and matter in distinction to colours, tastes, smells and the like which do not exist in themselves but are merely responses of sense organs to the onrush of atoms. The primary qualities belong to the atoms themselves whereas the secondary qualities are explained in terms of the primary qualities. In his opinion, the so-called 'facts and truths' of men are mere conventions, and the so-called 'knowledge' is mainly knowledge of the phenomena. Hence, Demokritos as an atomist explained the large in terms of the small, and the perceptible in terms of the imperceptible.

It appears that ancient Greek mathematicians also used another mathematical method of reasoning in competition with the rigorous method of exhaustion of Eudoxos of Knidos, an older method due to Demokritos which was based on the concept of the 'geometric atom'. In this method a line segment, an area, or a volume was thought to be built up of a large but finite number of indivisible 'geometric atoms'. This intuitively founded method of 'geometric atom' had one great advantage over Eudoxos' rigorous method of exhaustion, it provided the means to find new results. The modern limit concept has made it possible to make the method of 'geometric atom' as rigorous as the method of exhaustion, and, therefore, the method of 'geometric atom' is still used in a modern form today in the solution of mathematical problems in physics and engineering.

Demokritos introduced the intuitive method of 'geometric atom' to establish theorems on the volume of the pyramid and the cone. He filled the volume of the cone or the pyramid with innumerable thin slices of cylinders or parallelpipeds, and by making these slices thinner and thinner and by increasing their number, the stratified volume of the stack of the thin slices of the cylinder or the parallelpiped was made to approach the volume of the cone or the pyramid. In this intuitive, infinitesimal method, Demokritos arrived at the formulae for the ratios of the volumes of the cone and its circumscribed cylinder, and of the pyramid and its circumscribed prism, results which had been known empirically to Sumerians and Egyptians countless centuries ago. It has been said that Demokritos himself puzzled about the stack of innumerable, atomlike, tapered, parallel layers which built up to such solids as cones and pyramids when made thinner and thinner: are the 2 volumes equal or unequal for there is an obvious difference between the stratified cone or pyramid and the smooth cone or pyramid? This query of Demokritos involves the question of the limit. Simplikios of Kilikia (6th cent. A.D.), however, wrote that Demokritos regarded the slices to be infinitely divisible in the mensuration of the cone, but this would be uncharacteristic of such a confirmed atomist as Demokritos. Logically rigorous proofs for these theorems were first given by the brilliant Eudoxos of Knidos, who employed the so-called deductive method of exhaustion. In infinitesimal analysis Demokritos apparently went far beyond the problems of the cone and the pyramid when he studied the 'horn angle' which consisted of the angle formed by one circle touching another from the inside because that leads to the idea of infinitesimals of the second order.

Following Anaxagoras, Demokritos also published a tract on the theory of perspective (***ekpetasmata***), but it has not survived the ravages of time. He wrote 2 treatises on macrocosm and microcosm, entitled < The Large Arrangement > (***Megas kosmos***) and <The Small Arrangement> (***Mikros kosmos***), in which he asserted that "man is a universe (***makrokosmos***) in small (***mikrokosmos***)." Already Alkmaion of Kroton, the Pythagorean physician, had regarded the human body to be a microcosm, reflecting in the small the universe as a macrocosm in the large.

Demokritos, who had a universal mind, was interested in all branches of philosophy and in all branches of science. Demokritos had encyclopædic knowledge according to Aristotle, yet for a polymath he made a remarkable statement: "Do not try to know everything if you do not wish not to know anything." He also said: "He that contradicts and keeps on talking is unfit to learn what he should." Demokritos emphasised the basic Greek belief that talents have to be cultivated when he wrote: "No one is likely to prevail by native qualities alone." Demokritos had realised that to explain physical nature, man has to rely on his imagination when he wrote: "Man must know that he is far removed from how things really are."

Demokritos was an extreme skeptic, which he expressed as follows: "We know nothing; not even if there is anything to know ... We know nothing in reality for the truth lies in an abyss." He connected action to courage and chance as follows: "Courage is the beginning of action, but chance is master of the end." Demokritos expressed distain for men's lack of rational foresight: "Men have fashioned themselves an idol out of chance as a cloak for their lack of counsel, for chance opposes good judgement. Most of life's tangles are straightened out by a keen and intelligent penetration by reason ... Chance is a bogey invented to excuse stupidity." The last statement of Demokritos is reminiscent of an opinion of Perikles: "We commonly blame chance for whatever belies our calculation." Demokritos also expressed his contempt for the 'pseudo-intellectuals ' when he wrote: "Many much-learned men have no intelligence." Demokritos asserted cynically that ill-bred men without cultural refinement have an appetite for disgusting and offensive trash: "Swinish men are greedy for offal."

Demokritos was a universal man who embraced the entire knowledge of his time, and among his many accomplishments were pioneering works on a theory of knowledge, mathematics, biological theories, psychology, social evolution, astronomy, meteorology, geography, economics, perspective, and interjectional theory of language. Unfortunately, Demokritos lived in the shadow of his popular contemporary Sokrates who preferred the simpler elementary philosophy of ethics to the intellectually demanding and theoretically difficult natural philosophy as a mathematical science, and whose disciples rejected the materialistic philosophy and the model of the universe of Demokritos. Most of Demokritos' writings have been lost or, perhaps, even wilfully destroyed because Demokritos rejected Plato's idealism. Plato is known to have said that he would like to burn all the books of Demokritos. Our fragmentary knowledge of Demokritos' extensive writings consists of quotations from frequent, but usually unfriendly, references to his works by later Greek writers such as Plato, Aristotle and others. Aristotle refers to Demokritos almost always in refutation of the arguments of Demokritos. Demokritos wrote in prose the style of which was worthy of comparison with the style of Plato, at least in the opinion of Marcus Tullius Cicero, the famous Roman statesman, orator, Stoic philosopher and man of letters. The reputation of Demokritos in ancient, and also in mediæval times, was enormous.

Apparently, Demokritos, an unconventional and sarcastic person who did not suffer fools gladly, nevertheless had a carefree disposition because it was said that: "Herakleitos weeps, and

Demokritos laughs at all things." He was popularly known as the 'laughing philosopher'. He called cheerfulness, and often confidence, that is, a mind devoid of fear, the highest good. Demokritean ethics was based on happiness defined as serenity of the mind which is undisturbed by fear or other adversities. He said: "Happiness does not reside in strength or money; it lies in rightness and versatility." Control of appetites obtained by temperance and self-culture according to him is a necessary precondition for this state. Inward contentment is secured by doing a good deed for its own sake without any influence of fear or hope. The reward for doing a good deed is the knowledge of having done it. In order to be happy, Demokritos advised avoidance of evil in any of its forms: "It is not enough to abstain from evil; one should abstain from any thought or word about it, for words are the shadows of action." His moral ideas began to delineate the concept of the 'wise man' (***sophistes***) whose character is imperturbability (***ataraxia***), serenity (***haekonia***), and self-control (***sophrosyne***). His idea of democracy by implication was moral as well as political in which every man was a law unto himself. Demokritos made a profound statement about the political significance of wealth in his book on apothegms (***gnomai***), the earliest known Greek collection of proverbs and sayings: "Poverty under democracy is as much to be preferred to the so-called prosperity under an autocrat as freedom is to slavery."

Archytas of Taras, Kinematical Methods in Mathematics and Mechanics, Reaction Principle:

One important Greek scientist and mathematician was Archytas of Taras (428-c.347 B.C.), a democratic Greek colonial city-State in Italian peninsula. Archytas, a student of Philolaos of Kroton, was the first known full-time scientist as well as a man of action who was born the year Anaxagoras died and a year before Plato's birth. He had what has been called a lumbering kind of genius, being outstanding both in the number theory and in geometry, and in the mathematical theory of music as well, yet he was not very adept in making his ideas clear in writing. Besides being the head of the Pythagorean Society in Taras, the main haven of Pythagoreans in Italy, Archytas was also an outstanding statesman, a successful general (elected 7 years in succession the commander-in-chief of his city and was never defeated during his tenure), a philosopher, a mathematician, the founder of theoretical mechanics, and a mechanical engineer. Archytas is the founder of theoretical mechanics, because he wrote the first systematic treatise on theoretical mechanics in which mechanics was treated for the first time as a mathematical science with theorems and proofs. He gave the mathematical theory of the pulley, a labour-saving device of the Sumerians, and invented the mathematical theory of the cylindrical helix which is the geometrical basis of the infinite screw mechanism. Archytas' screw represented an entirely new elementary machine as a labour-saving device, but it is not known whether he attempted to construct screws as practical mechanical devices.

It is more than likely that Archytas originated the kinematical criterion of equilibrium of the lever, which was later used by Aristotle of Stageira, and by Straton of Lampsakos in the book < On Mechanical Problems > (***Problemata Mechanika***), because Archytas also treated geometry from the kinematical point of view. His mathematical theory of the action of the pulley and the screw almost certainly were based on kinematical methods. His book probably also contained other fundamental ideas of mechanics, which later appeared in the works of other ancient Greek mathematicians. He is known to have written several works on machines.

Archytas discovered the all-important reaction principle in mechanics, and built a wooden dove which sang whilst being propelled through the air by the reaction to a jet of compressed hot air or steam expelled from the dove. The paramount importance of the reaction principle of Archytas to technology was first demonstrated only in modern times in turbojet aircraft engines and rockets. This astounding fact is the best testimonial to the incredible genius of Archytas for his discovery of the reaction principle is now of vital technological importance to the modern civilisation.

Archytas was the first scientist to connect acoustics with the motion of air when in the mathematical theory of music he associated the musical pitch with the frequency of vibration of the air, and to give a number-theoretic foundation for musical scales by giving the numerical ratios for the intervals of the tetrachord on 3 scales: the enharmonic, the chromatic, and the diatomic. In the construction of his very elaborate musical scales he used the arithmetic, the geometric, and the harmonic mean, in which b is the 'arithmetic mean' of a and c if $b = (a+c)/2$, the 'geometric mean' if $a/b = b/c$, and the 'harmonic mean' if $a/c = (a - b)/(b - c)$. He also proved that there exists no integer that is a 'geometric mean' between two whole numbers in the ratio $n{:}(n+1)$.

In geometry, Archytas produced a number of new theorems using his kinematical method of reasoning. All his contributions in mathematics were important and pathbreaking. Archytas had recognised that a point.as an indivisible cannot make up anything that is continuous such as a line, because a point cannot be continuous with another point. Since no accumulation of indivisible points can give anything but an indivisible, he concluded that only by motion can a point as an indivisible generate a line which is continuous. By introducing movement into geometry, he founded the kinematical theory of geometry which unified arithmetic to geometry: a curve is a trace of a moving point, a surface is a trace of a moving curve, and a volume is a trace of a moving surface. Therefore in the geometry of Archytas everything moved. The kinematical geometry is still being used, and in many areas of geometry, such as in manifold geometry, it is one of the most powerful methods of study. Employing the techniques of geometric algebra, Archytas gave an ingenious 3-dimensional solution of the 'duplication of the cube' or the so-called 'Delian problem', which he solved using the geometric reduction method of Hippokrates by constructing a solution to the problem of two mean proportionals in which a point is produced by the intersection of 3 surfaces :

a right cone, a cylinder, and a torus resembling a donut without a hole, a remarkable solution of great sophistication. The intersection of these 3 surfaces locates a point $2^{1/3} a$, which gives the length of the line segment that represents the length of the edge of the cube which doubles the volume of the original cube a^3 . The remarkable mathematical feat of Archytas in his solution of the 'Delian problem' was that he solved it synthetically by higher geometry using the stereometric interpretation of a geometric mechanism without the assistance of coordinates and modern algebra, a method which is exceedingly intricate, and Archytas' success with it is a testimonial to his remarkable mathematical ingenuity. His 3-dimensional solution was one of the outstanding achievements in ancient Greek mathematics which demonstrates how far advanced was the Greek geometry at that time. Moreover, Archytas was the first to study geometry on a circular cylinder and to determine some of the properties of its oblique section, the ellipse, and to discover the cylindrical helix as the geometric image of the infinite screw, a new and important labour-saving device.

In this work, Archytas became the first mathematician to define a curve as the intersection of 2 surfaces. This definition of the curve led Menaichmos of Alopekonnesos, who was a student in the mathematical school of Archytas' student Eudoxos of Knidos at Kyzikos, to the study of conic sections, which was a milestone in the development of mathematics. Moreover, the intersection of the cylinder and the torus gave a curve of double curvature – the first such curve defined in the history of mathematics. Archytas originated the use of a mechanically motivated mathematical model (***mesograph***) in the solution of this very difficult geometric problem having the form of a diagram in which geometrical segments moved on fixed curves as they would in a mechanical model. His example of the moving geometric figures in the solution of geometric problems, which was based on the principle of continuity not yet clearly formulated, was followed by his brilliant student Eudoxos, and the latter's pupil Menaichmos of Alopekonnesos, the discoverer of the general conic sections. Plato, an arrogant erstwhile friend of Archytas who at best had only a superficial grasp of geometry, had the impudence to castigate such ingenious and profound mathematicians as Archytas, Eudoxos and Menaichmos for using 'mechanical methods' in geometry, a subject of pure intellect which was clearly beyond Plato's intellectual competence, as being 'unworthy' of a 'true philosopher'. Many ancient Greek mathematicians had the wont to call the method of construction of the loci of any curve other than a straight line or a circle 'mechanical'. Archytas had introduced Plato to Pythagorean philosophy and mathematics during Plato's voluntary exile in Italy, and he also had helped to save Plato's life when the latter was imprisoned in Syracuse by the tyrant Dionysios the Younger.

It appears likely that the analytical method in mathematics was first explicitly used by Archytas in his mathematical works. Archytas conducted significant research in number theory in which he established three kinds of 'means': arithmetic, geometric and harmonic. By the time of

Archytas' researches, geometric knowledge had increased enormously, and the sheer mass of the results motivated Archytas to write the whole of available mathematics into a single connected mathematical system of propositions. He built up a universal arithmetic that is based on a rational theory of relations in which the arithmetic, the geometric and the harmonic mean occupy the central position. Archytas believed that arithmetic alone, not geometry, can give a valid proof in all disciplines of mathematics. Thus, Archytas placed arithmetic above geometry, which represented the traditional view of Pythagoreans, for his teacher, the astronomer Philolaos of Kroton had explained the whole creation by means of numbers in an arithmetic procedure rather than by means of figures in a geometric procedure, which made his arithmetic ontological since it assigned objective reality to arithmetical quantities. Philolaos had emphasised that anything that can be known to man has a number because it is impossible to recognise or comprehend anything with the mind without it. On the superiority of arithmetic, Archytas had this to say: "The art of arithmetic is far superior to other arts, for it deals more clearly with its subject matter than they do – even geometry. For even where geometry is baffled, arithmetic can complete the proof." This was a profound statement. The arithmetisation of mathematics was ultimately carried out by the German mathematician Karl Weierstrass (1815-1897) in the latter part of the 19th century A.D., which introduced considerable clarity into all aspects of mathematical analysis as Archytas had predicted.

Archytas certainly had realised that mathematics by itself cannot produce physical knowledge, and that the value of mathematics lies in its role as an intellectual instrument by means of which the subtler implications of empirical discoveries can be revealed but not invented, and the results of observations can be extended. Therefore, Archytas thought that mathematics should help to discover hidden truths, but it could not help to invent them. He classified arithmetic, geometry, astronomy and music as the four mathematical sciences, which became much later the mediæval ***quadrivium*** of learning in Europe. It appears that Archytas sought to establish a mathematical foundation for all sciences of his day which reflects the Pythagorean, as well as the modern Western viewpoint of science.

Archytas as the leading Pythagorean was also a noted astronomer, because the Pythagoreans invented the astronomical system of the world as it is understood today. Archytas believed that the universe as an astronomical system was infinite in extent.

About 388 B.C. Plato came to visit Archytas, whom Plato considered to be the ideal prototype for a philosopher-king. He purchased the book of Philolaos on the Pythagorean doctrine through the mediation of Archytas.

Birth of the Inductive Method in Science

By the time of the Peloponnesian War between Athens and Sparta lasting from 431 B.C. to 404 B.C., science and religion had already reached a state of conflict. The important accomplishment of this period was the development of philosophy and sciences as independent disciplines. The famous physician, Hippokrates of the island of Kos (460-c.360 B.C.) became the first savant to separate science, in this case, the medical science, from Ionian natural philosophy. The natural philosophy had been almost wholly devoted to the enquiries or speculations about the Earth, the heavens, and the universe. Hippokrates of Kos divorced science from the speculative natural philosophy, and became the first man of science who systematically put rational conceptions to the test of experience. The Hippokratic method in medicine was inductive as a scientific procedure for it carefully generalised from actual particular experiences, a generalisation which relied on the principle of invariant universal sequence of cause-and-effect in the physical world. Hippokrates of Kos asserted that to find the fundamental nature, the ***physis*** of a thing, its ***dynamis***, that is, its capacity to act or be acted upon, must be carefully examined.

Plato, Academy and Principles of Knowledge:

With Plato [he was called in Greek ***Platon***, a nickname derived from ***platys*** meaning 'broad', probably on account of his broad shoulders, for he was a former Olympic athlete in ***pankration***, a combination of a boxing and wrestling, a kicking and strangling fight to the finish, and his broad scope of knowledge; his real name was ***Aristokles***], philosophy entered a new phase, in which it almost parted company with natural philosophy. A large part of Plato's philosophy was devoted to speculation on the human mind and human condition, and the progress of the same. Therefore, Platonic philosophy represented essentially a mental and moral, rather than a natural philosophy. In this respect, Plato was influenced by his teacher Sokrates.

Although Plato himself had meagre ability in mathematics, he held mathematical knowledge important, apparently having been impressed by his mathematics teacher Theodoros of Kyrene, the mathematician Timaios of Lokri, and the ingenious mathematician Archytas of Taras. After the execution of Sokrates in 399 B.C., Plato left Athens and travelled extensively abroad to Kyrene, Egypt, Sicily and Southern Italy, where he met the leading Pythagorean mathematicians Archytas and Timaios.

Plato learnt all that had been done in philosophy, subjected it to a searching criticism of his own, and subsequently established his own philosophical system on an unprecedented prodigious scale. Plato presented his discussions of question after question about the nature of reality and knowledge in the dialogue form which he expressed in an interesting language that makes Plato one of the most influential writers in the history of Western literature. Although Plato did not originate the dialogue as a literary form, for Sophron of Sicily had already written simple dialogues in the 5th century B.C., but he did give it a dramatic form. Plato demonstrated in his writings that philosophy can be a literature of considerable cultural merit. Most of Plato's popular writings are extant, and his dialogues have served as models of exposition to important Western writers throughout the history of Western civilisation despite the fact that he was careless, imprecise, prolix, obscure in meaning, and labyrinthine in his prose, particularly in his later years.

Plato returned to Athens in 387 B.C., when he was more than 40 years of age, and began to teach at the Academy (***Akademeia***), a school of higher learning which he established in a sacred grove of a hero, ***Akademos***, located 6 stadia (0.59 miles or 0.94 km) from the western gate of Athens near which Plato owned some property. It was a private institution which had the legal status of a religious association (***thiasos***) typical of all schools but without formal membership. Plato not only taught special knowledge, such as introductory logic and a smattering of elementary mathematics, but also the principles of knowledge, of education, of ethics, and politics. Plato's teaching was informal, a kind of symposium. Plato aimed to teach his students the love of knowledge and wisdom, and in this way, to make philosophers, and perhaps even statesmen of them. Plato's advice to his students was that they must become slaves to knowledge, instead of being slaves to the body and its lusts as men are by nature, which requires not only hard work but also unrelenting effort that withstands disappointment. The Academy, which resembled in organisation the Pythagorean school in Taras, Plato conducted according to the Pythagorean principle: the search for knowledge as the greatest purification of the soul. The basic subjects of study in the Academy were physics comprised of natural sciences such as zoology and botany, and mathematics consisting of arithmetic, 2- and 3-dimensional geometry, astronomy and harmonics. The last 4 subjects he adopted from the Pythagorean school in Taras which was under the direction of Archytas. Plato's Academy is the longest lasting educational institution in history for it existed over 9 centuries, from 387 B.C. to A.D. 529, when it was finally closed by the Byzantine Emperor Iustinianus for being a school of 'perverse' pagan learning.

In one aspect of education Plato, who as a dedicated misogynist rather disliked women, was surprisingly modern and progressive. He maintained that the gifts of nature are equally diffused in both sexes, and that all the pursuits of men are also the pursuits of women, since a woman is only a 'weaker man'. Hence, in Plato's opinion women are to be educated and made adaptable to the services in society as well as men are. The education of women is to be based on the same principles as the education of men, and to include the same subjects however much they may differ in detail. It took more than 20 centuries before the Western civilisation finally caught up with Plato's progressive idea on the education of women, but as astounding as it is the theocratic Muslim countries in their hoary backwardness still obstinately cling today to their religious bigotry against women by regarding what Plato called the'weaker sex' unworthy of education.

Plato had essentially a mathematical outlook owing to the influence of Pythagoreans, and he believed that geometry trains the mind for rigorous, logical, vigorous and correct thinking and, therefore, he filled his writings with mathematical discoveries, and attempted to demonstrate on every occasion the remarkable connexion between mathematics and philosophy. Plato placed an inscription over the porch of his Academy: "Let no one ignorant of geometry enter here (***medeis ageometretos eisito***)," the first known admission precept of a school. Thus, in the opinion of Plato, knowledge of geometry was a necessary preparation for the study of philosophy. When Plato was questioned about the occupation of god, he answered: "God always geometrises." According to Plato, doing mathematics was a divine occupation, and he sought in geometry and arithmetic the key to the understanding of the universe and the pathway to the truth. Plato said: "Geometry will draw the soul towards the truth and create the spirit of philosophy [the love of the truth]." Plato expressed himself about arithmetic, as follows: "... arithmetic has a very great and elevating effect, compelling the mind to reason about abstract number ... Those who are born with a talent for it are quick at learning, whilst even those who are slow at it have their intellect much increased by studying it ... No branch of education is so valuable a preparation for household management (***oikonomeia***) and politics (***poleiteia***), all arts and crafts (***techne***), and sciences and professions, as arithmetic; least of all by some divine art, it arouses the dull and sleepy mind, and makes it studious, mindful and sharp ... The study of mathematics develops and sets into operation a mental creation more valuable than a thousand eyes, for through it alone can truth be apprehended." In his old age Plato became extremely critical of people who lacked mathematical competence, when he shamefully admitted that he himself became acquainted with irrational numbers only late in life, and that many people who "hardly deserve to be called human beings" have never heard of the subject.

Plato believed that it is necessary for an intelligent man not only to acquire intellect but also to develop the will to see things as they really are in order to become a critical rational thinker, and this will man must cultivate in himself, by himself, for himself, and make it into his native habit. Yet Plato himself seemed to fall short of the willpower to see things as they really were.

Plato was fascinated by geometry and the wonders of numbers as much as he was fascinated by myths, but he did no original work in mathematics because he had no talent in mathematics. Plato's frequent grandiloquent pronouncements in mathematics were rather like desert winds deficient in solid substance. Although Plato himself was not actually competent in mathematics like Aristotle, he did encourage mathematical studies in his Academy, and challenged mathematically talented members of the Academy to improve the logical methods of mathematics. Plato himself tried to use elementary logic in his philosophy, and he often attempted to argue with words as if they were mere geometric symbols. He stressed the abstract nature of mathematics by insisting that mathematical entities are purely 'imaginary objects' of the mind. It is mainly due to the influence of Plato's reputation as the foremost Western philosopher and thinker who extravagantly extolled mathematics in his dialogues that mathematics first acquired its unified significance in Western culture. In response to Plato's suggestions, accurate definitions were formulated, questions of possibility considered, methods of proof criticised and systematised, and logical rigour emphasised by his mathematically talented members of the Academy. It is proper to assume that the philosophy of mathematics as a subject really began in the Academy, and it is principally through the influence of Plato's Academy that mathematics as an intellectual discipline has retained its importance in the academic and the technical education in the Occident till this very day.

The ingenious Eudoxos of Knidos was instrumental in the systematisation of analysis, which had been implicitly used by Hippokrates of Chios and explicitly employed by his teacher Archytas, through the establishment of the method of analysis as a legitimate instrument of geometric investigation by giving rules for its application. In ancient Greek mathematics, the terms analysis and synthesis had somewhat different meanings from their present meanings. Analysis was the reverse method to synthesis. The oldest extant definition of analysis stems from Eudoxos of Knidos: "Analysis is the obtaining of the thing sought by assuming it and so reasoning up to an admitted truth; synthesis is the obtaining of the thing sought by reasoning down to the inference and proof of it." Since the validity of the analytical method depends upon the reversibility of all the operations used, therefore in the analytic proof, one works from the unknown to the known, and the necessary condition is found for the truth of that which is to be proven. In other words, analytic proof consists of assuming the proposition to be proven to be true, or untrue, and then by working backwards, step-by-step, through the assumptions involved until a premise is reached the truth or falsehood of which is known at least under certain conditions. Leon, a disciple of mathematician Neokleides and a member of the Academy, made use of Eudoxos' analytical method, which led him to the discovery of a general method for the mathematical assessment of geometric problems ***(diorismos)*** consisting of the statement of the conditions which show whether or not the problem is solvable, whether there are any limitations to the solution, and what path the solution should follow in order to find all solutions. Leon was also able to assemble a mathematical treatise < The Elements > (***ta stoicheia***). The Greek mathematicians such as Leodamas of Thasos followed Eudoxos of Knidos by adding the synthetic proof to the analytic proof which consisted of the reversion of all operations in the analysis, since the purpose of the method of analysis was to discover synthetic proofs or solutions. The synthetic proof, in contrast, proceeds deductively from the known to the unknown with unimpeachable logical validity by demonstrating that the necessary condition is also sufficient. ***Reductio ad absurdum*** is a particular kind of analytic proof and so is an algebraic proof. The synthesis and the analysis together constitute the so-called 'if, and only if' proof in mathematics. It appears that Leodamas of Thasos, was the first member of the Academy to apply explicitly the method of analysis as formulated by Eudoxos to geometric proofs.

Plato objected to the solutions of the problem of 'duplication of the cube' as given by the ingenious mathematicians Archytas, Eudoxos and Menaichmos because they used mechanically motivated mathematical devices other than the admissible compass and ruler and, for this reason, he called their solutions 'mechanical' rather than 'geometrical'. Plato considered the use of mechanical devices in the solution of the mathematical problems a material vulgarisation and a debasement of mathematics, a discipline of pure intellect which is concerned with unembodied and incorruptible objects. Unfortunately, he was completely wrong because of his ignorance in such higher order mathematics. It appears that the Greek astronomer and mathematician Oinopides of Chios (c.500-c.430 B.C.), a younger contemporary of Anaxagoras and the first Greek astronomer to refer to the obliquity of the ecliptic, laid down the restriction that only the ruler and the compass are permissible for all 'plane' constructions, that is, for all problems which in terms of modern algebra are equivalent to algebraic equations of degree no higher than second. It is a method of construction which gives preference to the straight line and the circle as the favoured geometric figures. It has been established in modern times that not only the 'duplication of the cube' problem, but also the 'squaring of the circle' and the 'trisection of the angle' problem cannot be solved by means of a compass and a ruler as Plato thought in his mathematical ignorance, since these problems are equivalent to third degree algebraic equations which cannot be solved by a compass and a ruler, something that only an ingenious mathematician such as Archytas could intuitively recognised. Plato's rejection of 'mechanically motivated' mathematical devices in the solution of mathematical problems led to the unfortunate separation of mechanics from mathematics and, thenceforth, mechanics came to be regarded as a technical art ***(techne)***, a branch of study of military engineers.

Plato adopted the philosophical doctrine of ideas from mathematics, which took for granted that there exists a world of ideal forms (***noumena***), such as geometric shapes, and so on, of which everything material (***phenomena***) is only an imperfect reflexion of an idea. The ideal forms are imperishable and their recognition is intrinsic to man's mind, whereas the corresponding material objects are imperfect and perishable. This type of Platonic thinking is called 'idealism' the origin of which was in the Pythagorean theory of forms. In Plato's view, and in this he followed Sokrates, who in turn had followed Pythagoreans, all ideal knowledge already preexists in the mind of men at birth, and it only has to be 'led out', in Latin, ***ex ducere***, from which comes the term to 'educt' and to 'educate'. Thus Plato, by asserting that ideal forms [ideas] exist independently of the material particulars, or the concretes, indirectly depreciated the importance of sense perception and experience.

Being influenced by the explosive development of geometry from an empirical science to an abstract, deductive science, Plato suggested that other sciences be developed in a similar manner, a suggestion which did promote the advancement of scientific theories. In fact, in his dialogue ***Philebos*** Plato went as far as to say: "Each science is science only so far as it contains mathematics." Plato minimised the importance of sensory experience and, thereby, also experiment in science because he considered geometry, and now also other sciences, to be related to the ideal world of the forms which is accessible only through thought. In his approach to science, Plato was more of a cosmologist, a metaphysician, and a visionary, than a true scientist. His astronomical knowledge being of Pythagorean origin, was badly out-of-date and unscientific even in comparison with his Pythagorean contemporaries. In science, Plato never proved any of his wild and bizarre guesses or irrational fantasies expressed mostly in obfuscated riddles. In general, his vague, muddled and unintelligible 'scientific' language resembled more the jargon of a sorcerer than the concise and precise idiom of a scientist. Plato pompously demanded that every artist, like every philosopher, should have a 'true' knowledge of his art by thinking things through to their transcendental ideas which reveal their 'true' meaning.

Plato believed in the rational, mathematical structure of the universe, a conviction he adopted from the Pythagoreans due to the influence of Archytas, who was the head of the Pythagorean society at the time. Curiously, Plato's dogmatic belief in the mathematical astronomy and physics was influential in the progress of science some 2 thousand years later in Europe. Plato apparently believed that observation is inferior to abstract thought rather than observation is worthless as was implied later by Neoplatonic philosophers, as his promotion of 'save the appearance of the phenomena', an early example of a form of positivism which was evidently first proposed relative to astronomy by the visiting young scholar Eudoxos of Knidos, seems to indicate. Plato's Academy indirectly promoted the quest for a more detailed and elaborate knowledge of natural phenomena, although Plato himself was not competent enough to make any positive contribution to real science.

Plato attempted to give the doctrine of the constitution of matter of Empedokles of Akragas a logical form by renaming the 'roots' ***(rhizomata)*** of Empedokles 'elements'***(stoicheia)*** the original meaning of which was 'letters'. He imagined the combinations of the 4 elements into compound substances to be analogous to the combination of letters into words. This analogy with the alphabet Plato adopted from Demokritos of Abdera, who had used it in his explanation of the atomic theory in which atoms were analogous to letters (***stoicheia***), molecules to syllables, and material objects to words. Demokritos used the analogy of atoms to the alphabet in order to explain how atoms make up material objects just like letters make up words, and how a material object is more than the sum of its atoms just like a word is more than a sum of its letters. Moreover, Plato was probably the first to assume the 2 forces of Empedokles which unite and separate the elements to be 'immaterial', rather than material as Empedokles had thought, which was a truly valuable modern concept. He tried to give mathematical and theoretical reasons for limiting the number of elements to 4 by expressing them in a fanciful continued proportion: fire : air = air : water = water : earth. In another attempt he tried to assign geometric forms to the elements by using the regular polyhedra as given by the Pythagorean Philolaos of Kroton: earth as *cube*, water as *icosahedron*, air as *octahedron*, and fire as *tetrahedron*. Since Philolaos also gave a 5th regular polyhedron, the *dodecahedron*, Plato presumed that there must be a 5th element, ***aither***, which he ultimately believed was the constituent of heavenly bodies. All these mathematically motivated fantasies proposed by Plato as 'scientific' explanations remained vague and enigmatic, and only his idea of the immaterial interacting forces reappeared again many centuries later during the waning years of the Roman Empire. Sometimes Plato's vague statement: "How can that be real which is never in the same state?" was interpreted to imply that conservation of matter is operative in nature.

It is clear that Platonic theory of nature tended to produce the ***a priori,*** or formalistic thinker who strives to fit nature to his preconceived intellectual scheme. In this way Plato promoted the formalistic approach to science, particularly after the ingenious Eudoxos of Knidos had demonstrated in his mathematical astronomy a construction of the Solar system by means of an ingenious system of abstract homocentric spheres as a purely abstract mathematical concept.

It was a great consternation to Plato, that no perfect regularity could be discerned in the observed planetary motions. It motivated Plato to urge all students at the Academy to attempt to discover what set of ordered and uniform circular motions of the planets would account for the apparent movements of the planets according to a dialogue written by a member of the Academy, Herakleides of Pontos. Plato suggested to the scholars of his Academy to apply the Sokratic hypothetico-deductive method to the definite physical problem of the heavens. The first person to meet Plato's suggestion successfully was Eudoxos of Knidos, a visiting scholar at the Academy. Eudoxos, an ingenious young mathematician, proved that it is possible to represent the motions of celestial bodies by a mathematically expressed kinematical system in which the motions of the planets are fixed in order, although the causes or the rules producing the well-ordered motions of planets might not be known, yet one could be certain that there were such rules for order which could be called 'natural laws'. Therefore, Eudoxos' mathematical theory of astronomy lent support to the conviction that there exists in nature a general fixed order which can be expressed by well-defined mathematical laws about nature.

Plato equated order with intelligence, and supreme order of repetitive celestial motions with supreme intelligence. He thought that the eternal accuracy of the repetitious order of the planetary movements reveals the supreme divine intelligence of the planets. In the opinion of Plato, stars and planets must be gods who are in communication with men on Earth, which he thought is proven by their visibility to men on Earth, thereby indicating that something passes from the stars to men. Plato suggested in a number of his dialogues the adoption of the cult of the stars as an astrological State religion, since astronomy besides being the very pinnacle of scientific knowledge is also a rational astrological theology. Astrological divination became feasible after the general acceptance of certain assumptions and conventions, and after the 'scientific horoscopes' had been successfully established. Plato explained the astrological religion in his last posthumous work ***Epinomis,*** edited by Philippos of Opus, which served as an appendix to Plato's < Laws >, but Aristotle's endorsement of the astral theology in his early years as a young man at the Academy when he still accepted Plato's metaphysics, but later rejected in his scientific investigations, made the new astral religion seem rational, and thereby contributed to its popularity in Hellenistic times as a 'kind of science' that was accepted by the intellectual elite both in Hellenistic Greece and in Roman Empire.

Plato is popularly known as the foremost Occidental man of letters and learning, but regrettably his enormous prestige is to a great extent a legend. The cult of Plato as a man of universal learning began during the Byzantine period in the 9th and the 10th century A.D., then continued under the patronage of the School of Chartres in the 11th and the 12th century A.D., and ultimately under the patronage of the Platonic Academy in Florence during the Italian Renaissance in the 16th century A.D.. The legend of Plato as a supremely learned man of the West was mostly fabricated by the literati who worshipped the grandiloquent language of Plato for its beauty but who deliberately overlooked, or just did not understand what Plato, a mere sciolist, actually wrote about science. The vagueness, obscurity, and bizarre absurdity of Plato's fantasies about science were taken by the literati for its profundity, and downright nonsense was accepted as his unique originality. Plato's irrational eagerness to mathematise everything conceivable was taken for his profound insight into the nature of science. For centuries most literary scholars have regarded ***Timaios,*** a dialogue of Plato chock-full of wild and woolly cosmological fantasies and scientific aberrations, as his main 'scientific' work. Actually, the works of Plato as a mathematician and scientist appear almost like travesties in comparison with similar works of such truly brilliant and ingenious contemporary mathematicians and scientists as Eudoxos of Knidos and his teacher Archytas of Taras, both of whom were men of indisputable genius. For the sake of Plato's legendary popular reputation, which is enormous, the scholarly translators of Plato's dialogues deemed it advisable to alter the precise meaning of some of Plato's statements in their translations.

Eudoxos of Knidos, Method of Exhaustion and Mathematical Rigour:

Eudoxos of Knidos, Ionia (c.408-c.355 B.C.), was a student of Philistion of Lokroi in medicine, and of Archytas of Taras in mathematics and astronomy. He was never a student of Plato. Quite to the contrary, Plato being conspicuously ignorant of genuine science and, particularly, of sophisticated mathematics needed to learn these subjects from Eudoxos, an ingenious young man, a born genius who was, and still is, one of the greatest mathematicians of all time. Eudoxos together with Archimedes of Syracuse (c.287-212 B.C.) rank as not only the greatest mathematicians of antiquity but also of modern age. In 385 B.C., during his scholarly journey to Athens as an impecunious 23-year old precocious philomath whose travelling expenses were defrayed by the physician Theomedon, Eudoxos paid daily visits to Athens where he attended lectures on oratory, natural philosophy, and also lectures at the Academy, which had been opened in 387 B.C., from the harbour city Peiraieus where he remained for 2 months after disembarking, because he could not afford living accommodations in Athens during his 2-months stay. It took him 2 hours to walk the 6 miles (9.7 km) from Peiraieus to Athens, and 2 hours back to Peiraieus each day. Eudoxos, who was a brilliant theoretical scientist in the modern sense, apparently became fed up with Plato's wild unscientific speculations and metaphysical fantasies about the cosmos after 2 months, and decided to return home to Knidos. About 380 B.C. Eudoxos went with the physician Chrysippos of Knidos to Heliopolis in Egypt where he spent 16 months learning astronomical knowledge from the priests of Heliopolis as well as making astronomical observations.

Eudoxos was a physician, mathematician, astronomer, geographer, natural philosopher, connoisseur of law, legislator, and an accomplished orator – in other words, a complete or universal man. In comparison with Eudoxos, Plato was an unaccomplished mediocre dilettante in all these learned disciplines. Eratosthenes of Kyrene called Eudoxos 'godlike (***theoudes***)' in his letter about the duplication of the cube problem to the King of Egypt, Ptolemaios Evergetes, who was a mathematician. After Egypt, Eudoxos went to the city of Kyzikos at the ***Propontis*** (the Sea of Marmara) where he founded his school of mathematical sciences to which many talented students were attracted. Eudoxos had also spent some time as a teacher at the court of King Mausolos of Karia in Halikarnassos, Ionia. About 368 B.C., Eudoxos, who was 40 years of age at the time and a distinguished mathematician, astronomer and natural philosopher widely admired for his enormous erudition, visited Plato's Academy in the company of a group of his pupils where at a festive symposium Eudoxos and Plato had an animated debate about the philosophy of science. Eudoxos was the greatest mathematician and the foremost theoretical scientist of the Hellenic age, whereas Plato in contrast was a mere speculative metaphysical smatterer in science whose exiguous mathematical competence and bizarre unscientific imagination were necessarily exposed to the public in this open debate with the erudite and brilliant Eudoxos.

About 370 B.C. Eudoxos solved the logical crises in Greek mathematics exposed by the logical paradoxes of Zenon of Elea by a deductive reorganisation of geometry on the basis of axioms, and a new emphasis on strictly rigorous geometry. He showed that irrational numbers could be represented in terms of continuous geometric magnitudes rather than in terms of natural discrete numbers of arithmetic by introducing the idea of magnitude as an abstraction for such entities as a line segment, an angle, an area, a volume, and time, which varied continuously but had no quantitative, that is, no numerical value. Therefore, Eudoxos' magnitudes were merely abstractions in mathematical logic and elements of reasoning in mathematical relations, and they reduced the mathematical concepts to their most general form with respect to the theory of proportions. It appears, moreover, that Eudoxos is probably the founder of the syllogism which Aristotle made later into a formal discipline of logic. He developed a general theory of proportions which became necessary because of the revolutionary discovery of irrational numbers (***alogos***) about 388 B.C. by Theodoros of Kyrene (*floruit* c.390 B.C.), Plato's teacher of mathematics, and by Theaitetos of Herakleia (c.415-368 B.C.), a disciple of Sokrates and a Pythagorean, who apparently created a systematic theory of numbers. Eudoxos precluded the necessity of dealing with irrational numbers as numbers by not assigning numerical values to his magnitudes. His purely geometric theory of proportions in a strict axiomatic form was a science of relations surpassing geometric shapes and numbers, since his magnitudes were comparable to modern algebraic quantities which geometrised the ratios of magnitudes and took into account the geometric continuity, thereby making possible its application to all ratios regardless of whether they were commensurable or not. His purely geometric theory of proportions in a strict axiomatic form was stated by him in the following postulate: If (A,B) and (C,D) are two pairs of magnitudes, then the two proportions $A : B$ and $C : D$ are equal if, and only if, $mA : nB = mC : nD$, whatever the whole numbers m and n. If $m\text{A} > n\text{B}$ implies $m\text{C} > n\text{D}$, then $m\text{A} = n\text{B}$ implies $m\text{C} = n\text{D}$, and $m\text{A} < n\text{B}$ implies $m\text{C} < n\text{D}$.

This definition depended upon an important postulate, the Axiom of Eudoxos: 'Magnitudes have a ratio to one another which are capable, when multiplied, of exceeding one another'.

Since the quantities of Eudoxos were all geometric, he had no need to give a definition of a number and, therefore, had no necessity to regard the ratio of two incommensurable quantities as a number. In geometrising the theory of proportions to exclude number-theoretical considerations, Eudoxos revealed his profound mathematical insight since the theory of numbers is an incredibly complex subject of mathematics even today. His purely geometric theory of proportions was ingenious, but like all good deeds there was a price to be paid for it and this price had an unfortunate effect: it veered Greek mathematics away from number theory because it drove a wedge between the number and the geometry, and made geometry the basis of virtually all rigorous mathematics for almost two millennia. The Pythagorean mathematics as presented by Eudoxos' teacher Archytas had stressed the number as the fundamental concept of mathematics. Eudoxos defined numbers as some points on a line ordered by increasing distance from one end, or what is now called a 'cut' as a division of this domain into two sections a and b, having no members in common where $b > a$. Such a 'cut' defines a number, now called the 'Dedekind cut', where a has a maximum or b a minimum.

But in other cases when a consists of all rational numbers such that $a^2 < 2$ and $b^2 > 2$, a will have no rational maximum and b no rational minimum. There will be a 'gap' given by 'a, b', and the 'cut' itself can be regarded as a new kind of number which is not rational, such as $\sqrt{2}$. This method is quite modern, since Eudoxos' postulate is virtually identical to the definition of real numbers in A.D. 1872 by the German mathematician Richard Dedekind (1831-1916), because it does separate the class of rational numbers m/n into 2 categories: $mA \leq nB$, or $mA > nB$. The ancient Greek mathematicians wished to avoid what are now called infinite sets of numbers because there are infinitely many rational numbers. Eudoxos made it possible by means of his theory of proportions to give rigorous proofs at least to theorems involving proportions, thereby meeting successfully the logical crises in Greek mathematics which had been created by the discovery of the 'incommensurable'. The modern exposition of irrational numbers as given by Richard Dedekind and the German mathematician Karl Weierstrass follows essentially the magnificent treatment of 'incommensurables' by Eudoxos, but because they were able to use modern arithmetical methods it opened up much wider mathematical vistas.

Another basic problem remained to be solved: the problem of comparing curved geometric figures with rectilinear figures. Demokritos of Abdera had derived the solution to the volumes of the pyramid and the cone, but his infinitesimal method consisting of stacks of thin indivisible atomic layers making up the cone and the pyramid was logically untenable to most Greek geometers. The method of Antiphon, based on the indivisible line segment, or fixed infinitesimal was conceptually too obscure, and violated the notion of infinite divisibility of space that virtually all Greek geometers accepted. Therefore, Eudoxos replaced Antiphon's controversial proof of the area of the circle with two alternate lines of reasoning: if the area of the circle is more or less than the product of half its circumference and its radius then contradictions arise which make both of these two alternatives absurdities. This rigorous method for solving such problems required two additional principles: an Axiom of Continuity, which is often mistakenly called the 'Lemma of Archimedes', and a proposition of 'exhaustion'. Eudoxos recognised that the Axiom of Continuity is a necessary ***a priori*** postulate, which is neither self-evident nor provable: Let A and B be 2 points of a straight line and C an arbitrary point to the right of B, then it is always possible to lay off the distance AB to the right of B a sufficient number of times to reach eventually a point D beyond the point C. Arithmetically, it can be stated as follows: let ϵ be a positive, arbitrarily small number, then a sufficiently large integer N exists such that $N\epsilon > 1$. This axiom, the cornerstone of number theory, is an intellectual feat which alone makes Eudoxos one of the greatest mathematicians of all time. This axiom of Eudoxos became very important when the modern arithmetic continuum was created in the 19th century A.D.. The principle of exhaustion of Eudoxos stated that if more than ½ (or any other larger fraction) of a magnitude is taken from the same magnitude, and again from the remainder more than its ½, and this process is repeated a certain number of times, then a remainder less than any assigned magnitude can be obtained. This proposition is equivalent to the modern statement that if M is a given magnitude, ϵ a preassigned magnitude of the same kind, and r is a ratio such that $\frac{1}{2} < r < 1$, then a positive integer N exists such that $M(1-r)^n < \epsilon$ for all positive integers $n > N$. This principle of Eudoxos is therefore an inchoate **(δ-ϵ)** method, which is equivalent to the modern theory of limits when $n \to \infty$:

$$\lim_{n \to \infty} M(1-r)^n = 0$$

Since Eudoxos did not have this formal symbolic subterfuge in mathematics available to him, he had to deal with the sequence of inequalities directly and substitute for the 'infinitely small magnitude' the finite concept of 'magnitude as small as we please'. The method of exhaustion is a genuine infinitesimal method that was based upon a rigorous concept of limit and, therefore, it could be easily transformed into a proof that satisfies all the requirements of modern analysis, which demonstrates the far-reaching genius of Eudoxos. He was the first to use inequalities in mathematics, and to study inequalities mathematically. This principle, which is the result of his discovery of the principal method of higher mathematics, the theory of limits, was not devised by Eudoxos to pass to the numerical limits but rather to avoid such limits. Eudoxos used the ***reductio ad absurdum*** argument, a logical device of the Eleatics, to prove this proposition which is the very basis of the 'method of exhaustion', a name given to Eudoxos' method by the Belgian Jesuit mathematician Gregoire De Saint-Vincent (A.D. 1584-1667) in his treatise ***Opus geometricum*** (A.D. 1647) in which he used the Latin word ***exhaurire*** (meaning 'to exhaust') for Eudoxos' method of quadrature of surfaces and cubature of volumes. Eudoxos applied his rigorous method of exhaustion to prove indirectly that the volume of a cone is ⅓ of its circumscribed cylinder, and theorems concerning the volumes of spheres and areas of circles. For instance, if Eudoxos wanted to prove that the ratio of the areas of two circles, a and A, are like the ratio of the square of their diameters d and D, i.e., $a/A = d^2/D^2$ then he proved by ***reductio ad absurdum*** arguments that the possibilities $a/A < d^2/D^2$ and $a/A > d^2/D^2$ are impossible because they lead to logical absurdities. By using the Antiphon's method of inscribed polygons, Eudoxos was able to prove that circles have areas proportional to the areas of regular polygons of *4*, *8*, *16*, *32*, ... sides inscribed in the circle. In his method the polygon could approach the circle as closely as desired by successive doubling, or subdivision of its sides, but it could never become a circle as a limit since that would mean that the process of subdivision of the sides of the polygon as a line segment had come to an end, a notion violating the postulate of infinite divisibility of space accepted by the ancient Greek mathematicians. Although Eudoxos could not use the numerical limit concept in his geometrical method of exhaustion, he was able to impose rigorously the geometrical limit concept which made the difference between the area of the circle and the area of the inscribed regular polygon as small as desired. The method of exhaustion does make Eudoxos the originator of the ideas basic to modern theories of continuum and infinitesimal calculus because he took the first decisive step using the rigorous geometrical rather than the numerical concept of the limit. Eudoxos was able to reduce problems which led to infinitesimals to problems involving only formal logic by means of his axiom and his geometric theory of proportions. The method of Eudoxos was logically rigorous but particular: a special demonstration had to be given to each particular case considered. It opened the way for the calculation of hitherto unapproachable problems of volume and surface area of curved bodies, because in Greek geometry circles and squares, for instance, were not commensurable with one another, but with Eudoxos' new geometric definition of dimensionless proportions it was possible to compare squares with squares, and circles with circles in the non-numerical ratios of magnitudes involved in the comparisons. His arguments were founded on finite, intuitively clear, and logically precise considerations. Eudoxos seems to have been the first to establish the deductive organisation of mathematics on the basis of explicit axioms, and to found the theory of irrationals on a thoroughly rigorous mathematical basis which is the only sound approach known to irrational number theory. He was the first mathematician to generalise the science of mathematics to encompass all existing mathematics of his time under the same system of axioms.

The remarkable researches of Eudoxos, and also of Theaitetos, had a direct cultural influence, for they raised the science of Greek geometry to a much higher intellectual level of sophistication.

As mentioned above, Eudoxos was the first to give an answer to the challenge 'to save the phenomena' of planetary motions. Any such theory of planetary motion had to be able to describe two observed facts: that the planets from time to time went into retrograde motion because of the compound effect of the motion of the planet and the motion of the Earth, and that such a motion deviates from the ecliptic. He founded the science of spherical geometry which was necessary for his kinematic theory of astronomy, and he is known to have written the first treatise on stereometry. He worked out in great detail the celestial motions of important planets based on his theory of homocentric spheres which represented mathematical abstractions and not material bodies whilst having scrupulous regard for the Egyptian astronomical observations, which, unfortunately, were few and not very accurate. In order to give a geometric account of the motions of planets, Eudoxos found that he needed 3 spheres each for the Sun and the Moon, and 4 spheres for each of the planets, making a total of 27 spheres, all rotating with different angular speeds about different axes. It was the first attempt by any man to represent very complicated natural phenomena in terms of an abstract mathematical model, and it was adequate for the qualitative description of most of the astronomical phenomena known to ancient Greeks, but not all. Eudoxos was able to make the planet attached to a sphere pass through its characteristic synodic motion in proper order: first, appearance; second, retrograde motion having a lemniscate (∞ -shape) trajectory; third, last appearance near the ecliptic during a reasonably constant time interval called the 'synodic period' of the planet, and move forwards along the ecliptic during the same period a reasonably constant length. Eudoxos was able to produce this motion by means of 2 concentric spheres with slightly tilted axes which rotated in opposite directions, whilst the 3rd sphere moved the planet forwards along the ecliptic by rotating the entire configuration of the spheres. The retrograde trajectory formed a spherical lemniscate, the axis of symmetry of which lay in the ecliptic. Eudoxos was able to produce the spherical lemniscate, called horsefetter (***hippopede***), by the method of his teacher Archytas, as an intersection of a sphere and a touching cylinder. However, Eudoxos' theory had certain shortcomings, which created doubts about its accuracy: it did not include the variable velocity of the Sun and made a small error about its path of motion; it was unable to produce the retrograde motion of Venus; it did not describe well the actual motion of Mars; and its failure to account for the great changes observed in the brightness of planets Venus and Mars cast doubt on the basic assumption of Eudoxos that these planets in their orbits remained at a constant radial distance from the Earth. In spite of these shortcomings, the kinematic theory of planetary motion of Eudoxos was an elegant and brilliant example of Greek rational thought. Moreover, Eudoxos imagined that the movements of the heavenly bodies were in complete accord with natural mechanical laws, and he realised that the movement of each planet along its orbit that was kinematically determined by the rotating spheres is governed by 2 opposing and invariable forces produced by the oppositely rotating spheres. He assumed these interacting forces to be proportional to the distances separating their points of origin from their points of application, but he did not think that these forces originate from the bodies themselves through mutual actions although he had a notion that equilibrium exists between the 2 opposing and interacting forces. Therefore, Eudoxos visualised what might be called a particular universal law of gravitation. With this great intellectual feat in which theory and observation were reasonably well balanced, he became the founder of scientific astronomy and one of the greatest astronomers of all time.

Eudoxos built an observatory at Knidos, where he made astronomical observations and discovered the star Canopus. He was the first astronomer to introduce the idea of the 'leap year', and to propose the establishment of a star catalogue in his work < Phenomena > (***Phainomena***), a practical treatise on astronomy, which he later published in a revised edition under the title < Mirror> (***Enoptron***). He wrote a work < Maps of the Earth > (***Periodos ges***) in 7 books which was the first work of its kind containing a vast body of geodesic and topographic data, information on natural history, medicine, ethnology, and also religion in which he noted the importance of Zoroastrianism and gave information on Egyptian gods Isis and Osiris. He drew a new map of the world which was better than the map of Hekataios of Miletos (c.550-c.476 B.C.).

Hekataios, who had studied with Anaximandros, applied the rationalist tradition of Thales to the surface of Earth in an attempt to continue the work of Anaximandros to map the world. In 517 B.C. he divided the land into the northern part (Europe), the southern part (Africa) and the far-eastern part (India), the 3 continents forming a circle on the Earth's disk which is encircled by ***okeanus***, the 'ocean river'. Hekataios also rationalised history, by writing the first Greek account of the deeds of men who, like himself, were skeptical and even scornful of myths. Therefore, Hekataios is the real so-called 'father of history', a title usually reserved for Herodotos of Halikarnassos because his history has survived whereas the history of Hekataios has not. Eudoxos was far superior to all geographers of the 5th century B.C., and a true forerunner of Eratosthenes of Kyrene (276-194 B.C.).

Eudoxos also wrote a didactic poem in verse < Astronomy > (***Astronomia***), < Eight Year Cycle > (***Oktaeteris***) discussed the 8-year cycle, and a number of other books on a great variety of subjects. He was the first Greek astronomer to attempt to prepare a map of the stars by dividing the sky for this purpose into degrees of latitude and longitude, a method later transferred to the surface of the Earth itself for geographic mapping. He also gave the earliest known estimate of the circumference of the spherical Earth as 400,000 stadia which, however, was too large in comparison with the later estimate of 252,000 stadia by Eratosthenes that is larger by less than 4 percent of the correct value. He also improved the solid celestial globe of Thales by marking it with constellations and fixed stars. Moreover, Eudoxos was known as an orator gifted with persuasive eloquence.

Eudoxos was the first geometer to study geometry on a torus. He discovered the sections of the torus cut by planes parallel to the axis of revolution, which were quartic curves that are now called 'Cassinian ovals' after Giovanni Cassini (A.D. 1625-1712), an Italian astronomer, who thought that these ovals were the true planetary orbits of which Kepler's ellipses were mere approximations.

More accurate observations of Kallippos of Kyzikos (born c. 370 B.C.), a pupil of Eudoxos, made it apparent that the 27 spheres used by Eudoxos were inadequate and that 34 spheres were required to match his own observations. Some further improvements on the Eudoxos' planetary theory were later made by Autolykos of Pitane (*floruit* 325 B.C.), in a work which is the oldest complete mathematical treatise that has survived, and by Aristotle who introduced 56 spheres. Unfortunately, Aristotle took a backwards step in rejecting the abstract nature of Eudoxos' purely mathematical kinematic planetary theory by assuming the interlocking spheres to be material and made of crystal according to his belief in physical reality. Autolykos of Pitane tried to explain the changes in the brightness of the planets Venus and Mars in his book on spherical astronomy but he had little success.

Menaichmos of Alopekonnesos and Conic Sections:

Menaichmos (375-325 B.C.) of Alopekonnesos in Thrakia, a student of Eudoxos, discovered the parabolic and hyperbolic conic sections. He was led to the conic sections by his solution of the 'duplication of the cube' problem (also called the 'Delian Problem'), which had been reduced by Hippokrates of Chios to the finding of 2 mean proportionals (x, y) between a straight line segment and another one twice as long. This reduction replaced a solution of a cubic equation by that of 2 quadratic equations. Menaichmos found that the search for the 2 mean proportionals (x, y) in the duplication of the cube problem led to 2 solutions of the 2 quadratic equations in which the intersection of two conic sections with coinciding vertices at right angles to each other determined the point (x, y):

(a) Two parabolas $ay = x^2$ and $y^2 = bx$ in the first case, when $a/x = x/y = y/b$, where $b = 2a$.

(b) A parabola $ay = x^2$ and a rectangular hyperbola $xy = ab$ in the second case.

Menaichmos constructed these curves as intersections of the normal plane and the right circular cone. Menaichmos' geometry was based entirely on postulates rather than axioms which reduced his mathematics to a study of logic consisting of finding all the logical consequences of certain initial premises accepted by convention and recognised as hypothetical. Menaichmos used 'mechanical methods' of Archytas to construct the conic sections, for which he was severely criticised by Plato. However, it was mathematician Aristaios of Kroton (*floruit* c. 330 B.C.), who first sliced acute, right and obtuse cones with planes normal to the sloping surface of the cone to produce, respectively, ellipses, parabolas and hyperbolas as intersections of the planes and the cone, and who wrote the first systematic work on conic sections.

The mathematical investigation of the conic sections by Menaichmos, and the later extensive investigations of the conics by Apollonios of Perge (c.262-190 B.C.) became the springboard of the Scientific Revolution for the German mathematician and astronomer Johann Kepler (A.D. 1551-1630) in the 17th century A.D. Europe, which has had a profound influence on the Western civilisation. Therefore, the rapid advance of Western science was the long-delayed consequence of the discovery of the conic sections by Menaichmos about 350 B.C..

The astronomer and geometer Menaichmos later became one of the teachers of Alexandros III, known as Alexander the Great of Macedon, who is reported to have asked Menaichmos for a shortcut to geometric knowledge, and to whom Menaichmos is reported to have answered : "O King, for travelling over the country there are royal roads and roads for common citizens, but in geometry there is one road for all."

Deinostratos of Alopekonnesos, brother of Menaichmos and another talented pupil of Eudoxos, was also an outstanding mathematician. He was the first to solve the problem of the 'quadrature of the circle' by using the trisectrix of Hippias in the application of which he needed to carry out a certain limiting process. The use Deinostratos made of the curve of Hippias in the quadrature of the circle is responsible for naming the curve 'quadratrix'.

Herakleides of Pontos and Geoheliocentric Planetary System:

Herakleides of Pontos (c.388-c.315 B.C.), a Pythagorean who for a time was attending Plato's Academy, admired Empedokles of Akragas and tried to emulate him. About 350 B.C. he developed his world system in which he conceived the universe to be infinite in extent and made up of jointless particles, in contrast to the atoms of Demokritos of Abdera, which were held together by attraction of the kind postulated by Empedokles. The astronomical observations by his time had shown that the inferior planets Mercury and Venus which were usually seen as the morning or evening stars never were farther from the Sun than approximately 29 degrees for Mercury and 47 degrees for Venus whereas the superior planets Mars, Jupiter and Saturn were located at any angular distance from the Sun. In order to account for these particular facts, Herakleides conceived a new planetary system, the geoheliocentric system, in which Mercury and Venus revolved round the Sun which in turn revolved round the stationary Earth, whereas the planets, Mars, Jupiter and Saturn revolved round the Earth as their physical center. Therefore, Herakleides' planetary system was geocentric for the Moon, Sun, Mars, Jupiter and Saturn, and heliocentric for Mercury and Venus, a system which led to relatively good explanation of the planetary theory. Herakleides treated the motion of the heliocentric planets Mercury and Venus by the epicyclic theory of his own invention that employed 2 circles, the deferent and the epicycle, in which the stationary deferent is concentric with the Earth and the center of the epicycle moves on the deferent with a constant speed whilst the planet moves along the epicycle with a different uniform speed. Herakleides remarked in his dialogue that at that time some astronomers were already using the eccentric theory of planetary motion in which a circle is rotating about the Earth which is eccentric with respect to the center of the circle whilst the planet moves with a uniform speed along the circle. About 2 millennia later, in A.D. 1583, another geoheliocentric planetary system was devised by the Danish astronomer of Swedish descent Tyge Brahe (A.D. 1546-1601), who was the last and the greatest naked-eye observational astronomer with the possible exception of the ancient Greek astronomer Hipparchos of Nikaia (c.186-125 B.C.).

Aristotle and Aristotelian Science:

Aristotle of Stageira (a city at the border of Macedon) in Thrakia is generally recognised as the greatest scientist and polymath who ever lived. Aristotelian science and philosophy is a formidable body of knowledge of which only those parts pertinent to science, technology and engineering can be discussed here. Aristotle was a philosopher, a scientist, a man of letters, and an encyclopædist who sought to organise and to unify the whole of human knowledge, a colossal undertaking for a single individual scholar. He had an enormous scope of intellectual interests and profound learning which makes Aristotle the best educated man of any age.

Aristotle, a Macedonian youth, attended Plato's Academy for a few years subsequent to which he spent about 20 years studying in Athens, and 3 years, from 347 to 344 B.C., in Assos where he married and really came into his own as a scientist. When he was attending the Academy, Plato called Aristotle 'the intellect of the school' (***nous tes diatribes***) because of the brilliance and intense scholarly sedulity of the young Aristotle.

Aristotle was the son of the noted personal physician Nikomachos to the Macedonian King Philip II, and he was appointed tutor of Prince Alexandros III from 343 B.C. to 336 B.C. at the Macedonian court in Pella. In 335 B.C., when Aristotle was 50 years of age, he returned to Athens and established a school and research center known as the Lyceum (***Lykaion***) on the grounds of the Temple of Apollo the Wolf-God (***Apollon-Lykaios***) located about 6 stadia (0.59 miles or 0.94 km) from the eastern gate of Athens where other teachers besides Aristotle also gave lectures. The Lyceum was much more like a school in the modern sense than the Academy. Aristotle used the covered walks (***peripatoi***) of the Temple for teaching, and for this reason the scholars of the Lyceum are usually called 'Peripatetics'.

Aristotle as a bibliophile collected the first great personal library of scholarly manuscripts worthy of its name. For the sake of scholarly literature he asked many of his assistants and students to write histories of various intellectual subjects: Theophrastos of Eresos (c.372-c.288 B.C.) [***Theophrastos*** meaning 'divine speech' was a nickname given to him by Aristotle who took great delight in his eloquent conversations; his real name was ***Tyrtamos***] was primarily a man of science and a prodigious scholar who wrote 227 treatises in his lifetime. He is regarded the founder of scientific botany who formerly had attended Academy like Aristotle. He later became one of the students of Aristotle at the Lyceum where he wrote a work about the views of the ancients on the main problems of natural philosophy, whereas Menon composed a book of extracts from the literature of medicine, Eudemos of Rhodos wrote a history of mathematics and astronomy, and Aristoxenos of Taras wrote a book on the history of music. The eloquent Theophrastos enjoyed a widespread reputation as a spellbinding teacher and lecturer.

After the death of Alexandros in 323 B.C., Aristotle was forced to leave Athens because he as a Macedonian was suspected of Macedonian sympathies, and he settled in Chalkis, a town on the Island of Euboia, where he died a year later. Traditionally, 322 B.C., the year of death of Aristotle, marks the end of the Hellenic Age.

After his death a major part of Aristotle's library and manuscripts became the property of his friend and successor, Theophrastos, who bequeathed them to his nephew Neleos of Skepsis. The heirs of Neleos sold a small part of Aristotle's library to Ptolemaios Philadelphos, the second Macedonian King of Egypt, who deposited the small Aristotle collection in the Library of Alexandria. The heirs hid the rest of Aristotle's manuscripts in a cave in Anatolia (now Asia Minor) because they were afraid that their own King Attalos of Pergamon might seize the rest of Aristotle's manuscripts to build up the royal Library of Pergamon. Many years had passed when a rich Peripatetic collector of books, Apellikon of Teos, bought the entire collection of Aristotle's manuscripts in the cave for his private library which he was setting up in Athens. Apellikon died before Athens was besieged and sacked by the Roman army commanded by General Lucius Cornelius Sulla in 86 B.C.. Apellikon's book collection which included Aristotle's manuscripts were absconded to Rome by General Sulla. In 72 B.C. a Greek grammarian known by his nickname Tyrannion was taken captive by the Roman army commanded by Lucius Lucullus Ponticus, Sulla's favourite General, and brought to Rome to catalogue and arrange the books of Apellikon. However, the first edition of Aristotle's manuscripts were edited and published about 70 B.C. by Andronikos of Rhodos which made Aristotle's works known to the outside world. The leading libraries of the Hellenistic age were in Alexandria, Pergamon, Athens and Rome.

The Lyceum under the leadership of Theophrastos, successor to Aristotle as the head of the Peripatetic school, was reorganised and enlarged with the help of his rich student Demetrios Phaleron, who bought the property in the grove of ***Lykeion*** for the Lyceum which now acquired the legal status of a religious association (***thiasos***) that was the custom of all schools in Athens. Under the tutelage of Theophrastos the Lyceum became very successful by attracting a large body of about two thousand students. Aristotle is the first well-known professional scientist who established the Western tradition of organised research based on scholarship, and who founded the scientific method. Although collaboration in research had been undertaken already in the Pythagorean society, in the medical school of Hippokrates of Kos, and in Plato's Academy, the kind of collaborative organised researches by teams undertaken and accomplished by Aristotle with his colleagues and students at the Lyceum far surpassed anything contemplated, let alone achieved before him, for the scope of research carried out in the Lyceum was immense.

Aristotle differed fundamentally from earlier thinkers because he was a student of nature who had an extensive knowledge of physical phenomena. He radically opposed Plato by rejecting Plato's contention that the true being of everything that exists is to be found in a transcendental world of Forms. He maintained that the subject of philosophy in general, and science in particular is formed by what is perceived by the senses, and all the knowledge acquired of the world originates in the sense-perception which the mind has to process and organise. These views of Aristotle represent a basically empirical attitude with respect to the phenomena of nature which recognises that true knowledge of nature can only be obtained from carefully collected observational data. He further emphasised the fundamentally empirical nature of knowledge: "In philosophy and in every science or branch of knowledge you must study facts. Experience alone can give you general principles on any subject." According to Aristotle, man cannot prove everything in science, for each science has its own "primary universal and immediate principle arrived at by intuition," and moreover, "... mathematical certitude is not to be sought in every science." Aristotle, therefore, reinstated the importance of sensation, and, thereby, observation in the sciences. He advanced a new method of enquiry consisting of studying special problems by observation, comparison and classification, and obtained reliable knowledge in several fields by this systematic procedure. Aristotle insisted on reviewing both the 'data' and 'common opinions' to discover the nature of a problem and as a first step in its solution. Thereby, Aristotle founded the organised historico-scholarly study of science.

Aristotle divided knowledge into separate categories and gave lectures in the Lyceum on the following subjects: theory of knowledge (epistemology), formal logic (later called ***organon***), ethics, poetry theory of government, politics, history of philosophy, literary analysis, psychology, astronomy, meteorology, physics, economics, chemistry, comparative anatomy, general scientific biology (a scientific discipline which he himself had created), and several other learned disciplines. Aristotle lectured in the morning ***esoterika*** to regular initiated students, and in the evening ***exoterika*** to public at large.

Aristotelian method produced the 'empiricist' who strives to fit intellectual schemes to what he observes in nature in contrast to Platonic method which produced the 'formalist' who strives to fit nature to his preconceived intellectual schemes. In this way Aristotle originated the so-called 'realist approach' to science in which physical reality was assigned to the geometric patterns and only those aspects of these patterns were retained which did not conflict with the physical reality. In the opinion of Aristotle, physical reality itself dictated the choice between various mathematical representations of a physical phenomenon.

Although Aristotle did not specialise in mathematics, he was a competent mathematician, and his lectures assumed the same competence from his audience. Aristotle was responsible for using the name ***mathesis*** when he referred to mathematical sciences. Aristotle did devote much of his attention to mathematical principles and demonstrated the unavoidability of postulates in mathematics, and the necessity of reducing their number to a minimum. He discussed in great detail the purpose and nature of mathematical principles, their basic system, and the method of proof. Aristotle scrutinised the idea of divisibility of continuous quantities such as geometric magnitudes but also physical concepts such as motion and time. He concluded that the infinite first appears in the continuous since what is infinitely divisible is by definition continuous. He not only examined carefully the nature of the infinite as well as the existence of indivisibles (or infinitesimals) but also issued a challenge to the scholars : enquire if there exists such a thing as the infinite, and if it does, what is it ? His own careful discussion of the potentially infinite, the actually infinite, and the continuous is still important today. His idea of definition is modern, and his discussion of the nature of mathematics as standing between physics and metaphysics and its relation to the material world has been very influential. His discussion of a sum which grows beyond any conceivable quantity and becomes mathematically meaningless implied the first insistence on convergence. Aristotle clearly recognised that laws established with the aid of geometric lines also apply to other kinds of magnitudes including numbers. He did succeed in proving a few theorems in mathematics which were later incorporated into the famous book on mathematical elements, < The Elements > (***Stoicheia***) by Eukleides. Aristotle was fond of giving mathematical illustrations for various topics he investigated and, therefore, he often used mathematical examples. He insisted on the separation of arithmetic and geometry contrary to the Pythagorean doctrine.

Historically, Aristotle is the first known author of systematic textbooks, and his textbooks, all of which exhibited his views on the discipline, were mostly written by his assistants under his guidance. All the extant works of Aristotle are essentially notes of his lectures prepared during his years of teaching in Assos, Pella, and Athens.

Since scientific pursuits often lead to disappointments, frustration, and even despair, Aristotle advised : "Time is the great physician, it dissolves all problems and tames all griefs."

Aristotle's most creative work was in descriptive natural history and biology where he demonstrated his enormous intellectual ability, his remarkable empirical method, his colossal knowledge, his profound systematic insight which brings order to the entire subject, and his uncanny gift for finding similarities and analogies. Ancient Greeks had created 3 methods of reasoning: by deduction, by induction, and by analogy, and Aristotle made use of all 3, but particularly the inductive method of reasoning which he had formulated as a rigorous logical procedure. He used his inductive method not only to formulate his comprehensive and completely integrated philosophical system but also to apply it most extensively to entirely new fields of theoretical research, which makes Aristotle the founder of practically most of the modern sciences.

Aristotelian Physics:

Aristotle classified sciences into three groups: *theoretical*, (aiming at knowledge for its own sake); *practical* (aiming at it as a guide to action); and *productive* (aiming at creating the useful and the beautiful). His theoretical science included metaphysics, physics, and mathematics, whereas his practical science included mechanics. In astronomy and physics, which were not his main scientific interests, Aristotle had the outlook: "The probable is what usually happens." In sciences Aristotle differentiated between axioms which he considered common to all sciences, and postulates which he regarded relative to each particular science.

Aristotle believed that all changes in physical world can be explained by motion considered in general as change which includes both qualitative changes, and changes of location in space. He conceived motion in general as a means by which some essence could realise its inherent purpose: whilst the purpose was still unrealised it was *in potency* (or ***dynamis***), and when realised it was *in act* (or ***energeia***, sometimes also ***enteleia***). Therefore, in the conception of Aristotle, motion was a reduction of the condition of ***dynamis*** to the condition of ***energeia***. In general, Aristotle regarded motion as a quality which does not increase or decrease through the joining together of parts as does a quantity.

In contrast to Plato who tended to assimilate material change with corruption, Aristotle conceived change as motion towards an ideal. Thus an acorn, according to Aristotle, is potentially an oak tree, as it carries within itself the 'form' of an oak tree. This illustrates Aristotle's theory of matter and form, and it is the form superimposed on the matter that makes the thing or object what it is. Aristotle's forms are immanent, that is, they are intrinsic to the things perceived, whereas the Forms of Sokrates and Plato were transcendent, that is, they were extrinsic to the things perceived. Therefore, in the conception of Aristotle the destiny of a thing was predicted by its intrinsic unrealised essence. Although in Aristotelian system matter and form together constitute concrete physical things, they are distinguishable only in thought. In the opinion of Aristotle, the idea of forms of Plato have no independent existence as Plato thought. Therefore, Aristotle clearly distinguished between material things and ideas about them. Moreover, Plato had rejected the possibility of progress in science and the material world, whereas Aristotle accepted it. The very idea of scientific progress is ancient rather than modern.

Aristotle claimed that all substances composed of 4 elements admit divisibility which is subjected to a natural limit. In his opinion, each substance possesses its own characteristic smallest particles as its natural minima, which might be compared to the molecules of modern chemistry.

In the broad Aristotelian conception of physics all concrete things that exist are changing towards an end which is potentially immanent in them and, therefore, their development is shaped by a purpose. The entire world is gradually being realised for its purpose because of the transcendental design, which may be called the 'divine providence'. Aristotle realised that the mechanism of change and the purpose of change in the development of things are complementary and inseparable aspects of nature and, therefore, in the study of nature it is necessary to seek either for a mechanical explanation or for the leading purpose of change. Since at the time of Aristotle virtually no knowledge of the mechanism of change in the development of things was conceivable because no scientific means existed for a detailed investigation of such material changes, only the teleological explanation of the purpose of change was possible. For this very reason, Aristotle attempted to answer the question 'why' things developed as they did rather than 'how' they developed and, therefore, he assigned his fundamental idea of purpose, the teleology, the validity of which could not be entirely proven, the primary place in his scientific physical theory. Although the teleological idea of Aristotle was more reasonable in biology than in physical sciences in general, it was at least an immense improvement upon the bizarre physical fantasies of Plato.

Despite his belief in teleology, Aristotle introduced four causes for the constitution of an object from matter and form. In the opinion of Aristotle: "... Science itself is knowledge of a cause (***aitia***)." Aristotle's ***aitia*** had a broader meaning than the modern word 'cause' because it signified everything that contributes to the production of an effect. According to Aristotle, in the constitution of a new object 4 causes are necessary:

1. *Material Cause* – substance out of which anything is made.
2. *Formal Cause* – something to give it a design.
3. *Efficient Cause* –its maker who induces the formal cause in the material.
4. *Final Cause* – its purpose or motive, a teleological principle on which the efficient cause acts.

In modern thought the efficient cause is considered the central consideration in the problem of cause, but for Aristotle the final cause had primacy.

Aristotle intended to establish a physical science of quality in contrast to the atomist Demokritos whose aim had been to use only physical principles which admit such quantitative determinations as extension of space, geometric form, position, arrangement and motion. Aristotle repudiated the fundamental proposition of Parmenides that 'Being' is not subject to change, that is, to generation and corruption, by pointing out that it is necessary to distinguish between several different meanings of the word 'being'.

Aristotle divided the universe which was finite and bounded by the sphere of fixed stars into two regions: the sublunar or terrestrial region extending from the Earth to the Moon, and the supralunar or celestial region stretching from the Moon to the sphere of fixed stars, because he assumed the constitution and the physical principles of the two regions to be entirely different. He thought the supralunar region to be a crystalline solid filled with divine crystalline matter consisting of the divine element 'æther' (***aither***) which forms the substance of all heavenly bodies, as Plato had assumed. The divine nature of this celestial substance was manifested in its immunity to all changes except movement. The celestial bodies such as planets and stars were subjected to a special kind of 'natural' motion along circular paths with uniform speeds by being eternally carried round the Earth on celestial spheres.

The matter and their behaviour in the sublunar region according to Aristotle was entirely different. He assumed, as Empedokles had presumed earlier which was subsequently adopted by Plato, that all sublunar or terrestrial matter is composed of 4 elements given in ascending order of weight: fire, air, water, and earth, but not of the fifth element, æther, which only exists in the supralunar, or celestial region. Each of the elements possessed two of the four basic qualities, in which the first named quality was the primary quality: 'fire' was hot and dry, 'air' was moist and hot, 'water' was cold and moist, and 'earth' was dry and cold. By a change in one of the qualities, an element could change into another element, such as water becomes air in fire. Every element had its 'natural' place: 'earth' and 'water' had 'gravity' by tending towards the center of the Earth; 'air' and 'fire' had 'levity' by tending to move away from the Earth. The 'natural' motion of a body composed of different elements is the result of the interaction of all such tendencies. The superlunary world consists of the 5th element, æther, which is the matter of stars. The 'natural' motion of bodies consisting of the 5th element is circular, therefore the motion of celestial spheres is circular.

The doctrine of 4 elements which Aristotle adopted from his predecessors inspired other fourfold divisions of knowledge, such as the doctrine of 4 humours in medicine: *blood* was warm and moist, *yellow bile*, warm and dry, *black bile*, cold and dry, and *phlegm*, cold and moist. The 4 humours were associated with the 4 seasons: blood with *spring*, yellow bile with *summer*, black bile with *autumn*, and phlegm with *winter*. The 4 seasons were in turn associated with the 4 ages of man, and with his 4 temperaments: the *sanguine*, the *choleric*, the *melancholic*, and the *phlegmatic*. In this manner, man became the microcosm, the little world, which reflected the macrocosm, the big world of the universe.

The terrestrial bodies made of the 4 elements were not immutable but were subject to 4 types of changes:

1. Change of *place*, or *location*– called 'local motion'.
2. Change of *substance* (when a log is burnt to ashes)
3. Change of *quality* (change of colour)
4. Change of *quantity* (increase or decrease of quantity of matter)

In order to investigate the problem of change, Aristotle had to examine in great detail not only the intellectual foundation of man's knowledge, the epistemology, but also man's very means of acquiring knowledge. Finally, Aristotle had to determine: how does man know that he knows?

Aristotle resolved all terrestrial local motions into 'natural' motion and 'violent' motion, a division evidently obtained from gross observations. From the 4 types of change in the physics of Aristotle only local motion became of central importance to the development of physics. In his treatment of the local motion Aristotle introduced the concepts of absolute heaviness (gravity) and absolute lightness (levity, which is equivalent to weightlessness), and thought that these 2 assumptions represented a great improvement upon the assumption of Demokritos of Abdera who had attributed weight to all substances, and for whom weight was a relative concept.

Aristotle held that bodies which fall naturally towards the center of the Earth behave that way because they are predominantly heavy in their constitution and, therefore, seek their natural place at the center of the Earth which is also the center of the universe. Bodies which rise naturally upwards are predominantly light in their constitution. He conceived 'fire' as absolutely light and weightless and, therefore, when unimpeded would rise above the 'air' and seek its 'natural place' below the Lunar sphere. Water and air according to Aristotle were intermediate elements having only relative heaviness and lightness. Therefore, 'water' when located below its 'natural place' within the Earth would 'naturally rise', but when located above the 'air' or 'fire' it would 'naturally fall'. 'Air' would fall when located in the 'natural place' of 'fire', and rise when located in the 'natural place' of 'earth' or 'water'.

According to Aristotle, 'natural movement' belongs to science, whereas 'unnatural or violent movement' belongs to technical art (***techne***), or technique. Aristotle explained the need for technique as follows :

> "In many things nature acts contrary to our needs. When, therefore, we have to do something contrary to nature, this perplexes us because of its difficulty, and we have need of technical art (***techne***). And so we call the branch of technical art that helps us in such perplexities mechanics (***mechanike***)."

In this connexion he recalled Amphion, the poet:

> "... by technical art (***techne***) we conquer where by nature we are overcome."

Since the science of physics of Aristotle is governed by the doctrine of 'natural place', a teleological principle, Aristotle regarded physical nature 'purposeful'. The anthropomorphic principle of teleology (in Greek, ***telos*** means, goal) may have plausibility in human affairs but when applied to natural phenomena it is apt to lead to false conclusions. The teleological principle of Aristotle made it necessary to enquire not into the origin of things but rather into their ends. His application of the teleological principle to zoology and biology at least appeared somewhat plausible, but it was almost useless when applied to physics or astronomy. Although Aristotle believed that nature itself refuses to accept the errors in men's assumptions about nature: "Nature refüses to be badly administered," his ideas led him into the false belief of 'final causes' and because of it, he was unable to make sound progress in physical sciences. As long as the Aristotelian qualitative doctrines were accepted in science, physical sciences remained stagnant.

Aristotelian Mechanics:

Since the teleological principle really explains very little or nothing at all about the physics of motion, Aristotle decided to present a causal explanation for local motion in terms of fundamental principle: Everything capable of motion, whether animate or inanimate, is moved by something else.

In the 'natural' movement this principle distinguished theoretically the mover from the object moved. If the object was animate then the soul of the animal was the mover and the animal's body was the object moved. In planetary motion, the mover was a celestial intelligence and the moved object was the planet. In both cases, the mover and the moving object were distinguishable but not physically, or spatially separable from each other. In the case of inanimate objects, the mover and the moved object were physically and spatially distinct both in the 'natural' and the 'violent' motion.

Although Aristotle did recognise that bodies accelerate as they approach their natural place, he treated such motions theoretically as if they were of 'uniform', or 'average speed'. In the case of the free fall of a body, he treated it as if the weight were the immediate cause of the body's natural downwards motion with uniform speed. He concluded that in 'natural' motion the speed of the body is directly proportional to the weight of the body and inversely proportional to the density of the medium through which the body moves. Unfortunately, Aristotle neither defined precisely the general concept of force nor the speed. He was able to define such quantities only for uniform speeds.

In the case of 'violent', or 'enforced' motion, Aristotle proposed a series of specific rules of speed in terms of the motive force F, the resistance R, the distance traversed S, and the time of travel T, rather than directly in terms of the 'average speed' or 'velocity V'. The Muslim and Latin scientists found it convenient to summarise all these specific rules in terms of the 'average speed V' in the metric Law of Velocity of Aristotle :

$$V \propto \frac{F}{R}$$

where R represents the total resistance operating against the motive force F which includes the resistances offered by the medium as well as by the body itself. In all his discussions about the resistance, Aristotle remained rather vague, and he never gave an objective method for its determination. The Law of Velocity of Aristotle does have the distinction of being the first statement of a law of motion in history.

This formula for the speed V is not how Aristotle might have expressed it because he could not give the speed of motion as a metric quantity in its own right. He could not separate the speed as a dimensional quantity because he used Eudoxos' theory of proportions which only admitted dimensionless magnitudes resulting from ratios of quantities of the same kind, such as two distances or two times. For this reason, ancient Greeks could not give a metric definition of speed as a dimensional quantity given by a ratio of space to time. Moreover, time for Aristotle is only the measure of motion which otherwise by itself has no independent existence. Aristotle had to express the relation of speed to motive force and resistance indirectly in comparative proportions by considering local motion in its separate stages, which is why mediæval commentators of his works found his rules of local motion difficult to interpret.

Aristotle did recognise the restricted validity of his rules of motion :

$$V \propto \frac{F}{R},$$

when $F \leq R$, the body will cease to move and his rules of motion would no longer apply. In a void $R = 0$, and, therefore, according to his rules: $V = \infty$, which is absurd. For this and other reasons, Aristotle repudiated the existence of void or empty space. Aristotle's discussions of the problem of local motion are scattered among his many works, but the most complete arguments are given in his books < Physics > (***Physica***) and < On the Heavens and the Cosmos > (***De caelo et mundo***). However, he failed to give a systematic and general treatment of local motion.

In 'violent' motion the initial mover is readily identifiable, but it is not at all obvious what is the source of the motive force that will keep a body, such as a projectile, in continuous motion after it loses contact with the initial mover. Aristotle postulated that the initial mover transfers to the medium through which the body moves, such as air, a certain quantity of motive power which makes the medium the source of motive force that by contact keeps the body in continuous motion through the medium. Therefore, Aristotle regarded the medium as the source of motive force as well as of the resistance to motion which brakes and slows down the body. Aristotle also gave the criterion that only one type of force F can act on the moving body at any one time. This criterion did not allow a vectorial combination of the 'violent' force of projection with the 'natural' gravity force, such as the weight of the projectile, though both act simultaneously on the projectile. This rule which precluded consideration of simultaneous action of both forces resulted in a trajectory of the projectile which consisted of two straight lines: one inclined in the direction of the projecting motive force which goes from the position of projection to the position where the motive force has been exhausted by the resistance, in which position the gravity force becomes active and makes the projectile fall down in the direction of the active gravity force thereby producing the second part of the trajectory in the form of a vertical line to the ground. If the action of both forces had been considered simultaneously then, mathematically, the incremental vertical displacements along the trajectory induced by the gravity force would have made the trajectory curvilinear.

Aristotle's theory of motion was insufficient to solve the projectile problem, because Aristotle had formulated the most commonplace experiences of motion obtained from gross observations as universal scientific propositions which, as the Muslim commentators of his works concluded, postulated proportionality between the average speed of motion V and the ratio of the motive force F and resistance to motion R :

$$V \propto \frac{F}{R}\ .$$

This Law of Velocity of Aristotle had the advantage that it was based on directly observable situations of everyday occurrence.

The modern mechanics with its inertia as an internal force of bodies offering resistance to changes in their states of rest or motion, is based on the principle of linear momentum that postulates a linear proportionality between the acceleration A and the resultant motive force F :

$$A \propto F,$$

which unlike the law of velocity of Aristotle, is never confirmed in everyday experience and, in fact, a direct experimental proof of it is fundamentally impossible.

The Aristotelian theory of motion, therefore, had an advantage of staying close to the concrete, observable motions in everyday experience, yet scientifically this advantage also proved to be its weakness, since everyday experiences in terrestrial mechanics are incredibly complicated. The great difficulty of terrestrial mechanics arises from the great complexity of natural phenomena, and Aristotle cannot be blamed for his failure because he lacked the great mass of experience which was available 2 millennia later in Western Europe.

Therefore, Aristotle made a mistake when he failed to treat 'acceleration' A as a concept distinct from 'velocity' V. By analysing motion entirely in terms of average velocity over a finite period of time, he was unable to incorporate 'initial' velocity of projection, or the force required to start a body moving, into his analysis of motion because his conception of force, or motive power, was restricted to a force causing motion that continues over a finite period of time. Many of the difficulties in Aristotle's analysis of motion would have been removed if the motion would have been analysed in terms of the 'instantaneous' velocity, a revolutionary change in the theory of motion which was first made in England in the 14th century A.D.. Aristotle had not overlooked this important idea since he had devoted a great deal of thought to the concept of 'instantaneous' kinematic state, and had reached the conclusion that 'instantaneous velocity' cannot exist in sensory perception: "Nothing can be in motion at present. ...Nor can anything be at rest at present," a judgement representing a categorical denial of the existence of 'instantaneous velocity'. His logical arguments concerning the intuitive perception of instantaneous velocity still carry considerable conviction.

Aristotle also presumed as a principle that any motion requires a motive force, which implies that motion is a 'process', an effect of a cause, and not a natural state of bodies. This basic assumption excludes what in modern mechanics is called inertial motion along a straight line with constant speed that is independent of any motive force. However, Aristotle should not be unduly criticised for this failure because it is possible to imagine that the so-called 'inertial motion' is actually due to the action of masses external to the Solar system the influence of which is ignored in modern mechanics. It is interesting that in his book < Physics > when discussing motion in a void, Aristotle actually presented in his arguments against the existence of a void the 'inertia concept' but only as an obvious absurdity. Besides the atomists, the Alexandrian mechanicians and the Stoic philosophers also admitted the possible existence of void.

The very foundation of Aristotelian physical science was built on his concepts of 'absolute heaviness' (gravity) and 'absolute lightness' (levity), his resolution of the 'local' motion into 'natural' motion and 'violent' motion, and many other physical assumptions, such as letting the resistance to motion always form a ratio with the motive force instead of reducing it, and concepts and arguments which he gave concerning these two contrary motions. The 'local motion' as a problem of physics occupied an important place in the development of physical science, but the concepts of Aristotle mentioned above when dogmatically accepted in such problems actually retard further progress.

Aristotle's physical science and his brilliant cosmology remained very influential because Aristotle had applied commonsense notions to his scientific problems which seemed to be supported by an enormous amount of everyday sensory experience. In the absence of a clearly defined experimental method and the qualitative rather than quantitative nature of the Aristotelian physics, there were few opportunities for a challenge of Aristotelian physical science. Moreover, the whole of Aristotelian scientific philosophy was so comprehensive and so tightly integrated in thought that it was hardly possible to explain a few of its details apart from their general context.

Aristotelian Logic as Scientific Discipline:

Aristotle had a complete understanding of man's faculty for abstraction by comparing the structure of human deliberation to that of analysis, and by demonstrating that Platonic forms were actually abstractions of things which can serve as the foundation for his formal logic.

Both Plato and Aristotle believed the world to be a product of rational design and, therefore, to be explanatory by means of rational thought which depends on deductive reasoning (***apodeixes***) and, hence, on logic (***logikos***). The Eleatic philosophers, Parmenides and Zenon, had introduced formal logic into reasoning in their method of deducing logically reasoned proof from primary assertions. Although Plato had already used it in his dialogues and Eudoxos had used syllogism in his work, it was Aristotle who in a number of treatises made formal logic into a comprehensive and systematic scientific discipline (which later became known as ***organon***) by classifying arguments according to their structure in his syllogistic logic which consisted of a major premise, a minor premise, and the inference, and by introducing logical principles such as the law of contradiction (nothing can both have and not have a given characteristic), the law of excluded middle (everything must either have, or not have a given character), and other principles such as the law of identity (*A* is *A*),which form the basis of indirect proof. Aristotle's ***organon*** and his doctrine of syllogism, an intellectual discipline unequalled in his time, contained the source of most branches of logic used today and it dominated logic for 2 millennia.

In Aristotle's syllogistic logic the 2 premises have 3 terms each, of which the middle term appears in both, but the logical inference does not contain the middle term, and it contains statements having qualitative adjectives such as 'all', 'some', and 'none'. In his class-calculus theory of syllogism, Aristotle had endeavoured to codify as much as possible the rich, intricate and subtle way ordinary verbal language communicates meaning, and the concept of propositional truth where all propositions were of the subject-predicate type. He worked out all possible arrangements of their terms to yield a valid syllogism in which conclusion follows from premises, but he overlooked some cases which were later discovered by Stoic logicians. He analysed the language used in the statements and contrasted the meaning of words standing alone with their meaning in sentences. Aristotle listed 10 categories for various types of term: substance, quality, quantity, relation, place, time, position, state, action and affection, which gave the most general features that things may possess. The substance in the argument represents 'what' is being discussed, and the rest of the categories 'how' its being discussed. For him a judgement or proposition was a linking of several separate meanings or concepts. He asserted that language is not haphazard but rather like a 'map' which reflects the real world as men experience it. He averred that concepts correspond to reality, and a judgement is true if the concepts in it are linked in the same way as the corresponding features of reality. For a long time his ***organon*** was considered complete until the Stoics discovered the 'logic of propositions', the various ways propositions can be connected in logical arguments which had been overlooked by Aristotle. Stoics were the first to use 'material implications' in formal logic which is a relation that holds between 2 propositions when if the first is true, the second cannot be false; and if the first is false, the second cannot be true. They also made important contributions to 'modal propositions' which use words such as 'must', 'can', and 'may'. In this connexion they were successful in giving a scientific basis to the study of Greek grammar invented by the Sophist Protagoras. Besides material implications and modal propositions, mathematics often uses propositions that are also not of the subject-predicate type but contain relations such as 'being between' and others, which also were not considered by Aristotle because he was not mathematically inclined. Perhaps the main defect in Aristotelian logic was his failure to develop a 'logic of relations, a defect remedied only in the 19th century A.D., although already noticed by the German philosopher and mathematician, Gottfried Wilhelm Leibniz (A.D.1646-1716). The fact became gradually known that syllogism is only one kind of inference among many, and that it is infrequently used in common thought and language. In mediæval Europe, some Scholastic philosophers began to develop a logic of terms used frequently in spoken language and to investigate the logical properties of spoken language employing terms such as 'and', 'or', and 'if-then' as logical operations in which those terms represent operators of symbolic logic. However, it took a long time before symbolic logic became of practical utility.

Aristotle introduced the formal doctrines of definition, induction and deduction. His inductive method concerned the establishment of one abstract premise from many particular arguments or conclusions, his deductive method consisted of inferring many conclusions from a certain established premise. Although the inductive and the deductive process of reasoning had been used by other ancient Greeks before Aristotle, he made them into conscious procedures of the mind for he was the first to formulate their logical character. As Aristotle pointed out his formal logic was concerned only with the validity of the arguments, and not with the truth of the premises which has to do with the subject matter of the argument and therefore has to be empirically decided, whereas the validity of the argument, in contrast, depends only on its logical structure. If the premises are true, then the conclusion is true, but not ***vice versa***: a true conclusion can be reached from false premises. Aristotle promoted understanding of causes by means of reasoning in which one passes from general premises to particular deductions, or from particular premises to general inductions. In other words, Aristotle is the founder of rational knowledge through syllogism.

Straton of Lampsakos, the Physicist:

A pupil of Theophrastos of Eresos, Straton of Lampsakos, the second successor to Aristotle as the head of the Lyceum (***scholarches***) from c. 287 B.C. to 269 B.C., wrote the first textbook on mechanics, entitled < On Mechanical Problems > (***Problemata Mechanika***), in which mechanical problems are solved by a combination of mathematical and physical theory. The supremely talented Straton, the best physicist in antiquity who was popularly called 'The Physicist (***ho physikos***)', had realised that the Aristotelian qualitative mode of thinking in physical sciences had to be supplemented by a mathematical mode of thinking. For this purpose, he sought for mathematically expressed general principles applicable to the action of mechanical devices such as oars in rowing sails in sailing ships, nutcrackers, gear trains, swing-beams in wells, wedges and pulleys in construction work, slings and capstans, wheels and rollers in transport, and motion of wagons including the problem of inertia. He attempted to give theoretical geometric explanations of mechanical phenomena in this book which contains adumbrations of the Principle of the Lever, the Principle of Virtual Velocities, the parallelogram of velocities, the concept of the center of gravity, and the concept of the center of density. It contains a study of accelerated motion when the acceleration is assumed to be proportional to the distance. Straton came close to the concept of kinetic energy when he discusses splitting the log with an axe: "Is it because all work is done by means of the movement and one weight is capable of imparting more movement to another if it is moving than if it is stationary?" He was puzzled by the fact that a heavy weight placed on top of the axe did not split the log, but when the axe alone was swung down onto the log, the log split. The brilliant Straton also gave the analysis of equilibrium of the lever loaded by two weights W_1 and W_2 expressed by the kinematic criterion of equilibrium :

$$\frac{W_1}{W_2} \propto \frac{V_2}{V_1} ,$$

where S_i $(i=1,2)$ is the distance travelled by weight $W_i(i=1,2)$, V_i denotes the speed of the weight W_i, and $T = S_i/V_i = S_1/V_1 = S_2/V_2$ is time of travel of the lever.

This kinematic criterion of equilibrium can be expressed in its modern metric form as a product :

$$W_1V_1 \propto W_2V_2 ,$$

or

$$W_1S_1/T \propto W_2S_2/T$$

that yields after cancelling T the proportional form of the principle of virtual work :

$$W_1S_1 \propto W_2S_2 .$$

This particular kinematic criterion of equilibrium of the lever very likely originated in the first treatise on theoretical mechanics written by Archytas of Taras, who was a proponent of the kinematical method not only in geometry but also in mechanics. Historically, the kinematic criterion of equilibrium of Archytas was the first statement of a law of statics in mechanics.

Straton considered the central and the tangential motion and discussed the parallelogram of velocities in compounding such orthogonal velocities into resultant velocity. If the ratio of 2 orthogonal velocities of a body compounded into the resultant velocity of the body by means of the parallelogram law is not constant in time the resulting motion would not be rectilinear but rather curvilinear. Like Aristotle, Straton also distinguished uniform speed (***isotachos***) from non-uniform speed. It was known to him from his experiments that free-fall is an accelerated motion.

Aristotle had asserted that time implies change, and thought that change can be mathematically defined, but he failed to separate time from space by abstracting it into an independent mathematical variable. He thought that both the time and the lines are continuous and that a continuum is: "That which is divisible into divisibles that are infinitely divisible ... Nothing that is continuous can be composed of indivisibles." A final division to him was inconceivable. The continuity of a line he based on the continuity of motion, because he thought that a magnitude is perceived by motion.

Since movement through continuous space is continuous, then the time taken up by the continuous movement must also be continuous. Straton did not like the term 'number', a discrete quantity, in Aristotle's definition of time because in the opinion of Aristotle both time and lines are continuous. Straton came close to conceiving absolute time when he defined time as "the measure of motion and rest," and "a quantity that exists in all actions," thereby seemingly having intended to eliminate kinematics from the definition of time as a uniform flux of time. For Aristotle time remained the measure of motion without independent meaning. Later the Stoics, having been influenced by Straton, defined time as a measure of slowness and swiftness.

Straton made many deliberately controlled experiments to confirm scientific hypotheses and fully founded the systematic experimental method of wide application. He stressed the primacy of experimental demonstration over the logical demonstration. He tried to eliminate Aristotle's vain search for 'final causes' in physics, and to avoid the artificial distinction between the 'light' and the 'heavy' body of Aristotle by accepting the view of Demokritos that all bodies have gravity (and none have levity) in their tendency to move towards the center of the Earth, a tendency Straton called 'gravity', although lighter bodies can be displaced upwards by the pressure exerted by heavier bodies. Straton, like his teacher Theophrastos, also severely criticised Aristotle's doctrine of the 4 elements. He maintained that every body consists of minute invisible particles of its material, but he denied the idea of Demokritos that all the qualities of things depend upon the size, shape and position of atoms.

Straton's treatise < On Motion > (***Peri kinesis***), in which he gave the first analysis of acceleration in terms of space and time from the kinematic point of view, is lost. Straton defined acceleration kinematically as "a movement such that equal spaces are traversed in succeeding periods of less time with a continually greater speed." He also discussed the free-fall of bodies and observed from his experiments that a body traverses the last part of its trajectory in the shortest time. He observed that if a body is dropped successively from greater heights, the body hits the ground with successively more powerful impact. Since the body had neither increased its weight nor was it impelled by a greater external force, the more powerful impact was merely due to its increased acceleration. Straton presented also experimental evidence to confirm the existence of acceleration in free-fall.

Straton did important research on hydraulics. He is responsible for the first statement of the hydrodynamic principle of continuity: "The smaller the cross-section of a flowing liquid with a given fall, the greater is its velocity." He was the first to state that the steam from the cauldron is rarified hot water ejected into the air.

Straton wrote a treatise < Meteorology > (***Meteorologika***) in 4 books based on Aristotle's lectures which covered not only meteorology, but also such topics as physics, astronomy, geology, and even chemistry. The 4th book of < Meteorology >, representing the first textbook of chemistry, is probably exclusively the work of Straton. Alchemists adopted the Aristotelian concept of the nature of minerals and metals from the 3rd volume of this treatise, since Aristotle believed that the elements in nature were continuously undergoing transformation from one element into another. The main objective of alchemists was to make this transformation of elements in nature take place at the will of man, a general conviction the alchemists had acquired from their practical experience in metallurgy. Although Straton rejected the idea of external continuous void (***kenon***) of Demokritos of Abdera, he did accept the existence of small, discontinuously distributed interstitial voids existing between the minute invisible particles of matter inside the bodies, a conclusion he drew from his experiments on air which he discussed in his book < On the Vacuum>. In his experiments on air he also discovered the elastic property of air, the so-called 'spring of air'. It is an impressive work for it took two thousand years to surpass it, and to bring its ideas to full fruition. Straton went as far as it was possible for him to go at the time because his ideas far outreached the possibilities of his experimental research.

It is quite likely that Straton also wrote a book entitled < On Audibles > (in Latin, ***De audibilibus***), which apparently dealt with the wave theory of sound, where he had laid the foundation for the correct theory of sound.

Straton had the opinion, which he expressed in his controversial style, that everything that exists is the work of nature rather than the acts of gods, since nature contains in itself all the causes, and that all the so-called 'divine power' is actually power which resides in nature.

He denied Plato's contention that true knowledge is independent of experience by emphasising that the source of all knowledge is in the experience. Moreover, Straton did original analysis in psychology that is still of fundamental importance and represented a significant advance over the brilliant psychology of Aristotle.

Birth of Mining Technology

Ancient mining required a large number of mining technologists (***metallikoi***) with great diversity of skills, many implements and tools, and a rather general management because it required tunnelling, ventilation, subterranean lighting, processes of washing, crushing and smelting, and various uses of by-products of mining.

A new mining technology was created in the Laurion silver mines in the Laurion region, which was rich in minerals, and located in the southern extremity of Attika a little before reaching the Sunion promontory. This region of about 50 miles (80 km) had been mined from time immemorial, certainly since the early Iron Age. The ancient Greeks were working it mainly to obtain argentiferous galera, an ore that included 65% of lead, and other metals, such as zinc and iron, and even gold, but too little of the latter to be extracted by the ancient methods. Laurion mines made Attika the sole source of lead in the ancient Greek world. But the main purpose of the Athenians in the working of the Laurion mines was to produce silver. After a richer body of ores was discovered in Attika, about the beginning of the 5thcentury B.C., the city-State Athens took charge of its exploitation which was so profitable that about 483 B.C. each citizen received a bonus. Athenian government devoted the revenues yielded by the Laurion mines to the building of a strong navy intended to repel the anticipated Persian invasion. Later the Laurion silver enabled Perikles to rebuild Athens, which had been burnt down by the Persian army in 480 B.C., in a magnificent way. For instance the construction of the Parthenon was made possible by slave labour and the income received from the Laurion mines. Since the Laurion mines were over-exploited in the 5th century B.C., by the middle of the following century only old workings were still open and there was no further prospecting being undertaken. Some efforts were made to revive the Laurion mines in the 3rd and 2nd centuries, but these efforts were jeopardised by labour troubles and they were finally stopped by a slave revolt in 103 B.C..

The Laurion mines were rather dry mines, so that there existed no great pumping problems to be overcome. The first daring mine shafts were sunk in the Laurion mines through rock to reach the deep-embedded pockets of silver-lead ore: the shafts had a cross-section of 4 by 6 feet (1.22 by 1.83 meters), and some such shafts reached a depth of 350 feet (106.68 m). In the mining galleries supporting pillars were up to 30 feet (9.14 m) long, and there were timbering and artificial supports for the roof of the mine. The Laurion mine was ultimately closed in the 1st century A.D. when it was under the Roman domination. By that time almost 2 thousand mine shafts had been sunk.

There were also other mines in the Greek world besides those in Attika, such as the mines near Mount Pangaios in Macedonia, in Thrakia, and on the islands of Siphnos and Thasos, but they were not as important as the Laurion mines in Attika.

Technology Enters Warfare

The unity between theory and practice never really developed in the Hellenic world mostly because the learned man as an individual was isolated from the world of work. In the Hellenic world, the man of learning never worked, and the working man seldom learnt natural philosophy unless he was a member of the military force, and this is the main reason why military engineering became one of the first technical professions. The army was the only body of organised craftsmen and engineers which had an accumulated corpus of practical experience with machines such as artillery. Only in the army was there a conscious, but slow effort made to unify theoretical mechanics with the design of machines of war, that is, to bring the theoretical mechanics to the practical level of application in machine design and that was how warfare was revolutionised by mechanisation and technology under the tyrant Dionysios I of Syracuse (***Syrakousai***), and later under the King Philip II of Macedonia.

In 399 B.C. Dionysios I of Syracuse in Sicily established the first known army ordnance – a corps of military engineers the sole purpose of which was to invent war machinery to be used against the Carthaginians, a group of Semitic settlers in Sicily. A catapult called ***oxybeloi*** was invented in the army ordnance to throw 6-foot (1.83 m) long darts against the enemy, and first used in the siege of the Carthaginian city Motye in Sicily in 397 B.C..

Greek Architectural Engineering:

About 350 B.C., Pytheos became one of the first Greek architectural engineers (***architekton***) to train his apprentices in his school of building construction, and to write handbooks and treatises for the builder in which he attempted to give rules of composition of structures as exact geometric relations, and to combine classical proportions with innovative building styles. With the help of his assistant Satyros and the famous sculptor and ***architekton*** Skopas of the island Paros, Pytheos designed and built the unique and widely acclaimed Mausoleum (***Mausoleion***), the tomb of King Mausolos of Karia (died in 353 B.C.) in Halikarnassos, Ionia, which combined a high pedestal with an Ionian colonnade topped by an Egyptian pyramid mound. This 14-storey building, which was twice as high as any other existing building, was decorated with 250 brightly painted life-size statues, and with larger than life-size statue of King Mausolos and Queen Artemisia riding in a chariot drawn by 4 horses on top of the roof of the Mausoleum. In the Greek world architecture was intimately combined with the plastic art of sculpture.

Skopas was responsible for breaking the classical tradition of Attic school of sculpture as represented by Pheidias (490-432 B.C.) of Athens, the famous Greek sculptor hired by Perikles to direct the decoration of the main buildings on the Akropolis. The classical Attic sculpture, transfigured human nature into the divine by idealising the purely human traits, such as individual personality, in their statuary of gods. Skopas in contrast to the classical Attic tradition created his statues in an intensely individualistic style which expressed strong emotions and sensibilities of men as well as depicting vigorous action and motion instead of the serene dignity and superhuman composure of the classical Attic sculptures. Skopas, and also Praxiteles of Athens (born c. 390 B.C.) who was a generation younger than Skopas, are regarded to be the founders of the late Attic school of sculpture. Praxiteles, whose statues of divinities no longer possessed the superhuman composure of the earlier Greek sculptures were instead exceedingly graceful and charming in their youthful human form. Praxiteles was considered the greatest sculptor of his generation who worked almost entirely in marble, and his treatment of marble surface in his statuary has remained unsurpassed. Praxiteles' statue of the goddess of love, Aphrodite, in Knidos was an idealisation of the body of a famous Athenian courtesan (***hetaira***) Phryne, who was widely admired for her physical pulchritude and considered the very symbol of perfect female figure. Phryne was also the inspiration for the famous painting of Aphrodite by Apelles of Kolophon, the foremost painter of Hellenistic age, who died whilst making a copy of his painting of Aphrodite years later in Kos.

One of the last works of sculpture by Skopas of Paros, whose creative years lasted from about 395 B.C. to 350 B.C., was the frieze of the Mausoleum depicting the battle of Amazons in which he was assisted by a group of other contemporary sculptors: Leochares, Timotheos, and Bryaxis, a Karian sculptor who was known for his statue of ***Sarapeis*** in the Temple of ***Sarapeis*** in Alexandria, called ***Sarapeion***. Skopas also decorated with his relief sculptures in marble the Temple of Artemis in Ephesos, called ***Artemiseion***, a temple burnt to the ground by a pyromaniac but reconstructed years later in a grandiose style by the Macedonian ***architekton*** Deinokrates of Rhodos. By that time Hellenic art had lost most of its traditional relation to magic and religion, since the artists had become mainly interested in the problems of their craft for its own sake.

The construction of the magnificent Mausoleum, which had 20-foot deep foundations, column drums connected by iron cramps and dovetailed stonework, was ordered by King Mausolos and his devoted wife and sister, Queen Artemisia (died in 351 B.C.). Artemisia proved to be a very resourceful military commander like the earlier Artemisia, the lady tyrant of Halikarnassos, who had fought so valiantly against the Greek warships in the Sea Battle of Salamis in 480 B.C. as the commander of her Karian warship in the Persian fleet that the victorious Greeks out of respect for her bravery and skill in the sea battle permitted her ship to sail safely home whilst the rest of the Persian warships of King Xerxes were being methodically annihilated by the Greeks, a humiliating spectacle Xerxes himself witnessed from his throne perched upon a high hill on the shore of the narrows of Salamis. This disaster made the angry Xerxes to complain bitterly that his ship commanders in the Sea Battle of Salamis fought like women whereas his Karian ship commander Artemisia, a woman, fought like a man. The widowed Queen Artemisia even surpassed the valiant deed of her namesake from the past by defeating the Rhodesian fleet with her clever battle tactics, and conquered Rhodos when Halikarnassos was attacked by the Rhodesian warships after the death of her brother and husband Mausolos.

About A.D. 1496 the remarkable Mausoleum was finally demolished by the Knights Templar. Its magnificent statues and friezes were broken up and burnt in limekilns to be used by Knights Templar as the building materials for their fortification which had to be very strong to withstand the cannon fire of the attacking Turkish armed forces.

The Greek ***architekton*** readily understood that building canons or codes should not be fixed forever, since he realised that what really matters is the search for such canons. If the canon be too rigid, it loses its true value, a matter well understood by ***architekton*** Pytheos when he produced his canon of construction, the first such written building code known.

In about 330 B.C., Philon of Athens, a learned engineer, builder and orator, extended the port of Peiraieus, originally planned by Hippodamos of Miletos, by adding the adjacent basins of Moynychia, Zea and the Bay of Phaleron to the fortified harbour complex. He built warehouses, ship sheds for the protection of 400 triremes, and an arsenal 400 feet by 55 feet (121.92 m by 16.76 m) in ground-plan and 40 feet (12.19 m) in height, at the shores of the harbour. The entrances to these ports were protected by chains, and the connecting roads between Athens and Peiraieus were enclosed by 2 continuous defensive walls, known as the Long Walls, which were about 200 yards (183 m) apart, almost 25 miles (40 km) long and 60 feet (18.29 m) high. A large part of the defensive wall was constructed from squared stone blocks clamped by iron cramps set in lead. A commentary describing this construction which Philon wrote has not survived, but it is known that he gave public lectures about the construction of the fortified port of Peiraieus.

The architectural engineer (***architekton***) usually was the chief builder in charge of constructing public buildings, and often he also designed these structures as well. The ***architekton*** generally worked under a contractual system. The city-State hired private craftsmen, such as masons and sculptors, who as master craftsmen brought along their own assistants. These subcontractors took some responsibility, but they still worked under the supervision of the ***architekton***. The building contracts, which were inscribed in stone and placed on the building site for citizens to read, contained specifications of construction in considerable detail to guide the workmen and to inform the public. Philon's four page specifications determined the important dimensions such as wall thicknesses, sizes of important stones, windows and doors, but less important details were given orally by the ***architekton***. The specifications of Philon of Athens are the best preserved building specifications of antiquity.

Alexandros of Macedonia and Hellenistic Age

[from 338 B.C. to 30 B.C.]

Hellenistic Technology and Engineering:

The ancient Greek citizen in Athens, or in any other Greek city-State (***polis***), lived under rather humble circumstances on a very small income and in modest housing because he appreciated the social life of the city community more than individual wealth and complete self-determination. Even his religion was a State religion, which formed an important part of the community life, rather than a personal religion of individual salvation and comfort. Greek art and architecture expressed the citizen's affection for his city-State as a community of likeminded people and were the results of voluntary community effort. The life of the city-State disintegrated after the Greek city-States fell under the hegemony and domination of the Macedonian King Philip II, a northern barbarian who pretended to be a Greek. Everything that an ancient Greek valued in his life began to disappear with the rapid decline of the autonomy of the city-State, and this decline robbed the citizen of the ***polis*** of his self-confidence which left him spiritually adrift and despondent. After the disintegration of the city-State and its communal life, the spiritual vacuum left by the gradual collapse of the city-State was being filled by the rise of incipient individualism and cosmopolitanism which further dissipated the closely-knit social organisation of the city-State, since the Hellenic Greeks were spiritually ill prepared to become completely autonomous as individual men. The self-determination of the city-State was completely eliminated when the actual political power became centralised in the hands of the Macedonian king, even though the self-government of the city-State in the formal sense was retained but only for the sake of appearances. The military conquest of all the Greek city-States by Alexandros III (Alexander of Macedon), son of Philip II, in 338 B.C. made this an accomplished fact.

Apelles of Kolophon, the foremost painter of Hellenistic time, was called to Pella to be the court painter to Alexandros. Lysippos of Sikyon was made the court sculptor, and Pyrgoteles was appointed the court engraver. All three men were accorded the same importance in their responsibilities to the court. Apelles' teacher was Pamphilos of Amphipoles, a student of geometry who operated a regular school of art in Sikyon where he not only demanded that his pupils have the knowledge of drawing, but of arithmetic and geometry as well. Pamphilos himself endeavoured to use perspective in his paintings.

In the new cosmopolitan life, every man had to take care of himself, spiritually as well as in matters of practical life, since there no longer existed a closely-knit community as such. A citizen could no longer take civic pride in a temple built by a Macedonian king, for it did not belong to him since he did not have anything to do with its creation. An individual in a cosmopolitan Greek city could only feel pride in his own personal accomplishments, which is a fundamental outlook of the modern Western man. As a result, the traditional class distinctions of the Hellenic Greeks world tended to break down in the new Hellenistic world dominated by Macedon.

Spiritually, the Hellenistic Age, the age of the Macedonian domination of the ancient Greek world, still lacked the firm belief in the great intrinsic value of the Earthly life of the individual man, which has been the great source of power of the European civilisation in its struggles to understand and control nature. Hellenistic Greeks had not yet discovered the spiritual dignity of every individual, and they had not yet convinced themselves that the individual man's welfare on Earth was of great importance in all creation and the intention of the gods. But despite this failure, the Hellenistic tendency was to consider the value, and the experience of a man more as an individual rather than as a mere participant in the community which had been the case in the Hellenic Greece before the rise of Macedon as a political power.

Much of the technological developments of the Hellenistic engineers were based on scientific knowledge, which constitutes an epoch-making advance in civilisation, but it needed an industrial revolution to turn the Hellenistic civilisation into a European type of industrial civilisation. Yet this advance never came because the Hellenistic man lacked a certain spiritual outlook which the later Western man possessed: there was too much traditional reaction against rugged individualism, too limited interest in the workings of the material world, and too much reverence for nature due to a still lingering effect of the ancient belief in animism, a pagan belief that all nature is animated. All of this interfered to a certain extent with the industrial progress of the Hellenistic civilisation. However, there developed in the Hellenistic age a growing professional spirit and an increasing exchange of ideas between learned men, which led to more systematic and organised professional research rather than to brilliant amateur speculations of the earlier Hellenic age.

Since longer sea voyages were undertaken by the Hellenistic Greeks, better knowledge of time mensuration, navigational techniques, and geography became necessary. Alexandria, being a commercial center of the world, encouraged commercial competition, which, in turn, brought about a keen interest in materials, efficient production methods, and improved technical skills. As a result of the new commercial interest, various technical arts previously neglected by the Hellenic Greeks, were again pursued by the Alexandrian Greeks, to the extent that many training-schools were established for various technical arts.

State supported institutions of higher learning and public schools were established in Alexandria to promote formal education. The Museum (***Mouseion***, the temple of the 9 Muses) of Alexandria, established by the Macedonian kings of Egypt, was a great research institute which was equipped with an observatory, zoological and botanical gardens, dissecting theaters, and staffed by about 100 scholars who probably trained their assistants and technicians. The Museum was located in the royal palace enclosure near the great harbour. It is possible that the great Alexandrian Library was also part of the royal palace complex and an integral part of the Museum.

Alexandrian scientists laboured their imagination to create scientific methods for they had realised that the problems of science were immense and demanded a patient effort from many generations. In Hellenistic times science was divorced from philosophy, and became separated into specialties or divisions, which science has retained to this very day. In the promotion of such divisions, particular schools were founded for the training of specialists.

King Philip II of Macedon, and his son Alexandros III owed their military successes partly to the efficacy of their military equipment, for Hellenistic armies composed of Macedonians and Greeks became highly mechanised. Some very ingenious engineering was done by the Greek military engineers in the design of Hellenistic war machinery. This technological outlook in the design of military equipment ultimately led Hellenistic Greeks in Alexandria to incipient scientific engineering and a high level of technology, yet its complete development took place more than a millennium later in Western Europe. The best Hellenistic engineers were mainly mechanical engineers who designed ingenious precision instruments, automata, and machinery in general. The science pursued in Alexandria, the commercial center of the world, tended to be more practical than the science that had been pursued in Greece proper. The Alexandrian mathematicians, who were influenced by the Babylonian numerical mathematics, began to apply numerical calculations freely to geometric problems and, furthermore, to ally themselves with engineers (***technites***), which motivated them to devote their geometry mostly to the calculation of lengths, areas and volumes that were useful in technological and engineering applications.

Military Equipment and War Engines of Hellenistic Engineers

Hellenistic Military Engineers:

About 365 B.C., Aineias, the Tactician, wrote a military manual < On the Defence of Fortifications >, which introduced venom-smeared weapons, but no mechanical engines of war. Pyrrhos of Epyros condensed it into an instruction manual for troops. About 350 B.C., the Pythagorean Zopyros of Taras invented an improved ***gastraphetes***, a stomach cross-bow or a mobile dart-thrower. Herakleides of Taras, chief military engineer for King Philip II, built a siege engine called ***Sambyke***. Military engineer Polydios of Thessalos built many war engines for Philip II.

Alexandros conquered the Persian Empire within a dozen years, from 334 B.C. to 323 B.C. when he died of malaria in Babylon, during which period he fought many battles that he won with his highly mechanised Hellenistic army which incorporated a corps of military engineers. Diades, chief military engineer of Alexandros, wrote the first treatise on siege engines, and invented the flying draw-bridge for ships so that Alexandros could land his troops near the breach in the wall of the Phoenician city, Tyre, produced by the bombardment of his ship artillery during the long siege of that city by the army and the fleet of warships of Alexandros. Diades and Charias, both of Macedon and both pupils of Polydios, designed borers, climbing machines, rams, siege towers and catapults for Alexandros. About 330 B.C., Poseidonios, a military engineer of Alexandros, designed a self-propelled siege-tower which was moved forwards by treadmills within the tower, according to Biton, who published a treatise on military war engines designed by the military engineers Charon, Poseidonios, Zopyros, Damios of Kolophon, and Isidoros of Abydos.

In 332 B.C., Alexandros assigned the celebrated ***architekton*** Deinokrates of the Island of Rhodos (in English, Rhodes), who was a native of Macedon, to plan and build a new city in the Nile Delta. Deinokrates was famous for rebuilding the magnificent Temple of Artemis (***Artemiseion***) in Ephesos on a grandiose scale soon after the old temple had fallen victim to an infamous arsonist Herostratos of Ephesos in 356 B.C.. Alexandros helped to pay for the rebuilding of the ***Artemiseion*** probably because he believed the fabulous story about the goddess Artemis being absent from her temple on the night of the fire to attend his birth in Macedon. Deinokrates incorporated the old platform, or stylobate, 377 feet by 180 feet (115m by 55m) constructed by Theodoros of Samos into his still larger platform 417 feet by 239 feet (127 m by 73 m) and built a new foundation on top of the pavement of the old temple, which raised the floor of the reconstructed temple 7.5 feet (2 m) above the floor level of the old temple. Although the rebuilt superstructure of the temple followed the specifications of the old temple, 127 columns of Deinokrates were 65 feet (20 m) high instead 41 feet (12 m) high as in the old temple. 36 columns at the front of the temple were decorated on their lower parts with relief carvings like in the old temple. The ***architekton*** and sculptor Skopas of the island of Paros was in charge of decorating the rebuilt Temple of Artemis with his relief carvings of the columns, the entablature and the frieze. Skopas was also responsible for the statuary in the new Temple of Artemis, such as the sculpture of goddess Artemis carved from cedar-wood.

This magnificent temple, called one of the 'Seven Wonders of the World', was looted of its fabulous treasures and burnt to the ground by the barbaric Goths in A.D. 262, but all the ships which carried the looted treasure sank to the bottom of the sea in a violent storm.

Deinokrates was charged by Alexandros with the building of his important new city Alexandria (in Greek, ***Alexandreia***), located at the crossroads of the East and the West on the site of an Egyptian fishing village, ***Rakotis***, a strip of land a mile and a half (2.4 km) wide between the Mediterranean, the rocky islet of ***Pharos*** and the marshy Lake ***Mareotis***. Deinokrates planned Alexandria according to the gridiron scheme of Hippodamos of Miletos, in which the two main avenues, the Kanobic Way running almost due east and west and the Street of ***Sema*** running almost due north and south, crossed at a place where later the stately tomb of Alexandros (***Sema***) was located. The main avenues paved with square granite flagstones and lined with marble colonnades were about 46 feet (14 m) wide. At first Alexandria was little more than the mile and a half (2.4 km) long islet of Pharos which was connected to the narrow strip of mainland by a mole, or a causeway, about 600 feet (183m) wide and about a mile (1.6 km) long, called the 'Seven Stadion' (***Heptastadion***). A 20-mile (32 km) long shipping canal, the Canal of Alexandria, was dug to a Western branch of the Nile by a mining engineer Krates from Chalkis, a leading city of Euboia in

Greece. Fresh water was supplied to the city from the canal through subterranean conduits which ran along the cross-streets to 350 subterranean cisterns. A branch of the canal connected Lake Mareotis to a harbour named 'Haven of Happy Return (***Eunostu Limen***)'. A mile-long (1.6 km) breakwater and nearly as long a causeway, the ***Heptastadion***, leading to the artificially connected rocky islet Pharos, were constructed to form a safe double-harbour for shipping, a type of harbour constructed earlier in Syracuse, Sinope, and Kyzikos. The eastern harbour, called the Great Harbour, was a natural harbour which contained naval dockyards and an inner harbour for royal ships. The western harbour, ***Eunostu Limen***, was built for the use of small vessels and fishing fleet. In the building of Alexandria, Deinokrates of Rhodos collaborated with the mining engineer Krates of Chalkis, who had served as a sapper and mining engineer in the army of Alexandros, under the auspices of the corruption-prone Kleomenes of Neokratis whom Alexander had left in charge of the finances of Egypt before he left for his final battles of conquest in the East. Alexandria at first was divided into 3 regions: the Greek, the Egyptian and the Jewish region. Later in Roman times the 4th official region was added which divided the city into 4 quarters.

In 324 B.C., on the order of Alexandros, Krates of Chalkis had attempted to drain the landlocked shallow Lake Kopais, a reed swamp, which stretched about 100 square miles (260 square km) at an elevation of 325 feet (99.1 m) from the sea level. Lake Kopais received the flow of the Kephissos River, the Herkyna River and a few other smaller streams, but its natural subterranean passages had become clogged, perhaps as a result of earthquakes. Lake Kopais was located in one of the most arable land regions of Boiotia in Greece, and its clogged passages prevented the proper drainage of this lake which caused yearly inundation of the entire region of this rich farm land.

Krates sank 16 shafts up to 216 feet (65.84 m) in depth along a curved alignment of the tunnel through the mountain to avoid deep shafts. He had driven two partially completed sections, each about 2,000 feet (610 m) long, of the planned, winding, 1.08-mile (1.7 km) long tunnels through the mountain, when he was forced to stop his work before its completion because of the unstable political conditions that prevailed in Greece after the death of Alexandros. One of his tunnels followed a winding pass through the hill. It appears that such drainage canals to Lake Kopais had been dug about a millennium before Krates by the Helladic engineers. In the 19th century A.D., a drainage tunnel was driven straight through the hill near one of the tunnels of Krates, which indicates the soundness of his engineering judgement.

In 305 B.C., Epimachos of Athens, a military engineer of Demetrios the Besieger (***Poliorketes***), constructed a colossal armoured 9-storey siege engine with catapults and battering rams for the siege of the city of Rhodos, the capital of federated city-States of the island of Rhodos, in the Hellenistic wars of the Macedonian generals called the Successors (***Diadochoi***) to Alexandros. This siege engine was from 100 to 150 feet (30.48 to 45.72 m) high, from 60 to 75 feet (18.29 to

22.86 meters) square in its base, and weighted about 125 tons, and it was able to withstand the impact of a 360-pound (163 kg) missile. This siege engine had 8 iron-tyred, castor-mounted wheels, and it was operated by 3,400 soldiers. In spite of the formidable war machinery and overwhelming numerical superiority, the assaults led by the brilliant military commander Demetrios ***Poliorketes*** with a military force of 40,000 soldiers and a squadron of pirates failed after a year-long siege. Demetrios attempted to force the federated city-States of the island of Rhodos to join his father Antigonos the One-eyed, a fierce and crafty Macedonian general of Alexandros, in an attack on Egypt ruled by another general of Alexandros, Ptolemaios, but his well-planned siege failed because the military engineers of the city of Rhodos were always able to devise ingenious military and technological countermeasures which neutralised the awesome power of the assaulting military equipment of the resourceful, bold but impatient Demetrios ***Poliorketes***.

Museum and Library of Alexandria

Rise of Scientific Technology and Engineering:

306 B.C. one of the generals of Alexandros and the appointed satrap of Egypt, Ptolemaios (in English, Ptolemy) I Soter [meaning 'Savior'] (ruled from c.307 B.C. to 283 B.C.), who together with Alexandros had also been a student of Aristotle, declared himself the King of Egypt after the death of Alexandros. He and his son Ptolemaios Philadelphos (ruled from 285 B.C. to 247 B.C.), made Alexandria the world capital of science and technology. The first 3 Ptolemaic kings of Egypt were scholars: Ptolemaios Soter was a historian, his son Ptolemaios Philadelphos was a zoologist, and his grandson Ptolemaios Evergetes was a mathematician (ruled from 247 B.C. to 222 B.C.).

About 300 B.C. Ptolemaios I invited Straton of Lampsakos, The Physicist (***ho physikos***), to tutor his son, and to found the Museum (***Mouseion***), the temple of the 9 Muses who were goddesses of humanities, the first government-supported research institute in the world. Straton, who excelled in all branches of learning but particularly in physics, organised the Museum to consist of 4 departments: mathematics, astronomy, anatomy and physiology, and literature after the example of the Lyceum in Athens. He deliberately did not establish a department for philosophy, a discipline dominated by the occult Neoplatonic philosophy that was inimical to science, at the Museum because it would have suffocated science. Therefore, the Museum was primarily an institute of scientific research, and it employed about a 100 government supported scholars, who established the Western tradition of organised group research and scholarship after the example of the Lyceum, and who held property in common. Straton returned to Athens in 288 B.C. after the death of his teacher Theophrastos, and succeeded his teacher as the head of Lyceum (***scholarches***), an institute which he directed from 286 B.C. to 268 B.C.. This was the 'golden age' of the Lyceum.

Ptolemaios I secured the services of Demetrios of Phaleron (c.345-283 B.C.)[Phaleron was the oldest harbour of Athens], an orator, writer and a former pupil of Theophrastos at the Lyceum in Athens who had been appointed governor of Athens by Kassandros, a son of the last general of King Philip II, Antipater, who had been governing Macedon and supervising much of Greece, including Athens, for Alexandros. In 307 B.C. during the wars between the generals of Alexandros, called the Successors (***Diadochoi***), Demetrios ***Poliorketes***, the proud, brilliant, but impatient son of the Macedonian general called the 'One-eyed Antigonos', conquered Macedon and subsequently invaded Greece where he restored democracy in Athens. Demetrios of Phaleron, who was sentenced to death by Athenians ***in absentia*** had fled to Egypt to escape execution but where he ultimately died from a snakebite. Demetrios of Phaleron after becoming the literary adviser to King Ptolemaios I convinced the King to found the Alexandrian Library of which his personal library and a small part of the library of Aristotle formed the nucleus. The Alexandrian Library grew from about 200,000 volumes to a collection of about 490,000 volumes, and it is possible that it finally may have reached a total of 700,000 volumes including the duplicates. The Library held literature from Greece, India, Egypt, and finally also from Rome. There was a remarkable inscription at the entrance to the Library which read: "A sanatorium of the mind." Soon State libraries appeared also in Antiochia and Pergamon, and a little later in Rhodos and in Smyrna. Ptolemaios Philadelphos gave the Museum its final form as an institution, and established an annex of the Library in the Temple of ***Sarapeis,*** called ***Sarapeion,*** dedicated to the combined cult of the Egyptian god ***Osiris*** and an infernal deity, the sacred bull ***Apis***. The ***Sarapeion*** initially contained about 42,800 volumes. The Museum as an institution was basically like a modern research institute, and it lasted about 600 years.

The years from 300 B.C. to 100 B.C. of the Museum, can be called the 'age of textbooks' and the most important and influential period in the existence of this institution, because during those years the habit and the art of writing systematic and logically composed textbooks, in which the topics were expounded from the first principles to the latest research results, were firmly established.

This period can also be called an 'age of technical training', which represents an important professional advance in the culture of the West. Specialisation in professions such as in engineering, science and medicine were developed to a very high and complex level which made special training a necessity for the practice of the profession. Elementary schools, once private, were now supported by the State, but with the State support came also bureaucratic control of scientists and scholars. In Hellenistic Egypt science was no longer pursued by freemen but by subsidised intellectuals who were told what type of science they had to pursue. The scholar no longer was free to present his own views on a topic if the State bureaucrats disapproved. Some scholars were persecuted, and even executed, for expressing 'wrong ideas' in their lectures. The scholars of the Museum seem to have been quite compliant and servile to the demands of the State, in sharp contrast to the scientists in the mediæval Europe who were far more courageous, individualistic and nonconformist. However, in the early years of the existence of the Museum the scholars of this institute were permitted to undertake and continue their investigations in relative freedom. Following the practice of Lyceum in Athens, research by teams of scientists was formally organised at the Museum.

A temple dedicated to any of the 9 Muses [7 Muses were patrons of literature in all of its forms but there was also one Muse for history, and one for astronomy] ancient Greeks called the ***Museion*** (in Latin, ***Museum***), and such temples existed in many parts of Greece. For instance, there was a '***museion***' in Plato's Academy in Athens, and Theophrastos founded a school of arts and letters in Athens which he named a '***Museion***' in honour of Aristotle, but all such institutions were small in comparison with the immense Museum in Alexandria which represented a greatly magnified institute modelled after the Lyceum in Athens. The Museum in Alexandria occupied a vast complex of buildings equipped for various scientific purposes in the royal district of the city called ***Brucheion***.

Sostratos of Knidos and First Skyscraper Pharos:

Architekton Sostratos of Knidos erected the marble lighthouse on the islet of Pharos for King Ptolemaios Soter and his son Ptolemaios Philadelphos from about 299 B.C. to 284 B.C..This lighthouse, called the ***Pharos***, a tower about 440 feet (134 m) high [Washington monument is 555½ feet (169 m) high] was the tallest building in antiquity. The lower rectangular part of the lighthouse was 213 feet (65 m) high, whereas the octagonal middle part had a structure consisting of heavy blocks of granite embedded in sheets of lead or bonded by gudgeons bound in lead. The top part which contained the fire for the beacon was cylindrical. Sostratos made use of glass in building the foundation of the lighthouse because it was the most water-resistant material available to him. The lighthouse had about three hundred rooms as well as accommodations for a garrison, and the lower rectangular part of the structure incorporated a wide winding ramp and broad balconies. At the summit of the lighthouse, the light of the fire in a furnace was magnified into an intense beam of light by a large mirror made of glass or polished metal which made the powerful beacon visible over a distance of about 35 miles (56 km). The fuel for the furnace of the lighthouse was hoisted from the ramp to the top of the lighthouse by means of a windlass. The lighthouse was partly destroyed by the Byzantine raiders in the 9th century A.D. when Egypt was under the Muslim rule. The ***Pharos***, which had stood for 15 hundred years finally crashed to the ground in the earthquakes of A.D. 1303 and A.D.1320. This lighthouse, the first 'skyscraper' in the world, was considered one of the 'Seven Wonders of the Ancient World'.

Pharaoh Canal, Postal Delivery Service with Camels:

Ptolemaios Philadelphos restored the Pharaoh Canal which the Persian King Darios had reconstructed, and early in his reign he began to drain Lake Moeris, which in the meantime had turned into a swamp, in order to recover much of the fertile land and to make this area in the Fayum district into a Greek settlement. Ultimately the swamp was reduced to a lake about the size of the present Lake Karun. He also established a caravan route from Koptos to Bernice at the Red Sea, and equipped it with wells and blockhouses. He organised a rapid postal service modelled after the Persian postal service, and a slower system of forwarding heavy parcels and persons based on requisitioning draught animals along the route. Ptolemaios Philadelphos instituted a postal service from Alexandria up along the Nile river using camels for transportation, since camels had endurance, were able to carry heavy loads, and travelled with great speed.

Chares of Lindos and Colossos of Rhodos:

Chares of Lindos was a favourite disciple of sculptor Lysippos of Sikyon, a self-taught coppersmith and a master of casting bronze statues, was the leading realistic style sculptor and the most celebrated artist of his time. He claimed that his teachers were nature and Polykleitos of Argos, whose canon of mathematical proportions of human figure he modified which made the human body more slender, sinewy and muscular. His sculptures were faithful to nature and emphasised extreme muscularity which is why he preferred athletes, heroes and gods as his subjects. He did not like to portray female figures. He was a great portraitist and the court sculptor of Alexandros. He and his brother Lysistratos of Sikyon, a sculptor primarily interested in making realistic portraits, devised a new natural sculpturing technique by using life-masks of plaster which consisted of taking plaster-casts from the faces of his models, and from such plaster moulds they were able to produce accurate copies of the faces of their models by pouring molten wax into them. This technique is known as the 'lost wax method' of casting. He was known for producing two colossal bronze statues, a statue of the mythological Greek hero Herakles, and the larger 60-foot (18.3m) statue of Zeus in the city of Taras in Italy, among his total of some 1,500 small statues which included many busts and statues of Alexandros. Lysippos reacted against the graceful, relaxed and delicate sculptures of Praxiteles of Athens, who was a generation older than Lysippos. Hellenistic realism in sculptures was mostly derived from the realistic style of sculptures by Lysippos.

From 292 B.C. to 280 B.C., Chares built the colossal bronze statue of the Sun god ***Helios-Apollon***, popularly known as the 'Colossos of Rhodos' which had a massive internal supporting structure and reached a height of about 120 feet (36.6m), on the Island of Rhodos. This giant statue was built over the span of 12 years from 220 tons of moulded bronze sheets rivetted together, and its huge cost of about 20,000 pounds of silver was financed by the sale of vast quantities of bronze weapons and war machinery abandoned by Demetrios ***Poliorketes*** after his unsuccessful year-long siege of the island in 305 B.C.. Reportedly Rhodos, a city which was widely known as a center of arts, had over 3,000 statues of which about 100 were of giant size.

The size of the Colossos of Rhodos was first surpassed by the 151-feet (46m) high colossal Statue of Liberty made of moulded copper sheets weighing 225 tons by the French sculptor Frédéric Auguste Bartholdi (A.D.1834-1904), who was the 19th century counterpart of Chares of Lindos. The moulded copper sheets were rivetted to an internal iron framework designed by the famous French engineer Alexandre Gustave Eiffel (A.D.1832-1923), and the colossal copper statue was erected in A.D.1886 on an island at the entrance to the New York Bay.

The Colossos of Rhodos, known as one of the 'Seven Wonders of the Ancient World', stood for 56 years but was finally toppled down to Earth in an earthquake of 224 B.C. which broke the colossal statue at its knees. In A.D. 654, after the Saracens had conquered the Island of Rhodos, an Arab general shipped the fragments of the crashed colossal statue as scrap metal to Syria in a fleet of several dozen ships, and sold it to a Jewish merchant of Emesa who had to use more than 900 camels to cart away the enormous fragmented remnants of the colossal bronze statue.

Eukleides of Athens and Axiomatic Mathematics:

Many outstanding scientists and engineers of the Hellenistic Age were scholars at the Museum. Eukleides (in English, Euclid) of Athens (c.330-260 B.C.), a contemporary of Straton of Lampsakos, was not only a leading scholar and a prolific writer, but also one of the prominent mathematicians of antiquity. In mechanics he may have been the author of the monograph, < On the Balance > (***Peri zygon***), in which a purely geometric proof was given to the principle of lever that was based on the principle of statical moment: the 'effective force' is measured by the product of the weight and the horizontal distance from the vertical force to the fulcrum of the lever, which in modern mechanics means that the 'effective force' is measured by the statical moment of the force about the fulcrum (***hypomochlion***), a remarkably original idea for an ancient Greek.

Eukleides wrote his famous encyclopædic treatise < Basic Principles >, now called < The Elements > (***Stoicheia***), in 13 books which made him the first mathematician after Hippokrates of Chios, Leon of the Academy and Theudios of Magnesia, to establish a broad synthesis of all mathematical knowledge obtained by others and by himself in which all propositions are placed into a strictly logical order. Eukleides, who had an extraordinary genius for synthesis and exposition, wrote many large treatises of encyclopædic nature which were distinguished by the best logical order and expositional lucidity, whereas his predecessors had written monographs or short treatises that were soon judged to be incomplete and obsolete in comparison with the encyclopædic treatises of

Eukleides and, therefore, the scribes ceased to copy them. In this way < The Elements > of Eukleides, which besides geometry also included geometrical algebra and the unbelievably complex theory of numbers, rapidly superseded the three previous works on the basic principles of mathematics. In this systematic work, axioms, postulates and deductions are differentiated with strict logical rigour. This treatise which contained 467 propositions in its 13 books, among which a considerable number of propositions were his own discoveries, had an amazing richness in content, and it is the most influential work of mathematics in the history of the subject. Next to the Bible, < The Elements> of Eukleides had the largest circulation of any book with more than 1700 editions, and it is the most reproduced and widely studied book in the history of the Western civilisation. In it he also proved the distributive and commutative laws of algebra by means of geometry, since Greeks had a cumbersome and awkward number system. Eukleides' favourite method of proof was the Eleatic method of reasoning called ***reductio ad absurdum***, which he adopted from the works of Eudoxos of Knidos. Book I explained fundamental concepts of his method such as definitions, postulates, axioms, and other basic geometric propositions. Book II treated an essential part of geometrical algebra, Book III the geometry of the circle, and Book IV the regular polygons. Book V gave the new theory of proportion of Eudoxos of Knidos in its application to both incommensurable and commensurable quantities, and Book VI the applications of the theory of plane geometry. Book VII to Book X were devoted to arithmetic and the intricate and complex theory of numbers. Book X contained his original theory of irrational lines. Book XI was devoted to solid geometry. Book XII applied the method of exhaustion of Eudoxos of Knidos to the mensuration of circles, spheres, pyramids and other geometrical figures. Book XIII covered the theory of regular polyhedra as the final topic in solid geometry.

Optics became the next successful science to astronomy and virtually all Greek natural philosophers speculated about the nature of light, vision and colour. Empedokles, in particular, had asserted that light has a great but finite speed, but in all these early speculations the theoretical considerations of light were always made independent of vision. However, the first ancient Greek who developed a geometrical theory of light was Eukleides. He wrote a treatise < Optics > (***Optika***), a bold and original work on the theory of vision and perspective in which the beam of light is mathematically abstracted into a pencil of rays emanating from the eye without regard to the physical nature of light. The major purpose of the treatise was to determine geometrically the apparent sizes of objects within the context of visual angles, as well as to demonstrate by means of his geometric optics how to find the sizes of objects that are seen as images in a plane mirror, an aspect of optics which in time developed into a new theory of perspective. In his speculative perspective theory Eukleides refers to the 'cone of sight', the 'law of reduction', and the 'picture of depth' with lines coming from the right and from the left side. He also discusses the 'aerial perspective' and its effect.

This entire work contained 58 geometric propositions on visual optics. In contrast to Plato's concept that vision could be explained by a series of rays going out from the eye to the object seen, a concept later used by Eukleides, the Stoic philosophers were the first to suggest that vision was due to rays of light entering the eye from the object seen.

It is not certain that Eukleides also wrote a work < Mirrors > (***Katoptrika***) which dealt with visual images given by reflected light rays from plane, concave and convex mirrors. In this remarkable work the Law of Reflexion of Light (first used by Aristotle in his theory of the rainbow) is given which is of fundamental importance to geometrical optics.

Eukleides wrote another influential work < Phenomena > (***Phainomena***) which was essentially a treatise on spherical geometry of great value to astronomers. The 18 of its 25 propositions were on spherical geometry, the rest on uniformly rotating spheres. A lost work in three books entitled < Porisms > (***Porismos***) dealt with methods of solution and proofs of mathematical existence by geometric construction. ***Porism*** might have been an ancient equivalent to the modern equation of a curve, something quite comparable to modern 'analytic geometry'. It also contained the seeds of modern projective geometry. He wrote another lost textbook < Fallacies > (***Pseudaria***) for the training of students in mathematics at the Museum in which he demonstrated correct and incorrect geometric proofs, and a small tract < Division of Figures > (***Peri diaireson***). Eukleides wrote another work < Data > (***Dedomena***) that was probably meant to be a companion volume to the first 6 books of his < The Elements > and used as a guide to the analysis of geometric problems at the Museum. This work, which is still extant, gave many applications of algebra to geometry and solutions to quadratic equations in a strictly geometric form. He may have also written a lost tract on < Introduction to Harmonics > (***Eisagoge harmonike***), which was probably a treatise on music, and a treatise on the doctrine of sound in which he treated the subject in an axiomatic and deductive manner reminiscent of his < Optics >. In this work sound was presented as movement of air and the pitch of tone was dependent upon the number of motions in air in a given time known as frequency, and the frequency of tone in a musical string instrument was considered to be inversely proportional to the length of the string. Eukleides wrote an elaborate treatise in 4 books on conic sections entitled < Conics > (***Konika)*** but, unfortunately, it is one of his lost works which apparently was used by Apollonios in the writing of his famous treatise on conic sections. Another lost work of Eukleides is a treatise in 2 books on < Surface Loci > (***Topoi pros epiphaneia***) which probably dealt with curves lying on the surface of revolution such as a sphere, cone, cylinder, torus, ellipsoid, paraboloid, and hyperboloid.

***Ktesibios of Askra and Mechanical Inventions*:**

Ktesibios of Askra (*floruit* 283-247 B.C.), known as 'Edison of Antiquity' and the founder of the Alexandrian school of mechanics, was a son of a barber, an engineer and a paid retainer of the Ptolemaic kings. In his school, mechanics was applied to the design of war engines, to all kinds of amenities, and to miracle-working gadgets of all sorts for the Temple of ***Sarapeis***. However, applications of mechanics to industry in general were conspicuously absent in Ktesibios' work.

Ktesibios, who is only overshadowed by Archimedes as the greatest engineer in classical antiquity, invented the all-important mechanical device for the transmission of power consisting of a cylinder fitted with a piston. He made use of the discovery of the so-called 'spring of air' by Straton of Lampsakos, and thereby became the founder of pneumatics and the first inventor of pneumatic machines. He designed the first force-pump consisting of two bronze cylinders fitted with pistons. This device with slight modifications was used in European fire engines as late as in the 19th century A.D..

He invented a hydraulic organ operated by his pump mechanism which forced water into a series of tubes that were separated by valves from air pipes of varying length. A musical keyboard controlled the flow of water by operating the valves, and produced musical sounds as water forced air from the pipes. The keyboard device of Ktesibios was extended to string instruments only in the fifteenth century A.D. in Europe. It appears that some of these hydraulic pumping devices were driven by waterwheels.

Ancient Egyptians had used for centuries a water-clock which gave information only over a certain length of time. Ktesibios invented his water-clock, called ***klepsydra***, which indicated continuous passage of time. He made use of constant hydraulic pressure which he obtained with constant head of water provided by means of a 3-vessel system that allowed water to flow through the ***klepsydra*** at a constant rate. The second vessel was fitted with an overflow duct to maintain constant head of water in the chamber. In order to prevent clogging and wear, he used onyx apertures. Time was read by means of a pointer moved up by a rising piece of floating cork in the third vessel. He later invented a better time-measuring instrument called the 'parastatic clock', which also used a pointer rising with water at constant rate in the middle of a drum to mark hours in a series of lines drawn on a vertical cylinder. The flow of water could be controlled by an adjustable, cone-shaped valve, or by changing the mounting of the cylinder, which allowed for seasonal changes in the length of the day. Ktesibios invented a rack-and-pinion gearing for his water-clock, and employed toothed gear-wheels (***tympani***) in his other mechanical designs. He invented the bent syphon for the drawing off of liquids by means of atmospheric pressure.

In the design of a catapult, which was powered by compressed air in two cylinders, he used the principle of the 'spring of air', but apparently it was not used successfully in practice, perhaps because the art of metalworking at the time was unequal to the task and could not provide strong enough material and proper sealing for this kind of pneumatic power source. Ktesibios is responsible for the invention of the first elastic metal spring made of bronze which stores energy in its deformed state. He also made the first 'self-acting' machines after the pioneering bird-automaton of Archytas of Taras. It is not known whether Ktesibios was only a practical mechanic, or whether he also gave scientific background to his inventions.

Aristarchos of Samos and Heliocentric Astronomy :

About 280 B.C., Aristarchos of Samos (c.310-c.230 B.C.), a talented student of Straton of Lampsakos who was learned in music, geometry, astronomy and other sciences, proposed a modified version of the planetary system of Herakleides in which the Sun was fixed in the center of all the concentric circular orbits of the planets, a system which was proposed again more than 17 centuries later in Europe by Nicolaus Copernicus (A.D.1473-1543). In his planetary system the Earth not only revolved round the Sun but also rotated about its own axis. Aristarchos considered the Sun to be a 'fixed star', and the 'fixed stars' to be distant suns. His heliocentric planetary system enjoyed certain advantages over the traditional astronomical system of the ancient Greeks: it gave 'variable' distances of planets moving with different speeds along their circular orbits of different size from the Earth at different times, distances which remained constant in Aristotelian astronomy. In spite of this advantage, the heliocentric planetary theory of Aristarchos was not accepted by other Greek astronomers because several objections could be raised against it on the basis of the Aristotelian theory of mechanics. The first objection was that such light bodies as the clouds would be left behind by a moving Earth because Aristotelian theory did not recognise inertia. The second objection was that heavy objects, which, according to Aristotelian theory, seek their place in the center, would fall off the Earth into the Sun, which in the heliocentric planetary theory is at the center of the universe. It is not known how Aristarchos met these two criticisms. The third criticism maintained that if the Earth moves, the relative distances between the 'fixed stars' as seen from the Earth must change as the Earth is being displaced in its motion round the Sun, which seemed not to be the case according to contemporary observations. Aristarchos was able to refute correctly the observational absence of the parallactic displacements of the stars by pointing out that the distances to the 'fixed stars' are so vast that the radius of the Earth's orbit is but a point in comparison and far too small to have any practical significance to parallactic observations of 'fixed stars'. The parallax of stars was first observed only in A.D.1838 by the German astronomer Friedrich Bessel (A.D.1784-1846) with a powerful telescope, an optical instrument which did not exist in antiquity, when he determined an annual parallax of 0.3 seconds of arc for the star 61 Cygni that is just visible to the naked eye, which corresponds to a distance of 10.3 [current value,10.8] light-years. Aristarchos wrote a treatise on his heliocentric astronomical system but unfortunately it did not survive the ravages of time.

Aristarchos is also credited with the invention of an improved Sundial (***skaphe***) consisting of a hemispherical bowl most of which was cut away and the vertical needle erected in the middle to cast shadows thus allowing the finding of both the height and the direction of the Sun.

His treatise < On the Sizes and Distances of the Sun and the Moon > (***Peri megethon***), which Aristarchos wrote about 260 B.C. and is still extant in manuscript form, contained the first general attempt to determine the distances of the Sun and the Moon from Earth and the relative sizes of these heavenly bodies. Aristarchos maintained that the Moon shines by the reflected Sunlight which enabled him to find the distance to the Sun by the geometry of the position of the Sun and the Earth at half-Moon. He had neither trigonometry nor a good value of π available at the time but his use of Eukleidean geometry was masterful. His estimate was that the Sun is between 18 and 20 times more distant than the Moon. The actual distance is 346-times the distance to the Moon.. He also found the ratio of the diameter of the Sun to the diameter of the Earth between 19/3 and 43/6. The correct value is 107. His values obtained by a correct method were made wrong only by the grossly inaccurate observational data obtained by primitive astronomical instruments available to him, which could not measure extremely small angles with sufficiently high accuracy for this type of heavenly mensuration. Eudoxos of Knidos was probably the first astronomer who had tried to determine the distances to the Sun and to the Moon. It is known that in arithmetic Aristarchos evaluated the irrational number $\sqrt{2}$, probably by a method similar to continued fractions. Judging from his extant work, Aristarchos was not only an ingenious and imaginative astronomer, but also an excellent mathematician. Aristarchos, moreover, wrote a lost treatise on light, vision, and colour

Philon of Byzantion and Military Engineering:

A prominent military engineer, Philon of Byzantion (*floruit* 250 B.C.) was probably a pupil of Ktesibios of Askra in Alexandria who later became a military engineer in Rhodos. He wrote an important treatise of applied mechanics and military engineering, < Systematic Compendium of Mechanics > (***Mechanike syntaxis***), a work divided into 8 or 9 books of which only a third has come down to the present time. Philon tried to treat in his treatise the engineering arts of war, both the offensive and the defensive military engineering, in a rather complete way. It contained chapters on the construction of harbours (***limens poiika***); construction of artillery (***belopoiika***); pneumatics (***pneumatika***); constructions of fortifications (***teichopoiika***); and methods of besieging (***poliorketika***). He also discussed techniques of cryptography and an optical telegraph for the transmission of messages over long distances. His book < Pneumatics > (***Pneumatika***) exerted great influence on the development of technological and engineering design. In it he described his experiments with vacuum in which he went almost as far as the Italian physicist and mathematician Evangelista Torricelli (A.D.1608-1647) and the French chemist Antoine Laurent Lavoisier (A.D.1743-1794) about 19 centuries later; he studied syphons, the means of keeping the level of water constant in vessels (necessary in water-clocks), the action of waterwheels, hydraulic pumps in the form of leather bellows, hydraulic toys, and water jets. He also designed a thermoscope in the form of an air-thermometer based upon his experiments on the expansion of air by heat which laid the foundation for the science of temperature measurement. He discovered that some air in a closed vessel was consumed by a burning torch, an observation used by Lavoisier to draw revolutionary conclusions in physical chemistry.

Philon devised a hydraulic reaction turbine for a fountain which worked on the principle of the modern rotatory lawn sprinkler. In his turbine a right-angle change in the direction of the stream of water flowing through the pipes created a reaction that produced a couple with respect to the vertical axis of the turbine which rotated the turbine about its axis.

He reduced applied mechanics to the single principle of Archytas of Taras as proposed by Straton of Lampsakos:

$$F_1/F_2 \propto V_2/V_1 \,.$$

Philon carried out empirical research for artillery design and gave the earliest known scaling laws: earliest empirical scaling formulae relating the sizes of elastic tendons in catapults to the weights of the missiles to be propelled. He mentioned that the trajectory of the arrow is circular when shot from the machine-gun shooting arrows (***euthytonon***). Philon gave the first known reference to elasticity in his discussion of the tendons, or skeins, and of metal springs in catapults. He is the first engineering scientist to call attention to 'lateral contraction' of elastic tendons [now, known as Poisson's Ratio], which he set equal to ⅓ of the longitudinal stretch of the tendon that were usually stretched by one-ninth of their original length. Since the tendons elongate in humid weather with a concomitant loss of their elasticity, he invented the elastic leaf-spring made of bronze to overcome this shortcoming. Philon was the first person to notice fatigue in the material subjected to repeated stretches. He also discussed the gimbal suspension, known today as the Cardan suspension, for an inkwell, and he may have known an elementary form of a universal joint.

Archimedes of Syracuse, Mathematician and Engineer Beyond Comparison:

There may be doubts about who is the greatest mathematician of the modern times but there is not doubt that the greatest mathematician and scientific engineer of antiquity was Archimedes of Syracuse (c.287-212 B.C.). It appears that Archimedes in his youth had pursued studies at the Museum in Alexandria. He was the most versatile and original mathematician-engineer of antiquity and a man of remarkably modern intellect. He not only devised highly sophisticated and elegant demonstrations and proofs in mathematics, but in mechanics as well, thereby making his theoretical mechanics as rigorous and as sophisticated a science as mathematics. Archimedes sought in his researches to prove by rigorous mathematical principles the practical understanding gained from experience. He was also considered to be an excellent astronomer for he not only had a wide scope of practical and theoretical interests, but also possessed outstanding mechanical skills.

Archimedes wrote a basic work on mechanics entitled < Elements of Mechanics > (***Stoicheia ton mechanikon***) in a series of 4 books constituting a single work:< On the Center of Gravity in Plane Figures >, < On the Equilibrium of Plane Figures > (manuscripts refer to both as ***Epipedon isorropiai***), < On the Center of Gravity in Solid Bodies > and < On the Squaring of the Parabola > (***Tetragonismos paraboles***). Archimedes was also the author of a famous work in 2 books < On Floating Bodies > (***Peri ochoumenon***), which laid the foundation for hydrostatics and contained his famous principle of floatation by means of which he determined the specific weights of bodies: 'A body wholly or partially immersed in a fluid loses an amount of its weight equal to that of the fluid displaced'. In his hydrostatics, Archimedes gave propositions on the motion of solid bodies in a fluid media that determined the positions in which such bodies will reach a state of rest, but without describing the motions necessary to reach such positions. He was able to give the most complete study of the configuration of rest and stability of a right segment of a paraboloid of revolution floating in a fluid with its base either upwards or downwards but subject to the condition that the base is either entirely above or below the surface of the fluid. He treated the stability of such bodies floating in water, and showed under what conditions a body when placed in water will either turn to or remain in a configuration of equilibrium, which are evidently idealisations of how ships would behave with different tilts in water.

In his youth, he wrote a tractate, < On Sphere-making> (***Peri sphairopoiias***), which described the art of construction of mechanico-astronomic devices, as well as his famous planetarium, a closed star-globe of constellations, made of brass and driven by hydraulic power, and its mathematical basis of operation. The planetarium of Archimedes reproduced the motion of the firmament, that is, the motion of the Sun, the Moon, and the planets, and it was capable of demonstrating the eclipses of the Moon. Its mechanism took the sidereal motions of the Sun and the Moon and produced from them the correct synodic waxing and waning of the phases of the Moon. He most likely had to use for the first time gears meshing in parallel planes to produce the correct mean periodic rotations of the seven celestial bodies and the synodic month. The Roman general Marcellus, who built a tomb for Archimedes emblazoned with the engraving of a sphere inscribed in a cylinder as Archimedes had wished, took the two planetaria of Archimedes to Rome as war booty, where one was kept in the house of Marcellus and the other in the Temple of Virtue. Therefore, it appears that Archimedes is the inventor of the first known gear-trains.

He is reported to have composed a book on his inventions but this work has perished. He invented his helical screw-pump named the 'water-snail' (***kochlias***), after having devised an ingenious analogy between the cylindrical helix and the inclined plane by wrapping a wedge cut out of a plane sheet around a circular cylinder which made a mathematical treatment of the helical screw-pump possible. In his work < On the Balance > (***Peri zygon***) dealing with the weight-lifting machine or power-lifter (***baruoulkos***), Archimedes invented the compound pulley (***polyspastos***) and the winch (***trispastos***), the steelyard (***charistion***) for weighing, various cranes and other machines of far greater power than had ever existed before. His cranes with iron hooks could lift 550-pound (250 kg) weights which far surpassed the previous crane capacities. He designed a set of peg and squirrel-cage gears which is known by his name. Archimedes also invented the first known 'feedback control' for his closed-loop water-clock.

Archimedes demonstrated to King Hieron II of Syracuse how his power-lifter worked by hauling singlehandedly a 3-masted merchantman together with its cargo and crew ashore without any help from others When the amazed king expressed the opinion that there must be some limit to the principle of multiplying the power which Archimedes had used in the design of his power-lifter, Archimedes gave his famous reply: "No limit. Give me another Earth to stand on, and I'll move the whole of this one." Apparently, he had invented the drive by wormgear in the operation of his power-lifter.

The naval engineer Archaias of Korinthos built for King Hieron II a gigantic ship, a double quinquereme, named <u>Syracusia</u> (***Syrakousia***), which was 420 feet (128 m) long and 57 feet (17.37 m) wide. This enormous ship, which could carry a 4000-men army, had four masts and twenty banks of oars, the longest oar being 84 feet (25.60 m) in length. About 2,000 men were required to row the 800 oars. The hull of this ship was sheathed by lead tiles, and it had 7 rams. Archimedes armed <u>Syracusa</u> with catapults hurling 180-pound (81.6 kg) stones, and 18-foot (5.49 m) long javelin-missiles, both having the range of 600 feet (183 m), artillery which Archimedes himself had devised. The catapult hurling 180 pound (81.6 kg) projectiles was the largest catapult ever built in antiquity, for the ordinary catapult hurled 60-pound (27.2 kg) missiles. He invented a capstan operating a worm-gearing in combination with a compound pulley system to launch the <u>Syracusia</u> with the help of a few men.

During the Second Punic War between Rome and Carthage which lasted from 218 B.C. to 202 B.C., the city of Syracuse had allied itself with Carthage against Rome, and as a result of this alliance, Roman army and fleet besieged that city from 213 B.C. to 215 B.C.. King Hieron II before he died in 215 B.C. had appointed Archimedes his General of ordnance in charge of the defences of the city, and in his capacity as the chief military engineer, he frustrated the vastly superior besieging Roman army for more than 2 years by building powerful war machines which wreaked havoc among the Roman army led by Appius Claudius Pulcher and the Roman fleet commanded by Marcus Claudius Marcellus who called Archimedes the 'geometrical Briareus' [a mythical giant with hundred arms]. The attempts of Carthaginians to break the Roman siege were successfully defeated by the Romans.

It is not entirely out of the question that Archimedes might have invented a steam-powered cannon which fired stone cannonballs held by a wooden plug in a wooden barrel incorporating a metal steam-chamber. The metal chamber when heated to about 750°F (400°C) temperature, and then quickly filled with cold water can turn the water almost instantly into rapidly expanding steam, which, in turn, creates a high steam pressure in the steam-chamber that can propel the cannonball from the barrel of the cannon after the removal of the wooden plug, thereby giving the projectile a remarkable range of firepower, from 990 to 1,300 feet (300 to 400 m), for his time. It is, however, quite certain that he constructed enormous cranes with iron hooks and grapnels to up-end the Roman warships near the city's outer defensive wall. Before the Punic War, he had designed a marine weapon called the 'dolphin', which consisted of an enormous weight made of lead that was suspended from the extremity of the ship's yardarm and could be slung against the hull of the enemy's ship by manipulation of a system of pulleys. He is also reported to have constructed an array of huge parabolic mirrors made of burnished metal with which he is supposed to have been able to set more distant Roman warships afire, but it seems that this may be an exaggerated claim.

In fortifying the defences of the city, Archimedes proved to be an outstanding military fortification engineer. He was responsible for the planning and construction of the formidable citadel Euryalos on top of the knoll in the city, and it proved to be a masterpiece of a defensive and offensive fortress built in antiquity. This exceptionally well planned and built fortress, a formidable structure, points to the amazing versatility of Archimedes as an engineer-scientist-mathematician. In spite of the remarkable engineering efforts of Archimedes in building the formidable defences of Syracuse and his ingenious war machinery which kept the Roman legions at bay for more than 2 years, the city ultimately fell into the hands of the Roman armed forces by a surprise attack by Marcellus helped by internal dissension and treachery whilst the Syracusans were celebrating a religious festival. Archimedes himself was killed in the sack of the city by a Roman soldier despite the order of Commander Marcellus to bring the 75-year old engineer-mathematician, who had already won a legendary reputation among Romans and Sicilian Greeks, to him unharmed.

The qualitative method of thinking of Aristotle was not able to produce an exact science which requires a mathematical form of expression favoured by Plato. Archimedes was the first ancient Greek who succeeded in carrying out the amalgamation of the two modes of thinking in statics by means of the axiomatic method employed by Eukleides in mathematics.

Therefore, in his theoretical works on mechanics, Archimedes introduced the concept of the mathematical model of a material body in which he dispensed with all the physical properties of the body that had no essential bearing on the mechanical theorem to be proven. His weights as forces were abstracted into geometric quantities and represented by abstract geometric concepts. In his work is buried the incipient notion of the so-called 'free-body' method. The statics of Archimedes rested not on experiments but on 2 fundamental axioms:

1. Two equal weights applied at equal distances from the fulcrum on both sides of the lever are in equilibrium.
2. Two unequal weights are in equilibrium if these weights are inversely proportional to their distances from the fulcrum.

His entire mechanics of equilibrium was developed on the basis of these two axioms of statics. He also established a mathematical form for the mechanical theory of the simple pulley systems initially studied by Archytas of Taras. The major work of Archimedes in statics and hydrostatics is < Elements of Mechanics > in series of 4 books, and < On Floating Bodies >. He was the first to study the stability of equilibrium by considering the state of the floating spherical segments relative to their equilibrium configuration in which he explicitly introduced the concepts of specific gravity and center of gravity. Archimedes demonstrated by means of proportions the conditions of stability or instability under which the parabolic conoids when placed in water will either turn or remain in a position of equilibrium. In this investigation which represented an abstract idealisation of the behaviour of ships when tilted in the sea, Archimedes came close to the concept of 'metacenter'.

Many mathematical researchers of Archimedes were inspired by his study of the works of other mathematicians such as Archytas and Eudoxos. His mechanical works leave the indelible impression of an engineer who was deeply concerned with the mathematical theory of mechanical problems. Archimedes, besides being the greatest mathematical engineer of antiquity, the kind of which were not to be met again for more than a thousand years until the late Middle Ages, was also the greatest mathematician of antiquity. He published a number of important mathematical tracts: < Quadrature of the Parabola > (***Tetragonismos paraboles***), < On the Sphere and the Cylinder > (***Peri sphairas kai kylindrou***) in two books, < On Spiral > (***Peri elikon***), <On Conoids and Spheroids> (***Peri konoeideon kai sphairoeideon***) and the renowned < The Method > (***Ephodos***), all awe-inspiring mathematical works endowed with a degree of mathematical precision and rigour not present in any of the works of his predecessors. Archimedes' geometry represented primarily geometry of mensuration rather than geometry of form. In mathematics, Archimedes refined and extended the method of exhaustion of Eudoxos of Knidos, and he made it into a powerful mathematical instrument of discovery by connecting it with infinitesimal considerations of

Demokritos of Abdera and the baricentric calculus (***kentrobarika***) in statics. Archimedes used the concept of 'statical moment' in his treatises < Quadrature of the Parabola > and < The Method >.

Archimedes explained his method of mathematical invention in the introduction to his memoir < The Method > (***Ephodos***), a work of 185 pages which he sent to Eratosthenes, who at the time was the custodian of the library at the Museum in Alexandria, and meant to be placed in the library. The introduction of this work is addressed to Eratosthenes:

> "Since I know you, as I have already said, to be a learned and excellent master of philosophy, and, if need be, you can appreciate mathematical researches, I have thought it well to explain to you the particulars of a method through which you will find it possible to gain a certain facility in treating mathematical matters by mechanical means. Besides, I am convinced that this method will be no less useful for the demonstration of the theorems themselves as well. In fact, I myself saw some things for the first time through mechanical means, and then I demonstrated them geometrically; for the research done in this way is not a real demonstration. But it is certainly easier, having in that way gained a certain knowledge of the question, to find the demonstration, instead of seeking it without any preliminary knowledge ... And on this occasion, I have decided to set down the method in writing, both because I had said I would do so and because I am persuaded that it will be of some use to mathematics ..."

In this introduction, Archimedes points out that whilst ***theoria***, that is, mechanical perception, does not provide a proof, it often helps the mathematician to find the deductive geometric proof if he has a clear idea of what is to be proven. Eudoxos of Knidos had been able to supply a rigorous proof to the propositions that the volumes of the cone and the pyramid were ⅓ of the volumes of a circumscribed cylinder and a circumscribed prism, respectively, but only because these results had been given earlier by Demokritos of Abdera without rigorous mathematical proofs.

Most of the mathematical results obtained by Archimedes by his mathematical procedures are in modern times obtained by means of integral calculus. Archimedes based his method of integration on the comparative study of the static moments of 2 geometric figures, one a figure with known geometric properties and the other a figure the geometric properties of which were sought. By means of the mechanical law of the lever, he balanced the 2 figures mathematically and determined the relative distances of the center of gravity of the 2 figures from the fulcrum which allowed him to determine the volume or the area of the figure the geometric properties of which were sought in terms of the same properties of the known figure. In this mechanico-mathematical procedure, Archimedes used a limiting form of the 'geometric atom' method of Demokritos of Abdera by assuming that surfaces were made up of infinitely many infinitesimal surface elements and volumes were made up of infinitely many infinitesimal volumes, because he had been able to devise a method of summing infinitely many infinitesimal elements in his mathematical theory of mensuration although other ancient Greek mathematicians did not accept the idea of infinity in mathematics. Knowing the answer to the question obtained by his mechanical and infinitesimal method, he was able to prove this result also indirectly and rigorously by means of the method of exhaustion and double ***reductio ad absurdum*** argument. As stated above, Archimedean method was equivalent to the operation of integration, and his concept of infinitesimals anticipated the concept of 'indivisibles' in the Middle Ages, which culminated in the calculus of indivisibles of Bonaventura Cavalieri (A.D.1598-1647) published in book form in A.D.1635.

Archimedes, who believed that projectiles move in a spiral trajectory, came closest to the modern form of integration in his study of the spiral $r = a\theta$, a curve which had been invented by his late friend, the astronomer Konon of Samos at the Museum in Alexandria, probably for the solution of the trisection and multisection problem of an angle. Archimedes defined the spiral of Konon kinematically, by rotating a line at constant rate about one of its ends as a center whilst a point is moving with constant speed along the rotating radial line from the center and tracing out a spiral. By the use of the parallelogram law of velocities, he was able to define the direction of motion and the tangent vector to the spiral curve as the path of motion. He showed how this spiral can be used to square the circle by letting the radial line make a 90 degree turn, $\theta = \pi/2$, and then demonstrate that the length of the polar subtangent is equal to ¼ -th of the circumference of the associated circle with the radius $r = a\pi/2$. Since the polar subtangent, the radius of the spiral $r = a\pi/2$, and the tangent form a right triangle, then the area of the triangle is equal to the area of the circle with radius $(a\pi/2)$. Since it is possible to replace a triangle by a square of equal area, Archimedes accomplished with this solution the squaring of the circle problem. Archimedes used a union of inscribed and circumscribed incremental sectors of the circle to approximate the area enclosed by the spiral from below and from above rather than by inscribed and circumscribed polygons which were used in the Method of Exhaustion. By letting these incremental sectors become smaller and smaller the difference between the sum of the areas of the finite number of inscribed sectors, or between the sum of the areas of the same finite number of circumscribed sectors, and the area enclosed by the spiral curve could be made less than any given magnitude. Unlike the method of exhaustion, this method of calculation of Archimedes was quite similar to modern integration. However, in his proof of the area of the spiral besides using his method of limits, Archimedes employed the double ***reductio ad absurdum*** argument of the method of exhaustion, which amounted to proving the uniqueness of the limit of a Cauchy sequence. In this solution, he constructed the tangent to the spiral, the first tangent established for a curve other than a circle, by means of the kinematic method using the parallelogram of velocities. In antiquity, this treatise of the spiral was considered to be the most difficult work of Archimedes.

Ancient Egyptians as well as Sumerians had recognised the sequence of numbers in an arithmetic progression:

$$a,\ a+d,\ a+2d,\ \ldots,\ a+nd,\ \ldots$$

where d is the common difference, and in a geometric progression:

$$a,\ ar,\ ar^2,\ ar^3,\ \ldots,\ ar^n,\ \ldots$$

where r is the common ratio.

For instance, the ancient Egyptian Ahmes (c.1500 B.C.) gave problems in his papyrus which involved both progressions, and he showed that he had rules for finding sums, and such other elements as the n-th term and the difference of terms. Ancient Greeks who inherited this elementary knowledge not only greatly simplified the treatment of the elementary series already known and introduced the study of higher types of series, but also took the first steps towards the investigation of infinite series. In the field of higher series the ancient Greeks were the first to make any progress.

Archimedes proved by means of geometry:

$$1 + 2 + 3 + \cdots + n = \frac{1}{2}\, n(n+1),$$

$$1^2 + 2^2 + 3^2 + \ldots + n^2 = \frac{1}{6}\, n(n+1)(2n+1)$$

and

$$3[a^2 + (2a)^2 + (3a)^2 + \ldots + (na)^2] = (n+1)(na)^2 + a(a + 2a + 3a + \ldots + na).$$

Archimedes was the first mathematician able to square a conic section, when he squared a segment of a parabola. In one of his proofs, he demonstrated that the area of a parabolic segment can be represented by that of the *n-th* inscribed polygon expressed as a geometric series:

$$A\,[1 + r + r^2 + \ldots + r^{n-1}],$$

where A denotes the maximal area of an inscribed triangle having the same base as the parabolic segment and the common ratio $r = 1/4$. He proved that this area can be neither less nor more than $(4/3)A$ by a double ***reductio ad absurdum*** argument, which was equivalent to summing the infinitely decreasing geometric series, a series first discussed by Zenon of Elea in his Paradox of Achilles and the Tortoise :

$$1 + r + r^2 + \cdots + r^n + \cdots = \frac{4}{3},$$

in which the common ratio $r = 1/4$. Archimedes proved that no matter how many terms of this series are added their sum would never exceed 4/3. Archimedes was unable to find areas of arbitrary segments of ellipses or hyperbolas by his method, because as we now know their integrals require transcendental functions, whereas the area of a parabolic segments needs only polynomial functions which he was able to treat by his method. Similarly, in the rectification of arc-lengths, which he postulated, he was unable to find the arc-lengths of parabolas, ellipses and hyperbolas because these integrals also require transcendental functions. However, he was able to square the area of a complete ellipse, $(x/a)^2 + (y/b)^2 = 1$, and prove that it was equal to πab.

He also studied geometric properties of figures of revolution generated by conic sections, and was able to find volumes of segments excised from ellipsoids, paraboloids and hyperboloids. He employed a method consisting of circumscribed and inscribed incremental cylindrical slices, the number of which can be infinitely increased when the slices are made infinitely thinner. Archimedes not only used his method of taking the limit of this infinite series, which made it a procedure of integration, but also introduced two inequalities as the upper and the lower bound, and used the double ***reductio ad absurdum*** in order to prove that the volume of the cylinder is twice that of the conoid. However, in the general sense, the method of Archimedes for all practical purposes can be considered to be a particular integration process.

In a tract entitled < On the Measurement of Circle>, Archimedes found the upper and lower bounds of π for the circle by using an inscribed and circumscribed regular polygon beginning with an hexagon and ending with a regular polygon of 96 sides: $3(10/71) < \pi < 3(10/70)$, an inequality which proved to be quite adequate for all problems of mensuration. In one of his lost works entitled < On Beam and Cylinder > (***Peri plinthidon kai kylindron***) Archimedes reportedly improved his approximation of π. In calculating the circumference of a circle by inscribed and circumscribed polygons of 6, 12, 24, 48, 96, ... sides, he demonstrated that the sequence of the areas of inscribed polygons is constantly increasing: $a_1 < a_2 < a_3 < \dots < a_n$ and that the sequence of the areas of the circumscribed polygons is constantly decreasing: $b_1 > b_2 > b_3 > \dots > b_n$ with the sequence of corresponding area difference: $\epsilon_1 > \epsilon_2 > \epsilon_3 > \dots > \epsilon_n$, where $\epsilon_1 = b_1 - a_1$, $\epsilon_2 = b_2 - a_2$, $\epsilon_3 = b_3 - a_3$, ... Therefore, for any ϵ however small, N can be found such that $\epsilon > \epsilon_n$ for all $n > N$. Thus, Archimedes at every step of his limiting process had an upper and a lower bound which approached each other in an unlimited way. The modern limiting process due to the Bohemian priest Bernardus Placidus Johann Bolzano (A.D.1781-1848) and the French engineer and mathematician Augustin Louis Cauchy (A.D.1789-1857) uses a single sequence of inequalities, called the 'Cauchy sequence': C_1, $C_2, \dots, C_n$ such that $|C_m - C_n| < \epsilon$ for $m,\ n > N$, but it can also be expressed in a double sequence of inequalities as preferred by ancient Greeks.

In proving the upper and lower limits for the square-root of number 3 which is an irrational number: $265/153 < \sqrt{3} < 1351/780$, he may have followed Aristarchos by employing a method similar to continued fractions which could be obtained from Eukleides' comprehensive theory of binomials, yet it seems more likely that he used successive linear interpolation, a method of algorism known to ancient Greeks. It enabled Archimedes to specify an irrational number by bounding it between two inequalities.

In the tract < On the Sphere and the Cylinder >, a work he valued above all his other mathematical researches, Archimedes proved by his method that the surface area of a sphere is equal to 4-times the area of its great circle, and that the surface area of the sphere is ⅔ of the surface area of the circumscribed right cylinder about the sphere including its bases, and that the volume of a sphere is ⅔ of the volume of the right cylinder circumscribed about the sphere. He also solved a very difficult problem consisting of cutting a given sphere with a planar section into two segments so that the volumes of the two segments are in a given ratio. He reduced this problem to the solution of the proportion :

$$(c - x) : b = a^2 : x^2 ,$$

which represents the cubic equation :

$$x^3 - c\,x^2 + a^2 b = 0 .$$

Archimedes solved it by finding the intersection of the parabola $x^2 = (a^2/c)y$ and the hyperbola $y(c - a) = bc$.

In these works, Archimedes was able to evaluate quantities equivalent to the modern integrals: $\int \sin x\, dx$, $\int x\, dx$, $\int x^2\, dx$ and $\int x^3\, dx$, but he seems to have been unaware that all his different geometric interpretations in particular cases had a single, general conceptual foundation, the modern concept of the integral.

Archimedes wrote a work entitled < Sand Reckoner > (***Psammites***), a work on an arithmetical system for representation of large numbers, in which he gave his ingenious method how to deal with very large numbers. Archimedes developed a counting scheme by 'octad', by the 8th power of 10, extending his number system as far as 10^{63}, and he not only used the algebraic exponential law :

$$a^m a^n = a^{m+n}$$

but also considered the fractional ratios such as $\sqrt{a^3} : \sqrt{b^3}$, i.e. $a^{3/2} : b^{3/2}$, which more than a millennium later led to exponential functions and logarithms. During the Middle Ages the fractional ratios were rediscovered by the outstanding English scholar and mathematician Thomas Bradwardine (A.D.c.1290-c.1349) in A.D.1328. His theory of large numbers in which Archimedes classifies numbers by orders and periods is now called the 'theory of indices of indices'.

On occasion Archimedes played tricks on his conceited Alexandrian colleagues, perhaps even on Eratosthenes of Kyrene, by sending them a few false propositions "so that those who pretend to have discovered everything themselves, without supplying proofs, may be trapped by claiming to have found something which is impossible."

He once sent to Eratosthenes < A Problem > (***Problema***) which was 'indeterminate' and practically unsolvable. It asked for 8 integral unknowns connected by 7 linear equations: the number of white, black, yellow and dappled bulls, which had to satisfy nine subsidiary conditions. Many years later, upon the urging of his friends, Archimedes published his proofs for this problem which finally led to what is known as the 'Pell Equation':

$$x^2 - (4,729,494)\,y^2 = 1$$

with the subsidiary condition requiring y to be a multiple of 9,304. The least solution is so formidable that the number of bulls requires a number of more than 206,500 digits, a number which has 68,848 periods of 3 figures each, which would fill 600 pages. In the last two works discussed, Archimedes demonstrated his supreme computational proficiency in which he was vastly superior to all other outstanding Greek mathematicians. Only the ingenious Eudoxos of Knidos, whose researches were of utmost importance to Archimedes, could be ranked his equal.

Other ancient Greeks besides Archimedes had some ideas about the combinatorial theory, for Xenokrates of Chalkedon (c.350 B.C.) had calculated the number of possible syllables capable of being made by Greek letters, and Chrysippos (c.250 B.C.) had found the number of possible combinations of 10 axioms.

In all of his works, Archimedes demonstrated a surprising originality of thought combined with a masterful computational technique and rigour of demonstration, an ability which makes him the foremost mathematicians of all time. All the works of Archimedes which cover a remarkably wide range bear the unmistakable mark of a genius, for he was able to carry them to the extreme limit of the capabilities of his time, and, beyond. Moreover, they are masterpieces of mathematical exposition quite comparable to the best modern works of mathematics. His work was about 2 millennia ahead of his time.

Eratosthenes of Kyrene and Size of Earth:

Eratosthenes of Kyrene, in North Africa, (c.276-c.194 B.C.) was a friend of Archimedes. In his youth, Eratosthenes had studied philosophy many years at the Academy in Athens and continued his studies later under Kallimachos (died c. 240 B.C.) at the Museum in Alexandria. About 235 B.C., King Ptolemaios Evergetes, the mathematician, appointed Eratosthenes to succeed Kallimachos as the custodian of the Library of Alexandria , and the tutor of the prince Ptolemaios Philopator, who reigned from 242 B.C. to 205 B.C.. Eratosthenes was called by his students ***pentathlos,*** since he had been champion in 5 athletic sports. Besides being an athlete, he was exceptionally talented in all the branches of learning of his time: he was a poet of note, a literary critic, an historian, an astronomer, a geographer, a philosopher and a mathematician. He was the first scholar to call himself a 'philologist'. He wrote scores of works in various disciplines : < Good and Evil >,< Measurement of the Earth>, < Comedy >, < Geography >, < Chronology >, < Constellations >, < Duplication of the Cube>, < Philologian and Poet >, and a selection of other works. Eratosthenes was also given a nickname **β** which may have meant a man of wide and varied learning who was second best in every field of knowledge. He was a quite capable mathematician and the first scientific cartographer of note after Eudoxos of Knidos. He is credited with the invention of the armillary sphere of the globe consisting of a skeleton of meridian and parallel rings. Eratosthenes earned a widespread reputation for determining the remarkably accurate value 11/166 of the complete circle (or 23° 51' 20") for the tilting of the Earth's axis of rotation which is responsible for the seasons. The modern value is 23° 46'. In arithmetic, Eratosthenes is usually credited with the invention of a method, the so-called 'Sieve of Eratosthenes' (***koskinon***), for a rapid systematic finding all prime numbers [a prime number is divisible only by itself and by unity] less than a given number *n*.

Eratosthenes won undying fame by determining the circumference of the Earth to an accuracy of 4% by means of a scientific method. He had a well dug in the island of Elephantine at Syene (modern Aswan) near the first cataract, a well still extant, which is 25 feet (7.6 m) deep and casts no shadow at noon. At the same time the needle fixed in the center of a hemispherical bowl, an instrument invented by Aristarchos and called ***skaphe***, cast a shadow of 1/25 of the hemisphere, and thus 1/50 of the complete circle, in Alexandria. Eratosthenes believed the 2 places to be on the same meridian (which is not quite correct as Syene lies 3° 4' west of Alexandria) and, therefore, he concluded that the well on the Elephantine Island near Syene was 1/50 of a complete great circle from Alexandria. Since the distance from Alexandria to Syene had been measured by professional geodesic 'pacers' (***bematistes***) to be 5,000 stadia, Eratosthenes calculated the mean circumference of the Earth to be 250,000 stadia, which was later changed to 252,000 stadia after further trials. Since there were stadia of different length at different times and in different places ranging from 7.5 to 10 stadia to a Roman mile of which the ancient geographers were hardly aware, it is difficult to decide which value Eratosthenes used. If he used stadia which went 9 times into a Roman mile, then his mean circumference of the Earth would be 25,890 miles (41,664 km) which is larger than the true value of 24,930 miles (40,120 km) by less than 4 %. Although other astronomers, such as Eudoxos of Knidos and Archimedes' father, astronomer Pheidias of Syracuse, had calculated the circumference of the Earth before Eratosthenes, his evaluation was remarkably accurate. Eratosthenes did estimate the average distance to the Sun as 804 million stadia, and the average distance to the Moon as 780 thousand stadia which when considering the relatively primitive instruments of observation available to him are respectable values. In a letter to King Ptolemaios Evergetes, Eratosthenes discussed the problem of the 'duplication of the cube' of the Sophists, and gave his own solution of the problem by means of his mechanical device, known as the 'mean-finder' (***mesolabon***).

Eratosthenes' work demonstrates that he was outstanding in geodesy and geography, and certainly one of the best geographers of all ages. He established the foundation for the mathematical geography of the spherical Earth and published his major contributions in geography, geodesy and cartography in his deservedly famous book < Geographical Knowledge > (***Hypomnemata***

geographika)consisting of 3 parts: Historical Introduction; Mathematical Geography; Measurement of the Earth and its Inhabited Part (***Oikumene***); and Mapping and Description (***Peri egesis***), in which he explained the nature and causes of changes in the Earth crust, and gave numerical data about the inhabited Earth.

Since Eratosthenes was also a historian, he wrote a history of philosophy, and part of his book < Geographical Knowledge > was history of geography. He realised that for all historical writing a scientific chronology which did not exist is necessary. Therefore, he succeeded to lay the foundation of scientific chronology beginning from the conquest of Troy to his own day, and he wrote 2 treatises on this subject, < Chronographics > (***Chronographiai***) and < Olympionics > (***Olympionikai***). In his time each country had its own means of registering dates of important deeds with reference to local standards which made correlation of different chronologies very difficult.

Eratosthenes starved himself to death, when he discovered that he was going blind from ophthalmia, a common regional malady of eye inflammation.

Pytheas and Geographic Mapping:

The famous ancient Greek mariner Pytheas of Massilia (modern ***Marseille*** in France) is reported to have fixed the latitudes (or more precisely recorded the noon's Sun altitude on the summer solstice) of a number of ports he visited on his celebrated voyage to the Faroe Islands or Iceland about 330 B.C.. In his account of his voyages < On the Ocean > (***Peri tou okeanou***), he was the first to recognise the relation of tides to the phases of the Moon and to direct attention to their periodic fluctuations in the spring and neap tides, and to record the difference between the length of the longest day in different parts of British isle as well as the climatic changes which took place in his travel towards the arctic circle. Although Pytheas' contemporary, Dikaiarchos of Messina had already suggested the use of 2 mutually perpendicular axes in geographic mapping, Eratosthenes of Kyrene was the first geographer able to draw his world map with crosslines representing latitudes and longitudes.

Kleon and Plans of Canal Engineering:

About 252 B.C., Kleon (*floruit* 258-252 B.C.), the royal engineer of the district Fayum and commissioner of public works for King Ptolemaios Philadelphos in Egypt, and his assistant and successor Theodoros, who replaced him when the King dismissed Kleon for accepting bribes from contractors, left extensive records of engineering works in canal construction and maintenance. These records contained the first extant engineering plans which specified dimensions for all construction and volumes of excavations amounting to 400,000 cubic yards (300,000 cubic meters) of Earth to be removed in an estate of 6,000 acres (2,430 hectares) of marshland to be drained by a system containing about 50 miles (80.5 km) of ditches and embankments.

Apollonios of Perge and Synthetic Geometry of Forms:

Another mathematician of the first rank in the Hellenistic era was Apollonios of Perge (c.265-170 B.C.), a younger contemporary of Archimedes who studied and perhaps even taught at the Museum in Alexandria and later lived in Pergamon and Ephesos. He ranks with Archytas of Taras, Eudoxos of Knidos, Eukleides of Athens, and Archimedes of Syracuse as one of the outstanding mathematicians of antiquity. He was a supreme master of synthetic geometry which he demonstrated in his development of the theory of conic sections discovered by Menaichmos of Alopekonnesos. In his major work < Elements of Conics > (***Konika stoicheia***) Apollonios intersected the same cone with planes at different angles to the generator of the cone, in a generalisation of the method of Aristaios of Kroton who had used three different cones for the same purpose, to produce all the characteristic conic sections: $y < px^2$ (ellipse), $y = px^2$ (parabola), and $y > px^2$ (hyperbola). He borrowed the names ellipse (***elleipsis***), parabola (***parabole***), hyperbola (***hyperbole***), from Pythagoreans who had used these terms in their method of application of areas. He discovered the focus of the ellipse and of the hyperbola, but not the focus of the parabola, and he failed to introduce the idea of the directrix for conic sections. Apollonios' unified theory of conic sections revealed the intimate relationship between the ellipse, the parabola, and the hyperbola, and by means of it he was able to give as coherent and sophisticated a theory for the conic sections as the theory for the circle. The sophisticated theoretical approach of Apollonios to conic sections changed the method of their study.

It should be mentioned that some of the most adverse critics of Apollonios accused him of having plagiarised, and then extended Eukleides' elaborate treatise on conic sections but, unfortunately, this work of Eukleides is lost and, therefore, it is no longer possible to determine whether this accusation was justified. It is possible that Apollonios' critics did not quite understand his sophisticated contribution to the theory of conic sections because in many branches of mathematics, but particularly in geometry, only Archimedes and Eudoxos surpassed Apollonios.

In < Elements of Conics > Apollonios demonstrated with great virtuosity how a theory can be exhausted to reach an amazing number of deductive results. In his 487 propositions Apollonios obtained nearly all the results on conic sections included in modern introductory analytic geometry. His study of the second order curves is unbelievably thorough. There is a possibility that his extraordinary powers of discovery might have been aided by his invention of coordinate geometry for he made free use of coordinates where he made a fundamental difference between abscissas and ordinates. Although the shortcomings in the algebraic notation of ancient Greeks militated against

Apollonios achieving a fully-fledged coordinate geometry, he, nevertheless, has to be considered the pathmaker to analytic geometry. The geometry of Apollonios was a geometry of forms, and not of mensuration like that of Archimedes, in which Apollonios strove towards generality. Perhaps it is proper to claim that he invented the general planar geometry. Apollonios was also an excellent arithmetician, which he demonstrated in some of his works. In his last treatise < Quick Delivery > (***Okytokion***) on the quadrature of the circle he took leave of the rigorous Greek mathematics and by improved arithmetical methods found the value of $\pi = 3.1416$, which is more precise than the same value given by Archimedes. In this work Apollonios might have introduced an incipient theory of uniform convergence. He wrote a treatise on unordered irrationals but it also has not survived the ravages of time. In fact, most of the works of Apollonios are lost.

In order to account for the apparent motions of the superior planets, Mars, Jupiter, and Saturn, Apollonios of Perge generalised the use of the theory of epicycles and helped to develop a 3rd kind of kinematic theory of planetary motion, the theory of eccentrics. He determined the points where the planets appear to become stationary and begin their retrograde motions with respect to the Earth. Apollonios of Perge appears to be the actual founder of 'Greek quantitative mathematical theory of astronomy', and his reputation as an astronomer almost equalled his reputation as a geometer for he was called in his own time and later, 'The Great Geometer'. Apollonios is also credited with the invention of a particular form of the screw pump of Archimedes, which consisted of a waterpipe in the shape of a tubular coil, or cylindrical helix, wrapped around the cylindrical drum (***kochleia***). He is credited with having written a work < On the Tubular Coil > (***Peri kochliou***). He also wrote a work on burning mirrors (***Peri pyriou***) in which he demonstrated that all rays of light emanating from one focus of the ellipsoidal mirror will be reflected to the other focus. The theory of conic sections of Menaichmos of Alopekonnesos in the Apollonian form laid the foundation for the Scientific Revolution in the seventeenth century A.D. in Europe, and it ranks as an unparalleled achievement in synthetic geometry. In addition to all his scientific talents, Apollonios was also highly regarded as a man of letters for his writings were distinguished by an excellent literary style which was not complicated by mathematical jargon.

Syphon Line of Pergamon:

In 180 B.C., King Eumenes, who ruled from 195 B.C. to 159 B.C., united the lower and upper city of Pergamon in Ionia, thereby making it into the most beautiful city of antiquity according to the Romans. A high pressure syphon line, 2 miles (3.2 km) long, was brought from the reservoir on Mount Hagios Georgios down through the valley, 640 feet (195.1 m) deep, up to the Akropolis of the city of Pergamon where the king's palace was located, approximately 123 feet (37.5 m) below the reservoir. These syphon pipes were under an unprecedented pressure from 16 to 20 atmospheres (modern syphons go up to 10 atmospheres of pressure). Only solid stone collars 4 to 5 feet by 24 to 27 inches by 8 to 10 inches (1.22 to 1.52 m by 0.61 to 0.69 m by 0.20 to 0.25 m), spaced about 4 feet (1.22 m) apart, each pierced with a 12-inch (0.30 m) diameter hole, remain of this incredible syphon line. Three 7-inch (0.18 m) terracotta pipes, 35 miles (56.3 km) long brought water from the mountains to the distribution reservoir. It is not definitely known what kind of pipe was used in the Pergamon syphon line, whether it was a metal pipe or a tile pipe encased in heavy perforated stone blocks, but it was probably a metal pipe. There were other syphon lines built in the Hellenistic world, such as the syphon lines in Patara, Methymna and other places, but none were under such great pressure as the syphon line of Pergamon. At Pergamon, the Hellenistic engineers built one of the few known Greek arch bridges which had a 27-foot (8.23 m) span.

Hipparchos of Nikaia, Free Fall of Heavy Bodies and Observational Astronomy:

After Aristarchos, Hipparchos of Nikaia, Anatolia (*floruit* c.130 B.C.) was the best astronomer and certainly the greatest mathematical and observational astronomer of antiquity. Hipparchos, who was an outstanding mathematician, studied combinatorial analysis, algebraic problems, invented spherical trigonometry and devoted great attention to the graphical solution of spherical triangles. He discovered the precession of the Earth's axis, a feat which enabled him to determine the tropical year as 365 days, 5 hours, 55 minutes, and 12 seconds, which is only six and a half minutes in excess of the modern value. He compiled a catalogue of more than 850 stars locating each by its own latitude and longitude on the basis of his own observations carried out by means of improved instruments of his own invention in the observatory of Rhodos.

Hipparchos' researches in astronomy made the mathematical planetary theory a great deal more complex in its geometry than the previous simpler theory of the rotating, homocentric spheres of Eudoxos. Hipparchos, and a generation later the Stoic scholar Poseidonios of Apameia (c.135-51 B.C.), clearly recognised that it is possible 'to save' the same astronomical phenomenon by alternate mathematical hypotheses, or models, since the method of eccentrics and the method of epicycles were kinematically equivalent and, therefore, mere mathematical expedients rather than fundamental descriptions of the workings of the heaven. Hipparchos used in his planetary theory both the epicyclic and the eccentric method by means of which he was able to reduce Solar and Lunar trajectories to combinations of circular motions whilst rejecting the heliocentric planetary theory of Aristarchos of Samos, mostly because the heliocentric theory based on 'circular orbits' did not account for the main irregularities he observed in the motions of the planets. The heliocentric planetary theory of Aristarchos became acceptable only after Johann Kepler discovered in A.D. 1609 that the orbits of planets were not circular but elliptic. Since heliocentricity of the planetary system did not lead to greater simplicity or precision his rejection of it was fully justified. Hipparchos' planetary and Lunar theories were partly based on extensive Babylonian observations which, however, he distrusted and checked as much as possible. He is responsible for having begun the synthesis between the Greek trigonometric method in which he must have known the equivalent of modern trigonometric formulae for sin($A \pm B$) and cos($A \pm B$), and the Babylonian arithmetic method in astronomy. Hypsikles of Alexandria had advanced the Babylonian idea of dividing the ecliptic into 360 degrees, but Hipparchos was the first to generalise this idea and divide every circle into 360 degrees, an idea which he used in trigonometry, a mathematical discipline which he was the first to make into a mathematical science. He published a work of 12 books on the table of chords equivalent to the table of trigonometric 'sine functions' by ½ ° increments from 0° to 180°. Either Eudoxos of Knidos or Hipparchos invented the method of stereographic projection (a method which is both projective and conformal) of spherical surface upon plane surface. Hipparchos invented the method of orthographic projection by means of which points and arcs can be projected orthogonally upon three mutually perpendicular planes. This method was principally used by the astronomer Klaudios Ptolemaios of Alexandria (A.D. c.80-c.168) for finding the position of the Sun at any given hour. The stereographic mapping of the celestial sphere on a plane made it possible for Klaudios Ptolemaios to solve problems of spherical astronomy by means of plane geometry and trigonometry. After Hipparchos' planetary theory, which was quite good for the Sun and the Moon but only partly good for planets, came to be accepted as the best astronomical theory, it was no longer possible to represent planetary motions by means of mechanical models with simple gearings, such as had been built by Archimedes. His astronomical theory, which established the basic principles of the discipline, accounted for the seasons, and predicted eclipses of the Moon quite accurately within hours, but it was less accurate in predicting eclipses of the Sun.

Hipparchos proposed to determine the geographic latitudes by means of the ***gnomon*** and the declination of the Sun. However, the longitude which was usually measured on land by route marches and on sea by log-line reckoning, both of which were not reliable, was a more difficult matter and, therefore, Hipparchos made it independent of surface measurements by suggesting to find the difference of longitudes between two places by observing the eclipse of the Moon from the two places, the difference of time of the eclipse between the two places being the measure for the difference in longitude. For this purpose he calculated the times of the eclipse of the Moon for a span of 600 years, but it was not taken up by other astronomers because it would have taken too long to accomplish this task since the eclipse of the Moon occurs too infrequently.

Hipparchos discovered and measured the annual precession of the equinoxes (the wobble of the axis of the Earth in its yearly rotation about the Sun) having a period of 2,600 years, found the accurate inclination of the ecliptic, gave the length of lunar month as 29 days, 12 hours, 44 minutes and 2.5 seconds which is within a second of presently accepted value, calculated the Lunar parallax, determined the perigee and mean motion of the Moon, and catalogued 850 fixed starts after 35 years of patient observation in the observatory of Rhodos. He determined the ratio of the distance to the Moon and the radius of the Earth as 67.74 (modern value: 60.4), and the ratio of Moon's radius to that of the Earth as ⅓ (modern value: 27/100), which were remarkable results for his time. His estimate for the distance to the Sun, which he evaluated to be 1,245 times the diameter of the Earth (modern value: 11,740), was greatly in error because the instruments he used to measure the angle of departure of Sun rays from parallellity on which his estimate depended is extremely small and only susceptible to accurate measurements by modern instruments with telescopic sight and Vernier scale.

Eratosthenes and Aristarchos had recognised that owing to the immense distance of the Sun its light rays could be approximated geometrically by parallel rays without any detectable error for all terrestrial problems. However, the light rays reflected from the Moon depart appreciably from parallellity owing to Moon's much shorter distance from the Earth. Hipparchos was able to measure with considerable accuracy the angular deviation of Moon rays from parallellity with the instruments at his disposal.

Hipparchos was probably responsible for the invention of the anaphoric clock about 150 B.C. which obviated the technical inconvenience of using the globe as Archimedes had done in the latter's planetariumlike device. Hipparchos, through the use of stereographic projection, was able to map the celestial globe conformally on a flat disk which could be fitted with a representation of the ecliptic and appropriate holes for the Sun and the Moon, so that the disk turned by a hydraulic clock behind a spider-web (***arachne***) invented by Eudoxos of Knidos and consisting of wires in circular arcs which map the horizon and equal altitude and equal azimuth for the place considered, showed the risings and settings of the Sun, the Moon and fixed stars, and by passing the wires of the spider-web indicated the hours of the day and of the night. In this way, the anaphoric clock afforded a remarkable representation of all the features of the diurnal rotation of the firmament. However, the movement of the anaphoric clock was not continuous since the disk had to be reset to its initial position every morning. The spider-web in the anaphoric clock was the stereographic projection of a part of the sky from the South Pole onto the equatorial plane which produced a sky map with constellations. Hipparchos, moreover, is the probable inventor of the quadrant, an important instrument of meridional observation in astronomy which remained in the service of astronomy over 2 thousand years, as well as of an improved astrolabe (***astrolabon organon***).

The importance of Hipparchos in engineering science stems from a tract he wrote on the downwards motion of material bodies, entitled < On Bodies Carried Down by Their Weight >, a work which is now lost. According to the references made to this work by other later writers, the following can be said about the content of Hipparchos' treatise: it presented a kinematic and dynamic study of accelerated vertical motion written in refutation of Aristotle's treatment of the vertical motion which Hipparchos considered implausible. In this work, Hipparchos took a tentative step towards the linear momentum principle when he implied that the upwards throwing force acting on the body creates in the body an upwards acting residual resisting force that is self-consuming by virtue of being continually reduced by the natural downwards pull of the weight of the body. In the case of a body falling freely from a height, Hipparchos thought that the force which held the body before the fall is still impressed on the body as residual resistance after release, and this residual resistance which is continually reduced by the downwards pull of the weight of the body remains with the falling body over a certain distance of the free fall, which accounts for the slower motion of the falling body at the beginning of the fall. Hipparchos' theory implied that an external motive power can impart an internal motive power to a body by acting on it only at the moment of its release. He considered every motion to be limited in duration unless the supply of motive power is inexhaustible.

The Monophysite Christian scientist and former Neoplatonic philosopher Ioannes Philoponos of Alexandria (A.D.485-555) took up the idea of the impressed power of Hipparchos again about A.D. 517 in a work which refuted the Aristotle's notion that the speed of a body in free fall is proportional to its weight on the basis of some simple experiments that were repeated in Europe more than a millennium later by Giovanni Battista Benedetti (A.D.1530-1590) and Simon Stevin (A.D.1548-1620).

Andronikos of Kyrrhestes and Horologion:

About 150 B.C. during the Roman hegemony, Andronikos of Kyrrhestes from Macedonia, built an elaborate timekeeping marble structure, the Tower of the Winds (***Horologion***), in the central square (***agora***) in the heart of Athens, a few blocks north of Akropolis. It housed an elaborate anaphoric waterclock, and had the first meteorological apparatus, a weathervane in the form of a bronze triton on top of the structure. Originally a Sundial, a gnomon with a set of markings underneath for telling time, projected from the top frieze on each side of the octagonal marble tower which was almost 43 feet (13m) high. The building itself, which represented a kind of Zeiss planetarium of the classical Græco-Roman world, is still standing.

Poseidonios of Apameia and Clockwork Calendar Computer:

In A.D. 1900, an intricate clockwork and mechanical calculating device of astronomical events such as the motions of the Sun, of the Moon and other planets was discovered in a ship wrecked near the Greek Island of Antikythera about 65 B.C.. This device contained a highly sophisticated train of mechanical gears consisting of a large number of gears with widely assorted sizes: 20 gear wheels, moveable slip-rings, some in planetary mountings, also a contrate gear to turn the drive through a right angle. The gears were meshed in parallel to give correct mean periodic rotations to seven celestial bodies and the synodic month. In order to reproduce the motions of the Sun and the Moon in perfect consistency with the phases of the Moon, a highly sophisticated gear, the so-called 'differential gear', was incorporated into the turntable mechanism. The differential gear in the Antikythera mechanism took 2 rates of rotation from which it generated a 3rd one by summing and differencing in the operation of the turntable. This is the first known differential gear in history. The input axle, that was probably connected to a clockwork, turned a crown-gear wheel which moved a big, 4-spoked driving wheel that by means of two trains of gears connected by axles to gear-trains on the other side of the plate led through an epicyclic turntable and terminated in a set of shafts which turned the dial pointers with various speeds round their dials. The front dial showed the annual motion of the Sun in the zodiac, whereas the back dials gave the motion of the Moon as well as the risings and settings, stations and retrograde motions of the planets. It had a scientific graduation and a very high order mechanical precision. There is some evidence in the remains of this device which indicates that it may have been activated by a crank, but it is not known whether the Antikythera clockwork calendar computer was automatically driven by water-power, or turned manually. The complex clockwork mechanism simulated the motion of the heavens by fixed gear ratios, but it calculated the Solar-Lunar calendar more on the basis of digital readings than by direct geometric modelling of the spatial trajectories of the planets. Its sophisticated mechanism was built to exhibit the cyclic sequence of sets of discrete phenomena rather than the continuous flow of events over continuous time and, therefore, the Antikythera clockwork calendar computer without escapement resembles more a modern analogue computer than an ancient Greek geometric model of the automatic celestial sphere or orrery of Archimedes of Syracuse.

This clockwork calendar computer was a creation of an ingenious mechanic associated with the Stoic school of mechanics in Rhodos under the direction of the Stoic polymath, scientist and mechanical engineer Poseidonios of Apameia (c.135-c.51 B.C.). It was apparently made about 82 B.C., almost at the time when the famous Roman orator and senator Marcus Tullius Cicero was a student of Poseidonios at the Stoic school of rhetoric and oratory in Rhodos. Gaius Iulius Caesar (c.102-44 B.C.) also studied rhetoric at the same school. This astronomical analogue clockwork computer of the ancient Greeks was a product of highly refined technology sustained by very sophisticated mechanical crafts and manufacturing processes that took full advantage of scientific theories and refined technical competence.

The Archimedean tradition of refined technology in the making of intricate mechanisms for astronomical clockworks and planetaria did flourish again in the Stoic school of Poseidonios on the Island of Rhodos, and the invention of the differential gear, a new and highly sophisticated mechanical device, is a testimonial to the surprisingly high technical level the mechanical design of the Hellenistic engineers had reached by that time. Unfortunately, this high technology was somehow lost when the practical Romans became the masters of the Western world. During this period, on the Island of Mykonos in the Cycladic archipelago, windmills with sails attached to spokes connected at their ends by ropes and set in a nearly horizontal shaft as a hub were employed as wind-powered motors.

Poseidonios carried out another evaluation of the circumference of the Earth which was first accomplished by Eratosthenes of Kyrene, but his value of 180,000 stadia seems to be appreciably in error. He used the position of the Star Canopus in place of the Sun, which was an improvement over Eratosthenes but somehow he appears to have made a mistake in the star's position due to the atmospheric refraction of light if the information given by the Stoic geographer, historian and a student of Poseidonios, Strabon (in English, Strabo) of Amasia (c.63B.C.-A.D.c.24) is accepted at face value. According to Strabon, Poseidonios in his mensuration of the Earth seems to have made a mistake of one sixth in the Earth's circumference, a measurement which had been rather accurately estimated by Eratosthenes to be 252,000 stadia. Since Poseidonios is known to have been the first astronomer to take the atmospheric refraction into account in his astronomical observations, it is more reasonable to assume that the stadion used by Poseidonios was longer than the stadion used by Eratosthenes. There were stadia of different length, such as 9, 8½, 8, and 7½ to a Roman mile, accepted at different times and places, and the ancient geographers such as Strabon were hardly aware of this situation. If Poseidonios used the long stadion of 7½ to the Roman mile then his evaluation of 180,000 stadia for the mean circumference of the Earth is in approximate agreement with Eratosthenes' evaluation of 252,000 stadia. Unfortunately, the ancient geographers assumed that there was only one stadion measure and they accepted the 180,000 stadia measure of Poseidonios. Poseidonios probably discovered the atmospheric refraction (***kataklasis***) from his knowledge of the vanishing coin trick in which a coin in the bottom of a vessel vanishes from sight when the vessel is emptied of water, and the Stoic belief that the Earth is surrounded by an infinite void. A Stoic astronomer Kleomedes (*floruit* c. 45 B.C.), who was probably a disciple of Poseidonios, wrote a treatise < The Cyclic Motion of Celestial Bodies > (***Kyklike theoria meteoron***) in 2 books in which he gave a summary of Stoic astronomy and also reported on the measurement of the circumference of the Earth by Eratosthenes and by Poseidonios. He assigned the atmospheric refraction as the cause for the Sun to be still visible when it is actually below the horizon. Poseidonios also estimated the distance to the Sun to be 6,550 (modern value is 11,740) times the diameter of the Earth which was a great improvement on Hipparchos' figure probably because Poseidonios used more precise astronomical instruments such as the ***dioptra*** produced with high mechanical precision in Poseidonios' school of fine mechanics. His estimation of the distance to the Moon was 26½ (modern value is 30) times the diameter of the Earth the margin of error of which was comparable to Hipparchos' estimate of 33.7 times the diameter of the Earth. Poseidonios regarded tides to be created by the joint attraction of the Moon and the Sun, and he travelled to the Atlantic Ocean to study them. He was the first to call attention to the spring and the neap tide.

The noted Stoic polymath Poseidonios of Apameia was a spellbinding teacher who had universal interests. He wrote works on astronomy, meteorology, history, descriptive and mathematical geography, and moral philosophy which had great influence on the Roman and the mediæval thought.

Impulse-Wheel as Horizontal Hydraulic Turbine:

Hellenistic engineers who built machines (***technoi*** or ***mechanopoioi***), converted a simple vertical water-lifting wheel (***noria***) used by the Caucasian mountaineers in Anatolia, into a horizontal impulse-wheel for the grinding of corn, but it was much too slow for its efficient operation since it could deliver only between half and one horsepower (373 to 746 Watts). This horizontal waterwheel was in wide use in Greece and Anatolia during the first century B.C.. For instance, in 63 B.C., a horizontal water-turbine, which was an impulse-wheel driven by water impinging on the blades from a steep chute or millrace, turned directly the millstone of a grain mill in the palace of the Parthian King Mithridates of Pontos. The direct power transmission from the waterwheel to the millstones, owing to the lack of gearing, made the most efficient milling speed impossible because the direct turning of the millstone was far too slow. This mill produced probably about 0.4 horsepower (298 Watts). Moreover, horizontal waterwheels could not be used in sluggish streams which were prevalent in the Hellenistic world, although many Asiatic rivers were made navigable for the first time by the Hellenistic engineers.

Seleukid kings improved and extended the royal postal roads and royal postal system of the former Persian empire. The Seleukid kings, for the first time in Western history, were able to provide all their requirements for metals from their own empire, yet the contemporary overland transportation was so expensive that it would have been cheaper for them to import metal by sea from the Atlantic coast of Europe.

Heron of Alexandria and Scientific Mechanics:

The last great Hellenistic scientist-mathematician-engineer was Heron (in English, Hero) of Alexandria (*floruit* c.150-100 B.C.) who was probably a contemporary of Hipparchos. Heron was apparently the founder and director of a polytechnical school in Alexandria which consisted of 2 main divisions: the theoretical branch (***logikon***) in which geometry, arithmetic, astronomy and physics were taught; and the practical branch (***cheirourgikon***) in which manual execution of metalwork (***chalkeutike***), woodwork, construction, surveying, painting and other practical technological skills were mastered. Heron considered a man who had been trained from his youth both in the practical and in the theoretical technology to be the best qualified engineer and inventor of mechanical devices. The science of mechanics of the Hellenistic Greeks consisted of two schools of thought: the Peripatetic (Aristotelian) school of mechanics and the Archimedean school of mechanics. Heron, a mathematically trained engineer, was the outstanding representative of both. His renowned treatise, entitled < Mechanics > (***Mechanika***), which consisted of 3 books including an introduction, an exposition of the theory of mechanical advantage of 5 elementary powers (***dynamis***) or elementary machines: the windlass, the lever, the pulley or tackle-block, the wedge and the endless-screw or the wormwheel, and some examples of their use by mixing theory and practice, was a remarkably mature work of applied mechanics. In this treatise, Heron relied mainly on the principle of dynamic equilibrium, the so-called 'golden rule of mechanics' due to Archytas of Taras as presented by Straton of Lampsakos. Heron had reduced theoretical mechanics to applied mechanics in the form of a single principle, now called the principle of virtual velocities: "That which is gained in force is lost in time." Since time and distance are interchangeable in this principle, because velocities are regarded as having been acquired in the same time interval, he was able to express the principle of virtual velocities also as the principle of virtual displacements: "That which is gained in force is lost in displacement." It was another form of the 'golden rule of mechanics': "The ratio of the times is equal to the reciprocal ratio of the moving forces." The quasi-static theory of Heron was used again in the late Renaissance period by Stevin and, particularly, by Galileo. Heron used finite velocities, or finite displacements, in the application of his principle. Infinitesimal displacements were formally introduced into this principle more than 1,500 years later by the French mathematician and philosopher René Descartes (A.D. 1596-1650). Heron's recognition of this very general principle of mechanics, which had a precise mathematical form and a broader scope of application in engineering design than the Archimedean principle of the lever, was one of the great achievements in the mechanical science of the ancient Greeks. It is important to note that in his treatise < Mechanics > (***Mechanika***), Heron combined theory and practice in designing his machines theoretically by using his principle of virtual velocities. In his works on statical equilibrium, Heron made use of the principle of statical moment and spoke of the condition of equilibrium in terms of the product of a force and its lever-arm to the fulcrum.

Heron's elementary machines (***dynamis***), the mechanical advantage of which he studied in great detail, were: the wheel, the axle, the lever, a system of pulleys, the wedge, the screw, and the inclined plane. They constituted the mechanical repertory of Heron, to which he applied his science of mechanics. Although Heron's theory of machines was restricted to the condition of balance between the effort and the load, he did consider the question of how much the effort had to be increased in order to move the load when he studied the effect of friction in machines. He did use friction wheels in his machines.

Following Archimedes, Heron imagined a cylindrical log which is balanced on a plane inclined at an angle α to consist of two segments produced by a vertical plane passing through the line of contact between the cylinder and the inclined plane. The larger segment tending to make the log roll down the plane, the smaller segment tending to make the log roll up the plane. The resultant of the two tendencies he regarded to be the force necessary to maintain the log in equilibrium on the inclined plane. If the weight of the log is *W* and the force maintaining equilibrium is *F*, then Heron's law of inclined plane can be expressed in modern form as :

$$F = W(2\alpha + \sin 2\alpha)/\pi,$$

instead of the correct law of Jordanus Nemorarius (*floruit* A.D. c.1230) given during the early Middle Ages :

$$F = W \sin\alpha.$$

Heron's law for the inclined plane is correct only for $\alpha = 0$ and $\alpha = \pi/2$, and approximately correct for small slopes, that is, for small α when π is replaced by *4*.

Heron designed a gear-train as well as a pulley-system in combination with a winch to solve the so-called 'Archimedean problem': to move a given weight of 1,000 talents with a given mechanical power produced by a weight of 5 talents. He invented variable-rate drives by means of friction disks, axial wheel trains, various reversible motion mechanisms driven by weights and operated by ropes, all sorts of reduction gears and cams, as well as star, crown and worm gearings. Heron used the endless screw as wormwheel invented by Archimedes in the hodometer and in the ***dioptra***, and gave its theory and method of construction.

In his mechanical problems, Heron made systematic use of the parallelogram addition of vectors such as velocities. He wrote a textbook on the construction of vaults, and on windlasses (***baruoulkos***). He designed the first known windmill (***anemourian***) with horizontal axle, which raised the heavy piston (***emboleus***) of the gravity-powered air-pump supplying the air-blast for his pipe organ; an improved hydraulic clock; an improved force-and-suction pump with the plunger and an elaborate fire engine, that was used by the Romans, and later by the Europeans in a slightly modified form from the 16thcentury to the 19th century A.D.; a watermeter the function of which was based upon the cross-sectional area of the aperture and the average velocity of water flowing through it; a ship speedometer which used for the first time the paddle-wheel principle; a hodometer for terrestrial vehicles operating by the differential screw-gearing principle; the first known ingenious tool to cut female screw-threads into wood invented for the manufacture of screw-presses; an improved compressed air-gun; and a variety of automata operated by descending weights, steam and compressed hot-air pressure, and vacuum.

In his mechanics, Heron like Hipparchos of Nikaia before him, presumed that every motion is limited in duration unless there exists an inexhaustible supply of motive force – an idea which ultimately led to the concept of impossibility of ***perpetuum mobile***. In pneumatics Heron recognised the law of persistence of uniform motion, and regarded force to be proportional to the velocity created by the force.

One of the Heron's great inventions was the small reaction steam turbine, the so-called ***aiolopyle*** (a term Heron himself did not use), the first significant device of converting thermal energy into mechanical energy, and a similar device producing rotary motion by means of steam and hot air. The first reaction device had been constructed by the founder of theoretical mechanics, Archytas of Taras, who had designed the first known automaton, a singing dove which flew, apparently in circles round a central shaft, being propelled by the reaction to a jet of compressed air. Heron described the ***aiolopyle*** in his < Pneumatics > (***Pneumatikon***),a treatise in two books, where he also explained his experiments with air based upon the concept first introduced by Straton of Lampsakos that air consisted of particles. He writes of the law of inertia for uniform motion and finds force to be proportional to the velocity created by it. He also invented a spherical watertube boiler for heating baths. In the introduction to this book, Heron uses a genuine scientific method to prove by an experiment that the accepted explanation for the action of the syphon was wrong.

He wrote a book < Artillery > (***Belopoiika***), which served as a manual to the army, and a treatise in 4 books, < On Water Clocks > (***Peri hydrion horoskopeion***), an important work on mensuration of time which unfortunately is lost. Heron knew that the rate of flow of water depends upon the 'head' of water. In his scientific engineering activities Heron evidently conducted many controlled experiments like Straton of Lampsakos did before him to corroborate his theoretical work.

Heron, besides being an excellent theoretical and practical engineer, was also a gifted and competent theoretical mathematician as his commentaries on < The Elements > (***Stoicheia***) by Eukleides reveal in which he proved many new theorems in the axiomatic geometry of Eukleides. He wrote a number of important textbooks on applied mathematics for his students, in which he showed Babylonian influence on his numerical mathematics for he treated arithmetic and algebraic problems quite independently of geometry. He wrote a textbook < Stereometry > (***Stereometrika***) on solid geometry of 3-dimensional objects including the theory of mensuration of various solids and a few practical problems of mensuration such as finding the seating capacity of a theater, the number of tiles required to roof a building of a given size and shape, and the number of jars that can be stored in the hold of a ship of given dimensions. Heron also published a work in 3 books on mensuration, < Mensuration > (***Metrika***), which dealt competently with mathematical theory and numerical mensuration and gave practical formulae for the calculation of volumes and areas for triangles, regular polygons, circles, cones, pyramids and other geometric figures and solids. In this manual, only occasional demonstrations for the formulae were given, such as the celebrated formula of Heron for the area of a triangle with sides a, b and c, which represented a reworking of the formula of Archimedes :

$$A = [s(s-a)\,(s-b)\,(s-c)]^{1/2}\,,$$

where $s = (a+b+c)/2$ denotes half of the perimeter of the triangle. He explained how to construct similar figures on a larger or smaller scale by the use of his pantograph.

In his work, < Geometry > (***Geometrika***), Heron gives theorems and rules for areas of planes and surfaces, and for volumes of a large number of geometric figures which are mainly the results obtained by other mathematicians, such as Archimedes. The book is immensely practical, and clearly demonstrates the influence of Babylonian arithmetic on Heron's work on practical mathematics since in most of his books he was typically interested in mensuration. In some problems, he even added dissimilar quantities to produce a numerically correct solution, because numerically, but not dimensionally, this procedure made sense. He used freely approximate results from the geometry of Egyptians as well as their unit fraction method, and also the arithmetic and algebraic geometry of the Babylonians. He was able to cast a considerable section of the geometric algebra of the ancient Greeks into rhetorical arithmetic and algebraic procedures of the Babylonians, since he employed words rather than symbols in these procedures. In his technical manuals written for surveyors, masons, carpenters and other technicians, he avoided such mathematical operations as the extraction of square and cube roots for the obvious reason that technical men lacked the required mathematical background and, therefore, he was not adverse to supplying them with approximate formulae and inexact rules for field mensuration. The algorism given by Heron for the finding of the square root by iteration actually represents the method of linear interpolation (in Latin, ***regula falsi***). Apparently, the approximate numerical computation (***logistika***) was not a new tradition but had existed for centuries in the technological practice of the ancient Greeks. Heron also discussed his scenography which dealt with the application of perspective to architecture or scenery in one of his lost works.

A Byzantine scholar of the 11th century A.D. composed a collection of mathematical extracts entitled < Definitions > (***Definitiones***), which consisted of a long catalogue of terms that are mostly geometrical but some are concerned with weights and measures. In is generally believed that these extracts were taken from the works of Heron.

Heron wrote a work < On Mensuration > (***Peri metron***) which was a collection of various topics on mensuration present in his ***Geometrika, Stereometrika*** and ***Definitiones***.

In Heron's famous treatise on a surveying instrument and methods of surveying,< On Theodolites > (***Peri dioptras***), he gives an account of a sophisticated surveying instrument of his own invention similar to modern plane table, which when used with his surveying poles outfitted with movable markers can measure accurately horizontal and vertical angles by using precise micrometric screw mechanisms, the Archimedean wormwheels, for all rotations and fine setting of sight. It was also fitted with a 5 feet 11 inches (1.8 m) long hydraulic level, but it did not yet incorporate the telescopic sight. He discussed various methods for the execution of particular surveying tasks such as laying out routes for water supply lines using gravity flow or pumping. In his theory of surveying, Heron demonstrated how to survey by a triangulation method an alignment of a tunnel through a high mountain when the tunnel is driven simultaneously from both of its ends. The use of his ***dioptra*** as an accurate sighting instrument was indispensable for this task. He gave methods for land measurement and division, as well as for geodetic distance estimation.

He used his hodometer, a wheeled taxometric vehicle for land distance measurement in which each turn of the wheel rotated by means of worm-gearing turned a pointer that recorded travelled distances up to one hundred miles. For the measurement of longitude difference of two places on Earth he gave an astronomical method based upon the occultation of the Moon. He gave a method to determine distances between two points of which only one is accessible, between two visible but not accessible points, how to find a perpendicular to an inaccessible line, and how to find the area of a field without entering it by means of his formula for the area of a triangle. He invented the cableway or ropeway for mountainous terrain.

In his optical researches given in his book <Mirrors > (***Katoptrika***), a distinctly mathematical work, Heron gave a proof of the basic law of reflexion, a law already known to Aristotle, by means of his principle of the least path, the first known application of the least action principle to physical sciences. Following Aristotle, Heron assumed the speed of light to be so great that owing to its least action it moves along a straight line when passing through any transparent medium. On the basis of this implicit least action principle he proved that a ray of light in reflexion moves along the shortest possible path between the object and the observer. Heron proved by means of his principle of the least path, the equality of the angle of reflexion and the angle of incidence. It represents the first minimum principle in physical science. The mechanico-optical analogy used by Heron in the solution of the reflexion problem became an important concept in the development of physics in modern times.

His book < About Making Automata > (***Peri automatopoietikes***) gave an account of the construction of two small-scale mechanical puppet theaters that were operated by the weights of heavy pistons moving down in cylinders filled with mustard seeds or dry sand which were gradually running out through the bottom of the cylinders. The motion of the heavy pistons was transmitted to the puppet theater by means of ropes and a winch. His designs utilised very closely the limitations of power available to him. Heron used ropes rather than toothed-wheel gearings to avoid the rather large friction created by such gearings. Heron anticipated the modern automobile differential by an ingenious axle design for complex motion of automata where each wheel turned independently of the axle and the other wheel by using ropes instead of gears. In his small-scale mechanical puppet theater Heron placed the figurines used in religious plays on wheels which moved over wooden rails in order to minimise friction. His design of the small-scale puppet theater incorporated the earliest known use of the idea of railroad in mechanical devices. It is also the first treatise about automation.

The abundance of physical principles and his understanding of their operation when they were applied with technical ingenuity to various complicated implements and apparatus by Heron is astounding. Heron was in complete command of the principles of hydrostatics and aerostatics and, particularly, of the action of syphons. He was fully cognisant of how to utilise the expansion of gases by heating, and of the pressures of compressed gases and saturated water vapours. He was thoroughly competent about the operation of the 5 elementary machines, and a number of more complex apparatus made of the 5 elementary machines.

What is even more astonishing is that Heron was in possession of almost as many physical principles and technical means as the 18th century A.D. mechanicians whose technological inventions made the industrial revolution in Europe possible. Yet Heron confines himself to the construction of ingenious but expensive instruments, contrivances and apparatus which were mostly without any practical utility insofar as relieving the burden of work on the common men, but which were rather intended to astonish and amuse them as idle spectators in the temples or at public parades.

Postscriptum

The mechanical designs of Heron as well as the highly refined mechanisms produced in the Stoic school of Rhodos represent the loftiest achievements in Hellenistic scientific engineering and high technology. Heron applied mathematics to scientific engineering in many fields more completely than any other Greek author, but the absence of applications to significant industrial processes in his work is conspicuous. There may have been too little respect at the time for the value of the individual man for his own sake, too much reverence for nature in order to interfere with the workings of nature, and, therefore, too little interest in using the powers of nature to do useful work for man. No doubt a lingering belief in the primitive animism played a certain role in the failure of the Hellenistic engineers to harness the forces of nature in order to relieve the burden of toil on the common man. The Hellenistic engineers were able to do small-scale mechanical engineering, such as the very intricate and remarkable astronomical clockwork-calculators and other astounding mechanical devices, such as a steam-powered vehicle built to drive in the annual religious parade in the streets of Alexandria, which were quite remarkable achievements even from the modern viewpoint. Yet, despite the ability for small-scale machine design, and interest in machines and their use, Hellenistic civilisation and the new masters of the ancient Mediterranean world, the practical Romans, failed to produce an industrial 'revolution' because the classical antiquity lacked the raw materials, the technical skills, the philosophy and the religious beliefs to surmount the threshold of the industrial modern age. It remained for Christian Europe and its technologically-minded monks to make the revolutionary breakthrough into industrial engineering and power technology, after a late and feeble attempt in the fourth century A.D. by the Roman engineers to industrialise the grinding of corn in their crumbling Empire.

Although the technological achievements of ancient Babylonia, Assyria and Egypt in the Near East, and of ancient China and India in the Far East were impressive, they lacked the essential background of science: the generalised conception of scientific explanation in logical form and the mathematical proof. The ancient Greeks were the ones who invented natural science as we know it today by their assumption of permanent, uniform, abstract order and laws by means of which the regular, observable changes in the material world could be explained by deductive reasoning, and by their bold and brilliant idea of the generalised application of conjectured scientific theory formulated according to the principles of noncontradictory logic and empirical tests.

Ancient Greeks took the practical, technological methods of reckoning and measuring which had been developed in Mesopotamia and Egypt and made them into the abstract sciences of arithmetic and geometry. They not only made the first attempt to give rational explanations of the observations made in astronomy and medicine, but by combining such observations with theory they greatly increased the practical use of these two sciences. The ancient Greeks explained the fundamental problem of the scientific method concerning the relation of theories to the related data such as: the inductive rules of collecting and ordering data; the establishment of causal connexions and the concept of causation; the process of discovery and the use of hypotheses; the criteria for the acceptance or rejection of a theory, or the preference of one theory to another; the questions of the existence of theoretical entities and of the place of concepts about nature in scientific explanation; and, finally, the problems of scientific procedure, the experimental data and the mathematical techniques.

Ancient Greek science as could be seen from the foregoing account tended to fall short of modern science in their restricted use of mathematically disciplined experimental techniques, which did exist in a nascent state in optics, statics and applied mechanics. Although observational science existed in astronomy, and observational and experimental science existed in zoology and physiology, it seems that they were not generally considered to be the absolutely necessary methods of scientific investigation. Only in the medical school of Hippokrates of Kos physicians made systematic use of deliberately controlled experiments in medicine.

Ancient Greeks were very talented philosophers, and they loved reason and all sorts of mental activity. They reasoned about abstract concepts and broad generalisations the intellectual method of which was the deductive reasoning. The rational deduction itself was an essential part of the Greek love of beauty both as an intellectual and an emotional experience. Beauty they associated with order, consistency, completeness and definiteness all of which they identified with reason. The great discovery of ancient Greeks was the idea of mathematical demonstration. Greek discoveries in geometry have no equal anywhere else, and in geometry they insisted on rigorous deductive proofs and existence proofs by precise logical construction. Unfortunately, the last 2 requirements when applied to mathematics with Drakonian absolutism were too restrictive and severe for creative mathematics, which definitely hampered the ancient Greek mathematicians and, for instance, prevented them from developing infinitesimal calculus. But they did confront the questions of mathematical truth, the cogency of proofs and their connexion with the associated philosophical concepts of causality which their Oriental predecessors had completely overlooked, for the mathematics of Egyptians and Babylonians were mere collections of empirical rules without any theoretical background whatsoever since they were only interested in practical methods of numerical computation, and not in general theoretical concepts of mathematics. The ancient Chinese contributed many ingenious devices for treating numerical higher equations, a subject that had no general interest to ancient Greeks since it dealt with mathematical approximations rather than with logical and precise mathematical results. In empirical arithmetic and algebra the Babylonians had some outstanding achievements to their credit, but in theoretical mathematics they were relatively crude and jejune when compared to the ancient Greeks.

All the glory of rational thinking belongs to the ancient Greeks because they were the only people who not only demonstrated the great power reason had in the life of man, but also showed what man can accomplish when he believes in himself.

CHAPTER VI

ITALIAN ENGINEERING: Rome and First Technological Empire

Etruscans:

[from c.1000 B.C.-200 B.C.]

Italian engineering began with the Etruscans, a people of unknown origin. It is most likely that Etruscans were native inhabitants of central Europe who had crossed the Apennines about 1000 B.C. and had subsequently occupied Tuscany, the region between the rivers ***Arnus*** (now, Arno) and ***Tiberis*** (now, Tiber). The ancient Greeks believed that Etruscans were seafaring Lydian immigrants from Anatolia, who had been forced to flee their homeland by the invasion of Phrygians, a group of fierce Indo-European warriors, who destroyed the Hittite Empire and spread all over Anatolia [modern Asia Minor], at the same time when the Dorians, another group of Indo-European warriors, smashed the Mykenaian Empire and its Helladic civilisation. The available fragments of Etruscan writings have never been deciphered for their meaning, mainly because these fragments are all too brief.

The Etruscans conquered the Indo-European immigrants such as the Latins, who occupied part of the Tuscany, and other autochthonous neolithic inhabitants of this region, and built their cities in this region which was later called Etruria. The role of the Etruscans in the civilising process of Italy was fundamental.

Although the Mykenaian Greeks had already traded with the Etruscans, the actual direct Greek influence in Italy began with the pioneer Greek colonists who first arrived in southern Italy about 700 B.C.: the Lakonians at Taras, the Dorians at Metapontion, Sybaris, Kroton and other places. Soon the Chalkidians of Euboia landed at Rhegion and Kumai on the Tyrrhenian coast, and also at Naxos, Katana, Leontini, Himera in Sicily, and other places. They were followed in Sicily by the Megarians at Megara Hyblaia and later at Selinous, by the Korinthians at Syracuse and its daughter-colonies; and a short time later, about 680 B.C., by the Cretans and Rhodians at Gela who, in turn, in 580 B.C. established the city-State Agragas.

In about 630 B.C., Ionian colonists from the city Phokaia, on the coast of Anatolia, began to found trading outposts on the coasts of the Adriatic and Tyrrhenian Seas, and on the Etrurian and Ligurian coasts, and even on coastal regions farther west.

The economic relations developed between the Etruscans and the Greek colonists, first with the Kumaians and later with the Phokaians on the Anatolian coast, were of great importance to the progress of Etruscan civilisation. Etruscans adopted the Greek alphabet from the Kumaians together with many Greek concepts in religion, art, and literature. From the Phokaians they derived all the features of the orientalising period of Etruscan art. The progress of Etruscan culture due to these contacts with ancient Greeks was so rapid that their culture, which was not a mere carbon copy of that of the Greeks, reached such a maturity that by the end of the seventh century B.C., and more particularly in the course of the sixth century B.C., the Etruscans acquired both political and cultural supremacy which reached down to the Gulf of Salerno. The Etruscan Empire included the Island of ***Ilva*** (modern Elba), and later also the Island of Corsica, and they gained hegemony in ***Latium*** by conquering Rome. Etruscan hegemony in Italy spread the influence of a number of new ideas and techniques, some purely Etruscan and some Greek which Etruscans had adopted, since by that time Etruscans had been thoroughly Hellenised.

About 534 B.C., Aristodemos, the tyrant of Kumai, repelled an Etruscan assault on his city, and thereby weakened the Etruscan Empire. Then in 509 B.C., the Romans expelled their Etruscan overlords from Rome, after which the Etruscan Empire, which actually consisted of two empires, one north of the Apennine mountains in the form of a loose federation, and the other south-east in Campania, began gradually to fall apart, and by 205 B.C. all Etruscan cities had been completely subjugated to the Roman rule.

The area occupied by the Etruscans, called Etruria which stretched from the Bay of Naples to the Bay of Salerno, possessed most of the early mineral wealth of the Italian peninsula. It was mainly due to the iron deposits of the Island of ***Ilva***, and the copper and tin of the adjacent mainland that had facilitated the rise of the Etruscan civilisation, since these natural resources provided the essential means of economic exchange and the materials for manufacture, crafts and arts. Etruria also had rich deposits of good stone for building material, and, at that time, possessed an adequate supply of timber for shipbuilding.

Etruscans were seafaring people and they earned the reputation of being redoubtable sailors, and as a result of their naval prowess, Etruria became the supreme sea power of its time. It is probable that the Etruscans had established trading outposts as far as Balearic Islands and on the Spanish coast, and perhaps even on the Canary Islands. It is certain that Etruscan commercial influences reached the Rhône valley in France, most of Germany, and the Baltic Sea. The Etruscan ships had been trafficking in Greek waters and carrying on a brisk trade ever since the Mykenaian period.

The Etruscans were skilled craftsmen in metalwork and pottery, competent miners, expert metallurgists, outstanding civil engineers, and expert agricultural technologists. They apparently had learnt their refined art and engineering from the Greek colonists in Kumai, Italy. Etruscans became the inventors of dry farming since they had learnt to cope with the twin problems of erosion and flooding that was a serious threat in the sharply scarped landscape of southern Etruria (the modern Tuscany province) the subsurface of which is tufa, a volcanic sandstone, where the streams tended to erode the Etruscan roads and inundate their fields. They solved this problem by excavating elaborate complexes of underground tunnels, called ***cuniculi*** by the Romans, which acted as subterranean drainage in carrying away the excess surface water. These tunnels which made waterlogged areas arable for agriculture were about a foot and a half (0.46 m) wide and more than five and a half feet (1.68 m) high, and were furnished with vertical shafts for access. For instance, near the Etrurian city Veii there still exist nearly 15 miles of ***cuniculi***, some of which are still in use. Near Rome, there are more than 28 miles of ***cuniculi***. In Rome, the Etruscans drained a central swampy area by a giant, vaulted storm sewer called ***Cloaca Maxima*** by the Romans, still extant today, which discharged into the Tiber river and thereby laid the foundation for the first sewer system of Rome. This drained swampy area later became the famous Roman Forum. The vault of the ***Cloaca Maxima*** in Rome has a span ranging from 9.8 feet (2.9 m) to 12.8 feet (3.90 m), but it represents an accumulative work since the initial open sewer without vaulting was cut in 600 B.C.. All Etruscan towns were provided with sewerage and water supply systems, because they were master-builders of waterworks. Etruscans, who were city builders by natural inclination, surrounded their towns with walls of superb masonry which indicates their complete mastery of stone construction. They connected their cities with efficient networks of all-weather roads that were drained and cut into the soft tufa rock. Etruscans not only spanned their rivers with bridges, usually consisting of stone piers and wooden super-structure, but they also became the pioneer builders of stone arch bridges. Although Sumerians had invented the arch, which Assyrians had made into a central feature of their monumental building style, and it had also been used by some Ionian Greeks in their city walls, only the Etruscans built stone voussoir arches which were constructed without mortar in bridge structures. In about 500 B.C., the Etruscans built a stone voussoir bridge at ***Blera*** which had a span of 24 feet (7.32 m). There still exists another small stone arch bridge at ***Bullicame***, which has a 6.9 foot (2.10 m) span. Romans continued the Etruscan practice of building stone arches which they made their principal structural method in the construction of long-span structures. Therefore, bridge building became an impressive practical art only after arch bridges had been introduced by the Etruscans. In engineering Etruscan engineers used ***groma*** to lay out perpendicular lines, and ***chorobates*** to lay down profiles, both surveying instruments of the ancient Greeks.

Etruscan civilisation was unique among ancient civilisations, because Etruscan women were well educated and socially equal to their men, something that contemporary colonial Greeks bitterly resented and deplored. Etruscans had an almost fanatical devotion to music and a profound concern for religion and afterlife, and an overpowering sense of fate. They believe that the length of man's life was fixed at birth, and it was only possible to prolong it a few years by pleasing the gods.

Etruscans believed that everything in existence lasted only a fixed length of time, even their own civilisation which they thought will last 1,800 years. The accuracy of this prediction was astounding.

Romans: Foremost Engineers of Antiquity
Republic : from c.500 B.C. to 50 B.C.
Empire : from 50 B.C. to A.D. 476

A Republican Roman was a farmer at heart and he looked upon things and events as means to ends. Republican Romans were eminently practical, serious, reserved, and hardly ever spontaneous, free-spirited and imaginative like the ancient Greeks whom Romans considered to be childlike.

Typical Republican Roman character was distinguished by seriousness, gravity (***gravitas***), soberness, probity, reservedness, honesty, serenity, self-discipline, austerity, modesty, persistent will, and composure of manner. To a Republican Roman, a man's word was as good as his life. The mind of a Republican Roman was divided between two antithetical devotions: firstly, utter dedication to the life, prosperity and safety of the Roman State; and secondly, zealous insistence on absolute freedom, privacy and independence within the bound of his private property. This double consciousness of the self and the public interest made the Republican Roman unique among the ancient men and the progenitor of the modern Western man.

The Republican Romans subordinated all their interests, even their life, to one supreme end: the safety of the Roman State. Hence, Romans were statists in their political beliefs. The abstract sovereignty, the Roman State, existed for the Republican Romans as a higher will, in which the wills of the individual Romans voluntarily united in a compact. Therefore, the compact will, or the contract, was the very essence of the Republican Roman spirit, which recognised the paramount importance of self-discipline and the 'iron will' of the Roman citizen. The Republican Romans, through their incredible pertinacity, perseverance and unrelenting willpower not to yield to any adversary, in the course of time, inexorably wore down their enemies into submission. Yet, the Republican Romans were more prone to humane actions than other ancient nations. Some of this strengths the Romans derived from their adaptability, improvisation and thorough practicality.

A Roman citizen as an individual in the Roman Republic could compare himself to a voussoir stone in a Roman arch, an arch in which each stone is like a keystone: each stone supports the rest of the stones in the arch, whereas the rest of the stones supports the individual stone with the total strength of the Roman arch representing the Roman Republic (***res***-affair & ***publica*** -public) as a collective of Roman citizens. This view represents an excellent analogy to the significance of the

Roman citizen in the Roman Republic. Any Republican Roman to be recognised by other Romans had to accomplish something which benefited the Roman State.

The practical was the one result aimed at by the reflective character of the Republican Roman, and he believed in the value of honest toil. In a sharp contrast to the ancient Greeks, the Republican Roman did believe in personal privacy, which he sought to achieve within the bounds of his private property.

Romans had profound respect for the objective law. The Republican Roman concept of the rule of law and ordered liberty implied that true liberty exists only then when the law of the State is subordinate to the law of nature. The famous Roman lawyer, senator, philosopher, writer and orator, Marcus Tullius Cicero (106-43 B.C.) defined proper law in the following way: "True law is right reason in agreement with Nature. It is of universal application, unchanging and everlasting ...." Therefore, according to Cicero, justice is not possible if right reason does not reign. Since sensuality destroys reason, and, in consequence, virtue, Cicero regarded sensual indulgence to be a vice, a surrender to chaos and abandonment of the true order of reason. In Cicero's opinion, such a vice once set in motion cannot be stopped. Therefore,"... not even in retirement," said Cicero, " did I surrender myself to a life of sensual pleasure unbecoming to a philosopher"; and he continued, "for sensual pleasure, a most seductive mistress, turns the hearts of the greater part of humanity away from virtue; and when the fiery trail of affliction draws near, most people are terrified beyond measure." Cicero thought that a wise man curbed his sensuality by right reason, thereby checking the power of chaos by the power of divine intellect. According to Cicero, only when right reason and rational order ruled the society, could there exist genuine justice. He thought that his contemporary Gaius Iulius Caesar (c.102-44 B.C.), a voluptuary who believed in the cult of chaos as social regeneration and vitalisation in which to destroy order was to recreate order, was responsible for undermining Roman morals as well as Roman law: "Men reckon that our courts of law have no strictness left, no conscience – nay, by now, no existence worth the name. The result is that we are condemned and despised by the people of Rome. We have been groaning, and that for many years, under a heavy load of infamy." Cicero was intensely concerned with public morality and convicting criminals who committed crimes that were "engendered by greed, nourished by lust, and, finally, completed by cruelty," and because of the failure of Roman courts to punish promptly all committers of crime, he called Rome in 60 B.C. the "Romulus dunghill." Caesar's loose morals were scathingly attacked by Curid the Elder, a sober Republican Roman, in one of his speeches in the Senate in which he called Caesar "every woman's man, and every man's woman." Some decades later Octavianus, a nephew of Caesar who became the first Roman Emperor Augustus (63 B.C.-A.D.14), made a misguided attempt to legalise public morality, but it only succeeded to spawn a large crop of informers and blackmailers in the Roman society.

Western man has inherited much of the Roman consciousness and culture but without some of the contradictions of the Roman outlook. The very concept of culture is the idea of Cicero who compared the intellectual development of man's mind to the cultivation of the field in Roman agronomy. Cicero, by virtue of his popular treatises, has been the greatest of all conserves and transmitters of the Græco-Roman culture, and the greatest unifier and the chief shaper of the civilised language of the Western men. By such means, Cicero has attained a life beyond his grave. Even the dictatorial Gaius Iulius Caesar said in tribute to Cicero: "It is better to extend the frontiers of the mind than to push back the boundaries of the Empire."

Romans laid great importance on the spoken word because they considered what a man says, and how he says it, to be the accurate reflexion of his character and his personal culture. The Roman statesman and Stoic philosopher, Lucius Anneus Seneca (4 B.C.-A.D. 65), a native of Spain, expressed this view concisely: "As the man speaks, so is he." Seneca introduced many useful colloquial words into his good Latin prose, which lent remarkable flexibility to the Latin language. He wrote with a natural freedom in his < Dialogues > (***Dialogi***) and < Letters on Morals to Lucilius> (***Epistolae morales ad Lucilium***) which is quite reminiscent of modern prose. He invented many new words such as "inspector," "favourable," "vulnerable," and "temporary," and used freely infinitives and adjectives as nouns. Although Seneca's Latin assumed the versatility of modern Romance languages, and for a while even replaced Cicero's language as the literary model for Romans, it was Cicero who left the imperishable masterpieces of Latin language for posterity. In his popular philosophical works written in prose, Cicero showed a proclivity for the metaphysics of Plato and the Stoic ethics of Zenon.

Romans, the first people in history to take culture seriously, believed that a cultured person knows how to discriminate and make the proper choices between ideas as well as between things but, particularly, how to choose his company among men. Romans believed that it is the personal cultural quality that counts, not the race or the origin of the individual man. Cicero wrote that Romans have never worried about whence anybody comes from and, therefore, have commonly preferred virtue (***virtus***) to pedigree. For instance, if the man was good enough to fight for Rome, then in the opinion of the Romans he was good enough to be a Roman citizen.

Romans were not only outstanding soldiers, administrators and lawgivers, but also first-rate engineers because they had a natural inclination for practical arts in all of which they excelled. They had outstanding aptitude for learning from other people, and developing the borrowed acquisitions to their maximum possible efficiency. A famous Roman saying: "Never averse to learn from foe (***fas est ab hoste docere***)," was their leading motto expressing their willingness to learn from any source, in which ability they surpassed all other ancient people, including the Assyrians.

Romans were the eminent ancient men of sound commonsense and practical talent and, therefore, the Roman world was a world of practical affairs and not a world of abstract thoughts. Sextius Iulius Frontinus, the famous Roman ***curator aquarium*** (chief engineer of waterworks) under Emperor Nerva, expressed the Roman attitude in these words: "Will anybody compare the idle pyramids, or those other useless though renowned works of the Greeks with these aqueducts, these many indispensable structures?"

The most famous and influential Roman engineer, Marcus Vitruvius Pollio (*floruit* c.30 B.C.), expressed the grave and practical mind of Republican Romans in these words: "... those who rely only on theories are obviously hunting the shadow, not the substance."

Romans who were obviously talented in technology, showed neither interest nor aptitude for natural science or mathematics since they made not a single contribution to either one. Science was valued only as far as it gave practical, useful results for the Roman State. The famous Roman naturalist and writer Gaius Plinius Secundus (A.D. 23-79) (in English, Pliny) lamented that the Greek scientists in the past had been motivated by a desire to expand man's knowledge of the universe, whereas his own contemporaries were occupied with security and wealth. A well-known satirist Gaius Petronius (A.D. first century), popularly called the 'arbiter of elegance' (***arbiter elegantiae***), put it bluntly: "Astronomers had succumbed to the lure of cash," instead of exploring the skies for new discoveries they cast horoscopes for cash in Imperial Rome where conformity was considered a virtue.

However, the Romans made one landmark contribution to astronomy when the Greek astronomer Sosigenes (born c. 90 B.C.) reformed the Roman Lunar calendar into the so-called Iulian calendar on the order of Iulius Caesar in 45 B.C.. In the Iulian calendar the year had 365 days to which every fourth year was added one more day to make the calendar conform with the equinoxes. This approximation of a year's length in days was, however, too long by 11¼ minutes, and it added up to an error of a full day in 128 years. By the thirteenth century A.D. it had accumulated to a 10 day mistake, which was the reason for the so-called Gregorian reform of the calendar in A.D. 1582.

Vitruvian engineers learnt 'from practice and precise reasoning'(***ex fabrica et ratiocinatione***). Hellenistic State policy of sinecures and privileges for scientists and engineers were continued by the Roman Emperors. Whilst the priests advised and counselled the State, the bureaucratic officials of the State served and obeyed, because unlike the priests their livelihood and security was provided by the State. In antiquity science had remained closely associated with religion, since the intellectuals were usually priests, and all men were religious. The engineer had entered history as a priest and scribe in Sumer, but he departed in the late antiquity as a bureaucratic functionary of the Roman Empire. The engineer Marcus Vitruvius Pollio, a contemporary of Caesar and Emperor Augustus, stressed the vital importance of professional integrity and high principle of an engineer working under such conditions. The necessary professional qualifications of an ***architectus*** as an engineer, builder and contractor combined in one man, according to Vitruvius are:

"An ***architectus*** should be ingenious, and apt in the acquisition of knowledge, ... he should be a good writer, a skilful draughtsman, versed in geometry and optics, expert at figures, acquainted with history, informed on the principles of natural and moral philosophy, somewhat of a musician, not ignorant of the sciences both of law and physics, nor of the motions, laws, and relations to each other of the heavenly bodies. ... Moral philosophy will teach the ***architectus*** to be above meanness in his dealings and to avoid arrogance; it will make him just, compliant, and faithful to his employer; and, what is of the highest importance, it will prevent avarice gaining an ascendancy over him; for he should not be occupied with the thoughts of filling his coffers, nor with the desire of grasping everything in the form of gain, but by the gravity of his manners and a good character should be careful to preserve his dignity."

Roman Engineering

Romans are known to history as conspicuously outstanding engineers. Since Roman Republic, and later Roman Empire, was a republic of 'common men', all their engineering enterprises were undertaken to benefit the common Roman people. It was the Romans who were responsible for giving the Occidental world the very concept of 'the people', a concept unknown in ancient Greece. A Roman citizen as an individual by Roman law was a persona: a man with personal rights to life, liberty, and property rights which were declared and protected by the Roman State. Roman jurist rationalised and systematised the Roman law, which stressed 'due process', a legal procedure first introduced by Hittites, and made it into a science, something that the ancient Greeks had failed to do. The Roman jurist built up a system of laws that was not only one of the most impressive intellectual achievements of ancient times but also constituted a social revolution. Romans had a natural penchant for engineering as a practical art, but they were not scientifically minded like the ancient Greeks. Science was valued by the Romans only insofar as it yielded immediate practical and useful results for the Roman State, otherwise science seemed to be a rather frivolous pursuit to the Romans. Since the intellectual ideas in the Roman world were essentially Greek, Romans acquired all their science and art from the Greeks, which they also freely acknowledged and appreciated. Even the Roman methods of engineering and technology were developed by the Romans from the Greek and Etruscan precedents.

Since the practical and economically minded Romans wanted to comprehend everything, including science, at a glance, they tried to make all knowledge conveniently available to public at large by producing several Roman encyclopædias which in time helped to bring about the unification of science. The Roman practicality and talent for organisation facilitated the integration of practical science and empiricism into society which ultimately led to the development of modern science in Europe.

Many Roman engineers were Greeks, as a letter of Emperor Traianus (ruled from A.D.98 to A.D.117) to Plinius the Younger indicates: "It is usually from Greece that they [***architecti***] come hither." Licinius Crassus (115-53 B.C.), who was one member of the First Triumvirate together with Pompeius Magnus (in English, Pompey) and Caesar, schooled slaves in engineering for the purpose of hiring them out for engineering tasks. Emperor Hadrianus (ruled from A.D.117 to A.D.138) established the first Roman public institution of higher learning, ***Athenaeum***, staffed with salaried teachers. Afterwards, philosophers, rhetoricians, and grammarians were publicly appointed to lecture. About A.D. 228, under the Emperor Marcus Aurelius Alexander Severus (ruled from A.D.222 to A.D.235), a college for mechanical engineers was established in Rome, but no further information about this technical school is known.

Alexander Severus, a shrewd ruler, had all glass factories by law restricted to a prescribed district of Rome so that the industrial smoke could not pollute the entire city. It is the first known public measure taken against industrial pollution. Similar measures of public safety had been taken by Augustus and Traianus concerning the height of apartment buildings, called ***insulae***, because many of them were fire traps which frequently collapsed. Emperor Augustus limited the height of ***insulae*** in Rome to 75 feet (23 m) by law, which Traianus later reduced to 60 feet (18 m).

Although Romans lacked the keen imaginative curiosity of the Greeks, which makes general scientific and technological innovation possible, they became the foremost ancient engineers because engineering consists of much more than the machines and the mechanical processes. The most important aspect of the engineer's task in large-scale engineering is the ability to marshal effectively the resources at his command, to understand the potentialities and limitations of his tools, materials and manpower, and to organise skilfully the available manpower and material resources for the efficient execution of the engineering project at hand. It is precisely in the last category where the Roman engineers particularly excelled and far surpassed all other ancient engineers. The Romans, using the basic tools which came down to them from previous times, and which had been improved by the inventions of the Greeks and further refined by the Romans themselves, accomplished feats of engineering on a scale that remained unmatched until relatively modern times. The large number and the monumentality of Roman construction works, such as the long aqueducts, extensive networks of roads, colossal buildings, and massive bridges that have withstood the ravages of time and some of which still render useful service, give testimony to the soundness and high quality which the Roman engineer, called the ***architectus*** (chief technical organiser), built into his engineering works.

Roman engineering skill represents a triumph of human organisation that is unmatched by any other ancient people, and they displayed the same organising skill in law, government, and military matters. Another very important, and unique aspect of Roman engineering was the fact that it was firmly based on sound economic principles: for each engineering enterprise the Roman engineers established exact specifications and made detailed contracts, and they took into account the varieties of materials and types of construction best suited to particular conditions and projects. Apart from the Roman aptitude for organisation, Romans had a penchant for standardisation, for they produced the first known standardised technological products known in antiquity such as the standardised water outlets in the Roman public water supply. It appears that Roman technology and engineering was a highly refined rule-of-thumb technology and engineering of craftsmen, a skilful practical art rather than a scientific modern technology and engineering.

Romans were the first people of antiquity to engage in all existing fields of engineering and technology at the same time. For the sake of their far-flung Empire, Romans became the civil engineers of antiquity ***per excellence*** for they were outstanding builders of roads, canals, aqueducts, bridges, docks, dams, stadia, theaters, temples, triumphal arches, monuments, enormous public baths, and many other structures. In the Republican period the Romans developed a devotion to public works, a tradition which continued throughout the era of the Imperial Rome – the first technological Empire in history.

The greatest difference between the Roman engineering and the engineering of other ancient people was the dramatically magnified scale of Roman construction. In the Imperial times, Romans built about 180,000 miles (289,674 km) of paved roads, 55,000 miles (88,512 km) of main highways, thousands of bridges, and more than 200 aqueducts all over the ancient world. The four centuries of vast programmes of Roman public works in the West constitutes the very source of modern tradition of civil and military engineering.

During the Roman era each trade as well as the skill of its ***magistrus*** (craftsman) was closely controlled by an organisation called ***collegium***, a Western tradition that endured into the Middle Age.

Land Reclamation and Public Works

The Mount ***Albanus***, which lies about 16 miles (25.7 km) southeast of Rome (in Latin, ***Roma***), is of volcanic origin and in the depressions of its huge crater are situated two picturesque lakes, Lake ***Albanus*** (modern Lake Albano) and Lake ***Nemorensis*** (modern Lake Nemi).

Both of these lakes were landlocked and had to be provided with tunnel outlets, or ***emissaria***, in order to control their water levels. Virtually nothing is known about the ***emissarium*** of Lake ***Nemorensis***, but the ***emissarium*** of Lake ***Albanus*** according to records stems from 396 B.C.. Lake

Albanus lies about 10 miles (16.1 km) southeast of Rome and north of ***Via Appia***, the first major Roman road. This lake rose to an unprecedented level in 398 B.C., and it was decided to build a drainage tunnel from Lake ***Albanus*** and use the lake water thus drained for the irrigation of suburban farms on the outer slope of the Mount ***Albanus***. At the time Rome was engaged in a protracted war with the Etruscans, and the Roman army was besieging one of the last Etruscan strongholds, the Etruscan city of ***Veii***, which lay about 10 miles (16.1 km) northwest of Rome. Despite the war conditions a Roman deputation was sent to Delphi, Greece, in order to consult the oracle, and possibly to import Greek mining engineers to direct the driving of the tunnel. A tunnel of 1½-mile (2.4 km) length was driven through Mount ***Albanus***, which was a solid hill of volcanic pepperino rock intercepted in places by basalt layers, and it passed through the mountain at the 430-foot (131.1 m) level below the mouth of the crater. The height of the tunnel varied from 5 to 10 feet (1.52 to 3.05 m), and its width is at least 3½ feet (1.07 m) or more. This tunnel was cut by chiselling, or picking out, the rock. The tunnel was driven from vertical shafts and inclined adits spaced at about 300-foot (91.44 m) intervals. At the inlet to the tunnel a vertical shaft was sunk at first from the high water level, and then the shaft was broken to a lower level to allow the lake water to flow into the tunnel. This process was continued until the level of the lake was the same as that of the tunnel, which maintained the constant high level of the lake. A long covered reservoir with 5 outlets for distributing water to irrigation channels was constructed at the outlet of the ***emissarium*** .

The lowering of the Lake ***Albanus*** was soon followed by the construction of the Appian Way (***Via Appia***), and the Appian aqueduct, the ***Aqua Appia***, which initiated the famous Roman practice of public works that continued all through the imperial period. The ***emissarium*** of Lake ***Albanus*** was one of the first great Roman engineering works.

About 30 B.C. another tunnel was cut under the direction of the engineer Cocceius Auctus, an assistant to the ***aedile*** Agrippa, from the city of ***Cumae*** through the Mount Gillo to Lake ***Avernus***. This tunnel was ⅔ of a mile (1 km) long and it was wide enough for two carts to pass. The tunnel was lit by daylight from oblique lightwells or ventilator shafts, and it had its own aqueduct in the form of a gallery within a gallery that was furnished with its own niches, ventilator shafts and adits for access. Cocceius is known to have built other tunnels in the ***Phlegraean*** fields, a volcanic plateau of ***Campania***, and a seashore between the cities of ***Cumae*** and ***Neapolis*** (modern, Naples).

Drainage of *Pontine Marshes*

The ***Pontine Marshes***, a belt of swamps from 4 to 9 miles (6 to 15 km) wide, stretched about 37 miles (60 km) from ***Nettuno*** to ***Tarracina*** along the Appian Way. This malaria-infested region was drained about 160 B.C. with an extensive drainage system consisting of open trenches and drain pipes, and turned into a cultivated land with fields and gardens. This elaborate drainage system required constant supervision and maintenance. After the fall of Rome the drainage system was neglected, fell into disuse and, therefore, deteriorated into new swamps which spread malaria among the inhabitants of this region. This disease decimated and scattered the population of the ***Capania*** (modern Campagna) region, which contained the ***Pontine Marshes***, to such an extent that it was virtually depopulated almost until the modern time. Another important reclamation of land by means of drainage was engineered about 109 B.C. in the center of the Po valley at ***Placentia***.

Emissarium of *Lake Fucinus*

Already Gaius Iulius Caesar, a prominent general and politician, had urged the drainage of the landlocked Lake ***Fucinus***, located high in the Apennine mountains about 50 miles (80.5 km) west of Rome, to augment the available rich farming land as a source of food supply for Rome. This project was first carried out under Emperor Claudius who reigned from A.D.41 to A.D.54.

A tunnel 3.5 miles (5.6 km) long and having a 28-foot (8.53 m) drop was driven through Mount Salviano and the Palentine Plains to provide an outlet, an ***emissarium***, for the Lake ***Fucinus*** into the river ***Liris***. About ¾ of this tunnel passed through limestone, but two long sections under the plains, and at the great depth of 328 feet (99.97 m), were underground. The tunnel was 6 feet (1.83 m) wide and 10 feet (3.05 m) high and it was worked from 40 shafts, the deepest of which was about 400 feet (122 m). An impressive engineering survey was carried out for this tunnel for Roman engineers using ***chorobates*** were able to set a gradient as small as 1-to-2000 !

It took 11 years for a 30,000-man workforce to complete this engineering project. The ***emissarium*** of the Lake ***Fucinus*** remained the longest tunnel in the world until the modern Mont Cenis tunnel was completed in Switzerland in A.D. 1876. It is not known how successfully the ***emissarium*** of Lake ***Fucinus*** accomplished its intended purpose, but it is known that the completion of this ***emissarium*** was celebrated with a naumachy (***naumachia)*** on the Lake ***Fucinus*** in which 19,000 prisoners were forced to participate.

In A.D. 112, Roman engineers cut a 3-miles (4.8 km) long tunnel through the Mount ***Affilius***, but it was not as long as the ***emissarium*** of Lake ***Fucinus***.

Roman Roads

Romans were the greatest experts of communication engineering in ancient times. In the military conquests of the Imperial Rome, and in the maintenance of the Roman Empire, the means of communications were of the utmost importance to the Empire, and the Romans were keenly aware of it. For this reason Romans became the first systematic large-scale road builders in history. In the imperial times, Romans built about 180,000 miles (289,674 km) of paved roads and 55,000 miles (88,512 km) of main highways. The vast Roman Empire was covered with a tight network of roads from one end of the Empire to the other. In the Italian peninsula, the Roman cities were connected with Rome by a network of excellent highways: Appian Way, Flaminian Way, Aemilian Way, Latin Way, Aurelian Way, Cassian Way, Valerian Way, Tiburtina Way, Salarian Way, Ostian Way, and Emilian Way. The Flaminian, Salarian and Tiburtina Ways joined Rome with the Adriatic Sea on the east coast of Italy, whereas the Ostian Way went west to the port of Ostia at the Tyrrhenian Sea on the west coast of Italy. The Cassian and Emilian Ways traversed the Apennine Mountains to the north to join Rome with the Po valley. The best-known Roman road is the Appian Way (***Via Appia***), built by the blind censor and the first great Roman writer, Appius Claudius Crassus, in 312 B.C., which ran from Rome to ***Capua***, and was later extended to ***Brundisium*** (modern, Brindisi).

Major Roman roads were usually named after the ***censors*** who had charge of the public lands and public works during the Roman Republic, and who directed the building of roads. A good Roman road design essentially consisted of a foundation, a binder and a pavement. The main Roman roads had well-drained subgrades, ditches, culverts, and sharply cambered surfaces. A Roman road had a thickness from 3 to 8 feet (0.91 to 2.44 m), with the pavement slabs laid in pozzuolana cement (***pulvis puteolanus***), a cement made out of volcanic ash found near the city ***Puteoli*** (modern Pozzuoli), which when mixed with water dried out to rocklike hardness. The main roads were 80 feet (24.4 m) wide, and consisted of the 40-foot (12.19 m) wide road surface and two sidewalks, each 20-foot (6.10 m) wide, which were separated from the road surface by low stone walls, or by grass strips. The average life of a Roman road was between 70 and 100 years. It was possible to travel more than 2,500 miles (4,023 km), all the way from Britain to the Euphrates river, on good Roman highways.

The ***cursus publicus***, the State's postal and messenger service, was the means of passenger transport, but this combined postal, passenger, and goods service was strictly regulated by the State.

At every 10 miles (16.1 km) of these highways there were posting stations (***mutationes***) with stables of 40 fresh horses, ostlers, veterinarians, blacksmiths, and other services, such as military police. At every 30 to 40 miles (48.3 to 64.4 km), larger stations and hostels (***mansiones***) were located for overnight stay and supplies, such as road maps (***itinerarii***). The ***mansiones*** also served as central offices for all taxes paid in kind. The express service could be used only by high officials, their families, and the imperial messenger (***tabellarii***). The average speed of the imperial post was about 5 miles (8 km) an hour, whereas special messengers averaged 10 miles (16.1 km) an hour. Cicero as a governor of Sicily travelled 24 miles (38.6 km) a day in 51 B.C..

Postal service was first used only by the State, whereas private post sent with merchants and travellers was long-delayed and frequently lost. After the 2nd century A.D., private companies also forwarded letters and parcels. On special occasions for short trips the messenger could travel about 100 miles (161 km) a day and more with frequent changes of horses. The messenger wore breeches, heavy woollen cloak and a flat hat resembling that of Mercury, the messenger of the gods. The known record of travelling speed on Roman roads was achieved by Tiberius, who later succeeded his step-father Augustus as the Emperor. Tiberius travelled 200 miles (321.9 km) in a single day in his furious drive to reach his brother Drusus who lay dying at ***Lugdunum*** (modern Lyons) in Gaul (Roman province France). He wore out 3 light chariots in this record breaking travel.

The most magnificent Roman road map was the map of the Roman Empire in the bedroom of Emperor Augustus, which consisted of a large sheet of gold with engraved roads and main cities laid in precious stones. Emperor Vespasianus (in English, Vespasian), a general who ruled from A.D.69 to A.D.79, installed in the Roman Forum a vast map of Roman Empire with all the roads and towns carved in marble.

In the late period of Roman Empire, the Egnatian Way was constructed from ***Tergeste*** to ***Byzantium***, which remained the important link between the Western and the Eastern Roman Empire after the division of the Roman Empire in A.D. 395.

Aqueducts

Romans were avid builders of aqueducts wherever they went in the ancient world. By A.D. 300 the city of Rome itself had 11 aqueducts supplying 220 million gallons (1,000 million liters) of water daily, which provided about 120 gallons (545.5 litres) of water per capita per day. The contemporary rate of water supply in Rome is about 60 gallons (273 litres) per capita per day. The use of Roman water in the Empire period was about 17 % industrial, 39 % private, and 44 % public. The public water supply provided water for 95 public buildings, 39 public baths, 591 fountains, and 19 military barracks. Excess water of the aqueducts was used for the sewage disposal in ***Cloaca Maxima***. Lead pipes with standardised calibrated nozzles (which could not be closed because there were no cocks in them) distributed water into houses. Water users had to pay for the nozzle size and not for the actual quantity of water used.

The Roman aqueducts lost about half of their water originally extracted from the sources through leaks and unauthorized tapping. In 9 B.C. a special Water Board was established by the Emperor Augustus. Under the Emperors Nerva and Traianus, Iulius Sextus Frontinus (c.30/35-103/104 A.D.), a former general and provincial governor of Britain, was appointed the head of the Water Board (***curator aquarium***) from A.D. 85 to 104. Frontinus, who wrote 2 books < On Water Supply > (***De Aquis***) and 6 books on other engineering subjects, is next to Vitruvius the best known Roman author of engineering books. He restored the corrupt water administration to efficiency, carried out periodic personal inspections of aqueducts and wrote the first ancient survey of water waste. He discovered 10,000 special pipes drawing the overflow from the fountains, old ducts illegally drawing water after the new ducts had been installed, and a number of pipes illegally bringing water to shops, irrigated fields, and places of entertainment. After making needed repairs on the existing aqueducts in Rome, and correcting all the faults mentioned above, Frontinus doubled the water supplied to Rome. The Water Board had a staff of 700, which included surveyors, inspectors, masons, pavers, and administrators. Potable water was tested for its quality by evaporation in bronze or copper vessels, by sedimentation, and by colour and taste of cooked vegetables.

Aqueducts of Rome:

	Name:	Builder:	Length: miles (km)	Specus: (roofed water channel) in feet (meters)
312 B.C.	***Aqua Appia***	Appius Claudius Crassus	10.29 (16.6)	2 by 6 (0.61 by 1.83)
272-269 B.C.	***Anio Vetus***	Manius Curius Dentatur	43 (69)	3.7 by 8 (1.13 by 2.44)
144-140 B.C.	***Aqua Marcia***	Quintus Marcus Rex	60 (96 .6)	4.6 by 9 (1.40 by 2.74)
125 B.C.	***Aqua Tepula***	Caepio & Longinus	11.00 (17.7)	2 by 3.5 (0.61 by 1.07)
27 B.C.	***Aqua Iulia*** (concrete)	Marcus Agrippa	14.35 (23.1)	2.3 by 4.6 (0.70 by 1.40)
19 B.C.	***Aqua Virgo***	Marcus Agrippa	12.97 (20.9)	2.2 by 5 (0.67 by 1.52)
2 B.C.	***Aqua Alsientina***	Augustus	20.39 (32.8)	5.8 by 8.7 (1.77 by 2.65)
A.D.38-A.D.52	***Aqua Claudia***	Nero & Claudius	43.34 (69.7)	3 by 6.2 (0.91 by 1.89)
A.D.38-A.D.52	***Anio Novus***	Claudius	62 (99.8)	4.3 by 9 (1.31 by 2.74)
A.D.109	***Aqua Traiana***	Traianus	35.4 (57)	3 by 5.7 (0.91 by 1.74)

A.D. 226	***Aqua Alexandrina***	Hadrianus & Alexander Severus	13.7 (22.0)	2.5 by 4.3 (0.76 by 1.31)

The earliest aqueduct, the ***Aqua Appia***, was built in 312 B.C. by Appius Claudius Crassus, called 'Ceacus' because he was blind, who also built the highway ***Via Appia,*** and is the first known Latin writer of prose or verse whose name has been transmitted to modern times.

The ***Aqua Appia*** was about 11 miles (17.7 km) long, and its workmanship was rather crude. It brought spring water to Rome but only 300 feet (91.44 m) of the aqueduct was on arches, the remainder being underground. It entered Rome 60 feet (18.29 m) above the sea level.

During the next 40 years after the construction of ***Aqua Appia***, Rome increased substantially in size and, therefore, needed a much more abundant supply of water. The ***censor*** Manius Curius Dentatus, a favourite hero of Romans and the very symbol of Republican Roman simplicity, frugality and disinterestedness, directed the construction of ***Aqua Anio Vetus*** which tapped the river ***Anio***, a tributary of the river ***Tiberis*** (modern Tiber or Tevere). This aqueduct began some 20 miles (32.2 km) northeast of Rome but it wound around so much that its length became about 43 miles (69.2 km). Since most of this aqueduct was underground, only about 1,100 feet (335.28 m) was on masonry structures above the ground. The ***Ponte Lupo*** and other parts of this magnificent aqueduct bridge were made of arches of tufa and travertine. The ***Ponte Lupo*** was a colossal arched structure, 365 feet (111.25 m) long, 100 feet (30.348 m) high, and 70 feet (21.34 m) wide at its base.

The ***Aqua Marcia*** built by Quintus Marcius Rex was about 60 miles (96.6 km) long, but only 12 miles (19.3 km) of this aqueduct was carried on masonry arches in 3 tiers constructed of red, brown and yellow cut stones, 18 by 18 by 42 inches (46 by 46 by 107 cm), laid in cement. In some places this aqueduct superstructure of masonry arches was 70 feet (21.34 m) high. It was reconstructed in 1869, and is still in use. The structure of ***Aqua Marcia***, which was much influenced by Greek architecture, was so substantial that the two succeeding aqueducts, ***Aqua Tepula***, which was built by the ***aediles*** Caepio and Longinus on a higher level than Marcia but with a smaller capacity and which brought slightly warm water from volcanic springs in the ***Albanus*** Hills, and ***Aqua Iulia*** which was built by ***aedile*** Agrippa, were constructed on top of ***Aqua Marcia***. ***Aqua Marcia*** was the first aqueduct of Rome built mostly above the ground and it delivered water to Rome at an elevation of 150 feet (45.72 m) above the sea level.

The successful Roman military commander, talented organiser and administrator, an orator and writer of some repute, Marcus Vispanus Agrippa (63-12 B.C.), a man of even temper who showed no trace of Roman ruthlessness, was responsible for most of the military successes of his close friend Octavianus, nephew of Caesar, who later became Augustus, the first Emperor of Rome, because it was Agrippa who defeated the forces of Pompeius and, later, of Marcus Antonius (in

English, Marc Anthony) (c.83-30B.C.) and Cleopatra (69-30B.C.) in two famous naval battles at ***Actium***. Moreover, Agrippa not only was, but also looked like an ideal, serious, determined, self-confident, square-jawed, rugged, practical and able Roman. Augustus appointed Agrippa the ***aedile***, a magistrate in charge of the aqueducts of the Roman Empire, in which capacity Agrippa directed the building of two aqueducts of Rome, the ***Aqua Iulia*** and ***Aqua Virgo***. The latter aqueduct, built in 18 B.C., had a 14-miles (22.5 km) long channel, of which 12 miles (19.3 km) was underground. It brought water from the springs 8 miles (12.9 km) from Rome, which lay only 80 feet (24.38 m) above the sea level, to supply his ***thermae***. His most outstanding work was the massive aqueduct of ***Pont Du Gard*** in Gaul (Roman province France) built in 18 B.C., which crossed the valley of the river ***Gardon*** (modern Gard) and was part of the 24-miles (38.6 km) long aqueduct to the city ***Nemausus*** (modern Nîme). It is one of the best preserved, the most beautiful, and the most substantial Roman aqueduct bridge extant. It is built in 3 tiers, each consisting of a series of circular arches. The lower tiers have the longest arch span of 80 feet and 5 inches (24.51 m), other arch spans range from 51 feet (15.54 m) to 63 feet (19.20 m). The length of the entire structure is 885 feet (269.75 m), and its height is 161 feet (49.07 m). The water channel **(*specus*)**, has the cross-section of 4 by 6 feet (1.22 by 1.83 m). The aqueduct bridge has dry masonry construction without iron cramps except the ***specus***, which was poured in concrete. Apparently the so-called 'flying scaffolds' were used in the construction of the arches, as the projecting stone-supports seem to indicate. It appears that many Roman engineers preferred 'flying scaffolds' supported on projecting stones to tall scaffolds built up from the ground. Altogether, Romans provided more than 30 cities in the Roman province Gaul with aqueducts**:** ***Marseilles*** had 3, ***Aix*** had 4, ***Vienna*** had 3, and ***Antibes*** had 2, of which one is still in service.

In Rome, ***Aqua Alsietina*** was completed for Emperor Augustus by 2 B.C.. It was a 25-miles (40.2 km) long expensive structure that brought water from the Lake ***Alsietinus*** for the ***naumachia***, the mock naval battles which were staged in the circus arena flooded for the occasion by a complicated system of pipes and sluices or, sometimes, in an artificial lake. The special basin dug for this ***naumachia*** of Augustus was 1,200 by 1,800 feet (365.76 by 548.64 m). Since the water of ***Alsietina*** was unfit for drinking, its surplus was used for irrigation.

The aqueducts, ***Aqua Claudius*** and ***Aqua Anio-Novus***, begun by Emperor Caligula in A.D. 38 but finished by Emperor Claudius in A.D.52, were meant to supply water to the highest hills in Rome. Both aqueducts were carried on the same arches a distance of miles (12.9 km) across the Campagna, and much of this aqueduct is 105 feet (32.0 m) above the ground, the highest in Rome. ***Aqua Anio-Novus***, which is 62 miles (99.8 km) long, is carried on the loftiest arches.

Another aqueduct, now called ***Aqueducto de las Ferreras***, which were built in the beginning of the Roman Empire in ***Tarraco*** (modern, Tarragona) in Spain has a length of 22 miles (35.4 km) and it crosses a valley at the height of 98½ feet (30.02 m) in a structure consisting of 2 tiers of arches, the lower tier having 11 arches and the upper tier 25 arches. The length of this structure is 682 feet (207.87 m).

The most daring skeletal stone structure erected by the Romans is the aqueduct structure in Segovia, Spain. It was constructed under the sponsorship of the Emperor Marcus Ulpius Traianus (in English, Trajan), who hailed from Spain and ruled from A.D. 98 to A.D.117. The Segovia aqueduct structure was part of a 60-miles (96.6 km) long aqueduct which brought water to the city of Segovia from the Guadamarra Mountains. The aqueduct superstructure is ½ a mile (0.8 km) long, 119 feet (36.27 m) high, and 8 feet (2.44 m) wide at base. It is a 2 tier arch structure consisting of 128 arches, with the longest arch span of 15 feet (4.57 m). It is of dry masonry construction without iron cramps and, surprisingly, it is still in daily use today.

Roman Syphon Lines

Romans also constructed Greek syphon line when it was economically sound and technically feasible. The most highly pressurised syphon line of the Roman construction was in the Aqueduct of ***Alatrium*** located some 50 miles (80.5 km) east of the city of ***Alatrium*** (modern Alatri) in central Italy. It had a vertical drop of 340 feet (103.63 m) with a pressure in the syphon line of 150 psi (1.03 MPa), more than 10 atmospheres. The diameter of the lead syphon pipe was 3⅞ inches (9.9 cm), and the thickness of the pipe was ⅜ inch (1 cm). It was built by the engineer Betilianus Varo.

The city of ***Lugdunum*** (modern Lyons) in Gaul during Roman times was served by 4 aqueducts which delivered about 28¼ million cubic feet (80,000 cubic meters) of water a day and accommodated 9 syphons. The 30-mile (48.3 km) long Gier aqueduct was the longest, and it accommodated 3 tunnels and 4 syphons with the total drop of 361 feet (110 m). The syphons consisting of 9 lead pipes 9 ⅞ inches (25 cm) in diameter and 1⅝ inches (4.0 cm) in wall thickness descended from the header tank on the 45° slope to the level part of the syphon called the 'belly' (***venter***), carried on a masonry bridge on which the number of pipes was increased to 18 lead pipes 6 ⅝ inches (16.8 cm) in diameter. The syphon pipes ascended again on a 45° slope from the ***venter*** to the receiving tank. The hydraulic gradient of a syphon had to be about 10 times the normal slope of the aqueduct to carry an adequate volume of water. The total length of the 9 syphons in the water supply lines to ***Lugdunum*** was about 10 miles (15.6 km) containing about 93 miles (150 km) of piping made from about 15,000 tons of lead. The two largest syphons were built into the aqueduct at Soucien, which was ¾ miles (1.2 km) long, 305 feet (93 m) deep, and at Beaunant, which was more than 1 ⅔ miles (2.6 km) long and 404 feet (123 m) deep. The next longest was the Brevenne aqueduct which ran 41 miles (65 km) in a step-like fashion of alternating cascades and plateaus and required one syphon over its total drop of 1,148 feet (350 m). The 17-miles (27 m) long Mont d'Or aqueduct had a total drop of 295 feet (90 m) and needed only one syphon. The 15-miles (25 km) long Craponne aqueduct had a giant syphon which was about 3 ⅔ miles (6 km) long and dropped about 328 feet (100 m) below the hydraulic gradient. The pressure in these syphon pipes reached as high as 12 atmospheres (1,200 kPa), and it is known that Roman syphon pipes usually failed at 18 atmospheres (1,800 kPa). These aqueducts were probably built on the order of Emperor Claudius.

Another famous syphon line was constructed on the Hebron-Jerusalem Aqueduct at the time of Jesus of Nazareth by the Roman governor Pontius Pilatus (in English, Pilate). The pipeline consisted of terra-cotta pipes passing through the perforations in interlocking stones which anchored the syphon line by weight.

The Aqueduct of Saint Remy, built by Agrippa, brought water to the city ***Arelate*** (modern Arles). One branch of it crossed the Rhône river in an inverted syphon consisting of lead pipes laid in the river bed. Sometime in the period from A.D. 81 to A.D.96, Emperor Domitianus (in English, Domitian) had an inverted syphon built to his palace on the Palatine Hill in Rome. Its lead pipe measured a foot in diameter and crossed a valley 133 feet (40.54 m) below the reservoir fed by ***Aqua Claudia***. Pressure in that pipe was 60 psi (0.41 MPa).

Central Heating

By 1200 B.C., at the end of the Hittite Empire and the beginning of the Trojan War, a central heating system had been constructed in the palace of the Kingdom of Arzawa, a Hittite vassal, in southern Anatolia.

Sometime between 80 and 40 B.C., central heating was reinvented by the Roman entrepreneur Gaius Sergius Orata, who first employed it in his villa at ***Baiae*** to heat his fish and oyster ponds at Lake ***Lucrinus***. This central heating system, called ***hypocaustum*** (fire below), was later used in the ***thermae*** and also in private homes.

Central heating reappeared in Europe after the fall of Rome only in A.D. 1908.

Palatial Public Baths: *Thermae*

In about 21B.C. Agrippa built the first and most renowned free public bath called the ***Thermae Agrippae***, located about 200 feet (61 m) south of the first ***Pantheon***, both built by Agrippa on his own expense. It is supposed to have incorporated a rotunda with a domed roof, but little is known about it since it was destroyed by fire in A.D. 80, and later restored and, in part, enlarged by the Emperors Hadrianus and Alexander Severus in which form it survived till the sixteenth century. The ***Thermae Agrippae*** was a complex of bathing facilities, exercise areas, shops and libraries. The other later public baths were designed by using the Agrippa's ***thermae*** as a model. The ***thermae***, besides bathing, tried to provide facilities for every kind of Roman leisure.

The ***Thermae Antoninianae***, or popularly called the 'Baths of Caracalla', was built from A.D. 206 to A.D.235. This ***thermae*** was begun by the Emperor Lucius Septimius Severus in A.D. 206, but most of it was built under Emperor Caracalla [this is a nickname derived from his favourite hooded tunic of Gauls which he wore as Emperor; his real name was Marcus Aurelius Antoninus (ruled from A.D. 211 to A.D. 217)] from A.D. 212 to A.D.216 when it was dedicated, but it was completed by Emperor Marcus Aurelius Alexander Severus (died A.D. 235) who ruled from A.D. 222 to A.D.235. The ***thermae*** stood on a 20-foot (6.10 m) high platform which was 1,150 feet (350.52 m) square. Underneath this platform were vaulted corridors, store chambers, hypocausts, hot-air ducts, and furnaces. The buildings which lined the platform were 2-storeys high with the shops and businesses occupying the ground floor. The stadium and the lecture halls lined the other half of the perimeter of the ***thermae***. The vault of ***tepidarium*** (warm bath) was carried by long bronze beams. Behind the stadium was located the great vaulted reservoir of water supplied by ***Aqua Marcia*** from which water was distributed to different parts of the ***thermae*** through lead piping.

The main building block of the ***thermae*** measured 750 by 380 feet (228.60 by 115.82 m) and occupied an area larger than 6 acres (2.43 hectares). The great central hall of the main building block had a size of 183 by 79 feet (55.78 by 24.03 m), and it was roofed over by enormous intersecting semi-circular vaults of concrete in three bays, which rested on 8 massive piers each 108 feet (32.92 m) high. The circular ***calidarium*** (steam bath), which was heated by wall flumes, was covered by a giant dome with a base diameter of 116 feet (35.35 m). The precursor of the colossal cross-vaulted enclosure used in the Baths of Caracalla was the 100-foot (30.48 m) span barrel vault that covered the lofty hall of the palace of the last Flavian Emperor, Domitianus, who ruled from A.D. 81 to A.D.96. The Baths of Caracalla also contained smaller domes which were supported on octagonal bases by means of pendentives. The pendentives which support huge domes resting on rectangular walls had been introduced into Roman construction in the rebuilding of the palace of the Emperor Domitianus on the Palatine Hill in Rome. The walls of the Baths of Caracalla were reinforced with bolted T-iron frames.

The ***thermae*** contained ***natatio*** consisting of a ***tepidarium*** (tepid bath) and a ***frigidarium*** (cold bath), the latter being an open air swimming pool. The interior of the ***thermae*** was elaborately and lavishly decorated with expensive building material. Even the giant vaults were richly ornamented with coffering, coloured glass mosaics, and modelled pointed stucco. The halls of this ***thermae*** housed some of the finest sculptures of antiquity, which had been brought from Greece, or were executed by Greek artists in Rome. The Baths of Caracalla accommodated about 1,600 bathers at a time.

The ***Thermae Diocletiani***, or the Baths of Diocletianus, completed in A.D. 302, was built by Emperor Diocletianus (in English, Diocletian), who ruled from A.D. 284 to A.D.308, and it was the largest Roman baths ever built in Rome. It had a rectangular size of 1,250 by 1,210 feet (381.00 by 368.81 m) which covered about 32 acres (13 hectares) of land, and resembled the Baths of Caracalla in its general architectural design. The great central hall of ***Thermae Diocletiani*** had a size 200 by 80 feet (60.96 by 24.38 m), and a height of 90 feet (27.43 m) and it is covered by an original groined cross-barrel vaulting in three bays, which sprang from 8 monolithic columns of Egyptian granite 50-foot (15.24 m) tall. Large parts of the ***Thermae Diocletiani*** have survived, and in A.D. 1563 its great hall was converted by sculptor, painter and architect Michelangelo Buonarroti (A.D.1475-1564) into the church of Santa Maria degli Angeli. The restoration of the ***frigidarium*** and the ***ephebeum*** of the ***Thermae Diocletiani*** gave a good idea of the sumptuousness of the original building. The ***Thermae Diocletiani*** accommodated about 3,000 bathers at a time.

Roman Bridges and Other Structures

About 150 B.C., Roman engineers discovered the Roman concrete ***opus caementitium***, now called pozzuolana concrete. It was made of a natural strata of trass Romans called ***pulvis puteolanus***, a porous reddish volcanic rock found near the city Puteoli, and also at and near Rome, and used as a substitute for lime. Pozzuolana was mixed with lime, rubble, potsherds, and crushed tufa brick shards set in alternate layers of large and small pieces to make concrete, which could be poured into formwork, and which set even under water and yielded rock-hard lightweight concrete. Roman concrete used ***caementum***, a large-size aggregate which was usually laid in layers and not mixed at random as is the case with modern small-size aggregate.

The first bridge built in Rome was ***Pons Sublicius***. It crossed the ***Tiberis*** (the Tiber River) at the foot of Mount Aventine and initially it was constructed of timber with a removable wooden deck. This bridge had a length not over 600 feet (182.90 m) and was built in 621 B.C. by Ancus Marcius, who ruled Rome from 641B.C. to 617 B.C. This bridge was destroyed about 500 B.C., but was twice restored by the chief priest (***pontifex maximus***). It was washed out by a flood in 23 B.C. and rebuilt in stone by Aemilius Lepidus, the last ***censor*** under the Emperor Augustus. This bridge was destroyed anew in a flood of A.D. 140, but again it was rebuilt. It was once more carried away by a flood in A.D. 780 and its remains existed until A.D. 1877, when they were finally removed to clear the river channel. ***Sublicius*** means trees, hence it must have been a bridge constructed on piles.

The next bridges in Rome were constructed in 291 B.C., when two wooden bridges were flung across the Tiber river connecting the Tiber island with both banks of this river. From 178 B.C. to 142 B.C., the ***censor*** Caius Flavius built a stone arch bridge, the first known Roman arch bridge, across the Tiber river below the Tiber island and below the ***Pons Sublicius***. This bridge had 6 semicircular arches the spans of which ranged from 44 to 54 feet (13.41 to 16.46 m), and the size of the piers ranged from 18½ by 29½ feet (5.64 by 8.99 m) to 15feet 2 inches by 29½ feet (4.63 by 8.99 m). This bridge was swept out by floods many times, and it was rebuilt at one time by Aemilius Lepidus, and renamed ***Pons Aemilius***. The new bridge again was repeatedly destroyed by floods, for the first time in A.D. 280. It was rebuilt several times and each time was renamed. For a while it was called ***Pons Palatinus***, then ***Pons Senatorius***, and finally ***Pons Lapideus***. The last richly ornamented reconstruction of this bridge stems from the time of Pope Julius III, but two arches of the last rebuilt version of the bridge were swept away by a flood in A.D. 1598. At present this old bridge has three arches and a long suspension span over the gap where the other arches originally stood. It is now called by the Italians 'Ponte Rotto' (Broken Bridge). It was originally built, like the old stone bridges of Rome, of peperino and tufa and faced with travertine anchored into the masonry.

The bridge now called 'Ponte Nona', located at the 9th mile of the ***Via Praenestina*** near ***Gaii***, in Italy, was constructed from 124 B.C. to 121 B.C. It has 7 semicircular stone arches of tufa and travertine, and an overall length of 225 feet (68.58 m). It is still in use.

In 109 B.C. ***Pons Milvius***, now known as 'Ponte Molle', which carried the Flaminian Way across the Tiber about 1½ miles (2.4 km) north of Rome, was probably built by censor Marcus Aelius Scaurus. It has 7 semi-circular stone arch spans ranging from 36 to 62 feet (10.97 to 18.90 m), and a width of 24 feet (7.32 m). The piers range from 16 feet 4 inches by 28 feet 8 inches (5.00 by 8.76 m) to 29½ by 28 ¾ feet (8.99 by 8.76 m), and are pierced with small relief arches. This bridge has been restored so many times that very little of its original material remains in the bridge. The last fundamental restoration stems from the 15th century A.D..

In 62 B.C., ***consul*** Lucius Fabricius replaced the wooden bridge connecting the Island of ***Aesculapius*** (modern Isola Tiberina), an island located in the middle of the Tiber river, with the eastern bank of the Tiber by a stone arch bridge of 2 spans 83-foot (25.30 m) each, and 3 smaller relief arches of 16 feet (4.88 m) span in the abutments which are now buried in the new embankments. The length of this bridge, which was originally named ***Pons Fabricius*** and is now called 'Ponte Dei Quattro Capi', is 250 feet (76.20 m). Its central pier is 33 feet (10.06 m) thick, and the archivolts, or the arch rings, making up the stone arch are 6 feet (1.83 m) thick. It is the oldest, perfectly intact Roman bridge which is still in use today.

The continuation of this bridge leading from the Tiber island to the west bank of the Tiber was built in stone by Rome's governor Lucius Cestius in 46 B.C., as a replacement to the original wooden bridge and called ***Pons Cestius***. A new caisson method of foundation construction was used: a shoal of rock and masonry was floated to place at low-water time and sunk, and the piers were built upon them. It has 3 arches, the central arch had a span of 76 feet (23.16 m), whereas the

2 lateral arches were smaller. This bridge was rebuilt several times, for the first time in A.D. 365. In A.D. 370 it was renovated by the Emperor Gratianus after which it was called ***Pons Gratiani***. Between A.D. 1888 and A.D.1892 it was destroyed and a new bridge built in its stead which is now called 'Ponte San Bartolomeo'.

A little earlier, in 55 B.C., Iulius Caesar ordered his engineer Mamurra to build a temporary military bridge over the river ***Rhenus*** (modern Rhine) near the city ***Bonna*** (modern, Bonn) in Germany. It had 50 spans and an overall length of 1,800 feet (548.64 m). The sloping piles constituting the piers were driven into the river bottom at 25 feet (7.62 m) intervals by pile drivers. Each pier consisted of 4 inclined piles and was protected by 3 fender piles at the upstream side of the bridge. Logs were used for girders, and for the beams spanning between the girders. Wickerwork was used for decking and fenders. This bridge, which was built in 10 days with the aid of pontoons, was destroyed according to the order of Caesar after his return from an 18-day punitive campaign in the enemy territory across the Rhine river.

The construction of ***Circus Maximus***, a gigantic chariot race track, which in its final form accommodated over 250,000 spectators, was first begun under Iulius Caesar about the middle of the first century B.C.. In its final form, the ***Circus Maximus*** was finished under the Emperor Traianus in the beginning of the 2nd century A.D..

From 27 B.C. to A.D.14 the finest of all the Roman bridges was built in Narni some 60 miles (96.6 km) northwest of Rome, and it carried the Flaminian Way across the Nera river. It was sponsored by Emperor Augustus and built in white marmor. This bridge had 4 arches: **2** arches with 75-foot (22.86 m) spans, 1 unsymmetrical arch with 143-foot (43.59 m) span, and 1 arch with 114-foot (34.75 m) span. The height of this bridge was 105 feet (32.00 m). The Narni bridge was of dry masonry construction with stones clamped in place by iron cramps laid in lead. It had a cofferdam foundation which rested on piles driven to the bedrock. The arches of this bridge consisted of 5 archivolts in the form of projecting arch rings. The main arch span, the longest known Roman arch ever constructed, was the only known unsymmetrical Roman arch having its springings on top of 2 piers at different levels. The roadway of the bridge was not level but had a fairly steep gradient. The main arch of this fairly massive bridge was destroyed in a flood in A.D. 1304, and one of its piers collapsed in the beginning of 20th century.

From 31 B.C. to A.D. 14, the Emperor Augustus had a skew bridge built over the ***Ariminus*** (modern Marecchia) river in the city ***Ariminum*** (modern Rimini) at the end of Flaminian Way. It is a well preserved bridge and the most ornamented of all known Roman bridges. This bridge, called ***Pons Augustus***, now known as 'Ponte Di Augusto', has 5 spans of semi-circular arches ranging from 24 to 29 feet (7.32 to 8.84 m) arranged in a skew alignment which involved complicated problems of stone cutting and fitting. The stones in the archivolts are so finely joined that they appear to be ground together. Above the heavy piers of the bridge are panels formed by columns supporting entablatures and the heavy stone cornice of the deck is carried on dentils. At one time marble porticoes stood above the roadway. It is made of excellent travertine stone that looks like marble.

From A.D. 60 to 64 a bridge called ***Pons Neronianus***, which connected ***Campus Martius*** with the Gardens of Agrippa, the circus of Nero and the Vatican meadows, was built in Rome.

In A.D. 40, Emperor Caligula had a pontoon bridge flung in a crescent shape across the narrow point in the Lake ***Lucrinus*** (modern, Lucrine Lake) in ***Sinus Cumanus*** (modern Bay of Naples) between the cities ***Baiae*** and ***Puteoli*** which were located on the opposite sides of this lake. It had a length of more than 3 miles (4.8 km) and its deck was supported by a double row of boats and pontoons. The roadway, which was made of planks covered with earth and gravel, was lined on either side with shops and houses, and was illuminated at night with torches. The remains of the mole of this bridge, which was made of giant square blocks of concrete, were still extant at the turn of twentieth century. Caligula is supposed to have built this bridge to surpass the pontoon bridges of Xerxes flung over the Strait of Dardanelles (***Hellespont***).

From A.D.70 to A.D.80, the Emperor Vespasianus and his son Titus built the famous ***Amphitheatrum Flavium***, which is popularly known as the ***Colosseum*** because opposite to this amphitheater, at one time, stood the colossal 120-foot (36.58 m) high bronze statue of the naked Emperor Nero which Emperor Hadrianus later changed into the statue of Sun-god Helios. The major diameter of this oval arena is 620 feet (188.9 m) and the minor diameter is 513 feet 5 inches (156.36 m). The arena was surrounded by rising tiers of seats incorporated into the 4-storey outside structure enclosing the arena which was 175 feet (53.34 m) high. The entire arena was covered by a retractable canvas awning (***velarium***) suspended from poles and operated by a squad of sailors. The canvas could be stretched radially over the arena by means of ropes to shield the audience, often consisting of 50,000 spectators, from the Sun. This huge arena was built where an uncompleted artificial lake intended for Nero's huge villa, the Golden House (***Domus Aurea***), was located which required a complicated drainage system before the arena could be built. This lake was occasionally used to flood the arena for the staging of ***naumachia,*** the mock sea battle. This arena was still used for animal games as late as A.D. 523. The ***Colosseum*** in Rome remained the largest arena in the world until the construction of the 'Yale Bowl' in New Haven, Connecticut, in 1914.

Engineering of Traianus (ruled from A.D.98 to A.D.117)

Marcus Ulpius Traianus (in English, Trajan) (A.D.c.53-117), a native of Spain, was primarily a scrupulous military commander who spent his life in military campaigns which extended the Roman Empire to its maximum limits. Emperor Marcus Coccelius Nerva died shortly after adopting

Traianus in A.D.97 as his colleague and successor. Traianus was the first outstanding Roman general to occupy the Emperor's throne. Traianus was a powerfully built, broad-shouldered man who was genuinely modest. He never indulged in any grandiose personal projects, but only built useful public structures on as large a scale as was technically possible in his time. The churchmen of the Middle Ages considered Traianus to have been the exemplary Emperor of almost Christian virtues for he was the very model of simplicity, honesty and fair play. Traianus was no less capable as a political administrator and he devoted more attention to the details of government operations than any emperor before him. He established a very high standard of efficiency in administrative processes and left a tradition of excellence both in the conduct of government and in the staffing of important government posts in the Imperial civil service. He also dismissed the secret police of the Roman State, and banished all spies, a system of informers first established by Emperor Augustus. The times of Traianus were rather felicitous for Roman citizens, and its tenor was aptly expressed by the historian and proconsul Cornelius Tacitus (A.D. c.55-died after117): "Modern times are indeed happy as few others have been, for we think as we please, and speak as we think."

Traianus sponsored many engineering works all over the Roman Empire but most of his important structures were built in the provinces. In Rome, he built the 11th aqueduct, the 35-mile (56.3 km) long ***Aqua Traiana***, in A.D.109 for the sole purpose of supplying the ***Thermae Suranae***. From A.D.107 to A.D.113, ***architectus*** Apollodorus of Damascus built for Traianus his masterpiece of civic construction, the vast complex of ***Forum Traiani, Basilica Ulpia***, the neighbouring libraries and markets. The libraries flanked a smaller courtyard of this complex in the center of which stood the celebrated 125-foot (38.10 m) high column of Traianus (***Columna Traiani***). This column was faced with a 625-foot (190.50 m) long helical scroll carving of the Dacian campaign of Traianus, and it was topped with the statue of Traianus. This column is still there except that the statue of Traianus has been replaced with that of Apostle Paul. North of ***Forum Romanum***, Apollodorus built in A.D.112 the 5-storey Traianus Market (***Emporium Traiani***), consisting of a large market hall surrounded by a beehive of 150 shops and offices, as part of this complex. It was a vast concrete structure faced with brick and built on 3 levels. The Traianus Market, the precursor of the modern shopping center, was functional in the extreme by introducing the austere, utilitarian building style based on modular planning.

Traianus, true to the tradition of Roman Emperors, also built in Rome the large Public Baths of Traianus (***Thermae Traiani***). His engineers built the most daring, slender, and functional Roman structures. Emperor Traianus, and his successor Hadrianus who was his nephew, reopened the blocked ***emissarium*** of Lake ***Fucinus***, but the control of this lake was made secure only by a modern tunnel cut in A.D. 1876. Traianus substantially improved the harbours of ***Ostia*** and ***Ancona***, and constructed the harbour ***Centum Cellae*** (modern Civitavecchia). He restored the ***Via Appia*** (Appian

Way) and built new roads and bridges all over the Roman Empire. He partially drained the Pointine Marshes with a network of canals.

From A.D. 104 to A.D.105, Traianus ordered his Greek ***architectus*** Apollodorus of Damascus, the foremost ancient engineer, to construct a famous timber bridge over the lower ***Danuvius*** (modern Danube) river near the modern Turnu-Severin in Transylvania, Rumania. The length of this wooden bridge was anywhere from 3,720 to 4,500 feet (1,133.86 to 1,371.60 m), its height was 150 feet (45.72 m) and its width was 60 feet (18.2 m). The bridge consisted of 20 wooden arches of center-to-center span of 170 feet (51.82 m). The 170-foot (51.82 m) span stood as a record bridge span for 16 centuries. The piers had a size of 60 by 50 feet (18.29 to 15.24 m) and were 150 feet (45.72 m) high. The piers were made of clamped cubical stone blocks of 2-foot (0.61 m) dimension and erected on 120 by 80 feet (36.58 by 24.38 m) sunken caisson-foundations set on piles driven to the bedrock. The Danube river had a depth of about 18 feet (5.50 m) at this location. This giant bridge was constructed in one year, a record in Roman construction, because Traianus needed it urgently for the conquest of ***Dacia*** (modern Rumania). In A.D. 120, the next Emperor, Hadrianus, ordered a partial dismantlement of this bridge through the removal of its deck in his effort to consolidate the boundaries of the Roman Empire which, in his opinion, had been militarily overextended by Traianus. Since the maintenance of the bridge was discontinued, the timber arches soon fell into disrepair. Emperor Constantinus restored the bridge in A.D. 328, but only a few piers of this structure still remain today because it was later destroyed in the wars with semibarbaric Germanic tribes. The lower Danube river was not bridged again until the 19th century A.D..

Apollodorus also provided Traianus with illustrated designs of various war machinery in a treatise which he edited for the Emperor. A few centuries later another well-known technological treatise was written by Flavius Renatus Vegetius (*floruit* A.D.375-392), who was not a military engineer but a high Roman official concerned with organisation and administration, the 4th book of which contained information on the art of fortification and engines of war. Their source seems to have been the book of Athanaios, a famous ancient Greek military engineer, on the subject.

From A.D. 98 to A.D.105, Traianus' engineer Gaius Iulius Lacer built one of the finest Roman bridges in the boldness of its conception and execution at Alcantara, in Spain, a city which lies on the road to Portugal. It is known as the Bridge of Alcantara, and it crosses the river ***Tagus***, which flows in a deep gorge, at a height of 130 feet (39.62 m). In spring floods the fierce waters of the ***Tagus*** have occasionally risen up to the arches of this bridge. The Alcantara bridge has an overall length of 627 feet (191.11 m), and a width of 26 feet (7.92 m). It has 6 spans of semi-circular arches made of granite ranging in span from 92 to 98 feet (28.04 to 29.87 m). The thickness of the piers is 29½ feet (8.99 m). The Alcantara bridge is of dry-masonry construction and it is the loftiest Roman bridge known. It is an exceptionally well preserved bridge which is still in use. The engineer Lacer built a chapel at one end of the bridge, in which he inscribed : "This bridge was built by famous Lacer with divine skill to stand forever through the centuries of the world (***Pontem perpetui mansuram in saeculi mundi fecit divina nobilis arte Lacer***)." Lacer was not boasting, he knew that he had built one of the finest bridges in the history of Roman Empire.

Traianus also had the longest known Roman bridge built in the 9th largest Roman city ***Augusta Emerita*** (modern Merida) in Iberia, Spain, which spans the ***Anas*** (modern Guadiana) river. This bridge consists of 64 granite arches with an average span of about 35 feet (10.67 m). The overall length of this bridge is 2,500 feet (762.00 m), almost ½ a mile (0.8 km), its width is 21 feet (6.40 m) and the average height is 33 feet (10.06 m). The Merida bridge has small relief arches over some piers, and it is still in service.

Traianus died on his return from his successful military expedition against Parthia in which he had advanced as far as the Persian Gulf.

Engineering of Emperor Hadrianus (ruled from A.D.117 to A.D.138)

Publius Aelius Hadrianus (in English, Hadrian) (A.D.76-138), who as an orphaned nephew of Traianus became a ward of his uncle, was educated in Rome, and under his uncle Traianus occupied high offices of the Roman Empire by being the Emperor's military and administrative assistant. After the death of Traianus he was proclaimed the next Emperor by the army for Hadrianus was Traianus' choice for his successor, and his appointment was ratified by the Roman Senate. Hadrianus had distinguished himself as a commander of the Roman legions by displaying great military skill and decisive commandership in the war, particularly in the Dacian campaign.

The autocratic Hadrianus was a most unusual Roman Emperor because he was a genuine gentleman, an intellectual in the ancient Greek tradition, and a passionate Græcophile. Hadrianus was educated by the leading Peripatetic Greek scholar and the celebrated author of the biographies of famous Greeks and Romans, Ploutarchos of Chaironeia (c.A.D.50-120). Hadrianus was called by Quintus Septimius Florens Tertullianus (c.A.D.160-230) "a universally curious explorer (***omnium curiositatum explorator***)." He spoke Greek as proficiently as Latin. He drew, painted and sculpted. He demonstrated his informed command of architecture, engineering, science, mathematics, literature and arts. He wrote poetry, and was a good singer. He was also a knowledgeable historian. In other words, Hadrianus was a scholar, philosopher, poet, artist, æsthete, and also an ***architectus***. Moreover, he was as scrupulous as Traianus, and proved to be an exceptionally gifted administrator who was blessed with an extraordinary memory, boundless energy, subtle imagination, excellent judgement, and great decisiveness. In other words, Hadrianus more than satisfied the Vitruvian requirements for an ***architectus***. It is likely that, as the trusted lieutenant and military assistant of

Traianus, Hadrianus took an active interest in the design of some of the outstanding structures built during the later period of the rule of Traianus.

Hadrianus was curiously modern, but unlike Traianus, simplicity was not one of his virtues. Hadrianus was a Græcophile who genuinely appreciated Greek culture, and he was the first Roman Emperor to wear a full Greek beard. However, Hadrianus, despite all his remarkable intelligence, had a chink in his armour: he became a great embarrassment to his wife Sabina, who was a grandniece of Traianus, by making himself ridiculous to the Roman public in his mania for a Greek youth from Bithynia, who ultimately committed suicide by drowning himself in the Nile river. By the time Hadrianus died of tuberculosis and dropsy in A.D.138, he was almost universally despised for this degrading affair and for the objectionable covert methods of his secret police, called ***frumentarii***, who were even spying on his own close friends. However, Hadrianus was quite competent as an architectural engineer, and he took an active part in the planning and overall design of many important structures built during his rule. Hadrianus reorganised the service to the State into military and civil branches, and appointed Salvius Iulianus in A.D. 131 to codify all the Roman laws into a single Roman Law Code (***Edicta perpetua***) which Hadrianus made the foundation of all legal decisions throughout the Roman Empire.

One of the finest and most remarkable Roman building is the ***Pantheon*** in Rome, which was designed by Hadrianus and his engineer Apollodorus of Damascus and built from A.D.120 to A.D.124. It consists of a rotunda and an entrance portico. In this building, for the first time, all the architectural emphasis was placed on the interior and not on the exterior design composition which was typical of Greek buildings. Hadrianus constructed his rotunda directly over the rotunda of the original ***Pantheon***, which had been built in 25 B.C. by Agrippa's assistant engineer Valerius of ***Ostia*** in honour of Agrippa's naval victory over the naval forces of Marcus Antonius (c.83-30 B.C.) at ***Actium***, but it had burnt down twice, for the first time in A.D. 80 and again in A.D. 110. The new ***Pantheon Hadriani*** incorporated a number of unique and remarkable engineering features. The rotunda, which has a diameter of 142 feet (43.28 m) and a wall thickness of 20 feet (6.10 m), rests on a foundation in the form of a ring-beam made of concrete containing layers of basalt as inert aggregate. The ring-beam is more than 33 feet (10.06 m) wide and 14¾ feet (4.50 m) deep. The drum of the rotunda was provided with recesses in such a manner that the rotunda contains every conceivable type of buttress concealed within the wall of the drum which offer a safeguard against any possible horizontal thrust that may be exerted by the roof of the ***Pantheon***. Moreover, these recesses also facilitated the drying of the mortar and concrete in the thick wall.

The roof of the ***Pantheon*** is a huge dome which has an internal base diameter of 142 ½ feet (43.43 m). In order to minimise its outward expansion and the turning moment it exerts on the structure, the dome incorporates an unglazed circular opening (***oculus***) of 30-foot (9.14 m) diameter at the apex of the dome which not only lit the interior of the ***Pantheon*** but also eliminated a great deal of dead weight at the center of the dome. Moreover, the thickness of the dome was reduced from 21 feet (6.40 m) at the support to 4 feet (1.22 m) at the central opening, and the entire dome was coffered in order to reduce its dead weight. Even the aggregate of the concrete within the dome was well graded to reduce the dead weight of the dome towards the center. The lower part of the dome has brick as aggregate, the middle part has alternate layers of tufa (a porous volcanic rock) and brick as aggregate, and the upper part has layers of tufa and pumice as the lightest aggregate. Since Roman engineers built non-shallow hemispherical domes, the dead weight of which exerted relatively small horizontal thrust against the support, although such domes were subjected to a large circumferential tension near the support. In order to reduce both, Apollodorus added stepped rings over ⅔ of the dome round the support which increased the thickness of the dome where this circumferential tension is the largest, and after the subsequent radial cracking of the dome into orange peel-like segments the stepped rings acted as continuous pinnacles of dead weight which directed the oblique thrust of the archlike cracked segments of the dome downwards. Owing to this technique of dome construction, Roman domes looked saucer-shaped from the outside whereas from the inside they looked spherical.

Hadrianus and Apollodorus used permanent brick or stone walls as formwork for the liquid lightweight concrete, which exerted considerable lateral pressure before hardening. In the second century A.D. the Roman engineers had learnt to construct niches and recesses in the walls of buildings which acted as buttresses to absorb the horizontal thrusts, and Apollodorus took full advantage of this type of buttressing in the structural wall rotunda of the ***Pantheon***. The roof over the entrance porch of ***Pantheon*** was supported by a 40-foot (11.8 m) long rivetted bronze roof truss erected by Apollodorus, which was melted down by the order of Pope Urban VIII in A.D. 1625 for the purpose of casting a bronze cannon for the defence of Rome.

The ingenious structural design of ***Pantheon*** exhibits an exceptional intuitive appreciation of structural mechanics by Apollodorus. ***Pantheon***, which was converted into a Christian Church in A.D. 609, is the most perfectly preserved classical building in Rome, and it is still in use today as the 'Church of Santa Maria Rotunda'. This structure is now known as the ***Castel Sant'Angelo***.

Roman concrete allowed Roman engineers to build vaults of unprecedented large spans which were not surpassed until the introduction of steel as building material. The dome of the ***Pantheon*** remained unequalled until the 143-foot (43.59 m) ***Duomo*** of Florence was built of masonry by the Renaissance engineer Brunelleschi in A.D. 1436, but by no other structure until the 19th century A.D.. Moreover, the use of lightweight concrete in structures by Roman engineers was economical of skilled labour, since Roman engineers always selected their building materials very carefully from the viewpoint of ease and economy in execution, and of engineering purpose. Roman buildings were constructed in a much shorter time than the Gothic cathedrals and the Renaissance buildings, structures erected many centuries later.

Hadrianus built a 3-tier aqueduct in ***Emerita Augustus*** (modern Merida) in Spain using a new kind of arch design in this structure: the slender piers of this aqueduct superstructure were arched over at the top and braced by lower jack-arches. This form of construction was also used in the Aqueduct of Cherchel in Algeria, North Africa, the 115-foot (35.05 m) tall piers of which have a concrete core and a permanent formwork in cut stone and brick facing.

Hadrianus built Rome's largest temple dedicated to ***Venus*** and ***Roma Aeterna*** from A.D.123 to A.D.135. This temple, which had a size of 160 by 83 feet (48.77 by 25.30 m), had two separate cellas built back-to-back as a pun, for ***Venus*** was the goddess of love and ancestress of all Romans, and love in Latin language is ***amor***, that is, ***Roma*** spelt backwards. This huge temple facing in two opposite directions was designed by Apollodorus of Damascus and Emperor Hadrianus. It has been reported that the autocratic Hadrianus ordered Apollodorus executed after Apollodorus had put a professional slight upon Hadrianus' design suggestions for this dual temple.

Hadrianus built over many years a huge villa complex, a veritable town occupying 180 acres (72.9 hectares), located 15 miles (24.1 km) from Rome in ***Tibur*** (modern Tivoli), that was popularly known as 'Hadrian's Folly'. The spectacular villa of Hadrianus had a 600 by 1,000 yards (548.64 by 914.40 m) ground plan and occupied about 7 square miles (11.3 square km) of land. It was essentially a large park containing a skilfully connected loose complex of large and small palaces, an island villa surrounded by a moat, guest quarters, dining rooms, baths, a number of large halls, pools, a wrestling ground, a stadium, a library, porticos, slave quarters, barracks for military units and firemen, and a vaulted temple of ***Sarapeis***. It outdid Nero's 'Golden House' in opulence and exhibited an extravagance untrammelled by limitations of cost or engineering. Hadrianus had planned his sprawling villas as an empire in miniature in his private possession. Despite its opulence, Hadrianus' villa was an entirely modern building design motivated by the lightness of structural and architectural design. This villa, which was intended as a winter palace, was almost finished when Hadrianus returned in A.D. 134 to Italy, after spending 13 long years in travelling through the Roman provinces. He died from dropsy 4 years later, before the final completion of this enormous project.

Hadrianus, the great consolidator of Roman Empire, built defensive military walls at the vulnerable parts of the outlying frontiers of the Roman Empire: the so-called 'Hadrian's Wall' (***Vallum Hadriani***), which runs 73½ miles (118.3 km) across the British Isle, was built to keep out the savage Scots and Picts from the Roman Britain. 'Hadrian's Wall' was 20 feet (6.10 m) high, and in places 10 feet (3.05 m) thick. It incorporated 17 forts distributed along its entire length with castles located at every mile (1.6 km) between them. From A.D. 140 to A.D.142, after the death of

Hadrianus, the next Emperor Titus Aurelius Fulvus Boionus Arrius Antoninus, known as Emperor Antoninus Pius [Antoninus the Good] (A.D. 86-161) built another defensive wall, called 'Antoninus' Wall' (***Vallum Antonini***), across the British Isle about 75 miles (121 km) north of Hadrianus' wall. This wall was 37 miles (59.5 km) long, had a ditch to the north, and 19 forts on the southern side. It was abandoned about A.D. 185. Emperor Antoninus Pius was Hadrianus' choice for his successor because Pius had distinguished himself with exceptional ability and integrity that made him as good and as capable an Emperor as Traianus. In a temple built during his reign 3 huge stone blocks of the dimensions 63 by 13 by 10 feet (19.2 by 4.0 by 3.0 m), a record size for any building, were incorporated into its structure.

A 170-mile (273.6 km) long enceinte from the river ***Danuvius*** (modern Danube) north of the modern Ingolstadt, to the ***Moenus*** (modern Main) river, and a 120-mile (193 km) long enceinte from the modern city Frankfurt to the ***Rhinus*** (modern Rhine) river near the city ***Bonna*** (modern, Bonn) as a continuation of the ***limes*** (defensive wall) was built to keep out the fierce Germanic tribes. In Hadrianus' times ***limes*** was constructed as a wooden palisade.

From A.D. 117 to A.D.138, Hadrianus built with his engineer Messius Rusticus the bridge ***Pons Aelius***, now called 'Ponte St. Angelo', which served as an access to Hadrianus' Mausoleum (now called ***Castel Sant'Angelo***) located across the Tiber river. This bridge originally had 3 main arches of 62-foot (18.90 m) span, and 2 smaller arches of 26-foot (7.92 m) span at one end and 3 at the other end of the bridge. Two of the 3 smaller arches are now buried in the embankment. The piers of the bridge are 21½ feet (6.55 m) thick and 50 feet (15.24 m) high. The foundations of the piers of this bridge, which are set on a veritable forest of piles driven to the bedrock, were constructed within cofferdams. The dressed stones of the piers are anchored in all directions with stone keys and metal clamps set in lead. The foundations of this bridge are still in excellent condition and the bridge is still in service.

In about A.D. 305, the Emperor Diocletianus (in English, Diocletian) built his grandiose palace in ***Spalato*** (modern Split in Croatia) which was a vast fortresslike rectangular structure of the size 698 by 592 feet (212.75 by 180.4 m). It had many structural features that influenced later Byzantine structures such as arcades which spring directly from the capitals of slender columns. This arcade demonstrates that the Roman engineers had clearly recognised that the horizontal thrusts of continuous arches are mutually balanced, and that only the vertical reactions have to be supported by the columns. This principle had already been used in the design of the large cross-barrel vaults in the palatial Public Baths of Caracalla and of Diocletianus, in which the thrusts of the contiguous intersecting cross-barrel vaults mutually balanced each other and buttresses were only used to resist the thrusts acting in directions in which there were no contiguous cross-barrel vaults. This principle was rediscovered at close of the Middle Ages by the Italian engineer Taddeo Gaddi, and independently by a French engineer Jean-Rodolphe Perronet (A.D.1708-1794) in the 17th century. The very beginnings of the Byzantine, the Romanesque, and even the Gothic style of buildings were laid down in the design of the palace of Diocletianus.

A second novel structural feature was incorporated in the Mausoleum of Diocletianus which stood within the confines of the palace. Its roof was a hemispherical dome consisting of two contiguous shells of brickwork, each about 1 foot (0.30 m) thick, the inner shell of which was entirely made of brick arches arranged in a fish-scale fashion. This dome design represented the ultimate achievement in Roman vaulting and it anticipated Byzantine construction in which massive Roman concrete was replaced by a wide-jointed brickwork. Parts of the palace of Diocletianus have survived and are currently used as a museum.

In A.D.313, the ***Basilica Nova*** of Maxentius was built in Rome. Its roof consisted of a cross-vaulted structure in brick and concrete. This Basilica, which served as a model for mediæval cathedral builders, was begun under the usurper Emperor Maxentius but it was finished in A.D.313 by the first Christian Emperor Constantinus (in English, Constantine the Great) of Roman Empire, who defeated Maxentius in the civil war for the throne of the Roman Empire. Basilica was a Roman law court, a main business center and an official meeting place.

The Basilica which Maxentius and Constantinus built in Rome contained novel so-called 'flying buttresses' which much later, during the Mediæval Age, came into structural prominence in the Gothic Cathedrals.

About A.D. 530 the Mausoleum of Theodoric was built in Ravenna, Italy. Theodoric was an Ostrogoth and a remarkably able and intelligent King in the Western Roman Empire. His mausoleum has a monolithic shallow dome roof with a base diameter of 35 feet (10.67 m) which was hollowed out of an Istrian limestone monolith and provided with 12 stone bosses for lifting. The cylindrical wall on which this dome rests has indented and interlocking stone arches over the door and the windows to resist earthquakes.

Water Power

Manpower was the basis of all economy in antiquity and in ancient Rome. Until the late Roman period in the 4th century A.D., there was no urgent need in the Roman world to use hydraulic power, for the abundant manpower was definitely preferred. For instance, Emperor Vespasianus (in English, Vespasian) (A.D.69-79) gave a reward to a mechanical engineer who invented a water-driven hoist to lift heavy columns which afforded a cheaper way to transport such building material, but Vespasianus refused to make use of it because he did not want to take from the poor the work that fed them: "... lest the poor have no work." Therefore, the huge derricks, such as the so-called

trispastos with 3 pulleys in the tackle, still was operated by human muscles, or by men in the treadmill, very seldom by animals, and virtually never by hydraulic power.

The use of hydraulic power for practical purposes began in the late Roman period and led without a break to the complex hydraulic machinery of later times. In order to raise water the Romans used, besides the pump, the water screw and the ***noria***, a huge paddle-operated wheel with buckets. The Hellenistic engineers had converted the primitive ***noria*** used by the Caucasian mountain people for lifting water, to a horizontal impulse-wheel for grinding corn but it was much too slow for its efficient operation, and it was only able to develop between ½ and 1 horsepower (373 and 746 Watts). The Roman engineers converted this simple impulse-wheel into a waterwheel by means of mechanical transmission of power which made it into a more efficient vertical waterwheel machinery, or the water-mill. The water-mill with horizontal axle the power of which was transmitted at right angles through the pinion-and-lantern gearing of Archimedes was a quite sophisticated invention. Its appearance in the middle of the first century B.C. marks the very beginning of power engineering.

The Roman engineer and man of learning, Marcus Vitruvius Pollio (known as Vitruvius), who flourished about 30 B.C., wrote the most influential engineering work of antiquity entitled <On Architecture> (***De architectura***), which served as a standard reference work to Renaissance engineers such as Alberti and Palladio. In Rome the title ***architectus*** stood for a builder-contractor-engineer. In this book Vitruvius described for the first time a waterwheel as a continuous power source, the so-called 'Vitruvian Mill', which was a significant advance in power engineering. It was a geared version of a Greek water-mill consisting of the horizontal impulse-wheel with a vertical axle which was turned through a right angle to set the axle horizontal. The rotation about the horizontal axle was transmitted through right angle by a pinion-and-lantern gearing in the ratio of 1-to-5 to a rotating vertical shaft. The vertical shaft was attached to the grinding stone and the speeded-up rotation of the grinding stone was essential for the proper and efficient grinding of corn. This water-mill was capable of developing between 3 and 5 horsepower (2,237 to 3,728 Watts). The Vitruvian Mill is the first important prime mover using natural power, and the first important achievement in continuously powered machinery, which gave a significant beginning to power engineering.

Vitruvius' waterwheel was undershot which is not as efficient as the overshot waterwheel, because in the latter the weight of the water assists in turning the wheel. The Mediterranean rivers are not as favourable for waterwheels as the rivers in northern Europe because they carry widely fluctuating seasonal quantities of water. It is difficult to use the undershot waterwheel in a sluggish river with fluctuating level, because it works efficiently only in swiftly flowing rivers with nearly constant volume of discharge. The overshot waterwheel requires a well directed and regulated water supply, usually collected in a millpond by aqueducts, and then delivered through a sluice to a millrace and chute properly set for the correct impact of water on the top of the wheel. Therefore, millponds and control weirs were often constructed to provide a constant discharge of water. The output of energy by the Vitruvian Mill was considerably higher than that of any machine powered by men or beasts.

In A.D. 216 watermills were constructed in the ***Thermae Caracalla*** in Rome, to utilise the water used in this public bath for the milling of grain. There also existed an undershot 6-foot (1.83 m) diameter waterwheel at ***Venairo*** on the Tuliverno river, near ***Neapolis*** (modern Naples), which was fed by an aqueduct. It produced about 3 horsepower (2,237 Watts) and its millstones revolving at about 46 rpm ground about 360 pounds (163 kg) of flour an hour, which was many times more than the production of a donkey mill.

Between A.D.308 and A.D.316, the most efficient watermill, not common in the Roman Empire, was used in a large flour mill at ***Barbegal***, 5 miles (8 km) from ***Arelate*** (modern Arles), in Gaul (modern France) which ground flour for the Roman army. This mill had two sets of 8 overshot waterwheels of 7 feet 3 inches (2.20 m) diameter, 2 feet 4 inches (0.70 m) width, with wooden gear-wheels fixed with lead to iron axles, which turned 16 pairs of millstones. The waterwheels were fed with a constant stream of water from a brick and concrete aqueduct of ***Les Baux*** which collected water from the ***Arcoule***, the valley of ***Les Baux***, and the well of ***Manville***. The ***Les Baux*** aqueduct had a channel 6½ feet (1.98 m) wide and 18 feet 5 inches (5.61 m) deep, with a 30° degree slope at ***Barbegal*** where it doubled. The 8 pairs of waterwheels were built on a 30° slope into a cascade, each pair lower than the previous pair, over a total drop in the elevation equal to 61 feet (18.60 m). The water conduits ran down on both sides of the flour factory turning waterwheels on both sides. A millpond for water distribution was located on top of the hill with two sluices for both channels. This flour factory produced 28 tons of flour in a 10-hour day which was sufficient to feed 80,000 men. ***Arelate*** had a population of only 10,000 at a time, and it evidently was an important harbour supplying corn to Rome. It seems that this flour mill was built by the well-known engineer of machinery, Quintus Candidus Benignus. There seems to have existed similar flour mills at ***Pistriacum*** (modern, Prety) and near ***Tournus*** in Burgundy, which milled the corn grown in the Saône valley and supplied flour to the Roman army in the northern Gaul.

From A.D. 457 to A.D.474, an overshot waterwheel was built in the marketplace (***agora***) of Athens. The waterwheel had a diameter of 10 feet (3.05 m) and turned two sets of millstones. It had a wooden axle that was 11½ feet (3.51 m) long, and it turned in wooden bearings. This mill had a race with a single trap, and the millrace and the flume were 4½ feet (1.37 m) above the waterwheel.

There are indications that by A.D. 379 the Romans might have used water-driven saws to cut stone on the Ruwer at the Moselle river. It is also likely that in the 4th century A.D. watermills were used on the Ianiculum hill in Rome for which the water was supplied by ***Aqua Traiana***.

In A.D. 537, the Commander of the army of the Byzantine Emperor Iustinianus, General Belisarius, and his engineers devised the so-called 'floating mill'. When Germanic warriors Goths who besieged Rome cut the aqueducts to Rome, Belisarius stretched a hawser across the Tiber river and moored barges in pairs to it; a waterwheel was hung between each pair of barges, and connected by gearing to millstones on the barges, thereby solving the acute problem of milling flour for the population of Rome and for the army of Belisarius. The 'floating mill' is less dependent on the water level of the river, and, therefore, it is not so much influenced by the fluctuations in the flow of the river.

The ancient people, in general, were very reluctant to use the power of nature, because they believed in the animated character of nature. They believed the water to be the domain of water-nymphs and their supernatural powers, and ancient men never dared to harness the supernatural powers because such an attempt would have appeared to them as an intrusion on the privilege of the gods. The harnessing of the powers of nature had to wait for the advent of the Christians who had no pagan animistic beliefs about nature.

When Rome finally did fall, the last obstacle to natural power development vanished with it, because the pagan animism died in the West with the Roman State.

Roman Canals and Harbours

Canals did not play an important role in Roman Italy, because the Italian Peninsula is mountainous and its rivers are short. There is known to have existed an old canal beginning at Forum Apii, about 43 miles (69.2 km) from Rome, and running almost parallel to the Appian Way to ***Tarracina***. The first canal dug outside of Italy was the ***Fossa Mariana***, named after Gaius Marius (c.155 B.C.-86 B.C.), which was excavated in 101 B.C. in the delta of the Rhône river in Roman Gaul in order to facilitate navigation. Romans also undertook dredging and excavation work to improve the navigability of the Rhine river for military purposes. They established many naval stations at Mainz, Coblenz, and Cologne in the present Germany. The river bed of the Rhine river was maintained strong and clear by building embankments from 13 B.C. to A.D. 47. Navigation in the Tiber river in Italy required constant supervision under special curators.

If bridges and roads were mainly built for military purposes it was even more true of harbours, since many harbours were created directly for military needs. Romans became great harbour builders because there were virtually no natural deep-sea harbours in Italy, except in the ***Sinus Cumanus***, (modern, Bay of Naples). ***Puteoli*** in the ***Sinus Cumanus***, a natural harbour, had been the principal harbour of Rome until it was superseded by ***Ostia***. Tradition has it that King Ancus Marcius, who allegedly built the ***Pons Sublicius***, founded a Roman colony at the mouth of the Tiber river in the 7th century B.C. and named it ***Ostia*** (meaning 'entrance'), which during the

Punic Wars became a naval station. As the city of Rome grew, ***Ostia*** became its main port for the shipment of grain from abroad. In all imported goods ***Ostia*** competed with ***Puteoli*** as a port of Rome, because harbour of ***Puteoli*** was deeper and safer and, therefore, was preferred for more expensive and valuable cargoes.

In 218 B.C. during the Punic Wars the Scipio brothers built a harbour in ***Tarraco*** (modern, Tarragona) in Spain as a maritime base against the Carthaginians.

In 37 B.C., Marcus Agrippa became the supervisor of the organisation of the fleet of Octavianus (who later became the first Roman Emperor Augustus) in the Roman Civil Wars. In this capacity Agrippa built a naval station in ***Misenium***, a little bay at the tip of a small promontory in the ***Sinus Cumanus*** in order to allow the Octavian fleet to control the Tyrrhenian Sea. He built a subterranean reservoir of fresh drinking water, the so-called ***Piscina Mirabilis***, an enormous rectangular tank 225 feet 7 inches by 83 feet 7 inches (68.76 by 25.48 m) in base and 4feet 3 inches (15.00 m) high, which was supported by 48 pilasters arranged in 4 rows along the length of the reservoir. It had a capacity of 444,623 cubic feet (12,590 cubic meters).

In 36 B.C., Agrippa built a naval port, the ***Portus Iulius***, in Lake ***Avernus*** which lies about ⅔ miles (1 km) west of ***Cumae*** and about ½ a mile (0.8 km) north of the Lake ***Lucrinus***. The Lake ***Avernus*** is an old extinct crater which has a circumference of nearly 2 miles (3.2 km), a depth of about 200 feet (60.96 m), and precipitous banks that were covered with thick woods in ancient times. Agrippa cut the trees, drove a large tunnel accommodating 2-way traffic which was lit by daylight through 6 vertical or inclined shafts and contained an aqueduct with its own ventilation shafts and adits, to connect Lake ***Avernus*** with the city of ***Cumae***, and cut a wide navigable canal to Lake ***Lucrinus*** as a waterway to the ***Portus Iulius*** in the Lake ***Avernus***. He built a mole in the Lake ***Lucrinus*** to protect the new dockyards of ***Portus Iulius*** which he constructed in a small bay of this lake. Another tunnel, 660 feet (201.17 m) long, 12⅓ feet (3.78 m) wide, and 13 (3.96 m) feet high, without light shafts was later driven from Lake ***Avernus*** to Lake ***Lucrinus*** to provide a secret passage between these two lakes. In these maritime constructions Agrippa's resident engineer was Cocceius Auctus.

The old harbour of ***Ostia*** was not improved until the rule of Emperor Claudius, when public riots broke out as result of the grain shortages in Rome which occurred because of inadequate harbour facilities in ***Ostia***. Emperor Claudius sponsored the enlargement of the harbour of ***Ostia*** so that large ships could enter this harbour also in the winter and anchor safely within it. For this purpose Claudius had a new harbour built at a short distance from ***Ostia*** across the mouth of the Tiber river, because silting had over the years moved the shoreline seaward from ***Ostia*** proper, and made the old ***Ostia*** harbour too shallow for bigger ships. The ***Portus Claudius*** consisted of 2 curved jetties, which were built out from the shoreline and almost closed in a semicircle. In the opening between the two jetties a man-made island, a wavebreaker, with a 7-story lighthouse 200 feet (60.96 m) high was constructed to shield the harbour from the rough sea. The foundation of this island was made by sinking a large ship, earlier used to transport an Egyptian obelisk to Rome, filled with concrete. The entire harbour basin was excavated out of the mouth of the Tiber which had a useful water surface area of 803,337 square feet (74,630 square meters), and a depth from 15 to 18 feet (4.57 to 5.49 m). Unfortunately, this wavebreaker was ill placed because it was located almost along the curved centerline of the two jetties which exposed both of the harbour inlets to the full force of the wave action. The incorrect position of the wavebreaker had been chosen against the advice of the chief engineer. It took a 30,000-man workforce 11 years to build this harbour.

Harbours similar to ***Portus Claudius*** were built in other parts of the Mediterranean. Another famous port of this type was built over a 10 year period by ***Herodes*** (in English, Herod the Great) (c.73-4B.C.), King of Judea, in his new city ***Caesarea Philippi*** inaugurated in 9 B.C..

In A.D.62 a violent storm sank almost 200 ships in the ***Portus Claudius*** which convinced everybody that this harbour was unsafe, but it was Emperor Traianus, who much later undertook to build a safe inner harbour in ***Portus Claudius***. He excavated a hexagonal basin, with a surface area of 3.5 million square feet (0.33 million square meters) and a depth of 18 feet (5.5 m) and a supply canal, and built various harbour installations such as warehouses, an arsenal and a market. The inner harbour of Traianus proved to be a masterpiece of naval construction. He also built the excellent harbour of ***Ancona*** at the Adriatic sea.

The harbour of ***Puteoli*** had a breakwater of an original design to avoid swells. It consisted of two parallel arcades with a space between them arranged in such a manner that the arches of one arcade were in line with the piers of the other arcade, so that no wave could directly sweep through both arcades. The opening in the arcades dissipated the impact of the waves on the structure.

Most Roman harbours had lighthouses similar to the Pharos in Alexandria, but were smaller and more functionally designed. The lighthouse at ***Ostia*** was 7 storeys high; the lighthouse of Bologne in Gaul was a 12 storeys high octagonal structure of about 65-foot (19.81 m) base diameter; the lighthouse at ***Freius*** was about 75-foot (22.86 m) high circular structure of about 35-foot (10.67 m) diameter at the base.

The Romans built extensive masonry works below the water level, and the soundness of their marine structures was a result of their use of pozzuolana concrete, which set rock-hard under water. Romans employed cofferdams in their marine construction as the accuracy and refinement of their subaqueous stoneworks indicate. It is evident that Romans were able to drive heavy piles to build their cofferdams, and pump water in vast quantities.

Roman Dams

Romans were able to build many large dams, some of which were of enormous size, all over the Roman empire, because they had the talent to organise and administer enormous engineering projects and to overcome all technical problems with common sense and practical efficiency. Before Romans, the ancient people in general did not build dams to store water during the rainy season in great reservoirs in order to use this water in the dry season. Apparently as long as the required amount of irrigation could be obtained with diversion dams across rivers or valleys, the ancient people did not build more elaborate hydraulic structures. Therefore, their dams were relatively small in size. The Romans changed all this by finding new uses for the dams in which the size of dams increased dramatically. In all their dam designs, Roman engineers paid close attention to the important problems of hydraulic engineering such as percolation, erosion, spillway design, proper materials, and superior methods of construction. Dams were primarily built by Romans to divert and store the water.

Only 3 of the large dams that the Romans built were in Italy. In the vicinity of Emperor Nero's villa at the river ***Anio*** (now, Aniene) in the gorge above ***Subiaco***, Nero ordered 3 dams constructed across the river to create 3 artificial lakes the purpose of which was purely recreational. The middle dam of the 3 dams, built directly at the villa of Nero, was the highest dam ever constructed by the Romans. This dam had a height of about 164 feet (50 m), the highest dam in the world, and no comparable dam was built until some 1,500 years later. This dam must have been an arch-dam because the gorge at this location was too narrow for a gravity dam to be effective. It is assumed that the crest of the dam was 44 feet (13.41 m) thick, sloping towards the middle, and tiled for the normal overflow. One of the recreational lakes created by the 3 dams were later made useful by Emperor Traianus, when he ordered the intake of ***Aqua Anio Novus***, a defective aqueduct which originally drew its rather turbid water directly from the river ***Anio***, to be placed in the artificial lake lying above the former villa of Nero, where the river was at its clearest. This large dam collapsed in A.D.1305 because two monks had removed some stones in the dam to lower the level of the lake which had been flooding their fields.

The oldest known arch dam was constructed by the Romans in the town ***Glanum*** in Gaul, near the modern St.-Remy-de-Provence, which may have been constructed in the first century B.C.. This curved dam was about 20 feet (6.10 m) high, 12 feet (3.66 m) thick, and it stood in a valley which was deep and narrow.

Another arched dam was built by Romans in North Africa at Kasserine, about 135 miles (217.3 km) southwest of the present Tunis. This irrigation dam had the length of 500 feet (152.40 m), and the height of 32.8 feet (10.00 m). It had a rubble-and-earth core, and was faced with fitted masonry blocks bound with mortar. The water-face of the dam was vertical, whereas the air-face was stepped through 6 courses of masonry at the top and vertical below this, a distance of some 12½ feet (3.81 m). The dam was evidently designed to spill the overflow over the crest, as the top of the dam was faced with stones set in mortar to prevent scour. This dam was built in the second century A.D.. Romans built many other dams in North Africa for the purpose of flood control, water retention and soil conservation.

Many excellent dams were constructed by Romans in Spain. The Cornalvo dam in Merida was built to collect the water of the Albarregas river. It is 656 feet (199.95 m) long and 66 feet (20.12 m) high; the maximum base thickness is about 200 feet (61.00 m) near the center of the embankment, and its crest widens from 22 feet (6.71 m) at one end to over 40 feet (12.20 m) at the other. The profile of this earthen dam is trapezoidal, the air face slope is 1-to-3 and the water face slope is 2-to-3. The internal structure of the dam consists of longitudinal and transverse masonry walls dividing the dam into deep masonry boxes, which were filled with stones and clay and then covered with earth. Masonry facing was provided on the upstream side. This dam was rebuilt in A.D.1936.

The Prosperina dam is another Roman dam in Merida, located about 4 miles (6.4 m) north of the town. It collects the water of a small river to form a reservoir which has a perimeter of about 3 miles (4.8 km) when full. This dam has a length of 1,400 feet (426.72 m), a height of 40 feet (12.19 m) near the middle, and it is built of concrete, masonry and earth. On the upstream side of the dam is a thick wall. Its core is of concrete, and it is faced with large masonry blocks. The water-face of the wall slopes at 6° to the vertical, whereas the downstream face is vertical. The wall penetrates some 20 feet (6.10 m) into the foundation, so the total height of the wall is about 60 feet (18.29 m). The crest thickness of the wall is about 12½ feet (3.81 m). The 200-foot (60.96 m) earth embankment behind the wall supported the wall in resisting the water pressure. It is a buttressed dam. The masonry wall on the water side was provided with 9 buttresses as otherwise the earth might have toppled the wall into the empty basin. The buttresses are 2½ feet (0.76 m) wide and project from 3 feet (0.91 m) at the top to 12 feet (3.66 m) in the bottom. The Prosperina dam probably was built during Hadrianus' rule, and it is still in use. Since Cornalvo dam uses more sophisticated structural features it must be a later dam. These two Merida dams are the finest Roman dams to survive.

In A.D. 284, the Emperor Diocletianus had a dam built across the Orontes river in Palestine near the present city Homs, thus creating a large reservoir, the artificial Lake of Homs, which was 6 miles (2.66 km) long and 2½ miles (4 km) wide. It was the largest artificial lake in the world at the time. The collected water in the Lake Homs was used for irrigation around Homs and for water supply. When this Roman dam was reconstructed in A.D. 1934 after 1,700 years of use, it proved to have been a remarkable engineering success, for it had accumulated virtually no silt behind the dam after 17 centuries of use. This huge reservoir was initially tapped by a single canal at its eastern bank. It was a masonry dam bound by mortar and filled with rubble. The Orontes dam had variable dimensions: its greatest height was about 20 feet (6.10 m), and the greatest thickness was 23 feet (7.01 m) at the crest and perhaps as much as 66 feet (20.12 m) at the base, and its masonry wall had slightly tapered faces. Its water-face was steeply inclined whereas, typically, the air-face was stepped in large increments.

Mechanical Engineering of Romans

The second known crank mechanisms and the first known flywheel were used in two enormous ceremonial barges belonging to the Roman emperors. These barges, the larger one being 240 feet (73.15 m) long and having a 78-foot (23.77 m) beam, appears to have been constructed between 55 B.C. and A.D.31. It is known that Emperor Caligula was in possession of these barges during his reign from A.D.37 to A.D.41. These barges were discovered in the bottom of Lake ***Nemorensis*** (modern Lake Nemi), in A.D.1444, and a few years later the Renaissance engineer Leon Battista Alberti (A.D. 1404-1472) made an unsuccessful attempt to raise the two barges to the surface. Finally, between A.D.1927 and A.D.1932, Lake ***Nemorensis*** was drained by means of an ancient Roman drainage tunnel, and the two large barges were finally recovered.

These barges contained two endless chain-bucket bilge pumps operated by cranks which were fixed to solid wooden flywheels. These two ships also contained turntables. One such turntable was supported by 8 bronze balls, each had a pair of trunnions set into journals. Another turntable was supported by 8 conical wooden rollers set into journals.

There still exists a wagon made in northern Europe in the first century B.C., the wheels of which were supported by cylindrical wooden roller bearings.

Streetlighting

The first streetlighting was provided in A.D.450 in the city of ***Antiochia*** in Palestine.

Textile Technology

In weaving the warp-weighted loom was developed in prehistoric Europe, the horizontal loom in ancient Egypt and the vertical loom in ancient Syria. In the course of the first two centuries A.D new weaving techniques were devised in Mesopotamia and Syria such as weaving of weft twills in wool with the aid of a third harness added to the horizontal loom, and reweaving of imported silks with the introduction of the draw-loom, significant improvements in weaving which soon led the textile production in the Roman near-east to assume almost an industrial stage.

***Fons et Origo* of Christendom**

The inception of Christendom in the West began with the defeat of Maxentius, son of the former co-Emperor Maximianus, by Flavius Valerius Aurelius Constantinus (popularly known as Constantine the Great) in three battles of the civil war in A.D.312, the last battle of which Constantinus won in the name of Christianity near the Milvian Bridge with the Christian monogram χ emblazoned on his military standards, after having dreamt about a vision of a giant flaming cross in the sky with the inscription: ***In hoc signo vince*** (meaning : By this sign conquer). This experience motivated Constantinus to convert to Christian faith in A.D.313 in ***Mediolanum*** (modern Milan) by which time he had become the sole Emperor of the Western half of the Roman Empire. Emperor Diocletianus, a son of slaves and a ruthless autocratic persecutor of Christians, had divided the Roman Empire for administrative purposes into two parts, the Western and the Eastern part, which he ruled under the official doctrine of divine right of the Emperor jointly with his friend Maximianus. Diocletianus, himself, ruled the Eastern part of the Empire, where the greatest resources of the Empire lay, as its ***augustus***, and Maximianus ruled the Western part as its ***augustus***, although Diocletianus retained veto power to himself as the senior ***augustus***. Each ***augustus*** had a deputy, called the ***caesar*** as the heir-apparent, which completed the tetrarchy of the Roman Empire. Diocletianus, who was the first Roman Emperor to abdicate voluntarily, did so in A.D.305, and persuaded Maximianus to do likewise. He had particularly planned the tetrarchy to ensure sound rule and orderly succession, since the two ***caesars*** were the son-in-laws of the respective ***augusti***. Constantius, a skilful general, an efficient ruler and a son-in-law of Maximianus was the ***caesar*** of the Western part of the Empire, whereas Galerius, also a skilful general and a son-in-law of Diocletianus, was the ***caesar*** of the Eastern part. Upon the retirement of the two original ***augusti***, Constantius and Galerius became the two new ***augusti***. Whilst Galerius continued the vigorous persecution of Christians carried on by Diocletianus, Constantius was tolerant and left the Christians alone. Upon the death of Constantius in A.D.306 the succession in the West was thrown into disorder. Constantinus, the son of Constantius, a distinguished and humane general, was declared ***augustus*** of the Western part by his troops. Maxentius, who had been passed over in the naming of the ***caesars*** by his father Maximianus, was declared ***augustus*** by the Praetorian Guards in Rome. Galerius appointed his lieutenant Licinius as the lawful ***augustus*** of the East. After Galerius died in A.D.311, Constantinus defeated Maxentius as his major rival in A.D.312, and Licinius, who had succeeded Galerius as the ***augustus*** of the Eastern part of the Empire, in A.D. 324. Thus Constantinus reunited the Roman Empire in A.D.324 for the first time since its division by Diocletianus in A.D.286, and became the sole Emperor and the first Christian ruler of the Roman Empire.

Since the city of Rome was no longer the political, or geographic center of the Roman Empire, Constantinus built a 'New Rome' in the Greek fishing port Byzantium (in Greek, Byzantion), which was a replica of the old city of Rome on the Tiberis because it also had 7 hills and 14 regions and was located on the Strait of Bosporus where the West meets the East.

Constantinus ruled the Roman Empire from his new capital city, the 'New Rome', which after its founding ceremonies in A.D. 330 was renamed ***Constantinopolis*** (City of Constantinus) when it became the seat of power of the Byzantine Empire after the final separation of the Roman Empire into the Western and the Eastern Empire.

The reunification of the Roman Empire by Constantinus successfully infused the Western Germanic tribal vigour with the Eastern spirituality, for the Eastern part was much more extensively Christianised than the Western part. The embracing of the Christian faith by the Emperor Constantinus and his official edict of toleration in A.D.313, which not only ensured freedom of conscience throughout the Empire but also made Christianity acceptable to the Roman society, had important consequences to the later European civilisation, since Christian religion had been the only religion which had been banned for being subversive to the Roman State. When Constantinus came to power only the cult of God Mithras, a late version of Persian Zoroastrianism in which Mithras, a deity of truth and light, was a serious competitor to Christianity. This cult was a vigorous man's religion which divided the world between good and evil, and in which a battle between the powers of light and powers of darkness takes place. Some of its tenets and rites were quite similar to those of the Christian religion, and its adherents had joined Mithras to do battle against evil. Owing to its emphasis of combat for the cause of good, the cult of Mithras had become almost the unofficial religion of the Roman army by the time of Constantinus. Also, by that time Christianity had become less doctrinaire, so much so that it was openly conceded that one can be both a good Christian and a good Roman citizen.

The spread of Christian religion in the Roman Empire brought great changes in the way Romans regarded individual men. Under the influence of the pagan religions, Romans had treated poor people as victims of the gods, in which poverty of the poor was considered as punishment meted out by the gods for reasons unknown to men. The first change in this attitude of the Romans was brought about by the Stoics who proclaimed the universal brotherhood of man (***koinonia***) and urged people to cultivate philanthropy (***philantropia***) and humaneness (***sympatheia***) towards their poor and weak brethren. Since Stoicism was a rather ascetic philosophy with stern ethics by means of which man had to remain indifferent to, and unperturbed (***ataraxia***) by his lot in order to give him some sense of autarky (***autarkeia***), it had little appeal to the common Roman, but it had become the dominant ethical gospel of many educated and cultured Romans before the advent of Christianity. However, before Christianity, Stoicism did promote brotherly concern and generosity between all men, and declare natural equality (***homonoia***) of all human beings. Christianity went much farther than Stoicism by preaching ***caritas*** which meant much more than friendliness and hospitality towards one's fellow men: it implied that man has to value his fellow-man as he values himself, that is, he has to love his neighbour as he loves himself. Ancient Greeks had a tragic view of life that saw the gods as inscrutable and inexorable in their dealings with men. Christianity alleviated this tragic view of life by teaching Christian believers to have the serenity to accept their fate, no matter how intolerable it may be, because it can be spiritually ennobling.

Although Constantinus was tolerant of all religions, his personal commitment to Christian beliefs influenced the growth of Christianity. Under the influence of his Christian beliefs, Constantinus abolished crucifixion; established laws to protect peasants and children from abuse; guaranteed humane treatment to prisoners and forbade branding of criminals on the face (in his own words a human face is created "in the likeness of divine beauty"); protested against gladiatorial displays as "bloody spectacles displeasing in a time of peace and quiet;" and instituted a weekly day of rest, the venerable day of the Sun (Sunday), when all shops, factories and law courts were required to be closed, all of which showed his social consciousness and genuinely decent attitude towards the poor, the weak, and the oppressed.

The growth of Christianity under the aegis of Constantinus brought with it greater emphasis on mercy and just dealings in Roman society. Conversion of pagan Romans to Christianity brought significant changes in their attitude towards working men and slaves. This new attitude emanated from the Christian proclamation of the dignity of all work, including manual work because in Christian religion, in contrast to the pagan religions, manual labour acquired real religious significance, for Jesus of Nazareth himself had done manual labour. Christian belief demanded that free craftsmen be accorded an honoured position in society, and that any industrious labourer, whether a freeman or a slave, be accorded respect for his diligent work. Constantinus confiscated the treasures of pagan temples and made Christianity into a State religion by uniting the church and the State. In this new arrangement Constantinus himself served as the head of the church (***pontifex maximus***) for external affairs. But even Christianity failed to unify completely the Roman Empire under Constantinus because of the dissension in the Christian Church over the nature of Jesus between the Arians, who regarded Jesus as not equal to God, and their opponents who regarded Jesus coeternal with God. Constantinus called the First Ecumenical Council at Nicae in A.D.325 into session under his leadership in an effort to resolve this disagreement. Although at this meeting the Doctrine of Trinity was formulated in order to achieve greater unity, still some Arians refused to accept this doctrine, and the Christian Church remained divided over this question until A.D. 381 when the Christian Emperor Theodosius made heresy and paganism a crime, mostly because of the pagan rituals which Christians considered barbaric.

The Christian view of man had a profound effect on the Roman Civilisation, and after the Teutonic conquest of the Western Roman Empire it was reborn as the Christendom, the so-called 'Western Civilisation'.

Hellenistic Mathematics, Science and Engineering

The so-called 'Golden Age' of Greek mathematics came to its end with Archimedes of Syracuse and Apollonios of Perge, whose works besides rigorous deductive, geometric methods also contained quantitative methods useful to mensuration and astronomy. The mathematicians who came after these two men of genius were for a time able to maintain the high level of the classical Greek mathematics but most of their creative mathematical work was restricted to applied mathematics: trigonometry and sphærics as handmaidens of astronomy, mathematical geography, and mechanics. The works of Hipparchos of Nikaia, and of Heron of Alexandria were of this kind. In this respect, Alexandrian civilisation considerably broadened the scope of Greek mathematics, yet no works of brilliance comparable to those of Eudoxos, Archimedes and Apollonios were produced.

One of the most prominent applied mathematicians and astronomers of this period was Menelaos of Alexandria who was a contemporary of Ploutarchos of Chaironeia and is known to have made astronomical observations at Rome in A.D.98. He wrote a treatise in 3 books,< Sphaerics> (***Sphairika***) which was a substantial contribution to spherical geometry. It contained numerous new theorems in spherical geometry, among which was the theorem that the sum of the angles of a spherical triangle is greater than two right angles. He gave a fundamental theorem on the cross-ratio property of transversals drawn across a pencil of lines that is a veritable case of modern geometry.

During this time, the Alexandrian mathematicians were influenced by the earlier work of the Stoic philosopher Geminos of Rhodos, probably a pupil of Poseidonios of Apameia, who in his work < The Theory of Mathematics > (***Mathematon theorias***) probably issued in several books tried to give a complete overview of mathematics. He grouped mathematics into pure mathematics consisting of arithmetic and geometry, and applied mathematics consisting of mechanics, astronomy, optics, geodesy, logistics (computational arithmetic), and canonics (study of musical harmonics). In one of his tracts on astronomy, Geminos gave an exegesis of Poseidonios' <Meteorology > (***Peri meteoron***) in which he distinguished between astronomical and physical enquiry by pointing out that astronomical enquiry deals with facts and not causes and, therefore, is based on hypotheses which can 'save the phenomena'.

Klaudios Ptolemaios of Alexandria:

Klaudios Ptolemaios (in English, Ptolemy) of Alexandria (A.D. c.80-c.168), a member of the staff of the Museum who was influenced by the works of Hipparchos of Nikaia and Geminos of Rhodos, believed that only enquiries based on mathematics and corroborated by experimental investigations are trustworthy in science. He developed theoretical disciplines of his day as far as possible. In fact, he was a great applied mathematician but also a superb mathematical astronomer and mathematical cartographer, and he set himself a high intellectual standard: "He who is to follow philosophy must be a free man in his mind." Ptolemaios, like Eukleides (in English, Euclid), was an excellent expositor and teacher. Unlike his predecessors who had written monographs or small treatises, Ptolemaios wrote large encyclopædic type of treatises with perfect order and lucidity. Ptolemaios, like Eukleides, possessed a genius for exposition and an extraordinary power of synthesis.

Ptolemaios took up where Hipparchos of Nikaia (c.186-125B.C.)had left the astronomical theory by completing the theory of motion of the planets (Hipparchos had been only able to collect astronomical data for planets), and improving the theories of motion for the Sun and the Moon. He wrote an elegant and compact treatise on mathematical astronomy ***Mathematike syntaxis*** (Mathematical Synthesis) which had a completeness comparable to the geometrical treatise < The Elements > of Eukleides. This work consisted of 13 books in which he completed the work of Hipparchos and Menelaos of Alexandria in astronomy and trigonometry. There existed a collection in a single volume of smaller astronomical monographs by Autolykos, Aristarchos, Eukleides, Apollonios, Archimedes, Menelaos and Ptolemaios in the Alexandrian Library which was called collectively ***Mikros astronomumenos*** (Little Astronomy). When < The Mathematical Synthesis> was compared to this collection it was called ***Megale syntaxis*** (The Great Synthesis) and later the ***Megiste syntaxis*** (The Greatest Synthesis), and centuries later Muslim astronomers called it in Arabic, ***Al-magisti***. Ultimately, it came to be known in Mediæval Christian Europe under the corrupted title, the ***Almagest***. This treatise gave an astronomical theory that was so comprehensive that it was soon accepted in Christian Europe as the unchallenged theoretical method on the workings of the heavens. Ptolemaios' geocentric theory of astronomy for the Solar system in the ***Almagest*** was so brilliant in its mathematical method that despite the criticisms of it, which were plentiful and becoming increasingly more contentious as the number and accuracy of the astronomical observations increased, its supremacy lasted more than 14 centuries ending in the 16th century A.D.. Owing to the pervasive influence of the ***Almagest*** mathematical laws were soon accepted by astronomers as the proper theoretical means for the description of the workings of nature. Ptolemaios never attempted in his mathematical astronomy to find any physical explanation for planetary

½motions: "After all, in general, the cause of the first principles is either nothing, or difficult to interpret in nature."

The necessary astronomical and mathematical background work had already been done by Hipparchos, so that Ptolemaios was able to complete it by working out the necessary details, improving the geometric theories used by Hipparchos, and preparing new mathematical tables such as the extensive table of chords begun by Hipparchos for each angle from ½ to 180 degrees by ½ degree increments. Ptolemaios knew the equivalent of the law of sines although he expressed it by means of chords. He used plane trigonometry without its title as the main mathematical method in his astronomical works because he recognised that spherical geometry and purely graphical methods were not only inadequate but also inconvenient in astronomical theory. Ptolemaios fully understood and appreciated the importance of interpolations and approximations as an essential part in the foundation of applied mathematics.

His most innovative theoretical contribution to astronomy was his abandonment of the concept of uniform circular motion by introducing the idea of 'uniform equant motion' (an angular motion) to make the geometric theory of planetary motion fit the observed motion of some planets with better accuracy. It assumed that the radial line between the center of epicycle and a point at a distance equal to the distance between the center of the eccentric deferent and the stationary Earth (but on the opposite side) be subjected to a uniform angular motion. He introduced his equant motion for the superior planets Mars, Jupiter and Saturn.

Books I and II of the ***Almagest*** gave introductory information on astronomical assumptions and mathematical methods used in this treatise. Moreover, Ptolemaios proved in these books the sphericity of the Earth, and postulated the sphericity of the heavens and their revolution round the stationary center of the Earth. He also determined the obliquity of the ecliptic. Book III considered the length of the year and the motion of the Sun. Books IV and V mainly dealt with the length of the month, the theory of the Moon, sizes and distances of the Sun, the Moon and the Earth, and the construction of the astrolabe. Book VI treated the eclipses of the Sun and the Moon. The major part of Books VII and VIII was devoted to the fixed stars and the precession of the equinoxes. The end of Book VII and the beginning of Book VIII listed his Star Catalogue. The rest of Book VIII described the Milky Way and the construction of a celestial globe. His Star Catalogue listed 1028 stars arranged under 48 constellations together with each star's longitude, latitude, and magnitude that represented the brightness of a star expressed on a scale in which the brightest stars are numbered '1' and the faintest stars visible to the naked eye are numbered '6'. It is the earliest surviving Star Catalogue. Books IX was devoted to such astronomical generalities as the order of the planets from the Earth and their periods of revolution, and to the planet Mercury. Book X was devoted to planet Venus, Book XI to planets Jupiter and Saturn, Book XII to stationary points and retrogressions of planets in their orbits, and to longest elongations of planets Mercury and Venus. Book XIII dealt with motions of planets in latitude, magnitude and inclination of their orbits.

In observational astronomy Ptolemaios either invented or improved the meridian circle (***astrolabon organon***), the parallactic instrument, and the mural quadrant. His best achievement in observational astronomy, in which he was not very accurate in comparison with Hipparchos of Nikaia who was an excellent observer of remarkable precision, was his discovery of 'evection', a small fluctuation in the eccentricity of the Moon's orbit round the Earth due to the influence of the Sun. This discovery made it necessary for Ptolemaios to improve the epicyclic Lunar theory of Hipparchos. Hipparchos before his death had only been able to supply the geometric theories for the motion of the Sun and the Moon in which he took full advantage of both the epicyclic and the eccentric theory. In the ***Almagest*** Ptolemaios was eminently successful in employing the epicyclic, the eccentric, and the equant theory in a superbly balanced mathematical and observational science of astronomy which made this treatise the very summit of ancient Greek astronomy. In one of the books of the ***Almagest***, he solved the three-point problem of surveying now known as the Problem of Snel (A.D. 1617), a problem which has a long history. He, moreover, extended the fixed star catalogue of Hipparchos which had 850 stars to 1,028 stars. He checked the location of each star in terms of its ecliptic latitude and longitude by his own observations, and made corrections in Hipparchos' data where necessary. All the astronomical observations which Ptolemaios claimed to have made himself he actually fudged to fit his theory. Many centuries later the Muslim astronomers also fudged their astronomical data to uphold Ptolemaios' astronomy at all cost for Ptolemaios' astronomy made factual fraud relatively easy since in its practice it was merely a numerical scheme. However, the astronomical tables of Ptolemaios were in general more accurate than all Babylonian tables because Babylonians had no trigonometry.

Ptolemaios was not only an outstanding mathematical astronomer but also a first-rate mathematical cartographer. In this discipline, he wrote a treatise of mathematical geography in 8 books,< Geographical Guide > (***Geographike hyphegesis***), the best cartographic work of antiquity which is almost as important as the ***Almagest***. In this first general comprehensive work on geography which possessed an astounding diversity and wide scope, Ptolemaios brought together all that was valuable in the works of his predecessors. Since he was not interested in physical and human geography like his predecessor Strabon of Amasia, he did not include these subjects in his treatise. He metrified the entire surface of the Earth on his maps by means of the gridlines representing latitude (***platos***) and longitude (***makos***). Ptolemaios was probably the first geographer to use systematic listings of places by latitude and longitude. The entire work was actually the first 'atlas' which located about 8,000 places on Earth by their latitudes and longitudes, and it remained the standard work on geography for more than 14 centuries, although he did not have a really satisfactory practical means of accurately determining the longitudes. The knowledge of the world as presented in < Geographical Guide > is often inaccurate, but its scope and variety are nevertheless astounding. His knowledge of geography was in general derived from Eratosthenes of Kyrene, Hipparchos of Nikaia, Strabon of Amasia, and above all from Marinos of Tyre. Book I treated generalities, the sizes of the Earth and the known world, and the methods of cartographic projections among other pertinent topics. Books II through VII contained systematic descriptions of the world in tabular form giving the longitudes and latitudes of places for every country of which he had sufficient knowledge. Book VIII was the concluding astronomical part to his treatise in which Ptolemaios described the proper method of correct determination of the latitude and the longitude but it required good instruments for the measurement of time and angles, some knowledge of astronomy and trigonometry and, above all else, scientific collaboration of observers at different locations on the surface of the Earth. Ptolemaios readily recognised his indebtedness in cartography to Marinos of Tyre, who was the real founder of ancient mathematical mapping about A.D.120 by being the first to take full advantage of the star mapping of Hipparchos. Marinos' maps established a new standard by being more successful in locating places, "remarkable cities (***polis epistemoi***)," by means of gridlines of latitude and longitude and by using a prime meridian which ran through the Canary Islands, but without recognising the importance of projecting curved surfaces on a flat plane of the map. This mathematical shortcoming in Marinos' maps was remedied by Ptolemaios in his separate monograph < Planosphærics > (***Planisphaerium***) which contained the theory of stereographic projection for the celestial sphere, and in his monograph on Sundials < Taking-Up > (***Analemma***), in which he used orthographic projection on 3 mutually orthogonal planes to determine the position of the Sun at any time of the day. Both of these works are lost in Greek but survive in Latin translations from Arabic. In his estimation of the size of the Earth he unfortunately preferred the estimate of Poseidonios of Apameia to that of Eratosthenes of Kyrene which was more accurate. For this reason Ptolemaios' estimation of the length of the Eurasian continent was too long,180 degrees instead of 130 degrees in angular measure. This wrong estimate, which made the Pacific Ocean considerably narrower than it really is, much later encouraged Christopher Columbus (c.1446-1506) and other early explorers of the Earth to undertake their hazardous long sea voyages of exploration. Since Ptolemaios' coordinates were calculated on the basis of dead reckonings, travellers tales and very few scientific observations they were not very accurate. Both the ***Almagest*** and the ***Geographike hyphegesis*** remained the most influential treatises in their fields for more than 14 centuries.

Ptolemaios, as one would expect, also took a serious interest in optical phenomena by writing a comprehensive treatise in 5 books entitled < Optics > (***Optika***), in which he attempted to collect all that was known about optics in his day, and to extend this basic knowledge through his own original researches. It dealt with the physics and physiology of vision, with the optical geometry of mirrors, and contained the earliest known scientific experiments on the laws of reflexion and refraction of light. The correct law of reflexion was already known, but the law of refraction was not. The problem of refraction of light going from one transparent medium into another had already been raised about 40 B.C. by the Stoic astronomer Kleomedes of Lysimachia, a student of Poseidonios of Apameia, who in his treatise in 2 books < Circular Theory of Heavenly Bodies > (***Kyklikes theorias meteoron***) claimed that he had observed a Lunar eclipse before the Sunset, a paradox which he explained by postulating that light rays bend upon entering the atmosphere, which makes the Sun visible even when it is actually below the horizon. Both Poseidonios of Apameia and Kleomedes were certainly quite familiar with the refraction phenomenon (***kataklasis***) of light-rays from witnessing the thaumaturge's trick popular at the time which made a coin in the bottom of a vessel visibly change its position when water was poured into the vessel. The discovery of seeing the Lunar Eclipse before the Sunset by Kleomedes indicated the existence of empty space beyond the atmosphere. In the same treatise, Kleomedes made a statement about the immenseness of space: "The Earth is but a dot in comparison with the heaven."

On the basis of his refraction experiments, Ptolemaios prepared a table of angles of refraction, from air to water, from air to glass, and from glass to air, for angles of incidence from *10* degrees to *80* degrees at increments of *10* degrees. He postulated a quadratic rather than a trigonometric law of refraction :

$$r = ai + bi^2 ,$$

where r denotes the angle of refraction, i the angle of incidence, and both a and b are suitable constants, perhaps by drawing his inspiration from the Pythagorean formula for polygonal numbers. Ptolemaios could not discover the actual law of refraction from his experimental results, since he did not know the sine function. The really astonishing aspect of the < Optics > is Ptolemaios' method of establishing a mathematical theory of science by means of experiments, which required a careful preparation of special experimental equipment for testing. This work of Ptolemaios on refraction of light rays is a splendid example for the development of a mathematical science that is subjected to a strict satisfaction of experimental results.

Ptolemaios was aware that astronomical observations required a correction because the apparent observed positions of stars were nearer to the zenith than their actual positions owing to the atmospheric refraction. In this work, Ptolemaios also reported on the Principle of persistence of vision in the human eye, an optical after-image effect of the eye which has been technologically exploited in modern times to make cinema and television possible. This treatise on optics was the best ancient Greek work on the subject.

Ptolemaios wrote an influential treatise on sound entitled < Harmonics > ***(Harmonika)*** in which he had collected all available knowledge on sound and music into a unified treatment quite like his treatises on astronomy, geography and optics. His treatise not only dealt with physical acoustics but also with physiological aspects of the sense of hearing, and with the Pythagorean doctrine on the harmony of spheres.

He is known to have written other works, now lost, such as < About Balance > ***(Peri hropon)***, < About Dimension > ***(Peri diastaseos)*** in which he demonstrated that the possible number of dimensions is only 3, a book on mechanics, and 6 minor astronomical works which are still extant.

It is necessary to reveal another side of Ptolemaios which was probably quite characteristic of ancient Greek scientists who lived in an era of almost universal belief in divination. He was a confirmed believer in astrology ***(astrologika)***. Under the influence of Babylonian and Egyptian superstitions combined with Pythagorean mysticism, the so-called Alexandrian 'scientific astrology' as a kind scientific pantheism became firmly established when the belief that not only will the stars influence human destiny in general, for it was the customary view of the Babylonian and the Assyrian astrology that the Moon, the planets and the stars directly influence, and even control the affairs of the State, but also that the destiny, health and welfare of each individual can be predicted by means of horoscopes cast by the 'scientific' representation and interpretation of the relative positions of planets at the birth, or better yet, at the conception of the individual. The first known horoscopes were cast in Mesopotamia on cuneiform tablets already in 410 B.C..

The 'scientific' astrology was developed by the ancient Greeks living in Egypt who borrowed astrological models from the folklores of Babylon and Pharaonic Egypt. Even Aristotle had expressed the idea in the first book of < Meteorology > that the movements of celestial bodies influence the sublunar terrestrial world, because he thought that all the power present in the world of man is controlled by the movement of celestial bodies. In other of his works, Aristotle expressed his belief in the freewill of man, *i.e.* in the freedom of individual decision. Also Aristotle's former student and successor Theophrastos of Eresos wrote a work, now lost, entitled < On the Signs >, which dealt with Babylonian judicial astrology. Unfortunately, the astrological pseudoscience was lent considerable scientific respectability by Hipparchos, who accepted astral religion by believing in the interaction between the souls and the stars, and by approving astrology explicitly. The Stoics believed in the doctrine of the unity of cosmos and the interdependence of all of its parts, which meant that the terrestrial part of the universe depends upon the activity of the celestial part of the universe. Moreover, Stoics also accepted the Pythagorean belief in the identity of macrocosmos representing the universe with the microcosmos representing the individual man. Therefore, the Stoics believed that the actions of man as a terrestrial body are dependent upon the activities or movements of planets and stars as celestial bodies. This motivated the Stoics to accept determinism in their philosophy. Hence, the Stoic philosopher Poseidonios of Apameia approved of astrology and casting of horoscopes, and he wrote altogether 5 works on astrology which were extensively used by Ptolemaios. On account of the approval astrology had received from Hipparchos and Poseidonios of Apameia, astrology came to be considered a respectable science. Since the predictions of astrology could be used as black magic if so desired, a 'scientific' astrologer such as Ptolemaios tried to set down 'scientific' rules for astrological predictions in his very influential work on astrology in 4 books entitled < Mathematical Synthesis in Four Books > (***Mathematike tetrabiblos syntaxis***), a work on pure astrological doctrine which dealt with the terrestrial influences of heavenly bodies. Ptolemaios regarded the ***Tetrabiblos,*** a textbook of astrology, to be a natural addition to the ***Almagest***, a textbook of astronomy. The ***Tetrabiblos*** not only differed from the ***Almagest*** as astrology differs from astronomy, but the mathematics used in the two books were also very different: the mathematics in the ***Almagest*** was the logically rigorous, sophisticated and synthetic Greek geometry whereas the mathematics in the ***Tetrabiblos*** was replete with primitive Babylonian arithmetic devoid of any logical foundation. The ***Almagest*** of Ptolemaios made it possible to predict the positions of celestial bodies and the ***Tetrabiblos*** put forth the theory of their influence on terrestrial things. He even expressed his conviction that errors in astrological predictions must be assigned to errors in astronomy, and not to errors in the astrological doctrine. ***Tetrabiblos*** was mostly made up of material collected from Babylonian, Egyptian, and Greek folklore and even from earlier writings, although Ptolemaios frequently developed his own ideas on the subject. ***Tetrabiblos*** endured as a standard work on astrology over fourteen centuries because it was so complete and so well organised. It explained the technical concepts of astrology and dealt with the predictions of a general nature, and with predictions relative to the individuals. Horoscopes in the form of diagrams of the heavens showing the relative positions of planets and the signs of the zodiac were given and discussed in some detail for their use in calculating their influence at birth of an individual person, and foretelling the events in the life of a person. The ***Tetrabiblos*** became even more popular than the ***Almagest***, since superstitions change but do not progress like the science of astronomy. New editions of the ***Almagest*** are only of scholarly interest today, whereas new editions of the ***Tetrabiblos*** still give guidance to the contemporary practicing astrologers.

Astrology had many prominent advocates, such as the celebrated ancient Greek physician Klaudios Galenos of Pergamon (in English, Galen) (A.D.131-201). Ancient physicians, called iatromathematicians (***iatromathematicii***), used astrological signs in their decisions on the proper treatment of patients. Therefore, the Hellenistic astrology, which was personal rather than political, melded the astronomer as well as the physician with the astrologer. Astrology vanquished the conquering Romans and reached its peak in the time of Emperor Augustus, after which it endured through the Middle Ages and the Renaissance, when the liaison between medicine and mathematics via astronomy became even more pronounced, and it is still doing thriving business today.

Since the encyclopædic treatises of Ptolemaios were very thorough and excellent in exposition, the earlier works which had served as their foundation were soon considered incomplete and obsolete in comparison with Ptolemaic treatises and for this reason the scribes ceased to copy them, and as a result of this neglect the earlier treatises were superseded and vanished from existence. At the time of Ptolemaios, the gradual decline in the scientific research in Alexandria was temporarily arrested, but after his death, the decay in Alexandrian science continued unabated.

Religious Philosophy and Mechanical Theory of Motion

During the Roman hegemony in the Mediterranean world, there were important advances made in the problems of mechanics which had a direct bearing on one special aspect of military engineering: the ballistics. Great efforts were made by scientific engineers to bring the science of motion to the state which allows mechanical theory to be applied to artillery, and to the prediction of projectiles trajectories. All the scientific research in mechanics was done by the Greeks in Alexandria, and in Byzantium, the seat of government of the Eastern Roman Empire since the 4th century A.D. which was popularly known as the Byzantine Empire from the beginning of the 8th century A.D.. In the Byzantine Empire in its later stages, educated people no longer spoke Latin but rather Greek as their native language. By that time, the former Greek town Byzantion which had been rebuilt into a 'New Rome', and renamed ***Constantinopolis*** after Emperor Constantinus came to power, had become a leading cultural center like Alexandria. The reason why the theoreticians were all Greeks was best expressed by the famous Roman orator and man of letters, Cicero, who himself was a learned man educated at the Stoic school of rhetoric in Rhodos by the Greek Stoic scholar Poseidonios of Apameia: " The Greeks held geometer in the highest esteem; accordingly, nothing made more brilliant progress among them than mathematics. But we have established as the limit of this art its usefulness in measuring and counting."

About A.D. 200, Alexandros of Aphrodisias referred to air moving without being moved and, therefore, being 'self-moved' in the projectile problem. This argument of Alexandros contradicted Aristotelian mechanics.

Themistios (A.D.c.317-387) introduced the idea of 'storage of power' into ballistics by comparing the Aristotelian idea of air supplying the driving force for the projectile with the heat stored in water when heated which can heat bodies immersed in warm water by transferring its stored heat to the body as long as the water remains warm. This was a false analogy, according to which the projectile is moved by the projector as well as by the air through which the projectile moves and which itself is moved by the stored power it has received from the projector.

Certain Aristotelian concepts in physics were applied to religious philosophy by some Christian thinkers who had formerly been Neoplatonic philosophers and, thereby, were elaborated into new abstractions which, surprisingly, laid the metaphysical foundation for a purely mechanical theory of motion when the same abstractions were reintroduced into mechanics. Plotinos (A.D. 205-270), a famous Neoplatonic philosopher and teacher of Roman Emperor Gallenius, took over the Aristotelian idea of the relation between ***energeia*** and ***dynamis*** in physics and applied it to religious philosophy thereby disassociating these concepts from the tactile world of matter. Plotinos used the concept of ***energeia*** to describe the nature of One. The trinity of being (***ousia***), power (***dynamis***) and actualisation (***energeia***) was first used by Porphyrios (A.D.233-304), a Greek scholar and Neoplatonic philosopher who is famous for having written an antiChristian treatise in 15 volumes which were burnt in A.D. 435 by the order of Emperor Theodosios II for being perverse pagan literature corruptive to Christianity. These Neoplatonic ideas were used by the Neoplatonic philosopher and mathematician Proklos of Byzantion, and taken over by Pseudo-Dionysios and by some Christian religious thinkers, who considered the ideas associated with the concept of Trinity as obvious and requiring no explanation. The first Christian thinker who thought that the Trinity was necessary was John of Skythopolis, but the first Christian to express the trinity in fully Christian terms was St. Maximos. The trinity in religious thought was an abstracted version of the triadic nature of change in the physical world due to Aristotle, which existed only in the abstract world of the mind and spirit. Surprisingly, this abstraction lent the metaphysical basis for the erection of purely mechanical theory of motion, since it was now possible to consider matter as something that can be abstracted into the world of the mind and subjected to the ***dynamis*** of a force external to matter; thus ***energeia*** could now be conceived as an internal motive power to do work by virtue of its motion, the motion having been imparted to the body by an external power, ***dynamis***.

Diophantos of Alexandria and Algebra:

Another short period of revival of Alexandrian mathematics occurred about the time of Diophantos of Alexandria (*floruit* A.D.250-275), who was the last original ancient Greek mathematician of great brilliance, and whose work is of enormous importance to the development of algebra. It has been said with complete justice that in mathematics he was a giant in a century of pygmies. Virtually nothing is known about his person and even his dates are uncertain. Some historians believe that he lived a few centuries earlier, and that he was a younger contemporary of Heron of Alexandria. There is an arithmetic epigram about him in the book < Greek Anthology > collected by Metrodoros, a grammarian of the 5th century A.D.: "Diophantos passed one sixth of his life in childhood, one twelfth in youth, and one seventh more as a bachelor. Five years after his marriage was born a son who died four years before his father, at half his father's final age. How old was Diophantos when he died?" The correct answer is 84 years of age. This anthology is a collection of some 6,000 epigrams of which more than 40, including the epigram about the age of Diophantos, are mathematical problems leading to linear equations.

Diophantos is known to have written 3 treatises: < Arithmetic > ***(Arithmetika)*** in 13 books [6 are still extant], < On Polygonal Numbers > ***(Peri polygonon arithmon)*** of which only fragments are left, and ***Porismos*** and ***Prismata*** (Corollaries?) which are now lost.

His greatest work is < Arithmetic > which gives an analytic treatment of algebraic number theory that distinguishes its author as a genius in this field. There were 189 problems which can be classified into 50 different types, a classification which he himself did not establish. All problems which led to the first and second degree equations, and one particular problem which led to a third degree equation, are solved with unmatched virtuosity by ingenious special methods, for he gives no general method of solution. In his solutions, Diophantos accepted only rational solutions; solutions which were negative, irrational or imaginary he rejected and called such equations 'unsolvable'. In his solutions of simultaneous equations, he recognised the importance of symmetry in algebraic expressions. He made the mathematics of his syncopated algebra completely independent of geometry. Before his time only rhetorical algebra, in which everything was expressed in words, existed. His syncopated algebra used acronyms for words, which was a giant step towards the modern *symbolic* algebra. Diophantos is the first mathematician who made systematic use of signs for constantly recurring quantities and treated fractions as numbers. He assigned a symbol for one unknown quantity, and used ingenious devices to express other unknowns in terms of the single unknown which had a symbol. He introduced a symbol for subtraction, but addition is obtained by juxtaposition of quantities to be added. He gave a sign for equality, and had a symbolic way of expressing powers of the unknown. Reciprocals of various powers he denoted by the same sign as the powers but with a special mark attached. He had no sign either for multiplication or for division for which he used a special phrase. He attempted to create a concise method of solving equations based on Greek alphabet, which, however, was enormously difficult because every letter in the Greek alphabet stood for a unique number. Only certain sequences of letters did not have numerical meaning in ancient Greek arithmetic.

Diophantos solved determinate equations with one unknown in the first book, and in the rest of this work, he treated indeterminate equations of the second, and even of higher degree, having two or three unknowns. In regards to indeterminate equations, he was interested only in exact solutions rather than approximate solutions which Babylonian mathematicians had sought for both the determinate and indeterminate equations. His emphasis was on indeterminate equations which have more than one set of solutions, even an infinite set of solutions. He made important contributions to the theory of numbers, since the problems of indeterminate equations form a part of modern number theory. Indeterminate algebraic problems with rational solutions are now called 'Diophantine problems' in his honour. In notation, Diophantos is the founder of algebra because he was the first mathematician known to have used algebraic symbolism in the same algebraic sense as it is used in modern algebra today. < Arithmetic > of Diophantos is a remarkably original work and represents a true intellectual monument to the founding of algebra.

Pappos of Alexandria:

Pappos of Alexandria (*floruit* c. A.D.284-300), a younger contemporary of Diophantos, was the last creative ancient Greek mathematician and the last mathematical giant of antiquity. He was not a teacher like Eukleides but rather an erudite mechanical engineer of extensive and profound learning who mastered all existing mathematical methods of the ancient Greeks. This enthusiastic, prodigious and competent author of ancient Greek mathematics showed remarkable versatility and independence of judgement reminiscent of the great mathematicians of the 'Golden Age' of Greek mathematics although he was not very methodical like Eukleides. His greatest work < A Book of Mathematical Collection > (***Mathematikon synagogon biblia***) in 8 books of which the last 6 and a fragment of the 2nd are still extant, was a valiant effort on his part to revive interest in higher order geometry of the past which had been neglected for a long time. This compendium of ancient Greek mathematics virtually covered the entire field of Greek mathematical sciences. His prefaces to each book are of great historical value but regrettably the prefaces to Books I, II and IV are lost. Book II commented on Apollonios' method for the notation and operation of large numbers in terms of powers of myriads (that is, 10^4). Book III treated continued proportions and inscribed solids: Book IV gave a masterful investigation of higher order plane curves such as the spiral of Archimedes, the quadratrix of Hippias, the conchoid of Nikomedes, the cissoid of Diokles, and the curves produced by sections of torus discovered about 150 B.C. by Perseus, a contemporary of Apollonios. Torus (***spheira***) as a geometric solid had been studied already by Eudoxos of Knidos. About 180 B.C., Nikomedes invented the curve:

$$r = a + b \sec\theta,$$

called conchoid (mussel-shaped), with which he solved the problem of two mean proportionals, as well as the duplication of the cube problem. Diokles wrote <Burning Mirrors> (***Peri pyreion***), a work of considerable scope in which not only the burning properties of the paraboloidal, ellipsoidal, and spherical mirrors are studied, but also a new curve called the cissoid :

$$y^2(a+x) = (a x)^3$$

where a is a radius, with which he solved the problem of the two mean proportionals in the duplication of the cube problem. He also invented a mechanism to construct the cissoid and a method of solving the equivalent of a certain cubic equation by means of the intersection of an ellipse and a hyperbola. It also gave a method of integration for the spiral that was different from Archimedes' method.

Book V treated the maximum problems of isoperimetric figures based on the work by Zenodoros (*floruit* c.180 B.C.) entitled < On the Isometric Figures > (***Peri isometron schematon***). Zenodoros proved that of all regular polygons of equal perimeter, the one with the most angles has the greatest area, that a circle has a greater area than any regular polygon of equal perimeter, that of all polygons with the same number of sides and equal perimeter, the equilateral and equiangular polygon has the greatest area, that of all the solid figures the surface areas of which are equal, the sphere has the greatest volume. Pappos added to Zenodoros' isoperimetric theorems, one of his own: 'among all the segments of a circle having equal circumferences the semicircle has the greatest area'. He marvelled at the sagacity of the bees and the maximum-minimum properties of the hexagonal cells of their honeycomb: the hexagonal cells provided the maximum capacity to store honey with the minimum quantity of wax required to construct the cells. A later mathematician, Proklos of Byzantion, reported how in communistic societies of his time, some of the leaders who were knowledgeable of mathematics cheated their fellow members by giving them land of greater perimeter but of lesser area than they took for themselves, with the result that they earned a reputation of unimpeachable honesty when, in fact, they took more than their share of the produce. This deception was made possible by the popular misconception that a geometric figure with a larger perimeter has also a larger area. Book VI treated the sphere and served as an introduction to astronomy in general and the ***Almagest*** in particular. Book VII was devoted to analysis and it gave an historical account of twelve important Greek treatises on various aspects of mathematics in addition to his own theorems on the calculation of the volumes and surface areas of any solid of revolution of which he was justifiably proud, as well as the fundamental theorem of projective geometry due to Menelaos of Alexandria. In his quite original discussion of 'loci with respect to three or four lines', Pappos came close to discovering the coordinate geometry. It was an attempt to generalise this problem to n-lines that led the French philosopher and mathematician, Réné Descartes in A.D.1637 to formulate the method of coordinates. This book also contained the first reference to the focus-directrix property of conic sections. Book VIII for the most part dealt with mechanics and like Book VII, it contained much that was probably original with Pappos. For instance, it contains his solution for the motion and equilibrium of a heavy body on an inclined plane, which was, however, wrong.

The intention of Pappos in this renowned work was to set out the mathematical propositions of his famous, ancient predecessors which by his time were scattered and in many cases not even available for study, to generalise previous proofs or to give them more concise and precise form as well as better logical order, and to establish some new and useful theorems of his own. Pappos, who was an excellent creative mathematician, not only reproduced the original proofs collected from various sources, but also gave his own alternate methods of solution, improved proofs and extensions of the problems. The mathematicians who followed Pappos were no longer creative and none of the later authors were able to rise to his intellectual level. The ideas of Pappos were profound and they served to inspire Western European mathematicians to create from A.D.1637 to A.D.1640 such modern mathematical disciplines as analytical geometry, projective geometry, and centrobaric method which Pappos founded in his theorem for the calculation of volumes of bodies generated by the rotation of a plane figure about an axis, a theorem which was plagiarised by a Jesuit mathematician and goldsmith, Paul Guldin (A.D.1577-1643), in A.D.1635 and A.D.1641, although Guldin expressed Pappos' Theorem, which is also known as Guldin's Theorem, with more clarity but his proof was incomplete.

Neoplatonic mathematician Iamblikos of Chalkis (died c.A.D.330),a younger contemporary of Pappos and a student of Porphyrios, wrote commentaries on < Introduction to Arithmetic > by Nikomachos of Gerasa, on polygonal numbers and other works. He also wrote a short treatise on chemistry.

Hypatia of Alexandria:

In the fourth century A.D., Theon of Alexandria (*floruit* A.D. 365), a teacher of astronomy and mathematics at the Museum, wrote a series elaborate critical commentaries on the ***Almagest,*** revised and improved a new edition of < The Elements > (***Stoicheia***) by Eukleides, and published his own lectures on mathematics and philosophy. He had a brilliant collaborator in his illustrious, intellectually gifted but modest daughter, Hypatia (A.D.c.370-415), who was meticulously educated by her father Theon to make her into a perfect specimen of a supremely erudite young lady despite her conspicuous handicap: she was an exceptionally beautiful young woman. After Hypatia completed her scholastic journey to Athens and southern Italy, where she met great scholarly success on account of her brilliant intellect and profound learning, she returned to Alexandria and became a prominent teacher of mathematics and philosophy. Alexandria by that time had many separate schools for pagans, Jews and Christians besides the Museum. Hypatia as the first truly accomplished female mathematician taught at the Museum and assisted her father Theon with his scientific and mathematical writings. Hypatia and her father Theon of Alexandria were the leading mathematicians of their age. Hypatia, who was the preeminent algebraist of the period, wrote several critical commentaries on the treatise < Arithmetic > by Diophantos of Alexandria in which she gave a number of alternative solutions and many new problems that were subsequently incorporated into the works of Diophantos. She wrote a treatise in 8 books on the < Conics > of Apollonios of Perge that served as a popularisation of his works. She helped her father Theon to revise and improve the new edition of < The Elements > by Eukleides, which is the edition still in use today. Hypatia revised her father's commentaries on the ***Almagest*** by Ptolemaios, but her treatise < Astronomical Canon > consisting of tables for the movements of the heavenly bodies was in all likelihood a separate work from her father's works on astronomy. Most of Hypatia's writings had their origin in her textbooks which she had prepared for her students.

Hypatia was appointed the head of the Neoplatonic school in Alexandria about A.D. 400 where she was officially responsible to teach various philosophical doctrines including Plato's philosophy and the natural philosophy of Aristotle to all the students irrespective of their religious background. Hypatia as the leading mathematician of her time taught a mathematical form of Neoplatonic philosophy in a direct contrast to the occult Neoplatonic arithmetic, a form of number mysticism, taught at Plato's Academy in Athens which was no longer a school of higher mathematics. As a mathematician she was evidently also a connoisseur of the astronomical works of Ptolemaios, and the mechanical treatises of Ktesibios of Askra, Philon of Byzantion and Heron of Alexandria. Hypatia's eloquent lectures on mathematics, philosophy, astronomy, natural philosophy and mechanics in Alexandria were so widely popular that students came from all parts of the world to attend her lectures. Many of her students were reported to have become enamoured with the remarkably beautiful, erudite and sophisticated young lady. The only other well-known female savant who was contemporary with Hypatia was Asklepigeneia in Athens, whose father Ploutarchos of Athens was the director of Plato's Academy at the time. Hypatia's most prominent student was Synesios of Kyrene (A.D.c.370-c.413), who converted to Christian faith in his middle age about A.D.407 and became the prosperous and powerful Bishop of Ptolemais in A.D.410.

Hypatia took an active interest in practical technology and mechanical design, for she designed and built several scientific instruments such as a plane astrolabe, an apparatus for distilling water, an instrument for the measurement of the level of water, and, a graduated bronze hydrometer called 'baryllion', for the determination of the density of liquids, as the seven extant letters of Synesios addressed to Hypatia indicate. Her home soon became a center for the gathering of intellectuals in Alexandria where important scientific and philosophical problems were discussed. Hypatia was habitually consulted by city magistrates about the administration of the affairs of Alexandria which made her politically vulnerable.

Unfortunately, she was responsible for defending pagan learning such as Greek scientific rationalism and Neoplatonic philosophy against Christian attacks as the head of Neoplatonic school and a teacher of science and mathematics at the Museum in an increasingly Christian city of Alexandria. After Cyril (A.D.376-444), a nephew of Theophilus, the Patriarch of Alexandria , was elected to succeed Theophilus in A.D.412, an irreconcilable disagreement arose between Orestes, the Roman Prefect of Egypt, and the new Patriarch Cyril, a fanatical Christian zealot who harboured a passionate and unrelenting hostility towards Jews and pagans. The Patriarch Cyril, after becoming the Bishop of Alexandria, decided to put an end to pagan and Jewish learning once and for all. He began to persecute Jews for their criticism of Christian doctrine by demolishing their homes and driving thousands of Jews out of the city. By that time an open conflict flared up between the Christians, Jews and pagans, and angry partisan groups were habitually rioting in the streets of Alexandria which were no longer safe for the public. Then Cyril decided to expel from Alexandria all Neoplatonic pagans, who were considered dangerous heretics by the Christians since Neoplatonic philosophy representing Hellenism of the period began to assume a spiritual character whilst the Christians attempted to form a philosophical foundation for the defence of the Christian religious dogma against all kinds of charges and heresies, in particular against the Neoplatonic philosophy in its new spiritual cast. The expulsion of Neoplatonic pagans from Alexandria was categorically opposed by the Roman Prefect Orestes, a close friend and former student of Hypatia. Byzantine Emperor Theodosios I had proscribed pagan religions, and in A.D.391an edict of the Emperor ordered all Greek temples destroyed. Many pagan temples were converted into Christian churches, but in A.D.385 a Christian mob led by Theophilus, the Patriarch of Alexandria, destroyed the famous Temple of ***Sarapeis***, called ***Sarapeion***, together with thousands of volumes of pagan Greek treatises still stocked in this temple, the largest such collection in the world at the time.

Hypatia ignored the urging of Orestes to abandon her pagan ideals, to convert to Christian faith, and to give up her public speeches in defence of Neoplatonic philosophy. She was openly accused of being the very cause of the bitter hostility between Patriarch Cyril and Prefect Orestes. In March of A.D.415, when the beautiful philosopher Hypatia was driving home in her chariot, she was forcibly seized by a fanatical mob of enraged and raving Parabolan and Nitrian monks from the Church of St. Cyril of Jerusalem led by an enraged cleric named Peter, a church reader and a follower of the fanatical Cyril, who pulled her out of the chariot and dragged her into the Church called 'Caesarium', where they disrobed her, scraped her flesh off her bones with sharp oyster shells until she expired, cut her body into quarters, and burnt the remains of her body to ashes at a place called 'Cinaron'. Orestes, who after reporting this brutal murder and requesting Rome to institute an investigation of this grisly atrocity, resigned his office and left Alexandria. This investigation was repeatedly postponed under the conniving leadership of Bishop Cyril for "lack of witnesses," and ultimately the unscrupulous Bishop had the effrontery to pronounce officially that Hypatia was "alive and well, and living in Athens," a blatant and deliberate lie. It is not definitely known if Cyril had given explicit or implicit advice to his enraged monks and raving monastic followers to liquidate Hypatia, although it seems more than likely, but he was certainly personally responsible for inciting the barbaric religious massacres in Alexandria. In the 19th century A.D., Bishop Cyril was canonised 'Saint Cyril' by Pope Leo III for "his dedicated service in the defence of Christianity".

Thus the beautiful Hypatia, the first brilliant female mathematician, became one of the first martyrs of science. Hypatia's brutal murder ended the teaching of Neoplatonic philosophy in Alexandria, and soon in the rest of the Roman Empire, which had been Cyril's openly declared intention from the beginning of his bishopric tenure, and being an unscrupulously clever schemer he must have known that his particular objective to end the instruction of Neoplatonic philosophy in Alexandria made it necessary to dispose of Hypatia, the popular teacher and effective defender of Neoplatonic philosophy. This grisly act of savagery, which was much later sanctified by the Roman Church and the Pope as a valiant act of defence of Christianity, remained entirely unpunished, and the main reason for it was that the early Christian Church never genuinely liked women, particularly such an erudite and supremely talented woman as the beautiful Hypatia. The early Christian Church saw women as evil incarnations of Eve who had brought about the downfall of Adam. This narrowminded and asinine view of women is testified by the statement of John Chrysostom, a genuine Byzantine Saint: "Women are a necessary evil, a natural temptation, a desirable calamity, a domestic peril, a mortal fascination, a painted scourge."

Ever since this ghastly atrocity, which remained unpunished though her assassins were well known and still active in the Christian Church, Hypatia has been regarded as the symbol of the end of pagan learning and the beginning of the Age of Faith. None of Hypatia's treatises have survived probably because most available copies of her works were destroyed by the fanatical Christian monks.

The incredibly savage and brutal murder of Hypatia committed by the barbarous and bloodthirsty mob of fanatical Christian monks marked the beginning of the rapid decline of the Museum as a great institution of learning and research.

Proklos of Byzantion:

The last ancient Greek author of note in mathematics was the Neoplatonic philosopher and mathematician Proklos of Byzantion (A.D.410-485), who was educated at the Museum in Alexandria and studied Neoplatonic philosophy in Athens under Ploutarchos of Athens. He became the head of the Neoplatonic Academy in Athens because he had a remarkably broad range of learning. He was a very competent mathematician and it was his responsibility to teach this subject in the Academy in Athens. He was also an indefatigable author. He wrote commentaries on the works of Ptolemaios, Hipparchos, Eukleides, a treatise on astronomy, a work on higher plane curves, a tractate on clocks which has not survived the ravages of time, and as Proklos was also a believer in mysteries and myths, he wrote a brief treatise on astrology. Since Proklos had access to many works now lost, his historical commentaries on these works are of inestimable value to our knowledge of ancient Greek mathematical sciences.

Ioannes Philoponos of Alexandria:

A former Neoplatonic philosopher who after conversion became a Monophysite Christian scholar, Ioannes Philoponos [a nickname meaning 'lover of labour'; also known as Ioannes Grammatikos meaning, John the 'Grammarian'] of Alexandria (A.D.485-555) was a polymath who besides writing commentaries on 11 works of Aristotle, wrote on philosophy, grammar, rhetoric, theology, mathematics including a critical commentary on the < Arithmetic > of Nikomachos, and science. Philoponos and Simplikios of Cilicia were the foremost scientists of their time.

In science Philoponos followed the Platonic method of not searching for the actual causes of phenomena in the immediate experience but rather in the general ideas abstracted from experience by reason. Therefore, he held that the law of local motion was to be established as an idealisation found by abstract analysis of the diverse experience with the phenomenon of motion in the material world.

About A.D. 517, Philoponos wrote his critical commentaries on Aristotle's < Physics > (***In Aristotelis physicorum libros***) which contained a number of novel ideas on local motion. He rejected Aristotle's claim that the velocities of freely-falling bodies are proportional to their weights, an opinion corroborated by his free-fall experiments. Philoponos rejected Aristotle's fundamental principle which asserted that whenever a body is moved 'unnaturally', that is, is moved against its natural tendencies, it must be moved by an external agent in contact with it. He contradicted Aristotle when he held that a body moving in a void where there is no resistance still has a finite velocity, and not infinite velocity as Aristotle had claimed. He referred to the motion of the celestial sphere as an example of motion with finite velocity in the absence of resistance. It was evident in Philoponos' theory of motion that resistance was not an essential factor in the phenomena of motion. He maintained that in falling bodies and projectile motion velocity is proportional only to the motive power, and that the resistance of the medium serves only as an impediment to motion which merely reduces the velocity produced by the action of motive power. Philoponos advanced an important idea for the projectile motion by proposing that the projector imparts a certain incorporeal motive power, ***energeia***, to the projectile. However, this motive power is only 'borrowed' and it is reduced by the natural tendencies of the projectile such as gravity, and by the resistance offered by the medium, so that the 'unnatural' or 'violent' motion of the projectile eventually ceases. The original source for the idea of impressed motive power was the tractate < On Bodies Carried Down by their Weight > written by the ancient Greek astronomer Hipparchos of Nikaia. In contrast to Aristotle's theory of projectile motion in which the motive power was extrinsic, in Philoponos' theory of projectile motion the motive power was intrinsic.

Philoponos held that the speed of a moving body is proportional to the difference between the motive force and resistance rather than to the ratio of motive force to resistance as Aristotle had implied. According to Philoponos, motion of a body in resistanceless void satisfies the requirements of 'violent' motion of Aristotle because the impressed force acts as the cause of motion and the body itself functions as resistance. A medium such as air is only an impediment to motion by virtue of the resistance it presents to motion. Therefore, the speed of a body moving through a medium is proportional to the impressed force reduced by the resistance of the medium.

The remarkable idea of Philoponos that the 'violent' or 'unnatural' motion of a body can be maintained by an 'incorporeal motive power' or 'energy' impressed directly on the moving body was a fundamentally important concept in mechanics that re-emerged in Mediæval Europe as the 'cause of motion' known as 'impetus' in the dynamics of the early fourteenth century A.D., and finally reappeared as the 'effect of motion' known as 'momentum' in the Newtonian dynamics of the seventeenth century A.D. The qualitative law of motion of Philoponos can be expressed in metric form as the Dynamic Law of Differences :

$$V = const.\,(F - R), \qquad \text{for } F \geq R,$$
$$V = 0, \qquad \text{for } F < R,$$

where V denotes the speed, F the motive force, and R the resistance exerted by the medium through which the body moves. Philoponos explained that ***dynamis***, the 'kinetic power', is transferred at the moment of projection from the projector to the projectile as ***energeia*** or 'kinetic energy', and it was this transferred power that kept the projectile in its 'violent' motion: "The energies flow from one body to another in such a way that an 'impressed' force is transmitted to the projected body." Philoponos clearly indicated in his theory of motion that the medium, in this case, the air, was not essential to the initiation or the maintenance of motion of bodies.

It seems that the importance of defensive artillery to the welfare of Byzantine States was influential in increasing the scientific attention paid to the projectile problem. Byzantium, unlike Alexandria, was under frequent attacks by the enemies of the Byzantine Empire, particularly from the sea. Therefore, there was strong pressure exerted by the rulers of the Byzantine Empire upon the engineers and scientists to improve the artillery used in the defence of Byzantium. The ensuing engineering developments in the technology of the artillery tended to discredit the Aristotelian ideas in dynamics because these ideas did not seem to apply to technological design of artillery. The apex of the theoretical development of ancient Greek dynamics appeared in the work of Philoponos, which remained unmatched until the mediæval scientists in Europe took up the quantitative study of motion, and were able to surpass the qualitative achievement of Philoponos.

Olympiodoros and Principle of Least Action:

Olympiodoros, a contemporary of Philoponos, in his commentaries on < Meteorology > (***Meteorologika***) of Aristotle called attention to Heron of Alexandria's Principle of Least Path in the reflexion of light by emphasising the teleological principle: 'Nature produces nothing in vain, nor labours in vain', which was tacitly assumed by Heron of Alexandria to establish his minimum principle in optics. This was the first explicit statement of the Principle of Least Action in antiquity, and it was rediscovered by the French physicist Pierre Louis Moreau de Maupertuis (A.D.1698-1759) in A.D. 1744.

Another minimum principle in optics was established about A.D. 1640 by the French lawyer and mathematician Pierre Siméon de Fermat (A.D.1601-1665) in his Principle of Least Time in its application to the refraction of light, which he also based on the Principle of Economy of Natural Processes. The Least Action Principle was made into a powerful theoretical method of modern physics by the Irish mathematician William Rowan Hamilton (A.D.1805-1869) in A.D.1828 and in A.D. 1834.

Kallinikos and 'Greek Fire':

In a similar effort to improve the defences of the Byzantine states, a Hellenistic Greek ***architekton***, Kallinikos from Syria, invented about A.D.650 the 'Greek Fire' which was responsible for the ability of the Byzantine military forces to repel all the attacks of their enemies against Byzantium. The 'Greek Fire' was basically a mixture of quicklime and sulphur, and probably of other incendiary ingredients as well such as naphtha and saltpetre, which ignited when put in touch with water and, therefore, could not be extinguished with water. It was used in missiles, and flame-throwers operated by the double-barrelled pumps of Ktesibios. It was a lethal and effective weapon of defence which kept the besieging enemies of Byzantium at bay, and despite the well-known Byzantine intrigues, the formula for the mixture of 'Greek Fire' and its delivery system was successfully kept a Byzantine State secret for a long time. After Kallinikos invented the 'Greek Fire', the military engineers and technologists in Byzantium, Islamic Empire, China, and soon in Europe began to search for even more rapidly combustible mixtures. As chemical technology improved, the saltpetre used in these compounds was further purified chemically which accelerated the process of combustion into instantaneous detonation. The first revolutionary change in the firepower since the 'Greek Fire' came with gunpowder and firearms, particularly with the cannon. Both the 'Greek Fire' and the cannon as a single-cylinder internal combustion engine were simple thermomechanical devices which transformed thermal energy into destructive power under controlled conditions.

Roman Libraries and Schools

Libraries:

The first public library at Rome was established by Asinius Pollio in 39 B.C. on the booty of his Dalmatian campaign. This library was overshadowed by the renowned Palatine Library opened by Emperor Augustus in 28 B.C. as part of the Temple of Apollo on the Palatine Hill in Rome. This great library had several thousand volumes in both the Latin and the Greek division, and the volumes were classified under poetry, philosophy, history and oratory. The palatial public baths, also, had libraries, and represented intellectual resorts in which cleanliness was closely associated with culture. A great deal of instruction took place both in the libraries proper and in the lecture halls.

The third and fourth centuries A.D. were the periods in which many libraries were established in the Roman world. By the end of the fourth century, there were 28 public libraries in Rome alone. With the advent of Christianity, the pagan libraries were closed and replaced by Church libraries, but both libraries suffered from the ravages of barbarians, and by the time the sixth century A.D. was closing, all the libraries had been reduced to rather pitiful conditions.

Schools:

Under the Roman Empire, institutions of learning in the West had been consistently gaining in importance. Emperor Hadrianus had founded a university at Rome, named ***Athanaeum***, and thenceforth, similar educational institutions were founded all over the Roman Empire, but particularly in the fourth century A.D. which was a great century for schools. It was no longer necessary for young Romans to go abroad to finish their studies, as Cicero had to do in his time, since now students from other lands often came to do their advanced studies in Rome. By the end of the fourth century A.D., the subjects of the formal studies were included in the ***trivium*** and the ***quadrivium***. Romans studied Latin grammar and their first great grammarian was Lucius Aelius Stilo (c.154-74 B.C.) who studied under Dionysios of Thrakia in Rhodos. His best student was Marcus Terentius Varro (116- 27 B.C.) who wrote 25 books on Latin language of which 6 are still extant.

Beginning with Hadrianus, the Roman State had supported schools and supplied larger and larger funds for their maintenance. Various decrees concerning schools issued since Emperor Constantinus were collected together in the Theodosian Code in the second quarter of the fifth century A.D.. Constantinus had enacted rulings to provide comfortable salaries to professors, in addition to voluntary honoraria that parents might contribute. Constantinus was particularly concerned about the education of an adequate number of engineers: "We need as many engineers as possible. Since there is a lack of them, invite to this study person of about eighteen years of age, who have already studied the necessary sciences. Relieve their parents of taxes and grant the scholars sufficient means."

Constantinus' nephew, Emperor Iulianus, who was an apostate intent to revive the pagan cults of the Græco-Roman gods in A.D.361, proclaimed that the first quality required in a teacher is 'character', eloquence being only the secondary requirement. Iulianus strongly urged young scholars not to embark on the career of teaching too lightly.

Byzantium: Eastern Roman Empire

Diocletianus split the Roman Empire into two subsidiary parts in A.D. 286, and it was formally divided into the Eastern and the Western Empire during the rule of Emperor Honorius (A.D.395-423). After the conquest of the Western Roman Empire in A.D. 476 by the semibarbaric Germans, who deposed the puppet Roman Emperor Romulus Augustulus, the army of Emperor Iustinianus (A.D. 483-565) [an Illyrian peasant who ruled the Eastern Roman Empire known as Byzantium from A.D. 527 to A.D.565] under the command of general Belisarius reconquered a large part of the Western Roman Empire from the semibarbaric German invaders. Belisarius had improved the Byzantine army and navy by training them in all arts of war to an unequalled excellence.

Byzantine Engineering:

The Byzantine military construction had started on a grand scale under the Emperor Theodosius in A.D. 413 with the building of the Theodosian Wall across the peninsula, on which the city ***Constantinopolis*** (in English, Constantinople), was located. Since this defensive wall was destroyed by an earthquake in A.D.447, it was rebuilt with an additional outer curtain wall incorporating towers and a wide moat. The new defensive walls consisted of ashlar masonry and a Roman concrete core. The outside wall was 6½feet (1.98 m) thick and the inner wall was 15 feet (4.57 m) thick. A heavy iron chain was stretched across the Golden Horn, a gulf adjacent to the peninsula, at times of war. The Byzantine construction followed essentially the Roman practice although the Byzantine engineers were more concerned about earthquakes than the Roman engineers.

Emperor Iustinianus (in English, Iustinian) reconstructed about 700 fortifications throughout the Byzantine Empire, a record in military construction, and these structures served as models for fortification construction for Arabs and Europeans. It was military engineering of highly refined quality and quantity achieved at the price of oppressive taxation and intolerable burden of bureaucracy. Iustinianus ran the imperial administration as a military autocracy first established by Diocletianus which allowed no political liberty for the people composed of different races such as Greeks, Egyptians, Syrians, Armenians, Slavs and Bulgars, all called ***Romaioi***.

About A.D.520, Iustinianus constructed in ***Constantinopolis*** the famed underground 'Cistern of 1000 and 1 Columns', the Philoxenos Cistern, which lay 50 feet (15.24 m) below the street level and had a size of 210 by 184 feet (64.01 by 56.03 m). It had only 224 columns [not '1000 and 1'] in 28 rows. Its capacity was 9 million gallons (40 million liters). Another cistern which he built was even larger. The Basilica Cistern, which is still in use, has a size of 460 by 230 feet (140.21 by 70.10 m). Its roof is supported by 336 columns, each 26 feet (7.92 m) high, arranged in 12 rows of 28 columns each. From the inside these cisterns looked like immense basilicas.

From A.D. 532 to A.D.537, the first, and also the largest Byzantine dome was built in the Church of Divine Wisdom (***Hagia Sophia***, later known by its Latin name ***Santa Sophia***) in ***Constantinopolis***. It was designed by Anthemios of Tralles from Lydia, who was an eccentric engineer, mathematician and physicist, and Isidoros of Miletos, his colleague, successor and one of the later Greek mathematicians of note.

The central feature of this church was the shallow dome of 102-foot (31.09 m) in radius that is buttressed by 40 meridional ribs and supported by four 60-foot (18.29 m) high pendentives in the form of spherical triangles resting on a square base of size 120 by 120 feet (36.58 by 36.58 m). This Byzantine dome is shallower than the Roman semicircular domes, and therefore, is subject to a much smaller circumferential tension near its base but, at the same time, it exerts a much larger horizontal thrust in the radial direction which requires substantial external buttressing. The base of the dome rests on four 100-foot (30.48 m) high piers, 25 feet (7.62 m) square in cross-section and made of squared stones. The stone courses are set in lead to distribute the weight more evenly. Externally, the thrusts of the domes at the piers are supported in the east and in the west by semi-circular domes of 51 feet (15.54 m) in diameter. In the south and in the north, the thrust is absorbed by massive buttressing walls.

The entire structure was designed to resist earthquakes. All walls are tied together with timber members at 6-foot (1.83 m) centers and horizontal stringers of 5½ by 3¼ inches (14.0 by 8.3 cm) cross-section which are joined to transverse beams of 7 by 4 inches (17.8 by 10.2 cm) cross-section. The base of the dome is an interlocking ring of stones, and iron ties stretch over the entire dome surface as reinforcement. The bases of the columns are joined to the shafts with sheets of lead. Metal bands are used to strengthen the base and neck of the shafts. Metal tie-rods connect the arches in the arcades supported on slender columns.

The earthquake in A.D. 986 caused the western buttressing half-dome and with it the adjacent quarter of the main dome to collapse. In the earthquake of A.D.1346, the eastern buttressing half-dome collapsed and brought the adjacent quarter of the main dome down to the ground with it. After each disaster, the huge dome was repaired, and ***Santa Sophia*** still stands as the greatest glory of the Byzantine engineering, only that now it serves as an Islamic mosque instead of a Christian church. It stood for a millennium as the largest church in Christendom.

About A.D.538, a dam was constructed on the Byzantine frontier along the Persian Empire about 18 miles (29 km) northwest of Nusaybin, or 140 miles (225 km) northwest of Mosul. It was an arch dam designed by the Alexandrian engineer Chryses who was also in the service of the Emperor. He was in competition with Anthemios of Tralles and Isidoros of Miletos for this job, which was awarded to Chryses because the Emperor Iustinianus preferred his design. This dam had a crescent shape and was mortised into the cliffs on both sides of the ravine. It was built just outside the defensive walls of Daras to contain the floods of the river. This dam had two sluice gates at different levels for the control of the flood waters. The river led past the dam into a channel which carried the water into the town. Virtually nothing is left of this flood control dam.

Byzantine Science and Technology:

In conclusion, it has to be made clear that the Byzantine Empire as the Eastern Roman Empire never suffered the cultural disaster that overtook the Western Empire after the latter's collapse in A.D.476. ***Constantinopolis*** (the former Greek town Byzantion) as a city-State remained a center of Greek learning from its founding in A.D.330 until it was conquered by the barbaric Turks in A.D.1453. Since the 6th century A.D. the learned circles in Byzantium spoke Greek instead of Latin, and the scholars on the whole were more conservative than creative. The learning in Byzantium was almost exclusively recovery and reworking of ancient Hellenic learning which prolonged the ancient Greek culture for many centuries, and finally passed it to the Western Europeans before the close of the Middle Ages in A.D.1453. For instance, besides the University of ***Constantinopolis*** which was reopened in A.D.863, the builders of the ***Hagia Sophia***, Anthemios of Tralles (died c.A.D.534) and his successor Isidoros of Miletos, founded a polytechnical school at ***Constantinopolis*** in which mathematics, sciences and engineering were taught if not developed. Anthemios, who was an able mathematician, experimented in optics and with burning lenses, as well as with various engines powered by steam and hot air in a continued development of the model power engines of Heron of Alexandria. He wrote a book entitled < On Remarkable Mechanical Devices >, as well as a treatise < On Burning Mirrors > ***(Peri pyreion)*** in which he gave the complete mathematical theory of concave mirrors of spherical, paraboloidal and ellipsoidal shape using the focal-directrix relations. It appears that the earlier works on this subject by Diokles and Apollonios were no longer available at the time. He also gave the string-method of drawing ellipses. He simulated earthquakes by steam pressure and discovered how to use and improve combustible mixtures. Isidoros of Miletos, on the other hand, did research in mathematics, invented an instrument called ***diabetes*** for drawing parabolas, and formulated rules for drawing isosceles triangles which were incorporated by one of his students into the famous book of Eukleides, < The Elements > (***Stoicheia***). A mathematician and a friend of Anthemios, Eudokios of Askalon (born c.A.D.480) wrote commentaries on the works of Archimedes and Apollonios containing many valuable historical notes, which were made widely known by Isidoros of Miletos and his pupils at the polytechnical school. Much work was done on all kinds of labour-saving devices, mostly in connexion with military engineering and the army.

Postscriptum

The Byzantine Empire endured for over a millennium under great external pressures which is an adequate proof of its importance. Byzantium was the heir to the cultural tradition of the ancient Greeks and Romans, but particularly ancient Greeks, and all throughout the millennia they were able to preserve this valuable tradition. Byzantium passed its classic cultural inheritance to the neighbouring barbarians and thereby brought them within the compass of the Western civilisation. It gave the Slavs virtually all their past and formed out of such undisciplined tribes as Serbs, Bulgars, Croats and Russians new nations. It gave them their institutions, religions, taught their princes the art of government and gave them the very means of civilisation – the art of writing and literature.

Before the Crusades, Byzantium was the champion of Christendom against the infidels, and the center of civilisation in Christendom. Near its end Byzantium became a puppet state of the Venetians and the Genoese, and served the Ottoman Turks as a vassal until it was finally conquered by the Turks in A.D.1453, a year considered the beginning of the Modern Age.

Contrary to popular opinion, Byzantium was not a moribund society of decadent voluptuaries and doctrinaire theologians, but rather the most active and enduring political organisation the world had yet seen.

One of the great contributions of Emperor Iustinianus to Western civilisation is the compilation of the practice of Roman law in his ***Corpus Iuris Civiles***, the capstone of Roman law, which was collected for him by the able lawyer Tribonianus from A.D.529 to A.D.534. The so-called 'Law Code of Iustinianus', which has had a direct influence on the Occidental law, incorporated the earlier legal code of Theodosios II, the Emperor who abolished the Olympic Games as frivolous pagan exhibitions in A.D.438. It remained the last great work in Latin language.

The Byzantine Empire began to crumble whilst Emperor Iustinianus was still on the throne. Valiant efforts were made by his immediate successors to prevent the break-up of the Byzantine Empire, but after many epochs of recovery and cultural vigour the disintegration could not be prevented for long. After the death of Iustinianus, from A.D.550 to A.D.650, the Roman traditions were Hellenised and even the official language of the Byzantine State changed from Latin to Greek. Yet the Byzantine Empire remained the prominent defender of Christianity and the civilisation of the ancient Greece, and the guardian of the language, sciences, engineering, and technology of the ancient Greeks. The Byzantine Empire fell victim to a whole succession of disasters: the breaching of the Danube frontier by northern barbarians about A.D.580 and its abandonment about A.D.600, the result of which was the permanent settlement of Slavs in the Balkans as far down as in the Peloponnesos; the war with Persia, beginning in A.D.605 and climaxing in the siege of Constantinople in A.D.626; the rise of Arabs under Islam and the loss of Palestine, Syria and Egypt in theA.D.630's and theA.D.640's, and all of North Africa as far as Gibraltar to Arabs, culminating in the sieges of ***Constantinopolis*** by the Arabs from A.D.674 to A.D.678 and from A.D.717 to A.D.718. Part of the reason for these military debacles was a steady depopulation of the Byzantine Empire beginning with the great bubonic plague in A.D.524 which is believed to have killed about 300,000 people, about half of the population in ***Constantinopolis***. The Empire was further weakened by persistent natural disasters such as a succession of devastating earthquakes and long periods of drought. The persistent series of disasters and the sparsity of population may have been the main reasons why Iustinianus' Empire with its extremely long frontiers could not be held together. For instance, Italy in the middle of 6th century A.D. was described in contemporary reports as "empty of men." In consequence of the sparseness of population, urban life was virtually destroyed. The so-called 'Dark Centuries' fell on Greece about A.D. 580, when virtually the entire country was occupied by semibarbaric Slavs, whilst only a few coastal outposts such as Athens, Corinthos, Thessalonica and Monemvasia remained under Byzantine control. The lower town of Athens, which was abandoned, became completely desolate.

In Asia Minor, or Anatolia, no foreign occupation of the countryside took place, yet the conditions were still quite similar to those in Greece proper owing to the yearly devastations brought about by nearly 2 centuries of Arab raids, which reduced many cities to their fortified citadels inhabited only by a very small population. Any engineering work done between A.D.610 and A.D.850 was merely a patch-up construction of fortifications and water supplies. After many centuries of military conflict, the Byzantine Empire was finally reduced to the capital city of Byzantium, ***Constantinopolis*** itself, and the small peninsula on which it was built. Byzantium had withstood successfully countless fierce attacks by hostile Arabs until the young Sultan Mahomet (also Mohammed) II of Ottoman Turks decided to conquer ***Constantinopolis*** in A.D.1453 by making use of the new gunpowder technology in warfare. A Hungarian engineer Urban had designed a giant cannon which fired granite cannonballs 16 inches (0.41 m) in diameter and offered the plans of this cannon to the Byzantine Emperor Constantine XI who, however, considered it too expensive to manufacture. Urban then offered the plans of his huge cannon to Mahomet II who paid Urban to build and to test it. Urban found from his tests that the huge cannon was able to shoot 16 inch granite cannonballs up to a mile (1.61 km) and penetrate the earth 6 feet (1.83 m). It took 100 oxen and 200 men to transport the giant cannon, and one hour to load it. The recoil of this cannon was so powerful that it took almost 3 hours to realign it for the next firing. Mahomet II set up the huge cannon outside the main gate of ***Constantinopolis*** and by firing it 7 times a day, he succeeded to broach the massive defensive walls of the city which had withstood countless enemy attacks over many centuries. Byzantium had served as a bastion of European Christian civilisation against the relentless onslaught of Islamic ***jihad*** (meaning,'struggle') for almost a millennium.

In viewing the impressive ruins of the once magnificent Roman structures, the proper epitaph to the thousand years of Roman engineering seems to be:

Sic transit gloria mundi

[So goes the glory of the world]

CHAPTER VII

MEDIÆVAL TECHNOLOGY: First Industrial Power Revolution, Mechanical Clocks and Gothic Cathedrals

[from c.A.D.476 to A.D.1453]

Birth of European Civilisation

It is customary to divide history into different periods for convenience: Antiquity is usually thought to have ended approximately in the 5th century A.D. when the Mediæval Age began and lasted until the conquest of Constantinople by the Turks in A.D 1453, a year which traditionally marks the beginning of the Modern Age. The so-called 'Dark Ages' as the early part of the Mediæval Age lasted from the 5th century A.D. to the 9th century A.D. when Western Europe was under the domination of the Teutonic conquerors.

The Teutonic fury (***furor Teutonicus***) in the repeated onslaughts of the semibarbaric Germanic tribes, many of whom were native to the Baltic region and the Russian steppes, such as the Vandals, the Visigoths [Western Goths], the Ostrogoths [Eastern Goths], and the Franks, brought the debilitated and demoralised Western Roman Empire to its knees. In A.D.410, Alaric (A.D.370-410), the King of the Visigoths, sacked Rome – the first time Rome had been invaded by any foreign army. In A.D.455, the Vandals, who had conquered North Africa and before their defeat by the Visigoths had also occupied Spain, invaded Italy with their fleet and sacked Rome. In A.D.476, Odovacer, the King of the Ostrogoths, deposed the puppet Western Roman Emperor, Romulus Augustulus, and established in Italy the Ostrogothic kingdom of Odovacer.

In A.D.489, the Eastern Roman Emperor Zenon sent Theodoric, the King of the Ostrogoths who was an Arian Christian, to reconquer Italy for the Roman Empire and rule it wisely and well in the name of the Emperor, a task which Theodoric accomplished after 4 years of fierce fighting. Theodoric, who was a cultivated person and a good administrator, established the Ostrogothic kingdom which he ruled wisely and well from A.D.489 to A.D.526, but after his death, internal religious squabbles appeared between Orthodox Catholics and the Arian Christians, the followers of Areios (A.D.c.256-336), an excommunicated parish priest in Alexandria, who about A.D.318 began to preach that Jesus of Nazareth was not equivalent to God, who is unique, but only the best of God-created mortal beings. Despite this religious conflict, which weakened the Ostrogothic kingdom, Arianism still remained popular and the orthodox religious doctrine of Teutonic tribes for centuries, because the realistic and grave Teutons rejected, as Zarathushtra had done more than 6 centuries before, the hoary pagan custom of deifying mortal human beings and humanising immortal gods, an immemorial habit of primitive Hebrews in Palestine. Finally, between A.D.535 and A.D.556, after 20 years of relentless battles, the army of Eastern Roman Emperor Iustinianus subdued the Ostrogothic kingdom and made it a part of Byzantium, the surviving Eastern Roman Empire.

From the 3rd century A.D. forwards, the Western European society had become progressively less urban. Large-scale manufacturing gradually began to disappear along with townsmen and traders. Middle class, the very engine of civilisation and the future of the society, gradually disappeared, and the small-scale manufacture which still existed was virtually done exclusively on the remaining great estates. Commerce, or what remained of it, owing to the increasingly chaotic political conditions in Western Europe caused by the gradual breakdown of the central Roman authority, became increasingly restricted to local areas which led to decentralised economy. In this disintegration of the central authority, Western Europe was becoming, little-by-little, almost entirely an autarkic agrarian economy, and, in consequence, the venerable dictatorial authority of the Cæsars gave way to the 'laws of the barbarians' (***leges barbarorum***) which took the form of either the Teutonic folkright, or the decrees of warrior chieftains that in contrast to the Roman law, allowed a wide scope to the liberty of the individual.

The Middle Ages can be divided for convenience into two periods: the Early or Low Middle Ages from c.A.D.500 to A.D.1000; and the High Middle Ages from c.A.D.1000 to A.D.1453. The period from c.A.D.500 to A.D.800 is often called the 'Dark Ages' and the period from A.D.800 to A.D.1000 the Carolignian Age, a brief period of Germanic revival of the Christian Roman Empire in Europe.

After the fall of the tottering Western Roman Empire and the incursion of Germanic semi-barbarians, the classical learning in the Græco-Roman culture suffered a sudden decline. During the rule of the Ostrogothic King Theodoric in Italy, two men of learning, Boethius and Cassiodorus, were the first scholars who tried to stem the rapid decline of classical culture.

Before the final collapse of the Western Roman Empire in A.D.476, Martianus Mineus Felix Capella, a 5th century A. D. Christian cleric from Tunisia on the North-African coast of the Roman Empire, had written about A.D. 470 the most influential textbook on education in the West, < The Marriage of Philology and Mercury > (***De nuptiis philologiae et mercurii***), in which he classified intellectual learning into two basic groups: the ***trivium*** which dealt with discussional arts such as grammar, rhetoric, and logic (but was not concerned with the analysis of human phenomena); and the ***quadrivium*** which dealt with numbers and measurements such as arithmetic, geometry, astronomy, and music (considered as a study of measured tonal relationships), and was concerned with nonhuman natural phenomena. Owing to the influence of the pagan Roman and the early Christian indifference to science, teachers tended to lay far more stress on the discussional arts of the ***trivium***, which Aristotle had traced back to Zenon and the school of logic in Elea, than on the computational disciplines of the ***quadrivium***, which can be traced back to Archytas and his Pythagorean school in Taras. This book was extraordinarily popular in the schools of the Early Middle Ages and held its own besides the more scientific treatises of Boethius and the practical compendia of Cassiodorus.

Ancius Manlius Severinus Boethius (A.D.c.480-524), a Roman nobleman, philosopher and probably the foremost mathematician of ancient Rome, had been appointed in A.D.510, a consul in Rome by Theodoric, the King of Ostrogoths and the ruler of Rome. In A.D.523 Boethius was appointed ***magister officiorum*** (master official). Late in the rule of Theodoric false charges of treason were laid against Boethius, and in A.D.523 he was imprisoned in Pavia. A year later he was tortured, sentenced to death without a trial, and executed. Boethius, who was not an Orthodox Christian, knew both Latin and Greek, and he had planned to produce Latin translations of all the available works of both Plato and Aristotle. He was the first to attempt to use the logical method of Aristotle in Christian theology, because he realised the importance of the Greek intellectual methods in the defence of the Christian thought. Unfortunately he was not able to carry out his plan. During his imprisonment he wrote about A.D.523 his famous work, < Consolation of Philosophy > (***De consolatione philosophiae***), a dialogue between himself and the personification of philosophy which was a noble but not a very original work. Though written by a Roman, it contained so many aspects of Christian ethics that it was highly valued by schoolmen during the High Middle Ages. He also wrote 3 books: < On Music > (***De musica***), < On Arithmetic > (***De arithmetica***), and < On Geometry > (***De geometria***), works which long served to present Greek mathematics to the mediæval world. Boethius' book on geometry consisted mostly of some simpler propositions of Eukleides (in English, Euclid) but it only provided proofs for the first three propositions, and applications to mensuration.

For Boethius the things in this world were either discrete (***multitudes***), or continuous (***magnitudes***). ***Multitudes*** were represented by numbers, or in their ratios by music; ***magnitudes*** at rest were treated by geometry, and those in motion by astronomy, all of which together represented the ***quadrivium***. In < On Arithmetic >, Boethius wrote: "By all men of old reputation who, following Pythagoras' reputation, have distinguished themselves by pure intellect, it has always been considered settled that no one can reach the highest perfection of philosophical doctrines, who does not seek the heights of learning at a certain crossway – the ***quadrivium***." Evidently, Boethius regarded the pursuit of the ***quadrivium***, a term which he probably introduced, as the way to a complete mastery of philosophy. In many different ways, Boethius mediated between the ancient classical culture and scholasticism which represented the mediæval learning by reintroducing liberal arts consisting of ***trivium*** and ***quadrivium***, and promoting the use of logic in rational enquiry. Boethius prepared the ground for the famous mediæval controversy over the nature of 'universals' and the 'particulars'; a controversy which took place five centuries later, when Boethius discussed the general concepts or 'universals' as they were considered by the Greek philosopher Porphyrios of Syara (late 3rd century A.D.) in the work ***Isagoge***, and wondered whether species as such are real or only conceptions of the mind. Boethius himself seemed to support the Platonic view that the 'universals' are independent of man and exist apart from the 'particulars'. In fact, Boethius was one of the last Neoplatonists. He wrote a treatise on logic which greatly influenced the mediæval logic, and he also translated some logical works of Aristotle with commentaries from which the early mediæval scholars mainly derived their limited knowledge of Aristotle. His treatise,< On Music > (***De musica***) remained the unquestioned authority on music for a millennium. He, moreover, wrote a number of works on theology. Boethius had also taken an active interest in the reform of coinage, and in the introduction of time-measuring devices such as waterclocks and sundials. It was mainly through all these works of Boethius, that the Greek philosophy was transmitted to the Early Middle Ages.

Boethius' contemporary, Flavius Magnus Aurelius Cassiodorus Senator (c.A.D.480-583), was a Roman historian and the second most important preserver of classical culture. He was a contemporary of the Italian monk from ***Norcia***, called St. Benedict of Nursia (c. A.D.480-543), who founded Western monasticism with his influential book, < Monastic Rules > (***Regula monachorum***), a work probably composed about A.D. 515 which consisted of simple and practical rules designed to weed out the spiritually unworthy and strengthen the sincere believers. St. Benedict intended to institute a school 'for the service of God' and 'to amend vice and preserve charity'.

The Western monasticism was accepted by the early Christian Church mainly because it had been supported by St. Jerome (A.D.c.340-419) and by St. Augustine. Jerome was a son of well-to-do Christian parents from Iryllia (modern Albania), who had obtained an excellent classical education. The Western ascetism had been inspired by St. Paul, the first anchorite of the desert, whose life was a motive for monasticism. Jerome had been a secretary to Pope Damasus in Rome, but he left in A.D.385 to establish a monastery and monastic school at Bethlehem in Palestine, as a coeducational institution which included a convent. In this school classical education was given as a preparation for Christian education which made his school very popular and young monks flocked to it from all parts of Europe. Jerome was a born teacher and as a man of learning he belongs to the front ranks of scholars and humanists of all time. Jerome's main object in life was to put his scholarship at the disposal of Christian religion. Being restless, inquisitive and irascible, he was also a troublemaker. Jerome, who had a sharp tongue like most of the typical humanists, was capable of letting loose with a torrent of cultivated billingsgate if the appropriate occasion arose. He was a superb humanist, but unfortunately not a superb humanitarian, for he went about doing 'good' without regard to those who did not want it. Although he lived with his scribes, books and his pet lion in a den, he advised moderation in ascetism with the ancient Greek motto: 'Nothing too much (***ne quid nimis***)'. Jerome was the actual founder of the more liberal monasticism in which classical studies found an important place in Christian education. His Latin translation of the Bible called ***The Vulgate*** became the official Roman Church version of the Bible.

St. Benedict, who in contrast to St. Jerome was a mystic suspicious of intellectual education, made no provisions for the education of monks in pagan literature: monks were restricted to read only the holy scriptures. By the standards of the time, Benedictine Rules did not impose a great deal of austerity or ascetism on the monks but it did emphasise the spiritual ennobling of work in monastic life exemplified by St. Benedict's dicta: 'Idleness is the enemy of soul', and 'to work is to pray'. In A.D. 529, St. Benedict found a pagan temple of Apollo on Monte Cassino in Italy, which he tore down and built in its place his famous abbey. He founded 12 monasteries near ***Sublaqueum*** (modern, Subiaco) from which his monasticism was spread by his disciples throughout the central and western Europe during his lifetime.

Cassiodorus was of noble Roman birth and a Neoplatonist, and next to Boethius the most important person at the court of Theodoric. He became the secretary of State under King Theodoric, a consul in A.D.514, and still later, like Boethius, ***magister officiorum***. He was responsible for the collection of the King's official correspondence, which Cassiodorus published in < Miscellaneous Letters > (***Variae epistolae***). In it he quoted a memorable statement of Theodoric, an exceptionally tolerant Gothic monarch: "We cannot prescribe religion for no one can be forced to believe against his will," showing a remarkable insight into human nature. From A.D.530 to A.D.536, Cassiodorus together with Pope Agapetus planned the founding of a Christian university of learning in Rome but the death of Theodoric in A.D.526, the death of Agapetus in A.D.535, and the reconquest of Rome by the Eastern Roman Emperor Iustinianus made him give up this plan. Instead, Cassiodorus, who was 60 years old at the time, became a Benedictine monk in A.D.550. He founded a monastery in ***Bruttium*** near his place of birth in Southern Italy and called it 'Fish Pond (***Vivarium***)'. In this monastery Cassiodorus returned to the educational plan of St. Jerome which aimed to amalgamate two cultures, the Christian and the pagan Græco-Roman culture, in which the classical learning served as the very means to advance and strengthen Christian learning. Although in this new education reading was the basis of the curriculum, the divine still held the foremost place. Jerome is responsible for the inception, and Cassiodorus for the establishment of this system of education. Cassiodorus set forth his ideas on education in his work: < A Manual of Instruction in Divine and Human Reading > (***Divinae lectiones***).

Cassiodorus wrote a book < The Arts and Liberal Literary Disciplines > (***De artibus et disciplinis liberalium literarum***), in which he describes the basic Aristotelian classification of sciences as a natural philosophy consisting of 2 parts, the theoretical (***inspection***): physics (***naturalis***), mathematics (***doctrinales***), metaphysics (***divinales***); and the practical (***actualis***): ethics (***moralis***), economics (***dispensativa***), and politics (***civiles***). He divided learning, like Capella, into arts (***artes***): grammar, rhetoric, and dialectic; and into disciplines (***disciplinae***): arithmetic, geometry, astronomy, and music, which continued to be taught under the rubrics of ***trivium*** and ***quadrivium*** as used by Capella. Cassiodorus himself wrote books in which he gave the ancient Greek works on mathematics and astronomy in his own poor versions. Since such studies needed a library, Cassiodorus urged and encouraged monks to collect and copy classical pagan works, which made the Benedictine monks the preservers of classical literary relics, particularly during the so-called 'Dark Ages' when individual Benedictine monks were the main preservers of classical learning. The monks of the Western world became the first intellectuals in history to do manual work. In monks the practical and the theoretical for the first time existed in the same person, and they were mainly responsible for destroying the artificial barrier which had existed since the Græco-Roman times between the empirical and the speculative, thereby helping to create a favourable social climate for the development of science and engineering.

Boethius and Cassiodorus, however, were not the typical scholars of the time. A more typical man of learning of the period was Gregory the Great, who reigned as Pope from A.D.590 to A.D.604, and had come to his office from a monastery. He had been a Roman nobleman and the prefect of Rome, and he carried his ample administrative talents to the papacy. Surprisingly, Gregory had no use for the classics despite his own excellent classical education. He wrote < Dialogues > (***Dialogues***), a work which included the life of St. Benedict, and was meant to popularise the monastic life. His commentaries on the Book of Job was intended to make people behave better. Gregory's own literary style was vigorous but rather crude, and everything he wrote had its practical purpose.

Another man of letters of the period was Gregory (A.D.538-594), Bishop of Tours, who wrote a rather juvenile type of history of the Frankish ruling house, called the Merovingian dynasty. In the education of the clergy, Gregory of Tours advised: "If thou wilt be a priest of God, then let our Martianus [Capella] instruct thee first in the seven sciences [***trivium*** and ***quadrivium***]."

In Spain, Isidore (c.A.D.570-636), Archbishop of Seville, was another well-known scholar of the so-called 'Dark Ages'. He wrote a work in 20 books, < The Etymologies > (***Etymologiae***), a kind of encyclopædia containing material ranging from mathematics to medicine, which became the standard reference book for couple of centuries. Isidore's treatise gives not only an indication of his learning, which was remarkable for his time, but also of his superstition and ignorance.

However, the most prominent man of learning among the many cultivated men living during the 'Dark Ages' was an English Benedictine monk ***Beda Venerabilis*** (The Venerable Bede) (A.D.c.672-735), of Durham, who was a great master of vigorous and pure Latin, and a connoisseur of the Greek and the Hebrew language. He was the leading Anglo-Saxon scholar of his time and a first-rate historian. He worked like a modern scholar by consulting many documents, discussed their relative merits, and faithfully cited them as sources, a most unusual practice at the time. He spent his whole life at the monasteries of Wearmouth at Sunderland and Jarrow, where he taught Hebrew,

Greek and Latin languages. Bede was the author of about 40 historical, scientific, and theological works mostly written in elegant Latin. His most prominent book in science is < On the Nature of Things > (***De natura rerum***) and his treatise of chronology, but his best work is his remarkable <Ecclesiastical History of the English People > (***Historia ecclesiastica gentia Anglorum***) describing a period from A.D.597 to A.D.731, a work published in A.D.731 which made him the 'Father of English History'. He measured all his dates from the year of birth of Christ, a practice still followed today. By that time the leadership in learning had moved from the European continent to the British Isles, and Northumbria where Bede taught was considered the leading center of learning in Europe.

Bede, who considered the world to be a cause-and-effect universe, held that the Earth was a static sphere with 5 zones of which only 2 were habitable. He also gave a clear account of the phases of the Moon, and of eclipses, the general problems of time-measurement, arithmetical computation, astronomical phenomena, and historical and cosmological chronology.

He wrote 2 treatises on rational time-measurement in which he gave one of the clearest expositions of the principles of Christian calendar which had the problem that it was a combination of the Roman 'Iulian calendar' based on the Solar year and the Hebrew Lunar calendar. The year and its divisions into months, weeks and days belonged to the Iulian Calendar, but the date of the Easter was determined by the phases of the Moon and, therefore, the date of the Easter in the Iulian calendar varied within definite limits from one year to the next. The basic problem in calculating the date of the Easter was that the lengths of the Solar year, the Lunar month and the day are incommensurable: no number of days can make an exact number of Lunar months or Solar years, and no number of Lunar months can make an exact number of Solar years. To relate the phases of the Moon accurately to the Solar year in terms of whole days, it is necessary to use a system of ***ad hoc*** adjustments based on some definite cycle.

The ancient Greek astronomer Meton of Athens (*floruit* 440 B.C.) discovered in 432 B.C. that 235 Lunar months made up just about 19 Solar years. Therefore, he established a cycle of 19 Solar years consisting of 12 years of 12 Lunar months and 7 years of 13 Lunar months which makes the Lunar calendar match the seasons. This arrangement is called the 'Metonic Cycle' which may have been already known to Babylonian astronomers. The Greek astronomer Oinopides of Chios (c.500-430 B.C.) had earlier invented a cycle of 59 years for the return of the coincidence of the Solar and the Lunar year. The Metonic Cycle made the length of the Solar year 365¼ days plus 1/76 of a day which was more than 30 minutes too long, whereas the 'Oinopidean Cycle' gave the length of the Solar year as 365 days plus somewhat less than 9 hours. The ancient Greek calendar was based on the Metonic Cycle, and it remained the calendar of the ancient world until 46 B.C. when Iulius Gaius Caesar (100-44 B.C.), a man of letters who had a genuine interest in astronomy and who composed a remarkably popular work < On Stars > (***De astris***) containing combined data on stars, weather and the seasons, with the assistance of the Peripatetic astronomer Sosigenes of Alexandria (born c.90 B.C.) established the so-called 'Iulian calendar' consisting of a 365-day year 3 times in a row to be followed by a 366-day 'leap year', a system which with minor modifications has lasted till the present time. The 'leap year' was first suggested by Eudoxos of Knidos (c.408-c.356 B.C.). Jews retained the Greek Lunar calendar, and in Christianity the date of the Easter is still calculated by the use of Metonic Cycle.

Bede's treatise on the calendar remained the standard textbook for 5 centuries and were used even after the Gregorian calendar reform in A.D.1582. In its time Bede's science was a remarkable achievement, and it influenced the educational system of the cathedral schools established for Charlemagne by Alcuin of York in the Carolignian Renaissance.

It is evident from the previous discussion that classical learning was kept alive during the so-called 'Dark Ages' by Boethius, Isidore of Seville, and The Venerable Bede. Cassiodorus, Isidore of Seville and The Venerable Bede were important links between the Græco-Roman civilisation, particularly with regard to the ancient Greek mathematics and the early mediæval world, but it was Boethius who exerted the greatest influence on the early mediæval learning.

The Carolignian Age in the 'Dark Ages' began with the establishment of the Frankish State by the Merovingian King Clovis, who defeated the Gallo-Roman general Syagrius in A.D.486, repulsed the Germanic tribe Alemanni, and another Germanic tribe, the Visigoths, in the crucial Battle of Vouillé in A.D.507. He reigned as a converted Christian ruler from A.D.481 to A.D.511. After his death the Frankish State was partitioned among his sons according to the traditional Frankish custom, which always led to an internal struggle to unify the Frankish State. The powers of the Merovingian kings were gradually taken over by the mayor of the palace (a kind of prime minister), although he exercised that authority in the name of the king. In A.D.720, one mayor of the palace, Charles (in Latin, ***Carolus***) (A.D.714-741), who was later called ***Martel*** (The Hammer), made himself king in all but name. He was above all a warrior, and he was the first to organise the Frankish knights about A.D. 730 into a formidable cavalry based on a new military technique, the mounted shock combat of his own invention in which the stirrup, adopted from the Chinese, and the saddle substituted the power of the horse for the power of the man. The Chinese, who had adopted the stirrup from the nomadic horsemen of the steppes, who in turn had developed it from the Indian toe-stirrup in the 2nd century B.C., never devised any new military technique because of the stirrup. In the Frankish shock cavalry the lance was now supported by a saddle with a high pommel and cantle, and the shield became pointed at the bottom to offer better protection to the knight's left leg. The Byzantine and the Saracen cavalry adopted most of the Frankish warfare technology.

In A.D.732 Charles Martel defeated a Muslim invasion force from Spain at Poitiers. It was said of this famous battle that the 'Hammer of the Franks' struck the decisive blow that checked the advance of Islam into the West. The Frankish kingdom had thereby passed to the Carolignians. Charles Martel's grandson, Charlemagne (in Latin, ***Carolus Magnus***) (A.D.742-814), who was a formidable warrior with colossal energy and an excellent administrator, extended the Frankish State by conquest into a Carolignian Empire of Western Europe. Carolignian government was paternal, and the Church and the Carolignian State were so closely bound together that it was difficult to make any distinction between their jurisdictions. Charlemagne issued innumerable decrees concerning so many aspects of public and private life that he must be considered one of the great legislators of the Middle Ages. Many of his decrees dealt with economic matters. Trade had been hindered by the Muslims so much that it became more and more restricted to local needs in which barter was replacing money economy. Charlemagne, who was the prime protector of the Church, realised that the religion of his people was steeped in superstition, and that the majority of the clergy was too ignorant to instruct the people. He recognised that a better education of the churchmen was of great importance, and, therefore, he urged Bishops and Abbots to establish schools at monasteries and cathedrals for the training of priests. Charlemagne, himself, established a school of music and a palace school in ***Aux de Chapelle*** (modern Aachen in Germany) to which he summoned scholars from all parts of Western Europe, such as Paul the Deacon (in Latin, ***Paulus Diaconus***) who wrote the < History of the Lombards > (***Historia Lombardiensis***), from Italy, and Theodulphus, a Spanish Goth, whom Charlemagne later made Bishop of Orléans.

Einhard (Latin name, ***Eginhard***) (A.D. c.770-840), who had been educated at the monastery in Fulda and continued his education in A.D.796 at the palace school, was a historian and one of the few Frankish scholars at that school. Charlemagne employed Einhard as his ***architectus***, and superintendent of public buildings, diplomat and educator who later became the tutor of Lothair I, a grandson of Charlemagne. Einhard was the first mediæval scholar to study ***De architectura*** of Vitruvius Pollio, which helped to disseminate the knowledge in this treatise in the Carolignian Empire and, subsequently, in the Germanic countries. Einhard also wrote the biography, < Life of Charlemagne > (***Vita Karoli Magni***), which was translated into many vernacular languages.

The most famous scholar who helped Charlemagne to organise the palace school and direct its educational programme from A.D.781 to A.D.790 was the English scholar Alcuin of York (Latin name, ***Flaccus Albinus***) (A.D.735-804), who was born the year Bede died. Alcuin had studied under a disciple of Bede at the cathedral school of York and had become the principal of that school in A.D. 766. Alcuin helped to change the palace school into a serious educational institution where the seven liberal arts, the ***trivium*** and the ***quadrivium***, which became the curriculum for mediæval Western Europe, were studied. Charlemagne even ordered his nobles to attend the school to improve their education. Charlemagne himself attended his palace school and took part in learned conversations conducted there by Alcuin. Alcuin encouraged the preservation and study of ancient texts. Alcuin himself wrote much that was needed in the school, and took the lead in biblical scholarship, as well as in improving the handwriting of the scribes in monasteries who produced a regular supply of legible books. The survival of much of Latin literature is due to the efforts of these

Carolignian scribes. Throughout such scholarly endeavours, Alcuin had an important and lasting influence on the intellectual life in Europe.

Alcuin himself was the author of numerous letters, mostly on theological and educational subjects, and of a textbook on rhetoric entitled < Compendia > (***Compendia***), and of poems. He also wrote on grammar, on dialectic, on arithmetic and on seven liberal arts. Alcuin's learning was as extensive as could be found in his century, but his scholarship was rather limited. His scholarly reputation depended chiefly upon his several works on grammar. The humanistic studies of Alcuin, and his successors led to a revival of learning in Western Europe, and to the development of the Carolignian minuscule script which later influenced the Renaissance handwriting in Italy. In A.D.796, Charlemagne appointed Alcuin the Abbot of St. Martin monastery in Tours, the richest monastery in France, where he established his most important school which became the center of learning in France. These church schools ultimately became mediæval universities, the teachers of which were usually supplied by the mendicant Church orders, the Franciscans and the Dominicans.

Charlemagne himself spoke and read Latin as well as his native German tongue for which he began a grammar, and he knew Greek, but he never quite mastered writing, which he took up late in life, despite a determined effort.

In A.D.800, Charlemagne was crowned the first Emperor of the Holy Roman Empire by Pope Leo III in Rome, but as his friend and biographer Einhard wrote, he had done it reluctantly. When the Church baptised, or consecrated the Empire by crowning Charlemagne a Roman-style Emperor, it made the problem of conscience more complicated for the Christian society because a government which to all appearances is in tune with the Christian society can, for that very reason, betray this society with the greatest of impunity. The same was, and is still true also of the Church as an organised institution.

The Holy Roman Empire was actually propped up by the force of Charlemagne's imposing personality, for the Empire lacked any real ethnic or political unity. It was held together by the Teutonic belief in the loyalty to the worthy ruler and by a common bond of membership in the Roman Church. As soon as Charlemagne was dead, his Empire began to disintegrate, when the local influence of the aristocracy, the counts, the bishops, and great landowners began to rise because they gradually took over the rights and duties of the central government, a process which ultimately led to a political system called 'feudalism'. This process of dissolution of the Carolignian Empire was further accelerated by the semibarbaric invaders from the North, the Norsemen known as Vikings, who descended with unprecedented power and rapidity upon the Western Europe from the sea in their long ships propelled by oars and a large rectangular sail.

Already during the lifetime of Charlemagne, the Vikings began to make piratical raids from Scandinavia to the British Isles. The first such recorded raid took place in A.D.787. The Vikings were heathen Teutons from Scandinavia who raided the coastal towns of Europe, and who in the last year of Charlemagne's rule had already assaulted the coast of the Frankish Empire. The Vikings were tall, blond warriors clad in their ringmail and scarlet cloaks, who wielded their long swords and long-handled battle axes. Vikings were remarkably versatile individuals for they were industrious farmers, skilled fishermen, able traders, daring sailors, and fearless pirates, equally adept on land and at sea, and they combined reckless daring with sound practical sense. They were tough, vigorous and individualistic people who were remarkably intelligent. Though they were fierce, and indomitable warriors, and masters of hit-and-run warfare, the Norsemen had their own literate culture glorified in their epical literature, the < Norse Sagas >.

At first they came in small raiding parties and a few ships, but soon the frequency and number of their ships increased dramatically, and no place along the European coast was safe from the organised Viking fleets which often numbered into hundreds of ships. They prowled along the Atlantic coastline, penetrated into the Mediterranean, and some of the Vikings landed in Iceland and in Greenland, and even in Canada. They also took the eastern route of conquest through the rivers of Russia, to the Black Sea, and to Constantinople where they met other Vikings who had come via the Mediterranean through the Strait of Gibraltar. For this reason, no place along the coast of Europe was safe from the Vikings. At first they plundered and destroyed much what they found when they landed. They loved to raid monasteries where they obtained easy riches and, therefore, a great number of monasteries were completely destroyed, and with them a great deal of classical learning which had been preserved there.

They soon settled in Normandy which became their dukedom in France, in England, in Ireland, in Sicily, and in Russia where they established a kingdom which later became the Russian State. They adopted the speech, the Christian religion, and customs of the people among whom they now lived, and began to apply their considerable talents to the advancement of the society. No invaders of Europe have been so versatile and talented as the Norsemen, who have left their permanent mark on the European civilisation for Vikings added new energy, vitality and new elements of culture to the Western civilisation.

Teutonic dedication to personal independence was the source of the Norsemen's passionate belief in the ideals of loyalty, courage, individual freedom, and in the equality of individual rights. Loyalty to institutions - the hallmark of statism - did not exist among the Teutonic people such as the Vikings. They did not believe in institutionalised authority but recognised only authority that one individual can have upon another individual through mutual consent. They did not believe in delegating any of the important attributes of man and, for this reason, all their political relationships were based on personal loyalties. Teutonic people had democratic traditions based on limited government formed by an assembly of all freemen, and their chieftain was elected by all arm-bearing men. However, the chieftain was subject to the same laws as everybody else. In other words, the chieftain was only the 'first among equals' (***primus inter pares***). Fortunately for the European civilisation, the individualistic ideas of the Christians and the Teutonic Vikings triumphed over the Græco-Roman statist ideas, and these ideas became the very foundation of the European civilisation.

However, once these remarkable Teutonic people, who came from Scandinavia into the civilised world of Europe as wild, heathen semibarbarians and a terror to all, had accepted Christian religion and the civilisation of the kingdoms they had earlier plundered but later settled in, they demonstrated their genius for government and administration unequalled by any other people in history. For centuries the Norse Kingdom in Sicily was the most tolerant, enlightened, cultured, and by far the best governed State in Europe. Normandy, their independent Dukedom in France, was the best organised and governed part of France. They founded the trading State in Russia, where they were known as Rus people, which later became the Slavic Empire. In Iceland they established in A.D.930 the first 'constitutional democracy' in history which was founded upon the 'Constitution of Ulfiot', and they produced the first great European literature in their Norse Sagas, the < Eddas >. In Constantinople, the capital of the Byzantine Empire, Norsemen were recognised as the finest warriors, and they formed the personal bodyguard of the Emperor. They also were the distinguished military leaders of the first Christian Crusades against the infidel Saracens. Normans, the Norsemen who had assimilated with the Franks in Normandy, brought their political talent and influence to Great Britain when William the Conqueror invaded and conquered England in A.D.1066. The influence of Norsemen on the development of the European civilisation was decisive, since they were instrumental in the ultimate collapse of the Carolignian Empire, a Roman statist version of Christendom, therefore giving the impetus to the development of the European feudalism from which a decentralised European civilisation was born during the Early Middle Ages.

Feudalism

The Carolignian kings were quite incapable of protecting people against the lightning fast attacks of the Vikings and, therefore, Frankish people lost their confidence in their central government. Gradually the Carolignian Empire fragmented into many small, autonomous kingdoms in which the essential political functions were carried out by means of private contracts, or agreements between individuals [and not between a sovereign government and its people], a time-honoured ancient Teutonic custom. Individuals primarily sought personal protection, and out of it developed a custom of placing oneself voluntarily in a dependent relationship to a more powerful person. In this voluntary relationship, the superior came to be called a 'lord', and the inferior a 'vassal' [the Celtic term, ***givassawl*** meant, 'one who serves']. The great nobles, the vassals-in-chief, who served a king in some military or political capacity, were granted tenure on royal lands called ***beneficium***, which came to be known by the end of the 11th century A.D. as ***feudum***, or fief. The fief was a sociopolitical unit, which varied in size with the wealth and importance of the landholder. These vassals-in-chief divided the greater part of their fief into smaller fiefs, and granted land tenure of these fiefs to their own vassals, who thus became subvassals of the king. These subvassals in turn might grant land tenure to their own vassals, and so on until the fiefs became so small that it could support and supply only a single knight. Such a process is called 'subinfeudation'. All the vassals were noble-born and set apart from the base-born.

The basic socio-economic unit of a fief was a manor, which represented a largely autarkic farm community that became the foundation of mediæval society and mediæval economy. The manor as a rural institution outranked both urban and commercial institutions, although cities and towns never disappeared and trade never completely vanished not even during the so-called 'Dark Ages'. There were thousands of manors in the Mediæval Age, and many lords had grants for a number of manors. A manor was not a real estate of the feudal lord, since he did not own it for he himself was a tenant on his fief. All land in principle, but not in practice, was owned by the king. Thus, the fief (***feudum***) was a grant made to a lord by a higher lord. The term 'Feudalism' implies the military, political, and social relationship that existed between the lord of the manor and the individual from whom he held it. Only the upper class persons, such as 'nobles' and 'knights' had fiefs; 'commoners' did not have fiefs though they may have lived on a manor. The tenants of a manor were the farmers and herdsmen who worked on the land. They had homesteads of their own, usually grouped into a village, and their own plots, which they farmed for food. For a certain part of the week they had to work without pay on the lord's land, called the ***demesne***, and had to give a percentage of their own crops to the lord in compensation for which the lord provided military protection and safety to the tenants of his manor. The lord resided in his manor house or castle, as his predecessor of late Roman times had lived in his great villa, with his household and his private army of retainers. The size of the household, consisting of household servants, grooms, ostlers, and huntsmen depended upon the size and wealth of the manor. A fief could be any piece of land, a single manor, a group of manors, or even a whole province. A fief could also be a castle, the right to collect taxes or tolls, to coin money, or to collect fees levied by the court. In the Early Middle Ages, lords had 'household knights' who held no fiefs at all, but were supported and supplied by the lord for whom they fought.

A special Teutonic institution had been the ***comitatus*** (in Latin, ***comes*** meant a companion) which was a small unit of young men sworn to serve with absolute fidelity a strong, military chieftain who provided them with food, shelter and weapons. ***Comitatus*** ultimately evolved into the mediæval institution of vassalage. After a vassal had done 'homage' and sworn 'fealty' to his feudal lord as his suzerein, the lord invested the vassal with a symbol signifying the transfer of the fief to the new holder. The feudal contracts imposed obligations on both parties: the lord to protect the vassal and the fief, to respect the vassal's womenfolk, and to guarantee that the vassal receives justice in the lord's court consisting of his 'peers'; the vassal to give 'aid and counsel' to the lord in military campaigns [initially limited to 40 days], in ceremonies and entertainment. The feudal contract was usually oral, but in the Late Middle Ages, it was written down in the form of a charter, like the famous ***Magna Carta***.

The manor evolved from the ***latifundia***, or great estate of the late Roman period, which were owned by a ***magnate*** and staffed by a household of fighters, who later became knights and feudal vassals, and by a large number of ***coloni***, or agricultural workers who later became serfs. ***Colonus*** was often a descendant of a small landowner who had once been free but who, during troubled times of barbarian invasions, had turned over his property and free status to a magnate in exchange for military protection. At the same time, the social structure of a manor bore some resemblance to the ancient Germanic village community.

Serfdom, of course, was not slavery, since a serf was not owned by the feudal lord. The mediæval serf was tied to the land, but the land was also tied to the serf in hereditary fashion. Moreover, a serf had a soul and as a Christian he could not be treated without respect. Not all the peasants on a manor were serfs: some of the peasants were freeman, called ***villein*** (villager) in France and ***franklin*** in England, who only owed special manorial services to the lord and virtually owned the land they cultivated.

Feudalism was effectively a decentralised political system aimed to maintain a chain of authority over a large territory, which the Romans had accomplished by means of their army and bureaucracy. In the decaying late Roman period, large local landlords had assumed increasing responsibility for the people who lived on, and around their great estates, representing real estates which they actually owned. Such private persons performing a public function came to be known as ***magnates***, who were local bosses or chiefs. Some invading Germanic semibarbarians displaced Roman ***magnates*** as large landowners, but they still remained partially dependent on their own chieftains. The two most important titles of vassals-in-chief in the feudal hierarchy, the count and the duke, were originally the imperial agents of the late Roman Empire. The 'count' (in Latin, ***comes***) was a local, county official appointed by the Emperor to act as an imperial agent in fiscal, judicial, and, above all, military administration. The 'duke' (in Latin, ***dux***) was an imperially appointed official who carried out most of the official functions of a count but for a duchy, a more important and larger area than a county. Over a long period after the death of Charlemagne and the disintegration of his Empire into smaller new kingdoms, the former offices of counts and dukes fell into the hands of ***magnates*** because the new kings had to make concessions to the ***magnates*** who supplied money and provisions for the kings to conduct their wars. Through these concessions the ***magnates*** were granted full feudal status by becoming hereditary holders of property and hereditary executors of governmental functions. In this way the control, but not the ownership of the fief became under the jurisdiction of the ***magnate*** as a vassal-in-chief of the king who was considered to own the fief.

By about A.D.1000 the temporary Carolignian ***beneficium*** had become the hereditary ***feudum***, or fief, thus establishing feudalism in Europe. Even clergy, such as bishops and abbots were often vassals-in-chief of the king and landholders of fiefs, and some even fought as mace-wielding warriors in wars.

The mediæval feudal government was fundamentally honest in its professions, and its performance was better than its promise, which is a rarity in the history of governments. Thus, feudalism was an agreement entered into by free men and it entailed honourable service and mutual respect. Its requirements were complicated and exacting for both the feudal lord and the vassal. The base-born peasants, as mentioned above, were outside the pale of this feudal association, but the 'custom of the manor' became a body of rules behind which the untutored and defenceless villein, or even the serf, could stand up and resist the arbitrary demands of the lord of the manor by claiming his customary rights. Only in the Late Feudal Age did the serf come up to the level of the ***villein***, the freeman peasant. The serf was a party to the 'manorial contract' between two social unequals: himself and his feudal lord; in contrast, the 'feudal contract' was between social equals: the vassal and his lord.

The feudal government respected the value of the individual man as a person, but it did not treat all men as equals in a marked contrast to the modern totalitarian State which depersonalises man and treats all human life as of equal, but virtually of no intrinsic value.

Monachal Engineering and Power Technology

During the Middle Ages people admired individuals who had the will to live in close accord with their ideals and, therefore, the so-called 'sainthood' was a publicly recognised vocation for living men and women. In the mediæval times people would knowingly choose a 'saint' to public office, whereas in modern times, in contrast, people would knowingly sooner elect a knave, or even a lawbreaker to public office than a 'saint', because an unpretentious 'saint' as a virtuous person is generally disliked, and frequently almost detested for his, or her superior spiritual nobility by the envious and supersensitive mass-man.

As a result of the prevalence of Teutonic and Christian ideals, the Middle Ages gave birth, and brought to maturity, a distinctively European civilisation that is the origin of modern civilisation.

In ancient Greece and Rome the individual man was completely subordinated to the State. In these ancient countries an individual man had no right to exist apart from the State, of which he was considered a mere subsidiary component. The individual's value, dignity and rights were 'privileges' granted to him by the State, which could be removed from him at any time for any reason by the State. Without the patronage of the State, the individual man was next to worthless, and he had no inalienable, or God-given rights of any sort just because he was born a man.

Christians, particularly the early ones, absolutely refused to accept the subordination of the individual man to the State; in fact, the very early Christians even refused to recognise the State as an authority over the life of a Christian, a political stance for which they were atrociously persecuted by the Roman State as subversive enemies of Rome. An early Christian apologist, a former Roman lawyer, Quintus Septimus Florens Tertullianus (in English, Tertullian) (A.D.c.160-220), put the general Christian outlook into the following brief statement: "Nothing is as alien as a public thing (***res publica***)."

In the Christian view, an individual man as a child of God, is created in the image of God, and, therefore, man cannot be considered as a creature of the State to be used as an instrument of the State or as a means to ends by other men in authority. In the Christian belief, an individual man is endowed by God with a unique spirit and soul that is accessible only to God. Moreover, in the Christian view, an individual man has infinite value in the eyes of God and, therefore, only human beings are priceless. Therefore, to a Christian, an individual man as a person possesses an inviolable consciousness and conscience which constitutes his very inner sanctum - a private inner world in which resides his personal worth and dignity as a man. It was considered a sacrilege and profanation committed by any man who tried to violate the private inner world of any other man since they thought that only God should have access to a man's soul. The early Christians thought that any such act implies an arrogation of Godly powers on the part of the perpetrator of this vile act of disrespect for the dignity of another human being, and, therefore, it represented an evil deed. Evil, so the Christians believed, has its roots in the soul of the individual man who in his self-will abuses his power of free choice.

Since to a Christian each man is a child of God and, therefore, all men are 'spiritual equals' in the eyes of God, no man could ever be regarded as a mere chattel of any other man or State. For this reason a genuine Christian is always willing to sacrifice things for people, but never people for things. Slavery as an institution had always been quite alien to the way of life of the Teuton, the Nordic German semibarbarian. The Christian morality with its emphasis on the great worth and dignity of each individual man as a child of God further helped to bring the idea of slavery into general disrepute. For these reasons the institution of slavery of the classical Græco-Roman civilisation never had a real chance of survival in Christian Europe since the European civilisation was thought by Christians to be a 'Christendom', a kingdom of Christ on Earth in which the credential of citizenship was the Christian faith and baptism.

The Christians firmly believed that an individual man possesses a Christian ideal of perfection which transcends any reason or need of the State. Therefore, an individual man possesses personal dignity and worth that transcends the worldly State, and his right to exist for his own sake as a child of God is sacred. Even the most humble occupation of a moral and upright individual as a private person with inviolable inner self was considered a dignified occupation for a Christian. Social status in Christendom played no role in the dignity of the individual man, a view succinctly expressed by Apostle Paul: "God is no respecter of persons." By such fundamental beliefs, Christianity lent personal dignity to the humble, but morally upright man, and to his ***banausic*** activities.

In the Christian outlook, an individual was responsible for himself and for the salvation of his own soul through the grace of God by always thinking good thoughts, speaking good words, and doing good deeds, all of which was done for the sake of his own soul, that is, for personal spiritual reasons. Therefore, a Christian did not do a good deed primarily for the sake of other men, but rather for his own sake, because by means of doing a good deed he strove to improve himself, to make himself a better Christian and, thus, a better person who is more worthy of salvation. Therefore, a true Christian believer is 'selfish' in the sense of recognising that it is of self-interest to him to do everything possible for the sake of self-improvement of his person, and therefore in his treatment of his fellow men he is not only kind and generous, but above all else just, because a Christian cannot love his fellow man for his sins.

The Christian God, creator and architect-engineer of the world became in the opinion of the mediæval Christian also the Master Mechanic and the Divine Artist who sculpted man out of clay like a potter, and then commanded man to rule over nature and work productively to partake in God's creative process on Earth. All matter, so the Christians believed, was created by God for the spiritual and material purpose of man. Since the material world is God's creation for the edification of man, man can learn about God from his studies of nature as God's handiwork. For this very reason, matter is neither to be transcended nor despised by man. The early Christian believed himself to be following God's own example if he used matter as an artisan for righteous material ends. The more creative and productive man is, the more he approaches God's creative example. St. Basil (A.D. c.330-379), an early Church Father and founder of the Order of Basilian Monks, wrote about the importance of work to a Christian: "... work itself should be a prayer of praise and thanksgiving reverently rendered to God who has bestowed on man the faculties of work and the means of exercising these faculties." Basil's fellow monk and friend, St. Gregory of Nazianzus (A.D. c.329-c.389) said that manual labour was intrinsically valuable, materially productive, and spiritually enriching. Therefore, work for the Christians became a moral necessity and an important means of worshipping God. This Christian outlook was well expressed in the dictum of St. Benedict of Nurcia: "... To work is to pray (***laborare est orare***)", in his manual < Rules of Monasticism > (***Regula monachorum***) in A.D.515, since Jesus of Nazareth himself and his apostles had been working men. This outlook made every moment of man's life priceless, and, therefore, Christians strove to devise technical means to reduce human labour and, thus, save precious time for spiritual work. For this reason, 'time' for Christians became a priceless valuable of God which they could ill afford to waste. Therefore in Christianity, in a stark contrast to classical antiquity, voluntary manual labour acquired for the first time in history religious significance and human dignity. Every individual's responsibility to work had been already emphasised by Apostle Paul: "If any man will not work, neither let him eat." These Christian beliefs provided the European society of the Middle Ages with a cultural climate that was unusually favourable for technological development, and which led to the prodigious growth of European technology.

On account of the early Christian belief that the world was created by a rational God, the mediæval Christians thought that natural occurrences were related in a rational manner with antecedent conditions which are representable by general principles. Therefore, mediæval scientists confidently laboured in their studies of nature to discover something that is true about nature by means of human reason.

Christian religion eliminated the traditional Greek subservience to cosmos, and the pagan worship of nature. Christianity, with its 'cult of human saints', undermined the primitive belief in 'animism' which had still plagued the late Roman society and, thereby, provided the basis for a consistent naturalistic view of the world. By following the Christian command: "Be fruitful, and multiply, and replenish the Earth, and subdue it," the Western Christians believed in the reality of the physical world, and they imposed upon it the power of man's will in order to be productive and take part in the creative process of God. To the Christians only human beings are important and irreplaceable, whereas all material things are replaceable and, therefore, expendable. This fundamental Christian outlook concerning nature was essential in opening the way for the rational use of the forces of nature, and to usher in an age of highly developed technology. The ancient men had always based their science on 'animism', which was still a basic element even in the Neoplatonic philosophy. The ancient men never had the confidence that man can harness the powers of nature, which they thought to be the privileged domain of supernatural spirits. The Roman Empire was the last stronghold of this type of thinking in the West, and the last obstacle in Europe against the general development of natural power by harnessing the forces of nature for the benefit of man.

Since life on Earth was a precious commodity to monks, they became eminently practical men who combined in themselves learning with experience, theory with practice, and intelligence with diligence. In ancient times working men were not learned, and learned men did not work. Monks were the first men of learning in history who also worked.

Cistercian Monks and Industrial Revolution

Early Christians had a strong spiritual dislike of inhuman effort and monstrous human drudgery. They regarded such backbreaking physical work unworthy of man as a child of God, because it required neither individual exercise of spiritual choice nor application of human intelligence as a God-given gift of man. They believed that not only the human but also the animal power should be avoided in backbreaking heavy work if natural power could be substituted for it. This realisation motivated Christians to substitute the work of power machinery driven by the inanimate forces of nature for heavy and dispiriting human labour. For this, and other economic reasons the introduction of labour-saving power machinery in the Western Europe was in complete harmony with the Christian religious assumption of the infinite worth of even the lowliest, but otherwise upright person. Christians of the Middle Ages considered nature as a reservoir of vast forces which were there to be explored, harnessed and used for the benefit of man according to human needs and requirements. The substitution of mechanised power for human labour was one of the great achievements of the High Middle Ages, and it represents one of the spectacular technological advances in the history of man. In this context mediæval power technology was an important step in man's quest for freedom from the servitude to brute nature.

The Cistercian monks became the leaders both in the harnessing of power in industrial processes and industrial management. Before the Cistercian Order was founded, the Cluniac Order had been established in a renewal of Christian spirit which had been relaxed in the Benedictine monasteries by reviving the strict Benedictine Rules and enforcing it through a central authority. Thus, the Abbot of Cluny was the theocratic ruler of the entire Cluniac order. By the 12th century A.D., the Cluniac monasteries which were scattered in large numbers all over Europe had become prodigiously wealthy owing to the diligent work of Cluniac monks and their lay tenants despite the fact that their monastic ideal was poverty and humility. As a result of the accumulated riches, the Cluniac monks had developed considerable secular pride and had relaxed their rules of monastic life.

In a reaction against the laxity of the Cluniac order, a Benedictine monk Robert organised, in A.D.1098, a new monastic order at ***Cistercium*** in Burgundy, a dismal, uncultivated wasteland, in an effort to recover the ideals of the original Benedictines, where they became established as the Cistercian Order. The black habit of the Benedictine monk was replaced by an unbleached white cassock, which is why the Cistercian monk became known as the 'White Monk' who lived far from the distractions and temptations of secular life. However, the effective founder of the Cistercian Order was its 'second founder', Bernard of Clairvaux (A.D.1098-1153), one of the most important Christian leaders of all time, and the most influential personality of his age. In A.D.1115 Bernard led a group of 4 fellow monks and some 25 friends to ***Clairvaux***, another desolate site near ***Cistercium***, to establish a Cistercian house in an effort to return to strict ascetism and a life of poverty. Bernard founded the Cistercian abbey on the manual labour of the monks such that the abbey would be economically self-sufficient by producing its own provisions for all its own needs, a requirement which soon led the monks to make use of the natural power. He remained the Abbot of Clairvaux monastery all his life despite many efforts by others to promote him higher in the Church hierarchy. He excelled as an administrator and organiser of ecclesiastical order, and was an irresistibly persuasive orator. Bernard dominated his age by his personality, writings, and personal example in a way unparalleled in history for a person who possessed no political power. He upbraided clergymen for their religious laxity, helped to promote the Second Crusade in the Holy Land, advised kings of France, and tamed even the most powerful of feudal nobles. He stopped a wave of pogroms in A.D.1146, and repeatedly saved luckless peasants from the powerful feudal lords. Through his writings, Bernard exerted a decisive influence on the Roman Catholic spirituality, the ***devotio moderna***, which is still felt today. His book < On the Stages of Humility and Pride > (***De gradibus humilitatis et superbie***), published about A.D.1121, established Bernard as the founder of Christian mysticism of the Middle Ages. In this book he condemned the acquisition of knowledge merely for the sake of knowledge, since to him knowledge was only then justified when it promoted the purification of the soul and led towards union with God. Humility to him was the basic condition for this union. Bernard was an intellectual anti-intellectual, and he repudiated human reason as a means of attaining the divine truth in the following words: "You will find more in forests than in books. Woods and stones will teach you more than any master." This viewpoint of Bernard was taken up again by the Swiss political philosopher and writer, Jean-Jacques Rousseau (A.D.1712-1778) in the era called the Enlightenment and made the basis of his educational system, now known as 'progressive education'.

Bernard was a man of great integrity and sincerity, but being a mortal man he was not perfect since he often lost his temper, showed occasional envy and sometimes even behaved unjustly according to John of Salisbury, an objective observer. Shortly before his death, Bernard began to lose his influence with people at large mostly because of the disastrous results of the Second Crusade which he had promoted. Bernard was posthumously canonised in A.D.1174.

Cistercian monks being wary of the central rule of the Cluniac order which depended so much on the individual character of the Cluniac Abbot who held the central authority, founded their monasteries on a genuine self-rule, so that the Cistercian monasteries constituted great democratic corporations the abbots of which met yearly to discuss the general policies of the Cistercian Order. This federation of religious monastic corporations of the Cistercians integrated well into an ever-increasing complexity of the mediæval economic life. Under the leadership of Bernard of Clairvaux, the Cistercian order underwent a great expansion since even during his lifetime 68 Cistercian houses were founded near ***Clairvaux*** alone, and by the close of the 12th century A.D. there were altogether 530 Cistercian abbeys in Europe.

The Cistercian monks regarded farming their chief occupation, and they led the world in the development of new agricultural methods. The Cistercians were the first monks to make comprehensive use of lay brothers, called ***conversi***, who lived in their abbey under a separate discipline and assisted the monks in their farming enterprise. The Cistercian monks became the leading engineers in the world in land reclamation, land draining, metallurgical technology and harnessing natural power for industrial use, and they were responsible for spreading these technological skills throughout Europe. The monastery in ***Clairvaux*** about A.D.1136 was provided with water-powered machines for fulling, tanning, smithing, milling, shifting, and other industrial processes. The Cistercian abbey at Faigny in France had 14 wheat-mills, 3 smelters, 3 forges, a brewery, 3 presses and a glasswork, all powered by waterwheels. They built the first known iron-mills, and were responsible for the widespread use of the triennial crop rotation, and of iron slag as artificial fertiliser and the source of phosphates in agriculture. The dignity of technology in the monastic life was ably presented by a German monk, Theophilus, about A.D.1120, in his book, < On Diverse Arts > (***De diversis artibus***), in which many technological novelties introduced by the monks, such as a flywheel to smooth irregularities in rotational motion and to pass through the 'dead-center' in machines, are discussed. It was the first time when the flywheel is presented as an element in machine design.

The technological influence of monks as engineers on the lay people in Europe was decisive, and they led the mediæval people to discover for themselves the dignity and the spiritual worth of labour. The people of Europe began to build from the eleventh and twelfth century A.D. onwards a complex, and basically a modern civilisation which was primarily founded on natural power that made it a remarkable historical epoch in the conquest of freedom for the individual man, an epoch that was not brought about by economic necessity, but rather emanated from the voluntaristic tradition of the Occidental culture. The belief in the general social progress for the first time became prominent in society, and the spirit of initiative, enterprise and inventiveness rapidly pervaded the European Christendom.

The ancient Greeks had created the scientific man (***homo sapiens***), but the mediæval Europe produced the craftsman (***homo faber***) who through mechanical arts mastered the forces of nature and made such forces serve men. This fundamental change in civilisation was accomplished by Christianity which brought about a moral and social revolution in abolishing slavery and rehabilitating manual labour and the mechanical arts as dignified occupations of man.

In the period from A.D.1150 to A.D.1250 there was a great extension of the franchise in favour of urban expansion in Europe and a creation of the merchant and the industrial middle class based on technical progress. Mediæval invention was at its peak during the twelfth and thirteenth centuries A.D. when the first 'industrial revolution' became clearly discernible. Expansion of commerce, new trade routes, and trade in cloth, metals and agricultural products, in turn, stimulated technical progress, and led to balance of payments with the East. The new middle class in towns, the burghers, were no longer satisfied with mere literature recitals of the clergy and nobles, but demanded and created the European theater, a literature of far greater realism, and a growth of drama in liturgy.

Middle Ages, Knights and Professional Men

Just like Charles Martel, ***maior domus*** of the Merovingian Kingdom, had saved Christian Europe from the threat of the infidel Saracen with his decisive victory over the Muslim invaders near Poitiers in A.D.732, so during the 'Dark Ages' the mounted warrior who wielded a sword, a battle axe, and most importantly, a lance, in mounted shock combat saved the Western Christendom in Europe from the fury of the pagan invaders which had threatened the Occidental Christian civilisation. When peace finally arrived, the mounted warrior of the wartime emerged as a knight [in French, ***chevalier*** was a horse-mounted warrior], a social class, and he was expected to live up to the standards of comportment of his class. Since the mediæval man had an honest passion for codification, the standards of knightly behaviour were incorporated into a code of chivalry for knights. The first code of chivalry that emerged was the simple creed of warriors, and its ideals were the same as the ideals expressed in the ancient Germanic legends < Beowulf >, < Siegfried >, < The Song of Ronald > and others: physical strength and courage, prowess in battle and exceptional skill in the arts of war, general generosity, and a principled disregard of wealth. This code of chivalry made its first appearance in the Teutonic ***comitatus***, the group of knights in the household of a lord. The homage paid to Christ and the fealty sworn by the knight to his lord, together with the investiture into the knightly order administered by the lord was already a religious ceremony so that knighthood from its very beginning had a Christian foundation.

After the knighthood had been established as a social class, the idea of *noblesse oblige* gave rise to definite rules of conduct for knights: obligation to fight on equal terms, prohibition to fight an unarmed man, acceptance and giving of the word of honour, courteous treatment of captives of one's own kind, and the will for glory through fighting. In the absence of wars organised show combats, called 'tournaments', were arranged in which knights were able to exercise their fighting skills and chivalry by jousting in peace time.

The Catholic Church strenuously disapproved of tournaments, banning them altogether in A.D.1130. The Church also banned the internecine warfare, luxury, unchastity, and homicide in duelling, all of which were not uncommon among the members of the knightly class. In this effort the Church, as an institution, came to promote its own concept of chivalry by grafting to the code of chivalry more highminded spiritual virtues in order to produce a knight who was a true soldier of

Christ. In this new form of Christian knighthood the investiture became a completely Christian ceremony, a sacrament. The Christian knighthood represented a kind of monastic order of warrior knighthood the principles of which were chastity, austerity, humility, righteousness and service to God. These new knightly ideals were first put into practice in A.D.1095 in the Crusades which were religious wars against the Saracen infidels.

During the Crusades a code of courtly chivalry was created by minstrels called 'troubadours', or 'Minnesingers' in their entertainment of the lonely wives of knights who were left alone for years whilst their husbands were away fighting in the Crusades. The minstrels sang songs of love and devotion in which the chaste love of a lady was the inspiration for the great deeds of the knight. In this new code of chivalry the love of a lady had taken the place of glory and God. In this new romantic code of chivalry the lady of a knight was the very reason for his great deeds and the object of his service, a service in which he had to observe the responsibilities of loyalty, faith, secrecy, and reverence. The chivalric convention of courtly love has left a tradition of romantic love in Western culture which is unique to European society, for other people did not share it. The romantic knightly virtues finally emerged as nobility, loyalty, honour, righteousness, courtly love, prowess, courtesy, diligence, cleanliness, generosity, sobriety, and perseverance — a great demand placed upon the character of any man. Thus chivalry was much more than a code of courtly love which signified an almost religious devotion to the paragon of feminine virtue, since it also stipulated that the knight owed loyalty to his lord, devotion to Christ, and a duty to follow all the exacting requirements in the long list of rigorous masculine and military virtues which imposed a strict moral responsibility on the knight to use his strength with self-imposed restraint and consideration to others. Therefore, a knight as a nobleman had to be a Christian gentleman by virtue of being a gentle man of high principles. It has been noted that the mediæval knight at his best was one of the great civilising achievements of Western culture, as the life of the Frankish knight Sieur de Joinville (A.D.1224-1317), a crusader in the army of the French King Louis IX, so persuasively demonstrated.

By the 14th century A. D. the time of knights as the foremost fighting man had been brought to its close by the invention of the crossbow, the long bow and the cannon which made the knight as a warrior obsolete. As a result of his obsolescence, the knight was gradually replaced by a more worldly fighting man, the ***courtier***. The courtier was born during the Italian Renaissance, an age which derived most of its inspiration from pagan Rome. The courtier's code of etiquette was set down by Count Baldassare Castiglione (A.D.1478-1529) in < The Book of The Courtier > (***Il Libro del Cortegiano***), published in A.D.1528, one of the great literary works of the 16th century both as a literary masterpiece and an important historical document. The courtier was required, like the knight before him, to be skilled in the use of arms as well as graceful, but unlike the knight, the courtier did not necessarily have to be of noble birth. He was expected to be well-groomed, sophisticated, that is, accomplished in arts, expert at all sports, refined in conversation, dapper in attire, and polished and nonchalant in manners. The courtier was expected to pursue virtue as an æsthetic standard through the force of his character by doing any deed for the sheer beauty of it and for self-advancement, that is, always acting with an aim at personal fame and fortune.

The code of chivalry of the Christian knight and to a certain extent the code of the Renaissance courtier produced the unwritten cultural code of the professional man as a Christian gentleman: a private and autonomous individual, self-responsible, self-reliant, self-confident, courteous, honourable, competent, high-minded, dignified, modest, reliable and humble by virtue of being keenly aware that man is neither omnipotent nor omniscient. The professional man was expected at all times to rely on his own judgement, but to avoid arrogance by being always ready and willing to learn regardless of the source. He was expected to collaborate voluntarily in worthy group efforts, but he was never to relinquish his personal Christian morality for the sake of any morale of the group, an act considered immoral for a Christian as an autonomous private individual with personal conscience.

Therefore, it was the Middle Ages which provided the very foundation for the professional person of high and ethical moral standards, such as an engineer, a physician, a lawyer, and a teacher.

Philosophy in High Middle Age

The mediæval philosophy proper began in the 9th century A.D.. Earlier intellectual efforts in philosophy consisted merely of preservation and compilation of classical culture and the speculations of early Christian thinkers which lacked originality. The necessary organisations for philosophical studies were lacking and such organisations appeared first in schools which arose after the Carolignian reawakening of Western culture. The first important resurgence of philosophy took place at the palace school of the French King Charles the Bald (A.D.823-877), who was King of West Franks from A.D.823 to A.D.843 and Emperor from A.D.875 to A.D. 877, where the Irish monk John Scotus Erigena (A.D.c.815-877), who had greater scholarship than Alcuin of York, was the principal teacher. He came from Ireland, a region where the knowledge of classical culture and even Greek language had been preserved much more than in any other part of Europe. He was an independent thinker and his translations of ancient Neoplatonic treatises from Greek into Latin, as well as his own original works, exerted an enormous influence upon the mediæval thought. Scotus Erigena recognised only one reality, God, and, therefore, to him philosophical truths and religious truths were identical. He regarded reason no more than an instrument for the interpretation of commentaries on sacred texts by the early Christian writers since he thought that this type of authority must be subordinated to reason. He was what is called a 'philosophical realist' because he claimed priority of the genus over the species, and priority of the species over the individual.

With him began the longlasting conflict between 'realism' and 'nominalism' that was revived after a lapse of more than a century. Scotus regarded revelation in the Bible as the authority of God, which cannot be subject to reason.

The 10th century A.D. was a terrible century because it was a time when Europe was torn with battles and invasions which forced learning to become confined to cloisters where it became monastic learning for a long time. As a result of this confinement, the Benedictine monasteries became the principal repositories of philosophical as well as theological knowledge. The classical learning was not so much destroyed as it was dispersed, since no single monastery was in possession of much of the classical literature. The existing Christian theology which consisted of Christian thought combined with pagan Greek philosophy, particularly Platonic philosophy, was given in an incomplete form by Origenes Adamantius (A.D.c.185-254), known as Origen, the most accomplished early Biblical scholar who had been the head of the catechetical school in Alexandria, and in a mature form by Aurelius Augustinus (A.D.354-430), known as St. Augustine, who was a former teacher of rhetoric and oratory in his home town of Hippo in North Africa as well as in Rome. Augustinus was the principal author from whose works the ancient Greek thoughts passed to the Latin Christianity in Europe. Augustinus, who was strongly influenced by the philosophy of Plato and Neoplatonists such as Plotinos (A.D.c.203-270), sought for certain basis of knowledge which he found in the conception of 'eternal ideas', or 'forms' which exist quite independently of any material object as had been taught by Plato. Augustinus encouraged the use of pagan philosophy of the Greeks to examine the rational basis of Christian faith because both the Greek theologian Titus Flavius Clemens, known as St. Clement of Alexandria (A.D.c.150-c.220), founder of the Alexandrian school of theology and a Father of the early Christian Church, and his pupil and successor Origen had claimed that all knowledge was good since it was perfection of the mind, and that the study of philosophy and natural science was in no way incompatible with the Christian life. Clement ridiculed the fear of pagan philosophy among the early Christians by comparing it to children's fear of goblins.

Augustinus was a persuasive and prolific author and a master of brilliant Latin literary style. His famous Christian apologia < The City of God > (***De civitade Dei***) in A.D.413-426, a monumental defence of Christianity against pagan criticism, contained the first philosophy of history, and his autobiographical < Confessions > (***Confessionis***) in A.D.400, a work with no counterpart in the world literature, contained the first philosophy of the spirit. A great deal of his theology came from his polemical writings, and he is generally considered the actual founder of theology which combined Neoplatonic philosophy as such with Christian thought. His wide knowledge of Greek learning and, particularly, the thoughts of the Roman man of letters, Marcus Tullius Cicero (106-43B.C.), passed into the mediæval learning ***via*** the numerous works of Augustinus. From his writings emerged the mediæval viewpoint of 'faith seeking understanding' (***fides quaerens intellectum***), as he wrote: "I believe in order to understand (***credo ut intelligam***)." He also wrote: "If I could be deceived , I exist (***si fallor sum***)." Augustinus was the philosopher of the 'inner man', and he affirmed the ego as the highest criterion of certainty. He was a vigorous defender of freewill of man, and he advised man to enter the interior of his own self in order to find himself, and within himself, God. In the works of Augustinus the problem between faith and knowledge is first found.

Augustinus recognised the limitations of sense knowledge, but he did not believe that man's senses give erroneous sense impressions of appearances. He thought that errors arise from the manner with which man's soul judges the appearances. He believed that the world of eternal truth exists, which the soul of man can grasp because it is illuminated by God which enables man to discover the eternal truths, and to judge all things in their light. Augustinus utilised the themes of light and divine illumination in his theory, and it was readily adaptable to the Neoplatonic conception of creation as an emanation analogous to the diffusion of light from a single source.

His influence on Christianity is only second to that of Apostle Paul. His important influence on the Modern Age by leaving his mark on Christian dogma, philosophies of the spirit and history, and scholasticism, not only makes him the last ancient man but also the representative of the beginning of the great Mediæval Age in Europe.

After the canon of scriptures and the ecclesiastic hierarchies of the organised Christian Church in Rome, called the 'universal (in Greek, ***katholikos***) church', were established, the hierarchy began to demand that they alone can be the interpreter of the religious meaning of scriptures and the divine truth in the Bible. They denied man's ability to discover the truth by his unaided reason. In spite of this claim by the ecclesiastic authorities the problem of applying reason to religious knowledge which required interpretation of the language of the revelations as given in the sacred texts remained, and it became the main occupation of the schoolmen of the Middle Ages. The chief aim of the mediæval man in philosophy was to integrate all knowledge and Christian revelation by means of reason which became known as 'scholasticism', because it was the work of teachers, called schoolmen or Scholastics, at various cathedral schools.

Conflict of Nominalism and Realism:

The authority of the hierarchy of the Roman Church was first challenged by a French cleric, Berenger of Tours (A.D.c.1000-c.1088), head of the cathedral school of Tours, a follower of John Scotus Eringena (A.D.c.810-c.875) and a student of Aristotle's logic, by his bold claim for the 'right to reason'. He declared that if in any particular question authority and reason conflict, it is the reason which should be followed. He advanced the viewpoint that belief comes from understanding: 'I understand in order to believe' (***intelligo ut credam***). Berenger, who philosophically believed in the 'nominalist' point of view of the ancient Greek Sophist Gorgias of Leontini (c.485-c.380 B.C.) in contrast to philosophical realism, denied the actual existence of 'universals' and, particularly, the actual presence of Jesus at the Eucharist. His views were criticised by his former student, an Italian Benedictine monk Lanfranc (A.D.c.1005-1089), and after his dispute with Lanfranc the Church authorities, who did not like his answers, declared Berenger a heretic.

Lanfranc's pupil, Anselm (A.D.1033-1109), an Italian Benedictine monk who became Archbishop of Canterbury, was a faithful follower of Augustinus and he combined Platonic philosophy with Christian doctrine by adopting Augustinus' view on the relation between faith and reason:'I believe that I may understand' (***credo ut intelligam***). Therefore, according to Anselm, it was faith in search of understanding (***fides quaerens intellectum***), since in his opinion reasoned proofs are not meant to support faith but are themselves supported by faith, thus making belief a necessary condition for knowledge. He said: "The Christian should approach understanding through faith; he should not approach faith through understanding ..."

Anselm presented what is called 'logical realism' in which he argued for the separate existence of 'universals'. He was the first person to attempt to give ontological proofs for the existence of God, and his philosophical and theological works were primarily concerned with these proofs. Anselm was the second important philosopher of the Early Middle Ages after John Scotus Erigena, and his works contained the formal beginnings of scholasticism.

The question on the nature of 'universals' was not only important in philosophy, but also in theology, and the controversy between the so-called 'realists' and 'nominalists' about 'universals' became increasingly acute in the 11th and 12th centuries A.D.. This basic controversy actually first began between Plato and Aristotle. In his philosophy of idealism [properly,'ideaism'], Plato introduced his 'doctrine of ideas or forms' which stated that ideas were the true beings, the true reality of things, whereas the things of this world were mere shadows of the ideas. Therefore, Plato divided the reality into 2 worlds: the world of perceptible things, which he discredited, and the world of ideas, which to him was a true and complete being. Therefore, Plato's theory of ideas implied that the ideas of things are real whereas the things themselves are mere imperfect representatives of the ideas. It was the first theory of the so-called 'extreme realism'.

Aristotle, with whom Greek philosophy became complete and perfectly mature, was the actual source for 'nominalism' (in Latin, ***nominalis*** meant, 'pertaining to names'), a philosophical view first emphasised by the Sophist Gorgias of Leontini. Aristotle maintained that the true reality consists only of individual things, or 'particulars', and that 'universals' are merely ideas in man's mind, in contradiction to Plato's idealism which asserted that the true reality exists only in the 'ideas'. In general, 'universals' can be thought of as abstract objects such as concepts, qualities, relations, common properties of things, as well as numbers.

The debate over 'universals' in the mediæval Europe began about some remarks of Boethius in his books concerning the relation of universal ideas such as 'man', 'rose', or 'seven' both to individual things and numbers and to the human minds that knew them. Did the 'universal man' subsist with individual men or as an eternal idea apart from physical things, or had the 'universal' no counterpart in the real world by representing only a mere abstraction? The longlasting conflict in Europe between 'realism' and 'nominalism' began with John Scotus Eringena of Ireland who was the most noted successor of Alcuin of York in the palace school of Charlemagne. He had a much greater scholarship than Alcuin of York, and he introduced the Greek language and brought a wider knowledge of the ancient learning to Teutons. He had a much more liberal attitude towards pagan learning with which he was well acquainted. He laid more emphasis on the study of dialectic, and being somewhat heretical in his nominalistic views he stimulated unprecedented discussions in theology. There was an intellectual interregnum of more than a century in this conflict until it arose again in a debate between Guillaume de Champeaux and Jean Roscelin of Compiègne.

The 'realist' position of Plato, which had been accepted by Augustinus, was expounded in mediæval Europe by Bernard Sylvester (died A.D.c.1130), who taught at the cathedral school in Chartres, and by Guillaume de Champeaux (A.D.c.1070-1121) who taught at the cathedral school of Notre Dame, whereas the 'nominalist' position was promoted by Jean Roscelin of Compiègne (A.D. c.1050-c.1120), who taught at cathedral schools in France, in England and in Rome. Roscelin was an 'extreme nominalist' who opposed Platonic philosophy and all kinds of 'realism' by maintaining that 'universals' are mere terms (***vocis***), and that only 'individuals' exist in nature. In his opinion 'universals' and 'ideas' exist only in the minds of men as something posterior to things (***post rem***) and that they are expressed in words (***flatus vocis***) or marks, whereas the 'realists' argued that 'universals' exist prior to individual things (***ante rem***).

Pierre Abelard, Free Enquiry and Conceptualism:

The most outstanding dialectician of the Early High Middle Ages was a French scholar Pierre Abelard (A.D.1079-1142), a scion of a noble family of soldiers who studied first at the school of Jean Roscelin and then at the school of Guillaume de Champeaux. Abelard had a competitive personality and contentious nature in the great military tradition of his family, which earned him the nickname, the 'indomitable rhinoceros' (***rhinocerus indomitus***). He was not only the supreme dialectician, the best logician, a radically individualistic thinker, and the foremost intellectual of his time, but he was also renowned as a spellbinding teacher whose lectures were extremely popular with students who came to study under him from all parts of Europe. Abelard claimed for the school a place of importance in European civilisation in its own right, and not only as an agency of the Church or of the State, an attitude which makes him a precursor of the modern university professor. Abelard proudly declared that the European scholars were capable of composing dialectics of their own which owed little to the ancients, and that they no longer had to accept anything without question: an individual Christian should observe, discern, discriminate, define, classify and use rational deduction to achieve critical understanding. He taught his students that it was the primary responsibility of a Christian to use his critical reason, even in religion, and to think and to doubt. Abelard had been influenced by the logic of Aristotle which was available to him through the logical works of Boethius, since most of the works of Aristotle became available to European scholars only after the death of Abelard, and by the treatises of John Scotus Erigena. Abelard who is responsible for creating a new kind of learning in Europe, is generally regarded as the intellectual founder of the celebrated University of Paris, a center of theological studies and later of natural philosophy.

It was a requirement in mediæval schools that every teacher defend the important aspects of his teaching in open disputes (***disputationes***) before the assembly of the faculty and students at least several times a year. The pugnacious Abelard, whose supreme dialectical skill made him virtually invincible in any open debate, engaged in disputations concerning the problem of 'universals' with his teachers Roscelin and Guillaume de Champeaux, both of whom he defeated, although his own 'nominalist' viewpoint owed a considerable debt to Roscelin. He opposed the 'extreme nominalism' of Roscelin because he did not accept the view that universals were 'simply names',that is, 'mere abstractions'. He particularly opposed the 'extreme realism' of Guillaume de Champeaux, whom he succeeded as the Master of the cathedral school of Notre Dame in Paris, because, as he pointed out, if the only reality were the eternal 'ideas', or 'forms', then there could be no real differences between individual men or roses which meant that ultimately everything would be everything else. The utter defeat of Guillaume de Champeaux in his debate with Abelard forced the angry Guillaume to modify his teaching. Abelard himself was a Platonist in his theology, but an Aristotelian in his dialectics. In the dispute about 'realism' and 'nominalism' which had been going on for a long time, at first between Lanfranc and Berenger, and later between Anselm and Roscelin, Abelard struck a compromise between the two viewpoints that anticipated the 'conceptualism' of ***Thomas Aquinas***. In Abelard's solution, universals are thought-concepts existing only in man's mind yet having a basis in individual things: "... although there exist only individual men, although each one is independent of the other in existence, the mind nevertheless possesses the general notion of humanity which belongs to each of them; but this form of generality is a product of our conceptual activity and does not affect the real existence." The result of Abelard's criticism of the 'universals' was that, thenceforth, the importance of the individual material thing was emphasised, and observation of the 'particulars' was encouraged.

Abelard, a belligerent, passionate, and nonconformist individual with extraordinary personal opinions, was a highly cultured man who believed in freewill as the basis of all ethics. His life was a continuous string of tragedies which he recounted in his autobiographical work < A History of Calamities > (***Historia calamitatum***) in A.D.1132. His theological work was condemned and burnt, and Abelard himself imprisoned for a short period by the ecclesiastical authorities. His famous love affair with his pupil Heloise, a beautiful and learned niece of Canon Fulbert of Notre Dame, led to his emasculation by a band of angry relatives of Heloise who mistakenly believed that he had abandoned her. The romantic affair of Abelard and Heloise is the most celebrated love story in the European literature. Abelard, despite his personal difficulties and tragedies, quoted the Roman poet from Gaul, Publius Vergilius Maro (in English, Virgil): "Happy the man who has been able to discern the cause of things." Abelard, being an expert dialectician, collected in his book < Yes and No > (***Sic et non***) all the contradictory statements made by the Church Fathers and the 158 contradictions in the Christian dogma found in the scriptures. He laid down the guidelines for the rational method of weighing the arguments without giving solutions himself, for he was not prepared to risk his intellectual pride and academic reputation for the official doctrine of the Church. Abelard's work which promoted the scholastic method indicated how controversies could be solved by demonstrating how the same words were used in different senses by different authors.

Bernard of Clairvaux, the most influential French ecclesiastic of his time and a grim adversary of Abelard, charged Abelard with pride and arrogance in thinking that man with his puny mind could ever comprehend the great mysteries of faith: "He thinks himself able by human reason to understand God completely." Bernard of Clairvaux succeeded in having Abelard's teachings condemned in A.D.1141, and subsequently Pope Innocent II ordered Abelard to silence.

Peter Lombard and Method of Disputation:

Abelard's pupil, the Italian cleric, Peter Lombard (A.D.c.1100-1160), later the Archbishop of Paris, wrote a celebrated treatise < Four Books of the Sentences > (***Sententiarum Libri Quatuor***), which was based on Abelard's book < Yes and No >. By the 13th century A.D., this book had become the standard text of theology and remained so through subsequent centuries, and is not quite outdated even today. In his book, Lombard used and completed Abelard's method of disputation: the argument begins with 'whether' (***utrum***); the next step is 'for it seems so' (***quod sic videre***) with arguments in favour; then the next step is 'but on the other hand' (***sed contra***) with counter arguments; and, finally, the 'solution' (***solutio***) with master's arguments to reconcile the two viewpoints which carried no authority but the 'master's opinions' (***sententiae***). In the method of Abelard as presented by Lombard, the best opinion, and not the weight of authority, decides the issue, on account of which Peter Lombard became known as the 'master of opinion' (***magister sententiarum***). Peter Lombard held theological views which were quite similar to those of his teacher Abelard, but Abelard believed in rationalism, free enquiry and investigation, whereas his pupil believed in rigid scholastic orthodoxy. Abelard was condemned as a heretic, whereas Peter Lombard became the master authority of the University for 2 centuries.

Averroës and Theory of Double-Truth:

The Persian physician and philosopher Ibn Sina (A.D.980-1037), known in Europe by the name of ***Avicenna***, had united Neoplatonic and Aristotelian thoughts with Islamic religious doctrine, but the Aristotelian philosophy proper was promoted in Spain by the Arab philosopher, jurist and physician, Ibn Rushd (A.D.1126-1198), known in Europe by the name of ***Averroës***. ***Averroës*** worshipped Aristotle as a 'man chosen by God', and contrary to the Christian scholars, he regarded Aristotle to be the very summit of all rational understanding, and an infallible guide to sound knowledge of the world. He skilfully commented on all the works of Aristotle in his polemical writings directed against the Islamic divines. In his 'double-truth' theory, ***Averroës*** assumed that truth is accessible through philosophy as well as through theology, but only philosophy could reach it perfectly, and that philosophical truth could contradict theological truth, at least verbally. Moreover, ***Averroës*** taught that there is only one intellect for all men, and that the universe was eternal and not created, thereby denying the Creation, personal immortality, intellectual independence, and freewill of the individual man. He was violently attacked by the Muhammedan clergy, condemned, disgraced, and his books were burnt.

Robert Grosseteste and Aristotelianism:

A prolific English scholar and physicist Robert Grosseteste (A.D.c.1175-1253), rector of the Oxford University, was a linguist of ancient languages and the first European to translate and comment on the works of Aristotle directly from the Greek originals which were used by the first promoters of Aristotelian thought at the University of Paris.

The Christian doctrine of Averroism based on Aristotelian thought was taught by Siger de Brabant (A.D. c.1235-1281) at the University of Paris, the first center for Aristotelian studies in Europe. He upheld the 'double-truth' theory based on the teaching of ***Averroës***, and was ultimately condemned by the Church for heresy.

***Albertus Magnus and Aristotelianism*:**

The German Dominican monk and a teacher at the University of Paris, Albert von Bollstadt (A.D.1206-1280), who was a former nobleman, became known by his Latin name ***Albertus Magnus*** (Albert The Great) on account of his amazingly wide range of interests and his prodigious scholarship. ***Albertus Magnus*** was trained primarily as a scientist whose literary output was encyclopædic, and because of the universal scope of his learned interests, he was called the 'universal teacher' (***doctor universalis***). He was a connoisseur of the works of the Arab and Jewish Aristotelians as well as of Grosseteste's commentaries on Aristotle, and the first European scholar to interpret and endorse the complete system of Aristotelian thought. He wrote extensive encyclopædic commentaries on Aristotle and on the natural sciences of his time. Before ***Albertus Magnus***, the English scholastic philosopher Alexander of Hales (A.D.c.1180-1245), the first Franciscan teacher at the University of Paris, combined Platonic and Aristotelian principles in his theology, but it was primarily the works of ***Albertus Magnus*** which popularised Aristotelian studies in Europe. ***Albertus Magnus*** wrote about philosophy with great clarity but he was not successful in integrating Christian thought with the contemporary Aristotelian philosophy, since he was more of a commentator and a compiler of philosophical knowledge than a creator of such knowledge. However, he was the first mediæval humanist and the first European Aristotelian.

Thomas Aquinas and Compatibility of Christian Dogma with Aristotelianism:

Since it was impossible to ignore the Latin Averroism, the challenge of Averroism was accepted by the Italian scholar and Dominican monk Thomas of Aquino (A.D.1225-1274), known by his Latin name ***Thomas Aquinas***, who was the favourite student of ***Albertus Magnus*** and the most outstanding intellectual of the Middle Ages. He wrote on every known subject in philosophy and science, and produced a vast body of philosophical works, which were remarkably clear, precise, detailed, persuasive, systematic, and complete despite his relatively short life. His numerous tracts expressed a renewed interest of his time in reason, nature and worldly happiness as well as in religious faith and personal salvation. ***Aquinas***, in his criticism of Averroism, argued that the truth of faith and the truth of reason and sense experience as taught by Aristotle are completely compatible and complementary. The truths of natural sciences and philosophy are discovered by reasoning, from facts of experience whereas religious truths such as the mystery of incarnation are not irrational but rather superrational, and must be accepted by faith. According to ***Aquinas***, all human knowledge originates in sensation, which is the medium through which man grasps the intelligible only by means of acting on it with human intellect. He held that the will of man was corrupted when man revolted against God, but that the intellect of man was unaffected by his 'Fall from Grace'. Therefore, he thought man could rely on his own human wisdom, and was free to mix the teaching of the Bible with the teaching of the nonChristian philosophers. His theory of knowledge, metaphysics, politics and ethics were in the main derived from Aristotle, but he added to Aristotle's naturalistic ethics with its goal of worldly happiness virtues of faith, charity and hope, and the goal of eternal salvation derived from Augustinus. Before ***Aquinas***, limited emphasis had been laid by the mediæval man on the secular life, but owing to the influence of ***Aquinas***, the everyday world and man's place in it became much more prominent and important in the mediæval life.

Aquinas was a very prolific author producing altogether about 80 treatises. No single work of ***Aquinas*** contains the entire scope of his philosophy, called 'Thomism', which is enormous. He developed and completed Abelard's scholastic method of disputation which consisted of proposing a question, stating the 'pro' and 'contra' arguments, and then striking a balance between the two arguments by means of logical reasoning, a method he published in < Summary of Theology > (***Summa theologica***). Some 8 centuries later, Aquinas' method reappeared as the 'thesis', 'antithesis' and 'synthesis' of the German philosopher Georg Wilhelm Friedrich Hegel (A.D.1770-1831). In his philosophy of 'moderate realism' ***Aquinas*** like Abelard regarded 'universals' as objects of the mind, but thought the source of universals to lie in existing particular things. By such means ***Aquinas*** was able to reconcile reason and faith which resulted in a relatively successful synthesis of the philosophy of Aristotle, and the philosophical and religious teachings of Augustinus and other Fathers of the Christian Church, of ***Avicenna***, ***Averroës***, and other Muslim philosophers. This synthesis of ***Aquinas*** was so remarkably complete, that it still stands next to Aristotle's work as one of the greatest works of human thought in the history of man. It is a complete theory by itself and its principles are applicable to any aspect of modern life, which is a remarkable achievement for a man of the Middle Ages. The union of Augustinian theology with Aristotelian logic known as 'high scholasticism' or 'Aristotelianism', which had acquired its highest refinement in the brilliant works of ***Aquinas***, flourished from A.D.1250 to A.D.1350.

However there was a price Aquinas had to pay for his success: he had to transform a purely 'logical distinction' of Aristotle between essences and existence into a 'real distinction' to be able to justify by reason the foundations of faith and to prove that some Christian dogmas are not antirational but merely superrational, and to apply Aristotle's logic in a rather flexible manner, liberties which unfortunately tended to disrupt the total harmony of the Aristotelian system of thought.

His treatise < On the Unity of the Intellect Against Averroists > (***De unitate intellectus contra Averroistas***) published in A.D.1270 succeeded in turning the contemporary opinion against Averroists, who were finally condemned by the Church authorities and driven from the University of Paris. The Averroists found refuge at the secular University of Padua under the protection of the Italian Republic of Venice, where they devoted themselves primarily to the study of mathematics, kinematics of acceleration and medical Averroism.

Aquinas was called the 'angelic teacher' (***doctor angelicus***) because he was a very accomplished and cogent lecturer like Abelard, a clear and precise thinker who wrote admirably exact but uncomplicated Latin prose. Regardless of the monumental achievement of ***Aquinas***, a Dominican monk, many Franciscan monks were hostile to ***Aquinas'*** system of thought that represented a radical reworking of scholasticism which opposed many Platonic and Augustinian doctrines preferred by the Franciscans over the Aristotelian thought. ***Aquinas*** distrusted scholars whose interests were limited to a particular speciality for their narrow-mindedness: " I fear the man of one book (***Timeo hominem unius libri***)." ***Aquinas*** himself had urged objectivity in the search for the truth: "Ask not who is speaking the truth, but whether the truth is being spoken ... The aim of philosophy is not to know what men have thought, but how the truth of the matter stands ... What was well said by the ancients we will accept for our profit, what they said wrongly, we will discard." In A.D.1277, 20 of his theses were posthumously condemned by Etienne Tempier, Bishop of Paris, together with 219 other Aristotelian tenets such as determinism, and consequently his works were officially banned in Paris by a decree. However, since the Aristotelian thought was irresistible for its broad systematic quality this decree was revoked in A.D.1325, and soon afterwards ***Aquinas***' philosophy triumphed at the University of Paris with the help of his old teacher ***Albertus Magnus*** who had outlived ***Aquinas***, and even at the Oxford University where both the Platonic philosophy with its emphasis on mathematics and the Augustinian theology of divine illumination were still very much appreciated.

Aquinas brought the emphasis of Aristotle on the particulars, or individual things into the philosophy of the Late Middle Ages which established the background for the humanistic ideas that were taken up in the succeeding Renaissance Age, and set the basic problem of 'nature ***versus*** grace'. ***Aquinas***, in opposition to the Christian followers of ***Averroës***, held for independence of tradition, voluntarism, and freedom of enquiry. In contrast to Augustinus, who had dallied with the idea that the pagan philosophy and the Christian dogma were both immediate inspirations of God, ***Aquinas*** established the line of demarcation between reason and faith, which served to encourage the philosophers to begin to work in an increasingly independent and autonomous manner. Although ***Aquinas***' attempt to harmonise Aristotle's thought and Christian dogma ultimately failed, his great efforts to rationalise Christian dogma implicitly recognised the 'authority of reason'.

Since ***Aquinas*** had used intellectual tools such as logic for themes which were quite different from the themes for which Aristotle had created them, he had to bend these rules to the advantage of his subject, in particular to relax the rigour in logic. These shortcomings in the scholastic philosophy based on Aristotelian philosophy were meticulously criticised by two very talented mediæval logicians, the Franciscan friars John Duns Scotus (A.D.1270-1308) and William of Ockham (A.D.c.1285-1349).

Condemnation of A.D. 1277:

A great controversy had arisen at the University of Paris between the faculty of arts and the faculty of theology. The theologians were infuriated by the masters-of-art who claimed that theology is based on fables, and because of it theological knowledge does not improve knowledge. On top of it, the masters-of-art boldly proclaimed that the only wise men of the world are the philosophers. In A.D.1277, Pope John XXI asked Étienne Tempier, the bishop of Paris, to investigate this controversy, and within three weeks Tempier issued a condemnation of 219 propositions drawn from different sources all linked with Aristotle's philosophical naturalism including 20 propositions by ***Thomas Aquinas*** who had died 3 years before the condemnation. The effect of the condemnation of A.D.1277 was immediate and lasting. Theologians were inspired by it to launch a vigorous attack against the far-reaching and extensive claims of philosophers consisting of a searching criticism of knowledge, and strictly rigorous application of logic. They succeeded in humbling both philosophy and philosophers by demonstrating with rigorous philosophical arguments based on strict logic that the only basis for accepting theological dogmas and beliefs was faith alone, and that faith is entirely independent of human reason. Theologians had pointed out what disastrous consequences follow from the uncritical acceptance of Aristotle's teachings in matters that concerned theology. Since there was now no doubt that Aristotle had erred in theological matters, could he have also erred in philosophical matters? Both John Duns Scotus and William of Ockham thought that he had. This condemnation encouraged natural philosophers to subject Aristotle's natural philosophy to a critical study, and to search for plausible alternatives.

John Duns Scotus, Freewill and Voluntarism:

John Duns from Scotland, called Duns Scotus, was a precocious philosopher, metaphysician, and logician who criticised both Augustinus and Aquinas, and discredited their notion of matter, form and potency, the very underpinnings of the Aristotelian philosophy. As a critical thinker, Duns Scotus was more of a metaphysician than a natural philosopher who established a system of metaphysics, which contained not only subtle and fine distinctions but also very sharply reasoned logical arguments that led to important consequences in his natural philosophy. He understood under the term 'form' to a certain extent a 'perceptible property or quality of a thing' which existed before as a general concept. He advocated a variety of forms together with their changes in which he differentiated between the intension (***intensio***) and remission (***remissio***) of 'forms or qualities of things'. He inaugurated a quantitative treatment of change in the intensities of the qualities of things, by holding that an intensity of a quality was as admissible to measurement in numerical degrees as the magnitude of a quantity. For instance, the intensity of a quality such as heat could be measured in degrees of its temperature. Duns Scotus' method of intension and remission of 'forms' was soon developed into an important mathematical method of mediæval science at the Merton College in Oxford. Duns Scotus insisted on demonstrable proofs which led him to a demarcation between rationalism and empiricism, and developed an extremely subtle, original and very precise technical system of logic and metaphysics. He made the inductive method in natural philosophy considerably more practical by restricting himself to a limited number instead of complete enumeration of proofs which were 'sufficient' to establish the existence of a cause. He was a strong 'voluntarist' by insisting that the divine will has primacy over the divine intellect, which creates rather than follows the laws of nature and morality. In his searching criticism of knowledge, Duns Scotus found it necessary to develop his own theory of knowledge which he based on three principles: the primacy of the will, the intuitive cognition, and the pre-eminence of the freedom of man. He held that every existing entity contains a 'common nature'(***nature communis***) yet is rendered particular by an 'individuating principle'. He also developed a highly complex system of metaphysical distinctions including the 'formal distinction' of his own creation. His compromise between 'realism' and 'nominalism' consisted of declaring the difference between individual objects and 'universals' which characterise them as being a purely logical rather than a real distinction.

The contention of Duns Scotus that every 'concrete reality' has the metaphysical nature of 'universality' as well as of 'particularity' led to a renewed debate about 'universals'. He applied logic much more rigorously than earlier philosophers, and demonstrated that many doctrines previously thought to have been proven by precise scientific reasoning were not proven rigorously at all, and had to be accepted on the basis of faith alone. Duns Scotus, and his followers, restricted the domain of truth capable of being rationally proven by gradually increasing the rigour and precision in logical reasoning. Using his rigorous and precise reasoning, Duns Scotus came to the conclusion that faith and reason were independent faculties of man. He denied that natural law arises out of human nature, but thought that it was rather a voluntary mental concept (***mente concipio***) of man. His assertion that freewill of man is his primary attribute, and much more important than his ability to reason which Aristotle had considered the supreme faculty of man, was a revolt against the domination of religion by philosophy and the encroachment of 'naturalistic rationalism' on the autonomy of religion. Although in philosophy he was a 'nominalist', he did admit that there exists no 'science of the singular', but believed that this indicated only the limits of the human intellect and not of the reality. Duns Scotus further demonstrated that theology was not a speculative science but rather a pragmatic means of salvation, which was based upon revelation regardless of its rational content.

Both the sharp criticism of Augustinus and Aquinas by the brilliant Duns Scotus, which evoked resentment from his contemporary schoolmen who never forgave him for his effective undermining of their cherished beliefs, and the fanaticism of his immediate followers led his opponents after his early death to use his name 'Duns' ironically as a term for a stupid person in the English word 'dunce'. In his own time, the remarkable Duns Scotus, who taught at the universities in Oxford and in Paris, was known as the 'subtle teacher' (***doctor subtilis***).

William of Ockham, Logic, Empiricism and Nominalism:

The philosopher most responsible for the dissolution of scholasticism was the English Franciscan friar and a gifted logician and philosopher, William of Ockham, professor at the universities in Oxford and in Paris. Ockham, known as the 'invincible teacher'(***doctor invincibilis***), was above all a profound logician and he proclaimed the primacy of logical method in all intellectual disciplines. He severely restricted the scope of reason and natural philosophy by applying Aristotelian logic with absolute rigour to all issues, and concluded that the truths of the Scriptures are absolute, and neither admit nor require proofs of reason: theology stands upon faith alone. Therefore, by asserting that no theological doctrine was demonstrable by reason, Ockham was able to divorce theology completely from philosophy. In his own philosophy Ockham relied basically on 'empiricism', a venerable British tradition upheld by the Franciscans. After the condemnation of Aristotelian natural philosophy in A.D.1271, both Duns Scotus and Ockham were primarily motivated by their theological interests to express their skepticism and criticism about the natural philosophy of Aristotle which had been accepted into the high scholasticism of the 13th century A.D.. Ockham, like Duns Scotus before him, recognised that to undertake a critical examination of the Aristotelian logic and philosophy contained in high scholasticism, he had to subject the method how man acquires knowledge to a searching critical scrutiny which motivated him to develop his own theory of the method of knowledge, called 'epistemology'. His epistemology which was based on radical empiricism completely destroyed any relation between the knowledge of the universe and the knowledge of God. In his opinion, the divine action lies beyond any human rationality since God has 'absolute freewill', whereas reason is limited to man only. He pointed out that man also has freewill, but it is not absolute since it is limited to alternative choices.

Ockham was extremely critical of scholasticism of his day which consisted of a union of Augustinian theology of divine illumination, Aristotelian logic, and philosophy because it was loaded with all kinds of metaphysical concepts and fine distinctions the existence of which he denied. For this reason, much of Ockham's polemic was aimed at the 'common nature' and the 'formal distinction' between such a nature and its 'individuating principle' as introduced by Duns Scotus. Ockham produced the most radical criticism of the works of all his predecessors, and held that such works which abstract entities such as 'essences', 'forms', and 'universals' are merely referring words to other words rather than to actually existing things (***res absolutae***). In his opinion, 'universals' have no reality either in things or in the mind of God as eternal examples of things because they are mere abstractions of the human mind such as concepts (***conceptus mentis***) or terms. Ockham regarded intuition of the singular as the source of all concepts representing signs or symbols for the real. One of the main objectives of Ockham's logical enquiries was to define the criteria by which a thing could be said to exist. These arguments of Ockham undermined the Aristotelian notion of the knowable which had been generally, but uncritically accepted in the thirteenth century A.D..

Ockham revived the principle of parsimony (***lex parsimoniae***), a principle already used by Grosseteste and Duns Scotus, which is popularly called 'Ockham's razor': 'Entities are not to be multiplied beyond necessity (***entia non sunt multiplicanda praeter necessitatem***)', by means of which he excised a host of mediæval metaphysical 'forms' used as explanatory devices in high scholasticism. Ockham applied this principle to philosophical entities and descriptions used by natural philosophers in the explanation of the world and its natural processes where he always gave preference to the simplest explanations. Ockham formulated his 'modern logic' (***logica moderna***) also by the use of this principle. Ockham's 'modern way' (***via moderna***) in philosophy not only was based on empiricism and represented a precursor of the modern age of analysis, but it also marked the beginning of the end of scholasticism, because it gave philosophy a thoroughly modern orientation which would eventually free it from all domination by the theologians, and allow it, by means of its alliance with experimentation, to develop into natural philosophy as a theoretical form of natural science expressed in terms of mathematics, although Ockham himself used mathematics rather sparingly in his works.

Ockham, who probably died of bubonic plague known as the 'Black Death',was an intellectual skeptic and a most clear thinking logician. In logical clarity and consistency he was markedly superior to Renaissance savants, and his logic in several respects was more modern than that of Wilhelm Gottfried Leibniz (A.D.1646-1716).

Many followers of Ockham's 'extreme nominalism' were led to 'radical skepticism', and he was also responsible for preparing the way for various modern nominalist theories such as instrumentalism, pragmatism, semanticism and logical positivism. Ockham's nominalist philosophy represented the extreme development of the Franciscan thought in mediæval philosophy, which was modern in its direction but still cast in the scholastic mould. It became very popular in Paris where it was known as 'terminism'.

After the time of Duns Scotus and Ockham, scholastic philosophy fragmented and became gradually devoid of real substance, overloaded with fine points of logic, and minute and quite sterile subtleties of thought. After the middle of 14th century A.D., the vitality of public disputation began to decline into a degraded rigid formalism which gave Scholasticism a bad reputation in the Renaissance Age, a time of revival of classical literature and renewed interest in nature and secular life in Europe.

Political Philosophy and Birth of Rights of Man

Mediæval political concept stressed the limited character of the government under the age-old tradition of the Teutonic tribes which asserted that the sovereignty of the people was supreme, and that the original source of all political authority lay with the community. The Teutonic societies considered the consent of the people as an actually existing condition of all rightful rule, and that the State was subordinate to the law. The idea that the executive ruler should take counsel was a fundamental principle firmly planted not only in the Teutonic custom, but already in the Roman Republican custom as well. In other words, the State was subordinated to the law in the Teutonic custom, whereas in the custom of Imperial Rome the law was dependent on the State. In the Germanic tradition the law was regarded as that of the community, and not as that of the king. Moreover, the Germanic tradition required the recognition of each successor to the kingship by the community. The Republican Roman jurists had also set down the principle that all political authority lay with the Roman people. The famous Roman lawyer, Domitius Ulpianus (A.D. c.170-228), who wrote the work, < Book of Edicts > (***Libri ad edictum***), from which much of the Roman law code ***Corpus Iuris Civilis*** was extracted, defined the 'true philosophy of law' as justice:'... the art of the good and the fair," and the lawyer as the 'priest of justice'. Since both Plato and Aristotle had taught that the State, as it exists, was superior to the law because the latter served as the instrument of the ethical function of the former, which represented the classical Græco-Roman Statist tradition, the basic problem facing the mediæval man was how to reconcile the classical tradition maintaining that the law was subordinate to the State with the Germanic tradition maintaining that the State was subordinate to the law. On account of the mediæval conviction of the 'exclusive reality of individual personality', and the concept of the community (***societas***) as an artificial partnership of individuals resulted in an attitude which circumscribed every holder of authority by restrictions and bound him by obligations not only to those above him but also to those below him. The solution to this basic problem was reached by distinguishing between the law of nature (***lex naturalis***) and the positive law (***lex positive***). Whilst the State and its rulers derived their right from the higher authority of the natural law, and thus, ***a fortiori***, from the divine law (***lex divine***) as declared in the Old and the New Testament, and were consequently subject to its ethical obligations; the positive law (***lex positive***) as a variable application of the natural law to particular circumstances of place and time was a creation of the State which depended upon the State. Therefore, the result of the mediæval political theory was to broaden the concept of law in order to include within its reach the moral foundation and ideal purpose of a political society. The mediæval thinkers neither believed in the 'corporate personality' nor in the 'general will'. However, they believed that the 'concordant unity between the wills of the individual members was good, whereas the forsaking of such unity was evil. The 'concordant unity' between individual human wills they considered to be essential to a good disposition of human society.

Aquinas studied the relation between the individual and the State, and his insistence that the State exists for the good of the citizen, and not the other way round when the citizen exists for the good of the State as Aristotle had implied, stands as one of the first declarations of the 'individual rights of man'. He taught that political and social institutions were intended by God to promote the happiness and welfare of the members of the institution rather than the institution being the instrument of punishment for the wickedness of its members. ***Aquinas*** himself favoured a form of constitution, like the ***politeia*** of Aristotle, which united monarchy, aristocracy, and democracy. The prince should be elected by the people, and assisted by the nobility based upon the possession of eminent virtue. The prince should be subject to the 'guiding force' (***vis directiva***) and be entrusted with 'coercive force' (***vis coactive***) of human law. The monarchy, as a 'service from Gods enterprise' (***ministerium a Dis commissum***), a 9th century A.D. phrase, was considered an occupied 'office' which involved duties as well as rights. On this basis, the so-called 'doctrine of divine right' of the king implied that the 'power of the monarch was conditional on its proper exercise'. In the later Middle Ages this doctrine became the watchword of the imperialists who insisted that the authority of the secular ruler was directly obtained by God, and not indirectly through the Pope. According to ***Aquinas*** the monarch is a 'public person' ruling 'for the common good'. He has a threefold function: to establish good life in the community; to preserve it after being once established; and to promote its progress to a still higher level. Therefore, the monarch's power is necessarily limited by the duties of his office. His private and public personalities are entirely distinct. Any commands issued by the monarch ***ultra vires*** are null and void. The monarch is the representative of his people by 'bearing their person' as was expressed by John of Salisbury. The dignity of a prince is inalienable, because he did not confer it on himself, and, therefore, cannot of himself dispose of it: 'The authority of the prince is his only for use, for no prince can create his own authority.' John of Salisbury expressed the opinion of Augustinus, Bishop of Hippo: 'God willed not that the rational creature made in His image should have lordship save over irrational creatures. ... The condition of servitude is rightly understood as imposed on man as a sinner.'

In the opinion of Augustinus, man developed 'servile ownership' (***dominum servile***) owing to his fall from grace; with the discovery of Aristotle's ***politeia***, a very different theory of society, a political society, was disclosed. The Aristotelian political society with its forms of organisation and government did not stem from sin but rather from the social nature of man, in which man developed 'political ownership' (***dominum politicum***).

Aquinas accepted the Hellenic tradition because he thought that had man continued in his state of innocence, man would have developed ***dominum politicum***, in which the Garden of Eden would have been administered by a constitutional monarchy where men would not have been equal because there would have been grades of virtues and knowledge. Social preferences and lordships are creations of the 'law of nations' (***ius gentium***), and rest on reason.

According to both ***Aquinas*** and John of Salisbury, the State originated in a contract by which the people, who are the ultimate sovereign, transferred their rights and powers to a ruler, and thereby instituted a 'civil society'(***societas***), a term that had been applied by Cicero to the organised community. Roman law provided the 'peoples justice' (***ius gentium***) by which a free people could institute a superior. The promoters of autocracy could stretch the terms of the surrender of the rights of people in the interest of the monarch, whilst the advocates of 'popular rights' could insist on the inherent sovereignty of the people, and establish a theory of republicanism on the principle that 'the people is greater than the prince' (***populus maior principe***). The latter course was taken by three prominent political thinkers of the Late Middle Ages: English friar William of Ockham, Italian political philosopher Marsiglio of Padua (A.D. c.1265-1343), and the German Cardinal Nicholas of Cusa (A.D.1401-1464).

In the struggle between Pope John XXII and the Emperor of the Holy Roman Empire Louis IV of Bavaria over secular power, Ockham and Marsiglio of Padua collaborated in the defence of the temporal rights of the Emperor for which activity Ockham was excommunicated by the Pope. Ockham wrote a thorough discussion of political theories in his book < Dialogue > (***Dialogus***), in which he defended the rights of the secular government against the Papal claims for secular power. Earlier Ockham had been incarcerated for some time for his political views which reflected the Franciscan opposition to the political power of the Pope.

Marsiglio of Padua, an Italian publicist who was rector of the University of Paris about A.D.1312, wrote his famous political pamphlet < Defender of Peace > (***Defensor pacis***) in A.D.1324-1326, the most radical mediæval work on political theory. Marsiglio found that the only sound authority in a commonwealth is the 'whole corpus of citizens' (***universitas civium***), and that there is no law but the 'popular will'. According to him the right of legislation is inalienably vested in the people, acting as a primary assembly or through elected representatives; the ruler is appointed, and can be disposed by the people, and his authority is always subordinated to the popular will, and he acts merely as the 'defender of peace'. In his political pamphlet, Marsiglio promoted 'constitutionalism' and the 'idea of popular sovereignty, and asserted that the actual power of the Holy See is self-arrogated. He urged that the Church be absorbed by the State, an idea first advanced in England by a Canon of York. Thus according to Marsiglio in both the State and the Church sovereignty is restricted to people. Marsiglio went with the train of Louis IV to Rome for the latter's coronation, and attended the Emperor afterwards.

Nicholas of Cusa expressed in his political tract < Universal Harmony > (***Concordantia catholico***) the mediæval ideal of a perfect harmony between the order of the universe and that of human society in which the temporal and the Church authority are independent but harmonious instruments, governments stand on popular sovereignty, and the elective and representative principles are championed for both the Church and the State. The new spirit of nationalism was plainly evident in the work of Nicholas of Cusa.

Aquinas, and his successors, strove to base the institution of civil society on the 'natural law' (***lex natura***), and to harmonise the ingrained individualism of the Teutonic people with the metaphysical legacy of ancient Greece and the juristic legacy of Rome. He sought to reconcile the Teutonic conviction that the State was subordinate to the law, and the classical tradition that the law was subordinate to the State by distinguishing between the 'law of nature' (***lex naturalis***) and the 'positive law' (***lexpositive***). The law in Teutonic societies was regarded to be that of the community, and not that of the king, whereas in the doctrine of Imperial Roman, the Emperor was the supreme legislative authority.

It is quite evident that ***Aquinas*** preferred to take the middle course in his political philosophy whereby he demonstrated his consummate skill in harmonising the Græco-Roman cultural legacy with the ideas of mediæval society. He thought that Pope as the head of the institution of the Church had "an indirect rather than direct authority in temporal matters." According to the mediæval man such as ***Aquinas***, law was something to be 'discovered' rather than 'made', and it was believed 'to be found at the throne of God'. Augustinus' maxim that 'an unjust law is no law at all', was quite generally accepted in the Middle Ages.

The formal organisation of civil law in Europe began in A.D.1076 with the rediscovery of one of the copies of the ***Corpus Iuris Civiles*** of the Byzantine Emperor Iustinianus from the surviving two copies by the monk Irenarius, a liberal arts teacher at the monastery of St. Stephen. The Catholic Church was rapidly becoming an international State under the Pope as an absolute ruler, and the need for a compilation of a universal canon law became acute. The monk Gratianus, a teacher of law at Bologna, Italy, masterfully organised and interpreted the canon law modelled after the Roman law and based upon the scriptures and decrees issued by Popes and Church councils in his < Code of Canon Law > (***Decretum***), published in A.D.1141. A new codification of the canon law was later carried out under Pope Gregory IX in A.D.1234.

The mediæval conviction of the exclusive reality of individual personality was so deep-rooted that it was an insuperable obstacle to the growth of legal theory of groups and corporations. When the doctrine of 'corporate personality' was introduced into juristic theory by Sinibald Fieschi, who was the great master of canon law and served as Pope Innocent IV from A.D.1243 to A.D.1254, it was considered a pure legal fiction (***persona ficta***) by the mediæval men.

The mediæval men considered the selling of their thoughts ignoble and, for this reason, they had no sense of invention or literary property, and, therefore, no patent laws or copyright laws existed. The establishment of the proprietary right of an individual for his original thought or invention had to wait for the Renaissance. During the Middle Ages any member of the learned profession who was miserly of his personal knowledge usually forfeited the respect of his fraternity.

This important political outlook on individual freedom came from a deep-seated individualist tradition which was based on the mediæval conviction of the 'exclusive reality of the individual personality'. The mediæval concept of the society (***societas***) represented an artificial partnership of individuals based on a social contract as was declared by John of Salisbury. The doctrine of social contract resting on ***lex natura*** became the mediæval catchword of popular resistance against the growth of arbitrary power and despotism of the government as well as of the institutionalised Roman Church. The belief that government was founded on right and not on might was generally held by the mediæval men. For this reason, modern constitutionalism is the child of the Middle Ages. The entire structure of modern ethical and political thought from the 17th to the 19th century A.D. was essentially built on the ideas developed in the Middle Ages.

Man as Private Individual:

The emergence of the idea of the private individual as a social ideal for man in the Middle Ages represents one of the important 'revolutions' in the history of man. Individual as a 'private person' was created by the social revolution in the Middle Ages which created 'private property', a concept which came about in the 12th century A.D., and achieved its highest status in the 19th century A.D.. The pioneer of the formal concept of property was the Roman lawyer, statesman, orator, writer and Stoic philosopher, Marcus Tullius Cicero , who emphasised the concept that land is a patrimony of labour. Later another Roman statesman, writer and Stoic philosopher Lucius Annaeus Seneca (4 B.C.- A.D.65), whose tragedies influenced Elizabethan drama, readily recognised that 'property is an individual right'. Prior to the official recognition of private property, individuals as private persons did not officially exist – only the rulers and the ruled. A great individual example for a spiritual private person had been provided by Jesus of Nazareth himself, who had given many examples in his sermons for the evils that the institutionalisation of man's spirit brings upon the soul of a person to whom spiritual privacy has been denied

Almost from the very beginning, various organised social institutions, such as the 'organised Church' and the 'organised State', launched a 'reactionary' campaign against the 'autonomous private individual' from whom has come all that is of any cultural value in the European civilisation. After many centuries this reactionary campaign, which is now primarily conducted by the bureaucratic institutions of the State, and by various organised political and social pressure groups, is still going on unabated, and has become particularly virulent and belligerent in the Marxist-socialist political movements of recent time. This reactionary social warfare conducted against the private individual was enormously intensified in the 19th century A. D., just when the 'private person concept' enjoyed its highest popularity in the Western world, by political agitators of various socialistic convictions such as Lassalle and the arch-reactionaries, Marx and Engels, and their 20th centuryA.D. heirs Lenin, Stalin, Mussolini, and Hitler, who resorted to massacres in mass as the most effective totalitarian method for the liquidation of the independent, annoyingly recalcitrant and nonconformist private individuals.

The Occidental Christian emphasised praxis, activity, self-disciplined personal will, and voluntary good works done in person and not by proxy. The Occidental Christians recognised, like the ancient Greeks before them, that only self-discipline is worth having for its own sake, since any other discipline externally imposed upon an individual adult is a form of tyranny and a violation of the dignity of the private person as a child of God. The Christian belief in the spiritual rectitude of the individual man made Christians defiant of any externally imposed authority, since they believed that God spoke to man through an inner voice. Many Christians recognised that the acts of Jesus of Nazareth taught that self-improvement is the only important contribution an individual can make to his Christian society. In fact, the only really meaningful contribution an individual can make to improve his society is self-improvement, and the success of the individual at self-improvement is his greatest social service for it provides a worthy personal example and inspiration to his fellow men. It was recognised by some early Christians that a person who stops at nothing to 'improve' his fellow men against their will is actually an arrogant and sacrilegious tyrant because his coercive act implies that if the people he wants to 'improve' are men, then he thinks of himself as being something more than a man. Already the pagan Greek, Sokrates of Athens (c.470-399 B.C.), had posed a challenge to such an arrogant, self-deifying social 'uplifter': "Let him who wants to improve the world, first improve himself – and thus serve the eternity."

Islamic Interlude: Muslim Science and Technology

After the death of Mahomat, the founder of the religion of Islam (Arabic for 'surrender'), in A.D.632, the armies of Muslims (Arabic for 'those who have surrendered') swept out of the Arabian peninsula in their struggle (***jihad***) against the infidels and conquered Syria, Palestine and Egypt under the first three Ummayad caliphs (Arabic ***khalifa*** means 'successor') who were leaders of the Sunnites (traditionalists). The Abbasid caliphs, who overthrew the Ummayads, conquered Persia, Afghanistan, North Africa, and in 3 years, from A.D.711 to A.D.713, most of Spain from Visigoth, but their subsequent penetration into France was stopped by the Franks at the Battle of Tours in A.D.732, and they were driven back to Spain in A.D.769. The grandson of the last Ummayad caliph escaped the massacre of his family by the Abbasids, and fled to Spain where he and his descendants created the Ummayad Caliphate of Cordova which lasted until A.D.1036. Another caliphate called Fatimid, whose founders claimed descent from Mahomat's daughter Fatima, was established in Egypt with Cairo as its capital. As the Muslim caliphates rose and fell, and subdivided, the unity of the Islamic Empire and its military power declined. The Islamic Empire, which was larger than the empires of Persia and Rome as it stretched from Spain to the Indus river, was populated by many very different races of people. The Arabs who conquered this vast territory were crude nomadic Bedouin tribesmen from the desert whose main interest was the same as that of all conquerors: living space and booty. As long as Islam was a pure Arab movement, there was no intellectual development concerning matters of this world, because the traditionalism of Islam is incompatible with the free spirit of enquiry and the idea of progress. For the sincere Muslim, all truths worth knowing are contained in the book < Koran > (***Qur'an***, means 'recitation') representing both a dogma and a doctrine of faith, the prescriptions of which regulate even the smallest details of life. The fatalism of Islam was destructive to personal effort or any display of personal will, since everything was preordained for man, and the only sensible thing for him to do was to 'submit' without protest or complaint: whatever happens to him is the will of Allah. A fanatical belief in the afterlife with voluptuous pleasures was the only consolation to the trials and tribulations of a Muslim warrior in this worldly life, and the only reward for his self-sacrificing fanaticism in war. In the Islamic world women existed primarily for the gratification of the male and for breeding, any other worthy personal ambitions of women were forbidden. As amazing as it is, even today many supremely talented Muslim women are still denied by their religion their God-given right to be themselves, that is, to be at their personal best by excelling for their own sake.

This kind of mentality induced by Islamic religion tended to rule out restlessness, dissatisfaction with self, and a constant striving for self-improvement that were the very attributes of the Christian mentality. The consequence of this religious attitude was an external appearance of noble serenity which excluded all effort to improve the human condition, an attitude in tune with the Bedouin tribal life in the desert. Moreover, the religion of Islam also tended to rule out intellectual curiosity and paralyse the spirit of enquiry at the source that is so concisely expressed by the dictum: "Allah knows best what is (***Allah aalam***)," and characterised in the apocryphal statement of Caliph Umar, when the Muslims sacked Alexandria in A.D.646 and burnt the remaining books of the Alexandrian libraries to heat the Moorish baths: "If these books say the same thing the Koran says, they are useless; if they say anything else they are false and should be destroyed."

During the Ummayad Caliphate of Damascus from A.D.660 to A.D.750, the Islamic Empire was primarily an Arab movement under strong Byzantine influence. Since the Arabs were rarely complete masters in their own realm, they took over the Byzantine system of government intact with its bureaucrats and absolutism. The civil service of the Caliphate was operated by Greek bureaucrats from Byzantium, and Greek artists were employed by the caliphs.

The Ummayad Caliphate of the Sunnites [traditionalists] was overthrown in A.D.750 by Shiites [sectarians] who established in A.D.762 the Abbasid Caliphate in Baghdad which was founded on the claim for Muslim rather than for Arab loyalty. The Abbasid Caliphate lasted from A.D.750 to A.D.1258. The intellectual life of Islam began during the Abbasid Caliphate when the presence of Persians, Syrians, Nestorian Christians, Samaritans, Jews, Sabians and other freethinkers in their Empire had a decisive influence on the brave but otherwise crude and uncouth Bedouin Arabs from the desert. The influence of the old, but very refined civilisation of Persia upon the Islamic Empire was great, since the Muslim civilisation became a fusion of Arabian fanaticism, with the Persian and the Greek culture. The culture of Islam was mostly contributed by other converts to Islam, since Arabs themselves had little cultural tradition. The Nestorian Christians who had established a center of learning and medicine in Jundishapur in Persia were made personal physicians of the caliphs. It was the Nestorian Christian court physicians from the medical school who were responsible for spreading the knowledge of Greek philosophy and science among the Muslim subjects of the Islamic Empire. The Muslims had particular reasons to pay close attention to astronomy which was necessary in the determination of the direction the faithful had to turn in their prayers, and in obtaining precise knowledge of Lunar motions for the calendar. In general, judicial astrology was highly respected in the Near East.

The 3 remarkable and able Abbasid caliphs, al-Mansur, Harun al-Rashid and his son al-Mamun, who were contemporaries of the Carolignian dynasty of the Holy Roman Empire in Europe, showed wide intellectual interests and were as tolerant as their Islamic priests (***imams***) allowed. About A.D.809, Harun al-Rashid, in his effort to reduce the diseases rampant among Arabs with practical medicine, hired Nestorian Christians to translate the works of Greek medicine and of Aristotle into Arabic. He also engaged a Christian as the superintendent of his schools. His successor al-Mamun, the first great patron of science, became so disgusted with the vile conditions and the filth of the Near East that he decided to clean up the entire pest-ridden Empire. He sent his emissaries to Byzantium and to India to search for manuscripts of science and medicine, and they brought back a rich haul of ancient Greek learning. He employed Nestorian Christians to translate on an unprecedented scale all the priceless Greek learning into Arabic tongue, the common language of the Islamic Empire. He founded an academy, a splendid library known as the 'House of Wisdom' in A.D.830 and built several observatories, the most important observatory was erected in A.D.829 in Baghdad which made Baghdad one of the most important intellectual centers of the world if not the most important. After the University of Constantinople was reopened in A.D.863, various caliphates opened rival Muslim universities in Baghdad in the 9th century A.D., at Cairo in Egypt, and at Cordova in Spain in the 10th century A.D..

Although Islam did not encourage learning directly, yet, in the practical Muslim world it offered surprisingly little resistance to scholarly efforts and scientific work. The period of translations were followed by the so-called Golden Age of Muslim Science, from A.D.900 to A.D.1100. It was Arabian mainly in language since many important scholars were not Arabs and some were not even Muslims. They were mostly Syrians, Persians, Egyptians, Moors, Tadjiks and Jews with Arab names who had nothing from the Arab spirit. Although positive contributions by Muslims to sciences in general were not as significant nor as original as those of the versatile ancient Greeks, they did produce notable advances in practical medicine, chemical technology, applied physics, technical mechanics, astronomy and also in applied mathematics. Muslim scientists made particularly lasting contributions to optics, primarily by the able and versatile Ibn al-Haitham (died A.D.1043) who discovered spherical aberration, demonstrated that parabolic mirrors concentrated a parallel beam of light rays in a single point, and recognised that the speed of light is finite.

However, their service in preserving the learning of ancient Greece, which they obtained from Byzantium, and of India, was beyond price. They also introduced a new purpose for which science and mathematics ought to be studied. The practical Muslims did not study mathematics for its own sake like the ancient Greeks but rather for its practical application, and they did not study science primarily for the sake of understanding nature but rather for the sake of gaining power over nature.

Following the collapse of the Abassid Caliphate when the Seljuk Turks took Baghdad in A.D.1055, the Arab learning spread to Fatimid Caliphate in Cairo where the University of al-Azar was founded, and then moved to Cordova, the capital of the separate and independent Ummayad Caliphate in Spain, the wealthiest and the most cultured Muslim province, a showplace for luxurious living where the Almohad caliphs had inaugurated a new Golden Age of Islam. The University of Cordova established by the Almohad caliphs had more than 600,000 volumes in its library by A.D.900 which rivalled the Abbasid library in Baghdad.

One of the important Muslim scholars was Ibn Hadjan (A.D.721-815) known in Europe by the name of ***Geber***, who did important work in alchemy in which he assumed that all metals were composed of quicksilver and sulfur in different proportions; al-Biruni (A.D.973-1048) produced an important encyclopædic work on mathematics, astronomy, physics, geography, general geology, mineralogy, ethnography and history in which he recognised experiment as the chief method of research. In another treatise he described more than 50 minerals, metals and alloys, and for the first time determined densities of some minerals and metals. Ibn Sina (A.D.980-1037), a Persian scholar known in Europe by the name of ***Avicenna***, systematised all known medical science in his famous canon of medicine which remained the most prominent handbook of medicine for five centuries. Ibn Badja (A.D.c.1090-1138), a Spanish Muslim known in Europe by the name ***Avempace***, replaced the Law of Velocities of Aristotle: $V \propto F/R$ by the Law of Dynamic Differences of Philoponos: $V \propto F-R$, in which V denoted the velocity, F the motive force, and R the resistance to motion. He also wrote commentaries on Aristotle's philosophy interpreted in accordance with Neoplatonism. The last important Arab philosopher, Ibn Rushd (A.D. 1126-1198), a Spanish Muslim known in Europe by the name of ***Averroës***, was the outstanding commentator on Aristotle's works.

The remarkable Persian philosopher, poet, mathematician and astronomer, Omar Khayyam (c.A.D.1038/1048-1123/1131), who lived in northern Persia under the rule of Seljuk Turks, was famous for his reform of the old Persian calendar that led to an error of one day in 5,000 years, an achievement which was more accurate than the Gregorian calendar that leads to an error of one day in 3,330 years. Omar Khayyam was also an ingenious mathematician both in geometry and in algebra. In his treatise on algebra he presented a systematic study of cubic equations, and gave the solutions for the roots of such equations as intersections of conic sections by using the method of the ancient Greek mathematician Menaichmos of Alopekonnesos (375-325 B.C.). He discriminated between the 'geometrical' and the 'arithmetical' solutions, and showed that 'arithmetical' solutions exist only if the roots were positive rational. The brilliant Omar Khayyam besides discovering the binomial theorem, also wrote a treatise on the foundations of geometry in which he replaced the Parallel Axiom of Eukleides by the Hypotheses of the Obtuse, the Acute and the Right Angle, hypotheses now used in modern nonEuclidean geometry. He also replaced the geometric theory of proportions of Eudoxos of Knidos by a numerical theory, in which he anticipated the theory of the irrational and the concept of the real number.

The Almohad caliphs of Cordova had replaced the Almoravid caliphs who, in turn, had overthrown the Ummayad caliphs in A.D.1031. When the caliphate of Cordova fragmented into many caliphates, the centers of learning also multiplied. In spite of the political fragmentation which took place all over the Islamic Empire, it did retain considerable cultural and economic cohesion. Although the Islamic world contained many different races of people, the basic unifying influence between them was the Islamic religion and their common Arabic language achieved by the strict Muslim obligation to read the Koran in its original Arabic tongue. Islam rather than Arab nationalism was the important factor in Muslim patriotism. In the second half of the eleventh century, the political power of the Arabs began to decline with the taking of Baghdad by the Seljuk Turks, the reconquering of Aragon and Toledo in Spain and Palermo in Sicily by the Christians, and the conquest of Jerusalem in A.D.1099 by the Crusaders. The Caliphate of Cordova in Spain split into several smaller caliphates with capitals in Seville, Granada and Malaga.

When Toledo in Spain was conquered in A.D.1085 and Sicily was captured in A.D.1091 by the Christian Knights, the Europeans took possession of important centers of Muslim learning where much of the ancient Greek science had been translated into Arabic in the 9th and early 10th centuries A.D.. A veritable flood of Latin translations of a significant part of ancient Greek and Muslim science emanated from these centers under Christian domination, and the steady flow of such translations into Christendom, which continued well into the 13th century A.D., had an all-important influence on the spectacular rise of scientific learning in the mediæval Europe.

After conquering Jerusalem in A.D.1187 Sultan Saladin, a Kurd [a descendant of Indo-European Kassites and Medes], and particularly his nephew, Egyptian Sultan Malik al-Kamil, renewed the cultural efforts of the Ummayad caliphs by establishing a permanent center of scientific studies for scholars. The new Golden Age of Muslim learning inaugurated in the Almohad Caliphate in Spain spread to Cairo where it survived until Mameluk Turks (mercenary soldiers of Turkish race) conquered Egypt, as well as to Baghdad where it continued to exist until the capture of this city by the Mongol hordes in A.D.1258.

Expelled from Europe by the Christians, driven out from Asia by the Mongols, and subjected to Seljuk Turks in Egypt, the Arabs lost contact with Persians, Syrians, Christians, and Jews who had played a central role in the vitalisation of Islamic culture. The Arabs thrown back on their own resources, proved to be intellectually quite helpless, and after A.D.1200 they sank into a cultural torpor under the yoke of their fanatical Islamic priesthood (***imams***) who succeeded in suppressing all intellectual life, a state of cultural stagnation from which they did not completely recover until the coming of the Europeans in the 19th century A.D..

The Muslim supremacy ended soon after the 11th century A.D. because the Muslim genius was less vigorous and less fertile than that of the Christian Europe, where the power and knowledge of the Latin world was growing by leaps and bounds. Whilst the Latin Christendom as a civilisation was improving at a rapid rate in the 13th century A.D., Islamic civilisation was culturally already in a decadent and boasting state.

Mediæval Science as Natural Philosophy

Mediæval men regarded science as a branch of philosophy, called 'natural philosophy', rather than an autonomous intellectual discipline. The primary concerns in early mediæval society had been spiritual which influenced the early mediæval man to consider enquiries into nature carried out for the sake of curiosity or practical purposes to be unworthy or even frivolous. The so-called 'profane science' as it gradually came to be tolerated by the early Christian Church authorities was entirely theoretical consisting mainly of the astronomy of Ptolemaios of Alexandria, the natural science of Aristotle, and the medical art of Galenos of Pergamon. However, all experimental research which differed from these scientific authorities were suspected to be black magic, or even illegitimate traffic with the Devil. Alchemists who sought to create new physical elements, in particular, were considered to be in league with the Devil, and alchemy itself was stamped as 'one of the seven deadly sciences'. Any scientist who introduced a novel idea into his field of research was in danger of being declared a heretic. Unfortunately, the dogmas contained in the Bible were bound to impossible physics, biology and anthropology, which is why every discovery in these disciplines came into conflict with some statement in the scriptures, and for that reason alone could be condemned by the ecclesiastical authorities.

The scope of mediæval philosophy was far-reaching and included every speculative knowledge about the world which can be obtained by reason unaided by any revelation. Theology as a sacred discipline as well as practical arts, and such disciplines as grammar, mechanics and medical arts remained external to the purview of philosophy. Ethics was part of philosophy and so were logic, natural philosophy and metaphysics. Psychology as the study of the soul was regarded a branch of natural philosophy, and so were the disciplines of science: astronomy, physics, chemistry, biology as well as mathematics, although no general agreement existed about the way mathematical reasoning was related to natural philosophy, and disputes over this question ultimately led to the rise of mathematical physics.

The science of the Mediæval Age can be divided into two distinct periods:
1. The High Mediæval Science, which lasted through the entire 13th century A.D. into the first decade of the 14th century A.D..
2. The Late Mediæval Science, which occupied almost all but the first decade of the 14th century A.D., and continued through the 15th century A.D..

In the period of the High Mediæval Science, Jordan de Nemore created an original school of statics by mastering a problem the ancient Greeks had been unable to solve, and by proposing an ***a priori*** general principle in statics which was generalised into a dynamic principle many centuries later. In dynamics Jordan introduced valuable improvements to both the projectile motion and the free-fall of heavy bodies. But one of his most remarkable contributions was in the development of rates of motion.

In A.D.1269 Pierre de Maricourt (Latin name, ***Petrus Peregrinus***) wrote the important brief empirical pamphlet of mediæval science < Letter about Magnet (***Epistola de magnete*** >, which contained the description of the first systematic experiments on the properties of the magnet.

Gerard of Brussels wrote the first work on modern kinematics in which the velocity was considered for the first time as a magnitude in its own right.

In the period of the Late Mediæval Science, the dominant philosophy was nominalism promoted by William of Ockham which moved the chief interest in natural philosophy towards logical precision. A high order of philosophical sophistication was developed about the importance of hypotheses in scientific theories, the main emphasis of which was mathematical. The mediæval scholars of this period were successful in producing an admirable corpus of hypothetical science in the course of which they created significant concepts, definitions and theorems which were of vital importance to the new mathematical science of mechanics. The methods of quantification were amplified and applied to a wide assortment of qualities, and new calculation techniques were devised for the study of various types of imaginary motions embracing infinity, and implying infinitesimals. The nominalist tendencies and influences served to support the ancient Greek doctrine of 'saving the phenomena' and, probably, supplied the philosophical justification for its extensive application in physics and natural philosophy in general. The philosophical tradition of nominalism also tended to emphasise uncertainty, possibility and probability rather than certainty, necessity and precision in man's ability to discover the true physical reality lurking behind the physical appearance. This nominalist tradition encouraged the mediæval scientist to study all kinds of imaginary physical processes whilst paying little or no attention to physical reality or practical application.

In Western Europe, experimental science began in the 13th century A.D. with the influx of ancient Greek treatises in Latin translations from Spain and Near East. These treatises served to familiarise the Western scholars with the entire Aristotelian corpus of knowledge and the computational methods of antiquity. The newly acquired Aristotelian learning joined together with

Augustinian theological thought was taught at universities, particularly at Oxford. The Augustinian tradition was steeped in Neoplatonic philosophy, a Hellenistic philosophy which was quite favourably disposed towards the mathematical conception of reality. The empirical outlook and systematic scientific procedures of Aristotle were deeply appreciated by Western scholars for providing the indispensable means for the organisation of natural history and observational data which had survived the Early Middle Ages owing to the efforts of encyclopædist. The new methods of calculation were enthusiastically received by mediæval scholars with mathematical interests. The significant influence of all this new Greek learning was that new treatises began to appear which were the harbingers of modern science in the Middle Ages.

It is significant that most of the problems of natural science (***scientia naturalis***), particularly the fundamental problems formulated by Aristotle, have passed into a related discipline called philosophy of science where they still remain unsolved today, and where the 'realists' and the 'nominalists', now called 'positivists', are still divided over fundamental questions.

Gerbert of Aurillac and Revival of Greek Learning in Europe:

The scientific spirit was revived in Christian Europe by the remarkable Frankish cleric Gerbert of Aurillac (A.D. c.946-1003), who in A.D.999 became Pope Sylvester II. In A.D.967 he went to study in Spain where he came into contact with Moorish learning, and later continued his studies in Italy. He was an eager student who worked in mathematics and astronomy independently, and after obtaining knowledge of the astrolabe from the Muslims he was able to make more accurate astronomical observations in which he had become interested because of the problem of calculation of dates such as the Easter. He taught at the cathedral schools at Reims and Ravenna where he lectured on the 7 liberal arts, and where he particularly excelled in the knowledge of the ***quadrivium*** consisting of logic, mathematics, astronomy and music. He was a skilled maker of astrolabes and other instruments. He built celestial and terrestrial globes to assist his lectures on astronomy, and had a habit of exchanging them for manuscripts of Latin classics. He was an inspiring teacher and his influence as a teacher in Germany, as an adviser to the Holy Roman Emperor Otto III, as a Bishop, and as Pope, served to elevate the intellectual level of the clergy, who at the time were exclusively students of science. He stimulated the interest of the clergy in mathematics and logic by collecting the treatises of Boethius on those subjects. Gerbert himself wrote a treatise on the abacus and built an abacus with as many as 27 columns. Although already in antiquity the ancient Mesopotamians had been skilful in developing algorisms (the art of calculating in series of elementary operations to solve a problem) for the solution of certain algebraic problems, Gerbert proposed in his work about A.D.1000 the idea of mechanising the development of algorisms, an idea important to mechanised computation. He was probably the first Christian scholar to teach the use of Hindu numerals. He also wrote expository works on arithmetic and geometry.

In Gerbert's time the Christian Europe was not quite prepared for the theoretical development of mathematics. The practical mathematics had been kept alive in Benedictine monasteries during the Early Middle Ages, and at the close of the 8th century A.D. it was taught at cathedral and monastic schools founded by Charlemagne, but this mathematics was elementary and restricted to what was required to keep accounts, to calculate the date of the Easter, and to measure land for the purpose of surveying. Until the close of the 12th century A.D. European mathematics remained primarily a practical science.

About A.D.1100 new influences began to affect the intellectual life in mediæval Europe when the Europeans came into contact with the Byzantines of the Eastern Roman Empire, and the Muslims at the Mediterranean coastline, and began to learn about the ancient Greek works from the Byzantine Greeks as well as from the Muslims who had prepared translations in Arabic language from most of the important Greek treatises in philosophy, science, medicine, astronomy and mathematics.

Cathedral School at Chartres and Natural Science:

The new interest in Greek learning which had been promoted by Gerbert took place in episcopal and cathedral schools the establishment of which had been promoted by Charlemagne. The first such school to undertake a search for rational explanations even of biblical passages, and to express the need for mathematics in the study of nature was the Cathedral School at Chartres founded by Canon Fulbert, who had been a pupil of Gerbert of Aurillac. The Eukleidean theorems were first taught at this school which became the most important center of mathematical studies in Europe. Although the study of ***trivium***: grammar, rhetoric, and dialectics, had priority in their curriculum, the study of ***quadrivium***: geometry, arithmetic, music and astronomy, was also considered important. The first known attempts to explain the world in terms of natural causes in Christian Europe was made at the cathedral school of Chartres in the early 12th century A.D. under the leadership of Bernard of Chartres, a Neoplatonic master at this school from A.D.1114 to A.D.1119. The falling and rising of bodies was explained by the Neoplatonic natural philosophers of Chartres according to Plato's 'theory' of gravity which supposed that 'bodies of like nature tend to come together'. They also followed Plato's ideas by assuming that within the universe no void can exist because space is a 'plenum', and that matter is indestructible.

Bernard of Chartres recognised the accumulative aspect of scientific knowledge and their incalculable debt to their predecessors, which he expressed by paraphrasing the Roman Didacus Stella: "We are as dwarfs mounted on the shoulders of giants, so that although we perceive many more things than they, it is not because our vision is more piercing or our stature higher, but because we are carried and elevated higher thanks to their gigantic size."

In his attempt to find a rational explanation for the Creation, Thierry of Chartres, brother of Bernard and a chancellor of this school who died about A.D.1155, declared that it was impossible to understand the story of Genesis without intellectual training provided by the ***quadrivium***, that is, without the mastery of mathematical sciences: "... for on mathematics all rational explanation of the universe depends." For this very reason, natural sciences did receive a due measure of attention at the cathedral school of Chartres, which was steeped in Platonic philosophy and particularly influenced by the bizarre cosmological fantasies in Plato's dialogue ***Timaios***. A master at the cathedral school of Chartres, Guillaume de Conches, even adopted a form of atomism which sought to reconcile the atomic theory of Demokritos of Abdera and Epikouros of Samos with the 'visionary science' in Plato's ***Timaios***. Despite the theoretical curriculum, the masters at the Chartres school did not ignore the practical importance of applied sciences. For instance, Thierry recommended for study at the Chartres school a great number of books dealing with the application of science such as works on mensuration, surveying and practical astronomy besides the required theoretical treatises.

The Platonic conception of the universe was still influential about A.D.1245 when Roger Bacon (A.D. c.1214-1294) as a young man still used the Platonic point of view of the school of Chartres in his lectures on physics, although by that time the Aristotelian physics and Ptolemaic astronomy were already making inroads into the Christian learning at Chartres. At first the leadership and progress made in teaching scientific reasoning was confined to the cathedral school of Chartres where the Christian thought had introduced the idea of creation into science, but soon it spread to the newly founded University of Paris, and then to the Oxford University in England.

A talented teacher such as Abelard had attracted thousands of students from all over Europe to attend his lectures in Paris despite the fact that there was no organised instruction and no facilities for lectures beyond the rather limited educational organisation at the cathedral schools. Many students were young and undisciplined, and there existed no organised administration capable of controlling the great body of students wishing to receive instruction. A large number of students, among whom were many unruly foreigners, spilled over into the city far from the school where they often were responsible for many altercations with townspeople. In order to eliminate such troubles, universities of higher learning (***studium generale***) were officially organised as voluntary corporations of scholars and masters usually under the protection of some high official of the State. The first European universities were established in Italy: in Salerno about A.D.1000, in Bologna in A.D.1088, and later in Padua. The university in Bologna, which became an important center for legal studies, and the university in Padua were special institutions of the Middle Ages because they had a lay and democratic organisation in which liberal arts and medicine were taught in the same faculty. In the absence of theological control, the philosophy of the medical doctors as teachers of medicine was rather materialistic, even anti-clerical, and fairly consistent with the doctrine of Averroism. For this reason, these universities graduated astrologically minded physicians (***medici***), a number of whom became outstanding military engineers of their time. They were the most scientifically educated and literate engineers of the Middle Ages.

In Paris after many serious confrontations between the unruly students and the townspeople, in which the students claimed protection from the secular interference on account of their clerical status, the French king gave in A.D.1200 formal recognition to the school as the 'university of masters and scholars (***universitas magistrorum et scholarium***)', specified its rights of self-government, and endowed it with official clerical status which made it independent from secular control and only subject to the ecclesiastical courts. It became known as the University of Paris which offered courses in 7 liberal arts in the form of ***trivium*** and ***quadrivium*** taught by a recognised faculty for both groups of studies. It consisted of 4 faculties: theology, arts (philosophy), law and medicine. The largest faculty was the faculty of arts . The students and teachers of the faculty of arts were divided according to nationality, and their elected leader was the 'rector', who finally replaced the chancellor as the director of the university. The University of Paris offered the following degrees: the 'baccalaureate, the 'licentiate', and the 'doctorate' for the rank of 'doctor or 'magister'. The University of Paris which rapidly became the leading university in Europe was under the protection of the French king and the Pope.

In A.D.1214, the University of Oxford was founded in England, and by the 14th century A.D. the University of Cambridge was fully organised although its very beginning stems from the 12th century A.D.. Universities in Salamanca, in Coimbra, in Lisbon, in Naples, in Toulouse, in Montpellier, and in Orleans were established by the late 13th century A.D.. In the 14th century A.D. universities were also founded in Prague in A.D.1348, in Vienna in A.D.1365, and later in Heidelberg, in Cologne, and in Valladolid in Spain, and soon there were more than 80 universities in mediæval Europe. Natural science was not usually a separate field of study at these early universities, which offered a rival education to a purely clerical one. The development of science in the Middle Ages was essentially a contribution of 2 mendicant orders: the Franciscans and the Dominicans. At the beginning of the 13th century A.D. the two mendicant orders were formed which replaced the Benedictine order as the center of intellectual life in Europe. Giovanni Francesco Bernadone (A.D.1182-1226), known as St. Francis of Assisi founded in A.D.1209 the Order of Friar Minor, and Domingo de Guzman (A.D.1170-1221), known as St. Dominicus, founded in A.D.1216 the Order of Preachers mainly for the defence of Christian orthodoxy. The mendicant orders came about when the Roman Catholic Church realised that monasticism was no longer adequate since the Church had to cope with the ever-expanding urban life. Two immediate changes were necessary to accomplish this : firstly, the monks had to live the life of the people they served; and secondly, they had to mingle with the urban people at least until city churches were built. The two orders which arose to meet this challenge were called mendicant orders because their monks, called 'friars ' (in Latin, ***fratres***, means 'brothers'),who mingled with the people and ministered to their needs, took vows of poverty and lived on alms from the people according to the ideal of poverty. St. Francis of Assisi, a man of great charm, had commended his friars: "... to go into all the world and preach the gospel unto every creature." St. Francis is the first person in history who developed the stigmata, the wounds of crucifixion, after fasting and praying for 40 days on a mountain, a malady which afflicted him for 2 years before his death.

St. Dominicus lacked the personal charm of St. Francis, but he was intelligent, fearless and courageous, and his character was stamped on the order he founded, the mission of which was to win back heretics to the Church. He believed that the best way to fight heresy was to eradicate ignorance and to spread the knowledge of the orthodox Christian belief. The particular task of the Dominican friar was to study theology and to preach. St. Dominicus advised his friars: "Henceforth the world is your home; go forth into the world, teach and preach." Dominican friars believed that they were 'the hounds of the Lord (***domini canes***)', who kept the sheep from straying from the flock. Whilst the Franciscan friars tended to the bodies and souls of the poor, the Dominican friars cared for their minds.

The first known Dominican teacher at the University of Paris was the Italian scholastic philosopher Roland of Cremona, and the first Franciscan teacher was the English scholastic philosopher Alexander of Hales (died A.D.1245), who was known as the 'indisputable teacher' (***doctor irrefragabilis***) and the first to introduce Aristotelian principles into Christian theology. Thenceforth the most important intellectuals of mediæval times were friars of these two mendicant orders. The mendicant Dominican and Franciscan orders quickly established such a dominant influence upon the University of Paris that the University fell effectively under their control, but not without considerable polemics with the laymen. Ultimately it became a stronghold of Dominicans.

The Franciscans assumed effective control of Oxford University where the English Franciscans, who kept the Platonic and the Augustinian tradition alive, created the background for 'nominalist' physics on the basis of British empiricism which ultimately led to modern science. Oxford University became preeminent in the field of mathematics, optics and logic in application to exact sciences whereas the University of Paris became mainly the center of theological and dialectical studies since mathematics was not a subject of regular and required teaching at Paris as it was at Oxford.

Adelard of Bath and Right to Reason:

One of the earliest European thinkers to pit his own reason against the orthodox Christian thought was the English natural philosopher Adelard (Latin, ***Æthelard***) of Bath (*floruit* in early 12th century A.D.) who had studied in A.D.1130 at Toledo in Spain, and was a tutor of the English prince who became King Henry II. Upon his return to England after his studies at Tours and at Laon in France, and travels in the Near East, he published his tractate < On Difficult Questions of Nature > (***Per difficiles quaestiones naturalis***) about A.D.1130, in which he showed preference for the Muslim Aristotelianism over the existing Christian Platonism. Adelard confidently relied on deductive reasoning and railed against the bondage of tradition and authority: "Nothing is surer than reason ... Nothing is falser than the senses." He categorically rejected the explanation of natural phenomena in terms of the Will of God, and held that God acts through natural causes which is why men have to seek Him in nature. He seems to have been one of the first men of science to urge direct study of nature. Adelard, who was celebrated for his mastery of Muslim learning, translated < The Elements> (***Stoicheia***) of Eukleides (in English, Euclid) as well as the astronomical tables and commentaries on the arithmetic by the Persian astronomer al-Khowarizmi from Arabic into Latin in which he made use of Hindu numerals, composed < Rules of Abacus > (***Regulae abaci***) and boldly named the age of Abelard, 'modern'(***modernus***). He said that he would not listen to those who are "led in a halter, ... wherefore if you want to hear anything from me, give and take reason." In reference to learning without any sound substance he said: "I am not the sort of fellow who can be fed with the picture of a beefsteak." Adelard of Bath serves as a typical example for the spirit of intellectual awakening in Christian Europe.

Robert Grosseteste and Experimental Science:

In the 13th and 14th centuries A.D., the English and French universities assigned the development of physical problems based on the works of natural philosophy by Aristotle a prominent place. Special emphasis was put on the problems of mechanics, and on certain properties of thermal, optical and other phenomena. To the pioneers of this movement belonged the highly learned English philosopher and scholar Robert Grosseteste, who was educated at the universities in Paris and in Oxford. He was appointed in A.D.1214 the first chancellor (***magister scholarum***) of the Franciscan university in Oxford. In A.D.1224, he founded the Oxford Franciscan school and became a lector of Franciscan friars without himself belonging to this mendicant order. He was responsible for creating at the Oxford University general interest in physical sciences, mathematics and logic, as well as in ancient languages and Biblical scholarship. He stressed the necessity of placing all natural sciences on a mathematical basis as Plato had urged and, therefore, he not only interpreted Aristotelian science mathematically, but also introduced into his scientific logic the postulational method of Eukleides. He organised the tuition at Oxford to include the study of Greek language, mathematics and physical sciences. He was a connoisseur of the works of Aristotle and responsible for introducing Aristotelian learning to the Oxford University but without breaking with the Platonic and Augustinian tradition which was the dominant philosophy in this Franciscan institution of higher learning. In A.D.1235 he became the Bishop of Lincoln. Grosseteste who had been a witness to the signing of ***Magna Carta*** by the English King John at Runnymede in A.D.1215, fought for the maintenance of ***Magna Carta*** and foreshadowed the spirit of Reformation in his protest against the exercise of Papal power from Rome. In mediæval Europe, he was the most important person who revolted against the prevailing Christian dogmatism and the absolute correctness of Aristotelian science.

Grosseteste, a prolific scholar and able linguist, found the Arabic translations of Aristotle's works frequently not only inaccurate but also corrupted by Muslim commentators and, therefore, he himself worked out superior translations of Aristotle's works from their Greek originals which were available to him.

The conception of science of Grosseteste and his student Roger Bacon was based on their conception of physical nature the very 'form' (or 'essence') of which can be mathematically formulated, and their very objectives of scientific enquiry were the predictive mathematical laws rather than the essential definitions of Aristotle. Grosseteste introduced for his time a completely new idea by asserting that cognition of the real world rests on observation and experiment, rather than on the opinions expressed in existing texts recognised as authoritative by the Church hierarchy. He advocated free and rational enquiry as a bold new direction in science, and critical treatment of the recognised authorities in natural philosophy. Moreover, Grosseteste placed a high value on mathematics as the most important means of scientific investigation, and he was the first mediæval scientist to work out a method of physical science that ultimately led to modern science by promoting the scientific method which contained the first outline of the hypothetico-deductive method: the formulation of the hypothesis based on experience, followed by empirical verification or falsification of conclusions deduced from it. Grosseteste made the Aristotele's distinction between the 'knowledge of the fact' and knowledge of the reason for the 'fact' the foundation of his theory of science. In order to go from one to the other he had to develop a logical procedure which helped him to analyse a complex phenomenon into its basic elements and to discover the common cause of a group of events. In this procedure he employed three methodological devices: inductive, experimental and mathematical methods, which represent the three pillars of modern science. He recognised that the science of geometrical optics presented an ideal example for the requisite scientific methodology: 'observation and experience can supply the facts, but mathematics is required to learn the reason for the facts'.

He regarded induction as a method of discovering causes from the effects of perceptions of man's senses which stand for physical facts. Therefore, he used the method of induction for the resolution of the complex physical facts given by man's sense perception into their causes or principles, a procedure which was essentially a process of abstraction. If these abstracted principles could be recomposed to demonstrate the causal connexion with observed facts then a scientific explanation of a physical phenomenon had been attained. This entire process was called 'resolution and composition'.

However, Grosseteste realised that the task of identifying the causes of physical events was a highly sophisticated problem and it may not always be possible to reduce a physical effect to an actual physical cause by this orderly procedure. In such cases, Grosseteste considered it necessary to rely on intuition and conjecture in order to reduce a physical effect to an actual cause. But this procedure poses a basic problem: how to distinguish a true cause from a false one? In order to eliminate false causes and insofar as possible to identify the true cause, Grosseteste proposed a 'method of falsification' whereby the proposed causes were tested by comparing the consequences deduced from them with the experimental results. He even worked out primitive experiments, particularly in optics, to be used in the method of falsification.

Grosseteste used in his method of science both the 'principle of uniformity' and the 'principle of economy'(***lex parsimoniae***) in natural phenomena. He demonstrated the necessity of expressing physics, which had remained mostly qualitative, in terms of quantitative mathematics. Grosseteste wrote: "All causes of natural effects must be given in terms of lines, angles and figures." Although Grosseteste's conception of experimental science owed a great deal to Aristotle, it did retain its independence from him.

Grosseteste was responsible for the introduction of Aristotelian learning to Oxford, though his interpretation of it was strongly influenced by Neoplatonic thought. Plato was the first ancient Greek philosopher whose ideas were accepted into the mediæval thought owing to the influence of Augustinus of Hippo and other Neoplatonic writers. The works of Aristotle with the exception of his logical tracts, which had been translated into Latin by Boethius and thus made available to European scholars, had a minor influence in the Low Middle Ages.

Plato's thoughts on creation in his ***Timaios*** and ***Phaido*** were recognised as the best approximation to Christian views and, therefore, many Christian works written in the 6th century A.D. blended Neoplatonic thoughts with Christian doctrines. At the same time, Plato's belief that science is science only so far as it contains mathematics, was very influential in the mediæval world, but particularly at the Oxford University which was legally constituted in A.D.1214 and where Grosseteste was a secular master. Therefore, the mediæval tradition which was considerably influenced by the Platonic and the Neoplatonic thought was inclined to believe in the mathematical conception of reality.

Grosseteste accepted the Neoplatonic view of reality, and he incorporated the 'thesis of divine illumination' of Augustinus into his natural philosophy which can be described as 'metaphysics of light'. He firmly believed in the Neoplatonic conception of nature as being ultimately mathematical, and that the key to the understanding of physical nature is mathematics, and that the key to the understanding of all the actions of physical forces is to be found in the propagation of sensible physical light as the first 'corporeal form (***corporeitas***)' on account of its property to propagate rectilinearly in all directions simultaneously. The 'metaphysical light (***lux***)', which Grosseteste assumed to be the primary substance and the highest reality of nature that incorporates itself into the primordial matter according to mathematical proportions in order to produce things of the senses, he regarded to be different from the visible 'physical light (***lumen***)' and the 'very source of all causes'. The metaphysics of light of Augustinus had been promoted by the Spanish Arab philosopher al-Haytham (early 11th century A.D.), the best Muslim physicist and a talented mathematician who was known in Europe by the name of ***Alhazen***. Grosseteste postulated the propagation of 'metaphysical light (***lux***)' to be pulsory like the propagation of sound. He was influenced by the optical works of Eukleides, Ptolemaios and ***Avicenna***, but not by the works of ***Alhazen*** which had not been available to him, and he devoted much of his research to the study of optics and the laws of perspective since he believed that the study of optics based on the propagation of visible 'physical light (***lumen***)' was the most convenient way to learn about the propagation of 'metaphysical light (***lux***)' which he regarded as essential for the understanding of the physical world. His theory of propagation of light as a prototype for any extension of an action, which multiplies itself from point to point in a rectilinear movement through a continuous medium, has some affinity to the field concept of modern physics, particularly when 'energy' is substituted for 'light'. Evidently in the natural philosophy of Grosseteste optics was more fundamental to the physical science than mechanics.

Grosseteste was a trailblazer in the theory of infinity, and in the theory of continuum which he presumed to consist of infinitely many indirectly connected 'indivisibles',or 'atoms'. He discussed the question of comparison of different degrees of infinity which he expressed mathematically by divergent series.

His studies of light, lenses and mirrors were thorough and scientific. He tried to explain the shape of the rainbow by means of the double refraction of light in a spherical lens which he could study experimentally. He thought that the rainbow was created by the refraction of light through the cloud, where the whole cloud acted like a giant lens. However, an explanation of the rainbow by means of the refraction of light rays had been already cited by the ancient Greek Olympiodoros in the sixth century A.D., and its origin may date from the Hellenic period. Grosseteste was responsible for the theory of double refraction which remained the standard explanation for the spherical lens and the burning glass until the 16th century A.D.. Grosseteste did observe magnification through biconvex lenses and soon after his death spectacles with convex lenses came into use in northern Italy about A.D.1286. He was the first Christian scientist to suggest the use of lenses to magnify objects and to bring distant objects closer. Grosseteste's contribution to the science of optics mostly consisted of his emphasis on the importance of the experimental and mathematical methods rather than of an increase in the positive knowledge apart from double refraction. He tried to establish a geometrico-mechanical conception of the rectilinear propagation of light and sound by a series of waves or pulses. He, moreover, regarded heat as a form of 'violent' motion.

Grosseteste, who was the first mediæval scientist to elaborate a method of exact physical science which united the experimental and the rational method into a systematic theory of experimental science, had a lasting influence on the subsequent important development of mathematical sciences at the Merton College of Oxford University in the fourteenth century A.D., although Grosseteste himself had perished in the bubonic plague known as the 'Black Death' which ravaged Europe in A.D.1253 and killed almost half of its 90 million population.

Albertus Magnus and Aristotelian Science:

A younger contemporary of Grosseteste, a former German nobleman, Albert von Bollstadt, became the Dominican friar ***Albertus Magnus*** (A.D.1206-1280), who knew the translations and commentaries of Aristotle's works by Grosseteste and was a recognised connoisseur of Muslim literature on Aristotelianism. ***Albertus Magnus***, who was essentially a scientist, brought together Aristotelian, Muslim, Jewish and Neoplatonic thought, which included all the contemporary learning. He was knowledgeable of all the sciences, from astronomy to medicine, and practised and advanced them all. His Christian world view was that God had created a cause-and-effect world which has an objective reality, and man has the freedom to examine and learn from it, since God works through natural causes which can be investigated by man. Observation and experiment guided all his own extensive researches in science.

Albertus Magnus and his student ***Thomas Aquinas*** recognised, like Adelard of Bath in the previous century, that theology and natural philosophy frequently approached the same event from a different point of view, an event which could be both the act of Divine Providence as well as the result of a natural cause. Therefore, they established a distinction between theology and natural philosophy by assigning to each its proper sphere of action, so that there could not be any real contradiction between the truth as revealed by religion and the truth as given by reason. ***Albertus Magnus*** stated that what pertains to faith and morals it is proper to follow the apostles rather than philosophers, but in medical matters he would rather consult Hippokrates or Galenos (in English, Galen), and in natural philosophy Aristotle because they knew more about nature.

Albertus Magnus, who was the first promoter of Aristotelianism in Europe, used the natural philosophy of Aristotle not only as a foundation for metaphysics and theology but, even more importantly, as a general theory for the scientific study of nature. He, and his student ***Aquinas***, regarded physics as prior to metaphysics, and they were attempting to preserve the autonomy of physics from the more abstract disciplines of mathematics and metaphysics. Both ***Albertus Magnus***

and ***Aquinas*** insisted on the autonomy of physical principles from mathematical principles, since both of them never accepted the Pythagorean and Platonic idea that the structure of reality is essentially mathematical. For this reason, ***Albertus Magnus*** as well as ***Aquinas*** emphasised the empirical aspects of their scientific methodology rather than the mathematical aspects of it as had been done by Grosseteste, thereby disassociating themselves from the metaphysics of light and the mathematical physics of Grosseteste at the Oxford school.

Albertus Magnus was a particularly keen student of nature and very skilful at observation and systematic classification. He urged independence of mind and reliance on personal experience in science, and he frequently certified his observation by the statement: " I was there and saw it for myself (***fui et vide experire***)." He, moreover, advised repetitive experimentation under a variety of external conditions in order to reach scientific accuracy. ***Albertus Magnus*** professed a systematic theory of experimental science (***scientia experimentalis***), and he expressed his views on science in various statements in his treatises. In his book on herbs, plants and trees, he stated his basic experimental philosophy in science: "...in these matters experiment is the sole proof (***experimentum solum certificat in talibus***)," and in his book on minerals he emphasised scientific independence: "The aim of natural science is not to accept the statement of others, but to investigate the causes that were at work in nature for themselves." ***Albertus Magnus***, who was the best botanist between the ancient Greeks and the modern botanists, made notable observations in < On Vegetation > (***De vegetabilibus***). Moreover, he was the first chemist to produce arsenic in free form. He also made extensive investigations of metal alloys.

Albertus Magnus remonstrated the Schoolmen for their uncritical reliance on authority, particularly on that of Aristotle: "Had Aristotle been God he would have been infallible, but since he was a human being like the rest of us, he could, of course, be in error." He resolutely rejected the idolatry of the Muslim philosopher ***Averroës*** who considered Aristotle infallible. He carried out numerous experiments on the thermal effects of Sunlight, classified about hundred minerals, made comparative studies of plants with a remarkable sense for morphology and ecology, and investigated embryology and reproduction which included experiments on lower animals. He also pursued theoretical and mathematical interests in his analysis of motion which not only inspired his pupil ***Aquinas*** but later thinkers such as Ockham as well, and did much to promote the Ptolemaic structure of the universe in preference to the more orthodox Aristotelian views of his contemporaries. His literary output was encyclopædic, and his work on observation and cataloguing of nature was extensive and independent. On account of his amazingly wide range of interests and his prodigious scholarship, he earned the soubriquet 'The Great (in Latin, ***magnus***)', as well as the popular title the 'universal teacher (***doctor universalis***)'. He is the only man in history who received the title 'The Great' for his scholarship and not for his military prowess as was the common custom.

Both ***Albertus Magnus*** and Vincent de Beauvais undertook ambitious encyclopædic works in which they examined the whole contemporary knowledge according to carefully thought out systems of orderly classification inspired by Aristotle. ***Albertus Magnus*** also wrote encyclopædic commentaries on the works of Aristotle. These studies culminated in the colossal work of ***Aquinas***, the most talented student of ***Albertus Magnus***.

Albertus Magnus and his pupil ***Thomas Aquinas*** not only developed a new Aristotelianism known as 'high scholasticism' that not only accorded secular learning almost the same importance as the revealed truth, but also laid a firm foundation for the growth of mediæval science.

Roger Bacon and Universal Science:

Grosseteste's student, Roger Bacon, a Franciscan friar popularly known as the 'miraculous teacher' (***doctor mirabilis***), continued his master's teaching of methodology of sciences and became a promoter of inductive reasoning, empiricism and mathematics in science. He considered experience, experiment, and mathematics the three pillars of natural science, and like his teacher Grosseteste he cultivated arithmetic, geometry, astronomy and experimental sciences in his own scientific works. Bacon studied at Oxford with Grosseteste, and also at Paris, after which he became a most celebrated and zealous teacher at Oxford University. He was learned in Hebrew, in Greek [a language for which he wrote a grammar], in Arabic, and he knew thoroughly the works of Aristotle. In science Bacon stressed the importance of mathematics: "Mathematics is the gate and the key of sciences ... For he who knows not mathematics, cannot know any other sciences; what is more, he cannot discover his own ignorance or find its proper remedy." Bacon realised that a great deal remains to be learnt about nature but he severely criticised the purely deductive methods used in science by most of his contemporaries, methods which he perceived to be incapable of solving important physical problems, and their blind reliance on past authorities. He thought that the uncritical acceptance of Aristotle's natural philosophy by the scholastics was a serious obstacle for the attainment of sound science, and he went as far as to state: "If I had the power over the works of Aristotle, I would have them all burnt; for it is only a loss of time to study them, and a cause of error and a multiplication of ignorance beyond expression." He thought that the search for Aristotelian forms and species was an idle folly, and that the true ***prima philosophia*** should be constituted from all the fixed universal laws of nature. Bacon, like his teacher Grosseteste, advanced an entirely new principle of science by insisting that the cognition of the real world must necessarily depend upon observation and experiment, and not on the texts by authorities recognised by the Roman Church. He insisted that physics should be investigated mathematically because without it natural philosophy is no more than verbosity. He also called for a new method of enquiry based on controlled observations. Bacon bitterly criticised his contemporary ***Albertus Magnus***, somewhat unfairly it seems, who replied to Bacon as follows: "... some people wrote nothing themselves but criticised others much." Bacon was also an outspoken critic of his fellow clergy who wrote on science, and the stinging flavour of his criticisms can be sampled from some of his statements: "Authority may compel belief but cannot enlighten the understanding .... Whatever seems to be true to the many must necessarily be false. ... the common people are not guilty of the fourth fault, concealment of ignorance and assumption of knowledge; that is the peculiar property of the learned professors. ... the whole clergy is given up to pride, luxury, and avarice. Wherever clergymen are gathered together, as at Paris and at Oxford, their quarrels, their contentions, and their vices are a scandal to the laymen." Bacon thought that progress in wisdom was hopeless when the moral condition of those who should promote wisdom was so far below that of the teachers of the pagan world, meaning both the ancient Greeks and the infidel Saracens. With such statements Bacon launched a fierce attack on scholastic philosophy of his day, a philosophy which applied reason to revelation, and on the pretentious and pompous clergy. It is not difficult to see why Bacon suffered long imprisonment for his unorthodox and scathing views about his fellow clergy. Bacon wrote 3 well-known treatises: < Greater Work > (***Opus Maius***), < Lesser Work > (***Opus Minus***), and < Third Work > (***Opus Tertium***) as a complete encyclopædia of science. In the last treatise, he stressed the importance of experience in science in the following way: "The strongest arguments prove nothing as long as the conclusions are not verified by experience. Experimental science is the queen of sciences and the goal of all speculations." Bacon was the first mediæval scientist to use the term 'experimental science' which he adopted from Ptolemaios of Alexandria. In his first treatise <Greater Work > Bacon wrote on the usefulness of mathematics in geography, chronology, music, explanation of the rainbow, calendar-reckoning, State administration, meteorology, hydrography, astrology, astronomy, medicine, optics, perspective and vision, grammar, logic, ethics, metaphysics, and theology. He devoted an entire book in the < Greater Work > to the science of experiments which he considered to be a separate science of its own.

Bacon advocated the use of the use of science to gain power over nature which had been the guiding idea of Muslim science over several centuries. In his opinion the justification of theoretical sciences is the useful results which can be obtained from them. He emphasised the need to include the study of the practices of artisans and practical alchemists in any system of scientific education. Bacon himself gave elaborate descriptions of various practical sciences in his treatises.

Bacon gave a rule which expressed the grade of intensity of a mixture of two quantities having different grades of intensity, a rule which formally agrees with the 'calorimetric formula' that was discovered and experimentally proven by the physicist of Swedish stock, Georg Wilhelm Richmann (A.D.1711-1753), a native to Estonia, in the 18th century A.D.. Richmann was immortalised when he was electrocuted whilst trying to duplicate the electrical experiments of Benjamin Franklin (A.D.1706-1790).

Bacon sought to establish a universal science' which is valid in all scientific disciplines in contrast to modern sciences which are limited to particular scientific fields. Bacon at first had thought that he could be the chief synthesiser of science, but he soon realised that this was impossible. He then suggested in his book that the Pope gather together specialists in different fields of study and urge them to cooperate. Bacon outlined the specialties which should be represented and the cooperative scientific knowledge that the specialists should try to produce in order to show the possibilities of science. Unfortunately, Pope Clement apparently never had time to study Bacon's book, because he died the following year.

Bacon's work in optics is distinguished by its clarity, because he understood the nature of the optical action of refraction in convex lenses. He was the first to mention the use of lenses for spectacles, and to hint at the optical effects of combination of lenses which ultimately led to the manufacture of optical instruments.

In his < Greater Work > Bacon suggested the use of convex lenses to compensate for presbyopia. About A.D.1280 the first spectacles were produced by Salvino degli Armati, and this invention was made public in 1285 by his friend the Dominican friar Alessandro della Spina of Pisa, who made his own spectacles using crystalline beryllus lenses.

Bacon determined the focal length of concave mirrors experimentally, and suggested that Sun's rays be treated as parallel rather than radial emissions from the Sun to improve the explanation for the optical action of burning lenses and parabolic mirrors. He claimed that light travels much faster than sound which he justified by giving examples such as lightning and thunder.

Bacon understood how reliable knowledge can be obtained and he offered sound ideas how to go about it. He explored the causes that produce or prevent the advance of science, and speculated about the reform of the method of enquiry.

Bacon was a technological visionary, for he predicted the following future technological achievements: the telescope, the automobile, the aircraft, the submarine, and a world ruled by a technocracy of scientific supermen. Fortunately for the world the last prediction did not come to pass. Much of Bacon's work was propaganda on behalf of Muslim science, which he believed had been neglected in Christian Europe but could be used by Christians to their own great advantage if they were competent enough to read the works of Muslims which could be translated better. He urged Christians to carry 'crusades of learning' to the lands of Muslims in order to win them over to the Christianity although by that time Muslim learning was already in a precipitous decline.

Thomas Aquinas and Speculative Science:

Aquinas and most mediæval scientists regarded physics as a 'speculative science', but this speculation was not groundless since it was based on sense experience and sensible matter, that is, matter which possessed qualities that could be directly apprehended by the senses. For this reason ***Aquinas*** did not disregard quantitative physics, although the sense experience he considered was mainly qualitative, and his natural philosophy possessed the same characteristics. However, his methodology was basically empirical which held that no material knowledge comes to the mind of man without first originating in his senses. ***Aquinas*** was aware of the hypothetico-deductive methodology of science as proposed by Grosseteste, and he stressed the conjectural character of the scientific arguments which had not been so recognised by Aristotle.

To ***Aquinas***, natural philosophy was a 'science' (***scientia***) which could give true and certain knowledge of the material world through principles that could be discovered from experience by means of rational inference and serve as premises in strict deductive proofs. Experience meant to ***Aquinas*** the ordinary sense observation in which man was a passive observer and not an active experimenter. When ***Aquinas*** used the term 'experimental science' (***scientia experimentalis***), he did not mean controlled experimentations in the modern sense but only ordinary sense observations.

Aquinas resolved science into the following disciplines:

'Physics' as the least abstract of the theoretical sciences which always considers material objects that have sensible matter as part of their definition.

'Mathematics' as a more abstract of the theoretical sciences by leaving aside sensible matter and constructing numbers and figures in imagination out of the matter as pure extension destitute of sensible qualities.

'Metaphysics' as the most abstract of sciences by separating its objects entirely from matter and considering them purely from the aspect of being.

'Intermediate science' (***scientia mediae***) such as Ptolemaic astronomy and geometrical optics which use mathematical principles to obtain an understanding of physical objects and their behaviour was situated between physics and mathematics.

Separate from such an intermediate science are the physical principles which are proper for natural philosophy and which safeguard the autonomy of natural philosophy from mathematics as well as from metaphysics. By insisting on this autonomy, ***Albertus Magnus*** and ***Thomas Aquinas*** could not accept the 'light metaphysics' and its mathematisation.

William Ockham and Empirical Science:

A decisive change in the natural philosophy as a theoretical form of natural science was produced by the iconoclast but ingenious English logician William Ockham who represented the extreme development of Franciscan thought in his empirical 'philosophy of nominalism' and its emphasis on concrete empirical facts. One of the striking features of Ockham's work was his careful analysis of references of terms which later helped to clarify many issues in physics.

Ockham held the general nominalist conviction which asserted that what is not directly observable in experience is not real. His epistemology consisted of a 'radical empiricism' which upheld the idea advanced by Duns Scotus that all human knowledge is obtained from experience by means of intuitive cognition'. Such a cognition meant that objects external to the mind, as well as personal mental states, are grasped by the mind 'directly and immediately'. In such a direct mental apprehension a person would automatically know whether or not something existed. No demonstration was required for intuitive cognition, nor could it be produced in order to show the existence of anything apprehended by such means. Therefore, Ockham was a champion of 'intuitive knowledge' which had to be acquired empirically from experience with particular objects. As far as a man's mind was concerned Ockham rejected the prevailing Aristotelian psychology which partitioned the mind into different separate faculties with fine distinctions between them because in his opinion man's mind is a unity and the distinctions are merely formal or logical, and not real.

Ockham argued that knowledge of one existing thing does not empower a man to infer the existence of any other thing since contrary to Aristotle's opinion, 'necessary connexions' cannot be presumed between contingent things which are the only existents apart from God. Therefore, he denied any justification for inferences made from experience to what transcends experience.

In the matter of causation, Ockham rejected Aristotle's concept of 'final causes' which he dismissed as mere metaphors and, hence, he concerned himself only with 'immediate causes'. He held that something could be considered an 'immediate cause' when the effect it produces happens in its presence, all other conditions being equal, and fails to happen in its absence. Thus, in Ockham's opinion, only by experience, and certainly not by ***a priori*** reasoning, could sequences of events satisfying the given conditions be justifiably considered 'causally connected'. Therefore, according to Ockham, there existed considerable uncertainty in man's knowledge of causal connexion. As mentioned earlier, these causal conclusions of Ockham tended to undermine the concept of 'necessary cause-and-effect relationship' and the sense of the knowable in Aristotelian natural philosophy which had been widely, and rather uncritically, accepted in the thirteenth century A.D.. As a dedicated empiricist who rejected the reality of the unobservable, Ockham contended that the basic premises of science should be derived from experience, and since such premises could not involve necessary cause-and-effect relations, they have to be expressed as 'hypothetical statements'. Ockham averred that according to the philosophy of nominalism the 'universals' are not things but only symbols, and in as much as science is related to 'universals' which are mere symbols, science is not science of things but rather 'science of symbols'. Ever since Ockham, physical knowledge is conceived in general not as knowledge of things but rather as knowledge of symbols representing physical concepts.

In the fourteenth century A.D. Ockham's influence on the intellectual climate in Europe was at once profound and lasting, and it produced a widespread tendency among the men of learning to accept 'empiricism' as the foundation of whatever true knowledge was attainable by man. According to Ockham, general principles obtained from experience by induction are the proper foundation for the pursuit of science. The unobservable entities and the mediæval Platonic 'forms' were thenceforth rejected as 'unreal' and, as a consequence, they lost their former importance as explanatory devices in the natural philosophy representing physical sciences which was in accordance with Ockham's requirement that the sole aim of a scientific theory is to describe observed facts as correctly and economically as possible. The philosophical movement of nominalism that was promoted by Ockham in the Late Mediæval science not only moved the chief interest in natural philosophy towards logical precision, but also achieved a philosophical sophistication of great refinement about the importance of hypotheses in scientific theory, the main emphasis of which was mathematical.

The mediæval physicists began to emphasise the positive aspects of human knowledge by realising that even 'incomplete induction' could produce a degree of certainty which is quite adequate for making judgements in natural sciences. Therefore, they embraced empiricism as a thoroughly acceptable foundation for the sciences, the fundamental principles of which, though admittedly indemonstrable according to Ockham, had all the validity they needed for any practical application. The nominalist theory of science served to corroborate the doctrine of 'saving the phenomena', and to provide the philosophical justification for its extended application to physical sciences. In his effort to promote empirical science Ockham had suggested a more definite separation between 'experimental science'(***scientia realis***) and 'rational science'(***scientia rationalis***) which consists of concepts and logical constitution of the same.

Since in the Ockham's system of natural philosophy quantity as such became more of a question of language than of physical science, his followers became concerned with linguistic analysis with respect to quantity. Concerning substance, Ockham pointed out that man knows only its properties but not the fundamental substantial form as declared by Aristotle. In their various disputations about physical problems his followers often became bogged down in a multitude of logical subtleties. Despite this shortcoming, these analyses prepared the framework for highly imaginative, and sophisticated calculations of the time-space relationships between motions with different velocities.

It appears that a definite break with Aristotelianism was essential in order to change the mediæval natural philosophy into modern science, and this initial break came with Ockham's nominalist natural philosophy called the 'new way' or the 'modern way (***via moderna***)' which contained the source of modern science, and with the condemnation of certain Aristotelian themes in theology by Bishop Tempier in A.D.1277 that had served Ockham as an inspiration for working out his own system of thought. However, Ockham was not the most radical nominalist thinker in natural philosophy. More skeptical nominalist theologians than Ockham, such as Jean de Mirecourt and Nicolas de Autrecourt of Paris, rejected Aristotelianism even in a more radical way. Jean de Mirecourt considered most human knowledge as merely probable, since in his opinion sensory knowledge is deceptive, and truth can rarely be reduced to the 'principle of non-contradiction' because the omnipotent God can always intervene by miracle to produce a different outcome. Nicolas de Autrecourt also thought that all knowledge of man comes from sensation, and that there is only one valid criterion of certitude: the principle of non-contradiction. He agreed with Jean de Mirecourt that the senses can deceive, and since it is difficult to reduce any argument to the principle of non-contradiction, human knowledge is essentially restricted to 'probabilities'. Nicolas de Autrecourt, who argued from Ockham's point of view that the existence of one thing does not permit to infer the necessary existence of any other thing and that cause cannot be logically inferred from its effect, denied all the propositions of Aristotelian natural philosophy because in his opinion they were indemonstrable and, for this reason, inconclusive. He concluded that only 'probable knowledge' was possible for man.

Using such arguments in Aristotelian natural philosophy, and particularly when applying it to causality, Nicolas de Autrecourt concluded that the atomic theory of Demokritos of Abdera, which had been rejected by Aristotle, was just as likely explanation for the existing things as the Aristotelian conception which held that things are being compounded of form and matter, a conception that had been accepted by ***Aquinas***. Furthermore, Nicolas de Autrecourt held that even if causality existed in nature, it cannot be demonstrated, which makes him a precursor of modern empiricists. He proposed to relinquish the Aristotelian representation of change as a succession of different forms assumed by the matter and instead introduced the hypothesis that all changes in the material universe can be achieved by interaction, with or without contact, and by motion of elementary particles such as atoms. This hypothesis of Nicolas de Autrecourt was quite modern because it opened the way for 'field description' of such a phenomenon as gravitation, whereas Demokritos himself had assumed that atoms could only act upon one another by actual contact. ***Thomas Aquinas*** had argued before Nicolas de Autrecourt that in the problem of motion an actual physical contact between the mover and the moved is not essential, and that in some cases a 'virtual contact' (***secundum virtutem***) is sufficient. In concert with his basic atomic theory, Nicolas de Autrecourt proposed a 'particulate theory of light', a theory which was revived by the English mathematician and natural philosopher Isaac Newton (A.D.1642-1727) many centuries later.

Ockham's natural philosophy, the 'new way' (***via moderna***), had brought the scholastic natural philosophy of Grosseteste, ***Albertus Magnus*** and ***Aquinas***, called the 'old way' (***via antiqua***),a scientific theory which had already passed its peak, to a veritable standstill. The scholastic science owing to Ockham's theories fragmented into many opposing factions the proponents of which became embroiled in endless disputes over ever finer logical subtleties, later ridiculed by literary humanists of Italian Renaissance.

Mediæval Science of Mechanics

The science of Middle Ages was a corpus of knowledge in which man attempted to comprehend the world of nature by means of his unaided reason.

There already existed a tradition of mechanics since classical antiquity which was derived from the study of < Mechanical Problems > (***Problemata Mechanika***) by the ancient Greek physicist Straton of Lampsakos (c. 286 B.C.), the axiomatic statics of Archimedes of Syracuse, and the Alexandrian theoretical mechanics as given in the works of Heron of Alexandria (*floruit* c.150-100 B.C.), Philon of Byzantion (*floruit* c.250 B.C.) and Pappos of Alexandria (*floruit* c.A.D.284-300).

Conspicuous improvements to mechanics and mathematics were made in Europe in the early 13th century A.D.. The improvements in arithmetic and algebra were due to the works of two scholars of remarkable originality: Leonardo Fibbonacci, also known as Leonardo of Pisa, and Jordan de Nemore, also known by his Latin name ***Jordanus Nemorarius***. All the improvements in mechanics were contributions of Jordan de Nemore.

Jordan de Nemore and Positional Gravity :

One of the first mediæval authors of mechanics was the German mathematician Jordan de Nemore who flourished about A.D. 1230 and was the author of two treatises on mechanics, three on arithmetic, one on algebra, one on geometry, and one on astrolabe projections. He is the founder of the mediæval school of mechanics and might have been Jordan of Saxony, who was elected Master-General of the Dominican order in Paris in A.D.1222, and who is known to have drowned in a shipwreck on his return from Palestine in A.D.1237. Jordan wrote the tractate < The Elements of Jordanus in the Demonstration of Weights > (***Elementa Jordani super demonstrationem ponderis***), in which he resumed the study of mechanical theories of antiquity such as the Kinematic Criterion of Equilibrium of the lever of the ancient Greek mathematician Archytas of Taras (428-c.347 B.C.), the axiomatic treatment of the equilibrium of the lever and the center of gravity of Archimedes of Syracuse, and the works of Heron of Alexandria on simple machines. He formulated the concept of positional gravity (***gravitas secundum situm***), an ***a priori*** principle which contained the germ of the Principle of Virtual Work, to prove the Law of the Lever. This proof is based on the principle, usually called the Axiom of Jordan, that a force which raises a weight W over a height h, can raise a weight nW over a height (h/n). Jordan's 'positional gravity' is, therefore, the product of the weight and the distance it moves in the vertical direction or, as he stated, a straight line distance towards the center of Earth. In this principle Jordan recognised the importance of the concept of work in statics.

In the book < Mechanical Problems >, Straton of Lampsakos had discussed the idea of vectorial composition of the horizontal velocity V_2 and the vertical velocity V_1, of a moving object. However, if the ratio of the velocities V_1 / V_2 is not constant with respect to time, then the motion of the object is curvilinear rather than rectilinear. Jordan showed that if he applied the reverse of this idea to an object falling along a curved trajectory, then the motive power or force at any given instant could be resolved into a 'violent' horizontal force of projection and into a 'natural downwards gravity' acting towards the center of the Earth. The component of gravity acting along the trajectory he called gravity relative to position, or positional gravity (***gravitas secundum situm***). He showed that the shallower the trajectory the smaller was the gravity relative to the position. Therefore, the steepness of the two trajectories could be compared by measuring the distance fallen in a given horizontal distance. This basic revision of the Aristotelian theory, which had assumed that only one type of force can act on a moving body at any one time, proved valuable and was later taken up again by Leonardo da Vinci, Simon Stevin, Galileo Galilei, and René Descartes.

The second book, < Treatise of Jordanus on the Theory of Weights > (***Liber Jordani de ratione ponderis***), corrected and superseded the first book which may have been written by one of Jordan's pupils. In this book the principle of moment is correctly used in the treatment of the equilibrium of the angular lever a problem which, unbeknownst to the author, had been already solved correctly in antiquity by Heron of Alexandria in his book < Mechanics >. The author studied the conditions of the stability of the balance and derived the correct law of equilibrium of a heavy body on an inclined plane, a problem the ancient Greek mathematician Pappos of Alexandria had failed to solve, by demonstrating that ***gravitas secundum situm*** of a body remained the same at all points on the plane. This treatise, which is better than many that were published by learned societies in the seventeenth and early eighteenth century A.D., gave the earliest statement of the problem of the elastic curve or ***elastica***, and made the earliest distinction between the static and the dynamic loading with respect to deformation. The hydrodynamic principle of Straton of Lampsakos, which stated that the smaller the section of a liquid flowing with a given fall the greater its velocity of flow, was included in this book. The numerous propositions on fluid flow, resistance, fracture, and elasticity given in this treatise were all original.

In his studies of the free fall of heavy bodies, Jordan correctly held that the speed is directly proportional to the time of fall. However, he did not state that the free fall is uniformly accelerated nor did he give the distance of free fall in terms of time. In another theorem, Jordan appears to say that the 'impulsion' I, a term used in classical antiquity which seemed to imply 'impetus' is proportional to the speed of fall V, *i.e.*, $I \propto V$, and that the speed is either proportional to time, *i.e.*, $V \propto t$, or proportional to the distance of fall S, *i.e.*, $V \propto S$, which is incorrect. The mistaken notion that the velocity of free fall is proportional to both the time of fall and the distance of fall was accepted and still used after 3 centuries by several prominent scientists such as Galileo and even the mathematician Descartes who should have known better.

Jordan de Nemore was also a competent mathematician, although he was not quite as able as his older contemporary Fibonacci. He wrote < Arithmetic > (***Arithmetica***) in which he used letters suggestive of parameters for numerals, however, all coefficients in his equations were still numerical. His < Tractate on Division of Numbers > (***Tractatus de numeris datis***), a leading book on mediæval algebra, dealt with a collection of algebraic rules for finding from a given number other related numbers according to given conditions. Jordan was the first mathematician to prove that stereographic projection of spherical circles are circles.

Jordan, moreover, wrote < Demonstrated Algorithms > (***Algorithmus demonstratus***) which contained a capable exposition of arithmetic rules that was used for three centuries, and < On The Triangle > (***De triangulis***), a book on geometry in 4 volumes containing 72 propositions. He devised a sophisticated method for trisecting an angle by means of a curve called the 'Limaçon of Pascal' in the 16th century A.D..

Leonardo Fibonacci and Mathematics:

In the same period, mathematics in Europe had a rebirth in the works of an older contemporary of Jordan, Leonardo Fibonacci of Pisa, popularly called Leonardo of Pisa (c.A.D.1170-1250), a layman who had studied under a Muslim teacher and who was the most original and capable mathematician of early mediæval times. He published his famous book, < Book on Abacus > (***Liber abaci***) in A.D. 1202, in which for the first time an effort is made to combine geometry and number theory with Hindu algebra and Hindu positional numeration based on the Sumerian principle of position. He devised the idea of generating arithmetical sequences by means of algorithms, and he gave many identities today known by the names of Viète, Euler and Lagrange. Leonardo Fibonacci advocated the adoption of the so-called 'Arab notation' in mathematics, that is, the Hindu 'place-value notation'.

In A.D.1220, Fibonacci published another book < Geometric Practice > (***Practica geometriae***) which was probably based on a lost work by Eukleides, < On Division of Figures > (***Peri diaireseon***), and on < Mensuration > (***Metrika***) of Heron of Alexandria. In this tractate he solved many surveying problems by means of the trigonometric method.

Fibonacci published his book < Flower> (***Flos***) on 'indeterminate' and 'determinate' problems in A.D.1225, which is reminiscent of Diophantos in the handling of indeterminate problems, and Eukleides, the Arabs and the Chinese in the treatment of determinate problems. In it he proved that no exact algebraic solutions constructible with straight edge and compass exist for the cubic equation $x^3+2x^2+10x = 20$, and gave approximations for positive irrational roots for it as sexagesimal fractions to half a dozen places apparently by means of the so-called 'Successive

Approximation Method' of Horner, a method which the Chinese discovered about A.D. 1247. It took 3 centuries to surpass the accuracy of Fibonacci's solution in Europe. In A.D. 1819, the English mathematician William George Horner (A.D.1786-1837) rediscovered independently this ancient Chinese method which was no longer used in the practice of mathematics in China.

In the same year, Fibonacci published another book, < Book on Quadrature > (***Liber quadratorum***), which was an outstanding work on 'indeterminate analysis' containing many algebraic problems he had solved in the mathematical contests held at the court of Emperor Frederick II (A.D.1197-1250), a Norman ruler with considerable scientific interests and talent, in Sicily. It also contained the 3-dimensional form of the Pythagorean Theorem.

Fibonacci was essentially an algebraist who used algebra to solve geometric problems, but a major part of his work was far too advanced to be understandable to his contemporaries. He was the most outstanding mathematician in indeterminate analysis between Diophantos and Pierre Siméon de Fermat (A.D.1601-1665).

Gerard of Brussels and Kinematics:

The kinematics of antiquity was developed further by Gerard of Brussels in his tractate, < On Motion > (***De Motu***) written sometime between A.D.1187 and A.D.1260, in which he implicitly distinguished kinematics from dynamics and exclusively examined kinematic problems. He attempted to reduce various curvilinear speeds of lines, surfaces, and solids to the uniform rectilinear speed of a moving point. In this effort, Gerard anticipated the 'mean-speed theorem' later established with mathematical precision by the Mertonian scholars in Oxford, when he equated the linearly varying rotational motion of a circle's radius with a uniform translational motion of its midpoint.

Gerard of Brussel's introduced in his work another critical improvement which was of fundamental importance to the development of modern mathematical mechanics by treating speed for the first time in history as a 'magnitude in its own right', something Aristotle had failed to do.

The mathematical treatment of kinematics by Gerard of Brussels served as the starting point of the mathematical studies of kinematics by the mathematicians at the Merton College in Oxford.

Thomas Aquinas and Motion:

A number of other studies on the motive power and resistances in relation to Aristotelian rules for the comparison of motions prepared the basis for the gradual substitution of the concept of force, such as the 'innate force' (***vis insita***) and the 'impressed force' (***vis impressa***), for the Aristotelian idea of cause, which made the subsequent, more sophisticated studies of gravitational and projectile motion possible.

The mediæval scientists in the late 13th century A.D. introduced a new type of resistance, the 'internal resistance', to supplement Aristotle's 'external resistance'. They also replaced the Aristotelian concepts 'heaviness' and 'lightness' in 'natural' motion by oppositely acting forces within the bodies consisting of mixed elements. In falling bodies, heaviness was taken as the motive force and lightness as the resistance. In rising bodies lightness was taken as the motive force and heaviness as the resistance. However, these concepts were of limited value to 'violent' motion.

Thomas Aquinas also examined briefly the problem of motion and came to the conclusion that an actual physical contact between the mover and the moved is not absolutely essential, and that in some cases a virtual contact (***secundum virtutem***) is sufficient. Although sometimes ***Aquinas*** refuted the theory of impetus, he did use it in order to explain how a ball rebounds from a wall. He reasoned that the hand throwing the ball imparts to it a certain impetus for motion (***impetus ad motum***) which is conserved during the impact, and it enables the ball to be carried away from the wall. In his commentaries on Aristotle's < Physics >, ***Aquinas*** was the most important critic of Aristotle's Law of Velocities. He preferred the Dynamic Law of Differences of Ioannes Philoponos of Alexandria (A.D.485-555) to Aristotle's Law of Velocities and accepted the idea that all motions are 'violent', but he was in agreement with ***Avicenna*** and Roger Bacon when he refused to accept the concept of Philoponos that an incorporeal impressed force can produce continual 'violent' motion of a body.

In his explanation of the projectile motion, he remained faithful to Aristotle and accounted for the motion of the projectile by the contact action of the medium through which the projectile moves. Roger Bacon by using the interpretation of ***Averroës*** also asserted that the projectile invokes a natural motion in the medium which by virtue of its power carries the projectile along.

Aquinas supported ***Avempace's*** argument that even in the absence of resistance all motions of bodies must still take time because the body has to traverse an extended distance. Therefore, he believed that motion in a void was finite because in his opinion a void as empty space is an extended dimensional magnitude in which a body must traverse the intervening empty space between any two points in the same manner as it traverses a space filled with some matter. This explanation of ***Aquinas*** was quite generally accepted by other natural philosophers.

In the 13th century A.D. isolated individuals were responsible for the reformulation of the science of antiquity, and for the initiation of mathematical analysis as well as experimentation. The primary intention of the researches of these individual scientists was to establish the workings of nature, particularly among the English savants such as Grosseteste and Roger Bacon. In the next century, the 14th century A.D., these developments were carried out more completely by groups of individuals active at the Merton College in Oxford, and at the University of Paris.

Dietrich of Freiberg, Optical Theory and Experimental Method:

The mediæval scientists worked mostly in the discipline of mechanics in which they primarily stressed logic and mathematical analysis that led to abstract scientific formulations which were not immediately put to experimental test. The active balance between theory and experiment in science was never achieved in the 14th century A.D., except in optics. In the 13th century A.D., Grosseteste had attempted a quantitative description of refraction but he made an error in the angle of refraction by assuming it to be half of that of the angle of incidence. However, a German Dominican monk, Dietrich (in Latin, ***Theodoric***) of Freiberg, wrote a work on the rainbow in A.D.1304 in which he correctly explained the production of the rainbow through the reflexion and refraction of light rays, thereby demonstrating his skill in both theory and experiment. He explained that the primary rainbow is caused by light falling on spherical drops of rain which become refracted outwards again, and the secondary rainbow is caused by a further reflexion before the secondary refraction. This explanation of the rainbow is the current one, although it is usually attributed to René Descartes (A.D.1596-1650) who gave a superior mathematical exposition of it. Dietrich carried out a model experiment with a spherical glass vessel representing a raindrop by means of which he made the important discovery that light was reflected at the inner concave surface of each raindrop. In this experiment, Dietrich made a remarkable advance both in the experimental method and in optics, and in the technique of reducing a complicated problem like the shape and colours of the rainbow, to a number of simpler problems which could be separately investigated by specially designed experiments. This work, which was methodologically very close to modern science, included experiments designed either to verify or falsify alternative hypotheses. Although his methodology was a perfect blend of theory and experiment, he committed some errors in his geometry and measurements which made some of his results erroneous.

William Ockham and Mechanics:

In natural philosophy Ockham tended to follow Duns Scotus by admitting the actual existence of primary matter. He regarded 'form' as the figure (***figura***) given to matter in space by geometrical extension rather than accepting the metaphysical concept of substantial form (***form substantialis***) which, according to ***Aquinas***, confers actual existence to composite matter.

The researches of Grosseteste and Ockham made a new approach to dynamics possible. Ockham had set down the requirement that the sole aim of any scientific theory is to describe observed facts as correctly and economically as possible. In mechanics he held that motion could not be an absolute entity and, therefore, it was not a reality distinct from the body in motion. For this reason, he rejected Aristotle's definition of motion as being something quite different from the body moved and the end attained by it. He also rejected the venerable principle of Aristotle: "Whatever is in motion is put in motion by another (***omne quad movetur ab alio movetur***)," which brought him into violent conflict with his contemporary Aristotelians, who conceived motion of bodies as a 'process', that is, an 'effect' resulting from a 'cause' rather than being a 'natural state' of bodies. Every new effect according to Aristotle required a cause, but motion according to Ockham was not a new effect since it was really nothing but the body existing successively in different places, and movement as such had no reality to Ockham. That meant, according to Ockham, that local motion necessarily required no cause. In Ockham's view local motion was a 'state of the body' and not a 'process' produced by an agent, since the simplest assumption that can be made in dynamics was that a body in motion would continue moving unless it met some resistance. Therefore, he held that no moving force is absolutely necessary to produce local motion regardless whether it is located in the medium through which the body moves or within the moving body itself, since in his opinion, force was not an obvious essential for the existence of motion. Because Ockham applied this idea to all kinds of local motion it was not an adumbration of the modern inertia concept, but only the first step in the right direction. The scientific problem of motion as Ockham saw it, was to give a mathematical account of the changes in the spatial relations of a body with respect to neighbouring bodies in the simplest way possible. Moreover, Ockham was the only mediæval philosopher who considered 'action at distance' as a principle of mechanics, an assumption which he later discarded. In his tract < Exposition on Books of Physics > (***Expositio super libros physicorum***) Ockham clearly distinguished between dynamic and kinematic problems. He defended ***Aquinas*** for holding the opinion that where there was no resistance motion would still take time, and the length of time depends on the distance traversed. When there was material resistance to motion the length of time would depend on the proportion of the motive power to the resistance. This was Ockham's method to distinguish the kinematic measure of speed from the dynamic measure of the motive power, or force, in terms of the work done.

Ockham's 'nominalist philosophy', as well as other scientific investigations in the 13th century A.D., used mathematical analysis sparingly. However, in the 14th century A.D. the mathematical treatment of science changed dramatically after Ockham's influence had taken hold at Merton College in Oxford and, subsequently spread to the universities on the continental Europe.

Merton College and Mathematical Kinematics:

The principal innovations in the natural philosophy of the mid-14th century A.D. were new mathematical methods invented for physical investigations, and new kinematic, and dynamic concepts which made the mechanics of moving bodies into an exact science. In dynamics, mediæval scientists always thought in terms of resistance to motion, a phenomenon which could be observed in common practical experience. Even gravity itself was regarded as a form of resistance. The combined effect of the moving force F and the resistance R offered to the moving body was always considered. The mediæval scientist introduced a new kind of resistance into dynamics, a kind of resistance unknown to Aristotle, the intrinsic resistance (***resistentia intrinsica***), which they considered to be an inherent tendency in nature that sought to bring the moving body back to its 'natural state of rest'.

The mathematical influence did not emanate from Ockham, because he had made little use of mathematics and mechanics, but rather from the mathematical tradition of Grosseteste which was still present at Oxford University. It was at the Merton College in Oxford where the first mathematical and kinematical innovations were made, and from there they were transmitted to the University of Paris, and to other centers of learning in the European continent. The chief developers of the new natural philosophy at Oxford were the mathematically trained philosophers Thomas Bradwardine, and his students William Heytesbury, John Dumbleton, and Richard Swineshead, all of whom at one time were active at Merton College.

Thomas Bradwardine and Exponential Law of Motion:

The early attempts in the Middle Ages to mathematise physics, as Plato had urged in antiquity, resulted in the establishment of a few mathematical theories such as the theory of proportions, the theory of continuum, and the completely new theory of latitude of forms, in all of which remarkable results were obtained, but particularly in the theory of continuum by the outstanding English mathematician and scholar, Thomas Bradwardine (A.D. c.1290-1349), who was educated at Merton College of the Oxford University, where he taught from A.D.1325 to A.D.1335. Bradwardine, like his teacher John Maudith, who wrote the first European treatise on trigonometry in A.D.1310, was primarily a mathematician, although he also taught theology and logic in which he tended to prefer Ockham's philosophy of nominalism. Bradwardine was popularly called the 'profound teacher (***doctor profundus***)' because he was more erudite than his contemporaries. He was proctor of the Oxford University from A.D.1325 to A.D.1327, chancellor at St.Paul's Cathedral in A.D.1337, appointed royal chaplain in A.D.1338, and appointed the Archbishop of Canterbury by the Pope in A.D.1349, the year when he became a victim of the bubonic plague called 'Black Death'.

Bradwardine wrote 3 treatises on mathematics and one on mechanics. His < Theoretical Arithmetic > (***Arithmetica speculativa***) was an abridged version of < Arithmetic > of Boethius, but his < Theoretical Geometry > (***Geometria speculativa***) was a more original work in which his investigation of the star-shaped polygons was a completely independent contribution. Bradwardine's book on geometry, which was very highly regarded by mathematicians of the 14th and 15th centuries A.D., was printed in A.D.1495, and soon afterward 2 new editions were published. He also attempted, like Jordan de Nemore, to construct a symbolic 'word-algebra' in which letters were used for numbers.

Bradwardine developed a form of syncopated algebra for the expression of functional relationships. In his syncopated algebra letters of the alphabet instead of numbers were used for the variable quantities to achieve generality, whereas algebraic operations such as addition, subtraction, division, multiplication and others performed on these quantities were expressed in words rather than by symbols as in modern algebra. This algebraic method was used by other scholars in Oxford, particularly by the scholars called ***calculatores*** at the Merton College in the A.D.1330's and the A.D.1340's.

Muslim commentators of Aristotle's < Physics > had mathematically interpreted his set of rules for local motion in the form of comparative proportions to mean that the speed of motion V is directly proportional to the motive force F and inversely proportional to the resistance R offered by the medium impeding the motion, which can be given as a metric law of motion of Aristotle or Aristotle's law of velocities :

$$V \propto \frac{F}{R} .$$

Aristotle was unable to express his law of velocities in the metric form since he could not separately give the speed as a dimensional quantity in its own right, because he used theory of proportions of Eudoxos of Knidos that was based on dimensionless magnitudes which consisted only from ratios of quantities of the same kind, such as ratios of two distances, or of two times. For this reason, ancient Greeks could not give a metric definition of speed as a dimensional quantity in the form of a ratio of space and time. Therefore, Aristotle could express the relation of speed to motive force and resistance only by comparative proportions after dissecting local motion into its separate stages, all of which made the interpretation of his rules of motion rather difficult.

Aristotle claimed that no motion results if the motive force F is equal or less than the resistance R, conditions which were not satisfied by his law of velocities.

In the 11th century A.D., the Persian physician and philosopher Ibn Sina (known in Europe as ***Avicenna***) (A.D.980-1037) was the first Muslim savant who preferred the dynamic law of differences of Philoponos to Aristotle's law of velocities, but he modified Philoponos' concept of the incorporeal impressed power by maintaining that this 'borrowed power' in the absence of any obstacles to motion will persist indefinitely. This opinion contradicted that of Philoponos who, like Hipparchos before him, thought that every kind of motion of bodies is limited in duration unless an inexhaustible supply of motive power is available to the moving body, which is obviously not the case in the projectile motion.

In the 12th century A.D., the Spanish Muslim philosopher and dignitary Ibn Badja (known in Europe as ***Avempace***) (died A.D.1138) promoted the law of motion of Philoponos without acknowledging Philoponos as the author of this law of motion. ***Avempace*** argued that in a void a body would move with finite speed because despite the lack of resistance, the body still has to traverse a distance in the space of void. In contradiction to Aristotle, ***Avempace*** held that the medium, which in his opinion only serves to impede natural motion, was not at all essential for the phenomenon of motion. ***Avempace*** also believed that motion is conceivable in spatial as well as in temporal terms.

The metric form of Philoponos' law of motion is :

$$V \propto F - R,$$

which for motion in void becomes :

$$V \propto F,$$

since $R = 0$ in void.

Therefore, the speed of a body moving in a void is proportional to the motive force, and the speed of a body moving in a medium is given by its speed in a void reduced by its speed in the resisting medium :

$$V \propto R \quad ,$$

according to Philoponos' law of motion :

$$V \propto F - R,$$

which is why this law is also called dynamic law of differences of Philoponos.

Philoponos' dynamic law of differences was in better agreement with observed motion than Aristotle's law of velocities :

$$V \propto \frac{F}{R} \quad ,$$

which gave infinite speed for motion in void :

$$V \propto \frac{F}{0} = \infty \quad ,$$

since $R = 0$ in a void. For this and other reasons, Aristotle insisted that void, or empty space, did not exist.

Bradwardine rejected Philiponos' dynamic law of differences and accepted Aristotle's concept that average speed is dependent on the ratio of motive force to resistance. However, in order to remove some of the internal contradictions besetting Aristotle's law of velocities, Bradwardine undertook to reinterpret Aristotle's arguments in order to arrive at the 'true' Aristotelian law of velocities. He rejected Aristotele's law of velocities because he did not quite understand what really occurs when the force F and the resistance R change simultaneously, and also that according to this law an indefinitely small force can set an indefinitely heavy body into motion, which he thought contradicts experience. Bradwardine assumed instead that the proportion by which the speed V changes depends on the manner the proportion between force F and resistance

R changes. This proposition assumed that the addition of two ratios is given by the multiplication of these ratios, and that multiplication of a ratio by a positive rational number 'n' means that the fraction representing the ratio is raised to the n-th power. Thus the sum of ratios $a:b$ and $c:d$ is the ratio $ac:bd$, and n times the ratio $a:b$ is the ratio $a^n:b^n$. All this type of reasoning is due to the particular character of the theory of proportions of Eudoxos of Knidos, which remained a continuous source of misunderstanding in scientific expositions for centuries.

In his book on mechanics < Tractate on Proportion or on Velocity Relations at Motion > (***Tractatus proportionum seu de proportionibus velocitatum in motibus***) written in A.D.1328, Bradwardine expanded the treatment of ratios (***proportiones***) and proportions (***proportionalitates***) by developing the n-tuple theory of proportions in which quantities not only vary in the double or the triple or the n-th power proportion, but also in the subdouble or the subtriple or the sub-n-tuple proportion in which quantities vary as the second or the third or the n-th root. He proposed an alternative law of motion to the Aristotle's law of velocities in which to double the speed V created by the ratio F/R, it was required to square the proportion or ratio F/R, to triple the speed V it was required to cube the ratio F/R, and so on. In other words, Bradwardine held that if the ratio F/R varied arithmetically, the speed V varied geometrically with the ratio of motive force to resistance F/R.. Making use of this exponential relationship Bradwardine gave his exponential reformulation of Aristotle's law of velocities, called Bradwardine's exponential law of motion, which can be expressed in its modern metric form as follows :

$$V = k \log \left(\frac{F}{R} \right) ,$$

where k is a suitable proportionality factor, and where,

$$\log \left(\frac{F}{R} \right)^n = n \log \left(\frac{F}{R} \right) .$$

When the resistance equals the motive force, *i.e.*, when $R = F$ then,

$$V = k \log (1) = 0 ,$$

which satisfies the condition that no motion takes place when the resistance equals the motive force, a condition which Aristotle's law of velocities violated. Bradwardine thought that the great advantage of his law over that of Aristotle is that once the motion starts at given values of F and R when $F > R$, the ratio F/R could be divided by any positive rational number 'n' without the possibility of any motion occurring. If the ratio F/R changes in the manner described, it is possible to give the speed V any desired value. Bradwardine's functional formula gave a continuous gradual change of V towards zero as the ratio of motive force to resistance F/R approached 1.

It appears that Bradwardine was the first mathematician to use algebraic functions in the mathematical description of motion, and to demonstrate mathematically how the 'dependent variable' V is functionally related to two 'independent variables' F and R.

Bradwardine's exponential law of motion was called 'ratio of ratios (***proportio proportionum***)' in his own time and later. Bradwardine, like Gerard of Brussels before him, treated speed as a 'quantity in its own right' which represented an important mediæval innovation that made possible the modern concept of speed as a ratio of space to time, a ratio of two unlike quantities the limit of which produces 'instantaneous speed'. Bradwardine introduced in this work for the first time the important concept of 'instantaneous speed' and some computational apparatus which prepared the way to infinitesimal calculus. Bradwardine applied his exponential law of motion on few occasions to 'instantaneous speed', which he called 'qualitative' velocity, rather than to average or total velocity over some given period of time as required by Aristotle's law of velocities.

He also succeeded in broadening the field of functional relationships because his law of motion can be expressed as an algebraic exponential function which could be quantitatively tested, and this aspect of his work was not only of the greatest importance to the development of the mathematical science of mechanics but also a 'revolutionary' novelty in mathematics as well. The exponential law of motion of Bradwardine was very popular and widely accepted, although it did not represent the phenomena of motion as well as the dynamic law of differences of Philoponos. Bradwardine's mathematical formulation of dynamics in terms of algebraic functions made a profound impression on his students at the Oxford University, and later on the scholars at the University of Paris.

In his analysis of local motion (***motus localis***), Bradwardine abandoned Aristotle's method in favour of the empirical method of Ockham, and as a result of this approach, his researches introduced a new and quite distinct mathematical treatment into the study of motion, in which he gave the first clear-cut separation of dynamics from kinematics.

In connexion with his mechanical considerations, Bradwardine established the theory of compound proportions in a detailed exposition which contained the concept of fractional exponents. Bradwardine introduced the fractional proportions which correspond to $\sqrt{a} : \sqrt{b}$, but he was unaware that in this theory of proportions he had a distinguished precursor in antiquity in the person of Archimedes of Syracuse, who in his tract < Sand-Reckoner > had discussed fractional proportions corresponding to $\sqrt{a^3} : \sqrt{b^3}$. Owing to the influence of Bradwardine both the mechanics of Middle Ages as well as the fractional ratios soon became the subjects of more general development.

Bradwardine investigated the problem of continuum in his treatise < Tractate of Continuum> (***Tractatus de continuo***) written within the period from A.D.1332 to A.D.1335, in which he examined the theory of continuum and discrete medium, a subject which lies at the boundary between philosophy, mathematics and physics. He was aware of the basic problem of the structure of continuum, and he examined critically the five different concepts of continuum which existed at the time. Aristotle had argued that the continuum does not consist of atoms which are indivisible, but rather of parts which are infinitely divisible, a concept of the continuum that Bradwardine also supported. Bradwardine stated his basic viewpoint on the structure of the continuum as follows: "No continuum lets itself to be integrated or compounded from infinitely many indivisibles (***Nullum continuum ex indivisibilibus infinitis integrari vel componi***)." In this sentence, Bradwardine used the term ***'integrari'*** which was much later, in A.D. 1691, introduced as 'Integral' into infinitesimal calculus by Johann Bernoulli (A.D.1667-1748) and Wilhelm Gottfried Leibniz. Bradwardine concluded: "Every continuum is compounded of infinitely many continua of the same kind." Infinitesimals had for Bradwardine, like for Aristotle before him, only a potential existence.

In antiquity, Pythagoras of Samos (c.580-497B.C.) had assumed that the continuum consists of an infinite number of points, but Demokritos of Abdera (c.470-c.370 B.C.) insisted that the continuum rather consists of an infinite number of 'indivisibles' which he called 'atoms' whereas Plato (429-348 B.C.) thought that the continuum consists of a finite number of indivisibles. At Oxford University, Bradwardine's highly respected predecessor, Robert Grosseteste, had assumed that the continuum consists of an infinite number of indirectly connected 'indivisibles'.

Bradwardine undertook a very thorough, detailed, and in many respects original critical examination of the mathematical theory of the conception of the continuum as a set of indivisibles which led him to a complete refutation of the atomic conception of the continuum. He began his arguments with definitions and theorems the deductions of which he proved. Bradwardine presented a great number of arguments against the conception of the continuum as a finite set of indivisibles, and proved that the concept of continuum as an infinite set of indivisibles leads to paradoxes. Bradwardine studied the concept of infinity and specified two kinds of infinity: the unreachable transfinite, and the potential infinity which like natural numbers grows beyond all bounds. He showed that ***via*** one-to-one correspondence any part of an infinite set is itself infinite, thereby anticipating to a certain extent the modern theory of sets. It was not his intention to develop in his critical discussion of the basic concepts of the continuous and the discrete some kind of algorism for the solution of particular problems in geometry and physics, but rather to clarify with the help of mathematics certain general quantitative properties of space, time and motion without trespassing too far beyond the boundaries of the Aristotelian philosophy. Bradwardine's critical discussions of 'indivisibles' were much later presented by Francesco Bonaventura Cavalieri (A.D.1598-1647) in his treatise < New Geometry of Continuum of Indivisibles > (***Nova geometria indivisibilibus continuorum***) published in A.D.1635. Bradwardine had also presented all the counter-arguments against the Method of Indivisibles which were much later used by the opponents of Cavalieri's Method of Indivisibles. For instance, Bradwardine demonstrated that the Method of Indivisibles leads to the following paradox: A piece of surface of finite size can in an arbitrary proportion exceed a piece of surface of equal size. Bradwardine's researches contained a corpus of ideas which three centuries later made the seventeenth century A.D. scientific accomplishments possible. His researches on the basic concepts of the continuous and the discrete, and on the infinitely large and the infinitely small clearly demonstrated how motions can be mathematically represented and analysed. His mathematical method is reminiscent of modern 'intuitionism'.

Bradwardine's skilful, and original use of mathematics in physics and theology inspired other Oxford scholars to follow his example. Bradwardine's students at the Merton College, William Heytesbury (A.D.c.1313-1372), John Dumbleton (*floruit* A.D.c.1331-1349),and Richard Swineshead (*floruit* A.D. c.1344-1354), accepted Bradwardine's exponential law of motion in dynamics and, therefore, they turned their chief attention towards a more elaborate mathematical study of kinematics for which they established the basic terminology and definitions. The mathematically trained Mertonian philosophers were the first scholars to recognise in their speculative mathematical study of motion that an adequate basis for any quantitative analysis of continuity and variability of motion required a precise mathematical definition of these terms.

In Aristotelian natural philosophy, velocity represented a quality the local form of which was the intensity of motion, or instantaneous velocity at a point of a body or at an instant of time. To the instantaneous velocity as the intensity of motion corresponded the total motion, or the distance traversed as the global or extensive quantity. The Mertonian Scholars were successful in their study of the variations in the intensity of a quality such as velocity, or heat, from point to point of a body or from instant to instant in time.

These mathematically trained Mertonian scholars were the first theoreticians to distinguish systematically between the cause of motion, now known as 'dynamics', and the mathematical description of motion, now known as 'kinematics'. The Mertonian scholars abandoned Aristotelian analysis in favour of Ockham's nominalist analysis when they defined motion as essentially a ratio in which the 'formal cause' of motion was assumed to be the velocity.

In the works of the scholars of Merton College at Oxford University, the theory of the 'form', a concept going back to Aristotle, and its variability underwent an intensive development both in its mathematical and in its natural philosophic respect. It led to the so-called 'theory of latitude of forms' which contained the germ of the idea of 'functional relationship' and its graphical representation, the concepts and methods of which were finally completed in the 17th century A.D..

William Heytesbury, Limit Concept, Mean Speed Rule and Rise of Mathematical Physics:

Heytesbury considered motion as another quality, the latitude of which could be calculated and analysed by means of the theory of latitude of forms. This approach led Heytesbury to formulate and prove one of the most important contributions to kinematics in the fourteenth century A.D., the Mertonian Mean Speed Rule.

In Chapter VI entitled < On Local Motion > (***De motu locali***) of a large textbook, < Rules for Solving Sophisms > (***Regule solvendi sophismata***) composed in A.D.1335 for the first-year university students of logic, Heytesbury, a nominalist logician and mathematician who became Chancellor of Oxford University in A.D.1371, gave the first statement of the famous Mertonian Mean Speed Rule for uniformly accelerated motions: 'In a uniformly accelerated motion the distance traversed is equal to the product of the mean velocity and the time of travel (***velocitas uniformiter difformis correspondet gradui medio***)'. Heytesbury clearly differentiated between the velocity (***latitudo motus***) and the acceleration or deceleration of local motion (***velocitas intentionis vel remissionis motus localis***). Heytesbury's mean speed rule gives the distance traversed :

$$S = (1/2)VT.$$

Since the speed $V = V(T)$ at time T is obtained by a product of the constant rate of acceleration A, and the time of travel T, the speed at time T is :

$$V = AT,$$

which gives the well-known law for the distance traversed in a uniformly accelerated motion:

$$S = (1/2)AT^2,$$

as a function of time square.

Heytesbury made this result quite clear by his corollary which is his law of spaces: "When the acceleration takes place uniformly from rest, the distance traversed in the first half of the time will be exactly one third of the distance traversed in the second half of the time."

He did not offer a proof for the Mertonian mean speed rule in his textbook but merely stated that it can be proven. In this book Heytesbury gave definitions for 'instantaneous speed', 'uniform speed' and 'uniform acceleration'. He gave the first known proof of the Mertonian mean speed rule in his tract < Proofs of Conclusions > (***Probationes conclusionum***), a work which consisted of proofs for various conclusions reached in his textbook < Rules for Solving Sophism>.

During most of the Middle Ages, like in the antiquity, for example, in the case of uniform motion along a straight line the constant speed was not defined as a proportion of the distance travelled S to the time of travel T, *i.e.*, $S : T$, because according to Eudoxos of Knidos only the same kind of quantities can appear in the proportions. Therefore, in the Middle Ages like in the antiquity, in order to compare the speeds of two bodies, it was necessary to compare either the distances which were traversed by the two bodies over the same time interval, or the time intervals which were required for the two bodies to traverse over the same distance along the paths of motion. Under such mathematical restrictions, it was not possible to conceive the 'instantaneous speed' as a ratio of the infinitesimal displacement dS along the path of motion to the infinitesimal time interval dt required to make this displacement. The specific concept of speed which is directly related to the actual path of motion began rather slowly to make inroads into the works of mediæval scientists.

Heytesbury defined the 'instantaneous speed' in the following manner: "The magnitude of instantaneous velocity is to be determined by the path which would be described in a given period of time if a moving point were moved uniformly at the same velocity with which it moves at the assigned instant."

This intuitive definition of 'instantaneous speed' is quite comparable to its definition in some modern introductory treatments of calculus for laymen. In modern applied calculus based on the method of 'geometric atom' of Demokritos of Abdera the infinitesimal distance dS traversed from the given instant t over the infinitesimal interval of time dt is $dS = V(t)dt$, where $V(t)$ is the instantaneous speed at the given instant t which remains uniform over the infinitesimal interval of time dt. If, now, the infinitesimal time interval dt is made into an arbitrary finite time interval Δt, but the same given instantaneous speed $V(t)$ is still kept arbitrarily uniform over the finite interval of time Δt, then the arbitrary finite distance ΔS which would be traversed from the given instant t over the finite interval of time Δt is: $\Delta S = V(t)\ \Delta t$. This arbitrary finite distance ΔS represents a measure of the magnitude of instantaneous speed $V(t)$ at the given instant t. Heytesbury's definition of instantaneous speed is quite similar to that obtained by calculus based on the concept of the 'geometric atom' of Demokritos. Therefore, Heytesbury was able to define the difficult notion of instantaneous speed in terms of uniform speed. Moreover, Heytesbury was also able to derive correct definitions for uniform speed as well as for uniform acceleration in which its infinitesimal aspects were clearly evident. As late as in A.D.1638, Galileo still had to use these definitions of Heytesbury which he was unable to improve, in his well-known treatise < Two New Sciences >.

In treating the mathematical continuum, Heytesbury used the concepts of 'limit' and 'infinite aggregate' with subtlety and precision. In his discussion of variable physical quantities he came very close to a purely mathematical description. He recognised the value of the 'limit-concept' in the analysis of the instantaneous in time and motion, and by the use of such logical terms as 'to begin' and 'to cease' he was able to give an accurate treatment of limiting processes, which included even a 'limit of a quotient of infinitesimals' in one instance.

Heytesbury also recognised the value of the concept of 'infinite aggregate' in the analysis of the continuum, and applied the limit-concept to the bounding of the ranges of variables and aggregates. Moreover, he was also knowledgeable of the properties of the 'exponential growth function'. Heytesbury drew conclusions concerning limits and aggregates in his textbook which resemble those of the French mathematician Augustin Louis Cauchy (A.D.1789-1851) and the German mathematician Richard Dedekind (A.D.1831-1916) on the logical foundation of calculus. Heytesbury, a nominalist who viewed the world as a world of objects that needs no postulation of a mathematical substructure, used his mathematics for the classification of everyday speech which in his opinion needed mathematical precision.

'Sophism' as a term was applied by the Scholastics to propositions supported by an invalid argument which appeared to be valid or by a valid argument which for some reason appeared to be invalid, and to a proposition supported by a valid argument of which the premises were false although seeming to be true, or of which the premises were true although seeming to be false.

Richard Swineshead and Calculatory Sophism:

Richard Swineshead gave in his renowned treatise, < The Book of Calculations > (***Liber calculationum***), which was composed before A.D.1350, an intricate and extensive discussion of the changes of real and imagined physical quantities, and of sophisms involving variations of such quantities to infinity or to zero. In Swineshead's book, the 'intensity of form' appeared as a variable intensity of a property, such as the degree of heat or cold, as rarification or condensation, or as velocity of a mechanical motion. He analysed examples of changes of intensity but this analysis was purely abstract since no assumptions nor results were connected with real quantitative measurements or experimental data. He examined the problem how to reckon the degree of heat of a body, the parts of which are heated non-uniformly, and he solved the problem for a body *A* which is subjected to more and more heat, increasing arithmetically by unit increments to infinity like the members of the arithmetic progression *1*, *2*, *3*, ..., in its decreasing proportional parts, which are partitioned like the numbers of the geometric progression $1/2$, $1/2^2$, $1/2^3$, ... Swineshead showed that the solution of this problem reduces to the infinite series :

$$\frac{1}{2}(1)+\frac{1}{2^2}(2)+\frac{1}{2^3}(3)+\cdots+\frac{1}{2^n}(n)+\cdots=2$$

in which the infinitely increasing intensity of heat is compensated by the infinitely decreasing partitioning. He was able to show numerically that *A* should be denominated to have the same heat as another body *B* which is heated to 2 degrees throughout the entire body, thereby demonstrating by the mathematical equivalence that the sum of the infinite series converges to the limiting value 2. Swineshead's calculations were no idle and meaningless numerical exercises but rather constituted a valuable method of investigation of the validity of hypothetical principles. His general procedure consisted of stating the hypothesis as a mathematical relation between a number of variables, then assigning numerical values to the variables based on physical commonsense and imagination of the scientist rather than on the experimental data pertaining to the principle. Then these values were substituted into the mathematical equation, and if it led to results that were absurd or contrary to the commonsense, then the hypothesis was declared false and discarded. Although this method of calculations was not able to prove the validity of the hypothesis, it could prove the falsity of it.

When the Mertonian scholars considered the problem of the free fall of bodies which dealt with the cause of motion, they reverted to Aristotelian metaphysical and qualitative physics. When Swineshead considered falling bodies in a chapter entitled, 'On the Place of an Element (***De loco elementi***)', it was mainly to demonstrate that sophisticated mathematics is not readily applicable to motions found in nature. It apparently never occurred to the Mertonian scholars that the Mertonian Mean Speed Rule is applicable to the case of falling bodies. Swineshead did make an effort to clarify the meaning of the 'quantity of matter' (***quantitas materiae***) when he discussed the 'latitude' (***latitudo***) of rarity and density which implicitly defined how to determine the 'quantity of matter'. His definition is not significantly different from Newton's definition: "... the measure of the same arising from its density and magnitude conjointly."

In the Chapter < Rules of Local Motion > (***Regule de motu locali***) Swineshead gave an excellent account of Bradwardine's dynamics which he extended by attempting in great detail to relate various theorems of kinematics to different variations of forces and resistances thereby making Bradwardine's dynamics capable for a more complete and thorough examination of the comparability of all types of motions.

Swineshead was the first scholar to recognise the directional, or vectorial property of motion by observing that the displacement from *a* to *b* and the displacement from *b* to *a* have the same magnitude but different directions. It was the first time when the magnitude of motion is explicitly distinguished from the direction of motion. Therefore, Swineshead was the first mathematician to realise that kinematics and dynamics are vectorial, that is, directional sciences.

In his treatise, < The Tractate of the Local Difform Motion > (***Tractatus de motu locali difformi***), Swineshead markedly advanced Bradwardine's analysis of instantaneous velocity and other concepts required in calculus, and he gave four different arithmo-algebraic proofs for the Mertonian Mean Speed Rule in uniformly accelerated motion, which Heytesbury had omitted in his book < Rules for Solving Sophisms >. In many different aspects of mathematical sciences, Swineshead was the ablest of the four Mertonian mathematicians.This mediæval method of calculation induced Gottfried Wilhelm Leibniz to recommend the publication of a new edition of < The Book of Calculations > (***Liber calculationum***) by Richard Swineshead. In order to improve the method of calculations mediæval scientists began to search for better means, such as experimental data, to supply the necessary numerical values.

John Dumbleton and Graphical Methods in Mathematics:

The Mertonian mathematicians were called 'calculators (***calculatores***)' because they preferred arithmo-algebraic methods in their researches and never resorted to the descriptive geometric representations until John Dumbleton began to support his arguments in the theory of latitude of forms with geometrical drawings in his manuscript < Summary of Logic and Natural Philosophy > (***Summa logicae et philosophiae naturalis***) composed before A.D.1349. This work constituted a lengthy critical discussion of most of the major topics of contemporary physics. In this manuscript Dumbleton developed an extended Bradwardine's dynamic analysis by applying the ideas of 'intension and remission of motion' (***intensio et remissio motus***) to his study of various dynamic relations as functions of time differences whilst taking full advantage of graphical representation. References to Dumbleton suddenly stopped in A.D.1349, and it is quite possible that he perished in the bubonic plague known as the 'Black Death' which ravished Europe at the time.

Theory of Latitude of Forms:

John Duns Scotus of the Oxford University had introduced a quantitative treatment of variations in the intensities of a quality that a body might experience. In his opinion the intensity of a quality such as heat admits temperature measurement in numerical degrees in the same manner as the magnitude of any quantity.

The mathematically trained philosophers Bradwardine, Heytesbury, Swineshead and Dumbleton adopted this idea of Duns Scotus and began to treat variations in the speed of local motion in the same manner as Duns Scotus had treated variations in the intensity of a quality. In fact, the entire corpus of kinematical theory developed at Merton College in Oxford resulted from the study of the problem of 'intension and remission of qualities or forms' (***intensio et remissio qualitatem seu formarum***), also known as the theory of latitude of forms (***latitudo formarum***). The very purpose of this method as developed at Oxford was to express the numerical changes in a quality, or 'form' relative to some fixed scale. A 'form' represented any variable quality or quantity in nature such as local motion, growth and decrease, and qualities of all kinds such as light and heat. The intensity (***intensio***) or latitude (***latitudo***) of a 'form' was the numerical value that was assigned to it, and thus it was possible to refer to the rate at which the intensity, for example the speed, or heat, changed in relation to another variable form known as the extension (***extensio***) or the longitude (***longitudo***), for example the distance, or time, or quantity of matter.

A change was called 'uniform' when, as in uniform local motion, equal distances were traversed in equal successive intervals of time, and 'difform' when, as in accelerated or decelerated local motion, unequal distances were traversed in equal successive intervals of time. Such a 'difform' change was called 'uniformly difform' when the acceleration or deceleration was uniform with respect to time or space, otherwise it was called 'difformly difform'.

Ancient Greek geographers and astronomers had used a method of plotting the position of a point in relation to rectangular coordinates known as longitude and latitude, and this kind of graphical representation of the intension of a quality in relation to the extension by means of rectilinear coordinates had become quite commonplace at Oxford, as well as at Paris, by the early years of the 14th century A.D..

In the geometrical representation of the latitude of forms it was a common practice to use the horizontal line for the longitude and plot the perpendicular vertical line segment of specific length representing the latitude at each corresponding point of longitude. The 'line connecting the end-points of all the latitudes' (***linea summitatis***) described a particular geometric shape with respect to the horizontal line as the longitude thereby representing a 'functional form' relative to the horizontal line.

The theory of the latitude of forms was the very source for the idea of 'functional dependence', and the great advantage offered by this method was that functional relationships could be expressed descriptively by graphical means which made the theory of latitude of forms much easier to understand than its purely arithmetical theory. Roger Bacon had been the first scientist to use graphical representation of forms in one of his works. The latitude of forms became the second and easier method of the 14th century A.D. for the expression of functional relationships. It was a method of science which was completely independent of Aristotle's method of science.

The Mertonian scholastics studied the kinematics of uniform, uniformly difform, and difformly difform motion ***in abstracto***, that is, in isolation from observation of nature, which was also its greatest weakness. They included in their analysis all kinds of qualitative and quantitative changes in traversing a distance, or 'latitude' which is readily quantifiable. The Mertonian mathematicians generally used a 'letter-calculus' wherein letters of the alphabet represented ideas, and not magnitudes, which lent itself to subtle logical arguments, the so-called 'calculatory sophisms' (***sophismata calculatoria***). The 'calculatory sophisms' were decried by more traditional scholastics who lacked the sophisticated mathematical background possessed by the Mertonians scholars, and who found the Mertonian arguments incomprehensible, mostly because they were mathematically complex and demanding. Such Mertonian 'calculations' did suggest new techniques for dealing with problems of infinity, and also led to a sophisticated terminology for describing numerical rates of change with infinitesimal implications which had important applications in mechanics.The ***sophismata calculatoria*** was a kind of metaphysics of calculus which was applicable to all magnitudes and to all quantities that may increase or decrease.

It is quite clear from the account given above that the Scholastics of Merton College gave imaginative and ingenious treatments of kinematics but in a very abstract mathematical way without any reference to the motions taking place in nature. But despite this shortcoming, the Mertonian scholars Bradwardine, Heytesbury, Dumbleton, and Swineshead were important contributors to the modern mathematical apparatus by formulating a reasonably clear concept of instantaneous speed, thereby foreshadowing the concepts of function and derivative, and, particularly, by developing the infinite series and infinite processes, all of which made modern mathematical science and mechanics possible, because they demonstrated how variable motions could be conceived and analysed mathematically.

On account of the quantitative ***computo*** done by the Mertonian scholars, they were called the 'calculators (***calculatores***)' who preferred arithmo-algebraic deliberations which they offered in a purely verbal form, and they virtually never resorted to the descriptive geometric representation until John Dumbleton began to base his arguments in his manuscript < Summary of Logic and Physics > (***Summa de logicis et naturalibus***) to a certain extent on drawings. In his proof of the Rule of Uniformly Accelerated Motion, Dumbleton represented the velocity as a line segment along a straight line.

Bradwardine, Heytesbury and Swineshead had successfully prepared the foundation for a new mathematical kinematics, but it mostly concerned points and imaginary bodies moving in empty space showing little or no regard to the world of nature. It was in Paris where Bradwardine's mathematical methods were developed in the theory of physical dynamics. All the principal scientists in Paris who were concerned with the so-called Theory of Impetus show strong Bradwardine's influence in their works. They applied Mertonian calculatory methods to some motions found in nature. They developed the concept of impetus and searched for examples of motion in the universe that were uniformly accelerated, but surprisingly they failed to identify free fall with this kind of motion. They accepted Bradwardine's exponential reformulation of Aristotle's Law of Velocities and Aristotle's concept that resistance by a medium is essential to the motion of a body with finite speed.

The proofs given by the Mertonian scholars in kinematics were mathematically sophisticated and complex, but essentially sound. Simpler proofs by means of descriptive graphical methods were supplied a few decades later by the scholars at the University of Paris, particularly by the French mathematician Nicole Oresme, who was responsible for further development of the Theory of the Latitude of Forms. The Parisian scholars, Buridan, Albert of Saxony and Oresme, known as ***doctores Parisienses***, whose main interest was the study of dynamics, were quite partial to Ockham's philosophy of nominalism, but when they came to the study of physics they were unwilling to give up Aristotelianism altogether because to them it would have appeared like giving up natural philosophy. Therefore, the Parisian scholars, who were also called 'Terminists were 'realists' in their physics, but 'nominalists' in their logic since they used Ockham's ***logica moderna***.

The mediæval dynamics of the Oxford school which considered motion as a process requiring a cause, is in this sense closer to Aristotelian dynamics than to modern dynamics. However, unlike the ancient Greek dynamics, Mertonian dynamics was quantitative and not qualitative. The Mertonian scholars were able to formulate a fairly clear numerical concept of instantaneous speed, thereby foreshadowing the concept of a function and its derivative, and replace the qualities of Greek mechanics by numerical quantities which have dominated European science ever since. However, they carried out their research mostly in abstract, and overlooked the advice of both Aristotle and ***Aquinas*** that experiment is the only secure foundation for science.

Francisco de Marchia and Virtus Derelicta:

The concept of incorporeal impressed force proposed by Philoponos about A.D.517 to account for the continued 'violent' motion of a body such as a projectile was not accepted by ***Avicenna***, Roger Bacon and ***Thomas Aquinas***. Owing to the influence of Ockham and Bradwardine, Swineshead and Dumbleton rejected the theory of impressed power (***virtus impressa***). Not until the 14th century A.D. did some form of impressed force theory become popular, particularly in Paris.

In A.D.1323, an Italian follower of Duns Scotus on the faculty of theology at the University of Paris, Francesco de Marchia, composed a tract entitled < Sentences > (***Sententiae***) in which he discussed the causality of the Sacraments and used impetus to explain how both the sacraments and projectiles produce effects by means of a certain power which resides in them. He was the first scholastic to revive the concept of the impressed power of Philoponos. He proposed that the mover of the projectile imparts to the projectile a residual impressed power (***virtus impressa***), which he called the 'power left behind' (***virtus derelicta***). This residual power can move the projectile against its 'natural' tendency. However, it is not innate but rather a self-dissipating temporary power. This motive force (***vis motrix***) is determined by the mover and not by the goal of motion, that is, not by the teleological principle of Aristotle. De Marchia still compromised with Aristotle's theory by assuming that the surrounding medium also receives an impressed power from the mover which enables the medium to assist in the motion of the projectile by contact. The nature of motion produced, such as upwards, downwards, or even circular, is determined by the residual power (***virtus derelicta***) according to de Marchia. The case of circular motion allowed de Marchia to explain the motion of celestial spheres in terms of an impetus impressed upon them by their 'intelligencies', an idea which paved the way for the common treatment of the celestial and the terrestrial mechanics. In his theory of projectile motion de Marchia replaced Aristotle's extrinsic cause for violent motion by a combination of both an intrinsic and an extrinsic cause. This theory of projectile motion of de Marchia, but without the extrinsic cause, was used by Galileo about A.D.1590 in his first work on mechanics, < On Motion > (***De Motu***).

Jean Buridan and Dynamics of Impetus:

The basic problem of dynamics studied by Bradwardine was resumed by Jean Buridan of Bethune (A.D. c.1300-1360), a natural philosopher who became rector of the University of Paris in A.D.1327 and taught there in the Faculty of Arts from A.D.1320 to A.D.1358. Buridan and his pupils, Albert of Saxony and Marsilius van Inghen were concerned about the reality of motion in which the cause-and-effect of motion was the central problem. They incorporated the Mertonian kinematic ideas into Aristotelian dynamics, and effectively separated the study of motion into dynamics (***penes causam***), dealing with the cause of motion, and kinematics (***penes effectum***), dealing with the geometric effects of motion.

Since they were 'nominalists' in their logic but 'realists' in their natural philosophy at the same time, they were not entirely successful in resolving the inner contradiction this association implied. Buridan, Albert of Saxony and Marsilius van Inghen accepted the empiricism of Ockham, and asserted that knowledge acquired inductively from observations and experience could provide an adequate certitude for the requirements of natural science. They stressed the positive aspect of human knowledge rather than the uncertainty of human knowledge. Buridan thought that 'incomplete induction' could provide a degree of certainty in knowledge which is entirely adequate for natural science. Therefore, Buridan believed that the general principles of science arrived at through induction were a proper foundation for the development of science. Buridan and his students sought to apply 'calculatory' techniques of the Mertonian scholars to the phenomenon of falling bodies, to projectiles, and to the movement of the heavens, thereby taking the first important step towards the study of the world of nature with new mathematical methods.

Buridan rejected Aristotle's views on the motion of the projectile, and instead adopted the idea Philoponos proposed about A.D.517, namely, that 'certain incorporeal motive force is impressed by the projector onto the projectile'. Buridan replaced this qualitative assertion by a quantitative statement: "... by the amount more there is matter, by that amount can the body receive more of the impetus and more intensely," and "... by the amount the mover moves that moving body more swiftly, by the same amount it will impress a stronger impetus." Hence, Buridan's definition of 'impetus' comes close to the modern concept of 'momentum'. That impetus measures the tendency of a body to persevere in its motion, Buridan inferred from what he called "experience": observations of simple phenomena concerning tops, rotating millstones, lances, and ships.

Ockham had also considered the motion of the projectile, but he rejected the notion that the motive power resides in the medium, or in the projector for the following reasons: when two arrows collide in mid air, the medium has to supply two contradictory motions to the two arrows at the same place in the medium at the same instant, which is absurd; when the projector of the arrow is destroyed immediately after the projection of the arrow, the flight of the arrow is not arrested, which implies that the motive power is not contained in the projector after launching. The pragmatism of Ockham, however, made him reject the Aristotle's theory of motion as well as the contemporary doctrine of impetus.

The scholastic scientist who substantially advanced the concept of incorporeal impressed power of Philoponos of Alexandria was Jean Buridan. Buridan was the real master of the theory of impetus, and was the first to introduce impetus as a new quantified technical term in order to undertake a more systematic investigation of the concept of impetus in his effort to free dynamics from most, but not all, of its customary Aristotelian foundation. He assumed that it was a kind of motive force within the projectile, which is conserved in motion unless reduced by resisting forces. Therefore, impetus as a cause of motion in the form of a force impressed upon a body was different from ***virtus derelicta*** of de Marchia because it was not exhausted by the motion itself, that is, it was not self-consuming but rather reduced by externally applied forces counteracting the motion and resistances. In this sense, Buridan's impetus was an improvement on de Marchia's ***virtus derelicta***. As stated above, Buridan quantified the impetus by the product of the quantity of the primary matter of the projectile (determined by the relative density) and the speed imparted to it by the projector. He assumed that the impetus varied directly with the speed imparted and the quantity of matter (***quantitas materiae***) set in motion, a definition which is quite comparable to Newton's 'quantity of motion', or 'linear momentum', *mv*, except that Buridan's impetus was usually regarded the cause of motion as in Aristotelian dynamics, whereas Newton's quantity of motion is considered the effect of motion in the modern inertial dynamics. However, Buridan's impetus was regarded to be an internal cause of motion, whereas Aristotle's cause of 'violent' motion had to be external. Buridan assumed that the impetus would last indefinitely (***ad infinitum***), if not diminished by forces resisting the motion. Buridan applied his impetus concept also to circular motion in which the impetus of a body was considered to be an impressed force tending to maintain the initial motion whether rectilinear or circular. Although the concept of the circular impetus tended to obfuscate a clear understanding of inertial motion as being rectilinear, it did allow the mediæval scientist to see the celestial motion in a quite new perspective. He explained motion of the heavens by the impetus imparted to it by God at the Creation, and the acceleration of falling bodies by having gravity produce a small increase in speed that creates a small increase in impetus, which together with gravity, in turn, increases the speed, and so on. His impetus concept resembled the modern inertia concept but they were not really identical because he intended his impetus concept to be a further development of Aristotelian theory of motion in which motion in general is composed of 'natural' and 'violent' motions, and in which the impetus served as the cause of motion rather than the effect of motion. Despite the fact that the concept of a uniform, rectilinear motion which constituted the core of the principle of inertia was incompatible with Aristotelian dynamics, Buridan's impetus of indefinite duration possessed dynamic properties from which inertial motion could have been derived. Buridan thought that impetus would endure in a circle in celestial bodies and in a straight line in terrestrial bodies. It is interesting that Newton, before he conceived inertia as an internal force which gives bodies the capability to resist changes in their states of rest or uniform rectilinear motion, had assumed inertia to be very much like Buridan's impetus, an internal force which would cause indefinite rectilinear motion in the absence of external forces or resistances. But even in his famous treatise ***Principia***, Newton still gave the example of the rotating millstone under his inertia concept.

In the Middle Ages, rest and motion were considered to be contrary conditions and not as particular cases of motion. However, contrary to Aristotelian theory, Buridan's force would alter the motion and not just sustain it as was the case in Aristotelian dynamics. Since Buridan asserted that the effect of gravity (and thus of any other applied force) is to change the impetus of a body continuously with respect to time, it is evident that he applied a rather modern concept of force, in which the force is measured by the rate of change of impetus of a body, to the analysis of freely falling bodies and to the definition of gravity. Although Buridan failed to bring his dynamic analysis of gravitational motion into explicit relationship with the Mertonian kinematic law for distances traversed, his explanation of the projectile motion was markedly different from his predecessors, both modern and ancient.

Buridan proposed that impetus, like light, is reflected when it meets an obstacle. He illustrated the reflexional property of impetus by referring to the impact of a perfectly elastic ball with solid ground in which the ball is at first compressed in the impact with the stationary ground to a state of momentary rest but then the ball is restored to its original shape with the reflected speed in a rebound from the ground, to the oscillation of a string, and to the vibration of a bell after being struck. All these examples illustrated for Buridan the action of the reflected impetus that imply the principle of conservation of impetus as motive power, or the conservation of energy in the sense of Philoponos. In Buridan's theory, in the absence of resistance, the movement of heavens is perpetual, whereas under similar conditions motion in sublunary region is instantaneous according to Aristotle. Most schoolmen, except Ockham, Marsilius van Inghen and a few other radical thinkers, accepted motion as a process , and not as a state requiring no cause at all to sustain it.

Buridan expected his theory of impetus to give the solution to the problems of motion that arise within the scope of Aristotelian dynamics in which any 'violent' motion required a motive force (***vis movendi***). He sought to include both the terrestrial and the celestial motion in a single science of dynamics. For Buridan the power that kept the Earth in its orbit was impetus (or inertia) and gravity.

Albert of Saxony, Marsilius van Inghen and Mathematical Dynamics of Impetus:

The researches of Buridan's German student Albert von Rückmersdorf, popularly called Albert of Saxony, and his Dutch student Marsile van Inghen, called Marsilius of Inghen, made the impetus theory of Buridan popular. Albert of Saxony (A.D.c.1325-1390) taught at the University of Paris from A.D.1350 to A.D.1361 and was its rector since A.D.1353. In A.D.1366 he became the first rector of the newly-founded University of Vienna. Marsilius of Inghen (died in A.D.1396) was still teaching at the University of Paris in A.D.1379, and in A.D.1386 he founded and became the first rector of the University of Heidelberg.

Although the Paris Terminists such as Buridan, Albert of Saxony, Marsilius of Inghen and Nicole Oresme were known as 'nominalists' they preferred to be 'realists' in their theoretical works on dynamics in which they applied Mertonian calculatory techniques to motions found in physical nature. For instance, Albert of Saxony treated Bradwardine's Exponential Law of Motion several times in his works, and he applied Mertonian mathematical methods to both the terrestrial and the celestial mechanics. Albert of Saxony and Marsilius of Inghen applied the Mertonian mathematical methods to such problems of dynamics as the motion of projectiles, the motion of freely falling bodies, and the celestial motion. They both referred to impetus as an accidental and external force thereby upholding Aristotle's criterion of 'violent' motion.

Albert of Saxony, who was scientifically more able than Marsilius of Inghen, investigated the speed of freely falling bodies by assuming speed to be dependent upon the duration of fall, or upon the extent of fall. He rejected both alternative assumptions since both led to the conclusion that the body would reach an infinite speed after an infinite time of fall, or after traversing an infinite distance. He contended instead that in free fall bodies rather reach a limiting speed since impetus conferred by gravity increases more slowly with speed than air resistance. Albert of Saxony's researches on the problem of motion influenced most of his contemporary students of mechanics.

The Merton scholars had already demonstrated in the case of linearly accelerated motion in abstract, that speed is proportional to the time of motion and the distance travelled is proportional to the square of time, but unfortunately the Parisian scholars failed to identify free fall as linearly accelerated motion although they had been searching for such motions in the universe. In the theory of projectile motion Marsilius of Inghen went backwards rather than forwards in his theory of impetus by assuming that impetus was not only imparted to the projectile by the mover but also to the surrounding air, in apparent agreement with the idea of de Marchia. He also suggested a false analogy when he compared impetus with heat, which was weakest in that part of the body that was furthest removed from the source of motion just as a rod was coldest at the end furthest removed from the source of heat. He thought that after the body left its mover, impetus evens itself out throughout the body just like heat evens itself out in a rod after having been removed from fire, and finally impetus decays just like the rod loses its heat. The impetus school of thought began to wither after Marsilius of Inghen, and particularly decline in the 15th century although it was still taught at the beginning of the 16th century.

The graphical method in representing the latitude of forms first used by Dumbleton at Merton College in Oxford was frequently employed by Albert of Saxony and Marsilius van Inghen in their treatment of problems of kinematics, but the most significant improvements in the graphical method was made by Nicole Oresme.

Nicole Oresme and Graphical Method of Kinematics:

Another student of Buridan, Nicole Oresme (A.D.c.1328-1382), the most original of the Paris Terminists, was grandmaster of the College of Navarre from A.D.c.1348 to A.D.1362, and Bishop of Lisieux after A.D.1377. Oresme, who was primarily a mathematician, applied Mertonian methods to both the terrestrial and the celestial mechanics. Although Ockham, Buridan, and Albert of Saxony were all partial to the diurnal rotation of Earth, Oresme was the first who explicitly recognised this assumption and associated it with the theory of impetus of mechanics. He stressed explicitly the relativity of all motions: "... no experience whatsoever could prove that the Heavens rotate daily, and not the Earth." He asserted that the spin of the Earth like the rotation of heavenly bodies will continue indefinitely under the primary impetus conferred at the Creation. He explained the motions of the heavens by the analogy of a mechanical clock in proposing that God provided the celestial spheres with a celestial equivalent of a clock's escapement mechanism to keep them rotating at constant speed which would continue indefinitely under the primary impetus, because there was no resistance to arrest it. Therefore for Oresme, God had become both a master-mechanic and a master-craftsman. Oresme like other exponents of impetus theory believed that the universe has infinite extent, a viewpoint which became explicit in the work of Nicholas of Cusa.

In mathematics, Oresme generalised the Bradwardine's theory of proportions to include fractional and irrational exponents and rules for combining proportions : $X^m X^n = X^{m+n}$, and where $X^{\sqrt{2}}$ gave the first hint of higher transcendental functions, in his tract < Algorithm of Proportions > (***Algorismus proportionum***) where these rules were applied to geometrical and physical problems. He formulated the rule of summation of infinite series, and also gave the first known proof of the divergence of the harmonic series :

$$\sum_n (1/n)$$

when $n \to \infty$.

Mediæval studies of infinite series by Swineshead and Oresme in their verbal and geometrical form were very influential for they encouraged the acceptance of infinite processes in mathematics which in succeeding centuries were carried out by much more powerful techniques of arithmetic and algebra.

In kinematics, Oresme revived the kinematic geometry of the ancient Greek mathematician Archytas of Taras by stating that a moving or flowing point (***punctus fluens***) traces a line, a flowing line a surface, and a flowing surface a volume – ideas which in the sixteenth and the seventeenth century A.D. found their way into geometry and infinitesimal calculus such as Newton's Method of Fluxions.

In dynamics, Oresme no longer considered impetus to be only a function of speed but acceleration as well and, furthermore, he postulated that the impetus is self-expending in its production of motion. His concept of impetus was designed to explain accelerated motion, because he assumed that the acceleration of motion itself gives rise to an impetus which in turn generates a further acceleration. Acceleration in the free fall of bodies, in his opinion, is not due to natural gravity but rather to accidental gravity which in this case is synonymous with Oresme's impetus.

Oresme discarded the ancient idea that gravity and levity are absolute and opposite qualities. He rejected the assumption of Aristotle that gravity in free fall is an increasing quantity, since he maintained that natural gravity of a body was independent of the position of the body. In the problem of freely falling bodies, Oresme suggested that the speed of free fall is directly proportional to the time of fall, but he failed to apply the Mertonian mean speed rule to the problem despite the fact that he had given the first geometric proof of it. In his treatment of some special cases of motion, Oresme was able to sum the infinite series :

$$\frac{1}{2} + \frac{3}{8} + \frac{1}{4} + \frac{3}{16} + \frac{1}{8} + \frac{3}{32} + \cdots = \frac{7}{4} .$$

Oresme elaborated Bradwardine's dynamics in several of his tracts by following the methods of Swineshead and Dumbleton, in which he also included sections on the kinematic treatment of motion.

The Italian Franciscan friar, Giovanni di Casali (*floruit* A.D.1346-1375), devised a method of graphical presentation for velocity variation with time in his tract < On the Velocity of Variable Motion > (***De velocitate motus alterationis***) written about A.D.1350, which had been anticipated by Roger Bacon, but it was Oresme who substantially improved and generalised this graphical method in his treatise < Tractate on Uniform and Difform Intensities > (***Tractatus de uniformitate et difformitate intensionum***) by suggesting a method somewhat reminiscent of coordinate geometry. Oresme was responsible for the further development of the Theory of Latitude of Forms since he made this theory descriptive and easier to understand than the numerical theory of Swineshead by systematically applying geometric figures to the continuous quantities representing the intensity or latitude of forms. Oresme thought that everything measurable can be imagined as a continuous quantity and represented as a graphical function. Thus, he represented speed as latitude and time as longitude corresponding vaguely to modern ordinate and abscissa, which appears to be akin to modern analytic geometry, but is not because he was chiefly interested in finding the area under the curve which gives the distance traversed. The method of finding the area of the figure between the 'curved line connecting the tops of the latitudes' (***linea summitatis***) and the straight line of longitude is equivalent to performing graphical integration. However, he did not explicitly explain why the area under the curve is the distance traversed by a moving object. The most original and comprehensive treatment of the Intension and Remission of Qualities or Forms, also known as the Theory of Latitude of Forms, which is still extant is Oresme's tract < On the Configuration of Qualities > (***De configuratione qualitatum***) where the well-known geometric proof of the Mertonian Mean Speed Rule is given. His extensive studies of this topic, all written before A.D.1371, were scattered among a selection of tracts under various titles such as < Tractate on the Figuration of Forces and the Measure of Nonuniformity > (***Tractatus de figuratione potentiarum et mensura difformitatum***), <Tractate of Configurations of Qualities and Motion> (***Tractatus de configurationibus qualitatum et motuum***), among many others.

Moreover, Oresme suggested also a three-dimensional 'latitude of forms' in his < Tractate on the Figuration of Force and Measure > (***Tractatus de figuratione potentiarum et mensurarum***) in which the intensity of a form was erected graphically as a vertical height or latitude over two straight lines forming a cross in the horizontal plane, which represented extensive quantities as longitudes The intensity, therefore, depended on both extensive quantities and could vary differently with each, a representation which is reminiscent of a function depending on two independent variables in a coordinate space, but Oresme did not develop this mathematical concept any further. There was also a hint of geometry of 4 dimensions when he discussed the intensity of a form in a volume or in a body, a problem which really required an algebraic rather than a figurative geometry. He wrote a treatise on the 'latitude of forms' already before A.D.1361 and later prepared briefer versions of it. Although after the death of Oresme the vitality of the Paris school appears to have been exhausted, which left the study of natural philosophy to languish until the 15th century A.D., Oresme's 'latitude of forms' did remain a popular topic of study in Italian universities until the time of Galileo Galilei.

In economics, Oresme wrote a treatise < Tractate on the Origin, Nature, Law and Exchange of Money > (***Tractatus de origine, natura, iure, et mutationibus monetarum***) which was more of a magisterial condemnation of all debasements of currency than a treatise on money. In a quite scientific and realistic way Oresme anticipated a great deal of the modern orthodox monetary theory. In this work Oresme gave the first statement of the monetary law, later known as the Gresham's Law, which states: 'Bad money if issued in excess, drives good money out of circulation'. He also gave the first sound discussion of the problems associated with 'bimetallism' in economics. Oresme came to the conclusion that governmental depreciation of coinage leads to the lowering of living standard and to the creation of economic difficulties. This work on economics demonstrates that Oresme was a remarkably clear-thinking economist of his time.

Oresme's presentation of latitude of forms is reminiscent of the concept of a point-function in a continuum of 2 or 3 dimensions in which he defined the functional dependence either verbally or geometrically because contemporary algebra was insufficiently developed for the function concept, yet he did manage to give a classification of functions. Oresme succeeded in giving a unique classification of functions by means of a composition of distinct and geometrically irregular lateral forms over unequal intervals of longitude, which he obtained by mixing arc-lengths of similar kind. There is a remarkable similarity between Oresme's 'composite functions' and the 'mixed functions (***functiones mixtae***)' of the brilliant Swiss mathematician Leonhard Euler (A.D.1707-1783) which were defined over different intervals of the independent variable by means of distinct analytical functions.

Although Oresme's graphical method of intension and remission of qualities and velocities vaguely resembled analytic geometry its basic purpose was quite different. Oresme was not interested in plotting points with respect to rectilinear coordinates because he was primarily interested in the geometric figure itself. His intention was to represent a quality by means of a geometric figure of an equivalent shape and area hoping that the properties of the geometric figure might represent properties which are intrinsic to the quality itself. Therefore, Oresme attempted to give a geometric representation of physical reality which had a much wider purpose than analytic geometry. Nevertheless, Oresme's graphical method was an important step towards the invention of analytic geometry and the introduction of the idea of motion into geometry. It is quite apparent that the method of thinking of Oresme in some respects is very similar to that of Descartes in the seventeenth century A.D.. Although Oresme's theories contained some profound thoughts, the mathematical means of his time were quite inadequate for the solution of concrete problems. Nevertheless, Oresme in his researches had reached the very threshold of analytic geometry of Pierre Siméon de Fermat and René Descartes (A.D.1596-1650), and of the theory of indivisibles of Francesco Bonaventura Cavalieri.

Gaetano da Thiene and Application of Heytesbury's Doctrine to Mechanics:

The Italian scholar, Paul of Venice, attended the University of Oxford in the latter part of the 14th century A.D., and upon his return to Italy and University of Padua he taught the Mertonian methods to his students among whom was Gaetano da Thiene (died A.D.1465), who wrote an elaborate commentary on Heytesbury's treatise < Rules for Solving Sophisms > (***Regule solvendi sophismata***). In contrast to Heytesbury's highly abstract treatment of moving bodies and points, he gave many real mechanical problems as examples to demonstrate the practical utility of Heytesbury's doctrine. It represented another step in the direction of modern science of mechanics.

Nicholas of Cusa, Transition to Modern Science and Infinite Universe:

Nicholas of Cusa (whose real name was Nicholas Krebs) (A.D.1401-1464), was born at Kues (in Latin, ***Cusa***), in Germany. He studied law at the University of Heidelberg, and at the University of Padua where he received his degree in A.D.1418. He then entered the Church in A.D.1448, was appointed a Cardinal and governor of Rome, became a Bishop of Brixen in A.D.1450, and a Papal legate for Germany. Nicholas of Cusa, who was basically a philosopher and only incidentally a mathematician, not only started the tradition of scholarship combined with observation, but also exemplified the gradual transition from the scholastic to the modern science because he had a remarkable and uncanny ability to conceive ideas that were very close to the modern ideas in science and mathematics. In A.D.1440 he published a book in which he used mathematical ideas that opened the way for the transition from 'the closed world to the infinite universe'. He anticipated the planetary theory of Nicolaus Copernicus (A.D.1473-1543) by asserting that the Earth turns on its axis and moves around the Sun in a circular orbit, that there was neither 'up' nor 'down' in space which is infinite, that the stars were other Suns and carried in their hold other inhabited worlds. He was the first to express the relativistic view of the universe after an earlier brief remark made by Oresme: "If the universe is infinite then the Earth is not necessarily, or even possibly at its center. And if that is so, the Earth may well be circling the Sun. It is only the viewpoint of the observer as he stands on the Earth that makes him think it to be the center of the universe. And if everything were relative to everything else, the only way to know where you were, on Earth or on a planet, would be to find a way to measure the 'elsewhere'."

In A.D.1440 Nicholas of Cusa extended theoretical considerations in the mathematical science by introducing the concepts of infinity and continuity. He noted that a circle the radius of which becomes infinite as a limit, is identical with the straight line, thereby taking a giant step towards infinitesimal calculus. He was also one of the first to insist that celestial and terrestrial bodies obey the same laws of mechanics.

In his < On Learned Ignorance > (***De docta ignorantia***) Nicholas of Cusa states that every study of something unknown actually comes to the consideration of its resemblance to, and difference from something known that is reminiscent of two aspects in the forming of a mathematical ratio. He, therefore, concluded that cognition consists of the determination of ratios which cannot be realised without numbers. If a circle is considered a polygon with an infinite number of sides the infinite is brought within the range of intellectual cognition in a suprarational leap despite the limitation of man's reason, although the intellectual knowledge so obtained remains ***ignorantia***.

Therefore, the infinite which has no ratio to the finite, is unknowable to man and in this sense man remains shackled to ignorance (***ignorantia***), but since man recognises in this profound manner his ignorance he may be considered wiser and, therefore, his ignorance can be considered 'learned ignorance' (***docta ignorantia***).

He emphasised the absence of measurement in experimental science as the prominent weakness of the Scholastic science by asserting that knowledge must be founded on measurement (***mensura***). He stressed the importance of measurement in his < On Experiments with Scales > (***De staticis experimentis***), which preserved some of the mediæval experimental tradition, although most of his experiments were fictitious. He suggested many investigations, and experiments to which he was able to apply the elementary physical science using the experimental method based upon measurement in considerable detail, many of which were not carried out until a century and a half later. In general, he was adamant in his point of view that physical phenomena must be measured, such as weighing with a balance in experiments, or timing free falls with a water-clock. This work reveals Nicholas of Cusa to have been a remarkable thinker of great historical importance.

The speculative studies of motion by the mediæval natural philosophers led to subtle and sophisticated theorising about the infinite and the continuum which are fundamental concepts of modern mathematics. The scholastic disputes about such topics went on for centuries, and essentially contributed to the remarkable transformation from the ancient to the modern mathematical thinking by providing a foundation for such thinking. In this sense, even ***Thomas Aquinas***, who was not a mathematician, had taken a relatively important part in the development of mathematics. In geometry, ***Aquinas*** used the kinematic method of Archytas of Taras although he recognised that experiments never really verify a scientific theory because actual conditions never coincide with ideal mental concepts (***mente concipio***) of conditions.

Nicholas of Cusa believed that man's finite intelligence can approach truth only asymptotically. He thought that the infinite was the source and the means of the unattainable goal of all knowledge. He considered the infinite as terminus to be approached only by going through the finite, a capital idea which aimed towards the limit concept that was developed during the next five centuries. His philosophical doctrine, the Concordance of Contraries, led him to believe that the maxima and the minima are intrinsically related. In geometry, the triangle and the circle were in the conception of Nicholas of Cusa the polygons with the minimum and the maximum number of sides respectively. Similarly, zero and infinity were to him the lower and the upper bound of the series of natural numbers. On the basis of these ideas, Nicholas of Cusa proposed the quadrature of the circle by considering the circle to be a polygon of infinite number of sides the apothem of which is equal to the radius of the circle. The quadrature of the circle is then obtained by imagining the circle to consist of an infinite number of triangles which admits calculating the area of the circle as half the product of the apothem and the perimeter of the circle. He added to this method of quadrature of the circle, the classic proof by the Method of Exhaustion of Archimedes of Syracuse which used inscribed and circumscribed polygons and the ***reductio ad absurdum*** principle. When the method of Nicholas of Cusa was used a century and a half later by Simon Stevin (A.D.1548-1620) and Johann Kepler (A.D.1571-1630), the Archimedean proof was discarded and the elementary equivalent of the limit concept was regarded to be sufficient.

Although Nicholas of Cusa objected to the theory of atomism, he did attempt to connect the continuum with the 'indivisibles' by regarding a line as the unfolding (***explicatio***) of a point. He held continuous motion to be thinkable, but in reality to be impossible since motion is to be considered as composed of ordered series of rests, a view which has considerable resemblance to the modern mathematical theory of continuum and the static theory of the variable, although Nicholas of Cusa did not clearly state how the transition from the continuous to the discrete is precisely made. He did assert that in thought the division of such continuous magnitudes as space and time can be continued indefinitely, but that actually such a process of subdivision is limited by the smallness of the parts obtained such as the atoms and the instants. The lack of precision in the expressions of Nicholas of Cusa about the nature of the infinitesimal and the infinitely large was repeated two centuries later in the various methods of indivisibles to which his method had given rise, and these methods finally led to the invention of differential and integral calculus.

Nicholas of Cusa performed a careful experiment on a growing plant by weighing the seed, the earth and, in due course, the growing plant and its ashes as well as the earth in which it was growing in order to demonstrate that the plant had also drawn its sustenance partially from air as an explanation for the accession in weight of the growing plant. It was the first modern biological experiment which indicated that air has weight. This brilliant experiment of Nicholas of Cusa was pirated without acknowledgement by the Dutch Renaissance scientist Johann Baptist van Helmont (A.D.1577-1644) in the seventeenth century A.D.. In medicine, Nicholas of Cusa suggested counting of the pulse as a diagnostic aid. He was the first to make spectacles with concave lenses for the myopes, whereas earlier spectacles had used more easily ground convex lenses for the presbyopes.

Domingo Francisco de Soto and Law of Free Fall:

In northern Italy, especially at the University of Padua, the realist interest of the 13th century A.D. were combined with nominalist methods in physical sciences and such scholars as Paul of Venice, whose tractate < Summary of Natural Philosophy > (***Summa philosophiae naturalis***) published in Venice in A.D. 1503 was used as a textbook and, particularly, his student Gaetano de Thiene who also became a professor at the University of Padua were the typical influential scientists of northern Italy in the 15th century A.D. They succeeded to place the science of nature on a sounder foundation and, thereby, exerted an important influence on the scholars teaching at the University of Paris. Particularly effective was the influence exerted by da Thiene. The Parisian professors Jean Dullaert from Flanders, Alvaro Thomaz from Portugal, and Gaspar Lax and Juan de Celaya from Spain wrote several good physics texts, particularly good was the exposition of Celaya on Aristotle's < Physics > in his text of A.D. 1517. Celaya examined both kinematic and dynamic questions in his text and thereby made available much of the late mediæval work in mechanics, apart from statics, to scholars of the sixteenth century A.D.. The Spanish professors at the University of Paris to whom Celaya belonged, attracted a large number of Spanish students to Paris who later returned to Spain and became influential in changing Spanish universities such as at Salamanca and at Alcalá into schools of higher learning like the University of Paris. Spanish professors who tried to base their lectures upon the 'nominalist' concepts soon discovered that their students lacked adequate background in logic and natural philosophy.

A Dominican theologian and political philosopher, Domingo Francisco de Soto (A.D. 1494-1560), who had studied under Celaya at Paris as a layman and after his return to Spain became a professor at the University of Salamanca, was responsible for teaching natural philosophy to students who lacked adequate background in this subject, although he was not a physicist. It was his responsibility to write a series of simplified and abridged textbooks for his students from which they could rapidly learn what they lacked in their scholastic background. One of his textbooks was a commentary and a 'questionary' on Aristotle's < Physics > which was a much simplified and abridged version of the type of physics texts used at the University of Paris. Albert of Saxony had discussed motions which were not only uniform with respect to time but also with respect to the parts of the moving body. De Soto discussed motions in his textbook which were uniform only with respect to time or with respect to the parts of the moving body, but not both. He studied single variable motions. He gave examples of motions that were variable with respect to time alone, and then sought examples from nature to show how some natural motions are uniformly variable, and others are non-uniformly variable with respect to time. What makes this textbook remarkable is that among the many numerical examples presented in this book there is an example for the free fall of a heavy body. It is quite apparent from this example that de Soto had a thorough mastery of the uniform acceleration doctrine of the Mertonian scholars with its infinitesimal implications, and he was the first scholar to apply it to the problem of free fall in nature. He explicitly mentions that a freely-falling body accelerates uniformly and a body projected upwards decelerates uniformly. He recognised that the speed V in free fall is directly proportional to time T of the fall, and he was the first to apply the Mertonian mean speed rule to the uniformly accelerated motion of free fall in this numerical example and the first to publish the correct law of free fall which can be expressed in modern algebra as follows :

$$S = \frac{1}{2} VT = \frac{1}{2} AT^2 ,$$

where S denotes the distance of fall, V the terminal instantaneous speed of fall, A the uniform acceleration of fall, and T the time of fall. This law of time square, which de Soto implied was relatively common knowledge at the time, was given in his textbook < Questionary on Eight Books of Aristotle's Physics > (***Questions super octo libros physicorum Aristotelis***) first published in A.D. 1545, and in its complete edition in A.D.1551 in Salamanca. Francisco Toletus, who was a student of de Soto at the University of Salamanca, investigated and extended de Soto's study of free fall of bodies.

Scholastic Theory of Local Motion and Classical Science of Dynamics:

The mediæval scientists of the 14th century A.D. had developed some of the most important concepts, definitions, theorems and corollaries of local motion which were fundamental to the new science of mathematical mechanics, all results of a brilliant period of scholastic originality. These significant new ideas which had been created for particular cases of local motion they could have logically organised into a general theory of local motion of real bodies by basing it upon a few unifying fundamental principles and by abandoning the incompatible doctrines of motion of Aristotle, but they did not do it. The question is: why did they fail to do it?

The scholastic science was rich in new ideas, sophisticated analyses of concepts and logical criticism, but their approach to all this was abstract and removed from practical applications, perhaps mostly because the scholastic scientists were clerics who were on university faculties of art and theology where their scientific interests were rather incidental to their teaching. The main theories of mediæval science were developed almost entirely in their academic discourses based on Aristotle's books used in universities, since Aristotle's influence dominated, and virtually controlled all the intellectual work done in the universities. The mediæval scholar had to become a philosopher first and a scientist second almost out of necessity in order to learn the natural philosophy and logic of Aristotle, and the scientific tradition of ancient Greeks. In general, the clerics of the universities were responsible for the main theoretical conceptions of science, but their interest in science tended to be epistemological or metaphysical or purely logical rather than strictly scientific in the modern sense.

Mediæval Technology

To the ancient Greeks such as Plato, God was a master-mathematician, whereas to the mediæval man God was the great master-engineer-architect-craftsman. However, for both Plato and the mediæval man the world was the handiwork of God as the Master Creator. Tertullianus, an early Father of the Christian church, when discussing the Roman attack on Carthage described the Roman attack with the battering ram in Latin: "... the battering ram stunned the Carthaginians as a new foreign invention (***arietem ... stupuere Carthaginienses ut novum extraneum ingenium***)." From the Latin word ***ingenero***, which means 'to devise', derives the term ***ingeniator***, or engineer, who designed ***ingenia***, or ingenious machines of war. By A.D. 1100 the catapults were called ***ingenii***. By A.D.1200, a machine-builder in Europe was called ***ingeniator***, and later in vernacular Italian, ***ingeneri***.

History of technology in Europe after the collapse of the Roman Empire has been aptly described as a history of religion and the gradual mechanisation of manual labour. The mediæval man in Europe began to build his European civilisation on machine power rather than on the power of men or beasts. After the withdrawal of Roman legions the stable political organisation of the West collapsed. Subsequently Western Europe became dominated by the semibarbaric Germanic tribes and, therefore, all public works came to an abrupt halt which left Roman roads, bridges, and aqueducts to decay from neglect. Yet, as a result of the barbarian incursions, the Christian Europe became receptive to mechanical inventions and technological improvements. The only known public work which was constructed in Europe before the establishment of the Holy Roman Empire in A.D.800, was the aqueduct of Spoleto in Italy in the 7th century A.D., which was remarkable for its lightness, the height of its piers and its pointed ogival arches.

Only under the Frankish king, Charlemagne, were the first concerted efforts made to revive engineering in Europe. Charlemagne attempted to restore Roman roads, and to connect the Rhine and the Danube river with a navigable canal, but the last project was frustrated by the presence of quicksand. The navigable connexion between the Rhine and the Danube river was ultimately realised in the Neckar Canal, the construction of which was started only in A.D.1939. The first building of any importance constructed from A.D.792 to 802 in Western Europe was the minster, or the Palatine Chapel in Aachen (***Aix-La-Chapelle***) built by Charlemagne after the model of the church of San Vitale in Ravenna, which had been constructed by the Byzantine Emperor Iustinianus from A.D.526 to A.D.547. Charlemagne built the minster as his mausoleum. After the death of Charlemagne, the engineering activities in Western Europe again languished.

However, scholarship and learning did survive in the monasteries which were initially devoted mostly to mystical philosophy and religion. Since the mediæval monks were not only learned men but working men as well, in their desire to live up to St. Benedict's dictum: "Idleness is the enemy of the soul," they strove to relieve man from the backbreaking and monotonous labour, which inevitably led them to take a keen interest in technology. Therefore, the Christian Europe came to emphasise engineering rather than science during the Mediæval Age and, as a consequence, the mediæval monasteries became the institutional leaders in the revival of engineering in Europe. Since the progress of technology depends upon discovery and invention, both being products of man's desire for a better life, the basic inspiration for technological improvement came from the monks, who were also the spiritual leaders of the West

From about A.D. 900 the West began a serious effort to save human drudgery in physical labour by applying natural power to industry. By A.D. 983 a waterwheel powering a fulling mill was in operation in Serchio, Tuscany, Italy. The first known European application of the cam to machinery took place here. In A.D.1008 other water-powered mills were operating at Milan in Italy. In A.D. 1010 water-driven trip-hammers were used for forges in Germany and in A.D.1185 the first horizontal-axle windmill had been invented in Western Europe. The European horizontal-axle windmill was vastly more ingenious than the vertical-axle windmill introduced about A.D.640 in Seistan Province of Persia. The distant ancestor of the vertical-axle windmill might have been the Tibetan prayer-wheel in which scoops catching the impact of the wind rotate about a vertical axis. Aerodynamically the European windmill was a reversed air-screw allowing the wind to impinge on the whole area of the sail at the same time all the time, whereas in the vertical-axle windmill wind only impinged on part of the sail area which made its continuous rotary motion less efficient. The first Western windmills were of the fixed-tower type, but soon the post-windmills appeared in which the post was used to turn the entire windmill housing the horizontal axle of the windmill, in order to catch the full force of the wind. In the fifteenth century A.D., windmills increased in size to deliver more power, and as a result the post-mills became unwieldy. In order to overcome this difficulty, the European millwrights invented the turret, also known as the smock or the cap windmill, in which only the turret bearing the axle of the windmill is turned. One of the earliest turret windmills may have been built by Leonardo da Vinci in A.D.1502.

It appears that the Western windmill with horizontal axle may have been inspired by the Vitruvian watermill. The idea of the wind-vane may have been taken from the windmill (***anemourian***) of Heron of Alexandria (*floruit* c.130 B.C.) who had designed it to lift the heavy piston supplying the air blast to his wind-organ. The European windmill used a rigid latticed wind-vane that was much superior to the sail. By the 13th century A.D., every village in Western Europe had at least one windmill. For example, near the Flemish town Ypres there were about 120 windmills.

Even Gerbert of Aurillac, who became the first French Pope, Sylvester II, and who had revived interest in science in Europe, showed interest in technology when about A.D.991 whilst he was the Archbishop of Reims in France, he built a pipe organ at the bishopric school which was blown by air compressed by 'heated water' in the ***aiolopyle*** of Heron of Alexandria. Gerbert is reputed to have built a clock regulated by a pendulum at Magdeburg in Germany. However, it appears that pendulum clocks had been built by Muslim artisans before him. The Muslim astronomer Ibn Yunus (died A.D.1009) apparently used a pendulum for the measurement of time in the astronomical observatory at Cairo about A.D.1000. Gerbert also brought back from Spain a plan for a calculating machine which the Muslims had been unable to make work, but Gerbert's calculator performed no better than manual calculation. A Spaniard named Magnus is reputed to have made a calculator in the form of a brass head with figures appearing in the mouth of the head but nothing further is known about it.

Some time between A.D.1000 and A.D.1010, an Anglo-Saxon monk, Eilmer of Malmesbury Abbey in Wiltshire, built a mechanical glider with which he launched himself from the Abbey tower and flew more than 600 feet (183 m) before crashing and breaking both of his legs. He believed that the crash was caused by having neglected to install a tail on the rear part of his glider. It is the second known attempt by man to fly an heavier-than-air aircraft. The first successful glider flight had been made in A.D.875 by the Spanish Muslim Ibn Firnas in Cordoba. In A.D.1003 or A.D.1008 a Persian student of Arabic philosophy, al-Yauhari died in a crash when he attempted to fly in some kind of apparatus from the roof of the old mosque of Nishapur in Kherasan.

In the early A.D.1120's, a German canon in Paris, Hugh of St.Victor wrote an educational guide ***Didascalion***, in which he credits technology with intellectual quality by virtue of being an integral part of philosophy owing to its human necessity and the wisdom associated with it. Hugh of St.Victor regarded the traditional concept of philosophy to be pernicious because it tended to exclude from consideration everything that is technology or engineering. He divided knowledge in general into theory, practice, mechanics and logic. In mechanics he included seven sciences: the manufacture of cloth and arms, but also navigation, which ministered to the extrinsic needs of the body; and agriculture, hunting, medicine, and the science of theatrical performance, which ministered to the intrinsic needs of man. He went on to discuss in considerable detail various categories of these mechanical arts, but his opinion was largely ignored by his contemporaries.

Later in the twelfth century another popular classification of sciences was produced by Dominicus Gundissaunus in his book < On the Division of Philosophy > (***De divisione philosophiae***) in which he separated the sciences into theoretical and practical parts. Theoretical sciences consisted of physics, mathematics, and metaphysics. The practical sciences consisted of politics or the art of civil government, the art of family government which included giving instruction in the liberal and mechanical arts, and ethics or the art of self-government. The mechanical arts were concerned with making something useful out of matter. To each of the mechanical arts there corresponded a theoretical science which studied the basic principles put into practice by the mechanical art.

In the thirteenth century these ideas were revived by such men as Roger Bacon, ***Thomas Aquinas*** and Giles of Rome. Michael Scot and Robert Kilwardby (died A.D. 1279) wrote treatises on the classifications of philosophy. Scot thought that each of the practical sciences was related to a theoretical science by being the practical manifestation of it. He maintained that such practical sciences as medicine, agriculture, alchemy, the study of mirrors, and navigation corresponded to theoretical physics and such practical arts as business concerned with money, carpentry, smithing and stone-masonry, weaving and shoemaking corresponded to theoretical mathematics. Kilwardby's treatise, which was widely read for generations, expressed the importance of the practical side of science which is concerned with useful results. He included among the mechanical sciences: agriculture, viticulture, medicine, cloth-making, armouring, architecture, and commerce.

Pierre de Maricourt and Magnetism:

French military engineer, Pierre de Maricourt (in Latin, ***Petrus Peregrinus***, meaning Peter the Pilgrim), to whom his contemporary Roger Bacon referred as the "Master of Experiment (***dominus experimentorum***)," was the greatest experimental scientist of his time. Bacon said of Pierre de Maricourt: "What others strive to see dimly and blindly, like bats in twilight, he gazes at in the full light of day because he is a master of experiments." Pierre de Maricourt had become interested in magnetism after having watched compass-makers at work. He undertook a well-planned experimental research on magnetism as a cosmic force which was so remarkable that no further experimental study of magnetism on a comparable scale is known before A.D.1600 when William Gilbert (A.D.1544-1603), personal physician of Queen Elizabeth I, published his treatise < On the Magnet> (***De magnete***). Pierre de Maricourt wrote a letter to his friend Siger de Foucaucourt, entitled < Letter on the Magnet > (***Epistola de magnete***) in A.D.1269, during a crusade against Muslims led by Charles of Anjou, the younger brother of King St. Louis of France, when he was engaged in the siege of Lucera, a Muslim city in Southern Italy. In this work, Pierre de Maricourt explained how to identify the north and the south pole of magnets of the compass, demonstrated his knowledge of magnetic induction, and stated the laws of attraction and repulsion of magnetic poles. He described a number of magnetic compasses and experiments with required magnets. He was responsible for making the compass really practical by placing the magnetic needle on a pivot instead of attaching it on a piece of cork and letting it float on water as in the Chinese marine compass. He thought that the lodestone followed the directional powers of heavens and thus revealed the connexion between macrocosm and microcosm which would allow the production of perpetual circular motion on globular Earth. At the end of his Letter, Pierre de Maricourt offered his design of a wheel which he believed to be perpetually turned by the magnetic force of the rotating celestial sphere. Despite the fact that this machine could not work, it represented a historical forerunner of the modern dynamo. He described a globular lodestone, a ***terrella***, which he thought would rotate once a day when mounted without friction parallel to the celestial axis, and would serve as an automatic armillary sphere for astronomical observations, and as a perfect clock if properly inscribed with a map of the heavens. In his opinion this device would then replace all other chronometers. He was fully aware that the compass does not point to the 'true' north.

Owing to Pierre de Maricourt's researches on magnets, magnetic compasses were made which reached a high degree of perfection, and the availability of such refined magnetic compasses ultimately led to the conquest of the seas. William Gilbert lauded Pierre de Maricourt's monograph as "... a pretty erudite book considering the times," but he did not believe in the soundness of the perpetual motion wheel proposed by Pierre de Maricourt, and remained dubious about the supposed rotation of the ***terrella***.

Mediæval Technological Inventions and Innovations

The Cistercian monks under the guidance of Bernard of Clairvaux became the leaders in the application of waterpower to industrial processes and in the reclamation of barren wastelands. By the thirteenth century tens of thousands of watermills had been installed in France. Hellenistic engineers had invented the cam and gearing: the star, the crown and the worm gearing, and had produced very elaborate gearing mechanisms by the first century B.C., but they had used such mechanisms mostly in gadgets. The real technology of mechanical power began in the European civilisation the culture of which is a fusion of Christianity and Hellenism, and the European craftsmen rapidly demonstrated a distinctive originality in technological matters.

Beginning with the fulling mill at Serchio, Tuscany, in A.D.983, the technologists of the 11th and the 12th century A.D. applied the cam to a great variety of mechanical operations. In the 13th century the spring and the treadle (first used in China in the second century A.D. to operate a loom) and the automatic spring-feeder of saw-mills were discovered in Europe. In A.D.1215 a saw was operated by a pedal and overhead spring at Chartres. About A.D.1235 the heddles of a loom were operated by an overhead spring and a treadle in Rhineland, Germany. In A.D.1250 overhead springs were used in a lathe operated by a foot-treadle. About A.D.1280, the first known spinning wheel with a belt-transmission of power based on the flywheel principle and the differential speeds of rotation was used in Speyer, Germany. In the 13th century large silk-twisting and silk-reeling machines employing bobbins and flyers were developed in Lucca, Italy. In the A.D.1230's first functional button was invented in Germany which led to a revolution in costume design a century later. In textile industry, carding was a mediæval invention. Weaving looms were drastically improved and four-heddle looms, and looms for silk and other complicated works were developed in the fourteenth century A.D.. In the fourteenth century A.D. gearing mechanisms of great complexities were built. In A.D.1335, Guido da Vigevano combined two cranks at the axle-end of a Luttrell-type grindstone to form a compound crank. The connecting-rod was apparently invented in the Hussite Wars by a German military craftsman as a mechanical substitute for man's arm. About A.D.1420 a Flemish shipwright invented the bit-and-brace, which made continuous rotary motion in drilling possible, an invention which called for a compound crank. In A.D. 1430 machines appeared with double compound cranks having two connecting-rods. In the 15th century A.D., the establishment of the crank, the connecting-rod, the flywheel to pass the dead center, and the ball-and-chain governor vastly facilitated the conversion of reciprocating motion into continuous rotary motion. Advances made in the manufacture of iron and steel in the Middle Ages contributed to the marked improvement of tools. Over the next four centuries, the European technologists essentially refined and elaborated the many basic technological principles established in the Early Middle Ages. In A.D.1269 the lodestone had become the subject of theoretical study, the marine compass, the rudiments of which were first invented in China about A.D.1160 had come into general use, and the mechanical manufacture of paper was well established.

Paper had been invented in China by A.D.105 and after A.D.751, when the Islamic armies of the Caliph captured some Chinese papermakers in Samarkand, papermaking spread all over the Muslim world because paper was better and much cheaper for writing than either papyrus or parchment. Paper had been manufactured by hand-and-foot for a thousand years or more following its introduction. Papermaking was never mechanised in China or in the Muslim world but once it had reached Europe it was almost immediately mechanised by the technologically minded European craftsmen of the Middle Ages. In A.D.1238, paper mills producing pulp by means of water power in Xativa near Valencia, Spain, were established. In A.D.1268 the first water-powered paper-mill in Italy was located in Fabriano, and the second mill at Jativa in A.D.1280. In A.D.1326, a paper-mill driven by water-power was working in Moulin Richard de Bas, on the river Dore, near Amdery, department of the Puy-de-Dome.

About A.D.1280 spectacles were invented in Italy by the physicist Salvino degli Armati (1245-1317) of Florence, and he informed his friend the Dominican friar Allessandro della Spina (died in A.D.1313) of Pisa about his invention. Della Spina made public aware of the spectacles he made.

The Frankish military engineers were soon able to improve the explosive qualities of the gunpowder and to harness the exploding gases of the gunpowder in a metal tube to shoot projectiles, and soon after rockets made their first appearance in Europe at Cologne in A.D.1258. In A.D.1277, the first cannons were found. Cannon was both the first heat engine and the first internal combustion engine with one-cylinder. The real origin of the cannon lay in the Byzantine copper tube which exploded forth the 'Greek Fire'. Introduction of the rifling of gun barrels for increased accuracy of gunnery in its turn required improved surveying and better metallurgy. In A.D.1340, the first cast iron mortars were used. In A.D.1398, the use of hand-firearms were introduced, and soon after the first interchangeable parts of firearms were produced, which rapidly led to standardisation and classification of arms based on the strength of gunpowder.

By A.D.1000, power bellows were probably in use in ironmaking, and increased in size and effectiveness until by A.D.1384 at Liége in Flanders, the power bellows produced temperatures high enough to make cast iron in the first known blast furnaces. Between A.D.1066 and 1086, iron production trebled in England because of the introduction of power bellows. Laminated swords which had the cutting qualities of steel and the toughness of iron were produced by Germanic, Celtic and Slavic metallurgists north of the Alps after the original practices of Muslim metallurgists in Toledo, Spain.

About A.D.1430, a Bishop at the monastery of St. Georgenberg in Inn Valley, Germany, invented a hydraulic turbine, which was similar to the modern Pelton Wheel. The precursor of this hydraulic turbine was the Hellenistic impulse wheel with the vertical axle used in the first century B.C. which by the time of the crucifixion of Jesus of Nazareth was already in use in Northern Denmark, and for this reason it was later called the Norse Mill.

The gunpowder invented by the Chinese was a loose mixture of carbon, sulphur and saltpetre which was inhomogeneous, burnt slowly and lacked the instantaneous explosive power because of inadequate airspace between its constituent particles, both of which interfered with the efficient combustion of the mixture. The explosive properties of the gunpowder were first developed by the German chemists of Freiburg during the Middle Ages when they invented the 'corned gunpowder', which had an even distribution both of its constituents and air-space and produced a uniform and instantaneous combustion of the gunpowder. The instantaneous explosive property of the corned gunpowder made the cannon and the handgun for the first time formidable and efficient weapons of war.

The gunpowder and its application to technology developed in Europe far beyond anything achieved in the East. The invention of the powerful gunpowder led to an extensive development of chemical technology, a considerable part of which was taken over from the Muslims. Although the Muslim alchemists did not add to the scientific theory of chemistry of the ancient Greeks, they had been able to extend the chemical technology by improving distilling techniques, isolating a number of oxides, and producing new products such as sal-ammoniac, borax, soda, and potassium. The European alchemists of the Middle Ages invented new distilling apparatuses and made new discoveries: distillation of alcohol (brandy) by improved dehydrating agents such as potassium carbonate from wine (A.D.1100), of nitric acid by distilling a mixture of saltpetre, alum, and vitriol (A.D.1150), sulfuric acid (13th century A.D.), muriatic acid (15th century A.D.), mordants, pigments, dyes, camphor, tinctures and calomel (mercurious chloride, a cathartic) and other mineral acids which had been isolated by ancients only in their gaseous form. By A.D.1320, alcohol was used in herbal medicine, but with the availability of brandy drunkenness and public disorder had also increased alarmingly. Tile had been made since the 10th century A.D.. There was a development of glass products and stained-glass windows. Painting improved and was now based on drying oils. Soap-making was industrialised. By A.D.1453, the Middle Ages had launched the first wave of 'industrial revolution', which was powered by watermills and windmills, thus making the Middle Ages one of the most important periods of technological advance in the history of man. Enormous works were undertaken in towns to dig canals at the banks of which watermills could be installed. Tidal-mills were constructed in the lagoons at the head of the Adriatic, and from A.D.1066 to A.D.1086 tidal-mills were built at the entrance of Port Dover in England. Although tidal-mills as power sources were not entirely satisfactory because of seasonal fluctuations in the level of tides, the mediæval tidal-mills constructed on LaRance, near Saint-Malo in Brittany, France, were renovated and put into active use after World War II. In historical scale, the period of time within which this huge technological leap had been made was surprisingly brief. European craftsmen in the Middle Ages experimented with new techniques, new machines, and new devices to save manual labour and to improve the quality of life for the common man. There was a gradual revival of town life based on the re-emergence of trade, commerce and industry, which arose out of budding free-enterprise and business groups. The mediæval society believed in progress and did not adhere to outmoded traditions by mere habit if such traditions hindered technological advancement.

Guilds:

By the gradual disappearance of ***villeinage***, which tied man to the place of his birth, a greater labour force became available to towns. The craftsman in guilds was both a labourer and a capitalist until the growth of large specialised industries at the close of the Middle Ages wrecked the guild system in towns. The guildsmen in towns commanded a much larger share of the total wealth in their heyday than the rest of the middle class. Very often the guild, or the federation of guilds constituted the town government, just as warrior nobles had once constituted the feudal government.

In the early period of the Middle Ages guilds were free associations of craftsmen, who followed a common calling. Principles of sound craftsmanship, and protection against inferior products and cheap labour were carried out for the good of the community, which was possible because the craftsman pursued his calling openly and freely as an individual.

In 1347, a merchant ship from the Black Sea entered the Sicilian port of Messina bringing with it the great bubonic plague called 'Black Death' to Europe. In less than 3 years half the population of Europe was dead, more than 20 million people. After the 'Black Death' had ravished

Europe and returned virtually every two years in less lethal forms, work became scarce and as a consequence the guild principle became corrupted. In order to prevent competition between craftsmen guild membership was made compulsory, presently called a 'closed-shop'. By the end of the 15th century A.D. guild members were required to satisfy a number of strict conditions to prevent competition: individual innovations were forbidden; advertising of one's craft was forbidden; and it was regarded as illegal practice to employ anything but the traditional tools and techniques, or to work late by artificial light. Access to the guild was obtained by a boy as an apprentice under a master-craftsman to whom the youngster often had to pay a substantial sum of money. Boys commenced their apprenticeship at fourteen years of age, and most were expected to sleep in the workshop. After 7 years of training, the young man became a journeyman since he had no shop and had to journey to obtain work. Journeyman was an intermediate stage between an apprentice and a master-craftsman. The great expense of becoming a master-craftsman, that is, a craftsman who owns his workshop, prevented many journeymen from becoming master-craftsmen. Such unsuccessful journeymen were later to form themselves into dissident groups within the guilds.

As guilds became more and more self-centered, attempts were made to set up guild regulations which restricted entry to the guild by admitting only the sons and dependents of guild members in an effort to establish a kind of hereditary craft caste. These nepotistic guild regulations forced disgruntled journeymen to travel to towns where guild regulations did not apply, and where they would be able to open their own workshops. Much later during the Renaissance Age in the 16th century A.D., the guilds were sometimes successful to pressure the State to impose laws to establish uniform guild regulations throughout the realm, but the State legislation was ultimately unable to prevent the decline of the corrupt and moribund guild system. The future belonged to the entrepreneur who provided the raw materials as well as sold the finished products, whilst paying the craftsman wages for the latter's expert labour.

Near the end of the Middle Ages the master-craftsmen, particularly the master-builders, fought ceaselessly to defend their privileges, so much so that many such craftsmen spent more time in courts than at their work. In these corrupt guilds nepotism reigned supreme, so much so that often the most qualified artisan no longer became the master. The contemporary labour unions, as they operate today, resemble the corrupt guilds of the late Middle Ages a great deal, although the group method of terror, violence and vandalism organised by the modern labour unions against law-abiding citizens as individuals, which represents a vicious form of labour gangsterism that is tolerated by the modern social democratic governments, did not exist during the Late Middle Ages. When groups of dissident guild apprentices ran wild in a town and constituted a social menace, their lawless acts were not organised by the guild nor fostered by the government of the country. There were instances during the Renaissance, for instance in England in A.D.1517, when the royal authority charged treason against 13 boys of the guild for violation of the town laws and promptly executed them for vandalism.

Mediæval Agricultural Technology

One of the most remarkable technological advances made during the Middle Ages was in the agriculture. The plough had brought with it the first application of animal power to agriculture. The primitive scratch plough pulled by a pair of oxen produced a triangular furrow with undisturbed soil in between, and, therefore, the fields required cross-ploughing. The scratch-plough disturbed the soil only moderately and for this reason it only worked in relatively arid climates and light soil. In wet climates with sticky, but rich soil the scratch-plough was quite useless. Romans, in order to increase the efficiency of the scratch-plough had provided them with coulters. They had also used teams of eight oxen to produce a deeper tillage of the soil.

The heavy 'Saxon wheeled plough' for deep tillage which was invented some time in the 6th century A.D. in the Baltic region in northern Europe gradually began to move West with the Germanic tribes. The heavy Saxon plough had three functioning blades: the coulter, or a heavy knife which cut vertically deep into the sod; the flat plough-share set at right angles to the coulter which cut the earth horizontally at the grass-roots; and the mould-board which turned the slice of turf over. The heavy Saxon plough offered so much resistance that it required a team of 8 oxen to supply the power to turn the sod over, and on account of the deep tillage, there was no need for cross-ploughing which saved labour and permitted increased area of land to be cultivated. Since the heavy Saxon wheeled-plough was an agricultural engine, it was necessary to plough fields in long narrow strips which made efficient ploughing possible. Therefore, the lands of the village had to be reorganised into long, fenceless open fields consisting of strips that covered hundreds of acres, which aided agriculture as well as cattle raising.

About A.D.760 another great agricultural innovation was introduced when the triennial three-field rotation of crops replaced the Roman biennial two-field rotation of crops. The three-field system of rotation was a hybridisation of the Mediterranean autumn planting with the ancient Baltic spring planting. The triennial system of farming divided all arable land into three fields. In the Autumn the first field was planted with rye and winter wheat. In the Spring the second field was planted with oats, barley, peas, lentils, or broad beans. The third field was left fallow. Next year, the first field was planted with Summer crops: oats, barley, peas, lentils, or broad beans. The second field was left fallow. In the Autumn the third field was planted with winter grains: wheat and rye. In such a system of rotation of crops every field was left fallow, though ploughed twice, once in every three years, which was usually sufficient for the land to replenish itself.

On very poor soil such as in Italy and in southern France, even one year of fallow in 3 years was not enough for the land to recover, and, therefore, the Roman biennial rotation of crops was mainly employed in the southern Europe.

Fertilisers were also used to increase the productive capacity of the field. Cistercian monks, who were the leading agricultural experts in the 11th and 12th centuries A.D., used iron slag containing rich phosphates to fertilise their agricultural land. It may be that the special nitrogen-fixing virtues of legumes, such as peas and beans, were also known to the mediæval farmer. The rational theory of agriculture was promoted by a number of mediæval men such as ***Albertus Magnus*** who discussed manuring and other matters of planting based on his broad knowledge of botany. The English monk Walter of Henley, who was one of the first to use experimental methods in agriculture, discussed the importance of marling and weeding. He also wrote a book < Hosebondrie > (A.D.c.1250) which remained a standard work on the subject of animal husbandry until A.D.1523.

However, the best and most popular mediæval treatise on practical and rational agriculture was written by an Italian man of learning, Peter of Crescenzi, who had studied logic, natural science, medicine and law at the University of Bologna, entitled < Proper Farming > (***Ruralia commoda***) written about A.D.1306 which was translated into several European languages, and was much later printed many times. After retiring from his legal and political offices he settled on his estate and wrote this work, which was a critical compilation from books and observations, for the purpose of giving the intelligent farmer a rational and practical account of all aspects of farming, from the biology of plants due to ***Albertus Magnus*** to the arrangement of farm buildings and water supply. He discussed grafting of vines and trees, cultivation of cereals, legumes and vegetables, rearing of all kinds of farm animals, horses and their ailments, and hunting and fishing.

About A.D.800 the modern horse collar, the breast-strap type and the tandem harness which had reached Europe from central Asia made the horse commonly available for farm labour in northern Europe. The nailed horseshoe which had appeared simultaneously in Byzantium, in Siberia and in the West about A.D.900, permitted an efficient use of the power of the horse that proved the value of the horse as an effective power source. In previous times yokes had been used, but yoke-harness was only adequate for oxen, as it was too high for a horse to be able to put his entire weight into his pull. The new harness allowed the horse to pull from four to five times the weight in comparison with the pull the horse could exert with the antique harness. Since the horse consumed expensive grain, instead of the inexpensive hay consumed by the oxen, the peasant's meagre margin of production could not support a horse under the 2-field system of farming, whereas under the new 3-field system in the 12th century A.D. the surplus of oats and barley from the Spring planting gradually enabled most northern European peasants to replace the ox by the more efficient horse as the draught animal.

This new mediæval agricultural system having made steady progress through the introduction of new crops greatly increased the efficiency of the agricultural labour and more than doubled the production, making what had been hardly more than a subsistence farming under the old biennial crop rotation system into a surplus farming under the new triennial crop rotation system. The peasant for the first time in history was able to exploit nature in his agriculture. It was tantamount to an 'agricultural revolution'.

Naval Construction

In the 10th century A.D. the Italian shipwrights developed the modern skeleton-first shipbuilding method, which afforded more efficient and substantially less expensive naval construction. It appears that these less expensive and more numerous ships built skeleton-first, and the new efficient agricultural system which was very productive made the first Crusades to Palestine possible.

In the 12th century A.D. in Scandinavia the introduction of the rudder hinged to the stern post of a ship in place of lateral steering oars increased the size, the manoeuverability and efficiency of ships, a navigation device first used by the Chinese.

Military Engineering

Military engineering during the Middle Ages came closest to scientific engineering because virtually all military engineers were physicians who were educated at the universities. Medicine during the Middle Ages was connected with medical astrology which supposedly afforded therapeutic applications of the mathematical arts of the ***quadrivium***, and astrology required careful planetary observations and precise measurement of time for the preparation, and revisions of astronomical tables. Physicians soon discovered that the astronomical instruments of the classical antiquity and of the Muslims were far too crude for the requirements of the physicians, and, therefore, they had to make their own astronomical instruments and observations. Medical astrology ever since Hellenistic times was a required subject of medical study, and this tradition continued at the mediæval, and even at the Renaissance universities. These studies led some physicians to the development of various complex instruments, for instance, the weight-driven mechanical clock. Frequently, the physicians acquired such refined mechanical skills that they built their own intricate instruments.

The most famous physicians of the Middle Ages usually served as court physicians, in which capacity they had to accompany their ruler in the latter's military campaigns. A number of such mechanically skilled physicians were interested in military engineering, and became expert students of military tactics and war machinery. Virtually all important treatises on technology written in Europe during the 13th and the 14th century A.D., and the first quarter of the 15th century A.D. were produced by physicians who were also medical astrologers. The engineers of that period, who normally had little formal education, were practical men who had acquired their engineering skills through apprenticeship. The physician-medical astrologists, however, were some of the best university educated, literate men of the mediæval time, and they wrote virtually all the technological works of the period. The physician-medical astrologists were not loath to use their hands in ***banausic*** activities such as building instruments, an attitude which left a permanent impression on European civilisation.

Guido da Vigevano:

One of the first known physicians who was also a military engineer of note, was the Italian physician Guido da Vigevano. He served as a personal physician to the German Emperor Henry VII, and to Queen Jeanne of Burgundy, and was the author of a famous treatise on human anatomy written in A.D.1345. In A.D.1328, King Philip V of Valois planned to go on a crusade, and Guido da Vigevano was appointed a military adviser to the King. In his effort to assist the King on his prospective military campaign, da Vigevano wrote in A.D.1335 a treatise on military engines of war, < Machines of the King of France > (***Texaurus regis Francie***), a work which is composed of 13 chapters. Surprisingly, all the military machines devised, and given by da Vigevano, were prefabricated in order that they could be dismantled rapidly into individual parts for manageable transportation. His treatise contains defensive military instruments, bridges and other means to cross rivers, turrets and chariots. Therefore, da Vigevano's book mostly dealt with military ordnance in which everything was theoretically devised, but not entirely lacking in practical sense. The search for mechanical transmission of movement certainly was the major concern of da Vigevano. His ideas on military machines influenced a well-known Renaissance military engineer, Roberto Valturio (died A.D.1484), who produced a treatise, < On the Military Equipment > (***De re militare***) in A.D.1450. Da Vigevano's work has certain parallels with the ancient Greek and Roman works on military art.

Konrad Kyeser:

Another famous military engineer was the German physician, Konrad Kyeser (A.D.1366-1405), born of noble parents in Eichstadt, Bavaria, who had earned a doctorate in medicine from the University of Padua, and who combined medicine, astrology and technology in his professional work. He regarded theurgy to be a branch of technology, even above military arts. In A.D.1396, Kyeser fought in the Crusade against the Turks, and served under King Wenceslaus of Bohemia, and King Ruprecht of the Palatinate. During his military campaigns, Kyeser had seen a great deal of military engineering. He wrote an unfinished, illustrated manuscript on military technology entitled, ***Bellifortis*** (A.D.1400-1410), dedicated to Emperor Ruprecht of the Palatinate, which remained an authoritative treatise on the science of machines for more than a century. It was composed of 10 books dealing with chariots, siege engines, hydraulic machines, firearms, defensive weapons, military fireworks, fireworks for festivities, and tools and instruments. His chariots had a rudimentary artillery, first portable firearms, first multifiring gun (similar to the 'Gatling Gun' of American Civil War), handmill with rod and crank, hydraulic mills, boats with horse-driven paddle-wheels, observational 'aerostats' made of oiled paper stretched over wooden frames and filled with hot air for levitation. It contained the first picture of a rocket with launching pad, a conical spindle called ***fusee*** for spanning crossbows which a generation later was applied to portable timepieces driven by steel springs. He gave details of the ***trebuchet***, a powerful ballista operated by counterweights, which was so accurate an artillery that it forced all other forms of artillery out of the field by A.D.1199. The ***trebuchet*** was a European mechanical improvement of the inaccurate Chinese ***huo p'ao***, a pivoted sling-beam fitted with a terminal rope pulled on command by a group of soldiers. The whole work of Kyeser gives clear evidence that he had an eye for innovations.

Jean Fusoris:

Another well-known physician, astrologer and technologist, Jean Fusoris (A.D.c.1365-1436), who was not a military engineer but had learnt metalworking from his father, became a skilled instrument-maker whilst he was canon of Notre Dame in Paris. He made astronomical clocks, astrolabes and celestial spheres for prominent dignitaries in Europe. He constructed a new type of ***equatorium*** which mechanically initiated the combinations of cycles and epicycles thereby tracing out planetary trajectories in the Ptolemaic system. Fusoris' ***equatorium*** was a mechanical calculator which permitted the astrologers to dispense with astronomical tables and calculations. It was Fusoris who built the monumental astronomical clock for the Cathedral of Bourges.

Henri Arnault:

Henri Arnault of Zwolle, was a doctor of medicine and a student of Fusoris. He served as a personal physician and astrologer to Duke Philip the Good of Burgundy from A.D.1432 to A.D.1446, where he made planetaria and clocks of great complexity for his sovereign. He made the first known study of the mechanism of keyboard instruments in the light of the general concepts of machine design which was undergoing a rapid development at the time. He also devised a coiled steel-spring as a driving mechanism. His notebook on mechanics, which contains also military machines is still extant.

Giacomo Fontana:

A well-known physician-technologist of the period was the Italian Giacomo Fontana (A.D.c.1393-c.1415) of Venice, who studied arts and medicine at the University of Padua. He was appointed a physician of the Republic of Venice, and served the Venetian army at Brescia from A.D.1420 to A.D.1432. Fontana was more of a scholar than a practical engineer and, as it seems, a student of the works of Heron of Alexandria. He compiled a collection of machine designs entitled, < A Book on Instruments of War > (***Bellicorum instrumentorum liber***), the text of which was written in a cypher. This collection is more like a 'theater of machines', and the machines considered are mostly hydraulic machines, novel fountains (which accounts for his nickname 'Fontana'), water channels, automata (obviously inspired by Heron of Alexandria), a combination lock and magic lantern. He also studied natural history and physical sciences.

Feuerwerksbuch from Hussite Wars:

A German manuscript on military engineering entitled < Fireworks Book > (***Feuerwerksbuch***) was written about A.D. 1422 by an unknown military craftsman-engineer who fought in the Hussite Wars about A.D.1430. Its conceptual craftsmanship is better than that of Kyeser, and all of its machines seem to have existed in practice. It shows a compound crank mechanism in a handmill, modern diving apparatus, windmills, boring machines for pipes and cannons, and flywheels with hanging weights to overcome the dead-center. This was the last original work of the Middle Ages in military engineering.

Mediæval High Technology

Vitruvius Pollio, the celebrated Roman engineer, had written about 30 B.C.:
"... engineering and architecture is divided into three parts: building, clocks and machines."

In the period from A.D.1140 to A.D.1250, the cathedral builders had demonstrated their prolific inventiveness in the building of Gothic cathedrals for they seem not to have been content even with their colossal achievements in the Chartres or the Amiens Cathedral.

Mechanical Clocks:

By the middle of the 13th century A.D., timekeeping had become important in monasteries and in mediæval cities of Europe. There existed clocks operated by falling weights and controlled by the flow of mercury through small apertures in some monasteries. Some such clocks incorporated mechanisms for weight-driven hourly alarms. Similar timing devices had been developed for a number of astronomical mechanisms such as planetaria and mechanically turning star-maps. Although none of these timekeeping devices incorporated any system of gears, they did represent an essential part of the ancestry of the weight-driven mechanical clock. The first wheel-clock was probably built by Boethius in the 6th century A.D..

The second stupendous accomplishment of the men of the Middle Ages after the Gothic cathedrals was in the machine design, when in the period from A.D.1250 to A.D.1350 intricate mechanical clocks and textile machines were devised and constructed, as well as the automatic puppet theaters which were very popular throughout the mediæval times. Mechanical clocks and firearms were the first machines made entirely of metal. There existed a common interest among cathedral builders and technologists of the Middle Ages to install in the towers of Gothic cathedrals giant weight-driven mechanical clocks. Not only did the mechanical clock represent the motion of the heavens to the mediæval man, but they also thought that the sun and the planets were different from the Earthly bodies by being literally 'heavenly bodies', a notion representing the lingering influence of Plato on the mediæval mind. Their interest in mechanical clocks driven by weights was primarily created by the inconvenience and trouble they experienced with ancient water-clocks in the northern climate because these instruments froze during the winter. By the eleventh century A.D. in France the monks in the monastery, who had to pray at precisely-specified times during the day and early morning, had invented a rather ingenious alarm-device driven by a falling weight which they connected to their water-clock so that the alarm of the clock served to remind the monks of the time of the prayer. By such means the monks had converted their water-clock into an alarm-clock. By the next century, the monks had succeeded in developing a mechanical clock which was also driven by a falling weight like their alarm-device, and its uniform motion was controlled by an escapement mechanism of some kind. It is possible that the first weight-driven mechanical clock was already built in the late 9th century A.D. by Pacificus, the archdeacon of Verona in Italy, but its escapement mechanism was certainly not reliable. Apparently a mechanical clock regulated by a pendulum was built by Gerbert in A.D.991. It is known that in A.D.1271 European technologists were still searching for a perfectly reliable escapement mechanism of the weight-driven mechanical clocks. The invention of the mechanical clock in Europe ushered in a new way of life: a life regulated by time. The monk, who invented the mechanically operated, gravity-driven clock, lived by time, for time was his priceless valuable. Over many centuries, the weight-driven mechanical clock became an intellectual parent of the mechanically minded Western civilisation, because it is the key machine of the Modern Age. Before the advent of the mechanical clock the most complicated mechanical device in existence had been the pipe-organ.

Certainly one of the most influential technical achievements of the Middle Ages was the invention of the weight-driven mechanical clock, which was perfected between A.D.1277 and A.D.1300. It is possible that Bartholomew the Horologist of Saint Paul's Cathedral was responsible for devising a mechanical clock, as mentioned in A.D.1286, and that the new Canterbury clock of A.D.1292 as well as the first public clock built by Pierre Pipelart in Paris in A.D.1300 were of the same type. The weight-driven mechanical clock became possible only when a satisfactory solution for the escapement mechanism, which controls the uniform movement of the clock, was found. The first extant illustration of an escapement mechanism for making a figure of an angel rotate slowly so that its finger always points towards the Sun was given by the French master-builder Villard de Honnecourt in the middle of the thirteenth century A.D.. The first successful solution for the control of the uniform movement of the weight-driven mechanical clock was the verge-and-foliot escapement, an ingenious mechanism which had been elaborated in its perfected form in Germany by A.D.1278. By A.D.1330 two additional escapement mechanisms had been invented for mechanical clocks driven by coiled springs: the stackfreed and the ***fusee***. The more accurate and the more ingenious device of the two escapement mechanisms was the ***fusee***, which by A.D.1278 had been invented by German military engineers for the spanning of crossbows. A reliable and accurate escapement mechanism was an indispensable component of the weight-driven mechanical clock and of the clock driven by coiled elastic spring.

Richard of Wallingford and Equatorium:

Richard of Wallingford (A.D. c.1292-1335), Abbot of St. Albans Monastery (elected Abbot in A.D.1326) and a leper, invented about A.D.1320 a very intricate and expensive astronomical clock, and two more astronomical instruments. His elaborate astronomical clock was a mechanical device for finding positions of the sun, moon and stars and also the ebb and flow of tides, and, therefore, it represented a kind of mechanical calculator. It could be called an ***equatorium***. He also left a handbook giving information how this instrument was to be used. The first known astronomical computer, which was discovered in A.D.1900 in the hull of an ancient Greek ship wrecked near the island of Antikythera, was made by Hellenistic mechanical technologists on the Island of Rhodos about 80 B.C.. Richard of Wallingford's astronomical calculator was the most influential of such weight-driven, automatic, mechanical instruments of the Middle Ages.

Jacopo and Giovanni di Dondi, and Astrarium:

An Italian physician and medical astrologer from Chioggia, Jacopo di Dondi, who wrote a treatise on tides, designed another astronomical clock in A.D.1344 which was installed in the tower of the ***Piazzo Capitano*** in Padua. It included a twenty-four hour chapter ring, a calendar dial, and the signs of the zodiac, and it was supplied with a striking mechanism. This clock perished in A.D.1390, but was reconstructed in A.D.1434.

Jacopo's son, Giovanni di Dondi, who was also a physician like his father, designed another very complex astronomical clock-calculator named the ***astrarium***. It was installed in a castle at Padua in A.D.1364. When this clock broke down in A.D.1440, only one craftsman, a Dutch mechanic named Willem Zelander (Latin name, ***Guillelmus Zelanderus***), could be found in Europe who knew how to repair it. In A.D.1529, this clock went again out of order, and again only one craftsman, the Italian mechanic Giovanni Torriani, was knowledgeable enough to repair it. Not until A.D.1561 was another comparable astronomical clock built. This clock of di Dondi required very elaborate mechanisms, which included the segmental and the elliptic gearing having altogether 107 wheels and pinions, and it most definitely represents an important epoch in the history of machine design. Soon many European cities had mechanical clocks built into their town halls. The weight-driven mechanical clock had a enormous influence on the Western civilisation and on the development of Western scientific engineering, because this mechanical device had to be designed mathematically, and it represented a revival of the scientific engineering and refined technology of Hellenistic Greeks. The tradition of science and crafts in clockmaking was maintained by the scientific instrument-makers as a profession throughout the centuries, and it played an important role in the emergence of the modern industrial civilisation of Europe.

Mediæval Construction

Gothic Cathedrals:

The emergence of Gothic art, like the Gothic cathedral, reflects a fundamental change towards the natural environment, as things existing in this world ceased to be mere symbols, rebuses. The late Roman Empire in Byzantium had lived in a world of symbols rather than in the world of real facts, an attitude which was changed during the Middle Ages although it took some centuries to bring it about.

The Middle Ages was also the time of the most daring engineering construction in stone. The mediæval castle and the Gothic cathedral were two of the world's masterpieces in stone construction: the first, the most massive of cut-stone structures; and the second, the most daringly light 'stone-skeleton' structure. The Gothic Cathedrals were not only expressions of their structural engineering and their architectural art, the arts of painting, sculpting, glass staining, wood carving, and mosaic designing, all unified in the one dominant expression of their religious life but also their political activities, their æsthetic aspirations, their moral sympathies, and their intellectual development.

The ogival arch was probably first used in Buddhist India about the second century A.D.. The Sassanian Muslims adopted it and brought it to Syria by A.D.561, and it had become a common structural element by the late ninth century A.D. in Muslim Egypt. By A.D.1071 a porch with ogival arches and pointed vaults was incorporated into the structure of the new Benedictine church at Monte Cassino under Abbot Desiderius. In A.D. 1080, when Abbot Hugh of Cluny visited Monte Cassino, his engineers realised that the use of ogival arches they saw at Monte Cassino will avoid the structural problems the Romanesque arches would present in the construction of their church at Cluny erected from A.D.1088 to A.D.1120. The abbey church at Cluny, which became the most conspicuous church of northern Europe, incorporated 196 ogival arches and pointed vaults.

In the period from A.D.1130 to A.D.1144, Abbot Suger (A.D.1082-1155), counsellor and friend of King Louis VI and his son Louis VII (Suger, who was inspired by the political ideal of the partnership between the Church and the State, acted as the regent of France when Louis VII was on his ill-fated Second Crusade from A.D.1147 to A.D.1149), created a new and revolutionary design in the structure of his new royal abbey church at St. Denis, near Paris, when he acted as his own chief architect-engineer, although it is possible that he was assisted by the master-builder Gislebertus. St. Denis was a Cluniac Abbey Church the building design of which was based on a definite philosophy. About A.D.1104, the Cluniac Abbey Church of La Madeleine at Veselay was built. This edifice summed up the Romanesque past and forecast the Gothic future in European building. It was a Romanesque building with round arches supported by the characteristic cylindrical columns in the nave, and it had the first cross-vaults built in Western Europe, but its apse was built in pure Gothic style with ogival arches. The Roman engineers had bequeathed the mediæval master-builders two methods of enclosing large spaces: the barrel vaulting such as in the Palace of Domitianus, or the cross-vaulting such as in the baths of Caracalla and Diocletianus, and in the basilicas of Maxentius and Constantinus. The mediæval builders preferred the use of cross-vaulting method in covering large spaces.

Abbot Suger visited Monte Cassino in A.D.1130 and he began with his engineers to construct the royal abbey church in A.D.1135 which was built as the first true Gothic church right from its inception. Abbot Suger stressed light and unity of design in planning his new abbey church at St. Denis. In his design of the abbey church Suger emphasised light by stating that "light is holier than darkness" for he was influenced by the statement of Apostle John: "Men loved darkness rather than light." The religious metaphysics of light has its ancient roots in the Zoroastrian Wise Lord of Light, Truth and Justice (***Ahura Mazda***). The entire structure of the abbey church had to reflect the harmony in the universe as a design of God, for Christ to Suger represented literally Holy Light. In his philosophy of structural design, Suger employed all the available Christian knowledge: theological, moral, natural, and historical. He found an example for his structure in the abbey church at Monte Cassino and in the nave of the Cluniac Abbey church at Vezelay, as well as in the Cathedral of Sens in Burgundy which was being constructed in Gothic style under the direction of the French architectural engineer William of Sens at the same time as Suger's abbey church, but was finished only in A.D.1160. The Cluniac abbey church of Suger has some common features with the Cathedral of Sens, the first Gothic cathedral, and these common features might be due to the personal friendship that existed between Abbot Suger and Bishop Henry of Sens, who may have permitted his engineer William of Sens to consult Suger on the construction of Suger's abbey church. In A.D.1174 William of Sens was called to England to reconstruct the choir and the apse of the Romanesque Canterbury Cathedral, which he rebuilt in the new Gothic style that he had used in the Cathedral of Sens.

In Suger's 'Gothic' structure all superfluous was suppressed and everything necessary was in its proper place. All distinct structural elements in his abbey church had to harmonise with the correlated whole structure in order to lend the structure the unity and lightness of the Christian spirit. Suger's church was to be a place of soaring spiritual imagination, full of light and hope. Suger expressed this idea in the following words: "The dull mind rises to truth through that which is material," a quite revolutionary notion in the Middle Ages. The central idea in Suger's Gothic engineering which gave the form and the function of the Gothic structure was economy: to cover the maximum space with the minimum of material. This task was to be accomplished by :

(1) the use of the statically more efficient and structurally more adaptable pointed-arch, the ***ogive***, the axis of which follows more closely the line of thrust of the arch than that of the circular Roman arch, thereby undergoing less transverse bending than the Roman arch;
(2) the distinction between the load bearing structural elements, such as the stone skeleton, and the non-load bearing elements of the structure, such as the curtain walls, and subsequent elimination of pseudo-structural elements such as ornamentations;
(3) more expert and careful construction;
(4) the use of buttresses (later 'flying buttresses') to absorb the thrust of the vaulted roof structure;
(5) to make standard types of structural elements possible in such a logical treatment of structures.

Suger, also introduced the famous 'rose window' which depicts his own figure lying prostrate at the feet of Virgin Mary. Suger's design of Gothic structure reflected the spirit of a composed professional intellect concerned with the geometry and mathematics of structures, and serving spiritual and political ends of man. But, above all, Suger's Gothic style is light and has unity of design, and it achieved a remarkable synthesis between æsthetics and engineering.

The term 'Gothic' was coined during the Renaissance time, when the Renaissance artist and art historian, Giorgio Vasari (A.D.1511-1574), a propagandist for classical architecture, intended to degrade the ***forme ogivale***, the name by which the Gothic style of building was known in France, by implying that it was introduced by the barbaric Goths who overran the Roman Empire, whereas the classical style was the product of two ancient civilisations, Greece and Rome. The Italian Renaissance humanists called the Middle Ages the 'Dark Ages', which was meant as a derogatory term.

The Abbey Church of St. Denis finished in A.D.1144, was the first Gothic church, whereas the Cathedral of Sens, finished in A.D.1160, was the first Gothic Cathedral. Suger's abbey church in St. Denis was not completely pure Gothic on the outside for it had no 'flying buttresses'. Elemental 'flying buttresses' had been first used in the Roman basilicas of Maxentius and Constantinus. A bolder form of flying buttresses was introduced in the Durham Cathedral in England in A.D.1120, and finally made into an elaborate system in the Cathedral of Notre Dame in Paris in A.D.1178 which absorbed the thrusts of the vaults at the height of 110 feet (30.48 m) from the ground owing to the considerable weight of the vaults, and the pressure and suction of the wind. It took about hundred years for the Gothic structures to reach their classical phase. Between A.D.1150 and A.D.1280 about 80 cathedrals were built or rebuilt in France, many in commercial towns in the north. It appears that Suger by building his abbey church had initiated a new kind of crusade, a cathedral building crusade.

About A.D.1194, the second phase of the Gothic structure began with the building of the Cathedral of Chartres in which further slimming of the columns and changing walls into mere traceries of stain glass windows reinforced by iron bars were carried out. The construction of the Cathedrals of Reims, Amiens, Bourges and Beauvais, and others belong to this period. The drive to reduce piers and to build higher and higher vaults finally resulted in the collapse of the vault at the height of 158 feet (48.16 m) in the Beauvais cathedral. The vault was rebuilt in A.D.1274, only to collapse again in A.D.1284, which induced the master-builder to introduce intermediate piers. The crest of the choir roof, which collapsed, was at the height of 224 feet (68.26 m).

The mediæval builder had to surpass the Roman engineers in the skill of spanning large open naves with vaults because they did not use concrete that had been the essential building material in the Roman large-scale vaults. The mediæval engineer invented the light and slender skeletal compression structure of stone to accomplish what Roman engineers had done with a massive concrete structure.

The spire of the Cathedral of Chartres is 375 feet (114.30 m) high, that of the Cathedral of Strasbourg is 466 feet (142.04 m) high. The highest spire of any cathedral belongs to the Cathedral of Ulm in Germany, which was finished in the fifteenth century A.D.. The spire of Ulm Cathedral is 525 feet (160.01 m) high. Only in the nineteenth century A.D. was this height surpassed in the structure called ***Molle Antonelliana*** in Turin, Italy, which had a height of 550 feet (167.64 m).

The giant Catalonian Cathedral of Palma on the Island of Maiorca (south of Barcelona, Spain) the choir of which was completed in A.D.1327, is among the tallest Gothic cathedrals in Europe. The slenderness ratio of its piers jumped by almost 50% over any previously used in buildings, which makes the lithe masonry piers of this cathedral look more like modern reinforced concrete columns. It has an extremely high nave of 144⅓ feet (44 m).

In its final development the Gothic building had, in effect, become a framed skeletal structure of stone in which all members of the stone frame were only capable of transmitting compressive forces. In the absence of tension members such stone skeletal frames in the Gothic structures became quite intricate. At its best, Gothic structure is a rather perfectly composed static system which is designed by purely geometric rules and mathematical formulae that are concerned with form and composition like in the ancient Greek temples. Each detail of the Gothic structure served a double function, both structural and æsthetic. The structure and its beauty finally became unified in the mediæval building, particularly in the magnificent French Cathedrals.

The consummate skill of the master-builders of the magnificent Gothic structures, which are models of structural efficiency in stone, elicits great admiration. The secret of the Gothic master-builder in his design of these daring skeletal structures without the benefit of stress analysis was the fact that the criterion for the safety of such structures was determined essentially by their geometric proportions because the limiting stress virtually never governed the design in the skeletal compression-member structures since the stresses were relatively low in such structures. The mediæval building tools differed little from the Roman tools, and the mediæval builders used cranes and lathes operated by treadwheels as had the Roman builders in the distant past.

The mediæval masterbuilders and masons were fully aware of the importance of the geometry in building art, and many of them were taught in the cathedral schools which were the predecessors of universities (***studium generale***). Most master-builders were literate men who knew Latin and were in touch with academic geometry. ***Thomas Aquinas*** thought that an ***architectus*** was a man who knew how things should be ordered and arranged, and that this name could be applied to a philosopher even more than to a builder. The master-builder had a whole series of privileges attached to his professional status. They received very high fees, but they had to be masters of all phases of the work: architecture, structural engineering, mechanical engineering, sculpting, and general contracting. Their names were honoured, and their likeness depicted in sculptures or in the labyrinthine mosaics built into the floor of the cathedral in which the maze led to the image of the bishop as for instance in the Cathedral of Reims. Many master-builders were honoured with the title, teacher of masons (***doctor lathomorum***) on their tombstone. Some clerical intellectuals became envious of the master-builder who as architect-engineer directed the work "by words only" and seldom worked with his hands at the construction itself.

In the mediæval art of decorating buildings, the Italian painter Ambrogio Lorenzetti (A.D.c.1300-1348) introduced the geometric study of optics into his murals when he deliberately used central projection in his famous frescoes, 'Good and Bad Government' painted between A.D.1337 and A.D.1339, in the ***Sala della Pace*** of the ***Palazzo Pubblico*** in Siena, Italy. His frescoes served to revolutionise Italian painting in the 15th century A.D..

The cathedral builders, working in a society that recognised progress as a genuine good, were inventive, and the cathedrals at the end of the 13th century contained hundreds of novel features as a result of the spirit of research and innovation of their builders. The builders prepared careful plans for their structures, and organised the procedures of the construction in great detail. These itinerant masterbuilders, such as Gislebertus, Egbertus, William of Sens, Erwan von Steinbach, Gerradus Lapicide, Peter Parter, Alexandre de Berneval, Villard de Honnecourt, and many others, travelled all over Europe from country to country, from job to job, building cathedrals. The oldest surviving personal notebook of a masterbuilder dating from A.D.1245 is that of Villard de Honnecourt, who designed parts of the Laon, Reims, Chartres and other French cathedrals. Gothic cathedrals besides being places of worship became civic centers for secular activities, festivals, guild meetings, political assemblies, lectures, and general meeting places. Chapels became classrooms, and the naves became theatrical auditoria. For many serfs, the cathedral was a home away from home.

In France the Gothic cathedral as a petrified Christian spirit expressing a creed of hope that transcends all worldly things ended by incorporating in its structure engineering feats of extraordinary virtuosity, new subtlety, more delicacy, greater sensibility, and by inspiring loftier feelings in Western men. The famine which lasted from A.D.1315 to A.D.1317, the bubonic plague called the 'Black Death' brought by a merchant ship from the Black Sea to the Sicilian port of Messina in A.D.1347, which killed nearly half the population in Europe in less than twenty years, and the Hundred Years War which lasted from A.D.1352 to A.D.1453 effectively ended the building of Gothic structures in France.

The Cluniac spirit was born in the village of Cluny where William the Pious, Duke of Aquitaine, founded a monastery at the beginning of the tenth century. The Cluniacs revived the St. Benedict's Rule of Monastic Life by freeing it from secular control and insisting it should owe no service to the State. The resulting prodigious spirit of the Cluniacs diffused rapidly all over the Western World as the Cluniac monks covered Europe from Poland to Portugal with more than 1,400 Cluniac houses and dependencies. The civilising influence of the Cluniacs in Europe was very great. Since the Cluniac Abbot Suger at St. Denis had a decisive influence on the appearance of the new style of building – the Gothic Cathedral – the Cluniac monasteries brought about a great advance in the science of construction. As a result of the great productivity of Cluniac monks, the Cluniac Order became very wealthy, and they soon owned extensive land and other properties. The Cluniac churches were expensively built and decorated with sculptures and stained glass windows, and even provided with gold utensils. It was in a Cluniac house where Abelard spent his last days, whilst his life is enshrined in the famous but tragic love story of Abelard and his pupil Heloise.

Monasticism had resulted from a desire of men of faith to return to more primitive Christian simplicity, and the most influential promoter of monastic life in Europe was Saint Benedict of Nuncia. The Cistercian order was established as a reaction to the Cluniac order, which had become rich and, consequently quite secular, in a new return to the absolute strictness of the Rule of Monastic Life of St. Benedict. For this reason, Cistercian churches in the beginning were plain and bare, and without any towers or ornamentation, but after an initial hesitation, the Cistercian monks finally did adopt the Gothic style of construction because of its structural superiority and, thereby, they became responsible for spreading Gothic construction all over the mediæval Europe.

Mediæval Bridges:

Some time before A.D. 1050, the Pont d'Espalion was built over the Lot River in France. It has 4 arches of which one was almost semicircular, whereas the other 3 arches are slightly pointed, or ogival. The ogival arch spans are 26 feet 11 inches (8.20 m), 41 feet 2 inches(12.55 m), and 50 feet 10 inches (15.50 mm). The circular arch has a span of 41feet 4 inches (12.60 m). The width of the bridge varies from 16 feet 1 inch (4.90 m) to 16 feet 3 inches (4.95 m). The width of the piers vary from 12 feet 4 inches (3.77 m) to 19 feet 2 inches (5.85 m). According to the documents, this bridge construction was first ordered by Charlemagne, the Frankish King and the first Emperor of the Holy Roman Empire. It is constructed of red sandstone and originally 3 fortified towers stood on the bridge, one at each end and one at the center of the bridge.

During the Middle Ages monks organised brotherhoods for building, repairing and maintaining bridges to facilitate pilgrimages. The first such monastic group of bridge builders seems to have been the Alta Pascio Order at the Pilgrimage Hospice of St. James, near Lucca, Italy. In A.D. 1244 this monastic group was ordered by the Holy Roman Emperor Frederick II to build, and to maintain a bridge over the Arno river near Ficeclum for the service of travelling pilgrims.

Pont St. Benezet:

The most famous of such bridge-building monastic groups was a group of mendicant Benedictine monks in France, who formed a similar voluntary brotherhood of bridges, called ***Frères du Pont*** [in Latin, ***Fratres Pontifices***]. The leader of this brotherhood, a monk named Bénoit, who was later canonised as St. Bénezèt, built the renowned bridge at Avignon. Between A.D.1177 and A.D.1188, the Pont St. Bénezèt was constructed over the Rhône river at the city Avignon. Four of the original 20 arches of this bridge, which stood about 35 feet (10.67 m) above the mean low water level, are still extant. Arch spans of this bridge ranged from 65 to 115 feet (19.81 to 35.05 m). The piers were 25 feet (7.62m) wide, about a quarter of the arch span. The total length of this bridge which had a wedge shaped plan with a thirty degree break against the current was almost 3,000 feet (914.4 m), the longest stone masonry bridge built up to that time. This bridge has unique, unprecedented 3-centered arches which make the arches appear pointed because its central arc has the smallest radius. Since this elliptical type of arch is more efficient than the semicircular Roman arch, and its piers are only a quarter of the arch span instead of a third of the arch span as in the Roman bridges, this bridge represented a structural advance over Roman bridges. The arches of the Pont St. Bénezèt consist of parallel spans of stone rings, or archivolts like the Roman arches. The roadway of the Pont d'Avignon varied in width from 6½ feet (1.98 m) to 16 feet (4.88 m). St. Bénezèt died in A.D.1184 and was buried in the chapel on the bridge which has survived the ravages of time.

Old London Bridge:

Another very famous mediæval bridge is the Old London Bridge over the Thames river, which was built by the cleric Peter Colechurch in London, from A.D.1176 to A.D.1209. Its length was about 936½ feet (285.45m), and it consisted of 19 pointed arches, the spans of which ranged from 15 to 35 feet (4.57to 10.67m). Piers of this bridge constituted about half the length of the adjacent spans, and reduced the width of the stream to 503 feet (153.31m). The 'starlings' protecting each pier against erosion reduced the width of the stream to 245 feet (74.68m) at half tide. To make matters worse, waterwheels were installed in the end spans of the bridge which reduced the width of the stream further to 160 feet (48.77m), that is, to one-sixth of its original width. Evidently, it was not a good structural design owing to the heavy scouring action of the water, and because of it the Old London Bridge was in a state of constant repair, for it was continuously 'falling down'. This is not surprising for it virtually constituted a dam with holes in it, which created a 5-foot (1.52m) difference in water levels between the two sides of the bridge. Peter Colechurch, who died in A.D.1205, four years before the bridge was finished, was buried in the chapel built on the 11th pier which was larger than the other piers. Upon the death of Colechurch, King John hired the French engineer Isembert to finish the construction of the bridge. The London bridge apparently was constructed from both ends, a pier and an arch was completed approximately in every 18 months.

Pont Saint-Esprit:

From A.D.1265 to A.D.1297, the Pont Saint-Esprit was constructed over the Rhône, a treacherous river, below the confluence of the Ardèche. It was commissioned by the Cluniac abbot Jean de Tessanges. This bridge has 25 arches, of which 19 arches have spans ranging from about 78 to 108 feet (23.77 to 32.92m), and relief arches for spate water. The total length of the bridge is nearly 3300 feet (1005.84m), and its piers of 20 to 50 feet (6.10 to 15.24m) width have elbows opposing the current which make the entire bridge look like a pontoon bridge. This bridge was the last bridge built by ***Fratres Pontifices***, and it stood for centuries as the longest masonry arch bridge in the world.

After the 13th century A.D., the lay schools of ***maîtres des oeuvres*** replaced the religious corporations in both religious and civil constructions, and the cities and ***seigneurs*** (lords) no longer depended for their bridge construction on the monks of the ***Frères Pontifices*** or ***Frères Constructeurs*** for whom bridge building had been pious work.

Pont Truyere:

There exists a thirteenth century Bridge at Entraygues, Aveyron, France, over the Truyere river, which is also called the Truyere Bridge and is still in service. It has 4 ogival arches with spans of 50 feet 4 inches (15.33m), 54 feet 11 inches(16.75m), 46 feet 7 inches (14.20m) and 41 feet 8 inches (12.70m). The width of this bridge varies from 13 feet 5 inches (4.10m) to 14 feet 5 inches (4.40m), and the width of its piers varies from 15 feet 11 inches(4.85 m) to 16 feet 8 inches (5.07 m).

Pont de Montauban:

From A.D.1291 to A.D.1335, the Pont de Montauban was built over the Tarn river, and it consists of 7 pointed arches each spanning about 70-feet (21.34 m). The total length of the bridge is about 650 feet (198.12 m). It is a stone structure and its roadway lies 65 feet (19.81 m) above the river Tarn. Defensive towers about the size of those of the Pont de Valentre originally stood at each end of the bridge. It is the most monumental of all the French bridges of the Middle Ages which still stand. Etienne de Ferrieres and Mathieu de Verdun were the engineers of this bridge.

Aqueduct Bridge of Coutances:

In A.D.1277, the finest Gothic aqueduct bridge was built at Coutances, in Normandy, and it remained in service for a long time.

Fortified Bridges :

Mediæval bridges, such as the bridge of St. Bénezèt, were mostly fortified. The finest specimens of the Mediæval fortified bridges are:

The bridge called the Pont de Valentre was built over the Lot river at Cahours from A.D.1308 to A.D.1355 (or A.D.1378). It has 6 major pointed arches of 55-foot spans, and 3 defensive towers.

The Fortified Bridge was built from A.D.1321 to A.D.1339 at Ceret in the Pyrenees. This bridge has a single arch with the span of 149 feet (45.42m), and the width of 13 feet (3.96m). It is the earliest European open-spandrel arch bridge. It is still in service.

The fortified Bridge at Vielle-Brioude was constructed from A.D.1340, over the Allier river, by the engineers Estone and Greiner. Its semicircular stone arch had a span of 179 feet (54.56 m), then a record arch span, and a rise of 60 feet (18.29 m). The width of this bridge was 16 feet (4.88 m).

The great Fortified Bridge over the Adda river, at Trezzo in Northern Italy was built from A.D.1370 to A.D.1377 for Count Barnabo Visconti, Duke of Milan, as an access to his fortress castle. It spanned 251 feet (76.50m) in a single mammoth arch, the rise and the radius of which were 87 feet (26.52m) and 133 feet (40.54m) respectively. The single granite arch consisted of 2 courses: the inner course was 3¼feet (0.99m) thick, the outer course was 9 inches (22.9cm) thick, with the total arch thickness at the crown being four feet. The cross-section of the arch at the springing was 7 feet 5 inches(2.25m) by 29½feet (8.99m). This arch bridge represented a great structural advance over the Roman arches for it was equalled only in the second half of the nineteenth century, and finally surpassed by a concrete arch at the turn of the twentieth century. About A.D.1410 this bridge was destroyed by Carmognola in a local war. In A.D.1838 about 20 feet (6.10 m) of both abutments of this mammoth arch still survived.

Mediæval Roads:

Roman surface-paving had no provisions for expansion or contraction. The engineers of the Middle Ages developed a much cheaper and more efficient road building method than the Romans consisting of laying cubes of stone in a loose bed of earth or sand which permitted free expansion and contraction of the road surface and, moreover, made repairs of roads easy. Such flexible roads were in common use by A.D.1453.

Mediæval Canals:

The original source of European hydraulic construction is the Po river valley – the economic and technological heartland of Italy. In the period from A.D.1179 to A.D.1209, an 11-mile (17.7 km) long irrigation canal was dug tapping the Ticiano river, which in time was extended into the first major canal of Italy, the Naviglio Grande, that formed a moat around the city Milan. The first locks were built into it in A.D.1438 by Filippo da Modena and Fioravente da Bologna.

In A.D.1277, a great storm broke through the natural dunes which had acted as natural dykes of the ***Flevo Lacus***, a natural lake, and flooded it into the present Zuider Zee in Holland. Beginning in A.D.1400 the Dutch engineers were reclaiming the flooded Zuider Zee by building artificial dykes and pumping water out of the polders by windmill-driven pumps. In A.D.1373, the first pound locks were probably built in Europe at the junction of the Utrecht Canal and the Lek river, at Vreeswijk, in Holland, or perhaps a little earlier at Spaarndam.

The first European summit and sea-to-sea canal was built between A.D.1391 and A.D.1398. The Hanseatic League, a trading association of free cities in Northern Europe, built the Stecknitz Canal between the Baltic Sea and the North Sea, somewhat south of Denmark. The canal ran between Lübeck and Lauenburg and had a length of 42 miles (67.6 km). A 7-mile (11.3 km) stretch of this canal was the first summit canal in Europe: two pound locks raised the canal 16 feet (4.88 m). The entire rise was 56 feet (17.07 m) above sea level.

Industrial Pollution

Water-powered bellows produced draughts powerful enough to raise the furnace temperature to 2732° F (1500°C) in order to liquefy the iron ore, which had been crushed by water-powered stamping mills, in the blast furnace. The first known water-driven bellows were built in A.D.1323, and the first known blast furnace erected in A.D.1380. Water-powered trip-hammers delivered from 60 to 120 strokes a minute with 660 pound (300 kg) hammers, and 200 strokes a minute with 176 pound (80 kg) hammers in forging the bloom.

Construction of thousands of iron blast furnaces in hundreds of forests caused most of the deforestation in France and England. About 110 pounds (50 kg) of iron was produced from 440 pounds (200 kg) of iron ore and 883 cubic feet (25 m^3) of wood. One furnace could deforest an area of 0.62 mile (1 km) radius in forty days. A lime kiln could consume 250 oak trees in a year. In order to spare the forests the lime industry was the first to convert to the use of coal, and was soon followed by the iron industry. Then brewers, dyers and other industries followed suit. However, there is a cost involved in every act of man, even if it is a beneficial act. Burning coal to save forests produced the first known industrial pollution problem in the world.

The wealth of central Europe during the Middle Ages lay mostly in the mining and metallurgy. German miners, the acknowledged leaders in mining and mineral chemistry, were invited all over Europe to prospect for coal and new ores, and to establish new mining operations.

Coal mining had been primarily responsible for converting the mediæval agricultural environment into an industrial environment by A.D.1200, which can be recognised by the first pollution problems created by burning coal. Most coal mined at the time had a high bitumen content which gave off foul-smelling, choking, and noxious smoke that polluted the air. One of the main industrial uses of coal was for lime burning, and already by A.D.1307 the smoke produced by it had become such a nuisance in London that various attempts were made to prohibit its use. At the same time, industries such as slaughtering, and leather tanning polluted the rivers because the tanning process required acid and lime treatments.

Soon it became necessary to take counter measures, such as mining codes, to combat the 'new plague' of the Middle Ages: industrial pollution; for no benefits can be reaped by man without paying the price involved, in this case the pollution created by industry.

Mediæval Cooperation Between Science and Technology

In the Middle Ages the cooperation between science and technology was much closer than in antiquity. The mediæval scientists were keenly aware of the crafts, but they were usually unable to apply much of their scientific knowledge to crafts because this knowledge was mostly qualitative. In the thirteenth century A.D. the subdivision and mechanisation of industrial processes and crafts led to division of labour which, in turn, brought with it many professional and trade guilds that kept on multiplying. At one time in the textile industry in Italy there were about 16 guilds in existence.

Ramón Lull and Logic Circles :

A Franciscan monk, mystic, poet and a former wealthy courtier from Spain, Ramón Lull (Latin name, ***Ramundus Lullius***) (A.D.c.1235-1315), known as the 'enlightened teacher' (***doctor illuminatus***), was a man of singularly forceful personality and missionary zeal which inspired great admiration. He became dedicated to an ambition of converting the infidel Muslims to Christian faith, and, therefore, after teaching at Paris and Montpellier in France, he founded a college of Arabic studies in Mallorca in A.D.1276 and became an expert in Arabic language, literature and Muslim culture. He realised that to convert the infidels to Christian faith and to defend the Christian dogma against Muslim criticism, he had to master logic. He believed that theological knowledge had primacy over all other knowledge, and that logical reasoning could and ought to prove everything. He was convinced that the conversion of infidels required rational proof of the truth of Christian dogma. He wrote a long series of books in Latin, Catalan and Arabic based on his studies of diverse fields. In his tract,< The Tree of Knowledge> (***Arbor scientiae***), he drew attention to the scientific background of the crafts such as metallurgy, construction, clothing, agriculture, commerce, navigation, and military arts, which in his opinion were worthy of study by the scientists. Lull, who was an expert in naval engineering, advised navigators to make better use of geometry and arithmetic.

About A.D.1274, Lull conceived an idea to create a comprehensive and almost automatic method for the discovery of truth, which he called the 'great or general art' (***ars magna vel ars***

generalis), and he devoted several dozens of his works to this idea. In A.D.1275, Lull wrote a treatise, < The Ultimate General Art > (***Ars generalis ultima***), in which he gave a basis to serve all sciences and a key to invention and discovery, a work which was widely admired. His chief work, < Great and Ultimate Art > (***Ars magna et ultima***), was mainly a defence of Christian truth against the teachings of ***Averroës*** based on symbolic logic and combinatorial analysis. Lull thought it possible to obtain out of a combination of symbolic logical concepts a comprehensive system of general science (***scientia generalis***). He believed in the concept of a universal science of logic that could be applicable to all reasoning. In this work, Lull made the earliest known attempt in formal logic to employ geometric diagrams and mechanical demonstrators. He regarded every branch of knowledge to have a limited number of basic principles which could be represented by a set of terms standing for the principles or attributes of a subject in the form of letter symbols arranged in repeated concentric circles, called 'Lullian logic circles'. His combinatorial analysis consisted of rotating the inner circles to find all possible permutations which Lull believed will exhaust all combinations of the basic principles of the subject and, thus, reveal all the knowledge about the subject that the finite mind of man is capable of understanding. The number of Lullian logic circles varied from the usual 2 or 3 to 14 in his ***figura universalis*** which resulted in an enormous number of possibilities. This naive mechanical method of symbolic logic, which he called the 'great art (***ars magna***)', produced new ideas by combining the existing ones. The fundamental shortcoming in Lull's concept that it is possible to obtain cognitive knowledge of the world in a rational way by pure logic was that he left the significance of observation and experiment on cognitive knowledge entirely out of consideration. In the seventeenth century A.D., Lull's ***ars magna*** as a universal science of logic inspired the German savant Gottfried Wilhelm Leibniz to develop it rationally into his ***characteristica universalis*** which exonerated the possibility of automation of cognitive processes as envisaged by Lull. Today, it is possible to recognise in the thought processes of Lull the first notion of the possibility of mathematical logic and of the theory of mathematical machines such as computers.

Lull, a master of Arabic languages and a missionary in North Africa where he preached against the teachings of ***Averroës*** among the Muslims, met a gruesome end: he was stoned to death by a Muslim mob at Bougie when he was preaching Christianity to a crowd of Muslims.

Free Enterprise and Economics

A spirit of free enterprise and entrepreneurship developed in Flanders, the Low Countries,which brought about secular external finances and business organisations, from which all European countries learnt and benefited in the course of time.

The characteristic developments of the late mediæval society were the rise of the wealthy urban communities of burghers, expansion of commercial contacts and accumulation of capital to promote industry and to subsidise libraries and artists - all requirements for cultural advancement and maturation of a civilisation. The mediæval men instituted money economy, invented far reaching commercial enterprises and banking systems with double-entry bookkeeping which changed towns into populous centers of European culture.

It was the Lydian King Gyges who had first issued minted coins in the 7th century B.C., but their use was first made popular in the Persian Empire and the commercial Greek city-States Argos, Aigina, Korinthos and Athens. The Athenian tetradrachma with a relief of an owl on the coin became the international money like the English pound in the 19th century A.D. until the time of Alexandros of Macedonia, and like the English pound it was never debased in its value regardless of the vicissitudes of the time. Athenians created an exchange economy based on money, a commercial law, a system of weights and measures, and banking.

During the Early Middle Ages voluntary poverty was considered superior to wealth and even work because poverty was regarded as beatitude and the poor were seen "in the image of Christ." This attitude towards life was not conducive to commerce which is motivated by personal gains. Therefore, a merchant was rather despised as a sinner by the Church: "It is difficult not to sin when one makes a profession of buying and selling." Even ***Aquinas*** thought: "Commerce, considered in itself, has certain shameful characteristics and rightly so, because of itself, it yields to the greed for gain (***lucrum***), and gain knows no limit." Therefore, commerce was considered as one of the seven capital sins: avarice. It was also disliked because it led to moneylending at interest, called 'usury'. Moreover, taking of interest was regarded as equivalent to the selling of time, and time, so they thought, belonged to no man because it belonged to God.

The nobleman was expected to live with dignity, which meant that he should spend his money, and not hoard it, or invest it. His chivalric code expected him to loath money and to spend it lavishly on churches, pious endowments, tournaments, and fairs, since the Church condemned neither public nor private munificence. The churchmen of the Middle Ages had limited understanding of economic matters, but after the 12th century A.D. with the development of commerce on a larger scale, the theologians and canon lawyers had to make concessions, and soon the scholastic philosopher in his own right became quite an excellent economist and market analyst. There was one aspect of the economics which they could not rationally explain or justify, and that was the charging of interests on loans. They had a clear understanding of gaining profits from investments which were subject to risk, but because they believed in Aristotelian philosophy they accepted Aristotle's opinion that money as a means of commerce by itself is barren and unproductive, an opinion which unfortunately is not quite correct, although it was accepted as a valid opinion for almost seven centuries. For this reason, the mediæval scholastic economist could not see how pure interest on a loan when no ostensible risk of default is present can be economically and morally justified. Owing to the inability of the scholastic philosophers to find a rational justification for interest on loans on the basis of Aristotle's wrong assessment of the nature of money, the Catholic Church discredited all interest on loans as sinful 'usury'. For this reason, the Christians shunned the business of moneylending which was eagerly taken up by Jews, who were not members of the Western civilisation, the Christendom, and therefore not circumscribed by the moral code of the Christian society. The correct explanation of the interest on loans was first supplied by the Austrian economist Eugen von Böhm-Bahwerk (A.D.1851-1914) only in the late 19th century. He demonstrated that it is based on the concept of time-preference as a universal fact: the creditor is loaning the debtor money as 'present goods' whereas the debtor is giving the creditor only a 'prospect' of receiving money in the future, in other words 'future goods'. Since the time-preference makes 'present goods' worth more than 'future goods' the creditor will have to charge, and the debtor will be willing to pay, a premium called the rate of interest for the 'present goods'. The size of the premium is dependent on the rates of time preference of everybody on the market. Moreover, he showed that the normal rate of business profit is the rate of interest. Böhm-Bahwerk also demolished the incorrect concept of the labour-value of capital goods by demonstrating that such goods are not simply 'frozen labour' but also 'frozen time (and land)' and, furthermore, that the value of capital goods is a subjective, and not an objective measure. In view of this very late discovery of the correct economic concepts of value and interest, the mediæval man's mistaken economic assessment of charging interest on loans is quite understandable. For instance, even such economic experts as the Scottish economist Adam Smith (A.D.1723-1790) and the English economist David Ricardo (A.D.1772-1832), and their later followers believed in the incorrect 'labour-theory of value' and in its immediate economic consequences, all of which was fundamentally wrong.

When the mediæval scholastic economists were faced with large-scale trading, they were forced to recognise that merchants incurred risks which could result in heavy losses, and that money tied up in a loan involved the sacrifice of a possible legitimate gain elsewhere, and that a trader who travels far at great personal risk and peril in search of goods which are not locally available performed an essential service to his fellow men. The inflation of the thirteenth century A.D. made the risks run by all lenders abundantly clear to the schoolmen. Therefore, over the years the Catholic Church came to accept interest on public loans, contracts and bills of exchange as not only useful but also legitimate. Surprisingly, the mendicant orders such as the Franciscans were the most substantial defenders of the mediæval merchant.

Europe of the Middle Ages was regarded by its people as Christendom, that is, as the Kingdom of Christ on Earth. It was a closed society in so far as the Christian baptism was not only significant spiritually, but politically and socially as well: it marked the entrance of an individual into the European society in which only a baptised person was a fully accepted member. It is for this reason that a Jew, or a Muslim, who was not a baptised Christian was a non-person in the Christian commonwealth, and for that reason he could engage in occupations such as moneylending, which were otherwise forbidden to the members of the Christian society. The mediæval society, moreover, was a stratified society in which social status of an individual depended upon his membership in a closed corporation, whether a guild, a monastery, or rank in the feudal system.

Mediæval Trade and Merchant Leagues

During the Early Middle Ages interEuropean trade again began to develop, in particular trade in the wool of Flanders. For a time the city of Bruges in Flanders became the great capital of Northern trade in Europe, whilst European merchants became increasingly more capable in taking care of their own trade. For the purposes of keeping their markets in their own hands, the merchants of the northern German seaport towns formed guilds and a loose association of such guilds called the Hansa, which by A.D.1300 had been formally organised by the merchant guildsmen called the Hansards into the Hanseatic League. The Hanseatic League consisting of the merchant guilds of about one hundred towns was banded together for mutual benefit, and it dominated the trade in the North and the Baltic sea for two centuries. The leading cities of the Hanseatic League were Lübeck, Bremen, Hamburg, Danzig and such cities as Wisby on the island of Götland in the Baltic Sea, Reval (modern, Tallinn) and Pernau (modern, Pärnu) in Estonia, and such associated cities as London, Bruges and the far-away Novgorod in Russia. The League imposed stringent regulations upon its members to insure their monopoly in regional trade of certain commodities, such as fish, timber, amber, furs and metals. The League provided mutual protection to its members, but despite these arrangements rivalries between the members of the Hansa did not really disappear. The Hanseatic League built its own fleet of merchant ships, and provided the protection for their ships by putting down piracy and brigandage. The single-masted Hansa Cog, which evolved into a three-masted carrack by A.D.1453, was a sturdy little ship, the hull of which was braced and trussed to resist the heavy seas of the north. The Hanseatic League became so powerful that in a number of northern towns they controlled for a time their town governments, and by virtue of granting loans to monarchs they were even able to obtain concessions from foreign rulers. Hanseatic power became so great that in A.D. 1406 they were able to drive the English intruders out of the Norwegian fishing grounds, and even fight and win a war between A.D.1367 and A.D.1370 against the king of Denmark who tried to impose tolls on the Hanseatic ships.

The Hanseatic League became most powerful in the fifteenth century A.D. just before the trade routes shifted to the Atlantic after A.D.1500 owing to the discovery of the American continent, an event which helped to undermine the Hanseatic prosperity.

The trade in the Mediterranean was dominated by the Italian city-State Venice, just like the Hanseatic League dominated the trade in the Baltic. It was the marketplace for the commodities such as silk, sugar, spices and cotton from the East, and the woollen cloth from the West. Venice was also a great shipbuilding center in the Arsenal of which, a huge government-operated shipyard, the traditional, narrow oar-propelled galley was improved and converted into a faster and larger merchant vessel. The city-State Genoa in Italy, another powerful merchant city and the main rival of Venice, dominated the trade in the Black Sea. For a period of time Venice and Genoa were militarily and economically so powerful that the Byzantine State was reduced to their puppet.

Mediæval trade and commerce was given a great boost when in A.D.1397 the Medici family of Florence, Italy, opened banks all over Europe and began lending money for various commercial enterprises on an international scale.

Chinese Technology and Engineering

The pound lock was invented by a Chinese engineer Chiao Wei-Yo in A.D.984. He constructed in the Pien Canal 2 pound locks with 2 flash-gates about 250 feet (76.20 m) apart, which were operated by windlasses. Early in the twelfth century A.D., the Chinese built their Grand Canal, which ultimately had a length of 1,200 miles (1,931km). It was a summit canal. The construction of this mammoth canal was accomplished at an incredible cost in human life for over 2 million workers perished in its construction. The Emperor of China had absolute power over all life and limb in his Empire, and he used this power mercilessly. However, it is possible that the very first hydraulic structures such as sluices, and perhaps even a primitive kind of pound lock, were built during the reign of the Macedonian King Ptolemaios Philadelphos from 285 B.C. to 247 B.C. in his extention of the Pharao Ship Canal in Egypt.

The Great Chinese Wall, the construction of which began in 215 B.C. under the direction of General Meng T'ien (flourished about 220 B.C.), was essentially built during the Middle Ages under the rule of the Ming Dynasty from A.D.1368 to A.D.1644. This wall extends about 1,400 miles (2,253 km) across the northern China, and it incorporated about 25,000 watchtowers. Since the wall folds back on itself in many places its total length is closer to 2,800 miles (4,506 km). The building material used in this structure could make a wall 3 feet (0.91 m) thick and 8 feet (2.44 m) high encircle the equator. The construction of this colossal structure took an appalling toll in human life. It is estimated that at times about one-third of the able-bodied male Chinese were dragooned to build and defend this structure. All throughout the history, the Chinese people have despised this monstrous wall, which they called the 'World's Longest Cemetery' because the corpses of millions upon millions of Chinese workers who perished in the compulsory labour gangs building this useless wall were all buried in it. For instance, Chinese artists never depicted this despicable wall in the paintings of the landscape traversed by the wall, and its very existence was totally ignored in China until very recent times when ignorant Western visitors have taken an intense interest in the so-called 'Great Wall of China' which like the Volga Canal in Soviet Russia stands as a man-made monument built on millions of corpses. Cultural traditions in the European society made such gargantuan compulsory engineering projects quite impossible in the West. European people tended to be defiant of authority and frequently revolted over quite minor complaints, which stood in sharp contrast to the subservient Chinese who were always submissive to their superiors by virtue of their passive philosophy idealising conformity to nature and social station.

The Chinese ironmasters were in considerable advance over the European ironmasters. By 300 B.C., the Chinese ironmasters were able to maintain temperatures in their blast furnaces as high as 2,552°F (1,400°C) by means of a continuous forced blast of air from their horizontal, double-acting bellows which liquified the iron in the furnace so that it could be poured into moulds. Since cast-iron has a high carbon content which makes it brittle, the Chinese ironmasters discovered a method to remove surface carbon from the cast-iron and thereby create a steel-jacket around the cast which made it useful for practical applications. The European ironmasters were first able to make cast-iron only about 1,500 years later during the Middle Ages. The superiority of the Chinese blast-furnace stemmed from the superiority of the Chinese double-acting horizontal bellows, still in use in the Chinese countryside, over the vertical bellows used in Europe which produced intermittent blasts of air of much smaller volume.

In bridge construction Chinese engineers were also in considerable advance over the European engineers. In China some remarkable bridges were built, especially the celebrated Great Stone Bridge which was constructed from A.D.589 to A.D.618. It was an elegant, shallow, and slender segmental arch with an open spandrel which had a rise of 23 feet (7.00 m) and a span of 123 feet (37.50 m) giving a rise-to-span ratio of approximately 1 to 5. No comparable segmental, open spandrel arch bridge was built in Europe until about A.D.1400.

A remarkable engineering achievement of Chinese engineers was the famous South-Pointing Chariot constructed by an engineer called Yen Su in A.D.1027 which consisted of an arrangement of gears and wheels rigged to a vertical pole on which the south-pointing figure of a man was mounted. Once the chariot was set in the right direction in the beginning, the figure continued pointing south regardless which way the chariot was moved. A second such chariot built by the engineer Wu Te-Jen in A.D.1102 was more complex than the chariot of Yen Su by having a set of pulleys, and a great number of gears and weights. When the chariot changed its course, the pulleys lowered the weights which operated the gears to turn the figure so it kept its southward orientation. These two south-pointing chariots were not very accurate, since it is doubtful that they ever functioned properly, and apparently they were only used for court demonstrations. Such a chariot is supposed to have had a differential gear, but the late Derek de Solla Price, an expert of ancient mechanisms, did not believe that the extant literary description bears out this interpretation. However, these chariots are among the earliest known self-correcting machines which probably operated by the feedback principle first used by the ancient Greek mathematician and engineer Archimedes of Syracuse (287-212 B.C.).

Another exceptionally fine Chinese technological achievement was the giant hydraulic calendar-clock designed by Su Sung in about A.D.1086 which was housed in a 35 feet (10.67 m) high two-storey tower. The central feature of this structure was a giant clock driven by water power. Water flowed constantly out of a full tank into 36 scoops mounted on a driving wheel 11 feet (3.35 m) in diameter. The wheel turned an iron shaft which moved gears that operated the clock. On the lower floor of the tower, puppets came out of doors to announce the time with gongs, bells, drums and signs. A 20-foot (6.10 m) chain-drive operated a globe on the upper floor of the tower, and turned gears which operated models of the planets that moved over the surface of the globe in imitation of their motion in the heavens. On the roof of the tower there was a second sphere consisting of rotating rings on which the stars were marked. An astronomer could use it to scan the heavens through a sighting tube which automatically moved to follow a particular star as it traversed the sky. This astounding calendar-clock permitted very fine calculations of the positions of the stars on which any calendar could be based.

In A.D.1088 the Chinese technicians also made the first magnetic compass consisting of a magnetic needle floating on water. The first such mariner compass was described by Chu Yu in A.D.1115. The earliest known marine compass in Europe is mentioned in A.D.1190, but it may have been in use before that date.

Another Chinese invention was the humble wheelbarrow known to have existed in A.D.147. Some of the Chinese wheelbarrows had sails, but the first sailing wheelbarrows appeared in Europe only about a millennium later. The Chinese actually reinvented the wheelbarrow, since the ancient Greeks had invented the wheelbarrow already about 406 B.C. at Eleusis.

Chinese technologists having been inspired by the felt-making method of the Asiatic nomads, invented papermaking from rags, tree bark, hemp, old fishing nets, rope and other things as raw materials which were worked into a fine pulp by using mortar and pestle, and spread out on a frame to dry. The papermaking , the invention of which was probably the work of many technologists over a few centuries, was perfected by the eunuch Tsai Lun (A.D.c.50-c.118) and appears to have been in use in China by about 105 B.C..

Chinese engineer, Chang Heng, who is reported to have constructed the first crude south-pointing chariot already in A.D. 120, also invented the first known seismograph called the 'earthquake weathercock'. It consisted of a large, ornamented, cast-bronze vessel having a diameter of about 6 feet (1.83 m) with a domelike cover, inside of which was fitted a central column that operated the closing and opening mechanism by means of a heavy pendulum affected by the earthquake.

The unfortunate fate of all Chinese technological inventions was that they were 'stillborn' and never led to any further development in China proper. There must have been good reasons why such a bleak future awaited virgin Chinese inventions, and it must be sought in their religion, philosophy, social mores, and political ideals.

Failure of Oriental Civilisations to Develop Scientific Technology and Engineering

All the Asiatic civilisations came into being in the pre-logical era. They never succeeded to achieve the mental state of rational thought since the Oriental mind showed no concern about the concept of contradiction, a principle on which rational thought relies. They remained irrational in their search for the truth which they tried to find by means of intuition, symbolism, magic and mysticism.

Although the Western man and the Oriental man had virtually the same pessimistic opinion of the human condition as being precarious, tragic and fleeting, their particular attitudes towards it were quite different. The Western man attempted to improve his worldly condition by trying to gain mastery over nature, whereas the Oriental man wanted to escape his worldly condition by trying to gain mastery over himself. The Western man believed in the reality of the external world and in himself, whereas the Hindu, for instance, regarded the external world and the self as illusory, and sought to depersonalise and extinguish himself.

In mathematics, the Hindus were essentially interested in its arithmetical and computational aspects in sharp contrast to ancient Greeks who were fundamentally interested in the rational and geometric aspects of mathematics. For instance, the sharp logical distinction ancient Greeks recognised between the discreteness of numbers and the continuity of geometric quantities was not at all recognized by Hindus who thought such distinctions to be quite superfluous. They showed no concern about such logical paradoxes as presented by Zenon. For this reason, Hindu thought in mathematics lacked fine distinctions, and this neglect allowed them to take great delight in computational tricks that could be played in mathematics. Such profound logical questions as incommensurability, the infinitesimals, the infinite, the process of exhaustion, and other such mathematical topics leading towards the conception and methods of calculus were entirely overlooked in Hindu mathematics. However, in simple numerical algebra they not only recognised the irrational roots of quadratic equations but also the concept of absolute negatives, all novel ideas which were responsible for a change towards the modern view of the subject.

The Chinese were very industrious and thoroughly practical people who distrusted all theories. They demonstrated their native ingenuity in many original inventions, but they neither applied their inventive powers to industry nor developed scientific technology and engineering. The reason for this failure probably resided in their bureaucratic way of thinking, and in their values and beliefs.

The Chinese thought of the entire universe as a huge material organism in which all of its parts interact in a sympathetic and intimate harmony. They extended the sexual origin of every form of life to the whole universe by means of their principle of male (***yang***) and female (***yin***) which led to their peculiar sexual conception of cosmology. They did not comprehend the abstract notion of natural law and, therefore, they were unable to create fundamental abstract sciences. In the Chinese conception, nature as an organism was to be symbolically decyphered by means of a number of pseudo-sciences such as astrology, numerology, geomancy and physiognomy, all of which were incompatible with genuine sciences. Chinese mathematics was mostly derived from Hindu mathematics the original source of which was Sumer and Babylon, and it was limited to arithmetic and simple algebra. They developed certain ingenious devices for the treatment of numerical higher equations which were concerned with approximations and not with precise mathematical results. Their geometry, instead of being axiomatic and deductive which is necessary for a genuine science, was empirical and restricted solely to mensuration and they never applied mathematics to the theoretical study of nature. For all these reasons, Chinese physics remained confined to the metaphysics of ***yang*** and ***yin***, the five elements: water, fire, wood, metal and earth, and their symbolic affinities. They never distinguished between primary and secondary qualities, never had a complete understanding of the experimental method or its systematic use, and never theorised about nature in an abstract mathematical way. The Chinese being in awe of nature never tried to subjugate nature to their will, but rather sought to adjust themselves to the natural and the human environment. This submissive conformism of the Chinese people found its expression in two Chinese philosophies which dominated their lives: Taoism and Confucianism.

Taoism as taught by Lao-Tse (died 521 B.C.) ignored logic and urged men to return to their primitive state of innocence. All social virtues which men invent for the purpose of controlling their destinies were thought to be obstacles to natural order and regarded with profound contempt.

Confucianism as taught by Kon Fu-Tse (c.557-479B.C.) consisted of a theory of government and social ethics which enthroned 'conformism as a way of life'. Confucianism produced a rigid social ritualism that was further formalised by their written language which virtually stereotyped thought The limited structure of the Chinese language was another serious obstacle in the development of genuine science. The written Chinese language began with Sumerian type pictographs, which never developed into a phonetic alphabet but remained arrested in ideographs, a different sign required for each 'idea'. The characters or ideographs of the Chinese written language represent ideas, not sounds: it is an ideographic, not a phonetic written language. Consequently it has practically as many characters as there are ideas. These characters are not vocable, they have a meaning primarily for the eye and not for the ear. It is estimated that the number of these characters, exclusive of obsolete words and synonyms, is about 49,000. Considering those characters that are given a different meaning by a stress mark as totally different, it is estimated that the number is 260,000. When it is remembered that they have to be learnt like our alphabet, even the smallest number of the characters represents an appalling task of memory for a student. The fact that many of these 49,000 characters are seldom used in practice provides only an insignificant relief to the prodigious mental effort required to memorise them.

The Chinese literary language has relatively few sounds which can be combined in a limited way: only 412 different syllables are possible. Their linguistic rule that required one syllable for each word produced an absurdly small vocabulary. The use of different tones to distinguish otherwise identically sounding words extended the Chinese vocabulary to 1,280, a ridiculously small number for any civilised language. In their written language there are over 49,000 different ideograms but only 1,280 unique tones. Therefore, any one syllable may have over 30 different meanings, which can be distinguished by a system of compounding into polysyllabic words as is done in their spoken language, but the polysyllabic words have no literary form. For this reason, Chinese language is quite unsuitable for scientific thought which requires a large vocabulary of fine distinctions. In such a scientifically sterile environment, the Chinese studies of nature were based on superficial observations and æsthetic intuitions rather than on the hypothetico-deductive method of the ancient Greeks and Europeans which lies at the basis of any genuine exact science. Yet in their nationalistic arrogance, the Chinese not only considered their society to be perfect, but they also thought that there was nothing of value to be learnt from foreigners, an attitude which fostered xenophobia. Unfortunately, they were badly mistaken in both, for the mentality fostered by Taoism and Confucianism made a Western type of industrial progress in China entirely impossible.

Postscriptum

A rather detailed account of the achievements of the mediæval men has been given on the foregoing pages. There are two basic reasons for this: firstly, the Middle Ages created politically, intellectually, and technologically the very foundation of the European civilisation; secondly, the Middle Ages is the most maligned period of European history, and, therefore, the most misunderstood.

The greatest opponents of mediæval achievements and the main slanderers of the Middle Ages were the literary humanists of the Italian Renaissance, who reacted violently against their immediate past by pretending to be the heralds of a new age, and consistently dismissing and ridiculing the remarkable achievements of the men of the Middle Age. They scornfully named the mediæval building art, the most original and distinctive European architecture, 'Gothic' which implied 'barbaric' to the Italian Renaissance mind, and they vilified mediæval philosophy by saying that it was a mere playing with words. They presented their mediæval forebears as living in religious bondage to the Church, and being unwilling to think for themselves.

It is important to stress that a humanist is not the same as a humanitarian: humanist is merely a person interested in man, and in human life and affairs. Often a humanist is seriously lacking in humanism, and sometimes he is a person possessed with sarcasm and even vindictiveness. The literary humanists of the Italian Renaissance, who preferred Plato over Aristotle and venerated classical antiquity and its emphasis on arts, were the greatest opponents of mediæval achievements and scholasticism. Marcilio Ficino (A.D.1433-1499), head of the Platonic cult and an Italian Renaissance scholar, ridiculed the schoolmen from Padua, and Desiderius Erasmus (A.D.c.1469-1536), a Christian humanist, ridiculed the 'calculatory sophism' of the schoolmen from Paris, a topic that was really beyond his intellectual competence to appreciate completely. The interest of the Italian Renaissance humanists in philology moved them to make much out of original classical texts which they worshipped, thereby reintroducing a petrified reverence for authority, and giving birth to intellectual servility to ancient Greek thought, an attitude which the mediæval men would have expected from peasants and nobles, but not from scholars. The literary humanists of the Italian Renaissance did not return to the more substantial pre-Sokratic natural philosophy of the ancient Greeks for that lay beyond their ability. They condemned the schoolmen for having failed to study the original works of the ancient Greeks which, it should be pointed out, had not been available during the Early Middle Ages because at that time they were 'lost' works. The philosophy developed by the Italian Renaissance humanists themselves was a backwards step from the mediæval philosophy which hindered further development of philosophy into its modern empirical forms. The most important contributions to science by the literary humanists of the Italian Renaissance were their rather accurate literary translations of the famous works of Eukleides, Archimedes, Apollonios, Pappos, Diophantos and Ptolemaios which later scientists were able to study. The works of humanists which could be considered scientific were distinctly inferior to the mediæval contributions, and, if not, they were in some instances plagiarisations of mediæval works without acknowledgement of the original mediæval sources.

The outworn and distorted stereotype of the Middle Ages confected by the Italian Renaissance humanists, and still promoted by contemporary humanists and political atheists such as Marxists, who are hostile to religious thought and want to suppress the important corpus of knowledge which the religious mediæval men produced as the foundation of modern European civilisation, has been accepted ***in toto*** over many centuries by ill-bred uncultured men, and it is still dying hard today.

To counteract such rank ignorance, the previous pages give a rather extensive and detailed account of what the mediæval men actually accomplished for which the Western civilisation owes them a great debt. It is plainly evident that the mediæval culture was extraordinarily dramatic because giant efforts were made against great historical obstacles for freedom of thought in a mighty struggle between reason and faith, between freedom and authority, between miracle and natural law, and between tradition and progress. They were the first scholars to fight for the right to reason, to train us in modern logic and analysis, to give us our conceptual instruments of enquiry, to form the very vernaculars we speak in the Western civilisation, and to write the first vernacular masterpieces in every cultured European tongue. Since the vernacular tongues after A.D.1100 began to shape and channel thoughts of the people who spoke them, and these tongues when reduced to written language reclaimed the past in national terms, the national boundaries became sharply defined and thus gave rise to nationalism. The national states became clearly evident by A.D.1300, or later, in France and in England. Nationalism, the feeling of belonging to a nation, became strong in Europe when the common heritage from the past and the common aspirations for the future took precedence over local interest. Nationalism became a real social force with an effective leader who was representative of the group and its interests, and had to shape and focus those interests before he was able to lead them, yet he could focus only on what was potentially there in the first place. Many kings who had been reduced to feudal overlords with greatly diminished power during the feudal age, became powerful again on the swelling tide of nationalism in comparison with the institutional Church and the feudal lords.

The mediæval men instituted the right of private property, and as a consequence of it, the emergence of the autonomous private person, the very cornerstone of the Western civilisation, was made possible. They were the first to establish the rights of man, and to show the world how to use representative assemblies to limit the power of the government and to avoid the lawless State. They gave us the contract theory, resting on natural law (***lex natura***), which asserts that the government should be founded on the rights of man, and not on violence, and that the ruler of the country was circumscribed by binding dictates of ideal justice serving the best interests of the individual citizens.

The solution to the problem of the individual and society according to Plato and Aristotle was to be found in the intellectual nature of man which was possible only for the few and, therefore, it was aristocratic in its application. The solution offered by Christianity to the same problem was to be found in the moral nature of man which is common to all men and, therefore, universal in application.

Christianity in its original purity is a very individualistic faith which is concerned with the salvation of the soul of the individual man for he is responsible to God alone. A Christian does a good deed not only for the sake of the fellow man, but also for the sake of himself, for his own salvation, because doing a good deed for his fellow man makes him a better person more worthy of God's grace and salvation. A Christian is supposed to have ***caritas***, that is, loving kindness, but he cannot be optimistic about the perfectability of man, nor can it ever be pure humanitarianism since a Christian cannot love the sinner for his sins. Otherwise, a Christian has the responsibility not only to love the 'underdog', but the 'upperdog' as well, to the great consternation of many social reformers then and now. Christian thought distrusts the whole unaided, natural man and his appetites for gaining, fighting, vainglory, sexual indulgence, food and drink. Concerning food the Christian credo is: "It is better to eat in order to live, than to live in order to eat," otherwise the Christian as a child of God had to be truthful and act justly for his own sake, and certainly not in order to please or placate others. The Christian religion, the spiritual individualism in mediæval thought, and the sentiment were of cardinal importance in providing the cultural climate for the development of the distinctive European culture.

Thus the 12th and 13th centuries A.D. were eras of extraordinary social, political and cultural innovation in European history owing to the Western version of human action. In this era collective consciousness gave way to individual consciousness from which emanated comprehensive logic of opinion, belief and human action. Mediæval treatises of human action were really treatises on individual conscience. These remarkable centuries in Europe experienced critical breakthroughs in logic, political philosophy, arts and letters, sentiment, and rational scholarship in all forms of opinion, including scientific opinion. It gave the world the greatest philosopher since Aristotle in the person of ***Thomas Aquinas*** who is still without an equal.

The Early Middle Ages cannot be regarded as 'Dark Ages', a derogatory name invented by Renaissance humanists in their effort to defame Middle Ages, but rather as a period of gradual enlightenment culminating in the thirteenth and fourteenth centuries A.D. when clearly recognisable foundations were laid for modern European science, for the 'scientific revolution' is the child of the late mediæval science. The principal intention of scientific research of that period was to establish critical understanding of the workings of nature, since nature was considered to be the handiwork of God as the Divine Scientist-Engineer-Master Technician.

The scholastic period of Western science abounded with new ideas, profound and incisive analyses of concepts and logically motivated criticisms. The scholastic scientists were clerics whose approach to science was abstract and only sporadically associated with practical applications or experiments mainly because their philosophical and scientific interests were only incidental to their teaching in the university faculties of arts and theology. In contrast to the literary humanist of the Italian Renaissance, the mediæval scholar esteemed Aristotle with a certain respect, but they did not worship him nor regard him infallible. They were able to pass beyond him, and go so far beyond him as to deny some of Aristotle's assertions. They were definitely not servile to ancient Greek savants.

The conservative theologians who were concerned about the union of faith and reason, launched a brilliant philosophical attack against Aristotle, meant to distinguish clearly between the sort of knowledge accessible to human faculties and the kind only accessible by revelation. In the success of their attack they were able to move the entire metaphysics into the domain of revelation, thereby demolishing the entire Greek and Muslim concept of metaphysical nature of the philosophical undertaking, and inventing the empirical, that is, the modern notion of what philosophy is all about. Subsequently, Aristotle's qualitative, metaphysical physics was attacked by means of a new quantitative empirical physics, and, by means of some ingenious analyses, it was demonstrated that Aristotle's theory of moving bodies was erroneous, and an entirely new theory was put forth which was the point of departure for Newton. Unfortunately, the mediæval scientists thought that logical proofs of this new theory are sufficient and, therefore, mediæval science put limited emphasis on experiment. For this reason, their 'natural philosophy' was highly speculative and often very mathematical such as the admirable work produced at Oxford. In general, the mediæval scientist was dedicated to rigorous mathematical theories of structure and beauty. Before the success of the Mertonians in kinematics and the Parisian Terminists in dynamics, Jordan de Nemore had already surpassed the ancient Greeks by solving the difficult problem of the inclined plane and establishing the source of Virtual Work Principle in statics. These were remarkable scientific milestones which surpassed the achievements of ancient Greek scientists.

It is interesting to observe that during the Middle Ages science did not contribute to technology, but technology definitely stimulated science. Roughly speaking, technology is the way people produce and do things in their civilisation. Already in the ninth century A.D. Europeans thought that the advancement of technology is an aspect of Christian virtue. Even during the so-called 'Dark Ages' the technological skills of classical times were not only maintained, but considerably advanced.

Technologically, the Mediæval Age was one of the most innovative and daring age in the history of technology and engineering. Mediæval technology possessed an innovative boldness, largely lacking in ancient Græco-Roman times and in other civilisations, because it associated natural power with Christian idealism which produced important long-range results. The incentive afforded by this philosophical approach to technology proved so effective that mediæval engineering became quite precocious and far in advance of the limited scientific knowledge of its time, which makes the Middle Ages one of the most remarkable periods of technological advance. This kind of mediæval technology distinguished itself from that of antiquity by using new sources of power and better mechanical devices, and by applying mathematical analysis to mechanics and physics.

Mediæval time was an age of modern power technology, new chemical discoveries, new industrial processes, unique and daring structural engineering, efficient skeleton-first shipbuilding method, highly refined technology of mechanical devices, and new and very productive agricultural methods.

What any civilisation does with technology is influenced by the borrowing from other cultures and by attitudes towards technological change. Such attitudes basically depend upon what the people in the society think concerning their relation to nature, their destiny, and their principles for action, all of which are mostly broad religious questions that were quite successfully answered by the men of the European Mediæval Age.

Compared to all the numerous fundamental and distinctly 'revolutionary' contributions of the Mediæval Age to technology, engineering, sciences, industry, and philosophy, the Italian Renaissance contributions in fundamental matters, with a few exceptions, fell short of bold originality and daring by being in general relatively commonplace.

CHAPTER VIII

RENAISSANCE: Engineering as Practical Art
[from A.D. 1453 to A.D.1650]

Rebirth of Classical Culture

The Italian Renaissance consisted of the rise of republican city-States in northern and central Italy, and the birth of humanism which showed an intense interest in the secular life of man. The Italian Renaissance society in Europe was rather unique because it was virtually urban. The Italian peninsula was a land dotted with city-States the wealth of which was based on urban rather than agricultural economy. On account of its geographic location, Italy had become a commercial center of Europe already in the late Mediæval Age, and most of its cities in central and northern Italy were virtually independent republican city-States, which dominated their surrounding countryside, and as a result of their importance became the social, political, and economic centers for the whole Italian peninsula. Many feudal lords moved into these city-States and became neighbours of ordinary burghers, a situation which lessened the mediæval class distinctions. Although noble birth was still important, wealth or political power could be more important still. If prominent social status by birth be lacking, any conspicuous artistic or literary talent of a person could be sufficient to gain him access to the homes of the nobles and the wealthy burghers. For this purpose the idea of genius as a social ideology was invented by ambitious artists, sculptors, architects, musicians, and even poets in order to raise their social status and to justify snobbery. Unfortunately, this ideology did not promote education of engineering technologists in the universities since ingenuity cannot be taught.

A new commercial class emerged in Italian city-States who were largely responsible for the revival of classical learning which quickly became a Renaissance passion. This commercial class had trade connexions with the Byzantine State where they met Byzantine scholars who exposed them to classical Greek learning. Moreover, the free-enterprise method of business they had inherited from the Late Middle Ages required literacy from all individuals engaged in commercial business. The wealth created by the capitalist business enterprises enabled an increasing number of interested laymen to obtain a good education, and these people were financially able to participate in literature, and general learning, which further increased the secular interests of the Renaissance men. The new capitalistic methods in business and industry enabled many energetic and enterprising individuals to accumulate great wealth which permitted them to patronise art in such a generous manner that many lowborn but talented artists were raised high above the status of ordinary artisans. In this sense, there appeared to be no limit to what an individual man could accomplish through his ability and good fortune. In such a social atmosphere, an individual found great incentive to develop his native abilities to the fullest, and immortal fame in this world became more important to them than immortal life in the next. This outlook made the Renaissance men avid enjoyers of all that this world was able to offer which led them to develop all aspects of their personality in order to extract maximum pleasure out of life. Unfortunately, the eager development of all the faculties of man only too frequently meant the development of the baser as well as the loftier instincts in man. In the belief that the autonomous man being totally independent is his own measure, some Renaissance men came to consider themselves not only to be above the law, human or divine, but also independent of the Christian morality. A prominent goldsmith and artist, Benvenuto Cellini (1500-1570), who thought that ordinary morality did not apply to a genius like himself, conducted himself in his private life only marginally better than a common thug. Many Renaissance princes such as Visconti of Milan amalgamated in themselves the most refined appreciation of the arts with the remorseless, inhuman cruelty. The age of Italian Renaissance was an age of chaotic change in which there was still much that was mediæval and much that was modern. It was an age of contrasts and confusion in religion, in morality and even in individual character. Mediæval and modern characteristics existed side by side in the same person, and in the same society which was responsible for violent conflicts and inconsistencies. Countryside rebelled against the domination by the city-States. Within the city-States classes and parties fought for the control of the city government. It was a time of mercenary soldiers, who were organised in large bands under their own leaders, called ***condottieri***, who fought for no other cause save personal advantage and who sold the services of the mercenary band to the highest bidder. War to the ***condottieri*** was business and they conducted it for profit. It was in their interest to keep wars going, because to them peace meant unemployment. On account of the temporary nature of their employment, the ***condottieri*** had no time to train infantry and therefore had to depend exclusively upon cavalry, a form of military force which was really unsuited to the Italian terrain, and which left Italy without adequate defence against foreign invaders from the territorial States of Europe such as France.

Under such politically disturbed conditions the republican governments of these city-States were gradually overthrown by despots who were strong enough to keep order and impose peace at the expense of liberty. Many of the despots were ***condottieri*** who seized power by force of arms, some gained control of the republican government by using their wealth, and some gained despotic power by changing their temporary legal power into an extralegal power. Only the republican city-States Venice and Florence escaped actual despotism, but their governments were hardly more democratic because they were controlled by a small number of wealthy families. The despot, who ruled by force and cunning, recognised the binding power of no law, human or divine, and regarded himself to be above the law. A special Renaissance creation was the 'enlightened despot', who wanted to earn the respect, and even gratitude of the people if he expected a long rule. This desire to be respected, sometimes combined with a genuine love of culture, made many despots invite to their courts scholars, artists, and poets who were richly rewarded. Sometimes a city-State ruled by an enlightened despot, such as Milan, became an important center of learning and art. In the 15th and 16th centuries the major city-States of Northern Italy, such as Genoa, Florence, Milan, and Venice, became the important centers in the revival of classical learning, architecture, art, and engineering. Soldier-despots like Duke Federigo Montefeltro of Urbino, statesmen like Cosimo and Lorenzo de' Medici, the bankers who ruled Florence, and businessmen like the Florentine Palla Strozzi, were also scholars and cultured patrons of the arts. Yet many Italian statesmen, who were both enlightened and rational, formulated their policies by the assistance of auguries of charlatan astrologers. The external appearance of a refined and learned society in virtually every court in Italy usually hid a murky underlying immorality, which undermined the moral fibre of the society at large.

The inhabitants of an Italian republican city-State fancied themselves to be the heirs of the Republican Romans, and this attitude brought about a renewed interest in the classical literature and culture in Italy. The catchword of the Italian Renaissance was: '***essere humano*** (to be human)'. The Renaissance men attempted to combine knowledge of the past with their contemporary European ideas to achieve progress in the future. The Renaissance man, who was driven by a passion for self-realisation and control of his own destiny, added rational control of materials to the mediæval Schoolmen's logical control of arguments. In the Renaissance period, the mathematical tradition of Pythagoras and Plato was revived, and the numerical and geometrical structure of the world was again stressed. This renewed Platonic outlook was first applied in the theory and practice of Italian Renaissance engineering and architecture. Great importance was laid upon the proportioning of structures and it was supplied with the mathematical theory of the beautiful, which expressed the harmony of proper proportions. The Renaissance man thought like the ancient Pythagoreans that the existence of such mathematical proportions guarantees æsthetic perfection and that the mathematical proportions rule everything, even the human body. The engineering works of the Renaissance man, had to be not only functional and economical as the Romans had required, but also beautiful as the Greeks had emphasised. The renewed interest in the mathematical approach to nature ultimately led to the precipitous scientific development at the close of the Renaissance period and in the beginning of the Baroque era.

Renaissance signalled the rise of the well-rounded ***uomo universale*** (universal man), as an artist-engineer-architect-scientist-humanist, who was a scholar behind the draughting board. This artist-engineer replaced the academic philosopher-theologian of the Mediæval Age as the pacesetter of Western intellectual life. In the Pythagorean tradition of the Renaissance there existed no contradiction between the work of the scientific enquirer and the work of the artist-engineer because both were considered to be searching for the truth in nature through numbers and geometric figures.

Therefore, the Renaissance artist-engineer strove for a mathematical and scientific understanding of practical technology, and as a consequence of this effort, research and learning came out of the universities and became the pursuit of private academies, such as the Academy of Secrets of Nature (***Academiae Secretorum Naturae***), founded by Giovanni Battista della Porta (1537-1602) in 1560 but soon forced to close because of clerical suspicions, and the Academy of Lynces (***Academiae dei Lincei***), founded in 1603, in which technical problems were discussed in terms of science. Progress in science was now created by practically minded artist-engineers and by amateur scientists, whilst the idea of invention had become of central importance in the idea of progress. The direction of science now passed to self-made amateur engineers of natural genius, the so-called ***virtuosi,*** and the organs of the 'new culture' were no longer universities but the scientific societies and academies. The Renaissance period actually produced a relatively limited number of fundamentally new innovations in engineering and technology, since it was more an age of great expectations than basic contributions.

The Renaissance men attempted to combine the Roman ***gravitas***, the serious moral earnestness, with imaginative Greek intelligence. The birthplace of the Renaissance was the republican city-State Florence, where the chancellors who aspired to be scholars and practitioners of humanistic studies, saw in the Florentine Republic a revival of the classical virtues of ancient Greece and Rome. They cultivated excellence, beauty, and the spirit of criticism. They had rediscovered the Hellenic ideal of a well-rounded individual (***uomo universale***), the fervent belief in human genius, and the sense of harmony between man and his environment. They believed that there was no limit to the accomplishments of any man who relied on his own native ability and good fortune. The Renaissance society had a complete faith in man: he can do what he wills if given enough time, and they promoted business in all of its forms. The Renaissance businessmen were brilliant, clever, and curious, and they believed as was so well expressed by Alberti in 1434, that a freeman cannot set his hand to more liberal labour than working for profit and creating capital, since what he sells is his labour – the goods are merely transferred.

However, despite the presence of the so-called modern spirit in the Renaissance period, the typical Renaissance man harboured in himself a curious mixture of mediæval as well as classical Græco-Roman views and attitudes, of Christian as well as pagan beliefs, of metaphysical as well as empirical ideas, and of mystical as well as rational thoughts. It is indisputable that the secular and empirical aspects of the Renaissance life which are commonly regarded as 'modern' were already present in the mediæval society. It is probably correct to say that the Renaissance society, unlike the mediæval society, did not have a comprehensive and fundamental ideology which could have given unity and coherence to the Renaissance civilisation.

But soon the institutions of Church and State grew oppressive and placed ceremonies and conventional institutionalised piety ahead of serious personal piety – and even ahead of the truth. The grave and serious northern men of Europe recognised the institutional corruption that had overtaken the religious organisation itself, and they revolted against its attempts to oppress the spiritual autonomy of the individual man for the benefit of the institutionalised Church in Rome. These men realised that truth was no longer primarily pursued by the organised central church, and that the institutional corruption was being disseminated by the central institution of the church itself among the simple men of faith. The indolent and worldly Pope Leo X blatantly declared: "Since God has given us Papacy, let us enjoy it," and, "What profit has not the fable of Christ brought us."

The Protestant revolt against the oppression of the autonomous spirit and conscience of the individual man by the centralised church institution had a profound effect on the development of technology and engineering and, particularly, on the so-called 'Industrial Revolution' in the 18th century, since most of the important progress in technology and science was made by the dissenters who opposed the oppressive, large organised institutions, such as the Roman Church and the State. The dissenters had an authentic hero in the German Augustinian monk, Martin Luther (1483-1546), who was professor of theology at the newly established university in Wittenberg, and who denounced as fraudulent the late mediæval notion that good works prescribed by the Church regulations can save a man's soul. He particularly condemned the selling of indulgences by the Roman Church to people ostensibly to gain merit points for the individual towards his salvation and the remission of punishment for his sins. The Church in Rome had virtually made a 'protection racket' out of selling people privileges to sin. The legal experts of the Church toiled long hours to find new activities of the lay people for the Roman Church to forbid, which the Church could then make legal and right for a price. The Catholic Church, in order to make money for the building of St. Peter's Basilica in Rome, developed a growing market in absolutions, dispensations, and indulgences supplemented by benefices and papal bulls. Through such mercenary and unprincipled methods, the Roman Church had acquired a monopoly for selling in their sacraments salvation to men in exchange for money. A German Dominican cleric Johann Tetzel, a Papal travelling salesman for peddling salvation to common people, sloganeered in 1515: "As soon as the coin in the coffer rings, the soul from purgatory springs." The sale of indulgences became a big traffick, a sort of 16th century bingo. It was a lucrative racket. Luther, a man of powerful emotions and a strong sense of guilt, desperately sought for an assurance of salvation since without it his life seemed to be worthless to him. In 1505 he took his vows as an Augustinian monk, but the austerity and self-discipline of monastic life did little to quell his sense of guilt. The general corruption of the Popes and the widespread abuses practiced by the Catholic Church seemed to make a mockery out of the Church's claim to be the guardian of truth and the means of salvation. When in 1516 Desiderius

Erasmus (c.1466-1536) of Rotterdam published the original Greek text of the New Testament together with an accurate Latin translation it showed how much this apostolic original varied from the official Catholic Church version, The ***Vulgate***, the 4th century Latin translation of the New Testament by St. Jerome (c.340-419). It also demonstrated clearly how far the Roman Church had strayed in its aims and practices from those of the apostolic age. Even after Luther had devoted himself to extreme ascetism as an Augustinian monk, he still found no spiritual assurance that he was worthy of salvation. In 1515 after reading in Apostle Paul's <Epistle> the phrase: "The just shall live in faith," did he suddenly realise what it meant: man may be saved by faith, and by faith alone. This realisation brought him to the conviction that the 'good works' of the Church, such as fastings, pilgrimages, and even sacraments were unnecessary and meaningless, and that no man was dependent on the services of the Pope or the priests for his salvation. Neither through 'good graces' nor through penance could men obtain forgiveness for their sins. Luther believed that only faith and not works of any human merit, can bring salvation to man. Under the influence of rationalistic humanism of the Middle Ages, the Roman Church had taught ever since that salvation of a person was possible by means of good works, the efficacy of the sacrament, and faith. In the opinion of Luther, no man can perform the sacraments, for this is, as he asseverated, God's work. In the opinion of Luther, man can only be saved if he as an individual accepts God's grace through his own faith in God, because in Luther's view, there can be no middleman to bring salvation to any person. He thought that every man is his own minister and that his salvation depends upon the spiritual will of the individual man as well as on the grace of God. Luther's new ideal of piety was a Christian man with a free conscience by virtue of his faith. In this particular spiritual context, the popular Protestant revolt was a revolt of the independent autonomous man against the institutionalised heteronomous man, and a struggle of the individual against the oppressive central institution which denied the individual man his God-given right to control, and to attend to his own spiritual and secular life. The watchword of the Protestant Reformation was 'private judgement', a viewpoint which Luther had learnt from the example of Jesus of Nazareth, and through his personal example he encouraged others to do likewise. His views on faith and reason had been also influenced by the writings of the mediæval Franciscan friar William of Ockham (c.1285-1349).

Since Luther felt obligated to warn people not to put their trust in the indulgences, he prepared 95 propositions against indulgences in 1517 and posted them on the door of the church according to the academic practice of the time in declaring his willingness to defend his theses. Luther's intention was to make Tetzel stop this mercenary religious fraud: "I'll knock a hole in Tetzel's drum." To Luther's great amazement, for he was an unintentional social revolutionary, his theses carried great conviction among the German people and consequently, the sale of indulgences declined dramatically thereby drastically reducing the extra income of the Roman Church which, understandably, alarmed the Church authorities. Luther was called to Worms in 1521 to stand trial for his views before the Diet of the Holy Empire, where he had to face the hostile dignitaries of the Roman Church and the Holy Roman Empire. Luther resolutely refused to recant by declaring: "Here I stand, I can do no other." A few days after his trial, he was declared an excommunicated heretic to be burnt at the stake, a fate suffered about a century earlier by the Czech priest Jan Hus (c.1396-1415) (in English, John Huss) whose execution had led to the so-called Hussite Wars lasting from 1415 to 1436.

Luther had the courage of his convictions and his unyielding stand on the truth of Biblical faith in the face of his powerful enemies was heroic. Before leaving for Worms, Luther had written a series of pamphlets upon his beliefs, which were surprisingly influential among the German people and became immediately popular 'bestsellers'. Luther's comment on this unexpected success was: "Print is the best of God's inventions." His pamphlet < The Address to the Christian Nobility of the German Nation on the Improvement of the Christian Estate > was a soul-stirring appeal to German patriotism against the tyranny of the Church in Rome. Another pamphlet, < The Liberty of a Christian Man >, explained in a popular way the practical meaning of Luther's doctrine. These 2 pamphlets were written in powerful and effective German language, which reached a wide audience in Germany, for Luther was a masterful expositor of German, as well as of Latin prose. He also wrote a pamphlet in Latin entitled < The Babylonian Captivity of the Church >, which was a scholarly exposition of his views addressed to the learned audience. Luther's appeal received wide support from the urban middle class and the nobles which ultimately led to the success of Luther's views. By 1524 more than 300,000 copies of Luther's writings were on the market, and the use of cartoons in many of these publications brought Luther's basic arguments in this important religious conflict to the attention of the illiterate members of the European society. Political songs, catchphrases and slogans appeared and became very popular during this turbulent period. The defenders and dignitaries of the Catholic Church in Rome were fighting back by slandering Luther as the 'great heretic': ". . . a wild boor who has invaded the Lord's vineyards. A man so vile that he must have been spawned by the devil."

After his condemnation by the Roman Church, Luther was protected by Elector Frederick the Wise of Saxony (1463-1525) who had provided Luther with safe conduct to Diet, and who kept Luther safe in the castle of Wartburg where Luther used his exile to translate the New Testament into German language. The Old Testament he translated later, in 1532. Since Luther was a superb master of German tongue, his German Bible and his many hymns were as influential in the formation of the literary standard of the vernacular German language as ***Divina Commedia*** of Dante Alighieri (1265-1321) had been to the literary standard of the vernacular Italian language. Whilst Luther was translating the New Testament into German, his followers were establishing new churches relying upon Luther's evangelicalism. Luther was finally allowed to return to Wittenberg in 1522 to join his followers, after which more and more communities turned to Lutheranism, until a Diet held in 1529 forbade any further spread of Lutheranism upon which a group of German princes professing Lutheran religious doctrines lodged a formal protest at the Diet of Spires in 1529, thereby earning for themselves the name 'Protestants'. Subsequently, the entire religious movement set into motion by Luther became known as the Protestant Reformation which had become a major social, economic, and intellectual 'revolution' in Europe. Luther through his courageous attack on the primary authority of the Mediæval Age, the Roman Church, became the Great Reformer since by his unyielding heroic stand against a mighty central power he set loose a spirit of questioning and personal freedom among the European people and, thereby, he profoundly shaped the religious and cultural life of the Western world. After the Reformation had succeeded in northern Europe, and the Protestant churches became established in place of the Roman Church, the institutionalised Protestant churches gradually began to act rather like the Roman Church they had replaced: they became quite authoritarian. By that time, the princes had taken over the leadership of the Protestant movement and in many instances quite serious, even overwhelming mistakes were made when they did not act in accordance with the Bible as the guide in all matters of everyday life, something the Protestant Reformers had promised to the people. It definitely was not a 'golden age'. Luther himself passed a grievously unbalanced judgement concerning the Peasant Wars when he sided with the princes against the rebellious peasants, and said in an angry outburst: "Kill them, strangle them, ... strike, throttle, stab, secretly or openly." In Renaissance period people were wont of using extravagant language, and Luther, a man prone to violent emotions and temperamental outbursts, was no exception to this popular linguistic habit. The Reformation had spawned its own kind of radicals such as the Anabaptists, and some of the leaders of the Peasant Revolt of 1524-1525 went far beyond Luther by declaring that all men are equal in every respect, and that an unlettered man informed by an 'inner light' had as much access to God's truth and wisdom as had a priest or a man of learning. They claimed that all men had equal access to knowledge through divine inspiration, and in technical matters through spiritual intuition and experience acquired by craftsmen. These Protestant radicals thought that ordinary people with no theological training and learning whatsoever could take the reform of the Church and the State itself into their own hands. All this appalled Luther, a man of learning who valued scholarship, as an unconscionable distorsion of the truth and in his anger he severely condemned, too one-sidedly it appears now, the Peasant Revolt. Luther himself had only emphasised that every calling was of God, and that a farmer or a miner who tried to follow the teachings of the Bible in doing "his work faithfully ... is equal to the priest in God's sight. Each man, peasant or cleric, who helps his fellow man in Christian charity is equally regarded by God's standard." Therefore, according to Luther, all vocations can be equally worthy, which represented the doctrine of priesthood of all believers first expressed by the mediæval forerunner of the Reformation, John Wycliff (c.1320-1384), an English Franciscan friar and professor of theology and philosophy at Oxford, who was a champion of the people against the abuses of the Roman Church for which he had been condemned a heretic in 1380, and again in 1382. Wycliff was responsible for the first literal translation of the Latin Vulgate Bible into vernacular English tongue, a task finished by his followers. Wycliff's work and his belief that the source of final authority is the Bible and that salvation comes only through Jesus Christ, were further elaborated by Jan Hus, a professor at the Charles University in Prague. These basic religious views as pronounced by Hus had profoundly influenced Luther, and they became the basic ideals of the Reformation. Luther stressed the necessity of the clergy to know Greek and Hebrew languages so that they could interpret accurately the scriptures to the people, but he pointed out that this learnedness did not mean that they were nearer to God than the ordinary craftsmen or labourers. Luther's notion that an individual's ordinary daily work could be pleasing to God had considerable similarity with the 'work ethic' of the mediæval Cistercian monks which had been vigorously stressed by the leaders of the Cistercian order, particularly by St. Bernard of Clairvaux (1098-1153) whose theology had a direct influence upon Luther. The sense of work being a worthy vocation grew out of the profound Christian desire to help one's fellow men. Luther virtually despised the socially insulated life led by the monks in his time, but he did recognise that if the monastic life were led in the true spirit of St. Bernard, it could be of great value. Luther venerated the person of St. Bernard of Clairvaux who, temperamentally, had been quite similar to Luther.

The leadership of the Protestant movement was taken over by the Lutheran princes, who made the Lutheran Church into a State church. As could be expected, the Lutheran Church as an arm of the State tended to persecute rather mercilessly the more extreme Protestant sects such as the Anabaptists, thereby almost matching the malpractices of the Roman Church. Fortunately for the Protestants, the separation of law, sociology and science from the Church in accordance with Luther's view of this world as the Kingdom of the Devil, allowed a steady advance of intellectual ideas by virtue of being outside the Church's direct concern and control. Thus Luther's Reformation, and particularly Calvinism and Anabaptism, had considerable influence upon the growth of technology and science. Surprisingly, the ideas promoted by the Anabaptists which maintained that each individual man who accepts nothing on authority must seek the truth for himself, that each person is capable of divine inspiration, and that God is known through His works in nature, were eminently conducive to the growth of science and the development of technology.

The Roman Church had taught that salvation of man was possible by virtue of his faith, his good works, and particularly by the efficacy of the sacrament administered by the Roman Church, all in the context of the rationalistic humanism which was born in the Late Mediæval Age. In the romantic Renaissance humanism the emancipation of man meant to many proud Renaissance men the freedom to indulge in all the available vices. Luther and the Protestants rejected this attitude in the face of what they saw happening in Italy and in the Roman Church itself and, therefore, they put their reliance on faith alone because they believed as Apostle Paul had declared, that only faith justifies a Christian believer. The mediæval theologian and natural philosopher ***Albertus Magnus*** (1206-1289) had thought the human will and reason to be free, unless the human will yields to sin; but Luther denied that it was possible for man to choose deliberately and freely between good and evil because in his opinion man's will is held in bondage by his emotions. Neither did he believe that man's intellectual and rational faculties alone can provide him with his emancipation. Luther thought, quite correctly it seems, that reason might be helpful if used properly, but it was also a snare – the 'Devil's harlot.' He was led to this conclusion by observing the excessive sensualism, immoral recklessness, and intellectual corruption that had surfaced and overtaken the Renaissance society in Italy, a decadent condition he had observed during his pilgrimage to Rome in 1510 that cried out for correction. It appeared to Luther that an aura of total depravity had descended on the Renaissance society, and particularly on the Renaissance Roman Church. Many prominent Renaissance men, and even some of the high officials of the Roman Church, had become highly civilised men who were able to employ refinements in their cruelty and elegance in their depravity, all of which they rationalised and justified by specious arguments based upon the idea of emancipation. They asserted that beauty was not a snare, pleasure not a sin, and that a man can enjoy a voluptuous physical life to its fullest by finding pleasure in food, sports, and opposite sex. In judging the sorry consequences of the acts of the Catholic Church, Luther followed the example of Jesus of Nazareth who had taught that the practical effect of a belief is the real test of its soundness. Luther's main effect in his dissent with the Roman Church was to break the stranglehold the central institution had on the life of the individual man as a private person.

Both the Renaissance and the Protestant movements assailed authoritative traditions and made a direct appeal to the individual. Freedom had been introduced both in the north by the Reformation and in the south by the Renaissance, but in the south it went to licence, whereas in the north it did not. In the south it seemed that freedom undefined and without transcendent limits tends to culminate in anguish, or even in slavery leaving humanity naked, beautiful, but in chains. The Protestant Reformers were opposed to the Renaissance movement mainly because it was pagan in its aims and rested on the idea of complete autonomy of man. The Reformation, ultimately and indirectly, inspired the secular forces of nationalism, so clearly present in Luther's call: "Let us rouse ourselves, fellow Germans," but in its broader context it also promoted commercialism, capitalism, free-enterprise and the work ethic, and it widened the gulf between the mediæval and the modern society. Luther, himself, had no illusions about the benevolence of the States for he forthrightly declared that "princes are generally the biggest fools and worst knaves on Earth." Luther regarded a government not as a positive good but rather as a necessary evil – necessary because of the individual man's tendency to greed, arrogance and waywardness. Arrogance captivates a man's soul, casts his eyes downwards instead of upwards, and leads him to stagnation rather than to growth for it makes him see only inferiors instead of superiors, behold fools and knaves rather than the pure in spirit. Luther provided another useful example in his own person for the professional person, for throughout his life he examined himself critically which made him despair over his own violent temper, and the thought that he could be wrong caused him pain. He resented the calling of the Protestant movement by his name because he was a genuinely modest and religiously sincere man who did, however, have a volatile temper which profoundly grieved him. Yet, quite importantly, the Protestant Reformation promoted the work ethic of the Protestant man, and thereby inspired the individual man to be productive for his own sake, an outlook which greatly promoted technological development in the Protestant world. The importance of the work ethic was expressed by the Puritans in this descriptive sentence: "Satan finds work for idle hands." In fact, Protestantism rapidly became the ideological midwife for both the nascent entrepreneur, and his associate, the engineer. Calvinism, founded by Jean Cauvin [alias Caulvin] (1509-1564) (in English, John Calvin), a French lawyer who settled in Geneva, Switzerland, in 1536, even more so than Lutheranism, stressed the importance of energetic, empirical and rational conduct of the individual in working for profit as a means of fulfilling God's will. It promoted self-reliance and free-enterprise, and the combining of rationalism with empiricism. Calvin, who was influenced by the thoughts of Augustinus even more than Luther, considered God absolutely sovereign and man completely wicked. In his doctrine man was destined from birth to go to Heaven or to Hell. Calvin, a former lawyer, gave a more precise form to Protestantism in his < Institutes of the Christian Religion > (***Institutio Religionis Christianae***), in which he had assembled his harsh Christian ideas into a consistent system of Protestantism. He became the head of the State in Geneva where he set up a theocratic form of government based on his own theology and system of Church organisation. The difference of opinion between Calvin and Luther about the nature of the Lord's Supper caused the splitting of the evangelical Protestant movement into 2 factions: the Lutheran group and the Reformed group. The counter-reform movement of the Catholic Church condemned both the Lutheran doctrine of justification by faith and the Calvinist doctrine of predestination.

From 1526 until his death in 1546, Luther was plagued with serious doubts when he agonised over the question whether or not he had always taken the right course of action. Luther, an extremely conscientious and emotional person, was thoroughly shaken by these doubts and spiritual despair which he himself could not answer, so much so that he could not sleep well in the last 20 years of his life.

The campaign of the Roman Church in this conflict represented an organised spiritual warfare conducted against the private person and his autonomous conscience and God-given individual rights. This fundamental struggle between the individual and the institution is still going on unabated today for it is an eternal conflict, only the external form of this struggle changes but not its fundamental nature.

The revolting spirit of the dissenter, such as that of Luther, has animated many scientists and engineers throughout the history of Europe, for a man with a different viewpoint must necessarily disagree with his fellow men and this situation automatically catapults him into the position of a dissenter, and a dissenter must take a moral stand like Luther because dissent is a mark of freedom of a thinking person just as originality is the mark of an independent mind. Therefore, a dissenter is a moral intransigent, like Luther, who takes his moral stand against all odds. An inventor is a man who is dissatisfied with what is acceptable to his fellow men, and for this reason he is a dissenter of a particular kind.

The idea of invention as a unique individual act of creation soon became the very symbol of technological progress to the Renaissance man. One of the most important of such technological inventions was the mechanised printing. Certainly one of the greatest historical events to promote the cause of autonomous man was the invention of mechanised printing of books. It emancipated the individual man from his intellectual dependence on institutions and other men and, moreover, it made learning an individual pursuit, for the availability of printed books gave men freedom to study whatever they wanted and whenever they felt like it. The technology of mechanised printing as an industrial process came about at the end of the Mediæval Age, and in the beginning of the Renaissance era. It was an all-important milestone in the intellectual history of man. Printing as such was not entirely new since by A.D.688, block printing had first been developed in China, and in A.D.1045, a movable type made of baked clay had been invented by a Chinese craftsman, Pi Sheng. By the 15th century, cast metal type was already in use in Korea. However, textiles had been printed with woodcuts and clay stamps as early as in the Hellenistic period in Alexandria, and printing of religious pictures and monograms with wood-blocks had been a common practice in the 11th century Europe.

Mechanised printing with movable and interchangeable type was independently invented in Europe by two men, Laurenz Janszoon Coster of Haarlem, Holland, in the1430's, and by Johann Gensfleisch (c.1397-1468), usually called Gutenberg after the Gutenberg Manor owned by his mother, near Mainz, Germany, in the1440's. Gutenberg was a goldsmith and a metallurgist, and his metallurgical expertise was important in the development of mechanised type. Gutenberg found an ingenious practical solution for the mass-production of movable type as interchangeable, standardised parts in an inchoate industrial mass-production. He produced movable type of great precision by employing sliding forms. He cast the type from an alloy that melted at low temperature and solidified without distortion. He built a screw press to print pages, and his invention of printer's ink made from lamp black and linseed oil, the use of which lasted until the 19th century, were his other strokes of practical genius. Coster had cast his type in sand with wooden manually engraved originals as patterns, but it was a procedure which could not be developed into a practical method of mass-production. Moreover, there is no documentary evidence that Coster ever printed a single book by means of his method.

It took Gutenberg more than 20 years to develop his concept of mechanical printing. Finally, he was ready to build his printing presses and tools from 1450 to 1454, when he began to print the Latin Bible in which each page had double columns and 42 lines of type. He printed 300 copies of the so-called 'Gutenberg Bible' each one of which had 1,282 pages. The Gutenberg Bible was the first printed book, and it is still considered the most beautiful tome ever produced which has remained the most valued book in the world. Gutenberg had to borrow money twice from the goldsmith Johann Fust in Mainz to finance the building of his printing presses and tools in his printing shop. When he was unable to pay back the loan in time, he was sued by Fust. Gutenberg lost the lawsuit, and was forced by the court to turn over his printing presses, tools and printed products to Fust as compensation for his debt. Fust as the new proprietor printed and published the Bible with the help of his son-in-law and printer Peter Schöffer, both of whom had been associated with Gutenberg. Gutenberg never did reap any financial benefits from his revolutionary invention, and had to spend the rest of his life as an employed printer.

By 1454, printed books were produced by the mechanised process and, thenceforth reproduction of books became a mere mechanical operation. The appearance of mechanically printed books ended the time when information and learning, particularly for engineers and craftsmen, were difficult to obtain and the dissemination of knowledge was tortuous and slow. Moreover, the invention of the mechanised printing process broke the monopolistic stranglehold the institution had on the individual man as far as the life of man's mind was concerned, since learning now became an individual pursuit of knowledge obtainable from inexpensive textbooks which no longer depended on memorising. Most of the early printers were scholars genuinely interested in the dissemination of knowledge.

The first books printed were the Latin Bible, and the Greek and the Latin classics, but soon vernacular Bibles and other books on technology, mathematics, alchemy and medicine were produced in large quantities. One of the first non-religious books to appear in print was < Æsop's Fables> printed in England by the scholarly William Caxton (c. 1422-1491) who is famous for instituting the first lawsuit against the Crown for the freedom of the press. All of a sudden, the knowledge of a few could become the intellectual possession of the many who could read. Since the advent of the printed works has had a most profound influence on the cultural life of man till this very day, Gutenberg accomplished one of the most important technological feats of man.

Before the advent of the mechanised printing press, very little written instruction was available for the guidance of craftsmen because there were few manuscripts on crafts, and these manuscripts being handwritten by monks and professional scribes made them expensive and, therefore, put them beyond the reach of the lay-craftsman. Written information on the data and practice of the crafts became generally available with the first wave of printed technical handbooks in the late 15th and the early 16th century:

L.B. Alberti's ***De re aedificatoria*** (on building) (1485); Bayfius' ***De re navali*** (on naval technology) (1536); V. Biringuccio's ***De la pirotechnica*** (on metallurgy) (1540); N. Tartaglia's ***Questi et inventioni diverse*** (on artillery) (1546); G. Agricola's ***De re metallica*** (on mining) (1556); J. Besson's ***Theatrum instrument et machinarium*** (on instruments and machines) (1569); A. Palladio's ***Quatro libri dell' architectura*** (on building) (1570); L. Ercker's ***Beschreibung allerfurnemsten mineralischen Ertzt-und Berckwercksarten*** (on ores and mining) (1574); Guidobaldos's ***Mechanicorum*** (on theoretical mechanics) (1577); A. Ramelli's ***Le diverse et artificiose machine*** (on machines) (1588); F. Veranzio's ***Machinae novae*** (on machines) (1595); Lorini's ***Della fortificationi*** (on fortifications) (1597); V. Zonca's ***Nova teatro di machine et edificii*** (on machines) (1607); G.E. von Lohneiss' ***Bericht von Bergwerk, ...*** (on chemical technology and mining) (1617); G. Branca's ***Le macchine*** (on machines) (1629); and ***Treviso arithmetic*** (on arithmetic) (1478) by an anonymous author printed in an Italian town Treviso was the first printed book on arithmetic.

Early books on technology were called 'art' books, whereas books on painting, sculpture and so forth were called 'fine art' books. In the Renaissance time the chief engineer of a mine was called 'art master'. The term 'technology ' was first used in 1615 and came into general use only in the early 19th century.

In 1498 a scholar complained to the famous Italian printer who was also a scholar like most of the early printers, Aldo Manuzio known by his Latin name ***Aldus Manutius*** (1449-1515), that he could have bought 10 of the finest Latin manuscripts for the price of the 5 volume folio edition of Aristotle's works printed by Aldo Manuzio. This complaint caused Manuzio to begin printing large numbers of cheap pocket-sized octavo editions of classical books, where octavo indicated a size one-eighth of the folio page, by exploiting the principal virtue of printing: spreading the production costs over a large number of copies of a book. He invented a new type, called 'italic', which made possible the reduction of the book size so drastically that people could carry these portable books about in their pockets. This was the very first series in which important books were 'reprinted', a method of publishing still used today in various pocketbook editions.

Mechanical printing progressed so rapidly that by 1500 there existed up to 9 million printed copies of some 38,000 different books in circulation, more books than all the books produced before the existence of the mechanical printing press. The invention of the mechanised printing process was one of the most revolutionary creations of the late Mediæval Age and the early Renaissance era and it still retains its prominence in the cultural life of man. The invention of the printing press demonstrated that the solution in practice, which was achieved by Gutenberg over 20 years, was more difficult and required more ingenuity than the solution in principle which might have been a momentary inspiration. Therefore, Gutenberg's achievement was a truly magnificent, epoch-making technological accomplishment that created an astounding progress of Western civilisation.

Printing industry spread rapidly to important commercial cities in Europe: from Mainz to Cologne (1464), Basel (1466), Rome (1467) Venice (1469); Paris, Nuremberg and Utrecht (1470); Milan, Naples and Florence (1471), Augsburg (1472); Lyons, Valencia and Budapest (1473); Cracow and Bruges (1474); Lübeck and Breslau (1475); Westminster and Rostock (1476); Geneva, Palermo and Messina (1478), London (1480); Antwerp and Leipzig (1481), and Stockholm (1483). By the close of the 15th century there already existed the following number of printing presses by countries: Italy– 73, Germany– 51, France– 39, Spain– 25, Low Countries– 15, and Switzerland– 8.

Henry the Navigator and First Technological School:

A prince of Portugal, Dom Henrique o Navegador, popularly known as Henry the Navigator, (1394-1460), the third son of King John I and a great-grandson of King Edward III of England, was a noted patron of navigators and explorers, and thereby, a herald of the Renaissance. He fought in the battle at Ceuta in 1415, and was knighted for heroism. He resided at Sagres, near Cape St. Vincent, where he established an observatory and the first technological school in Europe, a school of navigators which was of central importance to the science of navigation and to the improvements in the engineering art of shipbuilding. He assembled all the available instruments used as aids in navigation at his school, and instructed his mariners in their use, which had a decisive influence on the development of naval exploration. Henry's main intention seems to have been to carry the Christian message to African natives and to find and join forces with the mythical Christian ruler Prester John who was supposed to rule in the African interior. His African explorations were, therefore, a byproduct of a new religious crusade by means of which he hoped to find out the territorial limits of the Muslim power on the African continent, and to locate new trade routes to the Spice Islands of the Orient. His ultimate aim was to circumnavigate Africa as the Carthaginian navigator Hanno had claimed to have done about 530 B.C.. Although, during Henry's lifetime, his ships had only reached Dakar and little political success had been achieved against the Moors, he did make Renaissance the golden age of geographic discovery since by the year 1600 the known surface of the Earth had been nearly doubled.

The increase in economic wellbeing of Europe, the discovery of the New World, and the development of powerful national monarchies provided an economic and political base for further technological expansion, and also for a widening of the horizons of mankind. By turning away from the intense spiritual emphasis of mediæval times and by renewing the secular approach to the world which had characterised the classical antiquity, the Renaissance produced in the Western man a state of mind which was increasingly receptive to further technological development.

Renaissance Engineering

The Renaissance man responsible for the first weakening of the hold of Gothic style on European building art was Filippo Brunelleschi (1377-1446), a goldsmith, architect, engineer, sculptor, geometer and, therefore, an unmistakable Renaissance man, in his design of the Hospital of the Innocents for the Medici family in Florence, Italy in 1421. Brunelleschi cultivated his theoretical and mathematical interests by collaborating with the mathematician and astronomer Paolo Dal Pozzo Toscanelli (1397-1482). He also developed a completely novel vaulted structure, the ancient corbelled structural system in a brilliant new form, in his octagonal, ribbed, and ogival double-shell masonry dome in which meridional ribs were supported by a series of parallel octagonal rings each a little smaller than the one below it, a dome which required no scaffolding at all in its construction, for the Cathedral of Santa Maria de Fiore built in Florence from 1420 to 1436. This cathedral had already been under construction for over a century. The average base diameter of this 25,000-ton dome, which in effect is the ancient corbelled system reappearing in a new and ingenious form, is 143 feet (43.59 m) and its height is 105 feet (32.00 m). The base of this huge dome lies 200 feet (60.96 m) above the floor of the cathedral. Brunelleschi built this outstanding structure in Italian Gothic style which united the Roman and the Gothic construction, and it is still the largest masonry dome in existence. In 1421, he devised and built his derrick to help in the construction of the great dome of the cathedral in Florence. Brunelleschi was the first engineer who clearly and explicitly recognised the existence of the circumferential tension in dome structures, and he proposed to tie a chain round the base of his octagonal dome to resist the circumferential tension. Against his better judgement, Brunelleschi was assigned an assistant, the sculptor-artist Lorenzo Ghiberti (1378-1455), who knew little about engineering and failed to design an adequate tension chain when Brunelleschi faked illness. After Ghiberti's failure, Brunelleschi designed his own octagonal tension ring made of oaken timber baulks bolted together, but his tension ring was also far too weak to provide the necessary circumferential tension. Fortunately, the double-shelled dome was strong enough by itself to withstand the circumferential tension without any assistance from the tension ring. Brunelleschi finished the construction of the dome in 1436, but the lantern weighing 600-tons was built after his death. The final finishing touches to the dome were given only in 1888. On account of the majestic dome which lends the Cathedral of Santa Maria del Fiore its unique appearance, this cathedral is now known as the ***Duomo*** [Dome]. Brunelleschi designed and built a number of other buildings, the most famous of which is the huge Pitti Palace for the Medici family.

In 1410, Brunelleschi made the first portable spring-driven clock which is the earliest domestic clock known.

In 1421 Brunelleschi obtained the first known patent for his invention of a canal boat equipped with a crane of his own design which he used to haul marble along the Arno river from Pisa. His patent, which was granted in the Republic of Florence, gave the inventor inclusive monopoly rights for 3 years to use this boat on the river. Unfortunately, Brunelleschi was unable to capitalise on this invention. In 1474, long after his death, the first official patent law was established in the Republic of Venice.

In the siege of the city Lucca by the Florentine army in 1430, Brunelleschi cut a canal to divert the Serchio river and to flood the city. Unfortunately, it also prevented the Florentine army from storming the city.

Brunelleschi discovered that realism in painting leads to mathematics and in his drive to make his paintings realistic, he developed the perspective method in geometry. The first principles of perspective are usually credited to Brunelleschi by the art historian Georgio Vasari (1511-1574), but it is difficult to know from Vasari's account precisely what were the principles of perspective discovered by Brunelleschi. It is known that he was able to paint a perspective view of the Palace, the Piazza, and the Loggia del Signoro with all the buildings around the Square. He also invented a small optical instrument containing a panel with a painted view of Florence which by means of mirrors gave an impression of a relief.

If the Renaissance age in its usual characterisation is the rebirth of ancient classical spirit and architectural form, then the work of Brunelleschi and his generation hardly satisfied this criterion though it might have been their rough intention. The first architect-engineer who laid the real foundation for Renaissance classicism in building was Alberti.

Already Marcus Vitruvius Pollio, a Roman engineer active about 30 B.C., demonstrated his familiarity with some of the principles of perspective: "Perspective is the method of sketching the front with the sides withdrawing into the background, the lines all meeting at the center of the circle." The Romans did not know 'one-point, central perspective' although they used a sort of perspective in the wall-paintings in Pompeii. The perspective to the ancient Greeks had been a new way of depicting space in a plane. The mathematical theory of perspective was developed further by a young friend of Brunelleschi at the papal court in Florence, Leon Battista Alberti (1404-1472), who was an artist, sculptor, philosopher, linguist of both the classical languages and vernacular Italian, musician, poet, architect, surveyor, cartographer, engineer, mathematician, and athlete and, therefore, the quintessential universal man (***uomo universale***). Further refinements in the theory of perspective were made by Paolo Uccelli (1397-1475) who is known to have written a book on perspective which is no longer extant, by Piero della Francesca (1416-1492), by Leonardo da Vinci (1452-1519) who was the first to combine the geometry of linear perspective with aerial perspective which considers shadows, colours, albedo and other subtle matters of art, and by Albrecht Dürer (1471-1528). Della Francesca, who was concerned with stereometry, published a fairly complete set of principles of perspective between 1470 and 1490 in his memoir < On Painted Perspective > (***De prospettiva pingendi***). In this treatise he showed his knowledge of the works of geometers of the past, and demonstrated 2 quite different methods of constructing perspectives: one extended Alberti's ideas of projection, the other apparently was his own method. He introduced the concept of the vanishing-point into perspective. Like Alberti, della Francesca gave theorems which he demonstrated by constructions or arithmetical calculation of ratios. His studies exerted an important influence on the development of geometric construction in painting. He also wrote a book on regular solids in which he solved the difficult problem of finding the volume produced by 2 cylinders intersecting at right angles, a problem which had been solved previously by Archimedes, but this solution had been lost and was only found in 1907. The solution given by della Francesca demonstrated his remarkable ability in geometry.

The Renaissance man was able to introduce the 3rd dimension into his painting by discovering that the section produced by the focussed lines of projection on a glass screen interposed between the viewer and the scene produced the same visual effect as the scene itself. The German artist-engineer-mathematician Albrecht Dürer, who studied geometry at the University of Bologna in Italy, called this section 'perspective', or 'seeing through' a glass screen. Tomasso Guidi known as Masaccio (1401-1428) had been the first painter who consistently tried to use central perspective, and it was he who influenced the painting of della Francesca, Leonardo da Vinci and other Italian painters, and who can be considered the founder of Renaissance painting. Leonardo da Vinci introduced the 'aerial perspective', which consists of the gradual diminution of intensity of colour with distance to compensate for the other eye. Shadings and shadows were also introduced as important aids to compensate for the same shortcoming. Although both Uccelli and della Francesca developed the geometry of perspective to a high level of technical complexity by painting scenes from the most unusual positions to solve the attendant geometric problem of perspective, it was Piero della Francesca who became the best painter-geometer of his time for all his paintings were geometrical to their minutest details.

The German artist, mathematician and engineer Albrecht Dürer, who invented the art of etching as well as typography in artwork, was the best mathematician among the Renaissance painters. Dürer was not only a supreme artist like his contemporary Leonardo da Vinci, but also a very capable, practical and efficient businessman who achieved material success as Leonardo did not. Dürer did not care about a subject unless he had a practical purpose for it, such as writing a book and printing it himself. He wrote and illustrated 3 treatises on mathematics, fortification engineering and human proportion which he produced in his own printing shop. He studied geometric transformations in his first book, < Investigations of Measurement with Compass and Ruler > (***Unterweysung der Messung mit dem Zirckel und Richtscheyt***) published by his own printing shop in ***Nürnberg*** (*Nuremberg*), in 1525, which is the first surviving text on applied mathematics that contained some remarkable novelties. The new complex curves constructed by Dürer were most important since he supplied each geometric construction with a careful geometric proof. He also was the first to make systematic use of orthogonal projections in space. His 2nd book < Some Instruction on Fortification > (***Etliche Underricht zu Befestigung***) (1527) deals with fortification engineering, and his 3rd book < Four Books on Human Proportions > (***Vier Bücher von menschlicher Proportion***) (1528) on human proportions was published posthumously. In graphic art, Dürer produced the best engravings and woodcuts, which he himself printed in his printing shop.

Leon Battista Alberti, 'uomo universale' beyond comparison:

Renaissance men believed that man can reason out the answers to all the important questions of life by beginning only from himself, which represented the basic outlook of humanism: man being a measure of all things. Leon Battista Alberti was an illegitimate son of an important member of a powerful merchant-banking family from Florence. He received an excellent classical education at a gymnasium in Padua, and then began his studies of canon law at the University of Bologna, the most famous and the oldest university in Europe for the study of law. Unfortunately a calamity struck Alberti during his first year at the university when both his father and his uncle, who was his guardian, died and left him penniless because certain members of the Alberti family took advantage of his illegitimate birth and appropriated his legacy. Impoverished, often sick from nervous exhaustion and overwork, Alberti supported himself and his legal studies by his literary work and mathematical studies, and he succeeded in earning his doctorate in canon law in 1428. After his graduation from the university, he became a secretary to the Bishop of Bologna, and travelled to France, Low Countries, and Germany. In 1432, Alberti entered the service of the Papal chancery in Rome which he held until 1464. He also took holy orders at this time after the Pope had issued his bulls to annul the prohibition against illegitimate children receiving holy orders. Alberti, a Renaissance man of supreme humanistic self-confidence, maintained that "to overcome all his weaknesses, a man can do all things if he will ... nothing is too difficult for study and determination to overcome," and he himself made great efforts to live up to his own maxims, for Alberti excelled over an astonishing range of physical and social accomplishments. He not only became the leading theoretician of the Renaissance by laying the foundations of Renaissance classicism in precept and practice, and thereby exercised a powerful influence upon his contemporaries, but also performed important physical experiments. Alberti was one of the foremost organists of his day, a composer, a singer, and a champion in the use of the vernacular Italian instead of Latin, a classical language in which he was also a recognised literary master. He wrote the first grammar of the Italian language; the first study of cryptography containing the first known frequency table of letters and the first known cypher wheel for coding and decoding secret messages; the first treatise on sculpture containing human proportions, and another one on painting, in which he established the theoretical and technical foundations of Renaissance art whilst discussing cultural ideas that were destined to have a lasting influence on European civilisation; a new translation of Ptolemaios' ***Almagest***, the ancient Greek work on astronomy; a treatise on jurisprudence; a treatise on ships and a treatise on lifting weights and diving which resulted from his efforts to raise a Roman galley from the bottom of Lake Nemi at the behest of Cardinal Colonna; a tract on the family; a funeral oration about his dog; works on ethics and moral philosophy, a treatise on music; and many literary works both in Latin and in Italian vernacular.

Alberti maintained that a painting which incorporates and reveals the mathematical structure of nature can even improve upon nature. He taught that art should reflect the structure of the universe, nature being the 'greatest artist'. In this connexion, he discovered the mathematical law of linear perspective. Alberti's investigations showed that form and position on the picture plane were relative rather than absolute factors in the perspective. He wrote all this in a treatise on painting in 1436, entitled < On Painting > (***Della pittura***), the first treatise to treat both the theory and the technique of painting. Alberti was the first to write a treatise on the theory of focussed perspective. He was the theoretical genius of the Renaissance on mathematical perspective, and his treatise which was mathematical also included a work on optics. The painter's problem, in Alberti's opinion, was to find the intersection of the picture plane with the 'pyramid of rays' from the eye to the object. He introduced the imaginary transparent screen and the section produced by the intersection of the projection and the screen. The trace of points on the glass screen he called 'the section'. Thus all objects in the distance were comparable in terms of proportions. Since the painter cannot see through canvas, he needs rules based on mathematical theorems for drawing the section on the picture plane. First, he gave the principle of foreshortening, and then the solution to what he considered was the fundamental problem of perspective which apparently gave great difficulties to painters: how to represent in the picture plane a square network on the ground the sides of which are parallel and perpendicular to the picture plane. In his solution, Alberti gave only the theorems and the geometric construction but did not supply the mathematical proofs which would have been clearly beyond the mathematical ability of his contemporary artists. Alberti also posed the fundamental question: If the eye looks at the same scene from 2 different positions, or if 2 different glass screens are interposed, both of which result in 2 different sections of the same original scene, then what is the mathematical relation between these 2 scenes? This basic question much later became the very source of projective geometry. Alberti gave no more problems on perspective in his treatise although it is quite clear that his knowledge of the perspective was not restricted to the problem solved in his book, for he certainly was able to present perspectives of figures lying above the ground plane. In this treatise, he also emphasised that "man learns by reason and by method, but he masters through practice," a distinction which is important to professional engineers. This treatise of Alberti was the most influential work on painting before Leonardo da Vinci's notes on the same subject in which Leonardo had copied many of Alberti's sentences. Since Alberti himself was not only a painter but also a sculptor, he wrote a mathematically formulated treatment of sculpture entitled < On Sculpture> (***Della statua***) about 1464, the first work in its field in which he devised an important method of mensuration for the sculptor, and gave the first Renaissance canon of proportions.

In 1437, the first Renaissance Pope Nicholas V, who was a former fellow law student of Alberti in Bologna, appointed Alberti his architectural and engineering advisor, and put Alberti in charge of the rebuilding of the St. Peter's Basilica and the Vatican in Rome, as well as constructing a new aqueduct ***Aqua Vergine***. Sometime in 1452, when Alberti was the architectural consultant to Pope Nicholas V, he wrote in elegant Latin the first modern manual on construction entitled < On Building > (***De re ædificatoria***), the source and beginning of which was Vitruvius' ***De Architectura***, and presented it to the Pope. Alberti's engineering manual was widely circulated among the engineers in its manuscript form, and it exerted a decisive influence on the engineering profession. It was posthumously printed in Florence in 1485, and it was the first mechanically printed engineering manual in the history of engineering. It is also the earliest printed treatise on town-planning including a discussion of water supply and sewage system. Alberti's manual gave detailed information on building techniques and materials, and standard specifications as mathematical rules on proportioning of all sorts of structures. Alberti was the first engineer-architect to propound the theory of different kinds of vaults based on the formal geometric features of the structure, for there was no possibility at that time to introduce the theory of mechanics of materials into the study of structures simply because it did not yet exist. He was the greatest Renaissance theoretician of vaulting and building. However, he did use a scientific approach in his study of the properties of building materials. He also suggested in the first discussion of the pound lock, the use of a double set of gates with an in-between basin to overcome the difference in water levels of canals which employed the portcullis type of lock-gates. Alberti tried to reconcile theory, engineering practice, and art in his treatise < Mathematical Diversions > (***Ludi matematici***), which he had written for the guidance of technicians in practical surveying and construction. In most of his works, Alberti made an attempt to apply mathematics to the understanding and control of nature, thereby putting the art of mathematics to the service of practical arts of painting, sculpture and construction. In his engineering treatise, Alberti had successfully transformed the Renaissance engineer from a craftsman of masonry into a white-collar learned professional.

Alberti's design for Palazzo Rucellai about 1446 for a rich Florentine merchant represents the first Renaissance use of a building system: the articulation of a facade by superimposed orders, in which the dimensions of the parts of the orders are interrelated by a module representing half the width of the column. Alberti's pupil, Bernardo Rossellino (1409-1464) executed Alberti's design of the Palazzo Rucellai in its actual construction. Alberti also designed the Tempio Malatestiano, his first building, and the churches San Sebastiano and Sant' Andrea.

In 1450 Alberti laid down the rules for the construction of new churches, the best example of which is his design for the Church of Santa Maria della Carceri in Prato near Florence. It was a centrally planned church in the form of a Greek Cross in which the proportion determined everything as an effect of the perspective. Its construction began in 1485 under the direction of Giuliano da Sangallo, 13 years after the death of Alberti.

He practiced his engineering art like a modern consulting engineer for his engineering and architectural designs were carried out in practice by his pupils and associates. Alberti's influence was enormous, and he founded an informal school of architecture by having his pupils such as Bernardo Rossellino, who built the first modern square at Pienza as the center of the city, carry on his influence.

Alberti was a remarkable athlete and as a high-jumper he was able to leap over a standing man. He as an expert horseman able to tame and ride the wildest horses wrote a well-known treatise on horses.

Alberti, an exemplary Renaissance man of Promethean powers in intellectual, literary, artistic and technological fields, had succeeded in acquiring such a complete command of a wide spectrum of human culture and profound universal learning that his contemporaries claimed him to be 'beyond comparison'. This claim is probably still valid.

Renaissance Engineers

Beginning in 1475, German architect-engineer Arnold of Westphalia (died 1480) dispensed with ribs in cross-vaulted structures, and began to construct prismatic, diamond-shaped, cellular folded-plate structures which obtained their structural rigidity from their geometric configuration. This folded-plate type of ribless vaulting, based on cellular, folding plate forms made of brick became rather popular and spread rapidly throughout the Renaissance world, and assumed in a very short time incredibly striking structural forms. This type of a folded shell structure came completely into its own only in the 20th century when folded-plate structures made from reinforced concrete became possible.

For the first time the craft knowledge of the past, as incorporated in the existing practice, was written down and published in books. However, the authors of these books made few technological innovations themselves. Technology still remained essentially the province of craftsmen who learnt their trade through a long apprenticeship rather than by means of book learning. In some cases the powerful guilds resisted changes in long-established processes, devices and techniques, which tended to hamper technological progress. Therefore, technology continued to be carried on by traditional means and on a relatively small scale.

Military engineering as a branch of engineering was considerably advanced in Renaissance Italy. Cannon was made into an efficient engine of war and the handgun was raised to a potent weapon. The first well-known Italian military engineer was Mariana di Jacomo, called ***Taccola*** ['The Crow'] (1381-1453/1458), of Siena, who was an unlettered contemporary of Brunelleschi. He wrote a well-known manuscript on hydraulic machines and military engineering, in which he described a double-suction pump operated by rod-and-crank method, chain-transmission system, the hoisting and positioning equipment of Brunelleschi in the building of the latter's dome, and a handmill with hanging-weight regulation of movement first given in the Hussite craftsman's manuscript. His military protective devices were similar to that of Konrad Kyeser (1366-1405), and he seems to have been influenced by German military engineers of the Mediæval Age. His work contained practically everything known in military engineering and it possessed certain technological erudition. Taccola's fame as an engineer was considerable, and he was given the ultimate accolade by his contemporaries when they called him the 'Sienese Archimedes'.

Another Italian engineer, Ridolfo Fioravanti [called ***Aristotile***] (c. 1415/1420-1485/1486) of Bologna became famous in Europe because at the beginning of his engineering career he almost specialised in difficult engineering tasks, such as straightening the tower of the Palazzo del Podesta in Bologna. In 1455, he moved a clock-tower weighing 87 tons about 99 feet (15 m) by means of machinery of his own design, a technical feat of a great master which made him famous everywhere in Europe. He was later engaged at the court of Duke Francesco Sforza of Milan, where he together with another Italian engineer, Antonio Francesco Averlino [called ***Il Filarete***](1416-1470) from Florence, built a bridge near Pavia. Later, Fioravanti was in charge of building fortifications and canals about Milan. Subsequently he was employed in the service of the Duke of Mantua, and then in the service of Pope Paul III. In 1467, he entered the service of the Hungarian King Matthias Corvin for whom he built a bridge over the Danube river. In 1475, he entered the service of the Russian Grand-Duke Ivan III in Moscow, where he built a cathedral in the Kremlin and other churches, poured cannons, founded bells, and directed the mint. In his activity as a military engineer, he built a pontoon bridge of ships in a military campaign against the Great-Novgorod. Another talented Italian engineer, Pietro Antonio Salario of Milan, also went to Russia together with Fioravanti and entered the service of the Grand Duke. Fioravanti was nicknamed ***Aristotile*** (Aristotle) because he had an encyclopædic mind: he was an architect, engineer, founder, metallurgist, and an expert in hydraulics, in fortifications and in pyrotechnics – a true Renaissance man whose reputation was enormous. In 1485, he fell into disfavour with the Russian Grand-Duke because of his courageous defence of a German physician who had been unfairly accused of malfeasance, but unfortunately he died soon afterwards. Fioravanti served as an important link between his generation of engineers and the engineers of the next generation.

Il Filarete from Florence, a younger contemporary of Alberti, was much influenced by the latter. He worked in Rome and at the court of Sforza in Milan where he collaborated with Fioravanti. He wrote a treatise on architecture and engineering entitled <Treatise on Architecture> (***Trattado dell'architettura***) in 1464, dedicated to Sforza, which was never published but it did exert considerable influence among engineers because it was widely circulated as a manuscript, and was so highly regarded that the Hungarian King Matthias Corvin had it even translated into Latin. His ideal polygonal city, Sforzinda, was a purely logical arrangement of structures without regard to the site or to the mediæval antecedents. He had borrowed freely from Alberti, but he proved himself to be more of an engineer than a theoretician. He discussed not only important buildings, citadels, cathedrals, palaces, hospitals, churches, housing, public baths, warehouses, but also seaports, bridges, water reservoirs, water channels, and even tunnels.

The versatile military engineer and artist, Francesco di Giorgio Martini (1436-1502) of Siena, who in the service of Duke Federico of Urbino wrote his great engineering work < Treatise on Architecture > (***Trattato dell'architettura***) from 1495 to 1501, in which he mainly followed Taccola's ideas in dealing with civil and military construction, and military defence and attack methods based on the effects of new firearms and explosives. Di Giorgio Martini is considered the inventor of the polygonal [also known as 'star-shaped'] and the rhomboidal fortifications which have irregular curtain walls without bastions and some external batter, and which proved to be much more effective against artillery bombardment than were the mediæval castles with their unbattered walls.

He thought that the security of a fortress depended more on its artifice than its shape or wall thickness. The fortresses built by di Giorgio Martini no longer were similar to the mediæval fortresses despite the fact that they contained some mediæval structural elements. He designed jet-operated compound crank-and-connecting rod mechanisms in military machines which were used in assaults on fortresses. In civil engineering he constructed dykes, water supplies for cities, and advised foreign courts and towns on all sorts of technical problems.

The Turkish army under the Ottoman Sultan Suleiman the Lawgiver ('the Magnificent') had failed in a month-long siege to take Vienna in 1529, mostly because the city which was enclosed by a 6 foot (1.82 m) thick defensive wall, had been fortified against cannon fire with thick earthen embankments constructed in a hurry by military engineers under the direction of the 70-year old German general Nicolas Graf von Salm, a cool professional soldier who was put personally in charge of the defence of Vienna by Duke Frederick, the top commander appointed by Charles V, Emperor of Germany and King of Spain. Graf von Salm had about 1,000 well-trained formidable German mercenary pikemen, and 700 Spaniards who were armed with new wheel-lock muskets which fired faster than the old Turkish matchlocks. Graf von Salm took charge of a garrison of 23,000 infantry and 2,000 mounted cuirassiers, and a total of 75 cannons compared to the 300 light field cannons of the Turkish army. Despite the numerous mine shafts dug by the Turks under the city wall, von Salm's brilliant countermeasures and battle tactics succeeded to beat back the Turkish army and defeat the Sultan's elite warrior slaves, the 'janissaries', despite their 10 times numerical superiority. The Ottoman Turks lost about 25,000 men in this disastrous siege of Vienna, several times higher than the losses of the defenders of the city. The defeat at Vienna marked the beginning of the decline of Ottoman Empire, although in 1683 the Ottoman Turks still dared to stage another disastrous siege of Vienna but by that time they were no longer a Muslim menace to Christian Europe. The serious threat of Muslim Turks to Christian Europe had been effectively eliminated by the disastrous defeat suffered by the Turkish fleet in the sea battle at Lepanto in 1571.

The method of defence of the city of Vienna served as an inspiration to the Italian military engineer Michele San Michele when from 1529 to 1548 he developed new type of bastions at Verona which were very effective in resisting artillery bombardments. This new type of fortress had sloping, bastioned front walls in stone, low ground-hugging profile, huge earthen embankments and ditches, and parapets tightly-packed with earth, all of which was well exemplified in his fortress at Turin built in 1538.

Leonardo da Vinci, 'uomo universale':

Another well-known universal man of the Renaissance was Leonardo da Vinci (1452-1519), who unfortunately published nothing in his lifetime. Although he was not a learned man like Alberti, he had a fertile imagination. In comparison with Alberti, Leonardo had some obvious shortcomings. He spoke a lower middle-class Florentine vernacular and acquired an adequate knowledge of Latin only late in life. His sentences were frequently ungrammatical, incomplete, and literally incoherent. Leonardo da Vinci despised the university scholars who took their entire learning from books and were dogmatic about their knowledge. He condemned men of book-learning who in his opinion strutted about puffed up and pompous, whilst adorned with the labours of others which they merely repeated, as reciters and trumpeters of other people's learning. Since he himself lacked formal schooling, Leonardo was snubbed by the men of learning and their insults made him indignant. He took it upon himself to study everything firsthand and, therefore, he undertook exhaustive studies of plants, animals, the human body, light, rocks, mechanics, engineering and countless other subjects. He believed in the maxims: "Theory is the general, experiments are the soldiers," and, "Theory without practice is powerless." Unfortunately, he lacked a scientific methodology in all his scientific investigation, and he knew little mathematics and virtually nothing of mathematical proof. For instance, he could not solve correctly a linear algebraic equation, although he praised the role of mathematics in science. Leonardo da Vinci was a true Renaissance man who was not only a painter and sculptor but also a botanist, zoologist, anatomist, geologist, musician, architect, and engineer.

His copious notes dealt with: the concept of force; composition of forces by statical moment, force parallelogram; trusses and structures; inclined planes; laws of friction (he was the first to state the laws of friction and propose specific experiments to prove their validity). In his notebooks he drew up an incredible variety of production machines and mechanical devices which provide the most extensive catalogue of machines of the period. He described an experiment to determine the thrust of an arch, and an analysis for the breaking strength of an arch under a discrete load at the crown. He analysed pulleys and levers by the method of virtual work, and had some very primitive notions on the principle of least action. He made the first known experiments on the ultimate strength of wires, columns and beams, and he might have established the formula for the maximum load on the column as being proportional to d^3/L^3, where d is the depth of the cross-section, and L the length of the column. Leonardo da Vinci was the first to describe the qualitative behaviour of elastic beams in bending by observing that in the bending of a beam of rectangular cross-section the longitudinal fibres on the concave side contract and on the convex side extend, thus leaving the fibres in mid-section, the so-called 'neutral fibres' unchanged in length. He noted that the extensions and contractions of the longitudinal fibres of the beam varied linearly from the 'neutral axis'. He also observed that the rectangular cross-section of the elastic beam becomes trapezoidal after bending: narrower at the extended fibres, and wider at the contracted fibres of the beam. Dutch teacher and engineer Isaac Beeckman (1570-1637) rediscovered the extension and contraction of the extreme fibres of a bent beam, and the existence of the 'neutral fibre' in 1620. Jacob Bernoulli (1655-1705) rediscovered the linear distribution of extensions in 1691, and Jean Adhémar Barré de Saint Venant (1797-1886) noted the trapezoidally deformed cross-section of the bent beam in 1837. Leonardo was the first to introduce a discrete model for a continuous body in his solution of a cable problem in which the cable was suspended from two different elevations. He was a pioneer of fluid mechanics, giving the law of continuity for fluid flow first discovered by Straton of Lampsakos (*floruit* 280 B.C.) in Hellenistic antiquity in particular cases, and studying descriptively the eddy currents in water. In hydrodynamics, he obtained at least qualitatively correct results. In the capacity of the ducal engineer for hydraulic structures in Florence, he proposed to change the course of the Arno river to create a navigable canal connecting Florence to the sea. In his studies of water flow related to his proposal, he examined the flow from a number of rectangular orifices spaced vertically above one another in a vessel. He demonstrated that if a jet of water issuing from an orifice in a tank containing water is turned upwards, the jet will rise to the level of the head of water above the orifice, a fact rediscovered by Evangelista Torricelli (1608-1647) in the middle of the 17th century. He concluded that the 'power (***potentia***)' is the same for all water-jets regardless of their location from the free surface of water in the vessel because "where the force of percussion is lacking, it is compensated by the weight of the waterfall." If 'energy' is substituted for 'power' and 'kinetic energy' for percussion, this qualitative statement reminds one of the fundamental theorem of hydraulics of Johann Bernoulli (1667-1748). Leonardo da Vinci appears to have recognised intuitively that the energy of fall of a water particle depends upon the relationship between the velocity of the water particle and the head of water over the orifice in the vessel. In this observation, he seems to have realised that energy was a function of position and motion, thereby making an instinctive distinction between the potential and the kinetic energy. Leonardo da Vinci made the first attempt to apply mathematical methods to a problem of fluid mechanics when he assumed that the speed of a falling water v as well as its impact force P on the blade of a waterwheel are both proportional to the height of its fall H: $v \propto H$ and $P \propto H$, an idea anticipated by Heron of Alexandria in the 2nd century B.C. , in his effort to develop a quantitative method in the analysis of waterwheels. In measuring the flow of water through an orifice he devised an anemometer fitted with vanes as a flow gauge.

Leonardo da Vinci devised a combined Archimedean screw-type hydraulic reaction turbine and pump that he called ***cichognola***, which consisted of 2 spiral snail-tubes attached to a conical surface, for lifting water. The larger tube on the outside was meant to be the driving engine operating on the action-reaction principle which Leonardo seems to have understood reasonably well.

Leonardo studied the centrifugal pump, detailed a universal joint and invented a parabolic compass based on a principle which was adopted only late in the seventeenth century. He invented the thrust-bearing, as well as the conical pivot-ball bearing without end-play, a bearing which was reinvented in the1920's. He not only discovered the principle of irregular gearing, and employed conical screws, link chains and spiral-gears in his machines, but also perceived how different elements of machines were interrelated and mechanically equivalent. He made the first known attempts to rationalise the basic mechanical problems of machine design, and his unfinished manuscript for a book on machine design has only recently been found in Madrid. It has also been recently discovered in a drawing of one of his pupils that Leonardo da Vinci apparently had invented the modern bicycle in all of its basic details but the pneumatic tires. It is possible that Leonardo da Vinci built the first turret-windmill in 1502 at Cesena.

About 1502, Leonardo da Vinci proposed to Sultan Bazajet II of the Ottoman Empire the building of a gigantic shallow arch bridge across the Bosporus Strait between Constantinople and Pera [modern Galata] that was rigidly supported at both sides of the Strait by split-abutments. The proposed arch bridge had a total length of 600 braccia (360 m) including the abutments, 400 braccia (240 m) across the Straight and 100 braccia (60 m) resting on land as the abutment of the bridge at both supports of the bridge. The bridge was 70 braccia (42 m) high above the water level and 40 braccia (24 m) wide. In the1950's, Leonardo's bridge design was deemed technically feasible. The first bridge over the Bosporus Strait was built only in 1836.

Leonardo da Vinci invented the digital counting principle for a mechanical adding machine and illustrated it in his notebook as a series of 13 ten-digit wheels which are turned in sequence by a handle. One revolution advances the first digit-wheel of units by one step, and after nine steps it returned to zero whilst it passed the action onto the tens-wheel which advances one step. This mechanism represented the basic principle of digital counting by adding one to make any number conceivable. This type of principle was independently rediscovered by the French mathematician and philosopher Blaise Pascal in 1642, who used it in the design of his mechanical calculator.

In his attempt to develop an internal combustion engine with one cylinder in military engineering, Leonardo da Vinci introduced a piston in place of the cannonball in the cannon bore, and used gunpowder for fuel. About 3 centuries later, this idea led to the design of piston engines. He introduced the pendulum as a governor of a reciprocating pump, an idea that hitherto had been overlooked. Somewhat earlier, a ball-and-chain governor attached to one of a pair of compound cranks to counterbalance the thrust of a connecting-rod on the second compound crank, had been introduced in Germany in 1420's.

In 1497, Leonardo da Vinci invented for canals the folded, mitred, lock gate with hinged wicket sluice doors, having one-sixth of the area of the entire gate, located at the bottom of the gate. He constructed 6 such lock gates in the canal near Milan. The technology of canal locks was finally mastered with the invention of the mitred gate by Leonardo da Vinci. His mitred gates are still used in canal locks.

Between 1500 and 1510, Peter Henlein [alias Hele] (c. 1480-1542), a locksmith in ***Nürnberg*** (*Nuremberg*),Germany, invented a portable watch driven by a steel mainspring for the use of town watchmen. The spring-drive had been invented in 1427 by a Dutch craftsman and medical astrologer Henri Arnault of Zwolle. Henlein's watch, which was cylindrical in shape, had only the hour hand, and it was hung from the neck with a strap. When wound up, it ran and struck for 40 hours. However, this watch was probably not very accurate because it lacked a suitable escapement mechanism which could supply a constant torque provided by the unwinding spring made of tempered steel to the miniaturised mechanism of the watch. Henlein is reported to have used hog-bristles for that purpose, but this device could not have supplied the watch with the necessary torque when the spring unwound. It is more likely that Henlein used the '***fusee***' device invented during the Mediæval Age for the regulation of his watchwork. The problem of high accuracy in spring-driven watches was first solved by Christiaan Huygens (1629-1695) and Robert Hooke (1635-1703) in the 1670's. Different parts of Henlein's watch were held together by pins and wedges, since screws were not used for such purposes until about 1550. However, Henlein's watch, which was popularly called the ***Nürnberg Egg,*** was not the first spring-driven timepiece, since there are at least two spring-driven clocks extant which preceded Henlein's watch, and that implies that he was not the inventor of the basic elements of the spring-driven movement of the watch. Henlein's basic achievement was the production of a small movement for a watch which could be carried in the pocket.

Francesco di Marchi (1504-1577) of Bologna, a professional soldier and not an artist, was the next most famous military engineer after di Giorgio Martini. He wrote a famous, comprehensive treatise < On Military Architecture > (***Della architettura militare***) which was posthumously published in 1597-1599. It contained a systematic exposition and development of di Giorgio Martini's simple polygonal and star-shaped bastions, which in di Marchi's treatment became complex designs of walls, moats, empty spaces and angular components of fortresses. Di Marchi is the most famous precursor of Sebastian le Prêtre de Vauban (1633-1707), the eminent fortress builder of the 17th century A.D. France. In fortress and military engineering theory, practice and mathematics were more closely related than in any other branch of contemporary engineering.

Several important inventions were made in the Renaissance period. In 1530, the spinning-wheel with treadle was devised. In 1578, the screw-lathe was invented. In 1589, Reverend William

Lee in England invented his knitting machine, the so-called 'stocking frame', a treadle-operated machine with a separate needle for each loop. It was not completely automatic, but it was a prototype for subsequent, completely automatic knitting and lace-making machines. In 1519, the compound microscope was invented.

In 1581, Italian artist-engineer-architect Andrea Palladio of Vicenza (1518-1580) reintroduced classical construction in his book < Four Books on Architecture > (***Quattro libri dell' architettura***). He became the first constructor of effective wooden truss bridges consisting of triangular truss elements, such as his bridge over the Cismone river near the Italian-German border, which had spans up to 100 feet (30.50 m). He reported that a friend of his had previously seen such truss bridges in Germanic Europe.

After Alberti, the theoretician of the new building style and the foremost creative master of it was Donato d'Agnolo (1444-1514), popularly known as ***Bramante*** ['he who wants'] The worldly warrior-Pope Julius II who restored the Papal States to the Roman Church assigned ***Bramante*** to build St. Peter's Basilica on the site of the ancient Christian basilica in Rome. ***Bramante*** designed a huge building the plan of which was in the form of a cross with a huge dome covering the central area of the cross. ***Bramante*** was able to erect the 4 main piers and the arches cast in concrete to support the dome before his death. He had rediscovered the Roman method of casting concrete in liquid state into a wooden formwork to produce cast-concrete arches which were able to support the dome. After the death of ***Bramante***, the new pope, Leo X, appointed Giuliano da Sangallo (1445-1516) together with Fra Giacondo (c. 1433-1515), and Raffaelo Santi (1483-1516), famous painter known as Raphael who had been named the successor to the deceased ***Bramante*** as the chief architect of the Vatican in 1541, to complete the construction of St. Peter's Basilica. The octogenarian Dominican monk Giovanni Monsignori of Verona (c.1435-1515) known as ***Fra Giocondo***, an acknowledged expert in foundation engineering, had to strengthen and consolidate the structural foundations of St. Peter's Basilica because they had been designed unsoundly and constructed too hastily by ***Bramante***. Sangallo, a follower of Brunelleschi who preferred elegance and clarity in building form, modified ***Bramante's*** architectural design of St. Peter's Basilica. After the death of Raphael a nephew of Sangallo, Giuliano da Sangallo the Younger (1485-1546), whose real name was Cordiani, was appointed in 1520 to succeed Raphael in the construction of St. Peter's Basilica, but his complex logical plan for the completion of the Basilica was not accepted owing to its severe, and massive style.

A number of successive Popes and their architect-engineers were attempting to solve the structural problems of St. Peter's Basilica by introducing little alterations in various parts of this building but all these efforts only resulted in a more confused project. Finally, Pope Paul III assigned the task of bringing the project of St. Peter's Basilica to an orderly conclusion to the famous sculptor, painter and capable engineer, Michelangelo, who had built fortifications at Florence and Rome. Michelangelo Buonarroti (1475-1564), known as ***Michelangelo***, redesigned this dome and prepared a model of it without accepting payment for his services, but it was again redesigned and finally constructed by the engineer Domenico Fontana (1543-1607) from 1590 to 1591. The diameter of this dome which weighs about 10,000 tons is 137.5 feet (41.91 m), and it has 3 iron tension rings resisting the circumferential tension at the base of the dome. Unfortunately, the iron tension rings proved inadequate and, as a result, some tensile cracks developed round the base of the dome, which required a theoretical reexamination of the dome and restoration work a century and a half later. Pope Benedictus XIV in 1742, and in 1743, assigned 3 Jesuit mathematicians, Thomas Le Seur (1703-1770), François Jacquier (1711-1788), and Ruggiero Giuseppe Boscovich (1711-1787) to carry out a theoretical study of the structural behaviour of the dome of St. Peter's Basilica. They used the principle virtual work upon the mathematical model of the dome which had fractured into orange peel type of sections. Since in their analysis the Jesuit mathematicians had used a constant resisting force acting in the tension chain, it was criticised by the Italian mathematician, astronomer and engineer, Giovanni Poleni (1683-1761), who carried out his own structural analysis. On the basis of these theoretical studies, architect-engineer Vanvitelli (1700-1773) installed 5 further tension chains in the dome. Domenico Fontana was a papal engineer-architect for Pope Sixtus V, who ran a remarkably corrupt reign, and he was one of the first engineers to emphasise explicitly that engineering design as an entity has 3 distinct aspects: the practical, the economic, and the æsthetic.

In 1586, Fontana erected the famous Egyptian's obelisk, which Emperor Caligula had brought to Rome, on the plaza in front of St. Peter's Basilica, and published his account of how the obelisk was transported to the plaza from its old location in front of Nero's circus in 1590. This 75-foot (22.86 m) tall obelisk weighed 327 tons, and 800 men, 140 horses, and 40 capstans were used by Fontana in its transport. The public executioner was in attendance to decapitate anyone who intended to sabotage the erection of the obelisk – a condition of construction resembling the conditions for the erection of obelisks in ancient Egypt. Fontana, as a papal engineer-architect, also built the Aqua Felice aqueduct and planned a number of great streets in Rome.

In 1592, Fontana was removed from his office by the next Pope, who accused him of diverting public funds. Fontana then became an architect and senior engineer in Naples.

Dutch and Italian engineers who were the acknowledged masters of hydraulic engineering in Europe in the 14th and 15th centuries built many canals in Italy, France, and England. Dutch entrepreneur-engineers and Dutch private finances carried out many large drainage projects in Europe. The secular financing and organisation of free enterprise had its beginning in Flanders in the 13th century and became prevalent in Italy and Germany in the 14th century.

One of the most remarkable hydraulic works of the Renaissance was the water supply system, called the ***Artificio***, built by the Spanish clockmaker and engineer of Italian extraction, Juanelo Turriano [alias Giovanni Della Torre Gianello] (c.1500-1585), for the city of Toledo in Spain from 1565 to 1573. He made a copy of the astronomical clock of Giovanni de' Dondi in the possession of the Holy Roman Emperor, Charles V, which no longer ran, and it took him 15 years to accomplish this task. Turriano left Italy after 1545 to join the court of the Emperor which was relocated in Toledo, Spain. When the pumping station and the pipes built by German mining engineers in 1526 failed after a period of operation, the Emperor commissioned Turriano in 1565 to build a hydraulic system supplying water to Toledo, which at the time had a population of over 200,000, from the river Tajo located about 1970 feet (600 m) below the city. Turriano built a new water supply system in 6 years, which was unique and certainly an engineering success. His water-lifting mechanism consisted of a combined waterwheel and noria which continually filled a trough-like container. This water was poured into one end of a 'cradle' as the central element of water transport system. The waterwheel also drove an ingenious reciprocating double row of rod-and-lever transmission system which rocked the whole chain of cradles so that water was poured from one ladle to the next one without spilling any water as the ladles were rocking to-and-fro. The movement of the entire system was so graceful that it was popularly called the 'ballet-dancing machine'. Its capacity was equal to the capacity of 300 mules working around the clock. This system of water supply could have been easily trebled by building parallel chains of such a 'bucket brigade'. Turriano's water supply system for the city of Toledo stands as one of the outstanding engineering works of the Renaissance, because it was not only practical but also æsthetically satisfying, a requirement important to the Renaissance engineers. This water-lifting machine of Turriano actually worked from 1573 onwards, but it was not a complete commercial success because the quantity of water raised by the machine was rather small and the need for repairs of the worn machinery was quite frequent. Turriano did construct a second water-lifting machine in 1581, but apparently, this machine kept working well beyond 1600, since it is known that some time before 1639, the citizens of Toledo returned to the old reliable method, using donkeys to transport water to the city. Shortly before his death in 1585, Turriano worked on the design and engineering of the Tibi dam, the first known high-arched dam.

Italian Renaissance scientist and man of letters, Gianbattista della Porta (1536-1615), was a precocious youngster who became one of the most active promoters of natural philosophy and a famous scientific writer. He was also a playwright who wrote about 30 comedies. During the Renaissance, scientific enquiry was quite general but unsystematic, as della Porta's voluminous writings, which range from quite fantastic speculations, magic, palmistry, physiognomy, chemistry and alchemy to classification of plants, magnetism, crystallography, pyrotechnic, cryptography, meteorology, mnemonics, farming, fortification and technology, testify. Della Porta's most important contributions were in natural history and horticulture, in optics and in mechanical application of steam power. His most important works were: < Natural Magic > (***Magiae naturalis***) in 4 books in 1558 (second enlarged edition in 20 books in 1589), < On Optical Refraction> (***De refractione optices parti***) in 1593, and < Three Books on the Spirit > (***Tre libri de'spiritali***) in 1601.

Della Porta's < Natural Magic > contained important experimental results on magnetism and optics, as well as a description of ***camera obscura***, which was fitted with a lens, thereby becoming a distant ancestor of the modern camera. He devoted much of his attention to the uses of lenses and presented various combinations of concave and convex lenses to improve vision at increased distances which makes him an early investigator of the compound microscope and telescope. He had considerable understanding of the experimental method but his massive learning led him astray.

In his book < Three Books on the Spirit >, della Porta gave information on some quite original uses of steam-power based on his experiments on the properties of steam. He had discovered that steam occupies a much greater volume than the water from which it is obtained, and that condensation of steam in a vessel leaves an empty space in the vessel, which can be filled by a liquid other than water when the vessel is connected to a supply of liquid open to the atmosphere.

On the basis of his fundamental discoveries about steam, della Porta devised a pump for fountains in which the steam in a heated vessel partially filled with water was permitted to escape through a valve and thereby create a partial vacuum which drew water from the well into the vessel, and where the steam-pressure from heating drove it up through another pipe into the fountain. This type of steam-driven pump was developed about half a century later by Edward Somerset, the Second Marquis of Worcester (1601-1667) in England. Della Porta had performed some experiments to measure the volume of steam by the quantity of water displaced by steam, which led him to make a distinction between steam and air, but he did not yet explicitly recognise it.

Della Porta travelled widely through Italy, Spain and France, and he was responsible for founding several scientific academies. Della Porta examined with care old fables, and in some cases, performed experiments to prove them to be false. He also invented a method to test the strength of lodestones by means of a balance.

The well-known Italian physician, mathematician, mechanical engineer and gambler, Girolamo Cardano (1501-1576), mentioned in an obscure manner in his book < On Judgement > (***De subtilitate***) in 1550 that an empty space is left by condensing steam, an idea he probably pilfered from the notes of Leonardo da Vinci, who had been a close friend of his father, Fazio Cardano, a jurist. Cardano, however, did not distinguish between steam and air. Cardano was a typical Renaissance intellectual who became successful in life by being willing to resort to unscrupulous methods, such as perjury, plagiarism and misrepresentation in order to acquire social eminence. Cardano, who wrote hundreds of tractates, plagiarised Leonardo da Vinci in his books < On

Subtleties > (***De subtilitate***) (1550), < On Various Things > (***De rerum varietate***) (1557), and < New Work > (***Opus novum***) (1570) which dealt with mechanical sciences and inventions. He developed the gimbal suspension of Philon of Byzantion (c. 240 B.C.) from Leonardo da Vinci's notes. He also applied optical lenses to the ***camera obscura***, an idea probably due to Leonardo da Vinci. However, Cardano's own contributions to the theory of algebraic equations and the theory of probability were quite fundamental.

The first to distinguish in a definite manner between air-pressure and steam-pressure was Salomon de Caus (1576-1626), a popular engineer-architect and prolific inventor from Normandy, who for a time was a tutor of the Prince of Wales, and an engineer to the Elector of the Palatine in Germany. His renown as an engineer stems from his designs of ornamental fountains in which water was raised by the power of steam. Salomon de Caus clearly recognised that steam is evaporated water, and that on cooling, the vapour returns to its original liquid state. He observed similar results in his experiments with mercury. In 1651, Salomon de Caus wrote his famous book < The Reasons of Moving Forces > (***Les raisons des force mouvantes***), also published in German language, in which he gave a number of propositions in the science of gases and gaseous phenomena that represented a considerable advance in the understanding of such phenomena. It made quite clear that there was great power present in steam pressure which was much larger than that found in air pressure, and that there are great mechanical possibilities in the use of steam. This was a scientific discovery of great importance, and it revealed the principles upon which the design of steam-engines could be based. Salomon de Caus himself did not produce any basically novel inventions in his steam-driven fountains, which were essentially based upon the concept of the steam-powered pump devised by della Porta. However, Salomon de Caus was the first to introduce the concept of work into mechanical science, and to call himself 'engineer'.

The court physician of Queen Elizabeth I of England, William Gilbert (c.1544-1603) of Colchester, a typical Renaissance man who believed in occultism and in an animate universe, was a talented experimenter who worked upon magnetism 17 years, and his efforts culminated in his deservedly famous book < On the Magnet > (***De magnete***) published in 1600 which was almost entirely nonmathematical and the first outstanding treatise on experimental method. He was the founder of the science of magnetism, and did pioneering work on the effect of heat on magnetism, which he considered to be an occult force, and conceived the concept of ***orbis virtutis***, the region of magnetic strength, or the field of magnetic force. He discovered the magnetisation without contact, the so-called 'magnetic induction', and recognised that the Earth is a giant magnet with its own magnetic field of force. He distinguished between electricity and magnetism and invented an electroscope to experiment with electric phenomenon. Gilbert made a spherical lodestone, ***terella***, in his effort to study the terrestrial magnetic phenomenon and to explain the magnetic declination and inclination with it, but he was mistaken when he assumed that the magnetic poles of Earth are identical with the geographical poles. He regarded the Earth to be surrounded by a magnetic field, and applied this idea to the entire solar system. This work of Gilbert introduced the study of terrestrial magnetism.

Gilbert left a manuscript < On Our World Beneath the Moon > (***De mundo nostro sublunari***), posthumously edited and published by his younger brother in 1651, which expressed his ideas on the mass, and the force exerted by Earth on the Moon thereby influencing Kepler's development of the gravitational concept.

Gilbert's treatise on magnetism could be considered the last important scientific contribution of the Renaissance period, a work appreciated by both Galileo Galilei (1564-1642) and Johann Kepler (1571-1630).

Early Italian Bridges Built in Late Middle Ages

From 1335 to 1345, Ponte Vecchio was built in Florence. This bridge has 3 shallow segmental arches, one arch spanning 95½ feet (29.11 m) and two arches spanning 85 feet (25.91 m), with a rise-to-span ratio of 1-to-6.5. The piers of this bridge are slender, less than 20 feet (6.10 m) wide. This bridge was designed by Taddeo Gaddi and, perhaps, built by a Florentine mason Neri de Fioravante. In the structural design of this very bold, shallow segmental arch bridge, Taddeo Gaddi had rediscovered that horizontal thrusts of contiguous arches of equal spans balance each other, an idea first exploited by the Roman engineers in the design of the arcades supported on slim columns in the palace of Diocletianus.

From 1354 to 1356, Ponte Castelvecchio [Scaligero Bridge] was constructed over the Adige River in Verona. This bridge has 3 segmental arches with spans of 160 feet (48.77 m), 93½ feet (28.50 m), and 79 feet (24.08 m). Its piers are 39 feet 5 inches (12.01 m) and 20⅓ foot (6.1 m) wide, and its arches have a rise to span ratio of 1-to-4. The engineers of this bridge were Jean de Farrare and Jacopo de Gozzo.

In China several notable segmental arch bridges had already been built centuries earlier. One of the most important of these bridges is the Great Stone Bridge built from 589 to 618, which is an elegant, segmental, and slender, open spandrel arch with a span of 123 feet (37.49 m) and a rise of 23 feet (7.01 m), giving it a rise-to-span ratio of 1-to-5.

From 1566 to 1569, the Ponte San Trinita in Florence was built. It resembles Ponte Vecchio, but its piers are wider, yet the span-to-rise ratio, 1-to-7, of its arches is more daring. Each of its arches consists of 2 parabolic arches which meet at the crown at an obtuse angle. This type of an arch was designed to replace the segmental circular arch. Its cofferdams, which were excavated to

14 feet (4.27 m) below the stream level, rest on 14-foot (4.27 m) long piles driven to the river bottom. Ponte San Trinita was designed by the well-known architect-engineer Bartolomeo Ammanati Battiferri da Settignano (1511-1592) [commonly called ***Ammanati***] .

The Rialto Bridge over the Grand Canal, Venice, was built from 1588 to 1591. The arch span of this bridge is 88½ feet (26.97 m), and the rise is about 21 feet (6.40 m), giving a rise-to-span ratio of 1-to-4. The Rialto Bridge was built by Antonio da Ponte (c.1512-1597).

Mathematical Contributions of Renaissance

Renaissance humanists did not contribute outstanding new results in mathematics but rather attempted to recover ancient Greek mathematics, and they succeeded to make some progress in two special areas of mathematics: geometric theory of perspective and the solution of algebraic equations. However, they did reestablish the close relation of mathematics with science and technology which had existed in the Hellenistic period. Their idea that the mathematical laws are the real aim of science, and that mathematically formulated investigations of practical problems in engineering and technology supply the best information for technical design was an important contribution to scientific engineering. However, the Renaissance style of mathematical exposition remained largely rhetorical, since they apparently did not yet realise the vital importance of symbolic notation to the progress of mathematics.

The ablest and most influential mathematician of the 15thcentury was the German mathematician, astronomer and technologist Johann Müller of the city of Königsberg [in Latin he called himself by the name of his city, Regiomontanus] (1436-1476), who was the harbinger of a new age and a link between the classical learning preserved in Byzantium and the early Renaissance movement in the West. He studied under Georg von Peurbach (1423-1461) who had been a student of Nicholas of Cusa (1401-1464), and had wide and varied interests befitting a Renaissance man. As a result of his ambition to translate and publish the scientific legacy of antiquity, he completed Peurbach's translation of Ptolemaios' ***Almagest***, and also translated from Greek some of the works of Archimedes, Apollonios of Perge, and Heron of Alexandria. In 1471 he moved to ***Nürnberg*** (*Nuremberg*) where he established the first European observatory, a printing press, and wrote 3 tractates on astronomy. In his printing shop ***Regiomontanus*** published Peurbach's < New Planetary Theory > (***Theoricae novae planetarum***) in 1472. He also built a mechanical eagle which flapped its wings and saluted the Emperor Maximilian I when the Emperor entered the city. It was regarded as one of the mechanical marvels of his age.

Regiomontanus' most important work was entitled < On All kinds of Triangles > (***De triangulis omnimodis***) which he wrote in 1464 but was printed at Nuremberg in 1533, almost a century after his death. This book gave the first systematic exposition of plane and spherical trigonometry. In some of the problems he obtains solutions by means of his algebraic geometry consisting of algebra and trigonometry. This work rendered European mathematics pre-eminent in trigonometry as an autonomous mathematical discipline. ***Regiomontanus*** was the most prominent mathematician of his generation who was not contemptuous of the Scholastic or the Muslim learning. He planned to reform astronomy, and had he lived he might have anticipated Copernicus. Unfortunately, he was invited to Rome by Pope Sixtus IV to reform the calendar, but was assassinated there by his enemies.

The first Renaissance algebra was written by a French physician Nicolas Chuquet (died c. 1500) about whom very little is known. The manuscript entitled < Three Parts in the Science of Numbers > (***Triparty en la sciences des nombres***) which Chuquet wrote in 1484 (but was printed only in 1884) consisted of three parts: arithmetic computation with rational numbers, irrational numbers and theory of equations. He recognised both negative and positive integral exponents and syncopated some of his algebra, but it was far too advanced for its time to exert much influence.

The best German algebraist of the Renaissance was Michael Stifel (1486-1567), an Augustinian monk and personal friend of Luther who converted to Protestantism. He was a peculiar personality and a mystic who believed in number mysticism although Luther advised him to forget all about that nonsense. He wrote a book on algebra, but his major treatise was < Integral Arithmetic> (***Arithmetica integra***) in 3 books in 1544 which dealt with rational numbers, irrational numbers and algebra, respectively. In the first book he pointed out the advantage of associating an arithmetic progression with a geometric progression, an idea which foreshadowed the invention of logarithms nearly a century later, and indicated a formula for binomial coefficients up to the 17-th order. The second book dealt with algebraic presentation of Book X of Eukleides (in English, Euclid). In the third book he dealt with algebraic equations for which he re-introduced the general symbolic algebraic notation that had been neglected since Jordan de Nemore. He introduces letters for unknown such as *1A, 1AA, 1AAA* for A, A^2 and A^3, respectively, and used symbols for operation such as + and – for addition and subtraction, respectively, and √ for the square root, but he discarded negative roots of the algebraic equations.

In 1494, Luca Pacioli (1445-c.1514), an Italian Franciscan friar, published one of the first mathematical books in print,< Summary of Arithmetic, Geometry, Proportions and Proportionality> (***Summa de arithmetica, geometrica, proportioni et propotionalita***), which summarised virtually all that was known of arithmetic, trigonometry and algebra of his time. It was a compilation from many sources but contained little of importance beyond what was in Fibonacci's ***Liber abaci*** apart from its superior syncopated notation. However, it did give an important treatment of double-entry bookkeeping. Pacioli closed his book with the statement that the algebraic solution of the equations:

$$x^3+mx = n, \text{ and } x^3+ n = mx,$$

was as impossible as the quadrature of the circle, a challenge that was taken up by the mathematicians at the University of Bologna, one of the largest and oldest universities in Europe and a famous center of higher learning. Copernicus, Pacioli and Dürer had been students at the University of Bologna. Scipione del Ferro (c.1465-1526), professor of mathematics at the University of Bologna, tried to find the general solution of the cubic equation, which could be reduced to 3 types:

$$x^3+mx = n, \quad x^3 = mx+n, \text{ and } \quad x^3+ n = mx,$$

where $m > 0$, and $n > 0$. Apparently, he succeeded sometime between 1505 and 1515 to solve all 3 equations, but he kept it a secret and never published it, since it was a Renaissance custom of mathematicians, and other professionals as well, to compete in public contests for money which made secret personal knowledge professionally valuable. All contestants in a public debate had to deposit a sum of money which was forfeited to the winner. However, del Ferro had revealed his solution of $x^3+mx = n$ before his death to his favourite student, Antonio Maria Fiore.

A mathematician in Venice, Niccolo Fontana (c.1506-1559), known by his nickname ***Tartaglia***, apparently rediscovered del Ferro's solution in 1535, and once it became known, Fiore, believing that Tartaglia was merely bluffing, challenged the latter to a public contest. All the problems proposed by Fiore at the contest reduced to the cubic equation solved by del Ferro as Tartaglia had suspected, and Tartaglia was able to dispose of them within 2 hours. Fiore was not able to solve any of the problems proposed by Tartaglia, most of which were reducible to the cubic equation $x^3+mx^2 = n$, the solution of which Tartaglia had established shortly before the contest. After this victory, Tartaglia was considered for a time the best algebraist in Italy. Tartaglia kept his method of solution a secret, but imprudently, he revealed it to a Milanese physician, Girolamo Cardano, who swore to secrecy but still published it in 1545, giving due credit to Tartaglia, in his famous work < Great Art, or On Algebraic Rules > (***Artis magna sive de regulis algebraicis***), the first book of which was exclusively devoted to algebra. In this historic treatise, Cardano went much further than Tartaglia by not only solving both cubic equations but also demonstrating how the general cubic equation could be reduced to the cubic equation solved by del Ferro when the term x^2 is eliminated. Cardano accepted negative roots, which he called 'fictitious', but he did not recognise imaginary roots although he did not disregard computation with square roots of negative numbers. He also recognised that the so-called 'complex roots', which he called 'sophistic quantities', always appear in pairs. He was aware of the so-called 'Descartes' rule of signs', had an idea of the number of roots of a cubic equation, and the relationship existing between the roots and the coefficients of the cubic equation, since he discovered that the sum of the roots of a cubic equation is equal to the negative of the coefficient of x^2, if the coefficient of x^3 is one. Since he used a rhetorical form of the cubic equations, these discoveries were by themselves quite remarkable. Cardano also gave a solution of a particular biquadratic equation which was due to his servant and pupil Lodovico Ferrari (1525-1565), who had discovered a method that reduced the solution of the general biquadratic equation to the solution of the cubic equation. He also gave a crude method of obtaining an approximate root of an equation of any degree. Despite all the merits of Cardano's book, it was not sufficiently advanced to be considered the source of modern algebra, although it is one of the great books in mathematics. After the publication of Cardano's book on algebra, an acrimonious and sordid quarrel ensued between Tartaglia and Cardano, with insults hurled both ways, which ended in Tartaglia's challenge to Cardano for a mathematical contest. On the day of the contest, Cardano, who failed to appear, sent the 20 year old Ferrari in his place. Despite the fact that both sides claimed victory in this contest, it appears that Tartaglia had the better of it. Tartaglia's opponent Ferrari, who had the temper of a fiend, broke up the meeting in a violent rage, and Tartaglia had to escape to save his life.

Tartaglia, like most of the prominent Renaissance men, was boastful, envious, truculent and, on occasion, even dishonest, for instance, when he published the solution of the inclined plane problem due to Jordan de Nemore as his own. Yet in comparison with Cardano, who was an exaggerated case of the common type of Italian Renaissance man with an incredible number of vices, Tartaglia was relatively respectable. Cardano was arrogant, conceited, vain, cantankerous, greedy, cunning, mendacious, humourless, envious, grudging, vindictive, lascivious, devoted to erotic pleasures, obscene, and incredibly superstitious. His popular fame was based on his numerous books on astrology, astronomy, physics, cosmology, gadgetry, medicine and a large variety of other topics, all impregnated with some magic and other nonsense which were popular at the time. By 1560, he had acquired a reputation as the most prominent mathematician, physicist and physician in Europe. After his eldest son, also a physician, was executed for murder, his younger son caught in burglary, and he himself accused of heresy and jailed, he had to take refuge in disgrace in Rome, where, surprisingly, the Pope considered Cardano worthy of Vatican's pension.

Cardano left 111 manuscripts and 138 printed books, among which were the posthumously published < Book on Games of Chance > (***Liber de ludo aleae***) (1643), the first book on probabilities, and his notorious autobiography entitled < On My Life > (***De vita propria***) (1643), in which he recounts both his virtues and incredibly numerous vices. His pupil, Lodovico Ferrari, was an extravagant, undisciplined and ill-tempered voluptuary, who became quite wealthy but was poisoned either by his sister, or by her paramour.

The last outstanding Italian Renaissance algebraist was Raffaello Bombelli (c.1526-1573), a member of a noble Bolognese family who was educated at the University of Bologna in hydraulic engineering and mathematics. Bombelli wrote a manuscript on geometry about 1550, and published his important book on algebra, < Algebra the Major Part of Arithmetic Divided into Three Books> (***L'Algebra parte maggiore dell' aritmetica divisa in tre libri***) in 1572, both of which contained a consistent theory of imaginary complex numbers. He was able to treat the irreducible case in the solution of cubic and biquadratic equations. It contained the most consistent and systematic treatment of algebra in an improved algebraic notation in Renaissance era, and the complex numbers lost some of their mysterious character in consequence of Bombelli's treatise, although a complete acceptance of complex numbers took place only in the 19th century. His treatise on geometry was also original and represented a departure from ancient algebra which led to modern analytic geometry.

The French lawyer and amateur mathematician François Viète (1540-1603), made further progress in algebra by reducing Cardano-Tartaglia's solution of the cubic equation to a trigonometric solution, which made the introduction of imaginaries unnecessary in the irreducible case. Viète's solution is usually given in modern textbooks of higher algebra. In his book < Introduction to Analytic Art > (***Isagoge in artem analyticam***) in 1591, he was one of the first to represent numbers by letters, + and – for addition and subtraction, respectively, and showed how algebra could be applied to the solution of geometric problems. What Viète was able to achieve in algebra in France was similar to what Bombelli did in Italy, except that Viète did it better and on a much broader scale. He applied geometry to algebra rather than algebra to geometry, which was done later by his countrymen Pierre de Fermat (1601-1665) and René Descartes (1596-1650) who because of it are the modern founders of mathematical physics. In his algebra Viète used letters for unknowns as well as for known quantities, which gave greater generality to his solutions and was one of his major contributions to symbolic algebra. His most important algebraic discoveries were established by means of trigonometry, a mathematical discipline in which he was a recognised master. His thinking in mathematics was rather geometrical, but of very high order comparable to that of the ancient Greek mathematicians Apollonios of Perge (c.265-170 B.C.) and Pappos of Alexandria (*floruit* c.A.D. 284-300).

However, Viète was not equally competent in astronomy. In his angry controversy in 1594 about the Gregorian reform of the calendar with the German Jesuit mathematician Christopher Klau (in Latin, ***Clavius***) (1537-1612), a talented teacher and highly regarded textbook author in mathematics and astronomy, Viète was entirely unscientific. Unfortunately, he rejected negative and imaginary roots which made it impossible for him to formulate a general theory of equations. Viète wrote numerous works on algebra, geometry and trigonometry, but not being concerned with his fame he published all his memoirs in limited editions privately at his own expense since he was a man of considerable means.

The last, properly Renaissance mathematician is the Flemish engineer, Simon Stevin (1548-1620), who entered Leyden University at the ripe age of 35, and later became a tutor of Prince Maurice of Nassau, quartermaster general of the Dutch armies, a member of Maurice's council, and superintendent of the financial administration, very important positions indeed. His mathematical and engineering contributions which were epoch-making are further discussed in ***Baroque Technology***. However, his importance to Renaissance mathematics is great, for he had an outstanding talent for introducing simplifying conventions in algebra and arithmetic which made further mathematical progress not only possible but relatively easy. Stevin is one of the greatest arithmeticians of all time.

His supreme achievement was his vindication of the decimal fractions in his book < Tithe> (***De Thiende***), published in 1585, which had the simplicity of a natural genius. The fractions in general use during the Renaissance were plane fractions such as *4/5*, sexagesimal fractions which were the most common in use, and duodecimal fractions in metrology and finances. Although decimal integers were in use, decimal fractions were not. Viète had used decimal fractions in 1579, and argued for their superiority over sexagesimal fractions, but it was Stevin who made the matter clear by explaining them simply and completely, and gave the decimals their utility and complete meaning by extending decimalisation to weights, measures and money. He demonstrated how easy it was to use decimal fractions together with decimal integers. Despite the fact that Stevin's notation was somewhat cumbersome because he treated his decimal notation as an exponential notation, <Tithe> was the supreme work of arithmetic of the Renaissance. Stevin's language in scientific and mathematical exposition was Dutch, and he boldly declared that it was superior to Greek and Latin.

Although his algebra was comparable to that of Cardano, Viète and others, he was profoundly more original in some aspects of the theory of equations. In 1594 he made an advance on the general theory of equations by stating that signs could be attached to quantities, that a subtraction is simply the addition of a negative quantity, $a+(-b) = a-b$, that every equation, even if some terms are missing, can still be regarded as complete if the coefficients of the missing terms are taken as zeros, that a division is multiplication by a reciprocal, that the negative roots may be considered as positive roots of another equation obtained by substituting $(-x)$ for x, and that every equation of the second degree the roots of which are real has two such roots. He also established rules for the solution of numerical algebraic equations of any degree. He showed that if $f(a) > 0$ and $f(b) < 0$, for $f(x) = 0$, then there exists at least one root between $x = a$ and $x = b$, and demonstrated how the decimals of a root can be obtained by successive approximations. Although the precise value of the roots for some equations cannot be obtained, it is possible to come indefinitely near to it by successive approximations. In all of these simplifying mathematical contributions, Stevin's genius in mathematics was plainly evident.

It would be remiss not to mention the late Renaissance English mathematician and noted astronomer, Thomas Harriot (1560-1621), who was the founder of English school of algebraists. In his youth Harriot was a tutor of Sir Walter Raleigh (c.1552-1618) who in 1585 appointed Harriot to be the geographer and surveyor of the team he sent to explore and map the Virginia territory (now North Carolina) in the American continent, an expedition led by Sir Richard Granville and financed by Raleigh. In 1588 Harriot wrote a brief report of the new found land of Virginia in the form of a large-scale statistical survey, probably the very first work of its kind. Harriot's outstanding systematic treatise on algebra < Practice of Analytical Art, about New Algebraic Equations ... Method of Solution > (***Artis analyticae praxis, ad æquationes algebraicas nova ... methodo resolvendas***) written about 1601 and published posthumously in 1631, set the standard for modern textbooks on algebra. It contained the construction of algebraic equations with prescribed roots, the relation of the roots to the coefficients of the equation, the transformation of algebraic equations into equations having roots differing from the original roots according to certain laws, as well as the numerical solution of algebraic equations. He expressed the known algebraic quantities by lower case consonants and the unknown quantities by lower case vowels, employed √ as a symbol for the cube root, and > and < as symbols for 'is greater than' and 'is less than,' respectively, and expressed products such as *xxx* by exponentials: x^3 . Moreover, he took definite steps towards analytic geometry.

Harriot has another, in this case a rather dubious distinction: he brought smoking of tobacco, an insidious drug habit of American Indians, to England because he mistakenly believed it to be beneficial to health. Harriot himself paid the supreme penalty for his folly for he died of lip cancer caused by his habit of smoking his pipe.

Postscriptum

The true 'renaissance', or rebirth of technology and engineering took place in the West during the Mediæval Age, not during the so-called Italian Renaissance which was essentially a 'literary renaissance' of classical works. In the Italian Renaissance great efforts were made to replace faith as the sovereign authority by reason.

The birth of true Renaissance spirit is ordinarily associated with 3 famous Italian men of letters from Florence: Dante Alighieri (1265-1321), Francesco Petrarca (1304-1374), called Petrarch, and Giovanni Boccaccio (1313-1375), who were responsible for founding the literary language of modern Italy. All three were actually men of the Mediæval Age. Dante was to literature what Thomas Aquinas (c.1225-1274) had been to philosophy: both tried to unite the Christian culture and the classical pagan culture. The Roman poet Publius Vergilius Maro (70-19 B.C.) was to Dante what Aristotle had been to Aquinas. Dante wrote < New Life > (***Vita Nova***), love poems which were very close to the mediæval tradition of the troubadours, and his magnificent major work <Divine Comedy> (***Divina Comedia***), completed shortly before his death, which has deep and profound beauty and is a work of genius of the highest order. ***Divina Comedia*** presented Dante's breathtaking imaginary journey through Hell and Purgatory under the symbolic guidance of the great Roman poet Vergilius, and through Paradise under the guidance of his great love in his youth, Beatrice, who was actually a Florentine noblewoman Bice Portinari (1266-1290), and after whose premature death Dante wrote ***La Vita Nuova*** in which he spiritualises and exalts the object of the poet's love, and which has one of the greatest verse sequences in Western literature. ***Divina Comedia*** is one of the superb works in the history of Western literature. Dante, who used Tuscan dialect as a literary Italian language, wrote < On the Common Eloquence > (***De Vulgari Eloquentia***) in Latin, in which he defended the Italian vernacular as a worthy literary medium. Dante was a mediæval man of enormous erudition which included virtually all the learning of his time.

Francesco Petrarca was much more like a true Renaissance man in his desire for immortal fame and in his passionate interest in classical antiquity, although his ascetic inclination still showed him to be a man of the Mediæval Age. He refined Dante's use of the Tuscan dialect, and influenced the form of Italian poetry. From Petrarca came a line of professional humanists, who as proud men of letters translated Latin, wrote speeches, and usually served the wealthy and powerful as secretaries.

Individuals who devoted their lives to the study of pagan classics in order to acquire ***humanitas*** were called 'humanists'. The term ***humanitas*** was coined by the Roman man of letters, orator, Stoic philosopher and Senator, Marcus Tullius Cicero (106-43 B.C.), who meant by it 'mental cultivation' which finds expression in refined literary form. To the Renaissance men it also implied a philosophy of life in this world, and not in the next world which had been the main preoccupation of the mediæval men. The humanists had to make their living as intellectual entrepreneurs apart from universities and the Roman Church and, therefore, they had to advertise themselves. Self-advertisement, after its first timid appearance in ancient Egypt, became a unique creation of the Italian Renaissance. In 1483, Leonardo da Vinci self-advertised himself in a letter to Duke Lodovico Sforza, the despot of Milan, offering his professional services in engineering in which he professed expertise in 15 branches of military engineering.

The products of the literary Renaissance humanists had to be shallow enough to be offered to princes, merchants and ladies in entertaining conversations at the courts and homes of wealthy burghers, since difficult topics such as natural philosophy of the ancient Greeks or Roman engineering were too weighty subjects for their lightweight fare. Their humanism expressed itself in their rigid reverence for everything ancient, particularly Greek and Roman. The human autonomy that the Renaissance men adopted was exclusively associated with the pagan Græco-Roman culture.

Giovanni Boccaccio, a worldly Florentine burgher, did not possess the profound spiritual insight and character of Dante and Petrarca. He learnt Greek language in order to study the classical pagan literature of the Græco-Roman world in its original languages. Boccaccio's translation of the Greek classics by Homer was one of the cultural stepping stones of the Renaissance which revived Greek literature after 700 years of relative neglect. He was a keen observer of life in Italy in his famous book, ***Decameron***, written in prose which served to create the style of Italian prose.

Owing to the influence of these three mediæval men, Italian literature underwent a rapid development which was cut short by the deaths of Petrarca and Boccaccio, and was not revived again until the second half of the 15th century A.D..

The general enthusiasm for classical Græco-Roman literature was raised to new heights after the conquest of Constantinople by the Muslim Turks in 1453, when a number of Greek scholars from the conquered city escaped to Florence and other northern Italian cities brought with them many classical manuscripts of ancient Greece and Rome.

The city-State Urbino became the center of Italian humanism under the patronage of Duke Federico di Montefeltro (1422-1482) and Guidobaldo di Montefeltro (1472-1508), both ***condottieri*** who were scholarly and cultured in their intellectual interests. Urbino soon became the most learned Italian city which had the best library in Europe.

The Italian princes from the Sforza family in Milan, the Malatesta family in Rimini, and the Montefeltro family in Urbino, all ***condottieri***, created the first centers of research where science and technology were pursued by humanistic engineers.

Duke Francesco Sforza in Milan was involved in building irrigation and navigation canals which had been under construction for centuries. The first major canal, Naviglio Grande, connecting Lake Ticino and Lake Maggiore with Milan, was a mediæval structure. The Martensa Canal connecting Lake Como with Milan was dug by Bertola da Navate, after which the canal from Milan to Pavia and to the Po river, which needed locks, was projected. Filippo degli Organi and Fioravanti of Bologna were the engineers who began the construction of this canal, but Bartolomeo della Valle finished it with the assistance of Leonardo da Vinci.

Sigismondo Malatesta in Rimini was a ***condottieri*** and a devotee of the art of war such as fortifications and engines of war, and he engaged his humanistic engineers in the design of war machinery. He himself probably designed the fortifications at Rhodes and at Ragusa, and it is possible that he even invented the bomb manufactured of wood slats held together with iron bands. Between 1438 and 1446, he had the Rocca Malatestina built which, however, was still quite mediæval in its building style. It is quite apparent that most of the construction carried out during the Renaissance period was done by military engineers in the employ of some despotic duke or prince.

In comparing the achievements of Renaissance engineers with those of the Mediæval Age, it appears that the Renaissance engineers usually had far-reaching and ample capabilities but they did not produce such important, fundamental contributions, particularly in the field of power and building technology, as the engineers of the Mediæval Age. The objective of the mediæval engineer had been to free men from their servitude to nature, so that men could serve God, whereas the Renaissance engineer being energised by his desire for personal fame was eager to serve himself. Therefore, the mediæval engineer promoted Christian virtues in his work, whereas the Renaissance engineer promoted himself. The Italian Renaissance engineer, like the ancient Greek ***architekton***, built structures that were beautiful, but like the ancient Roman ***architectus*** he also made the structures economical to construct through functional design. Therefore, Renaissance art had a direct influence upon Renaissance engineering, which was an important aspect of the Italian Renaissance culture. Above all else, the Renaissance artist-engineer saw himself as a 'universal man', ***uomo universale***, who combined engineering with mathematics, science and art in building economical yet entirely functional and æsthetically more satisfying engineering works.

Since the Protestant Reformers in northern Europe believed that science ought to be cultivated for the glory of God and for the benefit of mankind, the Protestant engineers pursued 'philanthropic' science and technology. According to the ideals of Lutherans such practical arts as technology and engineering should be used for the welfare of man, and not for pretentious display of wealth or power. The belief that the work and research of an engineer ought to benefit the public and mankind first appeared in Germany, the home of Protestantism, in the 1480's. The prevalent practice of the mediæval guilds had been to keep the art of the master craftsmen secret from the lay public. Already the German artist and engineer Albrecht Dürer (1471-1528) had written his works on geometry and on fortification engineering expressly for the betterment and improvement of all craftsmen who required measurement in their work, that is, to the public benefit of all experts and not for personal glory which was the purpose of humanist craftsman in Renaissance Italy.

The Renaissance was certainly a creative period in the human endeavour to excel, yet in the history of technology it does not rank nearly as high as the Mediæval Age which created a natural power revolution, fundamental agricultural and building innovations, and the first genuine advance in the science of mechanics beyond that of the ancient Greeks. In terms of basic inventions and radical improvements accomplished during the Mediæval Age, the Renaissance did scarcely more than develop and increase their size and scope. Machines became larger and more intricate in their mechanisms, and production increased but, surprisingly, there were very few basically new innovations. It is not an exaggeration to say that the Renaissance humanistic artist-engineer-scientist stood on the shoulders of giants when they began to study and develop the remarkable and brilliant works on science, mathematics and engineering of the ingenious men of the Mediæval Age.

The literary Renaissance humanists in Italy, whose mathematical and scientific learning was shallow, made a practice out of stinging their betters. They habitually sought to ridicule the mediæval scientists at every occasion by picking on the worst they could find in the Mediæval Age, yet they readily stooped to plagiarise the scientific methods and mathematical accomplishments originated in the mediæval works. At the same time the Renaissance humanists professed humble servility to the classical Græco-Roman literature with a rigid reverence befitting a mediæval monk. The abusive language, insults and outright obscenities some of the humanists were willing to use in their disputes proved their complete lack of genuine urbanity. It also demonstrates that the so-called Renaissance 'humanism' and the 'humanitarianism' were two completely distinct antipodal ideologies.

CHAPTER IX

BAROQUE TECHNOLOGY: Ascent of Modern Science, Scientific Technology and Scientific Engineering

[from 1550 to 1783]

In the so-called 'Baroque Era', the mathematical science of mechanics, which arose from the pioneering works of the ancient Greek mathematician and mechanical engineer Archytas of Taras (c.428-c.347 B.C.), was revived and revised by the European engineers and scientists. It was a time of preparation for important new scientific developments in technology and engineering. The idea of spontaneous action of nature was gradually replaced by the laws of mechanics, and the concept of 'natural law' anticipated by the ancient Greek natural philosopher and engineer Anaximandros of Miletos (c.610-547 B.C.) from Ionia became firmly established for the first time. In this new scientific atmosphere it was generally recognised that technology and engineering must proceed according to mathematically formulated laws of nature.

The recovery of science of mechanics, scientific technology and scientific engineering began in Italy and in the Netherlands. The explosive power of the gunpowder within the barrel of the cannon, and the ballistic problem of the flight of the cannonball led to the creation of two new sciences: chemistry and mechanics. The explosive force of the gunpowder which propels the cannonball from the barrel of the cannon presented to engineers and scientists the problem of the so-called 'internal ballistics' which led to the study of spontaneous combustion and, therefore, to chemistry. The subsequent motion of the cannonball presented to engineers and scientists the problem of the so-called 'external ballistics', which led to the modern development of mechanics, whereas the manufacture of the cannons and cannonballs led to improvements in metallurgy.

Tartaglia and Ballistics:

The flight of the cannonball as a projectile through the air is a particular case of general motion of bodies in a resisting medium in which the resistance offered by the medium primarily depends upon the speed of motion of the body. The first scientist who tried to determine kinematically and dynamically the trajectory of the cannonball shot from the cannon was the Italian mathematician and engineer Niccolo Fontana (c.1499-1557) of Brescia, who was popularly known as ***Tartaglia***, a nickname meaning the 'stammerer'. When Fontana was 6 years old, the French army plundered his native city. During the ensuing slaughter of civilians in the sack of Brescia, a French dragoon hit him in the mouth with a saber which inflicted an injury so severe that he never regained free use of his tongue. He taught himself to read Latin and Greek, and to master mathematics relying on his own intellectual resources with a diligence that was remarkable. Tartaglia, who had an outstanding mind, not only became a teacher at an early age but also a self-taught technologist, engineer, surveyor and bookkeeper. He earned his living as a mathematician and bookkeeper to bankers and merchants, and as a consulting engineer and technologist to the military artillerists of Italy.

Tartaglia wrote the two earliest treatises on the theory and practice of artillery: < New Science > (***Nova Scientia***) published in 1537 in 3 books, and < Queries and Diverse Inventions> (***Quaesiti et inventioni diverse***) published in 1546 in 9 books, the first 2 books of which contained the discussion of the ballistics problem. He was the first mathematician to insist that the theory of mechanics must be quantitative, and capable of making mathematical predictions, as well as the first theoretician to subject a practical art, the gunnery, to theoretical treatment. Tartaglia's study of the geometry of the trajectory of the cannonball led to the Aristotelian, or the so-called 'Peripatetic projectile trajectory' which consisted of 3 geometric parts: the first rectilinear part of the trajectory is joined to the second transitional part of the trajectory in the form of a circular arc the terminus of which is joined to the third rectilinear part of the trajectory in the form of a vertical line representing the path of the free fall of the projectile. The first 2 parts of the tripartite trajectory according to the ancient Greek scientist-philosopher Aristotle of Stageira (384-322 B.C.) represented what he called 'violent' motion, which counteracted what he called the 'natural' downwards tendency of the projectile as a material body, whereas the 3rd part represented the 'natural' downwards motion. Tartaglia noted that in the beginning of the trajectory the first 'rectilinear' part of the trajectory in the 'violent' motion is actually imperceptibly curved, an effect which he attributed to the influence of gravity, but this curvature is so slight that the trajectory appears to be rectilinear. Although Tartaglia as a theoretician accepted most of the opinions drawn from the experience of expert gunners, he did reject their traditional opinion that the increase of the power of impact of a cannonball is dependent upon the initial acceleration of the cannonball at firing. He maintained that the trajectories of the cannonball projected at the same inclination are dependent upon the initial velocity rather than on the initial acceleration at firing. He attempted to explain the ancient tripartite Peripatetic trajectory, and answer certain practical questions about the range and elevation of trajectories of the cannonball by a series of mechanically motivated propositions. As long as Tartaglia did not recognise the central importance of acceleration in the trajectory kinematics, and did not devote all his efforts to discover the law of acceleration in projectile motion, he could not succeed to find a theoretical method that mathematically gives the path of motion of the projectile, which still remained conceptually obscure and theoretically uncertain. On account of this conceptual confusion, Tartaglia struggled without success in his attempt to find a theoretical explanation, either kinematical or dynamical, for the path of motion of the projectile. He found empirically, and proved experimentally in 1532, that the 45° firing-angle of the cannon resulted in the maximum range of impact of the cannonball. He also gave a detailed description of an instrument, called the 'gunner's quadrant', for the setting of the firing-angle of cannons which was used in gunnery already before Tartaglia's investigations. Tartaglia succeeded to clarify various problems of the sighting of guns at pointblank range, and demonstrate that the extreme range is 10 times the pointblank range.

His second treatise which was written in the form of a dialogue between himself and Francesco Maria della Rovere, the Duke of Urbino, not only dealt with ballistics in the first two books but with artillery in general. The Duke thought that the velocity of the cannonball is the greatest when it leaves the cannon barrel, and from that time forwards the force of impetus and the velocity of the cannonball diminish, little by little, as the cannonball begins to sink, little by little, towards the ground, but Tartaglia's own 'more scientific' explanation of how the velocity and gravity of the cannonball mutually influence each other tended to confuse rather than clarify the ballistics of the cannonball. Tartaglia explained that the larger the velocity of the projectile, the less effective is gravity, and the smaller the velocity, the larger is the effect of gravity but he was unable to establish their mathematical relationship. Tartaglia came to the realisation that as the impetus, '*mv*', and the gravity act simultaneously on the projectile throughout the entire course of flight of the projectile, the 'conflict' between impetus, '*mv*', and gravity is continuous throughout the trajectory and, therefore, the entire trajectory must be curvilinear, which is known as the 'Tartaglia Theorem'. The notion of simultaneous action of two distinct forces upon a moving body had been first examined by the mediæval scholar Jordan de Nemore about 1230. Tartaglia performed many experiments on the influence of the charge, of the length of the cannon barrel, of the weight and the diameter of the cannonball, and of the caliber of the cannon, upon the cannonball's range of impact. His ballistic experiments were the first of its kind in history. Tartaglia's experiments upon the range of impact of the cannonball discredited the ancient Peripatetic explanation of the projectile motion.

Despite the shortcomings of Tartaglia's theoretical ballistics, it was the first systematic attempt to produce a scientific work on the projectile motion. Tartaglia's books on ballistics were so popular that they were still used by the Italian gunners a century later.

In mathematics Tartaglia published < General Treatise on Numbers and Measures > (***General trattado de' numeri e misure***) in 1556, and in 1560, in which he took the first step towards the binomial theorem by finding the coefficients of the expansion of $(1+x)^{n+1}$ from $(1+x)^n$ for $n=2,...,6$. This book contained a wide range of problems in commercial arithmetic, and a collection of mathematical puzzles. No other treatise in the 16th century contained so much information on arithmetic, either in theory or in application. Moreover, Tartaglia was one of the first mathematicians to use an incipient form of the function concept. He also published an Italian translation of < The Elements > (***Stoicheia***) of Eukleides (in English, Euclid).

The Portuguese mathematician Pedro Nunes (Latin name, ***Petrus Nonius***) (1502-1578), who was professor of philosophy and mathematics at the universities in Lisbon and in Coimbra, and the cosmographer of the King of Portugal, published in 1542 a book <On Obscurities> (***De Crepusculis***) in which he described a means to increase the accuracy of graduated instruments used in measuring small angles, the so-called '***Nonius*** scale'. This scale was later replaced by the so-called '***Vernier*** scale', invented in 1631 by the French military engineer and mathematician Pierre Vernier (1580-1637), in the instruments for measurement.

Copernicus and Mathematical Heliocentric Planetary System:

In 1543, a Polish clergyman of German extraction, Nicholas Koppernigk (1473-1543), known by his Latin name ***Nicolaus Copernicus***, published his celebrated treatise on astronomy, <On the Revolutions of Celestial Orbs> (***De revolutionibus orbium coelestium***), the writing of which he probably had finished in 1530. Copernicus' grandfather Niklas Koppernigk was a prosperous German banker and tradesman in Cracow. Copernicus was a genuine Renaissance man in his personal accomplishments: besides being an astronomer he was also a mathematician, physician, diplomat, political administrator, classical scholar, self-educated economist, and a skilled portrait painter. In the political administration of his Chapter of Ermland, he became involved in international finances which motivated him to write a Latin treatise on the general theory of money. In this treatise Copernicus was the first European economist after Nicole Oresme (c.1328-1382) of Paris to stress the tendency of 'bad' money to drive 'good' money out of circulation, a tendency which was rediscovered in 1558 by Sir Thomas Gresham (1519-1579), the founder of the English Royal Exchange, and is still known as the 'Gresham's law'. The astronomical treatise of Copernicus replaced the venerable astronomical work of Ptolemaios (in English, Ptolemy) popularly known by its corrupted title ***Almagest,*** which had been accepted by the astronomers as the best astronomical work for more than 14 centuries. Copernicus was quite familiar with the heliocentric astronomy of Aristarchos of Samos (c.310-230 B.C.), in which all the planets of the Solar system revolved in circular orbits round the fixed center of the Sun, and considered it the best and simplest astronomical system, which he adopted and made his own. Copernicus deliberately removed all references to Aristarchos in his original manuscript in an apparent attempt to leave the impression for posterity that the hypothesis of heliocentric Solar system was his own idea. The new heliocentric astronomy of Copernicus included much of the astronomy already presented by Nicole Oresme in his < Treatise of the Heaven and the World > (***Traité du ciel et du monde***). Also the German Cardinal Nicholas of Cusa (1401-1464) had anticipated the planetary theory of Copernicus by asserting that the Earth turned about its own axis and moved round the Sun in a circular orbit like other planets, and that there is neither 'up' nor 'down' in infinite space which makes any observer to assume that he is in the 'center' of such a centerless space. Nicholas of Cusa was also the first to express the relativistic view of the universe after an earlier brief remark made by Nicole Oresme. By the time of

Copernicus, it had become rather important to have more accurate astronomical predictions for the location of planets, because the knowledge of the precise position of planets was not only important to navigation but also to the reform of the calendar by the Roman Church. Copernicus in his treatise of astronomy virtually duplicated the method, the terminology, the mathematical system, the format, and the general arrangement of astronomical topics of the ***Almagest*** of Ptolemaios. Copernican treatise contained only relatively minor changes from the ***Almagest*** owing to the change from the geocentric to the heliocentric astronomy. The mathematical astronomy of Ptolemaios, which was concerned with angular motions of planets, was not a mathematical planetary system since it consisted of a complex mathematical theory which treated each planet separately and individually; instead of having a single mathematical relation that amalgamated all the different planetary models into a single mathematical planetary system, there was only a general similarity between the mathematical methods used for each planet. The most significant mathematical contribution of Copernicus was his recognition of a common feature in the separate planetary theories, and the use of the common feature in the amalgamation of all the separate planetary theories into a single mathematical planetary system. Curiously, Copernicus himself seems not to have been aware that he had set up the first mathematical planetary system. Qualitatively, Copernican astronomy gave simpler geometric explanations to 2 prominent irregularities in planetary motion, the retrograde motion of a planet and the apparent irregularity of planetary orbital period as observed from the moving Earth, by means of the relative motion between the planet and the Earth, which in Ptolemaic geocentric astronomy could only be explained by means of fictitious mathematical devices. Copernicus' mathematical planetary system was the initial step in enabling astronomers to present the orbit of a physical planet in space by the mathematical device of a circle. Copernicus, who sought in his mathematical cosmology to restore uniform circular motion to the entire planetary system, actually employed more circles in his heliocentric astronomical theory than Ptolemaios had used in his geocentric astronomical theory in the ***Almagest***. The general impression of Copernicus' treatise is that it was a rearranged imitation of the ***Almagest***, and that Copernicus as a successor to Ptolemaios was the last of the ancient astronomers who preferred to look backwards to ancient Greek astronomy for inspiration. He demonstrated that all mathematical techniques used in mathematical astronomy remained essentially unaffected by the change from the geocentric to the heliocentric planetary theory. Still, the mathematical planetary theory of Copernicus was not significantly more accurate in predicting the position of a planet than the complex geometric theory of Ptolemaios. He did not prove the heliocentricity of the planetary system nor the motion of the Earth round the Sun, but merely postulated it like Aristarchos had done in antiquity. The first practical proof that the Earth actually orbits the Sun was the discovery of aberration of light in 1729 by the English astronomer, James Bradley (1693-1762), who found that there is always an apparent shift in the position of a star towards the direction in which the Earth is moving at that moment, a phenomenon he called 'aberration of light', which is due to relative movements of the Earth and of the light from the star, although the shift due to Earth's orbital movement is large compared to that of the light, since the velocity of light is about 10,000 times greater than the 18 miles a second velocity of Earth. Moreover, Bradley discovered by 1747 a minor regular wobble of the Earth's axis called the 'nutation' that is caused by the Moon's attraction of the protuberances of Earth. Bradley also compiled a new star catalogue which surpassed all previous star catalogues in accuracy, and it is still important today in the measurement of individual motions of the stars. In early 1742 Bradley was appointed the Astronomer Royal to succeed Edmund Halley (1656-1742).

In one important respect the Copernican heliocentric formulation of the mathematical planetary system was of great importance to the history of astronomy: It prepared the way for the final physical explanation of planetary motion by means of the science of mechanics.

Professional interest in Copernican astronomy was raised by the publication of < Prussian Tables of Celestial Motion > (***Prutenicae tabulae coelestium motuum***) in 1551 by Erasmus Reinhold (1511-1553), senior professor of mathematics at the Protestant university in Wittenberg, since the tables calculated by Reinhold from Copernican theory were better than the < Alphonsine Tables > of 1272 which the new tables replaced. The new tabular values still had mediocre accuracy because the astronomical observations upon which they were based were insufficient both in their accuracy and number, but it was a step forwards since this book gave a practical demonstration of the value of the mathematical part of Copernicus' treatise and it remained unsurpassed for 80 years.

The Copernican astronomy was at first accepted as an astronomical theory 'to save the phenomena', but when some astronomers began to insist that it represented the world as it really is, which Copernicus himself had believed, in 1616 Pope Pius V declared heliocentric Copernican astronomy a heresy. Even Martin Luther (1483-1546), the German Protestant Reformer, strongly disapproved of Copernicus and Copernican heliocentric astronomy: "People give their ear to an upstart astronomer who strove to show that the Earth revolves, not the Heavens or Firmament, the Sun and the Moon ... The fool wishes to reverse the entire science of astronomy."

De Soto and Law of Free Fall:

A Spanish philosopher, theologian and political theorist, Domingo Francisco de Soto (1494-1560), a contemporary of Tartaglia who had studied in Paris as a layman, wrote a series of textbooks to alleviate the inadequate preparation of his students in logic and natural philosophy at the University of Salamanca in Spain. The inadequate preparation of university students in the two subjects was a common concern of university teachers at the time. De Soto wrote an abridged and simplified textbook on Aristotle's < Physics > in 1545 because, besides his specialties, he also taught physics at his university. In his textbook <Questionary on Eight Books of Aristotle's Physics> (***Questiones super octo libros physicorum Aristotelis***) published in 1555, de Soto proved himself to be the first author in complete command of the kinematical theories of Mertonian scholars from the Merton College in Oxford, who could discuss competently the Mertonian method of 'difform motion' with respect to time alone, and to give examples from nature for motions which are 'uniformly difform' and 'difformly difform' with respect to time [and not space and time simultaneously as had been the usual custom of schoolmen of the Mediæval Age]. De Soto derived the law of free fall as a uniformly difform motion by applying the Mertonian mean speed rule, which gave the distance S of free fall of bodies at time T expressed in terms of modern algebra :

$$S(T) = [(\tfrac{1}{2})V(T)]T = (\tfrac{1}{2})\, gT^2 ,$$

where the speed of free fall $V(T) = gT$, g is the constant acceleration of gravity, and T the time of free fall.

His numerical derivation of the law of free fall in his example, which represented the first triumph of modern kinematics, was accomplished without the assistance of symbolic algebra or geometry. De Soto explicitly stated that bodies in free fall accelerate uniformly, and that bodies projected upwards are subjected to uniform deceleration. It was certainly known in the Late Middle Ages that uniformly varying motion occurs in nature. The first correct published account of the free fall of bodies is in the book of the Spanish Dominican scholar de Soto. De Soto's numerical derivation of the law of free fall, which appears to have been common knowledge in his time, laid the groundwork necessary for the mathematical science of kinematics. Therefore, de Soto anticipated in his textbook the doctrine of free fall of bodies of Galileo Galilei (1564-1642) by almost a century. Francisco Toletus, a student of de Soto at the University of Salamanca, was responsible for his study of de Soto's treatment of free fall of bodies.

Brahe and Precision in Observational Astronomy:

The renowned Danish astronomer of Swedish descent Tyge Brahe (1546-1601), who is generally known by his Latin name ***Tycho Brahe***, was an astronomical observer of exceptional ability and the last important astronomer to obtain observational data on planets without the use of a telescope. He had realised that to improve the precision of astronomical knowledge much more accurate observations were necessary. Therefore, he improved his instruments of astronomical observation by considerably increasing their size. For instance, his mural quadrant had a 19-foot (5.79 m) radius and his celestial globe had a 5-foot (1.52 m) diameter. Brahe, by means of his carefully constructed large instruments, was able to reduce the limit of accuracy of his astronomical measurements to 2 minutes of an arc, whereas it had been about 10 minutes of an arc for both Ptolemaios and Copernicus. Brahe's careful observational data on the planet Mars, collected over

38 years, was remarkably precise and the analysis of this great mass of data by his assistant, the German mathematician Johann Kepler (1571-1630), led Kepler to his revolutionary planetary theory of elliptic orbits. Brahe's observations on Mars created modern observational astronomy by establishing the method of observation and the observational foundation on which Kepler, Robert Hooke (1635-1703) and Isaac Newton (1642-1727) based their astronomical theory. Brahe, an eccentric late Renaissance nobleman, had not only an excessively arrogant, overbearing, tactless, narrow-minded, and vindictive disposition, but also an explosive temper. He had a tendency to be obnoxious and ill-mannered which cost him the favour of his patrons. He sported a silver nose cemented in the place where his real nose had been before it was sliced off in a fencing duel, which he fought at the University of Rostock with a fellow student, who had made slight of his mathematical ability.

Brahe, a confirmed Protestant, adhered to the fundamental teachings of the Bible and believed the Earth to be fixed in the universe. He rejected Copernican theory primarily because he was unable to observe any stellar parallax which should have been a consequence of the Copernican planetary system. In 1577 he had made accurate observations on the position of a comet and shown that it was far off in space beyond the Moon, a region which according to Aristotle should be perfect and immutable. He found the parallax of the comet to be so small that it could not possibly be sublunar. Moreover, the comet moved along an oval orbital path that exceeded the orbit of planet Venus. Brahe contended that comets were astronomical objects which move in the celestial sphere beyond the Moon that according to Aristotle should be perfect and immutable. Brahe's study of this comet was a landmark in astronomy since only one comet, the comet of 1472, had been previously investigated with scientific competence by the German mathematician and astronomer, Johann Müller (Latin name, ***Regiomontanus***) (1436-1476), the best practical astronomer before Copernicus who had written the first book entirely devoted to trigonometry in 1464 after the pioneering treatise composed in 1310 by John Maudith of Merton College in Oxford. Brahe wanted to compromise between the Copernican concept of the universe which was hardly less complex than that of Ptolemaios or Aristotle and, therefore, he adopted the Herakleidean type of astronomical system, in which the Moon and the Sun revolve in circular orbits round the fixed Earth and the 5 planets revolve round the Sun in circular orbits but, unfortunately, his planetary theory did not have a better validity than that of Copernicus. Brahe gave his planetary system, and his observations of the comet made in 1577 in his book published in 1582: ***Astronomiae instauratae progymnasmata***.

Benedetti, Law of Free Fall and Law of Inertia:

Tartaglia's ideas on mechanics were much further developed by his talented but immodest former student, Giovanni Battista Benedetti (1530-1590) of Padua, who was mathematician, chapel master and chief military engineer to the Duke Orsini of Savoy. Benedetti, who had a good grasp of the law of inertia, proposed the correct the law of free fall in his treatise < Book of Diverse Mathematical and Physical Speculations > (***Diversarum speculationum mathematicarum et physicarum liber***) published in 1585. In this book and in his earlier treatise on the proportions of local motion <Demonstration of Proportions of Local Motion Against Aristotle and All Philosophers> (***Demonstratio proportionum motuum localium contra Aristotelem et omnes philosophos***) published in 1554, Benedetti rejected the rules of speed formulated by Aristotle. In the treatment of motion by Benedetti, the theory of impetus became an early form of the principle of inertia since he was the first to maintain clearly that impetus is conserved in a straight line and that any motion by itself is uniform and rectilinear. In the problem of free fall of bodies he showed that unequal bodies of the same material fall the same distance in the same time, a demonstration frequently incorrectly attributed to Galileo. Benedetti showed in his experiments that two equal masses joined by a thread did not fall twice as fast as predicted by Aristotle. He investigated various motions of bodies to find out what was faulty in the impetus theory, and to clarify the nature of circular motion using rigorous mathematical methods of ancient Greek mathematician Archimedes of Syracuse (c.287-212 B.C.). He observed that a stone swung around at the end of a rope when released flew off in a straight line along the tangent of the circle, and that impetus did not interfere with its kinematic condition. Benedetti asserted that the impetus '*mv*' imposed on a body always makes it undergo rectilinear motion, that a constant motive power applied to a body produces an accelerated motion, and that it is quite impossible to distinguish between an impetus for rotation and an impetus for rectilinear translation. These important observations in the historical establishment of the correct principle of inertia accord a place of honour to Benedetti. All these works of Benedetti were written with considerable mathematical sophistication. Benedetti's ideas were plagiarised by a Frenchman Jean Taisnier, who won wide acclaim for a piece of work that was not his. Many years later an Italian mathematician and engineer, Giuseppe Ballo (1567-1640) not only proposed the correct law of inertia in 1635, but also distinguished between the mass and the weight.

Benedetti published a letter in his book <Diverse Mathematical and Physical Speculations> (***Diversarum speculationum mathematicarum et physicarum liber***) in 1585, in which he discussed the application of hydrostatic pressure in communicating vessels and he almost came to the principle of the hydraulic press, which was discovered about the same time by Stevin in The Netherlands.

Stevin, Mathematical Science of Statics and Infinitesimal Mathematics:

The Flemish engineer, bookkeeper, businessman, and mathematician, Simon Stevin (1548-1620) was a practical scientist and a student of ancient Greek science and mathematics, particularly the works of Archimedes of Syracuse, who initiated his studies of statics with consummate skill.

After 1571 he travelled for some years in Scandinavia, Prussia and Poland in the capacity of an engineer, and upon his return in 1577 he worked in Bruges in hydraulic engineering. In 1581 he came to Leyden, and in 1583 became a student at a mature age of 35 at the University of Leyden, which was one of the first universities, if not the very first, to educate engineers. He was well prepared for university education. In 1600 he helped to organise the teaching of mathematics to engineering students in the engineering school recently established by Prince Maurice of Orange at the University of Leyden. At Stevin's urging the instruction in the engineering school was given in Dutch vernacular, whereas in the university lectures were delivered in Latin. Stevin wrote several books on arithmetic, a book on geometry, and 4 books on statics and hydrostatics under the auspices of Prince Maurice of Orange, who kept the original manuscripts in his possession even on his military campaigns but finally decided to have them translated into several languages and made generally available by publication. In 1592, Stevin was put in charge of the waterways of Delft, and in 1593 he was appointed by Prince Maurice of Orange quartermaster general of the Dutch armies, an important position which he occupied the rest of his life. Subsequently, Prince Maurice of Orange appointed Stevin a member of his council, and the superintendent of the financial administration of the State.

In 1586, Stevin wrote 2 books on statics entitled < The Principles of Statics > (***De Beghinselen der Weeghconst***), and <Practical Art of Weighing> (***De Weegdaet***), which contained the following topics: force triangle, force parallelogram, moment of a force, graphical statics, a new simplified proof of the lever principle, a new proof of the law of equilibrium on inclined plane, the vectorial principle of force, resolution of force into two orthogonal components, and the result of an experiment on free-fall with two unequal lead spheres, which he had carried out in 1585 with Jan Cornets de Groot, mayor of Delft and father of the famous jurist of international law, Hugo de Groot (in Latin, ***Grotius***), to disprove Aristotle's law of free fall that postulated the velocity of a falling body to be proportional to its weight. In a type of experiment which was apparently first performed by the Greek scholar Ioannes Philoponos of Alexandria (485-555) about 517, Stevin dropped 2 unequal lead spheres, one 10 times as heavy as the other, simultaneously from a height of 30 feet (9.14 m) onto a board, and found the sound of impact of the two spheres to be almost simultaneous which contradicted the Aristotelian theory of free fall of bodies. He based his original proof of the law of equilibrium on inclined plane and the hydrostatic equilibrium on the idea of impossibility of perpetual motion. He was willing to apply the principle of virtual displacements of the ancient Greek physicist, engineer and mathematician Heron of Alexandria (*floruit* c.130 B.C.) for the explanation of the sustained quasi-static action of simple machines without internal friction, but he did not approve of the principle of virtual velocities of Heron of Alexandria because he thought it absurd to deduce a condition of equilibrium from the considerations of motion, an opinion that overlooked the circumstance that the motion in this principle is the abstract 'virtual motion' which only exists in thought, and is not produced by the acting forces.

In 1586, Stevin also published his researches on hydrostatics in the book entitled <The Principles of Hydrostatics> (***De Beghinselen des Waterwichts***), which contained an original derivation of the floatation principle of Archimedes of Syracuse, and a demonstration that the total pressure on the bottom of the vessel is only dependent upon the head of the water contained in the vessel and the area of the base of the vessel but not the shape of the vessel. This phenomenon, known as the'hydrostatic paradox', Stevin provided with an experimental proof and an application that represents the so-called 'principle of hydraulic press'. In these derivations the transmissibility of the pressure within water, later called the 'Pascal principle', was implied but not explicitly mentioned. Stevin did not yet explicitly state that the pressure at any point in the fluid is the same in every direction although he used this idea in his theory of fluids. In his analysis Stevin introduced the 'principle of solidification': "A solid body of equal specific gravity to water keeps any place given to it in water." This principle was restated in 1743 by the French mathematician Alexis Claude Clairaut (1713-1765): "In any fluid at rest, if any portion be replaced by a rigid solid, the forces exerted by the remainder will not be altered." In 1605, Stevin applied the deduced hydrostatic laws to the study of communicating vessels, and approached the idea of the so-called 'metacentrum' in his treatment of top-heavy floating bodies in the 2nd edition of his book on hydrostatics.

To avoid the logical method of double ***reductio ad absurdum*** used by Eudoxos of Knidos (c.408-c.355 B.C.) in the method of exhaustion, Stevin took a direct passage to the limit in his calculation of the resultant hydraulic force of pressure exerted against a surface by using a method fundamentally the same as given in modern elementary textbooks of calculus. Therefore, Stevin rigorously calculated the resultant force exerted by water upon any inclined plane as the limit of the sum of pressures upon thin strips, when the strips are indefinitely diminished and their number is indefinitely increased. By this accomplishment Stevin became the first scientist to deal successfully with infinitely many forces and, thereby, he was an important link in the gradual transformation of the ancient Greek method of infinitesimal analysis used by Archimedes of Syracuse into the modern infinitesimal analysis of Leibniz.

At the time the academics in the universities preferred the use of the international language Latin to the European vernaculars, because then the weight of classical tradition lent uncritical authority to their own work. To counteract this deplorable neglect of vernaculars, Stevin, Galileo, Pascal and Descartes wrote deliberately in vernacular tongues to make their works accessible to the common people, and to promote the use of vernacular languages in the scientific literature of the important European nations. Stevin, a Flemish engineer who preferred Dutch language to Latin language, published his scientific and engineering books in Dutch vernacular. He was convinced of the excellence of the Germanic languages, and thought that Dutch in particular is the best language to express scientific ideas because it was clear, precise and more concise than Latin and Greek. He wrote <Discourse on the Dignity of the Dutch Language> (***Uytspraek van de Weerdichheyt der Deytsche Tael***) as an introduction to his <The Practical Art of Weighing> (***De Beghinselen der Weeghconst***) to prove by several examples the superiority of Dutch language in scientific discourse. In his day Dutch was as important a language in Europe as English is today. Stevin coined new Dutch words for scientific and engineering terms, and even wrote a dictionary of Dutch (***Deytsch***) language because he wanted to demonstrate that the vernacular Dutch language was not only as good as the international Latin language but, actually, a great deal superior as a means of scientific exposition. Stevin's influence on the Dutch language is still apparent today. In the early Italian Renaissance period Leon Battista Alberti (1404-1472) had been the pioneer promoter of vernacular European languages in science and technology by making the vernacular Italian into a literary, technical language, as did the artist-engineer-mathematician Albrecht Dürer (1471-1528) for the vernacular German, and the physician-mathematician Robert Recorde for the vernacular English.

In 1585 Stevin wrote an influential treatise in Dutch on decimal fractions, < The Tenth > (***De Thiende***), soon translated into French, English and Latin, which not only led to more accurate numerical calculations but also laid the groundwork for the later metric system. Before the appearance of Stevin's book, the decimal system had been used only for whole numbers whereas fractions were still given in the sexagesimal system of ancient Sumerians. Stevin, a man of genius, is one of the greatest arithmeticians of all time, and his work on algebra published in 1594 in French, < Algebraic Appendix, containing general rules for all equations > (***Appendice algébraique contenant règle générale de toutes équations***),which contained the general rule for solving numerical equations of any degree, was one of the highest and best achievements in the algebra of the Renaissance Age.

In 1599, Stevin published the last 16th century treatise on terrestrial magnetism < The Haven-finding Art > (***De Havenvinding***), which was not only widely read in the original Dutch but also in its Latin, English and French translations. In this book, Stevin recognised the value of declination measurements in navigation, although he was less optimistic than some of his contemporaries about its accuracy. In 1608, Stevin's books on statics, hydrostatics, and applied mathematics were published not only in Dutch and in French, but also in Latin translation entitled < Mathematical Memoranda > (***Hypomnemata mathematica***) in Leyden which made his works on mechanics widely known in Europe.

Stevin improved the scoopwheel design by reducing the number of blades from the standard 24 to 6, and by engaging the turning gears on their faces rather than on their felloes in an anticipation of bevel-gearing. From 1588 forwards he constructed in collaboration with his friend

Jan Cornets de Groot, a number of turret pumping-windmills (***watermolens***) incorporating his scoopwheels, the technical aspects of which Stevin abstracted into a mathematical theory in his treatise < About Watermills > (***De Watermolens***) in 1589, the very first book on the science of hydraulics which was influential in windmill design in Europe. In it, Stevin calculated the efficiency of windmills used in the drainage of polders. In 1589 Stevin patented his turret pumping-windmill which was 4 times as efficient as other such mills. However, Stevin overlooked in his calculations the effect of internal friction in the machinery that made him overestimate the pumping efficiency of his windmill, which could also be operated by a horsewhim. In mechanical engineering Stevin patented a special kind of winch for moving ships across shallow waters or dams, and a pivoted sluice-gate for canals and harbours. In 1600, he designed a successful sail-propelled chariot called the '***Zeylwagen***' that was built to the order of Maurice of Nassau, the Prince of Orange, who took a 14-mile trip in it with a group of 28 people. This ***'Zeylwagen'*** survived several centuries. Stevin also designed another, smaller sail-chariot which was still extant in 1802. Stevin's sail-chariots, which were capable of reaching speeds as high as 46 miles (75 km) an hour, earned him more repute with his contemporaries than all his other more important scientific and technological works. In 1589, he patented a remarkable version of a mud-hopper, a design which was about 3 centuries ahead of its time.

In his capacity as a military engineer, Stevin published in 1617 his dual treatise on castrametation and hydraulic defences, < Castrametation, Laying Out of Military Camps. New Kind of Fortification by Sluices > (***Castrametatio, dat is Legermeting. Nieuwe maniere van sterctebov door spilsluysen***), which was the first such work in Europe. He introduced the use of dykes and flooding as a method of defence against invading foreign armies.

Stevin also promoted scientific cooperation because, in his opinion, joint effort and contributions of many people are necessary for the advancement of scientific knowledge. He gave astronomy as a good example for such a cooperation, and he thought that what was true in astronomy was also true in all sciences and technology.

In 1608, Stevin also attempted to develop a general theory of tides based on the idea of Lunar attraction, and he gave a rough means of calculating the beginning of ebb and flow from Lunar observations. This imperfect theory represented the most important progress in the theory of tides before Isaac Newton's ***Principia***. He invented photogrammetry in his book on < Geometry > (***Wiskunde***) in 1605. Owing to his interest in fortifications, Stevin also wrote a treatise on the theory of perspective for Prince Maurice of Orange, which was one of the first theoretical studies of it.

Stevin was the best theoretician in mechanics in the long period from Archimedes of Syracuse to Galileo Galilei, and one of the foremost mathematicians of the 16th century A.D.. His mathematical proofs were rigorous and based on explicit hypotheses. Stevin's scientific work was founded on a sound and reliable background in experience and experiment, something that was mostly missing in the works produced by his successors in the 16th century. He made particularly clear the distinction between geometry, arithmetic, and also statics, which he considered to be a completely separate and independent branch of applied mathematics. Stevin demonstrated in his scientific works a remarkably competent and profound insight into the nature and function of theoretical sciences and, particularly, into the relation between rational mechanics and experimental mechanics - an insight which even many modern scientists seem to lack. Stevin was extraordinarily astute in the sharpness of his reasoning, and in the clarity, precision and effectiveness of his scientific exposition which was eminently superior to the journalistic style of exposition of Galileo. He was the most original man of science in the second half of the 16th century for he was conspicuously outstanding in many fields and, yet, he has not received all the fame which he fully deserves. Stevin's work gave a huge boost to the development of theoretical mechanics and scientific engineering, and the first person to launch his scientific investigations from that of Stevin was a Dutch physician, schoolmaster, scientist, and engineer, Isaac Beeckman (1588-1637), who in 1618 introduced the French philosopher, mathematician, and a former musketeer in the army of Prince Maurice of Orange, René Descartes de Perron (1595-1650), to the study of physics.

Kepler, Physical Astronomy, Instrumental Optics and Scientific Revolution:

The great revolution in science was launched by the German mathematician and astronomer, Johann Kepler, a mathematical genius of astoundingly rich imagination. He had a tendency to mysticism and his mind was a curious mixture of ancient Greek and modern ideas. In concert with his family tradition, Kepler was prone to rather extravagant speculations and occult fancies. One of his aunts was burnt alive at the stake as a witch, and when his mother was accused of sorcery, only Kepler's prominent position and appeal together with the generous help of influential friends saved her from a similar ghastly fate. Despite the irritable nature of Kepler, which was aggravated by chronic ill health, myopia, multiple vision and crippled hands resulting from a childhood bout with smallpox, he had a disarmingly dynamic personality and a keen lightning-quick mind. He was kind and considerate towards his fellow scholars, and particularly generous to his contemporary Galileo Galilei, who was manifestly unworthy of it. Kepler was the first mathematician to free astronomy from the trammels of the Aristotelian physics. He overthrew the ancient Pythagorean æsthetic belief in the prominence of circular motion in nature by regarding instead the rectilinear motion as the privileged one in the physical world. His creative intelligence revealed itself in the high order of his intellectual proficiency, the breath and profundity of intuition, exceptional mental astuteness, copious imagination and astounding knack for conceptual organisation. In his scientific imagination, Kepler was a dedicated believer in the inventive power of analogies, and in the precise mathematical formulation of sciences. Kepler's philosophical speculations in science, despite their enthusiastic nature, never failed to comply with factual analysis. Kepler scrutinised round a problem with a commanding touch and proficiency of intuition that was astonishing in its scope, which the begrudging Galileo was singularly unable to match. Although Kepler's science was in perfect harmony with his faith, his method of scientific enquiry was not only completely independent of all theological and philosophical tenets, but it remained distinctly different from similar methods in the ancient and the mediæval science. His prodigious industry, his inventive genius, his mathematical ingenuity, and his unfailing sense for significant physical facts are still awesome. Moreover, Kepler was a skilled expert in the art of computing, which he set upon a modern foundation by his computational procedures with logarithms, for he performed an immense amount of ingenious numerical computations in mathematical astronomy.

Kepler expressed his basic aim in astronomy as follows: "My intention is to show that the heavenly machine is not a kind of divine, live being, but a kind of clockwork (and he who believes that a clock has a soul, attributes the clockmaker's glory to his work), insofar as nearly all the manifold motions are caused by a most simple, magnetic and material force, just as all motions of the clock are caused by a simple weight. And I also show how these physical causes are to be given numerical and geometrical expression." The fundamental idea of Kepler that a single kind of force is causing the operation of the entire planetary system expressed in this statement was entirely correct, but this force is not magnetic as Kepler surmised, but rather gravitational as was later postulated by Robert Hooke and mathematically corroborated by Isaac Newton.

Kepler graduated from the University of Tuebingen with a degree of Master of Arts in 1591 earning second honours in a class of 14. In 1594 he was appointed district mathematician and lecturer in mathematics and astronomy at the Protestant Cathedral School [***Stiftsschule***] in Graz in Styria. In 1600 Kepler was appointed Imperial Mathematician by Emperor Rudolph to assist the celebrated observational astronomer Tyge Brahe in Prague. After the sudden death of Brahe in 1601, Kepler succeeded Brahe as the Chief Imperial Mathematician but at a reduced salary which was virtually always arrears. The Crown's debt of salary and gratuities to Kepler reached 12,000 florins by 1627. Kepler began his new job in an attempt to improve Brahe's observational data by eliminating errors owing to atmospheric refraction, which led him to his study of optics, and vision through different media, and to the optical function of the human eye.

Kepler had an intense and passionate interest in scientific principles, and a profound respect for the so-called 'stubborn facts' which, as he insisted, had to be strictly satisfied by precise mathematically formulated scientific theories. Kepler was the first scientist to recognise the fundamental significance and importance of the scientific law of nature, and he made an essential contribution to the modern conception of scientific hypotheses which were his two conspicuous achievements in celestial mechanics. Kepler thought that any basic question in science can be explained only by means of comprehensive hypotheses. He also broke new ground in his investigation of the meaning of the concept of force and mass in physical astronomy. In Kepler's treatises the law of nature for the first time assumed a crucial place in the foundation of modern mathematical sciences. Kepler insisted that his mathematical theory of physical astronomy not only be mathematically precise but also physically plausible. Copernicus had remained quite indifferent to physical reality in his heliocentric astronomy whereas Kepler could not ignore physical reality in his physical astronomy.

Kepler's physical astronomy created a veritable 'revolution' in the history of science, since it represented a critical turning point in the progress of science by ushering in a change towards the modern scientific method, which marks the very beginning of modern science. Kepler was the first scientist in history to formulate successfully the laws of physics in a precise mathematical form involving new conceptions of geometry and algebra, and to establish equation as the standard form of mathematical law in physical sciences, all of which made Kepler's science genuinely modern. He created a new scientific era with his neoteric method of science characterised by a consistent application of precise mathematical formulation and elaboration of scientific hypotheses, and with strict satisfaction of mathematically deduced results from his scientific hypotheses with empirical facts of high order of accuracy. Kepler was guided in the development of his scientific physical astronomy by his refined sense for mathematical formulation. He was the first scientist to cast physical laws successfully into their precise mathematical form. In retrospect, Kepler, more than anybody else, had a profound and lasting influence on the development of all physical sciences. Judging from Kepler's comprehensive work, mathematics more than anything else was responsible for the creation of modern science.

Kepler founded 2 new sciences: physical astronomy and instrumental optics. Few men in history have accomplished as much in founding a new science as Kepler in founding the physical astronomy. It was the most monumental problem man had ever faced, and Kepler's intellectual struggle in striving to establish physical astronomy was of epic proportions. He undertook to search for a physics which was valid alike in the heavens and on Earth. Kepler had a sound conception of the universe as a system of material bodies the arrangement and motion of which in space should disclose a common principle of design, and afford a universal generalisation which makes it possible to prove that the phenomena of 'each part' of the celestial system is consistent with a single general design. He tried to demonstrate that the Solar system consists of planets as material bodies the motions of which in space are governed by precise mathematically expressible laws regulated by physical forces. Like any important creator of a new science, Kepler accomplished much that was right but he also failed in much. In most of his voluminous works, Kepler always explained in great detail how he obtained his results in physical astronomy which included not only his thoughts, assumptions, errors and theoretical detours but also his self-criticisms that revealed his willingness to jest about his own follies and foibles. Kepler gave the following reason for his explanations: "The roads by which men arrive at their insights into celestial matters seem to me almost as worthy of wonder as those matters in themselves." Kepler was the founder of celestial mechanics by substituting a mechanical system for the purely formal schemes of earlier astronomers, the laws of nature for mathematical rules, and causal explanation for the mathematical description of planetary motion. He identified celestial mechanics with terrestrial mechanics, although he did nothing in terrestrial mechanics itself.

Kepler was interested in the Pythagorean conception of the relative sizes of the orbits of planets which the Pythagoreans thought were proportional to the lengths of the successive strings on a harmoniously tuned string instrument, a condition believed by the Pythagoreans to guarantee a harmony of the heavenly spheres that was satisfying to their general philosophical and æsthetic objective of celestial harmony. Kepler believed that there exists a correspondence between the planets and the regular solids or polyhedra known to Pythagoreans, and he considered it as a depictive form of an actual mathematical relation which governs the Solar system. He described the correspondence between the admirable proportion of the celestial orbits and the 5 regular geometric solids as the cosmographic mystery (***mysterium cosmographicum***). In his first major treatise, < The Forerunner of Dissertations on the Cosmography, containing the Cosmographic Mystery > (***Prodromos dissertationem cosmographicum continens mysterium cosmographicum***) published in 1596 (2nd edition, 1621), Kepler made his first determined effort to purge the Copernican astronomy from the remaining mathematical apparatus of Ptolemaic astronomy, as well as to pose the problem of finding the law connecting the relative distances of the planets from the Sun by means of geometry. Kepler's main intention all throughout his life was to find a mathematically expressible law which ties all the members of the Solar system together by revealing their distribution as well as their motions in space, and his first major treatise was the first step in this inspired aspiration. Kepler stated his intention as follows: "I undertake to prove that God, in creating the universe and regulating the order of the cosmos, had in view the five regular bodies of geometry known since the days of Pythagoras and Plato, and that He has fixed, according to those dimensions, the number of heavens, their proportions, and the relations of their movements." The conviction that God had designed the world according to size, number and weight (***in mensura et numero et pondere***) was already a popular notion during the mediæval times. Kepler wanted to prove that God, the great geometer of the universe, in creating and regulating the cosmos had partitioned the heavenly space according to the 5 regular solids [or polyhedra] known as 'Platonic solids' [cube or hexahedron, pyramid or tetrahedron, octahedron, dodecahedron, and icosahedron], which could be fitted geometrically into spaces between the 6 known planets, and set according to those dimensions their numerical relations and the relations of their movements. He separated the 5 polyhedra into 2 groups by the orbit of the Earth: 3 in one group (the cube, the pyramid and the dodecahedron) and 2 in the other (the octahedron and the icosahedron).The cube (or hexahedron) has square faces; the octahedron, icosahedron and the pyramid (or tetrahedron) have triangular faces, and the dodecahedron has pentagonal faces. The planet Saturn is circumscribed by a cube in which the planet Jupiter is inscribed, the planet Jupiter is circumscribed by the tetrahedron and inscribed by a dodecahedron, and so on. Kepler believed that the clue to God's mind was the geometric order and the numerical relations expressed in the geometrical features of the simple heliocentric scheme of the Solar system. Kepler was persistent in the pursuit of his deep conviction that there exists in nature a recondite and subtle relation which can furnish the key to the problems of the universe. In this treatise Kepler revealed an important discovery that all the planes of the planetary orbits lie nearly, but not entirely, in the plane of the ecliptic and pass through the center of the Sun, an important celestial condition overlooked by Copernicus which left his astronomical work in a certain sense incomplete.

Kepler attempted to determine the relative spacing of the 6 known planetary orbits by nesting them in and around the 5 regular polyhedra, but it failed to work out to his complete satisfaction. He felt that this geometric correspondence should reveal the master plan according to which the Solar system had been created by God and, therefore, provide the reason for the number of known planets, their sizes and their observed orbital diameters. It was an enthusiastic attempt to discover the 'hidden harmony' of the Solar system and link the 6 known planets and their respective distances from the Sun with the relationship between 5 regular geometric solids of the Pythagoreans. Such a 'celestial harmony' was only an abstract mathematical conception, and the infinity of the world only a metaphysical opinion to Kepler.

Already in this treatise, Kepler attributed the motion of the Moon to the attraction of the Earth (***luna potius trahitur***). In his opinion, to understand motion it is necessary to realise that all matter has the natural inclination for the state of rest (***inclinatio ad quietem***) which represents the force of inertia (***vis inertiae***),a term coined by Kepler, of all material bodies. Therefore an immaterial force (***vis immateriata***) is required to overcome the force of inertia of a material body such as a planet to set the planet into its orbital motion. This incorrect principle of inertia was a difficult obstacle for Kepler to overcome in the development of his physical astronomy, because he found it necessary to assume that each planet had to be subjected to the action of an immaterial force as the cause of motion emanating from the Sun, which he regarded as the very seat of all celestial power. This immaterial force as the cause of motion of the planets had to diminish in some mathematical proportion with the increasing distance from the Sun, whereas the speeds of planets decrease quicker than their distances from the Sun increase. At one time Kepler imagined that the immaterial magnetic force from the Sun emanates like a mighty vortexlike whirlpool that is responsible for the motion of the planets. Kepler frequently called the Solar force 'magnetic effluvium' (***effluvium magneticum***) because he always remained under the influence of William Gilbert who in 1600 presumed that the celestial forces emanating from the Sun were all magnetic.

This treatise of Kepler, distinguished with brilliant exposition, novel and significant scientific ideas, mathematical ingenuity, religious fervour mixed with metaphysical speculations and fantasy so typical of Kepler's works, was well received by his contemporaries, and served to bring Kepler to the attention of Brahe, who found Kepler's ideas not only interesting but also ingenious. Even the presumptuous Galileo, contrary to his usual pompous attitude, found this work of Kepler 'promising'.

The so-called 'three-body problem' of the Earth-Moon-Sun appears first in Kepler's treatise < On Lunar Hypothesis > (***De lunae hypothesi***) published in 1602, but he didn't have a clue how to treat such a problem of celestial mechanics.

In contrast to the ancient Greek astronomy, which was essentially celestial kinematics, Kepler wanted to find a physical explanation for celestial motions. In his concern for physical reality, Kepler endeavoured to find out the meaning of force in its application to heavenly bodies. He assumed a field of force to exist in space which emanates from the Sun and acts on the planets. Since Kepler believed in the concept of inertia based on common direct terrestrial experience that a body moves only when acted on by a force, but otherwise has the natural inclination to remain at rest, he could explain planetary motion round the Sun by assuming that the field of force created by the Sun is driving the planets. Kepler was the first scientist to introduce celestial dynamics as well as the idea of general gravitation (***gravitas***) to astronomy. However, in Kepler's celestial dynamics motion was a 'process', that is, a body moved only when a force was acting on it. In his physical astronomy Kepler was the first scientist to propose the principle of inertia of matter as the perseverance of matter in the 'state of rest'. Kepler did not realise that the general concept of inertia was the preservation of matter in any of its state of motion and, therefore, preservation in the 'state of rest' of matter is only a particular instance of inertia. Kepler's physical astronomy was the very beginning of celestial mechanics. Kepler thought of gravity as the tendency of cognate [material] bodies to unite, and if it were not for the motive power carrying the Earth and the Moon around their orbits, they would rush together and meet at an intermediate point. Kepler regarded this gravitational tendency to be caused by the tractive force (***virtus tractoria***) when he argued for the first time, that all attractions, such as gravity, which one body exerts upon another, are mutual (***mutuus***). His great originality was in making this attraction mutual, and expressing it in dynamic terms. Yet he never reached complete clarity about gravity. Therefore, Kepler thought that a satellite like the Moon was kept in its orbit by the tractive force (***virtus tractoria***) exerted externally by one body, such as the Earth, upon another body, such as the Moon, thereby propelling the Moon forwards in its orbit. He advanced many hypotheses on the nature of gravitational attraction, by speculating it to be subject to the law of inverse-square of the distance between two celestial bodies such as the Earth and the Moon in analogy with the photometric law for the spreading of light intensity from a source in space, and to be proportional to the masses of the two bodies, which he called ***moles***, but he did not pursue this capital idea any further. Kepler assumed that the attractive tractional force (***virtus tractoria***) of the Moon actually extends to the Earth because he assumed the ebb and flow of the tides to be caused by the Moon pulling the waters of the seas towards itself, a theory which had been foreshadowed by the English mediæval scientist Robert Grosseteste (c.1170-1253). He thought that a much stronger attractive force exerted by the Earth extended to the Moon and beyond. Kepler applied this concept of gravitation to the Earth and the Moon. He did make the following remark on gravity in his commentaries on the motion of Mars: "... a mutual bodily tending towards their union or function." Kepler reached out towards the idea of general gravitation but he stopped short of complete success. Although Kepler's revolutionary explanation of planetary motion by means of terrestrial dynamics was ultimately not tenable, it was of great historical importance because it attempted to establish celestial mechanics which was identical to terrestrial mechanics. It represented a definite break with the Aristotelian doctrine of the fundamental difference between the sublunar and the celestial world, a doctrine which had been questioned already in the Late Middle Ages. In all of his astronomical works, Kepler attempted to correlate astronomical observations with the mathematical formulation of physical events, and he was the first scientist to do so.

His painstaking masterpiece, < New Astronomy Concerning the Search for Causes ... of the Motion of the Star Mars from the Observations of Tycho Brahe > (***Astronomia nova aitiologetos, ... de motibus stellae Martis ex observationibus G.V. Tychonis* Brahe**), the first treatise of modern astronomy and an astronomical landmark, was finished in outline in 1605, and published in 1609 in Prague. In this treatise, Kepler announced the first two of his famous three planetary laws

[I] The Law of Elliptical Orbits - The planets move in elliptic orbits with the Sun located at one of the foci of the ellipse;

[II] The Law of Equal Areas - Every planet moves with nonuniform speed along its orbit in such a manner that its radius from the Sun sweeps out equal areas in equal times.

He found the second law [II] in 1600, long before the first law [I]. By that time Kepler had attained a greater clarity of various physical relations in his physical astronomy. Kepler intended to establish in the course of this work a new astronomy as the 'physics of the sky', which was based on causation and derived from his investigation of the motion of planet Mars. He inferred that gravity (***gravitas***) is a general property of all matter, and that the gravitational attraction of any body is proportional to its mass (***moles***), and for this reason the Earth attracts the stone more than the stone attracts the Earth. In this proposition Kepler was probably influenced by a suggestion made by William Gilbert in 1600 that the effect of a magnet is proportional to its mass. However, Kepler differed from Gilbert when he asserted that unlike a magnet, which attracts only in the direction of the pole, the attraction of a material body acts in all spatial directions. If 2 stones were at rest in space and free of the influence of the orb of the traction force (***orbis virtutis tractoriae***) of a 3rd material body, then the 2 stones would come together at an intermediate point along the straight line connecting the two bodies, each stone approaching the other in proportion to the other's mass. This is the earliest statement foreshadowing the principle of conservation of momentum. The 'intermediate point' in modern physics is the center of mass of the 2 stones. In general, all bodily substances located beyond the orb of influence of other bodies are everywhere in equilibrium in space. There are no 'absolutely light' bodies made of earthy substance, but merely 'lighter' or 'heavier' bodies, since contrary to Aristotle all bodies have weight relative to the Earth. Lightness of a body by definition meant to Kepler that it is merely less dense and, therefore, less attracted by the Earth. The Moon like any stone would crash on Earth under the gravitational attraction of the Earth if it were not held in its orbit round the Earth by the centrifugal force of its motion, whilst the moving force (***virtus movens***) imposed by the Earth drives the Moon in the tangential direction of its orbit. In this claim Kepler had a famous forerunner, the ancient Greek philosopher and mathematician, Anaxagoras of Klazomenai (499-428 B.C.), who stated: "...as the Moon and the stars are all heavy, they would fall on Earth if the centrifugal force would not prevent it." Anaxagoras also asserted that air is 'heavy', and that there are neither 'absolutely heavy' nor 'absolutely light' bodies.

Since in Kepler's conception the force of inertia offers resistance against 'every' change of state including the' state of rest', the impelling action of the moving force, which becomes weaker the further the Moon withdraws from the Earth, is essential. Kepler believed that there had to be 2 antagonistic forces, such as the moving force and the force of inertia, acting on any celestial body because a single force could produce neither an oval orbit nor periodic changes of speed.

Kepler had to determine the area of a sector in an ellipse and the length of an elliptic arc. Some of his calculations in this book correspond to approximations of modern elliptic integrals, such as his evaluation of the approximate perimetric length $\pi(a+b)$ for an orbital ellipse with very small eccentricity and the semimajor and the semiminor axis a and b, respectively, and the evaluation of another elliptic integral in this work was:

$$\frac{1}{\pi}\int_0^\pi r\,d\alpha \;,$$

where $r = \sqrt{1 + 2\, e\, cos\alpha + e^2}$, and $e = 0.09165$, using his surprisingly effective infinitesimal method. He evaluated the integral,

$$\int_0^{\phi} sin\phi \; d\phi = 1 - cos\phi$$

by a similar infinitesimal method.

Since the ellipse above can be produced from a circle of radius a by a transformation through which the ordinate of the circle at each point of the diameter as the abscissa is shortened according to the given ratio $b{:}a$, then it is possible to think of the area of the circle and the area of the ellipse as made up of the ordinates for points on the corresponding curves; as the ordinates of the 2 curves are in the ratio of $b{:}a$, the 2 corresponding areas must have the same ratio. Therefore, the area A of the ellipse and the area of the circle with radius a, πa^2, are in the ratio b/a : $A/\pi a^2 = b/a$, giving the area of the ellipse as $A = \pi ab$, a result which already Archimedes of Syracuse had rigorously proven in antiquity although it was not known in Kepler's time. In his investigation of elliptical orbits, Kepler found empirically the so-called 'Kepler Equation', one of the first transcendental equations, which gives the length of the radius vector r of the planetary orbit:

$$r = a - (a\, e)\, cos\, E\,,$$

and its direction,

$$r\; cos\, E_m = a\, cos\, E - (a\, e)\,,$$

where a is semimajor axis, e the eccentricity, E the eccentric anomaly from the aphelion, and E_m the mean anomaly. Kepler solved this transcendental equation in a particular case by means of special values.

On account of the very effective infinitesimal methods used in ***Astronomia nova***, this work is also important in the history of infinitesimal calculus, because Kepler was one of the important pioneers in differential and integral calculus.

This work, in which Kepler made the first major advance in astronomical theory, inaugurated the so-called 'Scientific Revolution' in Europe. Kepler discarded all qualitative speculations and based his physical astronomy on quantitative physical principles. The first and the second laws of planetary motion of Kepler yielded information on the motion of individual planets, discoveries which made Kepler inordinately elated, but he was not yet entirely satisfied because the two laws did not furnish any information on the mathematical relationship between the motions of different planets.

In his brilliant success with the Solar system Kepler had reached the very brink of general gravitation: "Gravity is the mutual bodily tendency between cognate [material] bodies towards unity or contact, so that the Earth draws a stone much more than the stone draws the Earth." Kepler also illustrated the gravitational attraction of the Earth with the example of a falling apple, a story which was later publicised as a popular anecdote about how Newton first discovered gravitation. Kepler assigned gravitation (***gravitas***) to act exclusively between the Earth and the Moon without any restriction and used it to give the correct explanation of tides. He taught that the force of gravitation was proportional to the masses of the Earth and the Moon, and further intimated that it was inversely proportional to the square of the distance to the Moon, but he could not make himself to apply this gravitational law to the other planets despite the fact that he was virtually at the threshold of the concept of general gravitation.

The year 1612 had been an exceptionally good year for the wine industry in Austria, but Kepler was astounded by the crude methods used by the wine merchants to evaluate the capacities of various wine kegs. He studied the problem and published his reflexions on it in a work printed in 1615, < New Stereometry of Wine Kegs > (***Nova stereometria doliorum vinariorum***), in which he found volumes of solids known to Archimedes of Syracuse in addition to some new solids. Although Kepler considered proofs of Archimedes absolutely perfect (***absolutae et omnibus numeris perfectae***), in this work he resorted to the idea of the 'infinitely great' and the'infinitely small' to avoid the labourious method of exhaustion of Eudoxos of Knidos. The idea of the 'infinite' and the 'infinitesimal' had been used with ingenuity by one of the best mathematicians, cosmographers, philosophers and certainly the most outstanding intellectual of the 15th century, Cardinal Nicholas of Cusa, whose works had a considerable influence on Kepler. He always spoke of the Cardinal as the "divine late Cusanus (***divinus mihi Cusanus***)." The mathematical work of Kepler incorporated the most complete expression of Nicholas of Cusa's mathematical thoughts on the infinite and the infinitesimal. Kepler, like Nicholas of Cusa, regarded the circle to consist of an infinite number of triangles having a common vertex at the centroid of the circle, and the circumference of the circle to be a regular polygon with infinite number of sides each one of these sides being the base of a narrow triangle. Then evidently the area of the circle is given by half of the product between the circumference and the radius of the circle. Similarly, Kepler regarded a sphere to consist of an infinite number of narrow cones with a common vertex at the center of the sphere, from which follows that the volume of the sphere is ⅓ of the product between its surface area and its radius. Despite the fact that Kepler did not introduce a clearly defined limit concept and a general method of summation of infinitesimal quantities, he was able to achieve correct results with very limited effort. By applying this 'geometric atom' method of calculus Kepler was able to find volumes of 93 solids obtained by rotating segments of conic sections about an axis in their plane. In his astronomical researches, Kepler made frequent use of graphical representation of geometric figures as functions. Using his numerical function method he established the 'stationary condition' of a function at its maximum or minimum value in the last section of this book by showing that the function has virtually equal numerical values immediately to the left and to the right of such an extremum value of the function. Kepler, who was concerned with numerical values of the volume, expressed his observation in terms of numerical 'increments' and 'decrements' of the volume near the maximum value of the volume. He observed that as the maximum volume was approached, the change in the volume for a given change in dimensions became smaller and smaller. Nicole Oresme had made a similar observation in the Late Middle Ages when he noticed that in the graphical representation of a semicircular latitudinous form, the rate of change of the latitudinous form became the least at the maximum point of the latitudinous form, an idea which gave the 'necessary condition' for the minimum and maximum of a function in modern calculus by means of the concept of derivative. Kepler's increment and decrement on the other hand led to the concept of the 'differential' which became the principal concept in calculus until replaced by the derivative in the early 19th century by the Bohemian mathematician and divine, Bernardus (alias, Bernhard) Placidus Johann Bolzano (1781-1848), and the French mathematician and engineer Augustin Louis Cauchy (1789-1857). In this section of the book, Kepler demonstrated that among all the right parallelpipeds having a square base the cube has the largest volume, and that among all the right circular cylinders having the same diagonal, the largest one has the diameter and altitude ratio of 2½ to 1.

Kepler's < New Stereometry of Wine Kegs > enjoyed considerable popularity which was later rivalled only by < Geometry of Continuum of Indivisibles > published in 1635 by the cleric Francesco Bonaventura Cavalieri (1598-1647) in Italy. Unlike the ancient Greek mathematicians who saw no way to connect the logical gap between the rectilinear and the curvilinear figures, Kepler used Nicholas of Cusa's scholastic 'principle of continuity' which recognised no 'essential' difference between a polygon with an infinite number of sides and the circle, that is, between the finite and the infinite. Kepler appears to have considered proofs obtained by the method of exhaustion, by the limit concept, by infinitesimal elements, and by indivisibles as equally valid. Kepler's method of infinitesimals was of tremendous importance to the invention of calculus for he was the first mathematician since Archimedes of Syracuse to make completely free use of infinitesimals with such surprising effectiveness which opened up a vast field of mathematics and made him one of the important precursors of infinitesimal calculus.

In 1619, Kepler, after 17 years of intensive work, finally found and published in the 3rd chapter of Book II of his treatise,< The Harmony of the World > (***Harmonices mundi***), his third law of planetary motion:

[III] The Harmonic Law - The squares of the periods of revolution of any 2 planets are as the cubes of their mean distances from the Sun:

$$T^2 \propto r_m^{\ 3} \ , \text{ or } \ T^2 = C\, r_m^{\ 3},$$

where C is a constant having the same value for all planets, T is the period of revolution of the planet, and r_m denotes the mean distance of the planet from the Sun which for elliptic orbits is the semimajor axis a. In contrast to his first two planetary laws, his third law was only approximate.

Kepler called his third planetary law, the Harmonic Law, because it established a very simple relationship between the orbits of planets. The third Harmonic Law [III] relates the mean distance of planet, r_m , from the Sun to the period of the planet, T, which is readily obtained from observations. In this way a complete geometrical model of the planetary system can be set up, and if one absolute value is known all the rest of the values follow from his Harmonic Law. Kepler's exuberance knew no bounds in his jubilation over the discovery of his third law of planetary motion which applied to the entire Solar system, since it confirmed his fundamental assumption that the Solar system has a common mathematical design. Finally, the entire Solar system was completely exposed in all its simplicity since the Harmonic Law linked together every single planet of the system by connecting their distances with their periods of revolution. He discovered later that his Harmonic Law also applies to the 4 satellites of the planet Jupiter.

It was in 1672 when French astronomers were able to obtain the first reliable measurement of the distance of planet Mars from the Earth, when this planet was at the nearest point in its orbit to the Earth, and from this reliable measurement the astronomers were finally able to find the distances to other planets from the Earth and reliable dimensions of the entire Solar system by means of Kepler's planetary laws as Kepler had predicted.

In this work, Kepler gave a correct explanation for the ebb and tide on the other side of Earth by the attraction of the Moon, and mentioned the creation of particularly high spring floods caused through the conjunction of the Sun and the Moon, which explicitly recognised the attraction exerted by the Sun upon the Earth. The ancient Greek Pytheas, a contemporary of Alexandros of Macedonia [alias Alexander the Great], was the first author to recognise the relation of tides to the phases of the Moon, and to draw attention to their periodic fluctuation.

Kepler formulated his famous 3 laws of planetary motion, which are the all-important landmarks in the history of astronomy and mathematical sciences, after many years of colossal mathematical effort in founding the science of astronomy from the accurate observations of the motion of the planet Mars made by Tyge Brahe, his former superior.

Kepler's mathematical study of harmonies led him to the problem of filling planes and space with regular figures. Kepler also made significant contributions to the subject of polyhedra when he discovered the cuboctahedron, rhombic dodecahedron [which occur in nature as garnet crystals], rhombic triakontahedron, and 2 out of 4 possible regular star-polyhedra, the dodecahedron of the 3rd and of the 7th kind described in detail in this work. Kepler's investigation of regular geometric figures belongs to the modern group theory. Unlike Galileo, Kepler was an effectual creative applied mathematician who followed the ideas of the ancient Neoplatonic Greek mathematicians Pappos of Alexandria (*floruit* c. A.D. 284-300) and Proklos of Byzantion (A.D. 410-485). 'Harmony of the world' meant to Kepler 'unity of all knowledge', which is why he attempted to associate physical facts with metaphysical and mystical ideas. Kepler's works were pathbreaking for they opened new vistas not only in modern physical astronomy but also in optics, and in differential and integral calculus. His theoretical results besides being very important were also endowed with imposing grandeur because of their intimate connexion with the solution of the most monumental problem science had ever faced – the problem of the Solar system. Three centuries of telescopic observations have shown that Kepler's planetary laws of motion hold save for some relatively small deviations due to perturbations that are well understood. In this treatise Kepler first used the term 'energy' (***energeia***) not for the precise work concept, but for the performance of the forces emanating from the Earth.

The science of geometric optics was established by the ancient Greeks, and one of the most influential optical treatises of mediæval times was < Optics > (***Kitab al-manazir***) composed in Cairo on the basis of the treatise of Ptolemaios of Alexandria by a talented Muslim astronomer and mathematician, Ibn al-Haitham (died c.1040), known to Europeans by the name ***Alhazen***, some time before 1039. Alhazen's treatise was translated into Latin by Gherardo of Cremona in the 13th century and it influenced Witelo (Latin name, ***Vitellio***), a Polish monk and mathematician in Italy, who wrote a treatise on physical optics about 1270 which contained relatively few independent investigations by the author on refraction and perspective, but otherwise presented an excellent review of what had been previously achieved in physical optics by scientists, particularly by Ptolemaios of Alexandria and ***Alhazen***, but it was published only in 1535. Witelo's treatise influenced Kepler, who wrote a pathbreaking pioneering work on optics in 1604 entitled <Introduction to Vitellio's Optics, Instruction to Optical Part of Astronomy> (***Ad Vitellionem paralipomena, quibus astronomiae pars optica traditur***),which put an end to Alhazen's tradition in optics and gave a new sound and vigorous beginning to modern optics. In the first part of this book Kepler laid down the basic principles of physical optics, and the second part was devoted to the instruction of astronomical optics. In this tractate Kepler established the foundation for modern physical optics on which the study of geometrical optics has been based ever since. In the purely optical theory, Kepler was concerned with the physiological problem of sight. The ancient geometric optics of Eukleides (in English, Euclid) was based on the visual cone, the base of which was located on the object perceived and the apex of which was in the eye. It was considered that the objects are seen in their organic unity in the act of vision.

Kepler completely reformed the physical optics by breaking down the object of vision into infinite number of points. Light in his new geometrical optics emanated from the point-sources in infinite number of rectilinear rays, where every point of a visible object could be regarded as a point-source. In Kepler's geometrical optics every point of a visible object produces a particular cone of rays, the apex of which is at the point and the base of it is at the pupil of the eye. Inside the eye, a second cone of rays has the same base at the pupil and its apex lies on the retina where a point-image of the visible object is formed, and a pattern of point-images comprises the vision of the object. An extension of the same geometric analysis gave Kepler the solution to the basic problems of reflexion and refraction of light rays. He did not study the optics of lenses as such, since at the time Kepler wrote this work the telescope was not known. It set for the first time the correct optical problem of refraction which offered a considerable improvement in the theory of atmospheric refraction and, moreover, it was abounding with new ideas and insights so typical of Kepler's works. Kepler who had already solved several outstanding problems in geometric optics gave in this work his remarkable new 'principle of continuity' for conics which was based upon an imaginative generalised point of view that makes all conic sections into a single family of curves, a point of view which was probably influenced by the ingenious use Nicholas of Cusa had made of the concept of infinity, and it has been of the greatest importance to mathematics. In this principle, the conic section is composed of two intersecting lines and two foci coinciding at the intersection point. By moving one focus gradually away from the other focus, the conic section moves through an infinite set of hyperbolas, and as the focus moves to infinity the conic sections become parabolas. As the moving focus leaves infinity and returns from the other side, infinitely many ellipses are produced until the two foci again coincide which reduces the ellipse to a circle. It was Kepler who introduced for the parabola two foci, one of which is located at infinity, and also coined the term ***focus*** (meaning 'fire place' in Latin). A few generations later Kepler's bold idea of 'points at infinity' was taken up by the French architect and military engineer Gérard [alias ,Girard] Desargues(1593-1662)in his novel 'synthetic projective geometry'. In this book Kepler also studied the optical problem of vision, and explained the working of the eye as an optical instrument in which he recognised the proper optical function of the retina as the light-sensitive organ of the eye first discovered by ***Averroës*** (not the crystalline lens of the eye as ***Alhazen*** thought). He explained correctly the optical phenomena of myopia and hypermetropia [also known as the 'old man's vision' called 'presbyopia'] and reduced the optical function of spectacles, which correct these optical shortcomings of the eye, to the laws of optics.

Although Kepler was the first to give a complete explanation for the optical function of the eye, it was the Italian scientist of Greek stock Francesco Maurolico (1494-1577) who first recognised that the lens of the eye functions just like a glass lens upon the curvature of which myopia and hypermetropia depend. He knew that convex lenses are convergent and concave lenses are divergent. He recognised that the lens of the eye acts optically like the artificial glass lens by creating an image of the visual object not on the lens of the eye but somewhere behind the lens depending on the curvature of the lens. If the curvature is too large, the image is formed too close to the lens resulting in myopia, which he held can be helped by concave spectacles. If the curvature of the lens in the eye is too small, the image is formed too far behind the lens resulting in hypermetropia which he held can be helped by convex spectacles. Although Maurolico did not know the important function of the retina because he did not test the eye itself, it was the first correct explanation of the optical effects of spectacles. Maurolico earned further fame in optics because he was the first experimenter to use a glass prism to break white light into its colour spectrum, which was the same colour spectrum as that of the rainbow. Maurolico published his researches a few years before his death in a large treatise < Photics of Light and Shadow > (***Photismi de lumine et umbra***).

After the telescope had become known, Kepler published another important treatise on geometric optics entitled < Dioptrics > (***Dioptrice***) in 1611 which gave a vigorous beginning to the modern theory of optics for lenses. In this work, which represented the most important advance in physical optics, Kepler established the scientific theory of geometric optics for the telescope and its lenses and objective glasses based on an approximate theory of refraction $i = nr$ (for $i<15°$), where i and r denoted the angle of incidence and the angle of refraction respectively, and $n = 1.5$ was the refraction coefficient when light passes through two media: air and glass. His optical theory of lenses remained incomplete because he had failed to discover the accurate law of refraction, although his approximate law of refraction was quite adequate for the optical theory of telescopes. The English astronomer and mathematician Thomas Harriot (1560-1621), who corresponded with Kepler about astronomical and optical matters, advised Kepler that the refractive power of a medium is not proportional to the density of the medium as Kepler thought for oil is more refractive yet less dense than water. Kepler's design of the telescope employed 2 convex lenses like in the modern telescope, which was a great improvement upon Galileo's telescope. He gave the focal lengths for biconvex, biconcave and planoconvex lenses in a form corresponding to the formula:

$$1/f = (1/a)+(1/b),$$

where f is the focal length, and a and b are the distances of the object and the image respectively, a formula given in 1693 by the English Astronomer Royal Edmund Halley (1656-1742), the inventor of the first compressed-air diving bell worthy of its name. Kepler's design of the terrestrial telescope incorporated a third lens which turned the image right-side up. The great scientific advantage of Kepler's telescope was that the cross-wires could be mounted in the focal planes of the eyepiece which made his telescope from an observational instrument into a measuring instrument. Kepler also improved upon Galileo's telescope by introducing a positive eyepiece which gives the real image formed by the objective at the focus of the ocular. Kepler's astronomical telescope was soon widely adopted for astronomical observations. He also gave in this work a new method for the finding of the longitude. This treatise of Kepler was the source for all later works on lenses.

Kepler's treatise < Epitome of Copernican Astronomy > (***Epitome astronomiae Copernicanea***) published in 4 volumes in 1618, 1620 and 1621, was his most voluminous work and the most important systematic exposition of facts and principles of astronomy based on his version of the Copernican system, which provided the foundation for his physical astronomy that gave a very simple geometrical picture of the Solar system with elliptical orbits without being cluttered up by such fictitious mathematical devices as epicycles, eccentrics and equants. In the 4th volume of this treatise, Kepler dealt with fundamental physicocosmic questions such as his unsuccessful attempt to find a physical basis for his third law, the so-called 'Harmonic Law'. He stated that heavenly bodies like terrestrial bodies have inertia because otherwise an infinitely small force could impart in a moment infinite velocity to such a heavenly body as a planet, and the finite periods of all planets prove that planets have inertia. In this volume Kepler extended the mutual attraction to all heavenly bodies which are now subjected to the inertia force (***vis inertiae***) and the mutual attraction. The Sun attracts the planets but this attraction is not mutual. Thus all the planets are subjected to the force of inertia as well as to the attraction of the Sun. The attractive force (***vis prensandi***) of the Sun grappling the planets is a bodily force which produces motion of the planets. Kepler assigned a gravitational attraction, which is proportional to the masses of two interacting bodies such as the Moon and the Earth. He accounted for the ebb and tide on the Earth by the gravitational pull of the Moon because he recognised that the influence of the orb of tractional force (***orbis virtutis tractoriae***) of the Moon reaches the surface of the Earth. Kepler, after demonstrating that the mutual attractive force acting between the Earth and the Moon is proportional to the product of the two masses (***moles***), investigated its dependance on the distance. He compared the distribution of the attractive force from the Sun to the spreading of the intensity of light which diminishes with the square of the distance from the Sun. Kepler stated in this treatise that if the Earth were transferred to the orbit of Saturn then the attractive force of the Sun acting on the Earth would be reduced according to the square of the distance. Hence, Kepler set the gravitational attraction of the Sun acting on Earth proportional to $[m_E \, m_S \,/ r_E^{\,2}]$, where subscripts S and E refer to the Sun and the Earth respectively. A few pages later, after Kepler had attempted to work out the mechanics of the Solar system, his correct ideas on gravity (***gravitas***) were lost again in some confusion, and he came to the wrong conclusion that the gravitational attraction of the Sun reduces according to the linear distance r_E from the Sun, *i. e.*, the gravitational attraction of the Sun acting on Earth is proportional to $[m_E \, m_S \,/ r_E]$.

In Kepler's cosmology the Sun creates a 'force field' throughout the space, but the force moving the planet is received out of space only where there is a planet. It is quite remarkable that

Kepler's 'force field' is reminiscent of the electromagnetic field of modern physics rather than Newton's gravitational force. Kepler's concept of gravitation was of considerable importance to the progress of celestial and terrestrial mechanics because it anticipated the law of universal gravitation first proposed by Robert Hooke, and then mathematically corroborated by Isaac Newton. The interesting aspect in the rise of the law of universal gravitation is that both Hooke and Newton had carefully scrutinised Kepler's works on physical astronomy before they commenced their own investigations of celestial mechanics, paying particular attention to the problem of gravitation between the Earth and the Moon, and Kepler's correct explanation of tides by the attraction of the Moon. Newton accused Hooke of exploiting Kepler's works on gravitation, whereas he recognised his own indebtedness to Kepler in his letter to Halley. Kepler, a man of infinitely richer mind than his contemporaries, particularly Galileo, invented in the course of his extensive investigation of the celestial dynamics an astounding abundance of original fundamental ideas, which didn't leave much that was entirely new for Hooke and Newton to devise.

Kepler's last work, < A Dream or Lunar Astronomy > (***Somnium seu astronomia Lunari***), was the first book on science fiction in the modern sense which gave a deliberately imaginary story about a dream of a journey to the Moon that was based upon contemporary scientific knowledge and educated guesses, which was edited by Kepler's eldest living son Louis because it was unfinished when Kepler died. This book was published posthumously in 1634 and it had great influence upon later writers of interplanetary travel. The scientific importance of this work is due to the numerous appended notes of astronomical, physical and geographical information that were more extensive than the main work itself, which indicated the wide scope of learning of its author. In one of these notes Kepler explained the particularly high spring tides as being caused by the attraction of the conjunction of the Moon and the Sun, that acknowledged that the Sun attracts the Earth, a proposition first advanced by the ancient Greek Stoic philosopher Poseidonios of Apameia about 80 B.C..

Kepler did not extend the correct law of gravitational attraction, which he had introduced for the interaction of the Earth and the Moon, to other planets, primarily because he did not know the correct law of inertia which made him devote a great deal of energy and hard work to the examination of a host of different hypotheses for the force causing the motion of planets that filled a large number of pages in his treatises. Although Kepler's explanation of the planetary motion in physical terms was ultimately not tenable, it was of the greatest historical importance because it was the first attempt to establish a celestial dynamics which paved the way for unifying the terrestrial and the celestial mechanics by means of the principle of gravitation. It represented a definite break with the Aristotelian doctrine of the fundamental difference between the sublunar and the celestial world, a doctrine the validity of which had been already questioned in the Late Middle Ages. In all his astronomical works, Kepler attempted to link observations with mathematical description and physical theory, and he was the first scientist to do so. Although these physical principles of Kepler were soon replaced by the new science of mechanics of Newton, Kepler was the first to propose a celestial dynamics as en extension of terrestrial dynamics and a sound concept of gravitation.

Kepler wrote: "Nature loves simplicity and unity," a fundamental idea which guided his approach to science. In general, Kepler attempted to integrate mechanical motion, purposive action, and archetypical constraints into his science of celestial mechanics. He had many idealistic, even mystical aspects to his scientific thought, but despite this tendency he did demonstrate a profound mathematical intuition of a great scientist. He further stated: "As the ear is made to perceive sound and the eye to perceive colour, so the mind of men has been formed to understand not all sorts of things, but quantities. It perceives any given thing more clearly in proportion as that thing is closer to bare quantities as its origin, but the farther a thing recedes from quantities, the more darkness and error adheres to it." Kepler saw the purpose of science in the following way: "The chief aim of all investigations of the external world should be to discover the rational order and harmony which has been imposed on it by God and which He revealed to us in the language of mathematics." Harmony to Kepler was always a purely abstract mathematical concept.

Kepler was plagued with illness, a string of personal calamities, and pecuniary difficulties all his life. Some times he had to cast horoscopes to survive, although he was not a firm believer in astrology. In 1595 after observing a comet, Kepler predicted famine, peasant uprising and war with the Turks and, surprisingly, was proven right by the subsequent events. Kepler was a pious man with a generous nature who was incapable of any self-seeking thought and lasting resentment. His landmark contributions to science received scant recognition in his lifetime. His very temperate acceptance of the general neglect of his work Kepler expressed in his statement in the Introduction to his treatise < Harmony of the World > : "The die is cast. I have written my book. It will be read; whether in the present age or by posterity matters little. It can wait for its readers ... Has not God waited six thousand years to have his works witnessed?" Fortunately for Kepler, in less than one hundred years his book did find 2 very competent readers: Robert Hooke and Isaac Newton who discovered in it Kepler's third law and the idea of gravitation which gave them a definite example for the formulation of the principle of universal gravitation. Kepler, a man of unequalled intellectual honesty, extraordinary industry and unflagging enthusiasm, was unable to realise completely the monumental significance of his own 3 planetary laws because of the inadequacy of the mathematical methods available at the time. Once the inverse square law of gravitation, which Kepler himself had introduced in < Epitome of Copernican Astronomy > but later neglected, and the equation of motion in mechanics had become available, the intimate connexion between Kepler's 3 planetary laws could be readily established. Surprisingly, in modern times the 3 planetary laws of Kepler have been found relevant to modern physics: it was demonstrated in nuclear physics that Kepler's laws can predict the motion of electrons round the atomic nuclei under the action of electrical forces. It has been pointed out with complete justification that Kepler was a forerunner of a modern theoretical physicist, who is trying to reduce the structure of atom to order as Kepler had sought to reduce the Solar system to order.

The first astronomers who appreciated the great significance of Kepler's physical astronomy were the English: mathematician and astronomer Thomas Harriot, and the cleric Jeremiah Horrocks [alias, Horrox] (1619-1641). Horrocks, a very young man, was a practical and theoretical astronomer of genius who was an early student and important correspondent of Kepler. He was the first astronomer to accept Kepler's elliptical orbits. In 1638, Horrocks extended Kepler's work by showing that the Moon moves in an elliptical orbit round the Earth located at one focus of the elliptic orbit, thereby completing the Keplerian astronomical system with respect to the Moon, something that Kepler himself had not managed to do because of the great complexity of the Moon's motion. Horrocks believed that the irregularities in the Moon's motion are due to the influence of the Sun. He also thought that the planets Jupiter and Saturn have mutual attractive influence upon each other in which he recognised the existence of universal gravitation. He amended < Rudolphine Tables > of Kepler with regards to the transit of the planet Venus across the face of the Sun, and predicted an occurrence of it on November 24th, in 1639. It was the first observed transit of Venus across the face of the Sun. Horrocks suggested that observations of the transit of planet Venus made from different observatories might set up a parallax effect for the calculation of the distance of Venus and, therefore, of the scale of the Solar system. This was eventually accomplished.

Napier, Bürgi and Logarithms:

John Napier [alias Neper] (1550-1617), a Scottish laird, had invented logarithms in 1594 which he published in his tractate < A Description of the Marvellous Rule of Logarithms > (***Mirifici logarithmorum canonis descriptio***) in 1614. Napier, who was not a professional mathematician, only showed interested in spherical trigonometry and, particularly, in computation. He had modified Stevin's notation for decimal fractions to ease computation by introducing the modern notation of the decimal point. Napier's logarithm (meaning 'ratio number') substituted a series of additions and a series of subtractions for multiplication and division as a practical method of computation, a technique which made it possible to perform any calculation by repeating the same operation several times and thereby making calculation by mechanical means feasible. In his efforts to eliminate tedious calculations he published ***Rabdologiae*** in 1617 describing the so-called 'Napier bones' which laid out the multiplication tables from *1* to *9* on bones so that they could be added diagonally, thereby making automatic carrying in multiplication feasible.

The Swiss court watchmaker, expert mechanic, instrument-maker, and assistant to the astronomer Landgrave (Count)Wilhelm IV of Hessen, Joost [alias Jost or Jobst] Bürgi (Latin name, ***Iustus Byrgius***)(1552-1632),who later became Kepler's assistant and court watchmaker of Kaiser Rudolph II in Prague, had invented logarithms independently of Napier about 1600. Bürgi, who was an ingenious mathematician, based his logarithms on the exponential formula of Archimedes:

$$a^m\, a^n = a^{m+n},$$

and constructed the first complete table of antilogarithms using the decimal base, although like Napier he had no general concept of the base of a logarithm for he did not use the relation $a^x = b$, which gives $log_a\, b = x$. He was the first to complete a small table of antilogarithms which he published anonymously in 1620 in his book < Arithmetic and Geometric Progress Tables > (***Arithmetische und Geometrische Progress Tabulen***). The basic idea underlying logarithms had been noticed by the German mathematician Michael Stifel (c.1486-1567) in 1544 when he observed that multiplication and division of two terms in a geometric progression, $1,\ r,\ r^2,\ r^3, \ldots$, can be performed by adding and subtracting the exponents of the corresponding terms in the arithmetic progression formed by the exponents $1, 2, 3, \ldots$, and he extended this idea to negative and fractional exponents as well. However, he did not use this relation between the two series to introduce the generalised concept of logarithms as exponents. Napier's mathematical treatment of logarithms was geometrical whereas Bürgi's method was algebraic.

After the Muslim astronomer Ibn Yunus (died 1009) of the observatory at Cairo, Bürgi was the first astronomer in Europe to use an isochronous pendulum-clock of his own construction, his 'planetary clock', about 1580 for mensuration of time in his astronomical observations in Cassel.

Schickard and General Purpose Calculator:

A friend of Kepler, Wilhelm Schickard (1592-1635), professor of Oriental and Hebrew languages, mathematics, astronomy and geography at the University of Tuebingen, as well as a Protestant minister, a good painter, a skilled engraver, and an expert mechanic who constructed his own astronomical instruments, discussed 'Napier bones' as a mechanical aid in computation with Kepler in 1617. In 1623 and 1624, Schickard described in his letters to Kepler a calculating machine he had constructed which used 'Napier bones' for arithmetic operations. Schickard's calculating machine had 6 sets of 'Napier bones' engraved on vertical cylinders which were adjustable by knobs so that any 6-digit number could be selected. A set of horizontal slides helped to select different sections of the 'Napier bones'. The result of a basic multiplication could then be added to an accumulator by turning a set of large knobs in the bottom of the calculator, and a set of small apertures enabled the storing of intermediate results. The only shortcoming in Schickard's calculator was that he used a single toothed gear in his carry-mechanism which could have damaged the machine if the carry-operation occurred in more than 4 columns since the force exerted on the single gear became too great for the mechanism to withstand. Despite the fact that Schickard's calculator was manually operated, its mechanical functions could be classified in entirely modern terms of computer engineering such as accumulator, register, memory and so on, because the functional design of his calculator was surprisingly similar to the design of modern computers. Although Schickard, his family, and his calculating machine perished in the period of plague and disaster brought about by the Thirty Years' War, a working model of it was made in Germany after the Second World War based on the information Schickard gave about his calculator in his letters to Kepler, and it proved to be a perfectly functioning calculating machine capable of performing addition, subtraction, multiplication and division.

Beeckman, Frequency of Vibration and Concept of Strain:

In 1618, Beeckman, continuing the tradition of Stevin's mechanics, solved the suspension bridge problem by demonstrating that a suspended cord to which equally spaced equal weights are attached assumes a parabolic configuration. In 1620, Beeckman was the first scientist after Leonardo da Vinci (1452-1519) to recognise that in the bending of beams the fibres on the concave side of the beam are contracted, whereas the fibres on its convex side are extended, which implies the existence of an unextended, the so-called 'neutral' fibre. In 1630 Beeckman discovered that the 'strain' $\epsilon = \Delta L/L$, rather than the 'stretch' ΔL of an elastic string, is the true deformation measure of the effect of a force acting on a material string of length L, which represents the first statement of the concept of strain as local measure of deformation. Moreover, Beeckman claimed to demonstrate that the frequency of vibration of a taut elastic string is inversely proportional to the length of the string, $f \propto 1/L$, which is correct for the first instant of motion. His reasoning supplied the earliest available mathematical proof in acoustics. In 1618, Beeckman also had formulated his conception of inertia: "What once moves, continues to move, if it is not interfered with." In the problem of the free fall of heavy bodies Beeckman correctly calculated that the distance traversed in the free fall is proportional to the square of the time of fall.

Simultaneously with his scientific work, Beeckman was busy in his technological and engineering activities: building and repairing waterworks for breweries and individuals, improving the efficiency of pumps and conduits, production of candles, and advising clients on various mill improvements, on new patents, and on designs of ***perpetuum mobile***, and improving lenses for telescopes. Beeckman was convinced that improvements in material aspects of life are possible only through the application of science and mathematics to technology and engineering. Beeckman kept a private ***Journael*** filled with his scientific and technological thoughts and activities.

Galileo, Kinematics of Trajectory and Strength of Materials:

The Italian mathematician, scientist, engineer and man of letters, Galileo Galilei, who also thought like Plato that real science is mathematical, had a wider popular influence than Stevin. Galileo expressed his thoughts on science in the following way: "Philosophy is written in that great book which ever lies before our eyes – I mean the universe – but we cannot understand it if we do not first learn the language and grasp the symbols, in which it is written. This book is written in mathematical language, and mathematical principles are the alphabet in which God wrote the world, without their help it would be humanly impossible to comprehend a single word; one would wander in vain through a dark labyrinth." The English mathematician Robert Recorde (c.1510 -1558) had made a more categorical statement on the value of mathematics to knowledge: "Besides the mathematical arts there is no infallible knowledge, except it be borrowed from them." A similar viewpoint was expressed by the German contemporary of Galileo, the brilliant mathematician and ingenious astronomer Johann Kepler, who was chiefly responsible for bringing about the 'scientific revolution' in Europe by introducing the ancient Greek theory of conic sections of Menaichmos of Alopekonnesos (375-325 B.C.), which had been exhaustively developed by Apollonios of Perge (c.262-c.190 B.C.), into his laws of planetary motion. Kepler stated: "... mathematical concepts and proofs must be applied to Earthly science ... mathematical laws are the cause of things being what they are." In science, both Kepler and Galileo were influenced by the Neoplatonic philosophy and the Pythagorean belief in the mathematical structure of the universe.

Galileo declared that scientific tradition was not very important, because in his opinion a scientist must decide for himself what is right and what is wrong. In this respect Galileo said: "Nor should it be considered rash not to be satisfied with those opinions which have become common. No one should be scorned in disputes on physics for not holding to the opinions which happen to please other people best," and, "In questions of science the authority of a thousand is not worth the reasoning of a single individual." But Galileo also said: "Nothing ever changes in nature to accommodate itself to the comprehension or notion of men."

All professors at the University of Pisa were required to wear academic robes at all times, a convention which the nonconformist Galileo scornfully dismissed: "Conventional clothes, like conventional ideas, are inventions of the devil."

Galileo adopted a system of methodological ideas of ancient Greeks, which had been delineated by Robert Grosseteste in its application to problems in physical science, that Galileo would refer to as the ***metodo risolutivo*** (method of analysis) and the ***metodo compositivo*** (method of synthesis).

Among the works of Galileo, the two important treatises are < Dialogue ... on the Two Great Systems of the World > (***Dialogo ... sopra i due massimi sistemi del mondo***) published in 1632, a work which caused his conflict with the Roman Catholic Church and made him a prisoner of the Catholic Inquisition, and his last major work < Discourses and Mathematical Demonstrations about Two New Sciences > (***Discorsi e dimonstrationi matematichi intorno a due nuove scienze ...***) published in The Netherlands in 1638. Following Tartaglia's precedent, Galileo wrote both of these works in the dialogue form. In the < Dialogue ...>, Galileo promoted the Copernican heliocentric astronomy in which the Sun is at the center of the world in contrast to the Ptolemaic geocentric astronomy in which the Earth is at the center of the world. Galileo, as a typical humanist of the Late Italian Renaissance, at first used in his polemical writings a language that could be characterised as a kind of vulgar billingsgate replete with coarse invectives, but he gradually improved his journalistic jargon by infusing it with biting wit, scathing satire and vitriolic ridicule - all expressed in his spectacular and bombastic journalistic prose, such as in his polemical masterpiece < The Assayer > (***Il Saggiatore***) published in 1624, and dedicated to the new Pope Urbanus VIII. In 1618 Galileo directed his vitriolic polemic against Orazio Grassi (1583-1654), a student of Brahe's works and a Jesuit philosopher, mathematician and physicist at the ***Collegio Romano,*** as well as the architect of Sant' Ignazio Church in Rome. Grassi had published a work on the nature of comets based upon Brahe's observations which Galileo called 'asinine' and 'villainous'. Galileo had a violent temper, a natural aversion against taking advice, and tact was not one of his native habits. Moreover, Galileo was afflicted with monumental vanity and conceit, professional envy, and overbearing self-righteousness which almost bordered on fanaticism. Already as a university student Galileo had revealed his contentious and obnoxious personality in his strident and supercilious deportment towards his fellow students, who called him the 'wrangler', for he was extravagantly dogmatic about his own opinions. Besides lacking conscience, subtlety and refinement, Galileo was brusque and inordinately blunt which fomented among many of his colleagues and men of learning an intense and unrelenting hostility towards his person. The large group of enemies spawned by Galileo's overweening and pompous behaviour finally included his erstwhile Florentine friend and patron, Cardinal Maffeo Barberini (1568-1644), a Jesuit pater who was elected Pope Urbanus VIII in 1623. Barberini, who felt personally responsible for the defence of the geocentric astronomy of Ptolemaios, thought that Galileo had lampooned him mercilessly in the < Dialogue ...> by representing Barberini in the person of Simplicio, a slow-witted foil who defended the geocentric astronomy of Ptolemaios, but was easily refuted and ridiculed as an incompetent simpleton and a fool at every turn. Barberini regarded Galileo's pretence of having presented both the heliocentric astronomy of Copernicus and the geocentric astronomy of Ptolemaios impartially, so that the reader is able to choose freely between the two astronomies, as patently insincere. In one of Galileo's several private discussions with Barberini about the true nature of the world, Barberini had given Galileo friendly advice: "Surrender to the inscrutable, speculate as you like, but do not believe that we can really know," after he had noticed the intellectual *hauteur* of Galileo in thinking that he alone can establish the true nature of the world purely by deduction from his arbitrary conjectured hypotheses. Galileo, like a typical humanist of Italian Renaissance, zealously craved for public recognition. In his messianic zeal to make everybody accept his scientific opinions , Galileo was not satisfied when other men of learning remained content with merely studying, discussing, and questioning the merits of his works. In his insufferably dogmatic attitude, Galileo insisted that they accept his scientific opinions as incontestable truths. He was a presumptuous and intolerant individual with a short temper who did not brook scientific opinions contradicting his. This serious fault and lack of courage in his character proved to be his undoing. In 1633, when Galileo was accused of heresy by the Roman Catholic Holy Inquisition, which in Roman Catholic dogma was not a court of justice to try heresy as a crime but more like 'a spiritual board of health' which applied a 'salutary' yet 'painful remedy', going as far as burning a refractory and unrepentant heretic alive at the stake to arrest the 'contagion of error', and thereby restoring the soul of the heretic within the boundaries of salvation. The openly declared objective of Holy Inquisition was not conviction, but rather submission like in the Islamic religion – not the truth, but obedient profession. The Roman Catholic Church claimed no motive of punishment or persecution behind their 'Holy Inquisition'. When Galileo finally had to face the moment of truth, his profoundly disappointing deportment during the Inquisition revealed that he was a cowardly blow-hard and, unlike the heroic Giordano Bruno (1548-1600),a first-rate philosopher and a disciple of Nicholas of Cusa who was a determined adversary of Aristotelian ideas. Bruno after 7 years of incarceration still refused to recant a word in his Copernican and anti-Aristotelian views and remained true to his convictions even after he was condemned to be incinerated alive at the stake where he still taunted his accusers as pusillanimous cowards. Bruno said: "Be that as it may, this at least the future ages will not deny me, let the victor be who he may be, that I did not fear to die. I yielded to no man in my constancy, and preferred a spirited death to a life of a coward." Galileo, contrary to his habitual pretentious bravado and bluster, lacked the courage of his convictions by cowering before, and collaborating in a degrading obsequiousness with his self-righteous, and autocratic accusers. The College of Cardinals had previously banned the works of both Copernicus and Kepler, and forbidden Galileo to promote their doctrine. As a man of science and natural philosopher, Giordano Bruno (c. 1548-1600), who taught at the ***Collège de France,*** in contrast to Galileo, was a man of honour and fortitude, and a dignified person deserving great respect and admiration.

Galileo intensely envied Kepler for the latter's native ingenuity and creative mathematical brilliance. He scorned Kepler's pathbreaking fundamental contributions to physical astronomy and Kepler's planetary laws in favour of Copernican circles. He also accepted the Aristotelian distinction between the 'natural' and the 'violent' motion. Since Galileo seemed to lack a fundamental appreciation of celestial mechanics as the 'physics of the sky', and never had any sound grasp of gravity, he scorned Kepler's revolutionary conception of ***gravitas*** which contained significant original ideas. Galileo never considered weight as an applied force since to him weight or heaviness was a unique property of bodies, and he always appealed to the Aristotelian concept by referring to the tendency of heavy bodies to move towards the center of the Earth as their 'natural place'. Galileo did not treat gravity as an external applied force acting on matter. Apparently, Galileo did not appreciate the celestial dynamics of Kepler. Galileo agreed with the ancient opinion that planets as spherical bodies 'by their very nature' orbited in a self-perpetuating circular motion, which remained his 'law of circular inertia'. He also proposed his 'principle of relative motion' which asserted that a motion common to all the bodies forming a given system has no influence upon the behaviour of the bodies relative to one another. Both principles were wrong because of their incorrect theoretical foundation, though both seemed to be approximately true for very short motions.

Although it must have been quite obvious to Galileo that Kepler was an ingenious creative mathematician who was intellectually his superior, Galileo made a spiteful and arrogant comment on Kepler's work by describing it as "so obscure that apparently the author did not know what he was talking about." It is true that Kepler's treatises tended to be abstruse composites of mystical and fanciful speculations combined with profound scientific insights, that Kepler often digressed from his topic, that his Latin was rather difficult and sometimes obscure, and that his thinking was more imaginative, fanciful and whimsical than that of Galileo, who wrote in terse journalistic jargon that was persuasive, occasionally even brilliant, and very influential among common people. Galileo like the typical Italian Renaissance humanist felt that as an intellectual entrepreneur he had to advertise himself to succeed in life, for journalism as a practical literary art form of self-promotion that Galileo practised was a creation of the Italian Renaissance. Kepler, in contrast, revealed in his writings all the details of his methods of solution because he was unconcerned about his personal fame. In contrast, Galileo in his writings not only had a habit of bragging, concealing his assumptions in his rhetoric and leaving unacknowledged most of the important sources of his work, but also scattering throughout his writings few lines of standard mathematical proofs for the easier and more trivial details of his exposition to lend the appearance of logic to what, in fact, was largely an ingenious guesswork.

Kepler's landmark contributions to astronomy remained unknown to René Descartes and, surprisingly, even to Marin Mersenne (1588-1648), a French Minorite Franciscan friar who had been a classmate of Descartes at the ***Collège de la Fléche***, and who taught philosophy and mathematics in Nevers and in Paris. He defended Descartes' philosophy against clerical critics, and opposed mystical doctrines such as astrology, alchemy, divination, and actively promoted experimentation. Mersenne served as an intellectual center of scientific interchange by being a channel of scientific ideas through his voluminous correspondence of over thousand letters with many outstanding scientific contemporaries such as Descartes, Beeckman, Galileo, Fermat, Pascal [both father and son], Pierre Gassendi [alias Gassend] (1592-1655), Gérard Desargues, Huygens and Gilles Personne de Roberval. In the days when no scientific journals existed Mersenne's correspondence rendered an essential service to science. Mersenne apparently gathered around himself in his Minorite Franciscan monastery at Paris a circle of intellectuals who had periodical meetings to which travelling scholars from any part of Europe were welcome. Mersenne was the chief promoter of Galileo's works outside of Italy. He published Galileo's pamphlet < On Mechanics> (***Le Meccaniche***) in its French translation in 1634, and translated into French the ***Discorsi ...*** of Galileo which was published in 1639 under the title of < The New Thoughts of Galileo >. Much of the information on the scientific work done at the time is known to posterity from the extant extensive international correspondence of Mersenne who himself wrote original works on ballistics, mechanics, impact and acoustics. Mersenne encouraged other scientists to experiment, to answer important scientific questions posed by him, and to publish their works. Mersenne's generous offer to mediate between Galileo and Descartes, was superciliously ignored by both pompous men of science. When Descartes went on a trip through Italy, he made it a point not to visit Galileo. It is also not surprising that the self-adulating Galileo, in his letter to his former pupil Francesco Bonaventura Cavalieri, a Jesuate who taught Kepler's astronomical theory at the University of Bologna where he was professor of mathematics, showed not a trace of gratitude to Mersenne for the Frenchman's generous help in disseminating Galileo's scientific researches outside Italy.

Mersenne himself did important experimental research on acoustics and music. He discovered and explained the so-called 'beats', introduced the term 'frequency' of vibration, and gave the Mersenne law: 'The square of the period of vibration varies with the length of the pendulum', and was the first to determine a sequence of simultaneous overtones emitted by a vibrating string. His findings in this discipline are the best ever obtained from purely experimental study of vibrations. Most, but not all of his results are given in his outstanding treatise on acoustics and music < Book on Harmony; Four Books on the Instrumental Harmony > (***Harmonicorum libri;Harmonicorum instrumentorum libri IV***) published in 1635. Mersenne published his own experimental researches on mechanics in his treatise, < Tractate of Theoretical and Practical Mechanics > (***Tractatus mechanicus theoricus et practicus***), in 1644. He also stimulated research in the theory of numbers.

Galileo investigated the kinematics of projectiles and studied the strength of materials in his treatise < Discourses and Mathematical Demonstrations about Two New Sciences Pertaining to Mechanics and Local Motion > (***Discorsi e dimonstrationi matematichi intorno à due nuove scienze attenanti alla mecanica e i movimenti locali***) published in 1638 in The Protestant

Netherlands. It was written in the form of 4 dialogues between 3 men over 4 days: the first 2 days were devoted to the strength of materials, a truly original engineering science, and the last 2 days to kinematics, but this treatise no longer had the literary significance and the crusading spirit of his landmark treatise, < Dialogue ... on the Two Great Systems of the World >. Galileo had paid many visits to the Venetian Arsenal, the largest industrial enterprise in Europe at the time, and many of his enquiries in strength of materials were inspired by his experience in the Venetian Arsenal, and by his discussions with its craftsmen. Surprisingly, the pompous Galileo expressed a sound professional attitude in his statement: "I never met a man so ignorant that something might not be learnt from him." His investigations on the strength of materials were inspired by the baffling experience of the shipwrights in the Venetian Arsenal expressed by their questions: "Why the resistance of a structure does not vary proportionally to the size of the structure or the quantity of the material used?" and, "Why is a large ship more fragile than a small ship, the proportions between the parts of the ships and the materials being the same?"

Galileo's argument for the rupture of ropes subjected to the pull of a terminal load was actually absurd, since according to it the rope does not break at all, or it breaks everywhere at once. His criterion, the 'critical limiting load' was not sufficient to explain the rupture of a uniform rope. In the case of a cylindrical beam in tension, Galileo assumed the rupture to occur when a certain force per unit cross-sectional area of the beam is reached. It appears that Galileo foreshadowed with this statement the concept of the so-called 'stress'. In his theory of strength of structural members such as columns and beams, which he regarded 'inextensional' before rupture, he investigated the relative strength of structural members based on the concept of statical moment first generally used by the ancient Greek mathematician and scientist Heron of Alexandria.

Galileo's criterion of failure of structural members was the 'limiting force'. In his theory of strength, Galileo assumed that the terminal load P required to rupture in bending the prismatic cantilever beam of rectangular cross-section (b x d), where b denotes the width and d the depth of the cross-section, is obtained from the balance of the moments at the lower edge of the beam at the support :

$$F \times (\tfrac{1}{2})\, d = P \times L\,,$$

where $F = K\,(b \times d)$ is the 'absolute strength', or the breaking force in tension acting in bending in the middle of the cross-section (b x d), K is a material constant, and L is the length of the cantilever beam. Then,

$$F/P = 2\,L/d\,.$$

Galileo gave this rule which compared the load P that will break a beam transversely in bending with the axial load F that will break it in axial pull [his 'absolute strength'], but it was basically wrong because Galileo ignored the bending of the beam before rupture. Already in 1639, Giovanni

Battista Baliani (1582/1586-1660/1666) of Genoa, in his letter to Galileo, referred to 2 weak points in Galileo's theory of strength, $F = K(b \times d)$ and ½ , but Galileo's vague arguments in his response did not face the issue raised by Baliani.

In 1638 Baliani had published a tractate < On the Natural Gravitational Motion > (***De motu naturali gravium***) in which he not only explained why all bodies falling in vacuum have the same speed, but also demonstrated the proportionality of mass to weight. He thought that the law of inertia is of universal application and not only restricted to horizontal motion as Galileo had assumed. Baliani, unlike Galileo, began to treat gravity as an action of a constant cause. He applied Buridan's theory of impetus to the free fall of bodies, and began to assume gravity to be an action of a force. He tried to discover how from constant gravity as an applied cause a uniformly varying motion can arise. Baliani, through the application of Buridan's impetus theory in which for each time interval the motion is due to the combined action of impetus present at the beginning of the time interval and gravity acting as if the motion had only just started, was led to his law of free fall: distances traversed in consecutive equal time intervals in the free fall are as the consecutive natural numbers, a law which differed from Galileo's doctrine of odd numbers. Baliani noted that if the time intervals were sufficiently diminished , then the difference between his law and the doctrine of odd numbers of Galileo became negligible. Baliani also noted the following ambiguity in the concept of impetus: sometimes impetus was regarded as the symptom of motion, and other times as the cause of motion. He thought that motion as such actually continues on its own accord, and that impetus was called the 'cause' of motion only for conceptual purposes.

Galileo noticed that a beam of a square cross-section with a cross-sectional area $(d \times d)$, and length L can carry a load proportional to (d^3/L) ,

$$P = F(d/2L) = [K(d \times d)/2](d/L) = [K/2](d^3/L) .$$

After some mysterious manipulation Galileo derived his law of the 'weakness of giants':

> "If one wishes to keep, in an immense giant, the proportions of the members of a normal man, it would be necessary to find a much harder and stronger material."

If the weight of a giant structure is W and the normal structure is w, and their respective sizes are L and ℓ, and the respective strengths of their materials are F and f, then Galileo's law of similitude becomes :

$$W/L^2F = w/\ell^2 f.$$

This 'law of similitude', which can be used to determine when a structure might collapse under its own weight, represented a mathematical scaling law: ' All effects are not proportional to size'. The first such scaling law had been empirically established for ancient catapults by the ingenious ancient Greek military engineer Philon of Byzantion (*floruit* c.240 B.C.).

In this case Galileo's important achievement was his refutal of the popular opinion that all effects are proportional to the size of structural members, and his setting up a theory of scaling. It is less important that his proportions are correct only for his hypotheses, which were not generally verified in practice, than that he was able to formulate a definite 'scaling law', regardless of whether they were right or wrong, because they indicate his immense insight and originality in this particular engineering discipline. Galileo's method in strength of materials was characterised by a complete absence of mathematical proof at important points of the development whereas strict demonstrations were given to trivial details, and no reference at all was made to experiments. His work on strength of materials was merely a chain of ingenious conjectures which were described with notable journalistic brilliance. It can be said that Galileo seemed to intimate the idea of stress but nowhere did he use the concept of 'interior stress'. Galileo recognised that the resistance of beams is due to the mutual action of its fibres, but as a practicing mathematician he lacked the ability to formulate a mathematical theory in which fibres occur. Galileo's criterion of failure was the 'magnitude of the load'.

Galileo made the following comment in the < Discourses... >: "...neither is the number of squares less than the totality of all numbers, nor the latter greater than the former." Thus Galileo indicated that the infinite class of all positive integers can be put into one-to-one correspondence with part of this class, such as all the perfect squares, for example. This property of equivalence in infinite classes, which was rediscovered by the Bohemian cleric and mathematician Bernardus Placidus Johann Bolzano in the 19th century, was a fundamental idea in the theory of sets which became influential in the development of modern analysis based upon a rigorous theory of infinite assemblages. Galileo did not consider the infinite from the point of view of magnitude like most mediæval mathematicians, but instead concentrated upon the idea of infinite as an aggregation like Plato. But he was somewhat confused when dealing with infinite classes and sets by concluding that such attributes as 'equal', 'greater', and 'less' are not applicable when comparing infinite quantities, or infinite quantities with finite ones. He confessed that infinity and indivisibility were by their very nature incomprehensible to him. Galileo believed that continuous magnitudes are made up of indivisibles, a concept which had been rejected by Thomas Bradwardine (c.1290-1349). Galileo failed to distinguish between the physical and the mathematical indivisible. He also failed to realise that the precise meaning of the sum of an infinite series can only be given by means of the limit concept. On the other hand, Galileo was able to demonstrate that the cardinal number of an infinite subsequence of the integers is that of the integers themselves.

Galileo was a typical Italian Renaissance man : proud, pompous, immoral, irreligious, and intensely concerned about his fame. He was particularly loath to acknowledge any achievements of the religious mediæval scientists which he was obliged to exploit in his own work. Yet Galileo had received an excellent education in rhetoric at the Jesuit monastery school of ***Santa Maria di Vallombrosa*** near Florence that served him well in his polemical writings. Like the typical humanist of Italian Renaissance, Galileo was determined to leave an impression that he was intellectually indebted only to ancient Greek scientists, such as Archimedes of Syracuse for instance, even if such acknowledgements were quite spurious. In the matter of personal fame Galileo himself was his own leading promoter. His fame in modern popular literature and mass media is mostly derived from discoveries and inventions he never made. For instance, Galileo did not invent the telescope, nor the microscope, nor the pendulum clock, nor the thermometer. He did not found the classical dynamics, nor discover the law of inertia, nor the idea that gravity induces uniform acceleration in all bodies, nor Sunspots, nor the parallelogram of forces or velocities. He did not prove the Copernican system of astronomy, nor contribute to theoretical astronomy, nor perform the classical free fall experiment from the Leaning Tower of Pisa. All these notable deeds are contrived literary fancies which make up the myth of Galileo as the heroic idol of science for the masses. His reputation is legendary, and it continues to shine brightly by virtue of its concocted mystique.

Contrary to popular opinion, Galileo was quite well-informed of all the important previous work on the problem of local motion which had been accomplished in Europe from antiquity to the 16th century by the 16th century authors, who were remarkably well informed and knowledgeable, and had incorporated in their writings the best of the 3 preceding centuries. Particularly valuable in this regard were the treatises and the reports of the lectures on natural philosophy by a number of professors at the ***Collegio Romano***, a Jesuit university in Rome, such as Muzio Vitelleschi, Ludovico Rugerius, Paolo Valla, Girolamo Borro, and Benedictus Pererius. These Jesuit professors were more interested in mathematical theories of physics than the secular professors at the universities in Padua and in Pisa, who were servile followers of Averroist Aristotelianism. In fact, many ideas and arguments in natural philosophy presented by Galileo were very similar to the ideas and sophisticated arguments more completely and more thoroughly discussed in the reports and treatises of the Jesuit professors.

Galileo was well informed of the important mediæval contributions to the science of local motion from the discussions in the reports of the Jesuits and, moreover, he was also quite well informed about de Soto's solution of the problem of free fall and the time-square law of the free fall of bodies. In fact, the mediæval scholars had developed all the significant concepts, definitions, theorems and corollaries for a general theory of local motion with strict mathematical rigour, but no mediæval scientist was philosophically prepared to attempt to organise all these significant results of local motion which they had developed with theoretical brilliance into fundamental principles that can be incorporated into a new general mathematical science of local motion. Although Galileo did not contribute any of these significant results in the theory of local motion, he was the first scholar to achieve their conceptual reorganisation which produced the new kinematical doctrines of falling bodies and trajectory motion. This accomplishment is important enough to justify the claim that Galileo is the founder of elementary kinematics of trajectory motion but, of course, he accomplished nothing in classical dynamics for Galileo believed until the day he died in the Peripatetic proposition that force is proportional to velocity, in particular the mean velocity. Galileo studied a few problems of motion the proofs of which required dynamical reasoning, but his solutions were correct in the sense of classical dynamics only as long as comparisons of motions of equal duration for the same particle were considered. In such cases, Galileo's proofs depended on the fundamental law of Peripatetic dynamics in which the mean velocity appears in the place of velocity. Galileo never had the fundamental insight that force is proportional to acceleration which characterises classical dynamics. In all his dynamical problems Galileo's thinking remained strictly confined within the scope of mediæval impetus theory.

In the section < On the Local Motion >(***De motu locali***) of his treatise < Discourses and Mathematical Demonstrations about Two New Sciences...> (***Discorsi e dimonstrationi matematichi intorno a due nuove scienze ...***) published in The Netherlands in 1638, Galileo stated his doctrine of free fall of heavy bodies as the doctrine of odd numbers: "The distances fallen in successive equal time intervals are proportional to the successive odd numbers."

Galileo knew the law of free fall of de Soto as the law of squares: "The distance traversed by a body in free fall from rest is proportional to the square of the elapsed time," soon after 1600. In order to derive it from the axiom $V = V(t)$, he applied the Mertonian mean speed rule demonstrated in its graphical form by Nicole Oresme (c.1328-1382) in the 14th century. Oresme, who was the first to realise the great theoretical utility of graphical representation of continuous quantities in the 'theory of latitude of forms', had already suggested that in the free fall of bodies the speed of fall is directly proportional to the time of fall: $V(t) \propto t$. Oresme represented the speed $V(t)$ of a moving point with respect to time in the graphical form as latitude and time t as longitude, which correspond in modern algebra to ordinate and abscissa respectively. He knew that the line (***linea summitatis***), which connects the tops of the ordinates representing speed $V(t)$ at various values of time t as the modern abscissa, encloses an area (***mensura***) with the abscissa which measures the distance traversed. His graph for the uniformly varying velocity of a moving point consisted of 2 geometric figures defined by their ***linea summitatis*** : the right-angled triangular figure represented the uniformly varying speed $V(t)$ over the interval of time from $t = 0$ to $t = T$, in which the maximum speed $V_{max}(T)$ is at $t = T$, superimposed on it was a rectangular figure representing the constant mean speed of magnitude $\frac{1}{2} V_{max}$ over the same time interval T. Since the areas of these two geometric figures on his graph were equal, and Oresme knew that the area (***mensura***) of each of these two geometric figures measured the distance traversed by the moving point, then the distances traversed by the two motions were also equal. Oresme had given in his previous works 2 arithmetic demonstrations, and one geometric demonstration by means of the mediæval theory of indivisibles for the Mertonian mean speed rule. Galileo's demonstration of this proposition was a faithful reproduction of Oresme's graphical demonstration, again without acknowledging the original source of his method, except that instead of considering the equalities of areas involved directly as Oresme did, Galileo considered the aggregates of the ordinates of the triangular and the rectangular figure which he interprets as a kind of total velocity with which a distance is traversed. On the basis of this demonstration, Galileo deduced the law of time square, the doctrine of free fall and its corollary, the doctrine of odd numbers. Much later Galileo found another 'proof' which he apparently based on the fundamental law of Peripatetic dynamics for comparison of motions of equal duration, but it does not make any sense since his term 'impeto' is used in this 'proof' with two entirely different meanings.

Galileo presented the discovery of the free fall as uniformly accelerated motion, the doctrine of free fall, and the graphical method of demonstration of the Mertonian mean speed rule as his own intellectual contributions to kinematics despite his knowledge that the first two belonged to de Soto, who had published his work almost a century earlier, and that the third belonged to Oresme. Galileo apparently thought that his lack of intellectual candour was not a ***faux pas*** in Renaissance Italy.

Galileo had obtained the notion of inertial motion from the works of Benedetti and, particularly, from the reports of the Jesuit lecturers at ***Collegio Romano,*** some of whom unlike Benedetti conceived the kinematic inertial motion as a 'natural' circular motion rather than a rectilinear motion. Galileo held that a body is indifferent to its state of motion, or state of rest, which was fundamental to his solution of the problem of motion on Earth. Galileo regarded 'rest' as an 'infinite degree of slowness', a concept relying on Nicholas of Cusa's idea of continuity between the finite and the infinite. Galileo claimed that man is indifferent to his state of motion in space, where he can move with immense speed and yet not perceive it. Galileo referred to circular motion in his works, but he was unable to give a kinematic analysis of such a motion. Galileo in accordance with his Platonic beliefs began with an idealised abstract case of motion without resistance of which the actual motion in the physical world represented only an imperfect version, whereas Aristotle began his theory of local motion, which always involved resistance, from ordinary experience. Galileo still followed Aristotle by separating motions into 'natural' and 'violent' motions which rendered a distinctly mediæval character to his treatise. Otherwise, his tractate ***De motu locali*** is an original work on local kinematics as far as the general conception and execution of the treatise is concerned. Curiously it is partly ancient, partly mediæval and, yet, conceptually almost classical. Galileo followed Benedetti's precedent, when he showed how sophisticated mathematical methods of Archimedes of Syracuse can be applied to the problems of local motion. Unlike his contemporary

Stevin, who was a brilliant original mathematician, Galileo was not a creative mathematician. It is surprising that he never took a serious interest in algebra. In general, Galileo's mathematics was neither original nor forward-looking, even somewhat awkward and clumsy, and already quite obsolete when his treatise appeared in print.

Galileo, whilst he was professor of mathematics at the University of Pisa from 1589 to 1592, wrote treatises on fortification, military construction and mechanics which dealt with simple machines such as the lever, the pulley, the screw and the inclined plane. In Italy of his time, teaching of mathematics involved teaching all these engineering topics. His salary was a puny 60 scudi (about $60) a year.

In 1593, Galileo had prepared a small set of notes entitled, < Mechanics > (***Le Meccaniche***), which he used in private instruction of his pupils when he was teaching at the University of Padua. In this book, which was published posthumously in 1649, Galileo treated the classic problems of 5 simple machines after Heron of Alexandria. By recognising like Heron that in an ideal machine without internal friction it was required to increase the forces necessary to maintain the machine in a state of equilibrium only by a very small amount to set it into uniform motion, Galileo analysed each simple machine dynamically by using the quasi-static principle of virtual velocities as Heron of Alexandria had done in antiquity:

(*Driving force*) × (*its velocity*) = (*Load*) × (*its velocity*).

Galileo followed Heron of Alexandria in the calculation of the power delivered by machines, but he was unable to surpass Heron in any substantial way. Although Heron of Alexandria had restricted his theory of machines to the condition of balance between the effort of driving force and the load, he did examine how much the effort had to be increased to move the load when he studied the effect of friction in machines. The ancient Greeks had understood mechanics not as a natural science, but rather as a technical art, or technique, by means of which man can overcome nature. Therefore, ancient Greeks regarded mechanics as a means used 'against nature' to make bodies move artificially against their 'nature'. Accordingly, in the opinion of ancient Greeks mechanics was not science but rather a technique (***techne***). Contrariwise, Galileo held that the motion produced mechanically can never be directed against nature since man can do nothing against nature, but rather that mechanics can produce motion only according to the laws of nature. Therefore, according to Galileo, mechanics is part of applied natural science.

Aristotle had given a fundamental rule in dynamics which assumed that no body can partake in two different kinds of motion simultaneously, but many astronomers regarded such celestial motions to be mutually independent. In the terrestrial motion of projectiles, Galileo adopted this view of astronomers with profit, and assumed that the horizontal motion and the vertical motion of the projectile are mutually independent and, on this basis, he derived a parabolic trajectory for the projectile. It was an important innovation in the kinematic theory of projectile motion. Galileo's approximate method, which ignored air friction, wind, and the spin of the projectile, served as the basis of the ballistic tables for centuries afterwards. Galileo's own thought on this approximation was as follows: "... hence in order to handle this matter in a scientific way, it is necessary to cut loose from these difficulties [air resistance, friction, etc.] and having discovered and demonstrated the theorems, in the case of no resistance, to use them and apply them with such limitations as experience will teach."

In 1581, whilst Galileo was a medical student at the University of Pisa, according to the legend, he had observed that the swinging of the lamp suspended by a long chain from the ceiling of the Cathedral of Pisa was for all practical purposes isochronous. He examined this phenomenon again in experiments with pendula consisting of suspended spheres made of different materials, and the results of his small-scale experiments seemed to corroborate his initial observation that the period of oscillation of the pendulum was independent of the material and the weight of the pendulum bob, and also of the amplitude of the swing. In 1637, based on this experience, Galileo developed a pendulum device as a vibration counter which recorded the number of oscillations in a given time. The idea of using an isochronous pendulum as a time-measuring device was not new, for it had been used by Gerbert (c.940-1003) in the design of a pendulum clock at Magdeburg in Germany, and by a Muslim astronomer IbnYunus, who used an isochronous pendulum for the measurement of time in the observatory at Cairo about 1000. Joost Bürgi had used his 'planetary clock', an isochronous pendulum-clock of his own construction, for mensuration of time in his astronomical observations at the observatory in Cassel, Germany, about 1580.

Galileo designed his mechanical clock regulated by the pendulum in 1641, when he was already blind and bedridden. He advised his son, Vicenzio, to construct a model of his pendulum clock, which lacked a drive, but Vicenzio delayed building the pendulum clock for fear that his father's invention might be pirated. Not until 1649 did Vicenzio have the framework constructed for his father's pendulum clock, but before he himself was able to proceed with the cutting of its gears, he died and left the clock unfinished. Galileo's pendulum-clock was built two centuries later from Vicenzio's drawings. In the meantime, the pendulum-clock had been theoretically designed and technically perfected by the Dutch physicist and mathematician, Christiaan Huygens, about a quarter of a century after Galileo's death, and some of the important details in Huygens' pendulum-clock were adopted to Galileo's pendulum clock.

Galileo expressed his appreciation of the great inventive value of mathematics in the following words: "Truly I begin to understand that although logic is a most excellent instrument to govern our reasoning, it does not compare with the sharpness of geometry [mathematics] in awakening the mind for discovery." Aristotelian mechanics of the Mediæval Age had basically concentrated its main interest on qualities, whereas Galileo proposed to concentrate his mechanics on quantities as Stevin had done. He sought descriptive knowledge of science consisting of a series of quantitative axioms as mathematical formulae deduced from a few fundamental principles. Galileo did not seek to discover the Aristotelian ultimate causes of the phenomena, because he thought such a search to be futile. He introduced mathematical functions in words and in the language of proportions, since the symbolic methods of mathematics were at the time under development, and he employed Oresme's graphical representation of functions without acknowledgement.

Galileo was not only a prominent scientist but also a practical engineer. He was appointed 'superintendent of waters' in Florence, and was co-author of a report on the River Bisenzio. Galileo improved a 'geometrical and military compass', an original invention of Joost Bürgi made several decades earlier in Cassel with the collaboration of his brother-in-law Benjamin Bramer who was known for his construction of a series of metrological instruments in Germany, by adding additional scales to this sector compass and employing skilled artisans in a profit-making workshop to manufacture it for sale. This sector compass of relatively low degree of accuracy had many scales, and it served as a portable calculator having a similar purpose as the modern slide rule. It was useful in solving many geometrical and mathematical problems, including extraction of square and cube roots. It was a good source of income for Galileo, and he claimed to have sold about 300 such instruments over a decade. He published a manual, his first book, on the elementary theory based on similar triangles of this instrument entitled < Instructions on the Use of the Geometric and Military Compass > (***Le operazioni del compasso geometriceo et militare***) in 1606. He also manufactured other instruments which he invented such as a hydrostatic balance, for which he wrote an instruction manual that circulated in manuscript form, and a thermoscope.

Already Muslim astronomers had used tubes without lenses to observe isolated stars. After the English scientist Roger Bacon (c.1214-1294) proposed in his treatise < Greater Work > (***Opus Maius***) in 1266 the use of spectacles with convex lenses to compensate for presbyopia, the lens-grinding industry had developed in several European centers. The combination of mirrors and also lenses suggested by Bacon were attempted by the English mathematician Leonard Digges (died c.1571) and his son Thomas (died 1595), but their apparatus was set on frames without tubes. The principle of the telescope was first mentioned by the Italian savant and man of letters, Giovanni Battista della Porta (c.1538-1615) in one of the several editions of his book < Natural Magic > (***Magia naturales***) in 1589. Apparently della Porta's telescopic instrument, which had a convex objective lens and a concave ocular lens, was manufactured in Italy about 1590 and subsequently taken to The Netherlands where the Dutch spectacle-makers attempted to improve it. The telescope which was improved empirically by the Dutch spectacle-maker Zacharias Jansen and his son Johann about 1590 was kept a military secret on the advice of Prince Maurice of Orange. A German spectacle-maker Hans Lippershey [alias Lipperhey] (c.1570-1619) working in The Netherlands obtained knowledge of Jansen's telescope which he improved before making it commercially available in 1609 when it came to the attention of Galileo. Galileo, after being informed of the telescope made in The Netherlands, built his own telescope by trial-and-error method since he did not understand its optical functioning. Galileo's own telescope had a planoconvex objective lens of a long focal length in combination with a diverging eyepiece, a system of lenses similar to that of modern opera glasses. The first telescope of Galileo had a magnification of 3 diameters. His last telescope had 33-power magnification, the limiting power for his optical system. Galileo surveyed the sky with his first telescope in 1609, but he was not the first astronomer to do so. In 1609 the noted English astronomer and mathematician, who corresponded with Kepler on astronomical and optical topics, Thomas Harriot, used the Dutch telescope in his astronomical observations in the summer of 1609 before Galileo had made his own telescope. Harriot succeeded to map the Lunar landscape more accurately than Galileo, and to discover the Sunspots and the satellites of Jupiter. Harriot, after surveying and mapping Virginia for Sir Walter Raleigh (c.1552-1618), also contributed to the notation and codification of modern algebra for his < Practice of Analytical Art > (***Artis analyticae praxis***) set the modern standard for textbooks of algebra. In 1607 Harriot had observed the Halley's comet before the telescope existed. Sunspots had been first observed by the German astronomer Christopher Scheiner (1575-1650) before Galileo, and the German court astronomer to the Elector of Brandenburg, Simon Mayr (in Latin, ***Marius***) (1570-1624) observed and named the 4 satellites of planet Jupiter, apparently also before Galileo. Galileo confirmed with his telescopic observation the claim of Copernican astronomers that planet Venus possesses phases like the Moon and, therefore, must revolve round the Sun as predicted by Copernican astronomy. Galileo thought that he had discovered through his telescopic observations a peculiar 'triple form' of planet Saturn, a grossly inaccurate observation later corrected by Christiaan Huygens, who discovered that Saturn is surrounded by a thin flat ring [later observed to consist of several rings] inclined to the ecliptic which does not touch the planet.

Huygens made his astronomical observations with a much superior telescope of his own design after inventing a new method of grinding and polishing lenses, and a new micrometer for accurate telescopic measurements of small angles. Galileo was not a theoretical astronomer like Kepler, but an astronomical observer who used a small and relatively primitive telescopic instrument. In 1635 Galileo proposed a new method of determining the longitude at sea based on the frequent eclipses of the 4 moons of the planet Jupiter as the celestial clock. Unfortunately this method did not work well at sea because the motion of the ship interfered with accurate observations of the eclipses of Jupiter moons, but it proved to be useful on land after 1668 when the Italian astronomer Giovanni Domenico Cassini (1625-1712) of Bologna published a set of tables on the Jupiter moons, and a new edition of the tables in 1693 which gave more accurate information on the motion of Jupiter moons.

In 1675 the Danish astronomer Øle Christensen Rømer (1644-1710), who was brought to Paris by the French astronomer Jean Picard (1620-1682) in 1671 to work with Cassini [an envious, opinionated individual] in the newly founded observatory at Paris, observed that the eclipse of the innermost moon of planet Jupiter and its emergence from the shadow cone of the planet did not always coincide with the values given by Cassini in his tables of Jupiter moons: it came too late when the Earth receded from Jupiter and too early when the Earth approached the planet. Rømer, a talented and ingenious astronomer, concluded from his observations that light takes time to traverse the distance from the planet Jupiter to the Earth. Twice in a year the Earth is in-line with the Sun and the Jupiter, once the Earth is between the Sun and the Jupiter, at the other time the Earth and the Jupiter are on the opposite sides of the Sun. At one time the eclipse of the Jupiter moon is seen 8 minutes earlier, and at the other time 8 minutes later than at the intermediate time. Rømer argued that the difference in times is due to the additional distance [the diameter of the Earth's orbit] the light from Jupiter has to travel to the Earth, and he estimated that the light has a finite speed, about 227,000 km a second [accepted modern value 299,792 km a second] – an estimate Rømer presented to the French Academy of Sciences in 1676 which was accepted by Picard and Huygens but rejected by the envious Cassini. Rømer, whose astronomical work was highly regarded, was invited to visit England where he met Newton, Flamsteed and Halley. He invented the transit circle, and a telescopic micrometer in 1676. In 1681 Rømer was called back to Denmark by King Christian V, and appointed Royal Mathematician, professor of astronomy at the University of Copenhagen, as well as the director of the observatory at Runde Taarn near Copenhagen where he introduced technical improvements in the method of astronomical observations with the combined use of the telescope, the microscope, the pendulum clock, and a mercury thermometer providing temperature corrections for his telescope ring and pendulum. In 1700 Rømer built the first meridian telescope. Rømer introduced in 1703 his thermometer which had fixed points at the melting of snow and at the boiling of water, the same fixed points used in the more refined thermometer developed later by the German-Dutch physicist, Gabriel Daniel Fahrenheit (1686-1736) of Danzig whose living accommodations had been provided by Rømer in 1708 and 1709. In 1705 Rømer was appointed the mayor of Copenhagen. Unfortunately, in 1728 the records of his extensive astronomical observations were completely destroyed in a widespread fire which swept through the city of Copenhagen.

Della Porta gave the first theory of the lens in his book < On Refraction > (***De refractione***) in 1593, but because he did not know the true law of refraction and the way sight comes about his conclusions were not correct The correct geometric theory of the lens and the human sight was first given by Kepler as discussed above, and he gave on the basis of his theory the principle of the astronomical telescope in which both the objective lens and the ocular lens were convex.

Galileo investigated the failure of suction pumps to lift water more than 33 feet (10.06 m) in a well intended to supply the palace of Grand Duke of Tuscany with water. Although he assumed that air had weight, Galileo was not able to explain why the suction pump failed to lift water to the height of 40 feet (12.19 m). His last assistant Torricelli made the correct explanation for the failure of suction pumps possible when in 1643 he proved the existence of atmospheric pressure by his invention of the mercury barometer.

Kepler's ingenious researches inspired 4 of his contemporaries: Willebrord Snel, Bonaventura Cavalieri, Gilles Personne de Roberval and Pierre Siméon de Fermat (1601-1665).

Willebrord Snel van Roijen (1591-1626), professor of mechanics at the University of Leyden, was the first Leyden professor to perform physical experiments. He discovered experimentally the law of refraction of light, which he stated in his unpublished manuscript: "For the same media, the ratio of the cosecant of the angle of incidence and of refraction retains always the same value." The law of refraction had already been discovered independently by the English astronomer and mathematician Thomas Harriot, but he never published it because of unstable political conditions in England. It was expressed as the law of sines :

$$\frac{\sin i}{\sin r} = n ,$$

where *i* is the angle of incidence, *r* the angle of refraction, and *n* is the constant of refraction, by René Descartes in his essay < The Dioptrics > (***La dioptrique***) in 1637, but without acknowledging Snel's priority. Descartes obtained the law of sines theoretically by basing it on 3 assumptions, 2 of which were wrong. His first assumption which claimed that the speed of light is greater in denser medium was criticised by Pierre de Fermat who deduced the law of refraction of Snel by means of his 'least time principle' based on the assumption that the speed of light is less in denser medium. Snel, moreover, followed the suggestion already made in 1533 by the Dutch scientific cartographer, mathematician and physician, Gemma Frisius (1508-1555), to use the so-called 'method of triangulation' consisting of establishing a network of precisely measured triangles over a particular territory to prepare accurate regional maps, and made a series of surveying measurements by triangulation in 1617 from which he determined the length of a degree of a meridian to be about 67 miles (107.8 km), a value which was later changed by one of his students to 69 miles (111.0 km) as a result of correcting some errors present in Snel's calculations, a value that lies within a few hundred feet of currently accepted value.

Cavalieri and Method of Indivisibles:

Bonaventura Cavalieri was inspired by Kepler's treatise on the wine kegs and, also, by Galileo's advice to give the first systematic account of the infinitesimal method. Cavalieri founded his method on the mediæval concept of the 'indivisible' which regarded a line to be made up of an infinite number of points. This method led him to the so-called 'principle of Cavalieri' which stated that 2 solids of equal altitude have the same volume, as long as their cross-sections at equal heights have the same area. This principle made it possible for Cavalieri to produce results equivalent to the integration of polynomials. He published his researches < New Geometry of the Continuum of Indivisibles > (***Nova geometria indivisibilibus continuorum***) in 1635, which presented a crude form of calculus by means of which he was able to solve many problems of mensuration. It was one of the most influential books of the 'Baroque Era' but its unrigorous method came under severe criticism, particularly by a Jesuit, Paul [alias, Habakuk] Guldin (1577-1643), professor of mathematics at the University of Vienna, who considered the method to be incorrect since it led to paradoxes as Thomas Bradwardine had already demonstrated by 1335. Guldin pointed out a number of fallacies resulting from the method of indivisibles. Another Jesuit Pater and mathematician, André Tacquet (1612-1660) of Antwerpen, who developed the concept of limits and gave the first actual limiting process in 1656, justifiably criticised the method of Cavalieri as neither legitimate nor geometrical. After his friend Torricelli showed Cavalieri that the method of indivisibles can lead to mathematical fallacies, Cavalieri introduced an interesting comparison of indivisibles of a surface with the threads of a piece of cloth, and the indivisibles of a solid with the pages of a book. Moreover, Cavalieri also used the kinematical conception of the ancient Greek mathematician Archytas of Taras that surfaces and volumes can be considered to be generated by the flux of indivisibles, an idea developed into a rigorous geometrical method by Torricelli which reappeared in the method of fluxions of Isaac Newton. Moreover, since the indivisible itself found an 'atomic' counterpart in the idea of the differential of Leibniz, Cavalieri's indivisibles did have a considerable influence on the development towards algorithmic procedures of calculus, although he did not succeed to give it a satisfactory logical basis. The 2nd edition of his book which appeared posthumously in 1653 contained his corrections and recent statements, but his arguments were essentially the same as the arguments of Nicole Oresme and Johann Kepler. Cavalieri's most significant contribution given in modern notation,

$$\int_0^a x^n \, dx = \frac{a^{n+1}}{n+1} \; ,$$

is valid for all positive integers n, a result which he gave in his book < Six Geometric Exercises > (***Exercitationes geometricae sex***). Another significant contribution of Cavalieri was his recognition of an important connexion that exists between the Archimedean spiral, $r = a\theta$, and the parabola of Menaichmos of Alopekonnesos, $x^2 = ay$. He showed how a parabola $x^2 = ay$ could be twisted around like the coiled spring of a watch so that it coincided with the Archimedean spiral $r = a\theta$, thereby giving the ordinates to the parabola which can be regarded as transformations of the radius vector r through the relationships $x = r$, and $y = r\theta$ between the rectangular coordinates x and y and the polar coordinates r and θ. This and other observations of Cavalieri on the twisted parabola were really a part of modern analytic geometry and calculus before these mathematical disciplines formally existed.

Roberval, Cycloid and Method of Indivisibles:

Another mathematician who was influenced by < New Stereometry of Wine Kegs > (***Nova stereometria dolorium vinariorum***) of Kepler was the French mathematician Gilles Personne de Roberval (1602-1675), since 1631 professor of mathematics at ***Collège Gervais*** and later at ***Collège Royal*** in Paris, a position he won by competition in 1634 and which he had to defend every 3 years in a competitive examination until his death in 1675. He belonged to the Mersenne group of scientists, and it was apparently Mersenne who suggested to Roberval to study the cycloidal curve first noted by Galileo, which Roberval named ***trochoid*** (meaning 'wheel' in Greek). In 1634, Roberval found the area under the cycloidal curve, and in 1638, he used kinematics to draw a tangent to a cycloid [a mathematical problem solved by Fermat and Descartes at the same time], and the volume generated by the rotation of the cycloidal arc about its base line. Roberval, who accepted Kepler's concept of gravitational attraction between two bodies in space, proposed in 1636 the Keplerian concept of gravity as mutual attraction between particles of bodies in space which the pompous Descartes, who was an implacable enemy of Roberval, unfairly ridiculed in 1646 as an 'absurd notion'. In 1639, Roberval developed a method of indivisibles in his memoir < Treatise of Indivisibles > (***Traité des indivisibles***) which, unlike the Cavalieri's method of indivisibles, was based on the ancient Greek 'geometric atom' method of Demokritos of Abdera (c.470-c.370 B.C.). Roberval maintained like Tacquet that geometrical magnitudes are made up of ***homogenea***, and not of ***heterogenea***, that is, in the 'geometric atom method' lines are made of infinitely small lines [not points], surfaces of infinitely small surfaces [not lines], and volumes of infinitely small volumes [not surfaces], which rendered his method of indivisibles more logical and precise. Roberval was able to show by means of his method of indivisibles, that the area under the cycloidal curve is 3 times the area of its generating circle, that the length of the first rotation of the Archimedean spiral $r = a\theta$ is equal to the length of the parabola $x^2 = ay$ from $x = 0$ to $x = 2\pi a$, a problem also solved by

Torricelli. He studied other curves, and constructed tangents to some curves by using the kinematic method of Archimedes of Syracuse. Unfortunately, Roberval did not disclose his methods of solution, probably because the professorial chair of mathematics at ***Collège Royal*** which he occupied became automatically vacant every 3 years to be filled again by open competition in a mathematical contest in which the questions were set by the last occupier of the chair. He kept his solutions secret for the sake of the regularly arranged mathematical contests which he had to win to keep his chair of mathematics, thereby losing credit for many of his discoveries which embroiled him in several bitter quarrels concerning priorities. His most acrimonious quarrel was about the cycloidal curve with Torricelli, who had made his discovery independently, and whom he accused of plagiarism. In evaluating the area of a surface, which in modern times is expressed by a definite integral, Roberval divided the surface into small surface elements which he let continually decrease in magnitude and increase in number, and then found the area by summing an infinite series by a method of arithmetical limit. Roberval's Method of Indivisibles was superior to that of Cavalieri which was based on fixed geometric indivisibles.

Roberval wrote a complete treatise < Treatise of Mechanics > (***Traité de Méchanique***) in 8 books which he had finished by 1650. Only manuscript fragments of this treatise have survived. In this treatise he gave a new convincing proof for the law of composition of concurrent forces that was even superior to the earlier proof of Stevin. A brief excerpt from Roberval's treatise of mechanics was inserted into the book < Universal Harmony > (***Harmonie universelle***), a French language edition of Mersenne's ***Harmonicorum libri,*** in 1634.

Desargues and Synthetic Projective Geometry:

Kepler's geometric idea of the 'points at infinity' bore fruit in the work of the French architect and musketeer Gérard [alias Girard] Desargues, a professional military engineer who gave some gratuitous lectures in Paris from 1626 to 1630 which impressed his contemporaries, particularly Descartes and Pascal, since he was a geometrician of great natural ability and originality. Desargues had an unorthodox view of the importance of perspective in geometry, an idea which found little support among other mathematicians and, therefore, he returned to his home city Lyon where he worked out a new and original geometry, now called the 'synthetic projective geometry', by himself. This new geometry was based on the concept of perspective and Kepler's principle of continuity in which he passed from the properties of the circle to the properties of other conic sections by means of the perspective, making use of poles and polars. This allowed Desargues to study the properties of the sections of the cone cut by a plane at different angles which remain invariant. In this new projective geometry of Desargues, parallel lines were regarded as pencil lines meeting in a point at infinity. In terms of generality Desargues' projective geometry had an enormous advantage over the metric geometry of the ancient Greek mathematician Apollonios of Perge, Fermat and Descartes since many special cases of a theorem were reduced into a single all-inclusive statement. Yet Desargues' contemporary mathematicians, who were apparently committed to the new achievements in algebra and geometry by Fermat and Descartes, actively opposed the new projective geometry of Desargues which represented too complete a break with the past. Descartes who had fought with Desargues at the siege of the city La Rochelle, considered Desargues' geometry to be unsound and even dangerous. Moreover, Desargues used a difficult style of expression and a most bizarre vocabulary in mathematics, and even the title of his book < Rough Draught of an Attempt to Deal with the Outcome of a Meeting of a Cone with a Plane > (***Brouillon d'une utteint aux événemens des rencontres d'un cone avec un plan***), which he privately printed in 1639 and distributed to his friends, was ponderous and laboured. On account of both the bizarre vocabulary with terms taken from botany, and the novel projective method to treat geometry that represented a complete break with the past, Desargues' treatise disappeared despite the fact that it contained an entirely new geometric discipline: the synthetic projective geometry. Fortunately, Desargues' projective geometry was saved from oblivion in 1847, when a handwritten copy of it made by his student Philippe de la Hire [alias Lahire] (1640-1718), a mathematically inclined architect-engineer who admired Desargues, was found in a library in Paris. La Hire in his work < New Elements of Conic Sections > (***Nouveaux élémens des sections coniques***) prepared in 1697 gave the first example of a surface given analytically through an equation in 3 unknowns which represented the first real advance towards solid analytic geometry. In 1685 he wrote < Conic Sections > (***Sectiones conicae***) which was a treatise on synthetic geometry treated from the projective viewpoint of Desargues. La Hire proved to be the first modern specialist in both the synthetic and the analytic geometry.

Fermat, Saint Vincent and Infinitesimal Mathematics:

The French lawyer and mathematician, Pierre Siméon de Fermat, author of the Principle of Least Time in the refraction of light in optics about 1640, was much impressed by Kepler's infinitesimal method and proceeded to extend Kepler's method in his development of an inchoative differential calculus in his study of maxima and minima of functions by defining an equivalent method to the derivative of a function $F(x)$:

$$E=0: \quad \frac{F(x+E)-F(x)}{E} \; ,$$

where E is a very small increment of x. In this ratio, obtained after division with E, he set $E = 0$.

Fermat was able to integrate by the use of his method of quadrature:

$$\int_a^b x^n\,dx = \int_0^b x^n\,dx - \int_0^a x^n\,dx \ ,$$

for all rational values of n, but for $n = -1$. In his method of quadrature, Fermat subdivided the area under the curve into small incremental elements of area in the form of narrow rectangles, and by letting the number of these elements increase to infinity whilst the areas of the elements become indefinitely small he evaluated the numerical limit of the sum of such elements. He appears to have appreciated the significance of every aspect of his quadrature but the operation itself, an operation now called 'integration'. Fermat's method of integration failed for $n = -1$, but this case was solved in 1647 by Fermat's older contemporary, Grégoire de Saint Vincent (1584-1667), a Swiss Jesuit teacher in Rome and in Prague :

$$\int_a^b \frac{dx}{x} = \ln b - \ln a \ .$$

Grégoire de Saint Vincent made implicit use of infinitesimals and, like Kepler, he regarded infinitesimal elements to make up any geometric figure in which the subdivision of the figure into infinitesimal elements proceeds to infinity to 'exhaust' [in his Latin, '***exhaurire***'] the figure by means of infinitesimal elements. He considered the subdivision to be varying, thereby approximating the method of limits. In this respect, he was closer to the modern concept than Cavalieri and Torricelli. Archimedes of Syracuse and Stevin had subdivided a geometric figure until the error was less than a certain amount, whereas Grégoire de Saint Vincent interpreted this to mean an actual infinite subdivision which brought him to the idea of the limit of an infinite geometric progression. But he was not the first to use infinite series since the Merton College calculators, Oresme and other Schoolmen of the Middle Ages had used infinite series in connexion with the latitude of forms. However, Grégoire de Saint Vincent was the first mathematician to state explicitly that an infinite series defines a quantity which can be called the 'limit of the series', and he attempted to formulate explicitly the limit concept in geometric terms, a concept that was implicit in Stevin's work. He also recognised that the Zeno's Paradox of Achilles can be explained in terms of the limit of an infinite series. Grégoire de Saint Vincent, like Nicholas of Cusa and Kepler before him, used an inscribed polygon of infinite number of sides to stand for a circle.

In 1629 Fermat became the first mathematician to discover analytic geometry, a mathematical discipline which not only marks the origin of modern mathematical physics but has had an important influence on the development of engineering sciences. Fermat, as can be seen above, discovered the infinitesimal analysis and the so-called analytic geometry, properly called coordinate geometry, which René Descartes discovered independently in 1632. He practically created the modern theory of numbers, which was an entirely new topic. He, together with Pascal, founded the probability theory in which Fermat's contribution according to Pascal was more substantial. Although mathematics was only a hobby to Fermat, no professional mathematician of his time made more important discoveries in mathematics. He was considerably more profound than Descartes in every subject they both studied.

It is appropriate at this point to recall that long before the works of Fermat and Descartes on coordinate geometry, the ancient Greek geometer Apollonios of Perge had already characterised conic sections by means of coordinates although he attached no numerical values to them. However, in the book < Geography > (***Geographika***), the ancient Greek astronomer and geographer Klaudios Ptolemaios of Alexandria used latitudes and longitudes which were actually numerical coordinates. Finally, the last creative ancient Greek mathematician Pappos of Alexandria, who had written the treatise < Mathematical Collection > (***Matematikon synagogon biblia***) comprised of 8 books, gave in the book < Treasury of Analysis > (***Analyomenos***), if the notation is suitably modernised, an application of algebra to geometry.

Descartes, Philosophical Principles and Vortex Theory:

Descartes in his dualistic philosophy attributed to matter the quality of being extended in space (***res extensa***) and to the mind the quality of knowing (***res cognitans***). Therefore, ***res extensa*** and ***res cognitans*** was the foundation of his analysis. He expounded a new mechanical philosophy of nature, which asserted that all natural phenomena are mere effects produced by inert material bodies moving according to immutable mathematical laws. Descartes assumed that motion can be transferred from one body to another by direct or indirect impact. He categorically insisted that there is only one mechanics valid both on Earth as well as in the heavens. Descartes had to invent an entirely new system of dynamics to make his vortex theory work. He maintained that there exist only 2 physical concepts: space or extension, and motion. He postulated non-existence of atoms, and maintained that matter and space are one and the same, and each admits unlimited divisibility. The 2 concepts, matter and motion, each being a fixed quantity in the universe, can neither increase nor decrease. Therefore, to remove matter and to leave empty space was not possible. For this reason, the only circumstance that physics has to consider is the communication of motion from one body to another: the laws of motion are, therefore, laws of the transference of motion from one body to another. He presumed that the total quantity of motion mv in the universe is a constant, an idea which introduced the concept of conservation, or invariance into mechanics. Descartes failed to realise that the 'quantity of motion (***quantité de mouvement***)', mv, is a directional [vectorial] quantity and not a scalar quantity as he assumed, although he attempted to distinguish between the speed of a body and its direction, but he never carried it to a satisfactory conclusion. Descartes took *mv* as a measure of force, and asserted the 'conservation of linear momentum' in essentially modern terms, but he did not claim it to be applicable to all problems of mechanics. Since this principle of Descartes did not hold in the simple pendulum problem, it could not be a general principle.

In 1644, in his < Principles of Philosophy > (***Principia philosophiae***) Descartes stated his law of inertia as follows: "All bodies moving in a straight line will continue in that motion unless there is an external cause". In this work he also introduced his principle of conservation of linear momentum in the world. Descartes, who lacked patience, never carried his enquiries far enough to discover that most of the principles he proposed were not only partly incorrect but also insufficient, and many were altogether wrong. He was convinced that his own theories were correct, and that in the experiments performed to test the theories the necessary conditions could not be actually realised. His law of inertia was one of the very few special principles of motion which he proposed that was not outdated soon after his death. Descartes and Pierre Gassendi were the first scientists to insist that inertial motion must be 'rectilinear', and that bodies which move in circles or along curves must be constrained by some external cause. Descartes was a confirmed skeptic: "In order to seek truth it is necessary once in the course of our life to doubt so far as possible all things," a principle on which he based his entire approach to science. As a general principle, Descartes advised : "Take false what was probable, take probable what was certain, and reject all else." The Christian scientist and former Neoplatonic philosopher, Ioannes Philoponos of Alexandria (485-555), had stated in 517: "The energies flow from one body to another in such a way that an impressed force is transmitted to the projected body," which is a theory of action by contact, and on this idea Descartes erected his entire science of mechanics. In his vortex theory, the Sun is the center of a vast rotating quantity of 'subtle matter' which men ordinarily do not perceive or detect, and this rotating matter keeps the planets moving in their orbits. Descartes used the idea of 'subtle matter' to explain the transmission of light, the action of gravity, the magnetic force, and other phenomena. Everything in nature that was not mathematical Descartes considered to be an illusion of the senses. Descartes' ideal scientific method was to treat natural science as mathematics: "The essence of science is mathematics," which is reminiscent of Plato who had written: "Each science is science only so far as it contains mathematics." Descartes introduced infinitesimal displacements into the principle of virtual work, and he was the first to sketch an entirely correct formulation of this principle. Descartes was the first scientist to regard work as the fundamental concept of mechanics which can serve as the foundation for the entire science of mechanics.

In 1628 a Benedictine friar, Benedetto Castelli (1577-1644), a former pupil of Galileo who taught mathematics at the University of Pisa and at Rome, published a treatise entitled < On the Measurement of Flowing Water > (***Della misura delle acque correnti***), which contained the principle of continuity of flow first proposed in a special case by Leonardo da Vinci. He also advocated the principle that the rate of efflux of water from a tank is directly proportional to the head of water, a wrong concept first used by Heron of Alexandria in the 2nd century B.C., and also by Leonardo da Vinci a century before Castelli.

Torricelli, Rule of Hydrodynamic Efflux, Barometer, and Principle of Stable Equilibrium:

A student of Castelli and Galileo's last amanuensis, the talented Italian mathematician and physicist Evangelista Torricelli (1608-1647),wrote a book < On Gravitational Motion ...> (***De motu gravium natur descendentium et projectorum***) in 1644, which is the source of hydrodynamics, because in it Torricelli connected the hydrostatics of Stevin with the motion of water. Torricelli asserted that under hydrostatic pressure a particle of fluid issues from an orifice nearly as fast as its speed v resulting in a free fall from a height equal to the head of the water h over the orifice of efflux:

$$v \propto \sqrt{h}.$$

Torricelli argued that a jet of water issuing from the orifice of a tank, if turned upwards, almost rises to the height of the head from the orifice, h, an observation that Leonardo da Vinci had already recorded in his notebook. The slight observed difference in the height of the jet and the head from the orifice Torricelli attributed to the influence of air resistance. In 1643, Torricelli gave in his letter to Matteo Angelo Ricci the first correct scientific explanation of the mercury-column barometer which he had invented, and the atmospheric pressure.

Torricelli, who was also an outstanding mathematician, established a minimum principle of stable equilibrium for a system of two connected masses:

$$\delta z_c = 0,$$

where z_c measures the height of the center of gravity of the two masses. He discovered the inverse relation between the quadrature [now called 'integration'] and the tangent problem [now called 'differentiation'] which represents the fundamental principle of calculus. Torricelli studied infinitesimal methods in great detail and employed the method of indivisibles used by Cavalieri, as well as the method of exhaustion of Eudoxos of Knidos (c.408-c.355 B.C.). He gave the quadrature of the cycloidal curve and constructed its tangent by the kinematic method of Archimedes of Syracuse. In his mathematical works, Torricelli came very close to the discovery of calculus in his memoir < On the Dimensions of the Parabola > (***De dimensione parabolae***), in which he stated that it is possible to inscribe within the parabola parallelograms of equal height which form a figure that can be made to differ from the parabolic segment by less than any given magnitude. This idea was implicit in Torricelli's work, and the limit concept would have readily followed from it if the quantities had been arithmetised. Unfortunately, Torricelli was influenced by Cavalieri to limit himself to purely geometric considerations, which led him more towards geometric indivisibles rather than towards numerical limits. Torricelli applied the kinematic method of Archimedes of Syracuse which made use of the instantaneous direction [thereby implying the 'limit concept'], in finding the tangents to a larger class of curves he called 'geometric spirals' which in modern notation are given as logarithmic spirals $r = ae^{b\theta}$. Torricelli did not treat these curves analytically but rather used ideas of synthetic geometry and kinematics to find the tangents, the length of curves and the areas bounded by them. It is possible that Roberval preceded Torricelli in employing kinematic methods in geometry, but since the unfriendly Roberval kept his mathematical methods a secret, it was Torricelli who made the kinematic method popular in geometry. For instance, Isaac Barrow (1630-1677) used it in his geometry, and his pupil, Isaac Newton, followed Torricelli's kinematic ideas in his method of fluxions.

Unfortunately, Torricelli's untimely death from pleurisy in 1647 was a severe loss to the immediate progress of science and mathematics, but his researches, particularly his efflux rule and the minimum principle of stable equilibrium, influenced some members of the French Academy of Sciences, particularly Huygens and Mariotte.

Pascal and Calculating Machine:

French mathematician, philosopher, physicist, and a former child prodigy, Blaise Pascal (1623-1662) generalised the notion of hydrostatic pressure in the so-called Pascal principle: "The pressure in a fluid is exerted in all directions with the same intensity to any point in the fluid." Therefore, according to the Pascal principle the pressure on a plane is independent of the inclination of the plane. This principle of Pascal which implies that pressure in a fluid is propagated in all directions with the same intensity without loss constitutes the technological hydraulic press principle, and its validity was demonstrated by Pascal himself when he constructed a model hydraulic instrument of force multiplication, the so-called 'model hydraulic press', which had a form of 2 interconnected cylinders fitted with pistons which had greatly differing cross-sectional areas. Pascal was not the first to use this principle, since it had been used implicitly by Simon Stevin and almost discovered by Giovanni Battista Benedetti in hydrostatics. In 1648, Pascal demonstrated by barometric measurements taken by his brother-in-law Périer, who carried a barometer to the top of the Puy de Dôme near Clermont in the mountainous district of Auvergne according to Pascal's directions, the correctness of his contention that the pressure of the atmosphere is hydrostatic in nature. Pascal subsequently wrote a tract on his barometric experiments <New Experiments Concerning Vacuum> (***Nouvelles expériences touchant le vide***), in 1647, and treatises on hydrostatics and aerostatics which were published posthumously in 1649 as a combined subject.

Pascal has been called, with some justification, the greatest 'might-have-been' in mathematics because he was the first mathematician to introduce in the memoir, < Treatise of Sines of the Quadrant of the Circle > (***Traité des sinus du quart de cercle***) (1658), what was later called by Leibniz ***triangulum characteristicum*** (characteristic triangle) for the change of the function in his quadrature [integration] of the functions $sin\phi$, $sin^2\phi$ and $\phi\ sin\phi$, in which the ratio of two infinitely small elements was determined by the ratio of two finite quantities, a method that led Leibniz to the invention of the differential calculus. Pascal accomplished the quadrature by the method of indivisibles that he had modified, and made more rigorous after studying Tacquet's treatise < Cylindrical and Annular Bodies > in 4 volumes (***Cylindricorum et annularium libri IV***) in 1854 by converting Cavalieri's 'totality concept' into the 'summation concept', and by distinguishing explicitly between the indivisibles and the elemental parts. He essentially generalised the concept of equality by equating 2 figures when the difference between them is smaller than an arbitrarily given amount. Pascal came closer to the concept of definite integrals than any of his contemporaries by clearly recognising that all integrations become arithmetical summations. However, Pascal did not use notational formalism because he expressed everything in words, but his work showed many details.

Pascal, moreover, studied the geometry of Archimedean spiral $r = a\theta$ with this method, which provided a link between the geometry of the Archimedes of Syracuse and infinitesimal calculus. Integral calculus would have been born if Pascal had made his triangle infinitesimally small, but it remained for Leibniz to discover the characteristic triangle in Pascal's 1658 memoir < Treatise of the Sines of the Quadrant of the Circle > and introduce it as an infinitesimal characteristic triangle (***triangulum characteristicum***) into infinitesimal calculus. Pascal failed to recognise the limit of a sum as the unifying concept of infinitesimal calculus, and the inverse nature of the problem of quadrature and the problem of tangents.

This type of characteristic triangle had first occurred in a work < Dutch Pilot > (***Tiphys Batavus***) in 1624, written by the remarkable Dutch mathematician Willebrord Snel van Roijen, who developed Gemma Frisius' method of determining distances by trigonometric triangulation and thereby established the modern art of geographic mapping.

The precociousness of Pascal can be recognised by his achievements. He began to study mathematics at 12 years of age. At 13 years of age, he discovered the celebrated Pascal triangle. Before he was 16 years of age, he had discovered the Pascal theorem, one of the fundamental theorems of the projective geometry. By 17 years of age he had derived by the use of his theorem 400 propositions in an essay on conic sections.

As a 19-year old teenager, Pascal rediscovered the basic principle of digital counting first discovered by Leonardo da Vinci and designed his celebrated mechanical calculator for additions and subtractions, which is the prototype for all mechanical desk calculators. Pascal used a set of wheels each of which was rotated by a stylus from 0 to 9, and transmitted by gears to a set of result wheels from which the answers could be read through windows. It handled up to six figures with a fixed decimal point. Tens were carried by a spring ratchet which rose with each unit step up to 9, and at 0 it dropped to advance the next result wheel one unit step. Subtraction was achieved by adding complements, and multiplication by repeated additions. Some of Pascal's calculators had extra wheels for addition of different coinage such as ***deniers*** and ***sous***, with 12 and 20 divisions, respectively. This calculating machine was not only far too complicated to repair, but also too expensive. It did not impress businessmen since it was cheaper to employ clerks to do the computations. The clerks also opposed the Pascal calculator since they feared it would lead to clerical unemployment. Therefore, Pascal's mechanical calculator, which is still extant, failed financially, but it brought him a considerable measure of fame.

Pascal wrote important essays on philosophy and philosophy of science, and he ranks with Descartes as one of the best writers of French prose of the 17th century. Although Pascal was a deeply religious person, he disagreed with many who asserted that nature proves the presence of God. In his opinion, nature proves God only to those who already believe in Him.

Pascal had a sceptical nature , and followed an extremely strict conception of hypothetico-deductive method. Before a hypothesis had been empirically verified, Pascal called it "a vision, a caprice, a phantasy or, at best, a beautiful idea," which accounts for his scepticism about the fantastic explanation of nature by Descartes.

Guericke, Vacuum Pump and Atmospheric Power:

The German physicist and engineer, Otto von Guericke [before ennoblement his name was Otto Gericke] (1602-1686), studied law in the juristic faculty but also attended engineering and science courses at the University of Leyden. He travelled in France and England, and served as an engineer for the German Protestant city of Erfurt. In 1631 the Protestant city of Magdeburg where Guericke lived was utterly destroyed in the most savage sack of the Thirty Years' War by the Imperial armies. Guericke and his family barely managed to escape alive. For a time he served as a military engineer in the victorious Swedish army, and upon his return to Magdeburg Guericke was appointed chief engineer of Magdeburg in the rebuilding of the city which lay in ruins. In 1646 Guericke became mayor of Magdeburg, a post he occupied for 35 years until his retirement.

In 1647, he began his experiments to create vacuum in an enclosed vessel on Earth in response to a cosmological question: Is it possible to produce spatial vacuum? If this be possible then it is also conceivable that planets may move in an empty space. Guericke's interest in empty space was evoked by the speculations on empty space in René Descartes' book < Meditations >

(***Meditationes***)(1641). After he discovered in 1650 that air could be pumped out of a vessel like any fluid, he built his first air [or vacuum] pump starting with the hand-syringe used to douse fires. His air-pump consisting of a cylinder, piston and receiver was the next important physical instrument after the telescope, microscope and barometer, with which he subsequently carried out important experiments on air-pressure in Magdeburg. Guericke, who was responsible for the introduction of systematic scientific experimentation into science, demonstrated with his experiments the existence of the immense force of atmospheric pressure by a method different from the Italian method, and the connexion that exists between the weather and air-pressure. He found from his experiments that the atmospheric pressure, which he knew depended upon the height above ground, was able to draw water up to a height of 19 Magdeburger ells (c. 32 feet). Since 1662 Guericke's house in Magdeburg had a water barometer more than 33 feet (10 m) high with which he was able to predict a storm hours before it happened, and to make the first comparative atmospheric pressure measurements in Germany. He also invented the Magdeburg air-gun which functioned by partial vacuum. In 1657, he pumped air out of two so-called 'Magdeburg hemispheres' made of brass and fitted together to form a hollow sphere about 3 feet in diameter with his air-pump, and he demonstrated in Regensburg before the Emperor Ferdinand III and an assembly of government officials the great power of atmospheric air-pressure when two teams of 8 powerful horses were not able to pull the 2 hemispheres apart. In his experiments, Guericke was the first person to observe the instability of thin shells under normal pressure, when some of his hemispheres buckled under air-pressure. Guericke demonstrated the great force of air-pressure also in an experiment in which a small boy pumped out the air from under a piston tightly fitted into a cylinder open to air above the piston, and the piston subsequently descended into the cylinder under atmospheric pressure, and thereby lifted a weight of 2,686 pounds (1,218 kg) which was connected to the piston by a rope running over a pulley. Guericke described his experiments on air pressure in his book < New Magdeburg Experiments of Empty Space > (***Experimenta nova Magdeburgica de vacuo spatio***), printed in Amsterdam in 1672. The account of his famous 'Magdeburg hemispheres' experiment was first published in 1657 by the Jesuit Pater Kaspar Schott (1608-1666) in the book < Mechanics, Hydraulics, Pneumatics > (***Mechanica, Hydraulica, Pneumatica***), a work from which other scientists in Europe first learnt about Guericke's air-pump. Guericke discovered that heat expands and cold contracts air, that air can be compressed but the compression has a limit, and that air has weight and therefore compresses itself.

Guericke's experiments led both the French Abbé Jean de Hautefeuille of Orleans (1647-1724) and the Dutch physicist and mathematician Huygens to suggest atmospheric engines as new power sources, since the experiments of Guericke clearly demonstrated the immense force of the atmospheric pressure, and indicated very clearly a method by means of which it could be harnessed to produce mechanical power. In 1678 de Hautefeuille proposed to supply the new Royal Palace of Versailles with water by introducing two cisterns into which water would be drawn by the vacuum created by exploding a small charge of gunpowder inside the cistern and thereby expelling air from the cistern through a nonreturn valve. The two cisterns were to be alternately evacuated of air by such explosions to maintain continuity of the water supply.

Guericke also discovered the electrostatic principle and designed the first frictional electric machine consisting of a sulphur ball attached to an axle to produce a continuous supply of static electricity by the friction of a hand pressing on the manually rotated sulphur ball. It opened up a century of experimentation on frictional electricity with other improved frictional devices. Guericke was the first important German physicist.

Boyle and Air-Pressure Experiments:

After the English experimental physicist and chemist Robert Boyle (1627-1691) received information about von Guericke's air pump in 1657 from Jesuit Pater Kaspar Schott's book, he constructed with the help of his young assistant Robert Hooke (1635-1703) a similar improved instrument which worked better than Guericke's air-pump, and had a glass receiver into which objects could be easily introduced for testing. Boyle performed a great number of experiments on air pressure and rarefied air with the help of Hooke all of which he discussed in his book < New Experiments Physico-Mechanical, touching the Spring of the Air and its Effects > published in 1660. He investigated the elasticity or spring of air [in Greek ***elater*** means a spring] and, particularly, the capacity of air to expand upon the reduction of external pressure. The first quantitative treatment of the elasticity of air Boyle gave in his book < A Defence of the Doctrine Concerning the Spring and Weight of the Air > in which he discussed the critical comments on his air-pressure experiments. Boyle's correspondent Richard Towneley (1629-1705), and also Henry Power (1623-1668) in his book on < Experimental Philosophy >, suggested that the volume and the pressure of the enclosed air are inversely proportional to each other, which Hooke had proven experimentally already by 1660, and succeeded to prove in a subsequent experiment even for the pressures below the atmospheric pressure. It represented the first quantitative law of nature apart from the phenomenon of motion. Boyle also noted that the pressure of an enclosed volume of air is increased by heating, but he failed to examine the phenomenon quantitatively, since at the time little attention was paid to the quantitative aspects of pneumatic phenomena. The so-called 'Boyle's law' appeared in the 2nd edition of the first book published in 1662. Boyle himself called this law, Towneley's hypothesis, although it was Hooke who actually had proven it scientifically by 1660, which Boyle also recognised. The French physicist Edmé Mariotte discovered in 1676 the so-called 'Boyle's law' given in his memoir < On the Nature of Air > (***De la nature de l'air***). Boyle was a founder of chemical analysis and a central figure in English experimental science during the 17th century. Boyle, like Hooke, was a supporter of Descartes' mechanistic philosophy of nature.

Marine Chronometer and Determination of Geographic Longitude:

One of the important age-old problems of science and technology was to find a reliable and accurate terrestrial or celestial clock because the determination of the exact position on the surface of the Earth and at sea required the exact determination of the geographic latitude and longitude. Klaudios Ptolemaios of Alexandria in the 2nd century A.D. had discussed the means for a correct determination of both latitude and longitude but it required accurate instruments for the measurement of time and angles, some knowledge of astronomy and trigonometry and above all else scientific collaboration of observers at different locations on the surface of Earth. It was the geographic longitude that was extremely difficult to determine with great precision, but particularly so at sea where it was of vital importance to navigation since every year the maritime nations suffered huge financial losses because of expensive shipwrecks in bad weather owing to the incorrect determination of longitude. Latitude could be determined conveniently by measuring the meridional altitude of the Sun from which the polar altitude could be found by means of a simple computation, if the declination of the Sun was known for every day from the declination tables. Such declination tables already existed in 1474, although they were not very accurate. Of course, the latitude can also be determined in the northern hemisphere by measuring the polar altitude, since the polar star is quite close to the North Pole. But the determination of the geographic longitude remained the critical problem to be solved by science and technology. As already suggested by Gemma Frisius in 1530, the exact determination of the longitude, or more accurately the difference of longitudes between a point on Earth and a fixed meridian reduces to the exact determination of the time difference between the astronomically established local time and the time at the fixed meridian. Therefore it was necessary to have either very accurate timepieces, or two observers who watch the same celestial phenomenon, for example a Lunar eclipse, as a celestial clock from two different places on the surface of the Earth and then take the difference of their local times. Since such celestial phenomena occur infrequently, the more practical solution to the longitude problem in navigation was to construct accurate mechanical clocks that can be transported on ships but are not affected by the rolling and pitching of the ships.

Huygens, Law of Centrifugal Motion and Conservation of Energy Principle:

The Dutch mathematician, physicist, astronomer, technologist and engineer, Christiaan Huygens (1629-1695), undertook to design and construct by means of the theory mechanics such an accurate and rugged timekeeper. Huygens solved the problem of the center of oscillation of a finite body by his axiom of energy, and his solution gives for the first time the moment of inertia quantity as a measure of rotational motion of a solid body. It was a milestone in theoretical mechanics. Unfortunately, Huygens' ingenious but quite special solution by his axiom of conservation of energy was not valid for the general motion of rigid bodies. Since the clock is the key instrument of the modern age requiring high precision mechanics, Huygens studied the mechanics of circular oscillation of the pendulum in 1658 the results of which he published in 1673 in his < Oscillatory Horology or the Pendular Motion Horology adopted to Geometric Demonstrations > (***Horologium Oscillatorium sive de motu pendulorum ad horologia aptato demonstrationes geometricae***). He was the first scientist to establish a correct law of motion in dynamics, the Law of Centrifugal Motion: $\frac{mv^2}{\rho} = F_n$,

where m denotes the mass, ρ the radius of the curvature of the path of motion of the mass-point, v the speed of motion, and F_n the centripetal force. Huygens derived the vectorial expression of centripetal acceleration, and presented the general curvilinear motion by a superposition of the centripetal and the tangential motion first considered by the ancient Greek physicist Straton of Lampsakos (*floruit* c.280 B.C.). Although Huygens compared gravitational forces with the centripetal forces of revolving bodies, he did not apply it to celestial bodies. He demonstrated that acceleration, like velocity, is a vectorial quantity, and he used Fermat's method of derivative to find the radius of curvature of a plane curve. Huygens sent a copy of his book to Newton.

In one of his early studies on the elastic impact of 2 spheres, which he succeeded to solve by his axiom of conservation of energy, Huygens investigated relative motion. His axiom of conservation of energy is sufficient with certain approximations to prove the isochrony of small pendular oscillations, but without some idea equivalent to rotary inertia it is impossible to calculate the period of oscillation. The solution of this problem by Huygens marks the very beginning of modern mechanics. Huygens also gave a mathematical solution of the suspension bridge problem of Beeckman.

In his study of the Galileo's problem of fracture of a simply supported heavy beam in 1662 Huygens applied the conservation of energy axiom for the first time to the fracture problem of the beam by equating the work done in the fracture by internal forces to the work done by the external forces :

$$M \Delta \phi = P_1 \Delta v_1 + P_2 \Delta v_2 + \cdots + P_n \Delta v_n .$$

In the conservation of energy principle of Huygens, the internal work was measured by the product of the moment of resistance M in the fractured cross section and the small angle-change $\Delta\phi$ at the cross-section of fracture of the beam which was set equal to the work done by the weight of the beam, represented by a set of discrete forces P_i, over the small displacements Δv_i produced by the collapse mechanism of the beam in which elastic bending of the beam is neglected. The fracture occurs at the section which makes the descent of the center of gravity, that is, the loss of potential energy because of the descent of the centers of gravity of the 2 parts of the beam, a maximum. This kind of virtual work method of Huygens which neglects elastic energy in the beam is still used today in the so-called 'limit analysis' of simple beams. The fracture mechanism of the beam was such as to make the center of gravity of the beam to undergo its maximum descent. Therefore, this solution of the fracture of beams can also be regarded as an application of the potential energy principle, and as the first use of an energy criterion of failure. Huygens' conservation of energy principle was an ingenious generalisation of the Torricelli minimum principle by equating the descent to the ascent of the center of gravity. Huygens' solution is equivalent to the criterion that the beam breaks at the section where the moment of applied loads is the greatest.

Huygens and Accurate Horology:

Accurate time measurement was made possible by Huygens who applied the science of mechanics to the clock design. The accurate mechanical timekeepers were indispensable for Huygens' own astronomical observations, but absolutely vital for the age-old problem of accurate determination of the geographic longitude at sea . Already in 1530 Gemma Frisius had proposed the use of clocks to determine the exact geographic longitude and suggested the use of a contemporary portable clock, the so-called 'Nuremberg egg', which worked with a spiral spring and ***fusee*** escapement. Unfortunately this clock was far too inaccurate for the precision required in longitude determination. Therefore, Huygens developed the principle of the pendulum for this purpose. Huygens made his first clock regulated by a pendulum in 1656. In 1658, Huygens wrote a treatise on the mensuration of time entitled < Horology > (***Horologium***) in which he introduced a 2-to-1 reduction gearing between the pendulum and the clockwork that reduced the arc of pendulum swing, since the smaller arc of oscillation of the pendulum reduces the error owing to the lack of isochronism in a larger arc of oscillation. In 1659, Huygens proved by his theoretical analysis with absolute mathematical rigour that isochronism results if the mathematical pendulum bob moves along a cycloidal arc.

In 1673, Huygens published his theoretical studies of isochronous cycloidal pendulum and compound pendulums in his book <Oscillatory Horology or On Pendular Motion ...> (***Horologium Oscillatorium sive de motu pendulorum ...***), in which he gave his design of the isochronous pendulum-clock using a bifilar pendulum the bob of which was swinging along a cycloidal arc that guaranteed isochrony regardless of the magnitude of the swing. The bifilar pendulum in this clock was swinging between two cycloidal cheeks. This treatise also contained his studies on the theory of evolutes, the effect of centrifugal force, free fall of bodies along curved or inclined paths, gravitational forces, motion in resisting medium, and possibilities of intelligent life elsewhere in the universe. Huygens designed, and built the first accurate cycloidal pendulum clock which made precise astronomy possible. Huygens was disappointed to learn that despite his efforts to test various modes of suspension of the pendulum, his pendulum clock was not successful at sea owing to the rolling and pitching of the ship, whereas on land his pendulum clock successfully met the standard of accuracy (a second a day) required for astronomical work.

Existing portable clocks had incorporated the verge escapement which drove a wheel or a bar-balance that unfortunately had no characteristic period of its own. In 1675, Huygens improved portable clocks and watches, by producing a watch fitted with a balance-wheel and a spiral spring drive which conferred isochrony to the timekeeper. A balance-wheel with a spiral spring drive had the advantage of having a natural period of its own like the pendulum, and, therefore, it gave the watch the same type of improvement in timekeeping as the pendulum gave to the pendulum clock. He calculated the frequency of vibration f of the pendulum :

$$f = \left(\frac{1}{\pi}\right)\left(\frac{T}{LM}\right)^{1/2},$$

where T is the period, L the length, and M the mass of the pendulum. A spiral spring of thin steel was fixed at the outer end of the spring to a flat base, and at the inner end in the center to a pinion turned by a balance-wheel with a heavy felloe. The self-reversing spring underwent approximately isochronous oscillations which performed the same function as the pendulum driven by gravity. The turning motion of the pinion was transmitted to the hands of the clock by means of a toothed contrate wheel. He provided his balance-wheel and spring-driven watch with an escapement which was able to maintain a constant torque as the spring unwound. When Henry Oldenburg (1626-1677), a German immigrant who was the first secretary of The Royal Society, published a description of Huygens' watch in Philosophical Transactions, a journal he published on his own expense, but he did not mention that Hooke had conceived the idea of the spring-driven watch first. Huygens' priority in the invention of the spring-driven watch was challenged by Robert Hooke, who claimed to have invented such a watch in 1658. In 1660, Boyle had shown one of Hooke's spring-driven watches to Viscount William Brouncker (1620-1684) and to Sir Robert Moray (1608-1673), the first president of The Royal Society, who offered to patent the invention for Hooke, an offer which Hooke could not accept because of an unfair clause in the patent agreement which stated that if anyone improved Hooke's invention then the improver, and not Hooke, will receive all the benefits from the invention. After this incident, Hooke decided to keep all of his horological inventions a secret until such unjust patent stipulations are abolished, which never occurred during his lifetime. In 1665 Robert Moray wrote Huygens 2 letters giving information about the design details of

Hooke's watches which Moray requested Oldenburg to communicate to Huygens. Subsequently Huygens, who benefited from this confidential information about the details of Hooke's spring-driven pocket-watch, offered the patent rights for his spring-driven watch in England to Oldenburg, who was acting on behalf of the avaricious Moray. Both Hooke and Huygens made working models of their spring-driven watches in 1674. However, the spring-driven watch was still not accurate enough for the exact determination of the longitude at sea, a problem of great interest to Hooke which was not solved for almost another century. It is very likely that the fundamental ideas for the details of the spiral spring-driven watch with spring-controlled escapement, in which the spiral spring was attached to the balance to confer isochrony to the watch, were first conceived by Hooke, who was recognised as the expert on all kinds of springs, rather than by Huygens. Huygens' and, particularly, Hooke's work on the technical details of more accurate timekeepers stimulated the development of more precise gear-cutting techniques among the instrument-makers in Europe, which substantially contributed to the development of chronometers of high accuracy. All of Huygens' chronometers were made by the clockmaker Salomon da Coster in Amsterdam. Hooke collaborated with the clockmaker Thomas Tompion in the manufacture of his double spiral spring-balanced pocket watches with spring-controlled escapements, 2 of which were presented to King Charles II in 1675.

Huygens had proven mathematically that, in isochronous motion, the pendulum bob has to move along a cycloidal curve but that for small amplitudes of the pendulum swing the circular curve almost coincides with the cycloidal curve. In Huygens' time, small amplitudes in pendulum clocks were difficult to control mechanically, but improvements in the escapement mechanism, such as were invented by Hooke, made the application of small amplitudes possible. Huygens was able to obtain the exact value for the gravitational constant $g = 31.25\ f/s^2$ ($9.81\ m/s^2$) from the oscillation of the pendulum. Hooke was the first physicist to use pendulum for the mensuration of gravity.

***Harrison, Longitude at Sea and Marine Chronometers*:**

For the sake of higher accuracy of timekeepers it became necessary to improve the escapement mechanism so that it would interfere less with the natural movement of the oscillating system, whether pendula or balance-wheels. Also the frictional resistance of the clockwork was greatly reduced by the introduction of jewel bearings, ordinarily rubies or sapphires, in 1704. The English clockmaker William Clement, who was often employed by Robert Hooke, used the anchor-escapement invented by Hooke in 1670, which was replaced by the dead-beat escapement of the English clockmaker George Graham (1673-1751) in 1715 that remained the standard escapement of astronomical clocks until the end of the 19th century because it eliminated recoil in the escapement mechanism. In 1721, Graham made a pendulum clock with the effective length of its pendulum being independent of temperature changes by providing the steel or brass bar with a bob containing mercury which had the opposite temperature effect. The change in temperature altered the dimensions of the metal parts of the pendulum clock, such as the pendulum itself, which affected its period of swing that was a serious source of inaccuracy in pendulum clocks. The English provincial mechanic and self-educated clockmaker, John Harrison (1693-1776), devised a gridiron pendulum composed of alternating rods of brass and steel which achieved the same temperature compensation effect as Graham's mercury bob pendulum. Graham also invented in 1721 the cylinder-escapement that allowed a slimmer design for watches, since it obviated the verge escapement in watches which had been in use for over 200 years.

In 1714, the British Board of Longitude set up a prize of £ 20,000 English pounds as an award for a marine chronometer which is not only capable of determining the longitude at sea with an accuracy of half a degree but also easily reproducible. The large sum of the award indicated the great importance of such a chronometer to maritime trade, since a great number of British vessels were shipwrecked because of errors in the estimation of longitude obtained by dead-reckoning which brought about heavy financial losses in maritime trade. Harrison, whose work on the marine chronometer was at first financed by a personal loan from Graham, finally succeeded with his 4th chronometer made in 1759, which kept time to within a 10th of a second a day. A replica of Harrison's 4th chronometer made by the clockmaker Larcum Kendall (1721-1795) was used by Captain James Cook (1728-1779) on his second voyage around the world, lasting 3 years from 1768 to 1771. Harrison's first accurate marine chronometer completed in 1735 had 4 balance-springs to compensate for the rolling of the ship. His first marine chronometer was operated by 2 mainsprings and worked like a clock in which 2 massive balances replaced the pendulum. His first chronometer weighing 72 pounds (32.7 kg) showed days, hours, minutes and seconds. His 2nd chronometer was even more massive weighing in excess of 100 pounds (41kg). All his chronometers incorporated special devices to prevent the timekeeper from stopping whilst being wound. The first 3 chronometers were mounted on gimbals but the 4th one rested on a cushion in a box. Harrison's 4th chronometer had a superb workmanship, a new verge type of escapement with diamond palettes, a cycloidal correction of the movement of the balance as well as reduced dimensions comparable to the dimensions of a watch. Harrison's 4th marine chronometer lost only a 10th of a second a day, and on a voyage to West Indies it lost only an additional 5 seconds. The temperature longitudes worked out for selected points by the traditional method checked perfectly with the values obtained by means of Harrison's chronometer. He had minimised the friction and compensated for temperature effects by varying the effective length of the balance-spring. The temperature effect is much more serious in balance-wheel timekeepers than in pendulum clocks, since the percentage change in the stiffness of a balance spring is 10 times as great as the percentage change in the length of the pendulum. Harrison used a bimetallic 'curb' to compensate for the change in the effective length of the balance-spring, circular steel balance wheel and the cycloidal correction of its movement. In brief, Harrison's method of compensating for the temperature variation was by means of thermocouples, and his method of compensating for the pitching and rolling effect of the ship was to employ counteracting balances. His 4th and the best pocket-size circular marine chronometer of 5-inch (12.7cm) diameter had the hour-hand, the minute-hand and the second-hand on the same dial. In fact, all the chronometers of Harrison were more accurate at sea than any other existing clock on land. The British Astronomer Royal, Nevil Maskelyne (1732-1811), who had accompanied Harrison's son William on the trip to the West Indies to test the accuracy of Harrison's pocket-size marine chronometer, kept the chronometer under observation at Greenwich Observatory for a year, and then issued an unfavourable and unfair report about its accuracy since the malevolent Maskelyne did not like clockmakers, particularly Harrison, which infuriated Harrison. After publishing a description of his chronometer in 1767, Harrison finally received the full award from the Parliament in 1772, but only after the young King George III had intervened on his behalf. Harrison's chronometer inaugurated the modern era of ship navigation, and the marine chronometer was only replaced a century and a half later when radio communication became well established in navigation.

The compensation for the temperature effect was produced by means of a new, ingenious detached-escapement which left the balance-wheel free during the greater part of its movement, and by a balance-wheel with varying moment of inertia controlled by two curved alcohol-mercury thermometers and oscillated by two oppositely-wound spiral-springs which were invented by the French clockmaker Pierre Le Roy [alias, Leroy] (1717-1785) who succeeded his father as the Royal Horologer (***Horologer du Roi***). Le Roy was the first clockmaker to lay down the principles upon which marine chronometers were later constructed in a prize-winning publication of 1770, but none of his practical solutions were adopted in the later chronometers probably because of his independence from contemporary ideas. In 1766, Le Roy constructed a marine chronometer which can be considered to be the prototype of the modern chronometer. Le Roy's contemporary, the Swiss clockmaker Ferdinand Berthoud (1727-1807) made 8 quite diverse marine chronometers, the last one completed in 1768 incorporated a temperature-compensated balance-wheel, controlled by bimetallic strips, which made his chronometer as accurate as that of Harrison since he had benefited from the inventions of Harrison and Le Roy. Berthoud, who made marine chronometers for 30 years, gave these timekeepers practically their modern form. Some attempts with varied success were also made to compensate for the fluctuating atmospheric buoyancy effect on marine chronometers.

Harrison's methods of chronometer design and construction were developed further after his death by Larcum Kendall and Thomas Mudge (1715-1794), but their chronometers could not be mass-produced since it took from 2 to 3 years to make each one of them. Therefore, the next generation of clockmakers in England and in France made great efforts to simplify the method of manufacture of chronometers by inventing more efficient components for them. In France, Pierre Louis Berthoud (1754-1813), a nephew of Ferdinand Berthoud [who had produced 2 or 3 chronometers a year], and in England, John Arnold (1736-1799) and Thomas Earnshaw (1749-1829), made great progress in the industrialisation of the manufacture of chronometers, particularly in France. Mudge had invented the detached-lever escapement as a replacement for the cylinder-escapement of Graham, which unfortunately was neglected for almost a century but was later used in the best of modern mechanical watches. In 1783 Earnshaw patented the free detent escapement [also credited to Ferdinand Berthoud], which was adopted in the manufacture of chronometers on account of its simple design and regular functioning. Arnold, who excelled in the manufacture of pocket chronometers, devised a helical spring of a particular form which induced the French engineer Edouard Phillips (1821-1889) to publish his mathematical theory of the terminal coils in spiral-springs in 1861, that enabled marine clockmakers to give the final improvement to their chronometers which came into general use only during the 19th century.

Huygens and Undulatory Theory of Light:

Among the many mathematical works of Huygens is the first treatise on the theory of probability based on the concept of expectation < Tractate on Reasoning in Games of Dice > (***Tractatus de ratiociniis in ludo aleae***) published in 1657. Huygens, who had studied and improved the infinitesimal mathematics of Grégoire de Saint Vincent, contributed to differential and integral calculus. He rectified the cissoid curve, studied the tractrix, and the catenary as a nonalgebraic curve. He applied infinitesimal analysis to conic sections, reduced rectification of the parabola to the quadrature of the hyperbola [*i.e.*, to the finding of a logarithm], found the surface area of a conoid [parabola of revolution], and found π with a new method representing the first definite improvement after Archimedes of Syracuse. Huygens was the first mathematician to use continued fractions as a means of deriving rational approximations. Huygens' mathematical works were written with Archimedean rigour, since he was the only mathematician of his time to take mathematical rigour seriously.

In 1672, Huygens proposed to produce vacuum under the piston of Guericke's cylinder by exploding a small charge of gunpowder, thereby finding a peaceful use for gunpowder. This method proved not to be entirely successful in the creation of vacuum in the cylinder and 'bringing perpetually fresh power to bear', for it was difficult to ignite the gunpowder and to evacuate the air adequately. Huygens thought that such an engine could be made small enough to propel vehicles and boats. He presented his gunpowder engine as one of his technological discoveries to Jean

Baptiste Colbert (1619-1683), the minister of France. Huygens was assisted in this work by the French physician, physicist and engineer, Denis Papin (1647-c.1713) of Blois. Huygens also experimented with static electricity by duplicating and investigating some experiments first performed by Otto von Guericke.

In the last decade of his life, which he spent on his family estate '***Hofwijk***' that is now a museum near The Hague, Huygens devoted his efforts to the development of his undulatory [wave, or pulse] theory of light, which postulated a serial transfluence of motion between interacting particles. This theory was temporarily eclipsed by the corpuscular theory of light of Newton, but both are now standard parts of modern physics in their modified form. Huygens explained both reflexion and refraction by his wave theory in a modern manner, including atmospheric refraction as well as double refraction. However, he could not account for the polarisation of light since his light-waves were longitudinal rather than transverse as in the pioneering wave theory of light of Robert Hooke, whose priority in wave theory of light Huygens also acknowledged. Neither could he explain on the basis of his wave theory the origin of colours, nor demonstrate theoretically that light travels rectilinearly in homogeneous media. His last speculative book about cosmos, ***Kosmotheoros***, in which he suggested life on other planets, appeared in 1698.

Huygens and his brother had learnt lens grinding from Baruch Spinoza (1632-1677), a Dutch philosopher who was by profession a lens-grinder, and with his own improved lenses, he was able to build in 1655 a high-resolution refracting telescope with a focal length of 210 feet (64 m). Using his telescope and a micrometer he had invented in 1658, which allowed him to measure minute angular separations between celestial bodies, Huygens discovered the Great Nebula in Orion, the surface markings of Mars, the ring and a moon of Saturn which he named Titan. In the mid-1680's, Huygens invented a compound eyepiece for telescopes, called the 'Huygens Ocular', which minimised the chromatic aberration by incorporating a second lens in his telescope that compensated for the aberration produced by the main lens. 'Huygens Ocular', is still used in modern telescopes. He not only understood infinitesimal calculus and improved on Fermat's method of maxima and minima, but also used the coordinate method of Fermat and Descartes. In 1671, Huygens with Johannes Hudde (1628-1704), who was a mathematician, statistician, an expert in microscopy, as well as burgomaster of Amsterdam for many years, made a study on the improvement of water supply in the Ysel river, a branch of Rhine river in Gelderland.

Huygens represents an outstanding example of a man with far-reaching talents who excelled in all of his professional activities: he was a rigorous mathematician, theoretical and experimental physicist, theoretical and practical astronomer, technologist, engineer, and a skilled portrait artist. Huygens' theoretical and practical works were always intimately related because he was equally interested in theory and in craftsmanship. In all his works Huygens relied on his experience balanced with reason (***experentia et ratione***).

Pardies and Principle of Equipollent Force:

In 1673, the French cleric, Ignace Gaston Pardies (1636/1638-1673) introduced the concept of the internal contact force, now called the 'stress resultant', which assumes that the action of any part of a heavy cord on its neighbouring part is equipollent, i.e.statically equivalent, to a tangential force acting at the imaginary cross-section cutting the cord. Using Stevin's 'principle of solidification', Pardies solidified the free-body of the cable cut at both sides by imaginary cross-sections, and replaced the action of the removed parts of the cable upon the remaining free-body of the cable by equipollent tangential forces acting at the imaginary cross-sections. By such consistent use of the imaginary section and the equipollent force principle, Pardies gave an elegant solution of the suspension bridge problem. Unfortunately, Pardies, who had frequent scientific intercourse with Huygens, died prematurely at the peak of his intellectual powers in 1673.

Hooke, Experimental Science, Universal Gravitation, Law of Springiness, and Balance Springs:

English physicist, engineer and technologist Robert Hooke was an extremely versatile and ingenious man of science and technology: he was a surveyor, city planner, architect, engineer, technologist, inventive experimental scientist, and a skilled artist. In his youth, Hooke had been an apprentice to the portrait painter Peter Lely, and to the miniature painter Samuel Cooper. In 1663, Hooke was granted M.A. degree by special recommendation of the Chancellor of the university in Oxford, and in 1691 a degree of M.D.(Doctor of Physick) was conferred on him at Doctors' Commons. In 1662 Hooke was appointed the first Curator of Experiments to The Royal Society, a demanding position he filled with great success for 15 years, and in 1665 Hooke was nominated professor of geometry at Gresham College in London. He was the leading experimental scientist of his time who demonstrated his brilliance in the great variety of ingenious experiments that he successfully performed. After1655 Hooke was employed by experimental physicist Robert Boyle to construct an improved air-pump. In a period from 1657 to 1659, Hooke devised 30 different methods of flying, and worked out the mechanism for the regulation of the movements of watches by means of balance springs. He served as a paid junior partner, consulting engineer and supervisor of the construction of many churches designed by his friend, Christopher Wren (1632-1723), a former professor of astronomy at the University of Oxford who later became famous as an architect. After a large part of London burnt down in the 'Great Fire of 1666', Hooke was appointed one of the 6 surveyors to supervise the rebuilding of London. Hooke designed a model for the rebuilding of the city, although Wren's reconstruction plan for London was preferred. Ultimately, neither plan was adopted by the city. The supervision of the rebuilding of London was a work of enormous proportions, and most of it was done with boundless energy by Hooke and Wren in collaboration. Hooke was the architect-engineer of the famous Bedlam Mental Hospital, Aske's Hospital, Royal College of Physicians, London Theater, Montague House, Raggle Hall and several other buildings and bridges in the rebuilt London. Hooke also supervised the construction of St.Paul's Cathedral, the architectural masterpiece of Wren, and advised Wren on the structural design of its double masonry dome.

Hooke was keenly interested in mathematical astronomy for the purpose of determining the longitude of ships on the open sea with mathematical precision. He was the first to recognise that the shape of the planetary orbits are obtained by compounding the celestial motion of planets of direct inertial motion along the tangent and attractive motion towards the central body, the Sun, where the attraction is determined by gravitational forces from the Sun obeying a given law of attraction depending upon the distance. Hooke was the first scientist to state clearly that the motions of heavenly bodies should be treated as trajectory problems in mechanics. Hooke emphasised that the fundamental problem of astronomy is the mathematical derivation of the planetary orbits from the law of gravitational attraction. Already in 1666, Hooke read a brief paper on curvilinear motion to The Royal Society entitled < Concerning the Inflexion of a Direct Motion into a Curve by a Supervening Attractive Principle > in which he postulated that the planets are subjected to the 'force of inertia' responsible for the rectilinear motion and to the gravitational attraction towards the Sun which produces the curvilinear path of the planets round the Sun. This viewpoint resulted from a remarkable intellectual effort which is entirely to Hooke's credit. Hooke added Kepler's concept of mutually opposing forces to dynamics: gravity pulling the planets towards the Sun and centrifugal forces counteracting this pull. What had been incomplete and untenable in Kepler's work, was reduced by Hooke in 1670 to the science of mechanics so that it could be incorporated into a theory of celestial dynamics. Therefore, in Hooke's opinion, all observable motions of heavenly bodies satisfy the following basic principles:

(a) principle of inertia, (b) all celestial bodies exert a gravitational force towards their centers, which means that all celestial bodies attract one another, (c) mutual attractions of celestial bodies represent reciprocal action and reaction.

This was the first statement of gravitation as mutual attraction between material bodies after Kepler, in which Hooke recognised the universal nature of gravitation, and he was the first scientist of his time to propose the principle of universal gravitation. Although, in general, Hooke accepted Descartes' mechanistic natural philosophy, in the matter of gravitation he was in basic disagreement with the French philosopher-mathematician who had categorically denied the validity of attraction as a scientific concept. In Hooke's inductive method, the planetary orbit was identified with the trajectory of the projectile, as was later effectively demonstrated mathematically by Newton, but Hooke was the first scientist to propose it. In the treatise of 1674 entitled < An Attempt to Prove the Annual Motion of the Earth from Observations >, Hooke put forth the following propositions paraphrased below:

(a) that all heavenly bodies have not only a gravitation of their parts to their own proper center, but that they also mutually attract one another within their spheres of action;

(b) that all bodies having a simple motion, will continue to move forwards in a straight line unless they are continually deflected from it by some other extraneous forces or powers, and bent into a motion describing a circle, an ellipse, or some other more compound curve;

(c) that these attractive powers are so much the more powerful in operating by how much nearer the body wrought upon is to their own centers;

which Hooke supplemented by the comment: "As to the proportion in which those forces an increase of distance, I own I have not discovered it although I have made some experiments to this purpose. I leave this to others, who have the knowledge sufficient for the task."

In these passages Hooke seems to have stated everything that Newton wrote in his ***Principia*** 13 years later, but unfortunately it was all expressed qualitatively, and not quantitatively which is absolutely essential for the mathematical proof.

In 1678, Hooke proposed the 'inverse square law of the gravitational attraction', a law first intimated by Kepler in 1609 which Hooke may have known from his study of Kepler's ***Astronomia nova*** (1609) and particularly ***Epitome astronomiae Copernicanea*** (1618-1621),but unfortunately he lacked the ability to prove mathematically that Kepler's planetary laws can be derived from his planetary hypotheses. Hooke clearly recognised the universal nature of gravitation. He was convinced that the power of gravity acts systematically throughout the whole world with varying degrees of force at various distances, although it may have a sensible limit at some immense distance. He informed Newton of the inverse square law of gravitation in his letter to Newton in 1680. Both Wren and Halley were convinced by 1684 that the inverse square law of gravitation proposed by Hooke was the very key to celestial motions. As Newton soon demonstrated, only the foremost mathematician in the world at the time had the mathematical ability to derive with adequate mathematical rigour Kepler's planetary laws from the theoretical planetary hypotheses including the Inverse square law of gravitation as proposed by Hooke. Since Newton was loath to recognise the true significance of Hooke's hypothetical qualitative contributions to the planetary theory which lacked the necessary mathematical formulation, it was responsible for engendering an acrimonious antagonism between these two brilliant Englishmen of science. Hooke had considered two alternative explanations for the physical cause of gravity: the magnetic and the vibratory cause; but ultimately he was inclined to favour the vibratory cause.

In 1678, Hooke, who was an extraordinarily talented, ingenious and prolific experimental scientist, published a treatise on elasticity, < Lectures ***de Potentia Restitutiva***, or of Spring Explaining the Power of Springing Bodies >, in which he gave experimental evidence that most material bodies behave like elastic springs. In this work, he proposed the celebrated Hooke's law– "As is the extension, so is the force (***ut tensio sic vis***)" :

$$\Delta L \propto F$$

which implies that the 'restitutive force' F of a deformed body such as a spring is proportional to its 'stretch' ΔL. On this type of constitutive law of materials is based the classical theory of linear elasticity and the mechanics of materials. He had already given his theory of elasticity or 'Springiness' as an anagram in an appendix to his previous work, <A Description of Helioscopes> published in 1675, a copy of which had been promptly sent to Huygens by Oldenburg. Hooke used his dynamical principle to find the speed v of a body attached to a spring in the form:

$$v \propto \sqrt{Fs}\ ,$$

where F is the force and s the displacement of the body in the direction of the force, a principle representing an elementary form of the principle of work in its application to the dynamical problem of a deformable elastic body. Some time later, Hooke proposed his dynamic principle as the 'general rule of mechanicks', which is an elementary form of the work-energy principle – "The force in moving bodies is in duplicate proportion to their celerities" :

$$Fs \propto v^2\ ,$$

where F denotes the magnitude of the force, s designates the distance moved, and v represents the speed acquired by the body. Hooke's treatise of 1678 contained a clear statement of the principle of synchronism, and the earliest treatment of simple harmonic motion of a deforming elastic body.

Hooke observed, as had Leonardo da Vinci and Isaac Beeckman before him, that the fibres of a bent beam are stretched on the convex side and compressed on the concave side, which implies the existence of the unextended, or 'neutral' fibre. Hooke called such bending the "compound way of springing," but he gave no hint how to relate the curvature of the fibres of the bent beam to the bending moment.

Hooke also gave in this treatise the earliest statement of the elementary principle of modern kinetic theory of gases, because in his kinetic theory of matter by means of which he attempted to unify all major universal phenomena he postulated the existence of countless exceedingly short vibrations of extremely high frequency within all material substances that he presumed to lie beyond the limits of human sensation. Hooke was also the pioneer promoter of wave mechanics in the theory of light, which was acknowledged by Huygens in his treatise on the undulating theory of light in 1690. In Hooke's theory, light was a wave motion taking place in a voidless plenum. In Hooke's wave mechanics of light, light-waves were oscillating transversely to the direction of light propagation. He anticipated the doctrine of interference and the phenomenon of diffraction of light independently of the Italian Jesuit Pater Francesco Maria Grimaldi (1618-1663), professor of physics at the University of Bologna.

Early in 1662 Hooke discovered experimentally that if the speed of a liquid flowing over a surface increases, the pressure it exerts upon that surface decreases. This relation of the speed of fluid flow and the pressure it exerts was rediscovered in 1743 by Johann Bernoulli in his treatise on hydraulics.

Hooke drew attention to the fact that the strongest and best form for the arch consisting of infinitely small voussoirs is the inverted catenary subject to inverted load in order that the arch will exert tangential thrust. Hooke's theoretical model of the voussoir arch reduced the problems of the arch and the catenary to one problem without giving the solution of either one.

Hooke proved experimentally that cables made faggot-wise were stronger than twisted cables, which had been first noted by the ancient Greek military engineer Philon of Byzantion (c.240 B.C.).

Hooke, like his friend and patron Robert Boyle, accepted Descartes' mechanistic philosophy of nature, although he did not agree with the ingenious Frenchman in all aspects of the latter's mechanistic concepts. Hooke accepted Descartes' concept of inertia and the doctrine of an all-pervasive æther filling the infinite space, although he rejected the existence of Descartes' celestial vortices because they contradicted his experience. Æther was the basic concept in his theories of light, magnetism, gravity and atmosphere. Hooke's main intention in his 'Science of Physicks' was to give physical explanations of natural phenomena, which is why he was always primarily interested in finding the physical cause of any physical phenomenon. He did experimental work in acoustics, metallurgy, gravitation, magnetism, light, celestial mechanics, geography, microscopy, and histology of plant cells. He was the leading proponent of many correct ideas in the theory of sound, but he made no advance beyond Beeckman and Mersenne. Hooke was eminently successful in experimental scientific research in which he was prominent as a pioneer. He originated the idea of using the pendulum for the measurement of gravity, and anticipated the experimental technique in the study of vibrating plates, used in 1809 by the German physicist Ernst Florens Friedrich Chladni (1756-1827), by strewing a vibrating bell with flour.

Hooke was a superb technologist and immensely prolific inventor. He invented and designed a wide variety of devices such as instruments and apparatuses for the measurement of air pressure, wind velocity, rain fall, and sounding the depth of seas. He also suggested a method of meteorological forecasting. He invented and improved micrometers, microscopes and telescopes, and designed a clockwork-driven telescope controlled by a conical pendulum which he had invented in the early 1660's. In 1658/1659, Hooke invented the anchor escapement for pendulum clocks, and a score of spring-controlled devices, a technological specialty in which he was the acknowledged leading expert. He also designed and built several heavier-than-air flying contraptions similar to modern helicopters, which he believed would fly if only powerful enough motors were available to drive the blades. In 1676, Hooke invented the universal joint [his own terminology], which is still of fundamental importance to the modern automobile technology. Hooke left his manuscript <Philosophical Algebra, an Art of Directing the Mind in Search of Philosophical Truths>, which contained a set of rules on how to make useful and significant discoveries about nature, unfinished.

Hooke is one scientist whose reputation has been unfairly neglected, because after Hooke's death the vindictive and unscrupulous Newton, who hated Hooke on account of the controversies Newton had with him concerning the theory of light and the gravitational theory, did everything in his power as the autocratic president of The Royal Society to traduce posthumously the reputation of Hooke as a scientist. Hooke deserves almost as much fame as Newton for having been the leading experimental scientist, technologist, engineer-architect, and a prolific inventor of Newton's time. That Hooke was not a leading mathematician of his era capable of proving mathematically his correct hypotheses of the mechanical planetary theory is not sufficient reason to overlook his impressive universal native talent, superlative imagination and originality, and remarkable ingenuity in experimental science, practical technology and scientific engineering that far surpassed anything Newton accomplished in this respect. In spite of the fact that Newton was quite aware that he was one of the leading mathematicians of his era, he harboured deep-seated envy and resentment towards both Hooke as well as Leibniz, whom he also succeeded to vilify posthumously, because these 2 intellectually gifted scientists in their own unique way rivalled Newton in creative thought and originality.

Hooke called the 'Physicks geometrically handled' together with induction the 'Synthetick Method', and the deductive method the 'Analytick Method', whereas Descartes called deduction from ***a priori*** principles the synthetic method and the methodical scientific search the analytic method. Newton, contrary to Hooke, called the making of experiments and observations analysis, and deduction from ***a priori*** principles synthesis. Hooke regarded the main fault of the analytic method to be its lack of certitude, because normally there is always a break somewhere in the long series of inferences. In natural philosophy, Hooke recognised that scientific explanations are usually established by induction from self-evident ***a posteriori*** truths obtained from sense experience. However, in his own scientific practice Hooke was by no means doctrinaire: he normally used the 'Synthetick Method', but in particular instances he felt justified to use the 'Analytick Method' where it offered a conspicuous advantage for doing so.

***Varignon, Funicular Polygon and Graphical Statics*:**

The inventor of the funicular polygon construction in statics is the French cleric Pierre Varignon (1654-1722) in his book < Project of a New Mechanics > (***Projet d'une nouvelle mécanique***) in 1687. It was used by another French engineer, Philippe de La Hire, a former artist, who in 1695 studied the stable equilibrium of the voussoir arches with frictionless joints by following Huygens' method in his treatise, < Treatise on Mechanics > (***Traité de mécanique***). This theoretical model of the arch, as La Hire soon realised, was unrealistic because for semicircular arches it required infinitely heavy voussoirs in order to produce a stable arch. In this work La Hire employed a modified graphical method of funicular polygon of Varignon, a graphical procedure which followed essentially the method of Stevin.

The clockmakers had early realised that the cogs, or teeth, of cogwheels in clockworks should have a shape which provides continuous contact with minimum friction between cogwheels. Mathematicians of the16th and the 17thcentury demonstrated that the teeth shaped like cycloidal curves satisfy these requirements. Much later it was demonstrated that involute curves were even better shapes for cogs. La Hire, who was called to design the gearing for the machinery in the waterworks of the Royal Palace in Versailles, founded the basic geometric principles for the design of cycloidal gear teeth. La Hire established the principle that uniform pressure should exist between the teeth in uniform motion, and that the surfaces of the teeth should roll on each other to avoid friction; and if the teeth of a gear are formed by a part of an epicycloid, the teeth of the follower should be part of a hypocycloid described by the same circle, a point of which generated the cycloid. La Hire stressed that involute or cycloidal shapes for gear teeth were not absolutely necessary since it was possible to obtain a constant speed ratio with countless number of teeth shapes as long as the shape of the driven teeth were designed in accordance with the shape of the driving teeth.

Another French mathematician and mechanician, Charles Etienne Louis Camus (1699-1768), found that even with cycloidal teeth, there is some sliding between the cogs which results in friction and wear. Therefore, Camus examined bevel-gears and used the principle of the rolling cone for their analysis. Camus developed simple methods for the design and construction of epicycloidal teeth, and was the first to demonstrate the method of design of bevel-gears with epicycloidal teeth. He, moreover, analysed the combination of a spur-gear and a lantern-gear, and a crown-gear and a bevelled-lantern. Some of the teeth of the pinions in his design were undercut and, therefore, were subjected to considerable backlash. The involute-type of gear teeth are of relatively modern invention and superseded the cycloidal gear teeth only in the1880's.

In 1712, in a memoir submitted to the Academy of Sciences in Paris, La Hire devised a practical way of taking friction into account in arch analysis by dividing the arch into 4 quadrants: the two central quadrants of 90 degree arc consist of frictionless voussoirs, whereas the outer quadrants are rigid abutments. For the stability of the arch the resultant force in his method had to fall within the abutment.

Mariotte and Experimental Mechanics of Materials:

A French Prior of the monastery of Saint-Martin-sous-Beaume near the city of Dijon, Edmé Mariotte (1620-1684), and Huygens had been engaged by the Academy between 1666 and 1670 to corroborate the validity of the Torricelli Efflux Rule with various experiments. They went further with their experiments and determined the impulsive force water jets exert against a plane surface as being proportional to the square of the speed of the impinging water, and established a formula for the impulsive force: $P = \gamma AH$, where γ denotes the specific weight of water, A the cross-sectional area of the orifice from which the water jet emanates, and H the head of water above the orifice. Both Huygens and Mariotte recognised that this quantitative formula could be used in hydraulic power technology. Mariotte took it upon himself to apply this formula together with the continuity principle, the efflux principle, and the idea that the impulsive force of a jet is proportional to the square of the speed of the water jet impinging on the waterwheels, in which he calculated the impact force due to the current of water acting on the blade of the stationary waterwheel. This approach to power unfortunately contained a basic flaw: the power of the waterwheel is not produced when it is stationary but rather when it is in motion. The static approach of Mariotte and Huygens to power had to be replaced by a dynamic approach, the first steps towards which were taken by 2 French scientists, Phillipe de La Hire and Guillaume Amontons.

Edmé Mariotte was given the responsibility by the King of France to advise on the design of the water piping system in the Versailles castle and the pumping station at Marly, which were built from 1661 to 1689. This extensive engineering project caused Mariotte to carry out experimental researches on the strength of structural members of his piping system, on the resistance to the flow of water in pipes, and on the efficiency of the waterwheels at Marly. Mariotte had finished his investigations and written the manuscript by 1683. Philippe De La Hire, who had assisted Mariotte in the surveying of the Versailles water-supply system, edited Mariotte's unfinished manuscript < Treatise on the Movement of Water and Other Fluid Bodies ... > (***Traité du mouvement des eaux et des autre corps fluides ...***) in 1686, which was a contribution to recently launched science of hydrodynamics by Benedetto Castelli and Evangelista Torricelli, and it incorporated Mariotte's experience obtained from the construction of the large hydraulic works at Versailles and Chantilly. A year before his death, Mariotte discussed the efficiency of the undershot waterwheel of the dam-fed type used at Marly for pumping water.

In the bending of beams, Mariotte independently discovered Hooke's linearly elastic law, and he was the first scientist to apply it to Galileo's problem of the strength of columns and beams.

Mariotte rejected Galileo's assumption of inextensibility of the material, because he observed the existence of contraction and extension on the opposite sides of a bent beam, and he realised that there exists a 'neutral fibre' within the beam which suffers no extension. He called this unextended fibre of the beam the 'axis of equilibrium'. Mariotte assumed the internal force in the beam to be proportional to the stretching of the fibre of the beam, which gave a triangular distribution to the internal forces, the tensions, in the bending of beams since he conceived the beam to be a collection of parallel fibres. At first Mariotte calculated the ultimate load P acting at the end of a cantilever beam of length L by the moment principle for a triangular distribution of tensions:

$$LP = (S/2)\,[(2/3)h] = Sh/3\,,$$

where S is the 'absolute strength' of the cantilever under axial tension. He almost immediately located the neutral fibre at the center of the beam having a symmetric cross-section and, thereby, obtained two wedges for distributed internal forces, the tensile and the compressive wedge of these forces. He wrote: "You may conceive that for half the thickness the parts are pressed together, those near the outside more than those near the middle, and that for the other half of the thickness the parts are extended." When Mariotte calculated the ultimate load for the case when the cantilever beam of a rectangular cross-section undergoes both tension and compression with the neutral axis being in the center of the cross-section, he substituted $h/2$ for h in the formula above to obtain the ultimate load P_t supported by the tensile internal forces:

$$LP_t = Sh/6\,.$$

The corresponding ultimate load P_c supported by the compressive internal forces:

$$LP_c = Sh/6\,.$$

Then the total ultimate load:

$$LP = LP_t + LP_c = (Sh/6) + (Sh/6) = Sh/3\,,$$

which is the same formula he had obtained for the triangular distribution of tensions. Mariotte made a mistake in his calculations because he overlooked that $(S/2)$ should have been substituted into the formula for the triangular distribution of tensions instead of S which would have given the correct result:

$$LP = Sh/6\,,$$

that can be expressed as a dimensionless proportion:

$$P/S = h/6L\,.$$

This result gives the failure modulus of $bh^2/6$, where b is the width and h is the depth of the cross-section.

In Mariotte's work, the basis for strength calculation of beams is effectively established. In his strength calculation, Mariotte made the mistake mentioned above, and he accepted this erroneous derivation because his rather crude experimental results seemed to tally with his incorrect formula.

Owing to this theoretical mistake, Mariotte obtained the incorrect modulus of the cross-section of the beam:

$$Sh/3 \propto bh^2/3,$$

instead of the correct one, $bh^2/6$. In his analysis, Mariotte had assumed that the beam failed under a linear distribution of extensions. Mariotte's elastic theory was essentially correct but his assumption that it should agree with ultimate strength tests was wrong. A few brittle materials behave elastically up to the fracture in tension, but they have a considerably higher compressive strength which makes the neutral axis of the beam in bending move towards the compression face. Most other materials lose their elasticity long before failure and the linear relationship between the load and deformation ceases to be linear. At that time only linear elastic theory could be established for bending, but only ultimate strength could be tested. This basic difficulty was part of the problem the early investigators of the beam theory such as Mariotte had to face.

Mariotte demonstrated that even brittle materials extend under load and he measured the extension of 4/5 line [1 line is 1/12-th of an inch, or 2 mm] of a glass rod 4 feet (1.22 m) long and ¼ line thick, which upon removal of the load returned to its original length. He was the first scientist to use the 'maximum strain criterion' as the criterion of material failure. On the basis of his 'maximum strain criterion', Mariotte was able to solve for the correct thickness of the pipe in his studies of the bursting strength of pipes. Therefore, Mariotte was the first to join the statical equations of equilibrium with the constitutive equations of the elastic material in the study of the ultimate strength of bending of beams. Moreover, Mariotte's work represents the first treatise on the 'experimental mechanics of materials'.

In fluid mechanics, Mariotte discovered that the actual orifice flow was only 7/10-th of the theoretical flow. He carried out a qualitative study of resistance of pipes to flow, in which he assumed the resistance to flow to be proportional to the velocity of the flow. In his studies of the impact of jets, Mariotte invented a dynamometer to measure the force of impact of the jet. He studied the force on the waterwheel blades and was, together with Huygens, the first to assume it proportional to the square of the current speed. Mariotte also discovered independently the Boyle-Towneley-Power Law but he had a much better understanding of it than Boyle and, therefore, it is frequently called the 'Boyle-Mariotte Law'. Actually, this law had been first suggested to Boyle by one of his correspondents, Richard Towneley as a hypothesis. The same law had been proposed also by Henry Power, but Robert Hooke was the first to prove it scientifically. Mariotte gave an experimental proof of this law in his treatise < Essay on the Nature of Air > (***Essai sur la nature de l'air***) in 1679, but he failed to found a barometric method for determining the heights owing to mathematical difficulties although his basic idea was correct.

Leibniz and Energy Principle

German philosopher, Gottfried Wilhelm Leibniz [also spelled Leibnitz](1646-1716), a man of universal talent who met Huygens in Paris, gave the work-energy principle , which he called the 'principle of live force':

$$m v^2 \Big|_{t_1}^{t_2} = m v^2 \Big|_{t_2} - m v^2 \Big|_{t_1} \propto \int_{s_1}^{s_2} F ds \ .$$

Leibniz asserted in this principle that the loss of the 'dead force'(in Latin, ***vis mortua***)given by the integral resulted in corresponding gain of 'live force' (in Latin, ***vis viva***). Leibniz's 'dead force' is the old 'force of position' known to the mediæval Scholastic scientists that is presently called the 'potential energy', but the 'live force' given as the mass times velocity squared is twice what is presently called the 'kinetic energy'. This principle of Leibniz was taken up by Johann and Daniel Bernoulli and made the basis of brilliant successes with special mechanical problems. Most if not all mechanical problems solved by Isaac Newton may be solved just as well with Leibniz's principle of live force, combined with Descartes' principle of conservation of linear momentum when it applies. The principle of energy and the principle of conservation of linear momentum are statements about the whole mechanical system not requiring, as do the Newton's laws of motion, the cutting of the mechanical system into its parts. But neither principle suffices to determine the motion of any but the simplest of mechanical systems.

Leibniz realised from his studies of the Pascal's treatise on the sines of the quadrant of the circle that the Pascal's finite characteristic triangle could be applied to any curve or function as an infinitesimal characteristic triangle of change (***triangulum characteristicum***). On the basis of this idea, Leibniz invented his differential and integral calculus independently of Newton, and it is his differential and integral method (***methodus differentialis et integralis***), instead of Newton's method of fluxions (***methodus fluxionum***),which is used today. Leibniz's success derived from his mathematical philosophy which contended that the mathematical notation itself be capable of doing much of the formal reasoning in mathematics, and his emphasis upon the algorismic nature of differential and integral calculus. The Leibniz-Bernoulli-Euler school of mathematical thought on natural phenomena triumphed completely over the Newtonian school of mathematical thought on natural phenomena.

Leibniz, Symbolic Logic and 'machina arithmetica':

Leibniz became interested in technology through his association with Huygens, who was his mentor in mathematics and science during Leibniz's stay in Paris. He became interested in calculating machines, and examined carefully the technological details of the mechanical calculators conceived by Blaise Pascal, and by Samuel Morland.

Samuel Morland (1625-1696), an English gentleman inventor who had studied mathematics at Cambridge and served as the master mechanic to the Royal household of King Charles II, invented and patented numerous gadgets and contrivances although none were financially profitable. In 1666 he constructed a calculating machine made of metal for the addition and subtraction of sums of money. It incorporated 8 dials which counted farthings, pence, shillings, units, tens, hundreds, thousands and 10-thousands of pounds. The first 3 dials were graduated into 4, 12 and 20 parts, and the rest into 10 parts. The disks within the dials which were similarly graduated and could be turned through any number of divisions with a stylus inserted into holes opposite each division. Each complete revolution of the disk turned a small counter disk through one of its ten divisions by means of a tooth on the large disk as a recording device. However, carrying amounts from one denomination to the next was not automatic but had to be done by the operator. Special procedures had to be followed in setting the disks, and turning the large disks depending upon whether addition or subtraction had to be carried out.

In 1673, Morland constructed another machine for multiplication and extraction of roots that operated on the principle of 'Napier bones' in which rotating disks had digits of each multiple at diametrically opposite ends. Multiplication in Morland's machine, like in Pascal's calculator, was done by repeated addition executed by turning a crank. Morland constructed still another machine for the solution of triangles and for the evaluation of trigonometric functions.

Leibniz conceived a calculating machine in 1671 which was completed in 1694 and is still extant. Another calculating machine which he constructed in 1704 is lost. Leibniz's digital calculating machine, known as ***machina arithmetica***, incorporated two important devices of his invention which were still used in modern mechanical calculators: the 'stepped reckoner' in the form of a stepped drum and the pin-wheel. Leibniz's stepped drum principle was an improvement upon Pascal's ratchet. The mechanical calculator of Leibniz was the first general purpose digital calculator the principles of which were still used in modern calculating machines. Leibniz's mechanical calculator performed all arithmetic operations such as addition, subtraction, multiplication, division, and even extraction of square roots. This mechanical calculator consisted essentially of two parts: one part which recorded the partial products obtained by repeated additions was fixed, whereas the other part was movable in order to admit these additions of the multiplicand being made in different groups of denominators. Leibniz's mechanical calculators were complicated machines and they did not work quite satisfactorily, although Leibniz spent large sums of money on their construction, mostly because the technological skill and mechanical precision at the time were not refined enough for this highly precise technological task. Even in the 18th century despite improvements in speed, reliability and convenience in manufacture, the technological skill and mechanical precision required to produce mechanical calculators in large quantities was not available. Besides numerical computation, Leibniz perceived another important use for digital machines in the testing of mathematical and scientific hypotheses, a capital idea which has only recently received serious attention in computer applications. The first to succeed in constructing a successful commercial mechanical calculator was a French inventor, Charles Thomas de Colmar (1785-1870), who in 1820 designed ***Arithmometer***, a mechanical calculator based on Leibniz's stepped drum having 9 teeth of different length which turned a small sliding-wheel that operated the counters. Colmar's calculators were primarily acquired by insurance houses in Paris.

Odhner and Industrial Calculator:

In 1877, a Swedish engineer Willgodt Theophil Odhner (1845-1905), a graduate of the ***Kungliga Tekniska Högskola*** (Royal Highschool of Technology) in Stockholm, invented a calculating machine mostly during his leisure hours whilst he was an employee of the firm of the Nobel family in St. Petersburg, Russia. He designed an industrial calculating machine which was not only small and simple but also easy to operate, and so inexpensive that anyone in need of a mechanical aid in computing would be able to afford it. Odhner's calculating machine worked by means of stud-wheels, which apparently were used in the first practical calculating machine that could perform all four fundamental arithmetic operations without any resetting of the machine patented in 1875 by an American mechanic Frank Stephen Baldwin (1838-1925). In 1878 Odhner was granted a U.S. patent for a calculating machine incorporating the stud-wheels which was very similar to that of Baldwin. The stud-wheel consisted of a disk fixed to a crankshaft and a rotary part with protruding studs. The number of cogs on a calculating dial was varied from 0 to 9 by a lever setting. The crank was turned clockwise for multiplication and counter-clockwise for division. The calculating capacity of the Odhner calculating machine depended upon the number of its stud-wheels which was increased to 18, thereby giving 18 digits. Odhner began to manufacture his calculating machine on a larger scale in his own factory in St. Petersburg in 1886, and altogether about 30,000 machines were produced by 1917 which were sold in Russia and in the rest of Europe. Odhner also invented in collaboration with a Russian engineer Orlov a multicolour printing press, the patent of which they later sold in England. Odhner's factory also produced other industrial products such as cigarette machines, nozzles for oil burners, control devices for railroads, phonographs, turnstiles with registering devices, instruments for naval artillery, and multicolour printing presses. Odhner's calculating machine was later developed into the well-known 'Brunsviga calculator' which was still being used in the middle of the 20th century. Another Swedish engineer Carl Fridén designed a number of desk-top calculators which he produced in his company founded in United States. These basic designs were later improved by other inventors who could take advantage of the rapidly advancing skills in technological design and manufacture. In all these calculating machines, the operator had to decide what was to be done, press the keys to do it, and then read the results. These machines fell far short of automatic, self-regulating calculating machines which accept the problem and return a completed answer without human intervention, a requirement needing logical power to make decisions and control operations as well as automatic means of receiving and storing information.

Babbage, Automatic Draw-Loom of Jacquard, and Computers as Computing Engines:

The automatic computing machine called the 'computer' is a computing engine in which the machine itself carries out the organisation of the mathematical program of calculation according to instructions fed into the machine by the programmer. The inventor of such automatic computing engines was the eccentric English mathematician Charles Babbage (1791-1871), a graduate of the Cambridge University and a man of genius. Babbage was a prolific inventor and his scientific and practical interests were far-reaching. He, for instance, founded what is now called the 'operational research' in his analysis of pin-manufacturing and publishing industries. He became the prominent promoter of machine tools and an avid advocate of mass-production. But his most enduring fame stems from his invention of two automatic calculating machines: the Difference Engine and, particularly, the Analytical Engine. It is interesting that Babbage also invented a speedometer which was actually a particular kind of analogue computer.

In 1812 when Babbage was still a student at Cambridge University, he and his friend John Frederick William Herschel (1792-1871), son of a famous astronomer Friedrich Wilhelm Herschel (1738-1822) who also became a leading astronomer and a pioneer in stellar photography, were assigned the task of preparing astronomical tables which involved checking the existing astronomical tables. Babbage and Herschel discovered several errors in existing tables. Babbage, like Leibniz before him, recognised that repetitive calculations from the basic formula required in the compilation of any mathematical table is the lowest intellectual occupation of the human mind because it involves intolerable tedium and monotony of repetitive calculations. Babbage maintained that such a method used in the compilation of mathematical tables always tends to lead to human errors which once committed become repetitive. For this reason, Babbage proposed to replace error-prone human computation by error-free machine computation.

In 1822, Babbage presented the Method of Differences for such a machine-computation in his paper < On the Theoretical Principles of the Machinery for Calculating Tables >. This method relied on the Principle of Constant Differences, which consisted of taking the difference of two successive tabular values, then taking the difference of differences and continuing this procedure until at some level higher than the first difference a column of constant differences is reached. Then the machine, working backwards, adds all these differences to the last tabular value, thereby obtaining the next higher tabular value without any need to calculate it directly from the mathematical formula of the table, and then print the machine-calculated tabular values without any human intervention. Babbage, however, was not the first to use the principle of constant differences in the design of an automatic calculating machine A similar principle was first used in the design of a calculating machine by the German military engineer, Captain Johann Helfrich von Müller who invented an automatic calculating machine in 1786 which functioned as a differencing machine, although as far as it is known he never built a prototype of it probably because of the inadequate technical means available at the time.

In 1822, after 2 years of work, Babbage succeeded to build a small pilot model of his Difference Engine, by means of which he produced tables of squares and values of quadratic polynomial functions to 6 decimal places.

After receiving financial support from the government in 1823, Babbage embarked on the construction of a full-size Difference Engine which he had designed to work to 6-order differences and 20 decimal places. For 10 years Babbage laboured with unflagging energy and dedication in the building of the full-size Difference Engine, because as a layman he had not foreseen the great technological difficulties encountered in the production of such a precision instrument. He had to supervise the machining of parts for his Difference Engine such as gears, cams, wheels, shafts and the like in the production of which he had to invent machines and hundreds of tools to facilitate the work. He encountered almost insuperable difficulties to machine the intricate parts to unprecedented tolerances required by the Difference Engine, despite the fact that he hired the best toolmakers of his time such as Joseph Clement (1779-1844), and later Joseph Whitworth (1803-1887) whom he trained to do this highly precise machining work. Although Babbage suffered a nervous breakdown in 1827 as a result of his all-out intensive effort, he was able to complete at least a part of his full-size Difference Engine which enabled him to demonstrate that his design principle for this machine was sound. By that time he had produced with Clement more than 200 drawings of the complete Difference Engine which, however, was not a general purpose calculator for it could only perform one specific mathematical programme.

In 1834, following numerous financial setbacks and bitter disappointments, Babbage finally relinquished work on the full-size Difference Engine when his chief instrument-maker resigned after an argument with Babbage, but by that time Babbage had already conceived his most ingenious invention: a general automatic universal digital computing machine capable of solving any mathematical problem. In the same year a comprehensive account of the Difference Engine was published in < Edinburgh Review >, which was carefully studied by Per Georg Scheutz (1785-1873) and his son Edvard (1821-1881). Per Scheutz, a lawyer, author, and publisher of a number of technical and trade journals such as the < Periodical of the Swedish Association of Industry >, realised that Babbage's mechanical design of the Difference Engine was probably even beyond the considerable skill of the British toolmakers and, therefore, he simplified and modified Babbage's design of the Difference Engine, and with the help of his son, who at the time was a student at the ***Kungliga Teknologiska Institut*** (*Royal Technological Institute*) in Stockholm, built a small model of it in 1837 working to 2 or 3 orders of difference and 5 decimal places. In 1854, after having received financial support from the Swedish Government, Scheutz and his son produced a larger and improved version of their Difference Engine which worked to 4 orders of differences and 15 decimal places and incorporated also an output device. In 1854 the Difference Engine of Scheutz was displayed in London and demonstrated at The Royal Society, after which an exact duplicate copy of it was made in 1854 by Bryan Donkin (1768-1855) in England, and used in the Office of the Register-General for the computation of life-expectancy tables. In 1855, Scheutz's Difference Engine was awarded a Gold Metal at the Exhibition in Paris. It is still on display in the Smithsonian Institute in Washington, D.C..

Babbage obtained his inspiration for the automatic universal digital calculating machine from his careful examination of the automatic draw-loom of Jacquard which was able to weave figurative silk cloth in any intricate design pattern. In this automatic draw-loom built by Joseph-Marie Jacquard (1752-1834) in 1804, the figurative weaving was mechanically regulated by a train of punched cards which automatically controlled the lifting and lowering of different selections of threads in the warp at each throw of the shuttle in order to form the pattern of weaving. After the death of Jacquard, his portrait was woven into a 57 inches (1.45 m) square silk cloth on the Jacquard automatic draw-loom which was controlled by a long train of more than 24,000 punched-cards. The woven portrait of Jacquard had such a fine detailed texture that it gave an impression of being an engraving. Babbage presented one of the woven silk portraits of Jacquard to Queen Victoria thereby hoping to raise the monarch's interest in his new invention inspired by the Jacquard draw-loom. Babbage was absolutely convinced that the Jacquard draw-loom can weave any design the mind of man can conceive, and since he realised that the patterns of punched-holes in the cards can not only represent numbers but also exercise control over numerical operations, an automatic universal digital calculating machine controlled by punched-cards in his opinion could solve any numerical problem man can conceive.

Babbage named this entirely original automatic digital computing machine which he had conceived the 'Analytical Engine', and this invention is the best evidence for the extraordinary brilliance of Babbage's genius. He was a man a century ahead of his time. The automatic calculating machine could organise its numerical calculations according to given instructions fed into the machine, and perform any type of digital computation. The Analytical Engine anticipated virtually all the basic parts and functions of a modern digital computer in a mechanical form because it was remarkably modern in its logical design.

Babbage's Analytical Engine incorporated 4 distinct units: an arithmetic unit called the 'mill' which fed instructions for calculation, do all operations of arithmetic and connect them together in any programmed sequence, the 'input' and the programme were both implemented by punched cards in which the patterns of punched holes in the cards represented mathematical symbols; a memory or 'store' unit capable of holding thousand 50-digit numbers, and an auxiliary 'store' of constants and programmes; a mechanical 'branching device', now called the 'conditional jump', which could compare partial results to one another in order 'to make decisions' with regards to the continued course of calculation; the 'output' unit was in the form of punched cards, direct printing or as type set ready to print. The programme cards were grouped into three sets: the number cards to supply the 'store' with numbers, the cards to transfer numbers from the 'mill' to the 'store' or from the 'store' to the 'mill', and the operation cards to direct the 4 basic arithmetic operations. In order to unite the programmes for cards, Babbage had to devise a new mathematical notation.

The block diagram of these functions of the Analytical Engine would be for all practical purposes identical to the block diagram of the equivalent functions of a modern digital computer.

In 1840, upon the invitation of the famous astronomer and table compiler Baron Giovanni Plana (1781-1869), Babbage presented his conception of the Analytical Engine in a series of lectures to a scientific congress at Turin in Italy. Luigi Federigo Menabrea (1809-1896), a Colonel in military engineering who later became a General and a Prime Minister of Italy, attended this congress and wrote a brief but effective account of Babbage's lectures in French: < Sketch of the Analytical Engine Invented by Charles Babbage, Esq. > which was published in a Swiss periodical ***Bibliothèque Universelle de Genève*** in 1842. Menabrea's account was translated into English and supplied with extensive notes by the daughter of the English poet Lord Byron, Augusta Ada Byron, Countess of Lovelace (1815-1852). The English translation prepared by Countess of Lovelace, which was augmented by her valuable explanatory notes containing many original ideas, had more than twice the length of Menabrea's original article. She was precocious and a brilliant mathematician, who was trained by the English logician and modern algebraist Augustus de Morgan (1806-1871). Countess of Lovelace became acquainted with Babbage and his works already in her early teens, and she was the first person to acquire complete mastery of Babbage's conception of the Difference Engine and, particularly, the Analytical Engine, and to contribute substantially to the theoretical development of the Analytical Engine and particularly to its programming.

Countess of Lovelace, and also Menabrea, not only suggested many possible uses for the Analytical Engine as a scientific instrument, but also outlined a number of applications for it which computer technology only began to approach in the 1950's. Countess of Lovelace readily recognised that although in the many calculations the Analytical Engine has to perform there would occur recurring patterns of instructions, but it is possible to reduce the number of punched cards since it is only necessary to prepare a single set of punched cards for the recurring computer instructions when advantage is taken of the 'conditional jump' facility of the Analytical Engine. She named the recurring sequence of machine operations a 'cycle', and recognised that a group of such cycles could itself recur to form a 'cycle of cycles' which are now respectively called a 'loop' and a 'subroutine'. She wrote the first computer programmes, and foreshadowed such modern computer techniques as automatic programming and subroutines. A computer programme is the translation of an algorithm representing a series of elementary operations to solve a particular problem into a well-defined computer language. She was the first to suggest the use of binary arithmetic of 0's and 1's in the computer language, instead of the decimal arithmetic used by Babbage. It was mainly due to the writings of Countess of Lovelace that the Analytical Engine as a sequentially operating automatic digital computer became comprehensible to persons interested in machine computation.

Babbage failed to complete a functioning computer because its construction was far beyond the technical facilities of his time. Only 100 years later, in the 1940's, were the available technological means adequate for building a computer of such high precision.

Torres y Quevedo and Electromechanical Computer:

The Spanish civil engineer Leonardo Torres y Quevedo (1852-1936), who became the President of the Academy of Sciences of Madrid, devoted his entire professional life to scientific research. He was particularly interested in the design and construction of a great variety of calculating devices and automata, such as radio-controlled torpedoes and boats, which he successfully demonstrated in 1906. He also built two chess-playing automata in 1911, and in 1922. In 1914, Torres y Quevedo wrote an important memoir < Essays on Automation > (***Essais sur l'automatique***) in which he emphasised the practical advantage of recent electromagnetic technology in computer design, and gave a schematic design for a special-purpose digital, programme-controlled calculating machine incorporating a completely developed system for conditional branching. In 1920, Torres built a calculating machine for the purpose of demonstrating that an electromechanical Analytical Engine of Babbage was technically quite feasible in his time, but he never built one although he was technically capable of constructing such a computer.

The first completely automatic computer, *Mark I*, was designed by Howard Aiken, Professor of Mathematics at Harvard University. It was an electromechanical machine as suggested by Torres y Quevedo, although Aiken was unaware of the work done on computers by the Spanish engineer. Aiken had already worked three years on the design of this computer before he discovered

Babbage's design of the Analytical Engine. Despite the fact that *Mark I* was a sequentially operating electromechanical digital computer, it was the first computer which followed essentially Babbage's concept, although it did not have the capability of 'branching its operations' like the Analytical Engine. *Mark I* digital computer used electromechanical components in the form of standard telephone relays as computing elements and its memory consisted of calculating wheels. It was externally programmed for all computing instructions were fed into the machine by a punched paper tape which advanced at a rate of 200 steps a minute. This type of externally programmed computing machine made it virtually impossible to incorporate stored-programmes within the machine and, therefore, it did not survive. The future belonged to stored-programme electronic computers.

Already Leibniz had become aware of the importance of mechanisation of thought, and he visualised the possibility of a reasoning machine in which mechanical processes of calculation could be made to correspond to mechanisation of thought. Leibniz was of the opinion that all logical processes of thought can be reduced to the manipulation of symbols, an opinion which foreshadowed the general trend of symbolic logic. René Descartes had studied the human body as a machine, which allowed the extension of the mediæval concept of the clockwork universe to living organisms. Descartes had dreamt of a universal algebra but it was Leibniz who first united calculus and logic in his attempt to construct a universal algebra and a calculus of logic by following the basic idea of the mediæval Spanish logician Ramón Lull (1235-1315). Since Leibniz had universal interests such as history, theology, linguistics, biology, geology, diplomacy, mathematics and the art of invention, he was mainly searching for a universal method by means of which he could obtain knowledge, produce inventions and comprehend the essential unity of the universe. He tried to build a general science (***scientia generalis***), which had many aspects, some of which led him to new discoveries in mathematics. His search for general characteristics (***characteristica generalis***) led him to permutations, combinatorics and formal logic. Since Leibniz's logic was completely independent of all concepts of space and number, it served as a prototype for future abstract mathematics. His search for universal language (***lingua universalis***) in which all errors of thought would appear as computational errors, led not only to symbolic logic, but also to a great many innovations in mathematical notation. Leibniz was the greatest inventor of mathematical symbols in history for few men have understood so well the unity of form and content. For instance, his invention of calculus resulted from his search for a ***lingua universalis*** of change, particularly of motion. In calculus, he introduced the infinitesimal characteristic triangle (***triangulum characteristicum***) whereas Pascal had used the finite characteristic triangle. Although Leibniz's idea tended to be more visionary than practical, it did foreshadow the basic ideas of mathematical notation and symbolic logic. Leibniz did develop his 'universal characteristics' as precursor of a 'universal algebra' which was later used as a model for a direct method of vector analysis. Leibniz's ideas on the calculus of logic and on the 'reasoning machine' later led to important developments in mathematics, and to computers.

Stanhope and his Logic Demonstrator:

The first logic machine was invented in 1777, about 70 years after the death of Leibniz, by the eccentric English statesman and scientific inventor Charles, the third Earl of Stanhope (1753-1816). The Logic Demonstrator of Stanhope was a simple, pocket-size instrument which could solve the traditional syllogisms, numerical problems in logical form as well as elementary problems of probability. Stanhope's Logic Demonstrator used a class logic which interpreted any proposition as an identity. It consisted of a block of wood provided with a central window behind which were two glass slides, the grey glass for the first premise and a red glass for the second premise. A logical conclusion could be reached when the grey and red slides were appropriately slid to fill the window and establish a relationship. Stanhope also invented two mechanical calculators in 1775 and in 1777 in which he used Leibniz's 'stepped drum' with modifications. His second calculator had a more complicated design.

Boole, De Morgan and Mathematical Method of Logic:

English self-taught ingenious mathematician George Boole (1815-1864), published his pathbreaking work, < The Mathematical Analysis of Logic > in 1847 and < An Investigation of the Laws of Thought > in 1854, in which he organised the laws of logic of Aristotle in terms of nonquantitative algebra. Boole separated symbols of mathematical operations from the things upon which they operate. He then investigated these operations in their own right and discovered that they were subject to some kind of symbolic algebra. Boole then set down the axioms for logic in their algebraic form like Eukleides had done for geometry in antiquity. Boole's noncommutative binary algebra is a two-state algebra which can be applied to any two-state system with definite rules, but it is not a generalisation of binary arithmetic since it does not follow all the same rules as binary arithmetic. His special law of logic: $aa = a$, which sets Boolean algebra of logic apart from the ordinary algebra, is quantitatively only satisfied by *0* and *1* that calls for binary mathematics, although *0* means the 'null set' and *1* means the 'universal set' in Boolean algebra.

Boolean algebra dealt with logic of classes and connecting words such as 'or', 'and', 'not' as algebraic symbols so that they could be used to analyse mathematically many forms of logical arguments, which made it into a powerful instrument in science and engineering. It organised the many rules of thumb given by Aristotle into a system, and was the first important step towards a modern symbolic logic as an answer to Leibniz's dream of a calculus of logic and a ***characteristica generalis***. Leibniz left an important contribution to computer engineering, when among his papers after his death was found a memoir on binary arithmetic in which he saw the very image of creation. In this work, Leibniz reasoned that since everything in the universe logically either exists or does not exist: "... the whole existence could be reduced ... into a universal calculus." George Boole carried out this idea of Leibniz by founding an algebra of logic based on 'zero' and 'one', the so-called 'binary Boolean algebra'. Boole's 'binary logic' made possible the mechanisation of logic, and it was discovered in 1948 that Boole's 'binary algebra of logic' was of crucial importance to the computer technology because it could be applied to the theoretical principles of design as well as to the function of the computers. All the so-called 'logic circuits' in electronic computers today work according to Boole's 'binary logic'.

Moreover, Boole also wrote a book < Finite Differences > in 1860 which is still a standard work on numerical computation important in science and engineering.

Euler, Venn, Jevons and Logic Machine:

The syllogistic arguments are made up of statements in one of four forms: 1. Universal affirmative (All *A*'s are *B*'s); 2. Universal negative (No *A*'s are *B*'s); 3. Particular affirmative (Some *A*'s are *B*'s); 4. Particular negative (Some *A*'s are not *B*'s). The letter symbols *A* and *B* stand for common nouns as the terms of a well-formed syllogism consisting of two premises and a conclusion. In 1768 the Swiss mathematician Leonhard Euler (1707-1783) in his popular lectures to the teenaged princess of Brandenburg, < Letters to a German Princess > (***Lettres à une princesse d'Allemagne***), an immensely successful book on popularisation of science which was translated into 9 languages and remained in print for 90 years in 12 French editions, 9 English editions, 6 German editions, 4 Russian editions, 2 Dutch editions, 2 Swedish editions, and one edition each in Italian, Danish and Spanish, invented the ingenious logic circle diagrams for testing the syllogistic arguments. The English logician John Venn (1834-1923) used Euler's logic circles in a novel way in which 3 Euler logic circles overlap in all possible ways, dividing the plane which represents the 'universal or universe class' into 8 regions. The English logician, economist and philosopher William Stanley Jevons (1835-1882), acquired considerable fame when in 1869 he invented his renowned logic machine which used a logical alphabet 4 terms to perform operations on the basis of Boolean algebra, and was the first logic machine with the power to solve complicated logical problems faster than the unaided logician. By such means, Venn and Jevons helped to change classical logic into its modern symbolic form. Thus in the middle of the nineteenth century George Boole, who had been strongly influenced by the symbolic logic of relations and propositions given in the book < Formal Logic > published in 1847 by the English mathematician and a man of great wit, Augustus De Morgan, opened a new field of logic now known as 'mathematical or symbolic logic'. Both De Morgan and Boole were reformers of Aristotelian logic, and initiators of an algebra of logic because they intended to mathematise logic. Almost contemporaneously, great progress was made by the German mathematicians Georg Friedrich Bernhard Riemann (1826-1866) and Georg Ferdinand Ludwig Philip Cantor (1845-1918) in the development of intellectually constructed mathematical theories, such as nonEuclidean geometries and transfinite numbers, respectively, which rested entirely on logical rigour and consistency.

Frege, Peano, Russell, Mill, Gödel and Symbolic Logic:

After the crucial discovery by the German mathematician Friedrich Ludwig Gottlob Frege (1848-1925) that the definition of a number can be given in terms of a purely logical concept of class which states that 'a number is a class of classes' he brought the mathematical systematisation of logic and the logical unification of mathematics together in his colossal work of 2 volumes <Foundations of Arithmetic> (***Die Grundlagen der Arithmetik***) published in 1893 and 1903, in which he derived arithmetical concepts from symbolic logic.

Frege's lifelong effort to derive mathematics from symbolic logic met a crushing intellectual disaster whilst the second volume of his gargantuan work was still in the galley-proof stage. In 1903 the young English mathematical logician Arthur William Bertrand Russell (1872-1970) sent Frege his paradox of 'class of classes not containing themselves as members' expressed wholly by means of logical notions that was germane to Frege's fundamental logical concept of the number as class of classes. Frege after careful consideration of Russell's paradox came to the conclusion that his logical system of mathematics was incapable of resolving this paradox. It remained a painful professional experience for Frege to insert into the 2nd volume of his lifework a paragraph stating that the logical foundation of his reasoning was undermined by Russell's paradox making the fundamental value of his treatise questionable.

In 1899, the Italian mathematician Giuseppe Peano (1858-1932), professor at the University of Turin, developed in his treatise < A Logical Exposition of the Principles of Geometry > a logically organised system of traditional mathematics in which he applied symbolic logic to the fundamentals of mathematics. By 1888 Peano had constructed a system of 5 axioms called the Peano Axioms, although they were first given by German mathematician Richard Dedekind (1831-1916), about the logical concept of number starting with the undefined concepts for zero, number, and successor, and deduced from them a logical unification of a wide field of mathematics. He also founded his system of mathematical notation for logic on the basis of these 5 axioms which should be properly named the 'Dedekind Axioms'. Peano's influence on other mathematical logicians was great, particularly on Russell whose major work < ***Principia Mathematica*** > incorporated a considerable part of Peano's logical work. Peano used logic for the improvement of the rigour of mathematics.

In 1903, Peano abandoned mathematics to develop an international language, ***Interlingua***, in which words were made of Latin stems without inflexion and combined with words taken from the German and the English language. Some contemporary scientific journals still give summaries of the papers they publish in Peano's ***Interlingua***.

After Frege's intellectual disaster, Russell and his teacher, the English mathematician and philosopher, Alfred North Whitehead (1861-1947), undertook an even more ambitious project of their own to derive all of mathematics from symbolic logic, a method called 'formalism'. Russell and Whitehead introduced symbols for connecting conjunctions such as 'or', 'and', and 'if' ... 'then' which had already been used by Frege, but they also introduced symbols for complete sentences which made their logical system intricate and much more complex. Russell and Whitehead published their ponderous work < ***Principia Mathematica*** > in 3 volumes from 1910 to 1913. For almost 20 years Russell and Whitehead were convinced that they had achieved mathematical certainty by having derived the entire field of mathematics from symbolic logic thereby unifying the 2 fields in one complete system of logic and mathematics. However, their confidence was shattered in 1931 when the brilliant Austrian mathematical logician, Kurt Gödel (1906-1978), demonstrated that no system of mathematical definitions can contain within itself the proof of its own validity. Gödel translated all the symbols of the symbolic logic into numbers in a systematic and inventive way, and then proved that it is always possible to construct a number which cannot be derived from the other numbers of his system. His ingenious proof demonstrated that every mathematical system regardless of its logical complexity can always be subjected to unresolvable paradoxes – that certainty in mathematics did not, and could not exist. The Gödel proof delivered the ***coup de grâce*** to the formalistic system of mathematical logic of Russell and Whitehead, just as Russell's paradox had delivered the ***coup de grâce*** to the mathematical logic of Frege. The Gödel proof finally ended the futile search for mathematical certainty by showing that all such attempts are doomed to failure, since the ideal of formalising the whole of mathematics in a single unified system was finally proven to be illusory. Mathematics cannot be reduced to logic since logic is simply too narrow for mathematical purposes, nor can mathematics be reduced to blind manipulation of meaningless formulas as in the method of formalism since the requirement of consistency is not enough.

In classical and symbolic logic, the truth of the conclusion follows from the truth of the premises with certainty. In the inductive logic the premises are evidence for the conclusion but the truth of the conclusion follows from the truth of the evidence only with a certain probability. The most significant contribution to inductive logic was made by the English philosopher of liberal humanism, John Stuart Mill (1806-1873), in his < System of Logic > published in 1843, where he formulated the method of proof with which he thought to characterise empirical sciences. In the twentieth century, the inductive logic has developed into a discipline known as the philosophy of science, and closely related to it is the branch of mathematics known as the probability theory.

Both classical and modern logic presume that any well-formed sentence is either true or false. Recently efforts have been made to develop logical systems of the so-called 'multivalued logic' in which an assertion may have some value other than true or false. In some such systems, it is a 'probability value' expressed as a fraction ranging from *0* to *1*, and from *-1* to *1*. Another development of logic has been to establish a system of modal logic, which represents logical relations between the assertions of possibility and impossibility, necessity and contingency, a type of logic first considered by the ancient Greeks called Stoics.

Leibniz, Mathematical Theories of Elasticity and Stress:

The extensive digression given above about the development of logic and, particularly, the precipitous advance in mathematical logic since the middle of the 19th century which can be called 'revolutionary', shows why the modern computer design owes its very beginning to this 'revolution', the origin of which lies in the works of Leibniz.

Leibniz was not only a theoretician but also a practical mechanical designer. In 1681, Leibniz worked as an engineer on the design of a wind-powered pumping engine to raise water out of the deep mines in the Harz mountains in Germany. The wind power in his pumping engine was controlled with a variable gear by means of a conical chain-wheel. His pumping engine operated by a windmill functioned well in steady wind, but in gusty winds or in windstorms the windmill exerted so much power that it could not be controlled and, in consequence, it finally broke down the mechanism of the mill. For this reason, Leibniz's wind-powered pumping engine was not successful. Apparently Leibniz was the first scientist to distinguish 'sliding' friction from 'rolling' friction in his engineering designs.

In 1708, Leibniz was also the first to propose and describe the working principle of an open-cycle hot-air engine in his letters to Denis Papin. In 1807, the aeronautics pioneer George Cayley (1773-1857) designed an open-cycle hot-air engine for his aircraft, but he continued to improve it as he went along, and in 1837 he patented the last version of his improved hot-air engine which he claimed would produce 5-horsepower. The first closed-cycle hot-air engine with a heat regenerator was invented by the Scottish clergyman Dr. Robert Stirling (1790-1879) and patented in 1816. In 1818, a hot-air engine of this type, which had an output of about 2-horsepower, was pumping water in a stone quarry in Scotland. Robert Stirling and his brother James produced several closed-cycle hot-air engines with improvements from 1820 to 1850. In 1843, probably the largest hot-air engine of Sterling with an output of 45-horsepower was working in a foundry in Dundee.

In 1684, Leibniz, by following Mariotte's researches, connected Hooke's law of linear elasticity with the extensions of the fibres of the beam in the fractured cross-section of the beam at the support [the rest of the cantilever beam he assumed rigid as an approximation]: "... their resistance is in proportion to their extension." He established the formula that the bending moment M for the beam at rupture in the fractured cross-section is proportional to the second moment I of the cross-sectional area A:

$$M \propto I = \int_A y^2 \, dA \ .$$

Leibniz considered the fibres of the beam to act like linearly elastic springs at the ruptured cross-section, and he assumed, like Mariotte had done before him, that the neutral fibre can be taken in the bottom of the cantilever beam. This memoir of Leibniz was the very origin of the mathematical theory of elasticity and the mathematical theory of stress.

Newton and Axiomatic Mechanics:

The English mathematician and theoretical physicist, Isaac Newton (1642-1727) synthesised theoretical mechanics of the particle in his monumental masterpiece in 3 books, < Mathematical Principles of Natural Philosophy > (***Philosophia naturalis principia mathematica***), published in 1687, by reducing particle mechanics to 3 basic axioms or laws of motion (***leges motus***):

Axiom (I)- Every body continues in its state of rest, or of uniform motion in a right line, unless it is compelled to change that state by forces impressed upon it.

Axiom (II)-The change of motion is proportional to the motive force impressed, and it takes place along the right line in which that force is impressed.

Axiom (III)-To an action there is always a contrary and equal reaction; or, the mutual actions of two bodies upon each other are always equal and directed to contrary parts.

Under Axiom (I) Newton included both the linear and the rotary inertia, but he gave here no mathematical definition to either one. Despite Newton's remark about the rotary inertia of a spinning top, inspired by the example of the revolving millstone given by Jean Buridan in the mediæval times, he did not attempt any particular theory of rotation of finite bodies, nor did he consider the problem of the oscillating pendulum as a finite body for which Huygens, under special assumptions, had published a correct energetical solution in 1673, nor did he indicate what principles govern the motion of a wheel on an axle.

His Axiom (II), which does not define here what motion means or how to determine forces, was apparently fashioned after the so-called ' principle of impulsive linear momentum', which in modern direct vector notation can be concisely expressed:

$$m \, \Delta \mathbf{v} = \mathbf{F} \, \Delta t \, ,$$

where m denotes the mass, $\Delta\mathbf{v}$ the incremental change of velocity, Δt the incremental interval of time, and $\mathbf{F}$ the applied force acting over the incremental time-interval Δt. It was the first general treatise of mechanics organised and derived from fundamental laws or axioms with mathematical rigour. All the major properties of motion of bodies Newton proved from a few relatively simple axioms. Newton took 'force' in the sense used in statics as a primitive idea, and introduced force into rational mechanics as an ***a priori*** concept, but it was illustrated rather than presented, explained, or explicitly justified. Before Newton, it had been a general practice to define force in terms of motion Although Newton regarded force as a 'mechanical' idea, he also mentioned 'electric' and 'magnetic' forces. In his treatise Newton made some headway in distinguishing 'mass' from 'weight', but his concept of the 'body' was still unexpectedly tentative. Sometimes 'bodies' in his equations were masses concentrated at isolated points, but other times, such as in the problem of attraction of spheres, his 'bodies' filled finite portions of space. Newton defined neither the 'momentum' nor the 'inertia' in this treatise. Newton's own ***leges motus*** are strictly insufficient for even what he himself claimed to prove from them. Newton gave no equations of motion for systems of more than two free mass-points or more than one constrained mass-point, and he left no evidence that he was able to set up differential equations of motion for mechanical systems. Most of the content of the first half of Book I, both physical principles and conclusions, was not entirely original and could be found in earlier writings, but Newton's presentation of the achievements of the previous century was concise, clear, and correct which evoked admiration from his contemporaries.

Wallis and Impulsive Linear Momentum Principle:

Needless to say no such analytical expression as the principle of impulsive linear momentum can be found in Newton's ***Principia*** since his mathematical method of exposition was geometrical. This law of dynamics was not an original creation of Newton since it had been presented many years earlier by a friend and older contemporary of Newton, the well-known English cryptographer and mathematician of remarkable ability and originality of his day, particularly in analysis, John Wallis (1616-1703) who presented this law of dynamics also in his tractate < Mechanics or Tractate on the Geometry of Motion > (***Mechanica sive tractatus de motu geometricus***) already in 1670, but he had made limited use of it. Wallis, a former child prodigy in numerical calculations who was appointed Savilian professor of geometry at Oxford University by Oliver Cromwell (1599-1658), wrote many works on mechanics and laws of motion, astronomy, geology, tides, sound, logic, philosophy, calendar (in opposition to Gregorian reform), and the compass. Wallis wrote the best and the most complete treatise on statics after Stevin. He was the first mathematician after Descartes to propose the law of conservation of linear momentum. He also conducted experiments in speech, and tried with some success to teach deaf-mutes to speak by using a method which he described in his book,

< Grammar of English Language > (***Grammatica linguae Anglicanae***), published in 1652. Wallis in his voluminous writings showed considerable genius in analysis, and he was the leading mathematician in England before Newton. He replaced the synthetical method by analytical method, defined conic sections as second degree curves of coordinates, and introduced infinite series as a regular part of analysis. Wallis recognised the importance of Cavalieri's method of indivisibles, which he arithmetised and systematised by combining it with Cartesian analysis, and he used it in the quadratures of algebraic curves in his treatise < Infinitesimal Arithmetic > (***Arithmetica infinitorum***) published in 1656, in which the concept of the limit and a completely arithmetised limiting process is more boldly and confidently applied than in the almost simultaneous work of Tacquet. Wallis sought to free arithmetic entirely from the geometric presentation, and in the pursuit of this goal he treated the passage to the limit as an independent arithmetical operation, thereby coming very close to the limit concept. He strove to establish infinitesimal calculus by arithmetical rather than by geometrical conceptions. Wallis, who made liberal use of interpolation and incomplete induction, did not worry too much about mathematical rigour in his arithmetisation of mathematics. He took the surface or the body as an algebraic sum of elemental parts and presented the relationship of two surfaces or bodies as a quotient of two series. In the same treatise Wallis introduced the symbol ∞ for infinity, as well as the reciprocal relations $1/0 = \infty$ and $1/\infty = 0$, and his ***triangulum characteristicum*** (dx, dy, ds), but he could not use it for the rectification of curves for he could not expand the differential arc element $ds = [dx^2 + dy^2]^{1/2}$ into an infinite series, which his method required, since he did not know the general binomial expansion theorem, the knowledge of which would have significantly improved his method.

In his < Geometry of Indivisibles > (***Geometria indivisibilibus***), Wallis pioneered in extending algebra into analysis with remarkable success. He failed to produce the quadrature of the circle by means of series because he did not know the general form of the binomial theorem which was needed, but he knew how to reach this result by another method. Wallis gave the equivalent length of the differential arc element ds of a curve in orthogonal Cartesian coordinates x and y:

$$ds = dx\,[1+(dy/dx)^2]^{1/2},$$

his most far-reaching discovery that linked the problem of rectification with the problem of quadrature. Wallis' treatise < Tractate of Algebra: Historical and Practical > (***De algebra tractatus: historicus et practicus***) written in 1673 but published in English in 1685 and in Latin in 1693, was the first treatise to give a complete exposition of a subject together with its history. In this book Wallis made the first attempt to represent imaginary numbers graphically by a method now in use, but he stopped short of complete success. In his theory of integration, which was his chief contribution apart from the mathematics of interpolation as a mathematical art of reading between lines, he generalised exponents to include negative and fractional as well as positive and integral numbers. His procedures were not always logically rigorous, but Wallis knew how to reach correct results. The most important contributions of Wallis to the development of infinitesimal calculus were in the theory of integration. The foundation for the concept of definite integrals was quite well set down in the works of Wallis and Fermat.

Newton and **'Principia'**:

Isaac Barrow (1630-1677), English mathematician and a divine, who was Newton's teacher at Cambridge University, published his masterpiece < Lectures on Optics and Geometry > (***Lectiones opticae et geometricae***) in 1669 with the assistance of his student Isaac Newton. Barrow disapproved of the arithmetisation of mathematics which Wallis pursued, and thought that arithmetic should be included in geometry, and held that algebra, which he disliked, should be part of logic rather than mathematics. Unfortunately Barrow did not fully appreciate the analytical methods of Descartes and Fermat, and did not properly recognise the fundamental importance of the arithmetisation of mathematics in the works of Wallis. However, it was Barrow who was the first to recognise in complete generality that differentiation and integration are inverse operations in mathematics. This capital discovery representing the fundamental theorem of calculus was stated and proven by Barrow, who laid the foundation for the differential and integral calculus geometrically by introducing the differential triangle of Wallis, and by bringing the quantities dx, dy and ds into the problem of tangents. In Barrow's work the recognition of the inverse nature of differentiation and integration are to be found for arbitrary functions such as curves for the first time. Barrow was the first who fundamentally reduced the inverse tangent problem by a formal method to a quadrature problem, that is, the problem of finding the properties of a curve from certain properties of the tangent of the curve. Barrow's major contribution to infinitesimal calculus was in the theory of differentiation, and in his recognition of the inverse nature of the differentiation and the integration operation. Differentiation is in general thought to be the fundamental operation, whereas integration is regarded simply as the inverse of differentiation. After Barrow's contribution to the infinitesimal calculus, what was needed was the creation of a formal symbolic method of calculation and a systematic set of analytical rules for infinitesimal calculus, a task soon accomplished by two eminent mathematicians of modern times: Newton and Leibniz.

Barrow was academically outstanding in mathematics, physics, astronomy and theology, and widely admired for his wit, bravery, scrupulousness and physical strength.

Newton succeeded Barrow to the chair of Lucasian professor of geometry when Barrow resigned the chair in Newton's favour. Newton expressed his idea on the foundation of all scientific enquiry in the following way: "... the best and safest method of philosophising seems to be first to enquire diligently into the properties of things, and of establishing these properties by experiments, and then to proceed more slowly to hypotheses for the explanation of them." When urged to give the cause of universal gravitation, Newton refused to propose a hypothesis for the cause of gravitation beyond the mathematical law of universal gravitation, and responded: "I do not fabricate hypotheses (***hypotheses non fingo***)."

In his scientific, but primarily in his mathematical work, Newton was particular, empirical and circumspect. He said that he relied on mathematics and used experiments mostly to make his theoretical results physically intelligible, and thereby convince the vulgar. He initiated many methods, but he did not emphasise them. He was a skilled master of approximate solutions, quadratures, and series expansions in definitely set mathematical problems. He devoted little attention to the form of his mathematics and, therefore, attached little importance to notation. He was quite satisfied with the series solutions of integrals. Leibniz, in contrast, was bold and had a propensity for speculations and generalisations, since he was always concerned with the form of mathematics and with operational formulae to produce a calculus of the widest scope. For this reason, it was Leibniz who set the system of rules and formulae for the calculus, such as integral tables and differentiation formula for $d^n(u\,v)$, something that Newton never cared to do. Moreover, Leibniz was always interested in finite solutions of his integrals. However, Newton's impressive application of calculus to important physical problems influenced the direction of analysis for more than 100 years.

Book I, *On the Motion of Bodies* (***De motu corporum liber primus***) of his < Mathematical Principles of Natural Philosophy >, began as the first treatise of general mathematical mechanics which was organised according to, and derived from 3 fundamental axioms or laws of motion. In it Newton gave his mathematical theory of the planetary motion in empty space, which was based on the general principle of mutual attractions of masses, first proposed by Kepler in 1609 and as a general astronomical principle by Robert Hooke in 1674, and inertia enabling material bodies to resist changes in their states of rest or uniform rectilinear motion, two dynamic states of bodies which in mediæval times had been considered to be contrary dynamic conditions. In justification of his mathematical model for such immense bodies as the Sun, the Earth and the Moon which he represented by mathematical points, Newton proved in a special solution that the mutual forces of attraction acting between two homogeneously layered spheres is independent of the diameter, and directed along the line connecting the centers of the spheres where their total mass can be imagined to be concentrated. His arguments based upon unstated statical assumptions depended on a rule of addition of infinitely many forces but no such explicit rule was given. He apparently regarded it sufficient to rely on the law of addition for pairs of forces given earlier as Corollary II to the laws of motion, but the proof of it resting on Corollary I was wrong. Newton treated the motion of heavenly bodies as the motion of mass-points subject to only 2 forces: universal gravitation and their own force of inertia. The second half of Book I is a completely original work, but in this part of his treatise Newton began to lose his grip on his method of deriving all his results mathematically from the axioms. Newton was able to reduce the two-body problem to an equivalent problem of one body attracted to a fixed center, but when he undertook to solve the three-body problem which cannot be so reduced, he was unable to give a solution or even an approximate solution to the problem, and his procedure of rigorous mathematical deduction from the axioms broke down completely, although he was able to obtain some correct inequalities and half-guessed approximate results. That it took the might of the enormous intellect of Newton to be able to extract this much from his rather primitive formulation of mechanics is demonstrated by the fact that it took more than 50 years before any improvement upon his results on the three-body problem was made. He gave no evidence of being able to set up differential equations of motion for such mechanical systems for which his formulation of the laws of mechanics was inadequate. The only motion Newton succeeded to reduce to mathematics was for a single point endowed with a finite mass. Newton demonstrated that the 3 planetary laws of Kepler follow from the inverse-square law of universal gravitation. Newton used the term 'body' quite vaguely with at least 3 different meanings, and his statements were generally correct only when applied to masses concentrated at isolated points.

Book II, *On Motion of Bodies* (***De motu corporum liber secundus***) in contrast to Book I, is almost entirely original but much of it is wrong. Newton speculated that heavenly bodies may also move in some kind of rare resisting medium, and since he accepted the opinion of Descartes that there is only one mechanics which is common to both the Earth and the heavens, he sought to learn about the resistance offered by the fluid media to the motion of finite bodies in Earthly experience. To find such resistance of the medium to the motion of the Earth, Newton thought it necessary to estimate precisely its effect on motion since he believed that a fluid medium can reveal the true nature of such a resistance. For this reason, Newton intended to determine mathematically the nature of motion in a resisting medium, but to study fluid resistance, he had to learn first the laws of fluid motion. Unfortunately, in this field of mechanics Newton had no foregoing pathfinder such as the ingenious Huygens. Newton conceived a fluid alternately as consisting of discrete particles 'fleeing one another', or as a 'continued' medium. The original half of ***Principia*** concerns fluids. Newton's brilliant but faulty analysis of resistance offered to bodies in rare and in dense fluids, the internal friction of fluids, the figure of fluid Earth, the spring of air, propagation of surface waves in water, the efflux of fluid from a vessel, oscillation of water in a bent tube, and for the propagation of sound waves in air, for which Newton had to invent new concepts, gave rise to the correct solution of all these problems in the 18th century. New hypotheses as well as stated and concealed assumptions were freely employed by Newton everywhere, but occasionally some stated assumptions were not used at all. Few of his devised concepts have been retained and few of his solutions were correct, which is not surprising considering the total novelty of the subjects, but it is remarkable that Newton was able, in each case, to grope and find his way to some definite answer. He studied bodies falling under gravity as well as the trajectories of projectiles, and resistances of cylinders and spheres spinning in a fluid with internal friction. He then described experiments with pendula swinging in resisting medium, and discussed the dynamic theory of fluids and spherical bodies moving in fluids leading to a study of solids of revolution offering the least resistance to the flow of a fluid past the body, the mathematical treatment of which was one of the first attempts at variational calculus. Finally, Newton advanced a proposition intended to destroy Descartes' vortex theory of planetary motion, but the proposition itself was not related to what went before, and was meaningless without the definition of terms used, and the 'proof' of it depended on an unsound principle of solidification. Newton was not able to find the right mathematical model for fluids in motion and, therefore, he alternated between the corpuscular and the continuum model whilst introducing various unsatisfactory ***ad hoc*** assumptions. Newton was the first theoretician to attempt a mathematical proof in fluid mechanics when he undertook to derive theoretically the Torricelli efflux rule:

$$v \propto \sqrt{h}$$

that gives the speed v of water issuing under the hydraulic head h from an orifice in the bottom of a vessel. In the first edition of ***Principia*** Newton's ' proof ' of this solution was essentially statical and wrong. In the second edition of 1713, a new 'proof ', which was even less plausible than the previous ' proof ', was based on a false ***ad hoc*** theoretical model of a fictitious ' cataract ' of melting ice sliding past an unmoved funnel of water, to which the law of free fall of bodies was 'presumed' to apply, in an effort to 'prove' the speed of efflux of water from a hole in the bottom of the vessel. In his original but false conjecture about the motion of water, he apparently tried to use Stevin's 'principle of solidification' in a novel but unsound manner, whilst he made no use of the concept of pressure nor of the principle of linear momentum. In his treatment of hydrodynamic problems, Newton claimed to solve each one of the problems by special reasoning, special hypotheses and special guesses which were only vaguely related to mechanical ideas and principles, but his theories of fluids were mostly wrong. In the first edition of ***Principia***, Newton maintained that the reaction of a jet from a hole in a vessel is the same as the force which would be required to keep the hole stopped. The correct solution of all these problems required the creation of the concept of the field. That some of the learned savants made definite progress upon such field problems without the benefit of the field concept proves the astounding virtuosity and profound talent of these men of genius.

This work on fluids by Newton in the ingenious but mostly unsatisfactory Book II is almost entirely original, and although faulty it constitutes one of the most brilliant original works ever written on mechanics, but as a treatise towards a unified mathematical science of mechanics it was a distinct failure. Despite this shortcoming, Book II succeeded not only to open new avenues of thought but also to identify the domains and define the problems for many investigations of the next century in mechanics.

Book III, bearing the title *Of the System of the World* (***De mundi systemata***) was devoted to the development of the concept of universal gravitation and to the detailed studies of the planetary orbits such as eccentricities, the flattening of the Earth at the poles, the variation of gravitational force over the surface of the Earth, the libration of the Moon, the disturbance of the Moon's orbit by the attraction of the Sun, the behaviour of comets, and a selection of other technical problems such as demonstrating that Kepler's third law applies to the motion of the Moon round the Earth, the planets round the Sun, and the satellites round the planets Jupiter and Saturn where they are maintained in their orbits by the gravitational forces which vary inversely as the square of the distance from the centers of their gravitational force. He demonstrated that the gravitational force acting on falling bodies near the surface of the Earth is the same kind of centripetal force which holds the Moon in its orbit round the Earth and it varies inversely as the square of the distance from the center of the Earth, *i.e.* that the terrestrial and celestial mechanics are the same as Kepler had assumed and Descartes had categorically asserted. Newton's < Mathematical Principles of Natural Philosophy >, usually briefly called ***Principia***, was an impressive pioneering attempt at rational mechanics by one of the foremost mathematicians of modern time, which as a treatise consists of inarticulated problems of motion some of which are solved well, some solved partially, some unsolved, and a few solved wrong. There was a profusion of problems of motion, but no general equations of motion. Nowhere in this treatise can the so-called 'Newton's equation of motion', $m\,\mathbf{a} = \mathbf{F}$, be found, for this general equation in astronomy was first published in 1749, not in 1687! Each motion given in this treatise stood as a new problem and was treated as such. There were many examples with ingenious concepts and a splendid approach, but no algorisms nor a general method. The history of rational mechanics being mathematical rather than experimental begins with Newton's treatise as a history of special problems for the solution of which new principles and methods had to be created. Newton, contrary to popular opinion, did not give 'classical mechanics' its present form, for his principles were neither clear nor definite enough to be able to do so. In his works, Newton himself gave no evidence of knowing that his laws of motion (***leges motus***) are sufficient for a general theory of mechanics. Newton did not treat rigid bodies, nor flexible bodies, nor elastic bodies by his method of dynamics because they were clearly beyond his theoretical range. Newton showed how to use statically conceived forces in dynamic problems, and mistakenly thought that 'forces' can be detected only when they give rise to motions, despite the fact that if this were true, then there would be no such science as statics! Newton demonstrated how to use knowledge obtained from the state of equilibrium to solve problems of motion, but his treatment of mechanics was the weakest where statics was involved. In the estimation of his contemporaries Newton's great achievement in physical science was the deductive, mathematical aspect of his mechanics.

Newton recognised the substantial intellectual debt he owed to Huygens, and he showed his great respect for this ingenious Dutchman by calling him ***Summum Hugenius*** (*Supreme Huygens*).

Newton devised his form of calculus a little earlier than Leibniz, but his conception and notation of infinitesimal calculus was inferior to that of Leibniz, and it did not survive the test of time, except for the trivial dot-notations of the velocity and the acceleration: $\dot{s} = v$ and $\ddot{s} = \dot{v} = a$, where s is the distance traversed, v the instantaneous speed, a the instantaneous acceleration, and $(\dot{})$ implies the time-rate of change, notations which are sometimes still used in engineering textbooks.

Jacob Bernoulli, Rational Mechanics, Bending of Beams and Principle of Lost Forces:

The Swiss mathematician of a Dutch merchant family hailing from The southern Netherlands, Jacob [or James] Bernoulli (1654-1704), one of the foremost mathematicians of modern times, investigated various topics of mechanics which Newton had not studied ***in extenso***, such as contact forces and contiguous action in continuous bodies, and the unification of statics with dynamics, which makes him, together with Newton, the founder of rational mechanics. From 1691 to 1694, Jacob Bernoulli, established the difficult mathematical theory of finite bending of beams when he attempted to unify the theory of flexible elastic lines with the theory of the bending of elastic bands, in his equation of bending:

$$C\,(1/r) = M,$$

where r is the radius of curvature of the bent beam, M is the bending moment, and C is a constant representing the geometric and constitutive properties of the beam. He encountered the beam problem in consulting a wainwright in Zurich who had experienced persistent trouble with the fracturing of his carriage wheels. In 1704, in his last paper, Jacob Bernoulli gave the first stress-strain law $\epsilon = f(\sigma)$, where the strain $\epsilon = \Delta L/L$ and the mean stress $\sigma = F/A$. He also investigated the bending of curved beams with initial curvature $(1/R)$, and established the equation of flexure of such beams:

$$C\,[(1/r)-(1/R)] = M.$$

When the observation of Hooke, Mariotte and Huygens on the existence of the neutral fibre within the bent beam was brought to his attention, Jacob Bernoulli tried to establish a theory by means of which the location of the neutral, unextended, longitudinal fibre in the bent beam could be determined. He was not successful in integrating over the cross-section of the beam as Leibniz had done for the linear distribution of tensions over the cross-section, because he was not prepared to introduce any special hypothesis representing the response of the material. Bernoulli tried to take into account the variations of tensions in the cross-section of the beam during bending, but since his own experiments with materials such as animal guts had made him suspicious of the linear Hooke's Law, he adopted a false general hypothesis which implied that the actual location of the neutral line is not important, although in one of his trial solutions he did place the neutral line at the center of the cross-section of the beam. Finally, he decided to place the neutral line at the bottom of the beam as Mariotte and Leibniz had done before him. Jacob Bernoulli tried in vain to establish a general equation of flexure for the bending of beams without the use of a constitutive law for a particular material, something he had accomplished before with complete success for perfectly flexible lines, or cables. He had been able to find 4 independent derivations of the general differential equation of equilibrium for perfectly flexible cables under arbitrary loading by the following 4 methods: (a) equilibrium of forces acting on an infinitesimal element; (b)equilibrium of moments acting on an infinitesimal element; (c)the principle of virtual work; and (d) the principle of minimum potential energy. However, this was not possible for the extremely difficult problem of finite bending of beams, a problem which has not been completely solved till this very day. Jacob Bernoulli replaced the action of all fibres of the cross-section by the action of a single elastic spring on the convex side of the beam, and not by a uniform distribution of elastic springs over the entire cross-section of the beam as Leibniz had done. Unfortunately, Jacob Bernoulli died before he could publish this particular paper, which contained important fundamental ideas on the mechanics of deformable bodies. This profound paper was published posthumously in 1744.

Jacob Bernoulli, in contrast to Newton who treated motion created from action at a distance, emphasised contiguous action in his researches of rational mechanics from 1691 to 1704 in which he was particularly interested in the relationship between statics and dynamics. The influence of the profound researches of Jacob Bernoulli on the development of rational mechanics is second only to that of Newton's ***Principia***.

In the solution of a famous problem of oscillation of a rigid solid about a fixed axis, the so-called 'center of oscillation problem' which Huygens had already solved by his ingenious but elaborate energy method in 1673 which was not valid for bodies in general motion, Jacob Bernoulli, after a somewhat faulty attempt in 1686 which he revised in 1691, gave in 1703 an entirely new approach to the state of motion of a solid body as a counterpart to the 'kinematic criterion of the static equilibrium of bodies' discovered by the ancient Greek mathematician Archytas of Taras about 400B.C.. In 1691 Jacob Bernoulli created a new approach to swinging bodies by assuming the Law of the Lever to be valid in statics as well as in dynamics, and he used it to relate Huygens' theory of a swinging body to the law of the lever in statics. In 1703, Bernoulli developed the method further, and found that for bodies in motion the system of applied forces is equipollent to the system of corresponding reversed accelerations per unit of mass.

In this paper Bernoulli resolved the acceleration of each mass into two components: the normal component to the path of motion is produced by the constraint of rigidity whereas the tangential component to the path of motion he resolved into acceleration of gravity, and the acceleration produced by the mutual interference of the adjoining masses. He concluded that the system of constraining forces of mutual interference in contiguous action must be in self-equilibrium. The application of Bernoulli's principle of the lever in dynamics to the problem of physical pendulum gave Huygens' elaborate solution from the axiom of energy directly from the relation of statics to dynamics.

Following Bernoulli's idea in a general sense, the actual acceleration **a** of the mass element dm of a solid body can be resolved into applied acceleration $\mathbf{a}^{(a)}$ and constrained acceleration $\mathbf{a}^{(c)}$:

$$\mathbf{a} = \mathbf{a}^{(a)} + \mathbf{a}^{(c)}.$$

If the applied force impressed upon dm is $d\mathbf{F}^{(a)}$ and the actual acceleration of dm is **a**, then the force 'lost' in motion owing to the internal constraints of the body is:

$$d\mathbf{F}^{(\ell)} = d\mathbf{F}^{(a)} - dm\,\mathbf{a} = -d\mathbf{F}^{(c)} \ ,$$

Then because of the parallelogram law of addition of forces:

$$d\mathbf{F}^{(a)} + d\mathbf{F}^{(c)} = dm\,\mathbf{a} = d\mathbf{F}^{(e)} \ ,$$

where $d\mathbf{F}^{(e)}$ is the 'effective force' which produces the actual acceleration **a** of *dm* if the body were free of constraints. Since Jacob Bernoulli asserted that, insofar as the constraint forces are 'lost' for producing motion, they must constitute an internal force system which is 'self-equilibrated'. In modern direct vector method, his concept could be expressed in the general form as follows:

$$\int_m d\mathbf{F}^{(\ell)} = -\int_m d\mathbf{F}^{(c)} = \int_m d\mathbf{F}^{(a)} - \int_m dm\,\mathbf{a} = \mathbf{F}^{(a)} - \int_m dm\,\mathbf{a} = \mathbf{0} \ , \qquad (1)$$

$$\begin{aligned} \int_m \mathbf{r}\times d\mathbf{F}^{(\ell)} &= -\int_m \mathbf{r}\times d\mathbf{F}^{(c)} = \int_m \mathbf{r}\times d\mathbf{F}^{(a)} - \int_m \mathbf{r}\times dm\,\mathbf{a} \\ &= \mathbf{r}\times\mathbf{F}^{(a)} - \int_m \mathbf{r}\times dm\,\mathbf{a} = \mathbf{0} \end{aligned} \qquad (2)$$

where $\mathbf{F}^{(a)}$ is the 'resultant equipollent applied force'.

In the solution of the so-called 'problem of the center of oscillation', Jacob Bernoulli on the basis of his new principle applied the moment equation (2) to the swinging body. On the basis of this new principle of rotating bodies in mechanics Jacob Bernoulli was able to incorporate Huygens' theorem on swinging bodies published in 1673 as an isolated statement into mechanics as whole science. The equations of motion representing the so-called 'principle of lost forces' of Jacob Bernoulli are valid for continuous masses as Newton's axioms of dynamics are not, and for this reason Euler subsequently used it in his solution of all dynamic problems of solid bodies. 'The principle of lost forces' of Jacob Bernoulli was the very first instance of the 'principle of rotational momentum' in its application to the dynamics of a swinging body, whether deformable or rigid, and soon it became in the works of Leonhard Euler the 'second independent fundamental principle of mechanics', but the moment of inertia of rotating rigid bodies was the creation of Huygens and Jacob Bernoulli.

The 'principle of lost forces' was used by Daniel Bernoulli (1770-1782) and by Euler to solve a host of special problems. The same kind of principle was used in 1743 in a general and slightly different but more obscure form by the French mathematician Jean LeRond d'Alembert. Today a particular version of the 'principle of lost forces' is known as the 'd'Alembert principle'.

Jacob Bernoulli was the first mathematician after Leibniz to learn Leibniz's differential and integral calculus, in which he was self-taught. After mastering calculus, Jacob Bernoulli taught it to his younger brother Johann, who became the foremost mathematician of his generation. Jacob Bernoulli is the creator of the modern calculus of variations, the probability calculus, the principle of the rotational momentum [also known as the moment of momentum], and the theory of elastica. In his very last profound paper which he finished before his death in 1704, Jacob Bernoulli was the first scientist to introduce a genuine constitutive equation: $\epsilon = f(\boldsymbol{\sigma})$, where $\boldsymbol{\sigma}$ denotes the mean elastic stress, for the elastic material as the so-called 'stress–strain relation' which is independent of the shape of the material body and, therefore, characterises a material property rather than a property of a particular material specimen, by connecting Beeckman's notion of 'strain' $\epsilon = \Delta L/L$ as a local measure of deformation, with the notion of the mean internal force acting over a unit area of the cross-section of the material specimen under tension that is now called the 'stress'. He was unwilling to regard the 'stress–strain relation' to be a linear function because it contradicted his own experiments with the deformation of animal guts and, therefore, he was content to regard the linear Hooke's law as only a special case. His arguments implied the so-called 'tangent modulus' of a nonlinear stress-strain relation rather than the constant modulus of elasticity 'E' of the linear stress–strain relation. All throughout his working life Jacob Bernoulli sought to establish the theory of bending of beams on the basis of a law of extensions for fibres, but he never succeeded.

In the works of Pardies, the resultants of internal forces or stresses, the so-called 'stress resultants' were conceived to be composed of mutually opposing, or 'conflicting' parts. This notion of internal opposition, or ontological 'strife', is reminiscent of the ideas of the ancient Greek philosopher Herakleitos of Ephesos (c.540-c.475 B.C.) in whose theory of nature the opposites in 'strife' maintain an internal balance as, for instance, a spanned bowstring is internally balanced by the bent bow. It is a noncausal assumption which involves no logical contradictions. Therefore, in this conception the internal stresses as contact forces exist in opposites, representing a noncausal mechanical postulate of interaction in the stress principle, known as the action-reaction principle of contact forces.

In 1699, de la Hire attempted to compare the work done by men carrying loads under various circumstances with the work done by horses. In his comparison, La Hire regarded both men and horses turning a crank of a capstan from which a weight was suspended. His approach was, however, statical in that the suspended weight had to be maintained 'stationary'. In the same year, a blind French physicist, Guillaume Amontons (1663-1705), who had designed a steam-wheel as a prime mover, attempted to measure the power of this device by the number of men or horses it could replace. Amontons was influenced by Galileo's mechanics, and, therefore, he recognised the importance of speed in the performance of his machine which he measured by the product of force and speed first proposed by Heron of Alexandria and adopted by Galileo in his pamphlet <Mechanics> (***Le Meccaniche***), a work which was well-known in France. Amontons replaced the statical method of Huygens and Mariotte for measuring power by the dynamical method of Heron of Alexandria. In 1699, Amontons proved experimentally that in the sliding friction the magnitude of the frictional force is ⅓ of the weight of the moving body, a proportion which is the same for all surfaces. Therefore according to Amontons, the magnitude of the frictional force in sliding solely varies with the magnitude of the weight of the moving body. Amontons also did research on the air thermometer in the theory of which he assumed the existence of an absolute zero temperature. In 1702, he proposed what is known as the 'Amontons law of gases'. In 1695 Amontons wrote a tractate on his physical researches, < Remarks and Experiments in Physics > (***Remarques et expériences physiques***).

In 1702, La Hire, who was inspired by Amontons' dynamic approach to machine power, employed both the statical and the dynamical method in evaluating the force required to pull boats upstream by horses, or by men. In this memoir, La Hire laid the theoretical foundation for calculating water power by amalgamating the hydraulic principles of Torricelli, Huygens and Mariotte with the dynamical method of Heron of Alexandria. La Hire established the mathematical formula for the force P necessary to move the boat with uniform speed v through stagnant water: $P = \gamma A\, v^2/2g$, where A denotes the cross-sectional area of the bow of the boat. In the case of a boat pulled against a stream flowing with the speed V, La Hire gave the force P by the formula:

$$P = \gamma A\,(V+v)^2/2g\,,$$

which recognised the relative nature of such an impulsive force.

Parent, Stress Principle and Maximum Efficiency of Waterwheels:

Although La Hire did not consider waterwheels, his memoir served as an inspiration to his former pupil, Antoine Parent (1666-1716) who produced the first scientific analysis of waterwheels. In 1700, Parent, who was a teacher of mathematics in Paris, not only had published an impressive work on spatial analytic geometry, but also had made efforts to give an algebraic proof of Amontons' dynamic method of evaluating the performance of machines. In 1701, he examined the mechanical efficiency of windmills and calculated the proper angular setting for the vanes of windmills to be *54* degrees and *44* minutes for maximum efficiency of windmills. In 1702, he published a memoir in which he attempted to represent the motion of animals by some principles of mechanics. In 1704, after 4 years of work, Parent presented his noted memoir on the maximum efficiency of waterwheels, in which he established the two limiting conditions under which the waterwheel would produce no effect: when the waterwheel is immobile, and when its blades move with the same speed as the water since then the water would exert no force on the blades of the waterwheel. Parent, by neglecting the gearing ratios, established the relation:

$$P/p = V^2/(V-v)^2 ,$$

which he solved for the output of the waterwheel, pv, and determined its maximum value in terms of the natural power PV of the stream by the first application of calculus to an engineering problem. Parent showed by means of his theory that an undershot waterwheel can deliver no more power than: $pv = (4/27)\ PV$, when $p = (4/9)P$ and $v = (1/3)V$, a result that surprised him. However, Parent's analysis had several shortcomings: he had assumed that only one blade of the waterwheel is immersed at any one time [which is not quite realistic], that the erroneous Huygens-Mariotte law:

$$P = \gamma AH ,$$

which took no account of the contraction of the water jet impinging on the blade (correct value $P = 2\gamma AH$) applied, that $P \propto V^2$ used by Huygens and Mariotte which overlooked oblique impact was valid, and that his analysis applied to all types of waterwheels [it was only valid for impulsive waterwheels]. Ever since the proof of the Torricelli efflux rule by Huygens and Mariotte, scientists had accepted the idea that gravity and impulse produce equal motive power and, therefore, they mistakenly regarded overshot and undershot waterwheels to be equivalent power sources. Had Parent only taken the reduction of the water jet in Huygens-Mariotte law into account, the value for maximum efficiency of waterwheels would have doubled to $8/27$,which is much closer to the correct value. This excellent work of Parent had considerable influence on the profession for in the 1740's it led to a lengthy debate about the correct solution of this problem, and to the criticism of his results, which substantially contributed to the establishment of a sound theory of power, and to the founding of the principle of energy.

In 1713 the resourceful Parent published another important research on the failure of beams in bending in which he corrected Mariotte's wrong section modulus at failure: $Sh/6 \propto bh^2/6$.

He gave the first correct static analysis of beams, and demonstrated that its equilibrium state requires the existence of transverse shear force in the cross-section of the beam.

Parent recognised that as the load approaches its ultimate value known as the 'failure load' in a cantilever beam, the neutral axis moves steadily downwards, which ultimately requires different moduli in the compression and in the tension zone of the cross-section, because the horizontal resultant of the compressive forces must balance the horizontal resultant of the tensile forces in the fractured cross-section. This work of Parent represented the first correct, and complete application of static principles to the forces of the fibres of the beam, and it foreshadowed the so-called 'stress principle'.

Johann Bernoulli, Internal Fluid Pressure and Hydraulics:

The younger brother of Jacob Bernoulli, Johann [or John] Bernoulli (1667-1748), a doctor of medicine, who was taught Leibniz's infinitesimal calculus by Jacob, and who became the leading mathematician of his generation until his pupil Euler surpassed him, was the first mathematician to give, in 1727, a precise mathematical formulation to the principle of virtual work which in modern direct vector notation is given by the equation:

$$\delta W = \Sigma_i \mathbf{F}_i \bullet \delta \mathbf{r}_i = 0,$$

where $\mathbf{F}_i$ denotes the force vector, $\delta \mathbf{r}_i$ the virtual displacement vector, and δW the virtual work.

The first time the linear momentum principle was applied to an element of a continuous body was in 1713 when the English mathematician Brook Taylor (1685-1731), a pupil of the astronomer John Keill of Oxford, applied the so-called 'Newton's second law' to a differential element of a vibrating string of density μ, but he failed to recognise in his expression:

$$T/r \propto F_n = \mu\, a_n ,$$

where a_n is the normal acceleration, F_n the normal force, T the tension in the string, and r the radius of curvature of the string, the differential equation of motion.

The first differential equations as complete statements of the laws of motion for deformable systems were obtained by Johann Bernoulli, d'Alembert, and Euler from 1742 to 1744. Johann Bernoulli was the first mathematician to introduce a single, fixed rectangular Cartesian frame of reference to which the motions of all bodies of a mechanical system were referred. In 1743, Johann Bernoulli, and the French mathematician and philosopher Jean Le Rond d'Alembert (1771-1783), obtained the first typical differential equations of motion. In solving the dynamical problem of a heavy cord in small oscillation, d'Alembert was the first mathematician to state a partial differential equation as the law of motion of a mechanical system.

In 1739 Johann Bernoulli was the first mathematician to isolate conceptually a differential slice of fluid of mass '*dm*' moving in a pipe, and to introduce the important concept of internal fluid pressure '*p*', with a difference '*dp*' in pressures on both sides of the differential slice as an internal interacting force moving with the differential slice of the fluid. He used a Newtonian type of principle to write down the equation of motion:

$$dm\,(dv/dt) = dp\,,$$

which he integrated along the pipe, rather than writing down the partial differential equation of motion. His pupil Euler immediately recognised the revolutionary nature of the introduction of 'internal pressure' *p* by his old teacher, and he made this concept into a fundamental principle of mechanics that unified much of the existing mechanics of his day. In his book < Hydraulics > (***Hydraulica***) in which he carefully distinguished between the kinematics and the kinetics of nonstationary flow, Johann Bernoulli established the celebrated Bernoulli equation of ideal fluids which Euler later gave in the following modern form:

$$(v_1^2/2g) + (p_1/\gamma) + z_1 = (1/g)\int_{s_1}^{s_2} (\partial v/\partial t)\,ds + (v_2^2/2g) + (p_2/\gamma) + z_2\ ,$$

where p_i is the internal fluid pressure, z_i the height of the fluid particle, γ the density of fluid, and v_i the speed of the fluid along the streamline '*s*'. This seminal work on the general equations of hydraulics for incompressible inviscid fluids was published in 1743.

In 1717 Johann Bernoulli founded the modern ballistics in the famous controversy between Newton and Leibniz about who was the first inventor of the calculus, and whose calculus was superior: Newton's fluxions or Leibniz's differential and integral calculus. A hot-headed partisan of Newton in this international controversy, John Keill (1671-1721), professor of astronomy at Oxford, imprudently challenged Johann Bernoulli to find the trajectory of a projectile moving in a medium which offers resistance to the motion of the projectile that is proportional to the square of the velocity of the projectile by means of Leibniz's infinitesimal calculus. Unfortunately the imprudent Keill issued this challenge in his blind passion to prove the superiority of Newton's method of fluxions before he had made certain that any British mathematician, including Newton, was able to solve this problem. Johann Bernoulli promptly dealt with the proposed trajectory problem by establishing the ballistic differential equation for it and, moreover, he also gave the differential equation for the ballistic problem in which the resistance to the motion of the projectile was proportional to any integral power *n* of the velocity. The ballistic differential equations of both trajectory problems Johann Bernoulli integrated with great theoretical brilliance, virtuosity and elegance which demonstrated the overwhelming superiority of Leibniz's differential and integral calculus over Newton's fluxions. Nobody in England, including Newton, could solve the two ballistic problems. After this disgraceful failure of British mathematicians, Johann Bernoulli subjected the inept Keill and British mathematicians in general to a contumelious public ridicule by calling them ***scurri anglicani*** (English buffoons), an acrimonious mockery that served as the final demolition of the reputation of Newton's fluxions. In their hot-headed partisan zeal, Newton's acolytes were completely unaware that the two Bernoulli brothers had made the differential and integral calculus (***calculus differentialis et integralis***) of Leibniz a powerful tool of analysis, particularly in its application to Newton's theoretical physics which made Newton's physics for the first time theoretically truly productive. Johann Bernoulli introduced exponential calculus, and he was fully justified to regard himself as the 'Archimedes of his age'.

Musschenbroek and Experimental Testing of Materials:

In 1729, the Dutch physicist, Pieter van Musschenbroek (1692-1761), built a testing machine with which he carried out experiments on small-scale iron rods, stone blocks, and wood under tension, compression and bending. He deduced from his tests the criterion for the buckling failure of slender struts by lateral bending under axial loads which are proportional to $1/L^2$, where L is the length of the strut.

Daniel Bernoulli, Hydrodynamics and Superposition Principle of Harmonic Oscillations:

In 1734, Johann Bernoulli's precocious son, Daniel Bernoulli, used the principle of lost forces of his uncle Jacob to give the basic differential relation :

$$d\mathbf{F}^{(a)} - dm\,\mathbf{a} = -\,d\mathbf{F}^{(c)} = d\mathbf{F}^{(\ell)},$$

where $d\mathbf{F}^{(a)}$ is the applied force, $d\mathbf{F}^{(c)}$ is the constraining force, and $d\mathbf{F}^{(\ell)}$ is the 'lost force' acting on a differential element '*dm*' of a vibrating heavy vertical chain. However, he failed to generalise it by requiring that the 'lost forces' of the entire chain be in a state of self-equilibrium. Daniel Bernoulli was trained in mathematics by his father and his older brother Nikolaus (1695-1726), a talented and original mathematician who died suddenly from a fever after swimming in the cold Neva River in St. Petersburg. Daniel earned his doctorate in medicine in Italy at 21 years of age, but was soon called to the Russian Academy of Sciences in St. Petersburg in 1725, together with his elder brother Nikolaus. Daniel Bernoulli made important and enduring contributions to anatomy, physiology, electricity, such branches of mathematics as probability and statistics, and all parts of mechanics. He was the first to give the mathematical definition of work done by mechanical action, an idea which was of major influence in the creation of the concept of energy in the 18th century. In 1738 Daniel Bernoulli gave the first analysis of fluid mechanics in his treatise <Hydrodynamics > (***Hydrodynamica***), his most famous work and the first book on hydrodynamics, which was based on the energy principle of Huygens. In this book, he established the relation existing between the speed of flowing water in the pipe, and the pressure it exerts upon the wall of the pipe. Daniel Bernoulli employed the speed formula in the form $v \propto \sqrt{h}$ instead of $v = \sqrt{2gh}$, but he did not use the important unifying concept of 'internal pressure' in the fluid continuum as his father Johann did in 1739. His pressure was always the pressure exerted by the vessel on the external boundary of the fluid, and not the internal pressure. In this treatise Daniel Bernoulli gave the theory of the reaction to a water jet streaming from a container, and he discussed the jet-propulsion of ships. Daniel Bernoulli analysed hydraulic machines driven by the impulse of a water jet, but he deviated from Parent's method when he implied that if the water jet were to impinge obliquely against the vanes, the maximum useful effect delivered by the water-driven machine would be different from that given by Parent. He also improved the technique of manometry, and introduced the pressure tube, first anticipated in 1594 by Carlo Fontana in the book, <A Practical Treatise of Running Water> (***Utilissimo trattato dell'aqua corriente***). In one chapter, Daniel Bernoulli gave the first quantitative treatment of the kinetic theory of gases , a theory first proposed by Robert Hooke. This book also contained a section on the internal ballistics in which he analysed theoretically the muzzle velocity of a gun functioning by compressed air, and showed that the 'work done' by the expanding air propelling the projectile equals the kinetic energy of the projectile at the muzzle.

In 1741 Daniel Bernoulli was the first scientist to linearise the geometrically nonlinear equation of bending of beams of his uncle Jacob for small deflexions, which is the form normally used in the current practice of engineering. He linearised the curvature change of a beam expressed as a function of transverse displacement $v(x)$ by assuming that $| dv/dx |^2 << 1$, then,

$$1/r \simeq d^2v/dx^2 ,$$

which resulted in the linear equation of the bending of beams:

$$M = B\,(d^2v/dx^2) ,$$

where $v(x)$ is the deflexion or the transverse displacement, and B is the bending stiffness of the beam. In 1739, Daniel Bernoulli informed Euler that the 'potential live force' of the elastica is $B\int(ds/r^2)$ and the differential equation of elastica can be found by minimising this integral. He asked his friend, the Swiss mathematician Leonhard Euler, to solve this 'minimum' problem by variational method, and prove that his minimum principle yields his uncle Jacob's Equation of Bending of Beams, $B/r = M$, a claim which Euler promptly proved in the appendix to his book on variational methods in 1743. Daniel Bernoulli's minimum principle for the bending of beams:

$$\int B\,(1/r^2)\,ds \;=\; Minimum ,$$

is now called the 'minimum strain energy principle'.

In one of his prize winning memoirs in 1752, Daniel Bernoulli suggested the replacement of sails in ships with windmill-like paddle wheel or a screw propeller he had invented.

In 1753 Daniel Bernoulli introduced his principle of superposition: any small oscillation may be regarded as a set of independent harmonic oscillations, each with its own frequency and amplitude. It is a principle of immense practical importance in mechanics by means of which complex modes of vibration can be produced by the superposition of many simple modes with suitable amplitudes. He claimed that any small motion of a string can be composed by a superposition of the so-called 'normal modes', each with its own frequency and suitably selected amplitude. Bernoulli's mathematical principle of superposition was particularly appropriate for the application of the trigonometric series, the so-called 'Fourier Series', to an initial value problem involving partial differential equations of motion, and it led in the 19th century to the so-called 'harmonic analysis'. He is responsible for the idea that a body may undergo small pure vibrations at only one of a series of definite frequencies called 'proper' [also called in German, ***eigen***] frequencies, to each of which corresponds exactly one proportional family of shapes called the 'normal modes', and that the higher the frequency, the greater is the number of stationary points in vibration called the 'nodes'. To make Daniel Bernoulli's principle of superposition mathematically successful the normal modes have to be orthogonal mathematical functions. Since Daniel Bernoulli refused to recognise partial differential equations as expressions of physical problems, he did not consider proving his superposition principle because to him it was rather a new law of physics. Nowadays Daniel Bernoulli's superposition principle is widely appreciated as a corollary to the laws of mechanics. Daniel Bernoulli was the first to compound rigid body motion out of translation and rotation in 1727.

He illustrated his principle in some relatively simple cases by calculating from his theory the frequencies and modes appropriate to the monochord, the flute, the chime and the conical horn, and demonstrating that the intervals of the overtones, the so-called 'harmonics', are generally far from harmonious. The musical quality and transmission of sound are understood today through the analysis of the distribution of energy among the Bernoulli components of a sound as was first suggested by the German physicist Georg Simon Ohm (1789-1854) in a remarkable paper published in 1843, in which he gave what is known as the 'Ohm's law of acoustics', that governs the combination of tones. This law states that musical sounds depend solely upon the distribution of energies among the harmonics and not upon the differences of phase – a law which saved acoustics from a basic confusion by solving the riddle of musical tone. Bernoulli's concepts which were extended and refined in the 19th century underlie theoretical and experimental acoustics today.

Both Euler and d'Alembert did not consider the principle of superposition of Daniel Bernoulli to be mathematically acceptable, despite the remarkable fact that Euler solved a purely mathematical problem in 1777 by means of a method that could have proven the mathematical validity of Daniel Bernoulli's superposition principle in mechanics. Euler solved the following problem of trigonometric series :

$$\alpha + \beta \cos \phi + \gamma \cos^2\phi + \ldots = A + B \cos \phi + C \cos 2\phi + \ldots,$$

where the trigonometric series on the left side of the equation is prescribed, that is, the coefficients $\alpha, \beta, \gamma, \ldots$ are prescribed; whereas the trigonometric series on the right side is to be found, that is, the coefficients $A, B, C, \ldots$ are to be determined. Using the orthogonality property of the trigonometric functions $\cos m\phi$ and $\cos n\phi$, where m, n are positive integers:

$$\int_0^{2\pi} \cos m\phi \, \cos n\phi \, d\phi = \begin{cases} 0 \text{ for } m \neq n \\ \pi \text{ for } m = n \end{cases},$$

Euler was able to evaluate in succession $A, B, C, \ldots$ by multiplying both sides of the equation above with $\cos m\phi$ and integrating each term between the limits $\phi = 0$ and $\phi = 2\pi$. It is downright incredible that Euler did not recognise that the validity of the Daniel Bernoulli's principle of superposition can be mathematically demonstrated by this method, but Euler had a strong dislike of trigonometric series, and only quite late in life he reluctantly admitted that they might suffice to predict 'all' motions of a vibrating string. In 1754 Euler noted that the possibility of superposition of simple modes results from the 'linearity' of the partial differential equation of vibratory motion.

Daniel Bernoulli made fundamental contributions to several branches of mathematics, statistics, probability, almost all branches of mechanics, and electricity. He also contributed to anatomy and physiology. As a physician and biologist, he introduced in his study of the pumping efficiency of the heart the mathematical definition of the 'rate of work', or 'power' by mechanical action which was of major influence upon the creation of the concept of energy in the nineteenth century. In 1725 his memoir won the great first prize offered annually by the French Academy of Sciences in Paris for the first of 10 times, setting a record second only to Euler's 12 first prizes. Daniel Bernoulli, who was also a brilliant experimenter, has never received all the fame he deserves, because as a mathematician he was overshadowed by his friend Euler, a supreme mathematician, and his simple but very effective experimental techniques did not reach the standard of precision expected in the next century. Any phenomenon Daniel Bernoulli investigated, he always constructed its theory first, and only then tested that theory by suitably selected experiments. Daniel Bernoulli wrote: "... there is no philosophy which is not based upon a knowledge of the phenomena, but to obtain any profit from this knowledge it is absolutely essential to be a mathematician." Whilst Euler was making mechanics into a profound general mathematical science, Daniel Bernoulli began to study electricity, magnetism, and physiology, and to write on tides, the nature and causes of ocean currents, and the inclination of planetary orbits.

Euler, Mathematician beyond Comparison:

Euler is not only the greatest mathematician, but also one of the foremost theoretical physicists of modern times. The brilliant and ill-tempered Johann Bernoulli, who considered no mathematician – not even Newton – his equal, finally had to concede and acknowledge the superiority of the prodigious Euler in mathematics in his letter to his former student: "I present higher analysis as it was in its childhood but you are bringing it to its state of manhood."

It is practically impossible to discuss all the pathbreaking contributions of the prolific Euler in science and mathematics in a brief account because of his enormous production of scientific work. In his lifetime, Euler wrote over 800 memoirs and 50 books and pamphlets in all branches of mathematical sciences and in some branches of engineering, as well as in music, philosophy, and even in religion. His average output of scientific work per year was about 800 pages of manuscript. His voluminous correspondence consisting of more than 4,000 letters, on which he set a high value, contained more of his brilliant original work not only in mathematics but also in science, engineering and other topics which he studied: experimental physics, electricity, engineering, chemistry, geodesy, geography, astronomy, philosophy, economics, demography, philosophy, logic, and religion. The classical mechanics as it is taught today largely depends upon Euler's work in mechanics. In differential and integral calculus Euler's notations and many of his results are still being used today. The so-called 'Newtonian mechanics' is actually 'Euler's mechanics'.

In 1727, in his first memoir, Euler assumed a linear variation of extensions over the cross-section of the beam, and as a result of applying the linear Hooke's law he obtained linearly varying tensions over the cross-section. He integrated the moment of the tensions over the cross-section thereby obtaining the bending moment of stresses. In this modern approach to the bending of beams, Euler united the method of Leibniz, who had considered variations of tensions in the cross-section of the beam but had neglected its bending, with that of Jacob Bernoulli, who had neglected the variation of tensions over the cross-section of the beam but had considered its bending. In his first research Euler gave the geometrically nonlinear Bernoulli-Euler equation of flexure of beams :

$$M = EI \frac{\dfrac{d^2v}{dx^2}}{\left[1 + \left(\dfrac{dv}{dx}\right)^2\right]^{3/2}} ,$$

where M represents the moment of the tensions in the cross-section of the beam. In this memoir Euler introduced the modulus of elasticity 'E' that characterises the elastic material and the second moment of cross-section 'I' that characterises the geometric property of the cross-section of the beam in bending. Euler was the first scientist to separate a general principle of mechanics from the constitutive property of the material, and the first to define the modulus of elasticity 'E' for the elastic material as a material constant. This memoir of Euler was published posthumously in 1862.

In < Addition I of Elastic Curves >, (***Additamentum I de curvis elasticis***) of his book on the calculus of variations < Method of Finding Maximum-Minimum Properties of Curves >, (***Methodus inveniendi lineas curvas maximi minimive proprietate gaudentes***), published in 1744, Euler gave a geometrically nonlinear theory of buckling of elastic columns, and the critical axial, or Euler load $F^{(E)}$ which causes lateral elastic buckling of columns. In his later work on elastic buckling of columns in 1776 and in 1778, Euler showed that if an axial tensile load equal to the large compressive buckling load were applied to the wooden strut a very small strain of 0.0007 would result. It was the first theoretical demonstration that very large stresses produce very small strains, and it lent support for the applicability of the Hooke linear stress-strain law to elastic deformation problems. He calculated the modulus of elasticity of wood, $E = 7.7 \times 10^5$ psi, using Musschenbroek's experimental data on the buckling of slim wooden struts.

In 1736, Euler published the first textbook on mechanics,< Mechanics, or Analytical Exposition of the Science of Motion > (***Mechanica, sive motus scientia analytice exposita***), in which he introduced the precise concept of mass-point and presented Newtonian dynamics of the mass-point in its analytical development. In his second textbook on mechanics, < Theory of Motion of Solid or Rigid Body > (***Theoria motus corporum solidorum seu rigidorum***), published in 1765, he treated the motion of solid bodies analytically. These 2 books of Euler established rational mechanics in its modern form, which made mechanics simple, straightforward and easy.

In 1738 Euler tackled the problem of ship's oscillation but discovered that all the principles of mechanics so far proposed were insufficient to solve the problem. He had to introduce a special hypothesis to solve it, which stated that any body has 3 orthogonal axes through its center of mass, about each of which the body may freely oscillate in small motion with arbitrary amplitude and frequency for each, but he was unable to prove it.

In 1744, Euler solved the first 'proper value' [or, ***eigenvalue***] problems by calculating the critical load in the buckling of elastic columns, and the natural frequency of the small transverse vibration of elastic bars.

From 1746 to 1750, Euler was the first to establish differential equations of motion for a general system of mass-points, which are called today the 'Newtonian equations'. Euler saw that these equations represent what today is called the principle of linear momentum which apply not only to the whole body but also to every part of every body. He applied later the principle of linear momentum to infinitely many parts of a rigid body and, thereby, obtained the equations that govern the motion of a top, or a planet, with respect to a fixed point but only after introducing an additional hidden assumption, the so-called 'exclusion principle' which implied that internal forces within a body contribute no motion to the body as a whole [which is false in general, but for rigid bodies it leads to correct results], that led him to claim that the principle of linear momentum is the only independent axiom of mechanics which, of course, is not true. This hidden false 'exclusion principle', that he used as an artificial device which avoided the use of the principle of moment of momentum [which he did not know at the time] in his discovery of the general equations of motion of rigid bodies, Euler had to eliminate in his later researches of mechanics. His analysis led him to the tensor of inertia of a rigid body, but he was unable to prove that every rigid body has an axis about which it may spin freely. Euler recognised the mutual actions of parts of a body upon each other, and the necessity to bring the interacting forces of those mutual actions into the open as specified unknowns. In 1746 Euler discovers that in general a rigid plane sheet cannot spin freely about an axis through its center of mass, and that permanent rotation about such axis is possible only if both products of inertia with respect to that axis are zero.

In 1748, Euler gave the least action principle for deformable elastic beams:

$$\int \mu \, ds \, [\int X \, dx + \int Y \, dy + \Sigma_i \, V_i \, dv_i + (B/2) \, (1/r)^2] = Extremum \, ,$$

where $X(x)$ and $Y(y)$ represent horizontal and vertical forces, and $V_i(v_i)$ represent forces directed towards a fixed center specified as functions of the distance v_i from the fixed center, r is the radius of curvature of the bend beam, $\mu(s)$ is the linear density of the beam, and 's' is the distance along the axis of the beam. Euler explained that the term which represents the work done by the 'stress couple', that is, by the bending moment M in the section at 's', is given by the integral:

$$\int M \, d\kappa = \int B(1/r) \, d(1/r) = (B/2) \, (1/r)^2 \, ,$$

where $\kappa(s) = 1/r$ denotes the change of curvature of the axis of the beam due to the action of bending moment M in the section at 's', and B designates the bending stiffness. The total 'quantity of action' of the bending moment M as a force of elasticity Euler gave by the integral :

$$\int ds \int M \, d\kappa \, .$$

This principle of Euler represents the so-called 'potential energy principle of elastic beams' undergoing transverse bending.

In 1750, Euler tested Amontons' conclusions on sliding friction, and agreed with Amontons that the magnitude of frictional force was ⅓ of the magnitude of the moving load.

In 1771 Euler gave the general dynamic field equations of the bending of curved bars:

$$(dT/ds) + (1/R)V = - F_t + \mu \, (dv_t/dt) \, ,$$
$$(dV/ds) - (1/R)T = - F_n + \mu \, (dv_n/dt) \, ,$$
$$(dM/ds) - V = 0 \, ,$$

where T is the tangential stress resultant, V the transverse shear stress resultant, M the stress couple [bending moment], R the initial radius of curvature of the curved beam, F_t and F_n the tangential and the normal load intensity respectively, μ the mass of the beam per unit length, and v_t and v_n the tangential and the normal velocity component respectively.

In static equilibrium, v_t and v_n are constants and, therefore, Euler's statical field equations for curved beams are:

$$(dT/ds) + (1/R)V = -F_t \ ,$$
$$(dV/ds) - (1/R)T = -F_n \ ,$$
$$(dM/ds) = V \ .$$

For straight beams, $R \to \infty$, hence $1/R \to 0$:

$$dT/ds = -F_t \ ,$$
$$dV/ds = -F_n \ ,$$
$$dM/ds = V \ .$$

In 1744, Euler was able to establish the bending equation for straight beams in its alternate form:

$$B(d^4 v_n / dx^4) = -F_n \ ,$$

where F_n is the transverse load intensity, and B denotes the bending stiffness of the beams. In the vibration problems of cantilever beams $F_n \propto v_n$, which led both Euler and Daniel Bernoulli to the differential equation:

$$(d^4 v_n / dx^4) = -c^4 \, v_n \ ,$$

where c is a constant. Since by 1739 Euler had found his method of obtaining general solutions of ordinary linear differential equations of n-th order with constant coefficients by superposition of particular solutions in the exponential form e^{mx} (m is a constant), he was able to integrate these differential equations and obtain finite solutions. Formerly, he and Daniel Bernoulli had integrated differential equations by means of series. Euler demonstrated that the 'superposition principle' is applicable in analysis as long as the pertinent differential equations are linear.

In 1774, Euler gave a complete statement of the stress principle for planar beams:

$$\mathbf{S}^{(+)} = -\ \mathbf{S}^{(-)} \ ,$$

where the stress vector $\mathbf{S} = T\ \mathbf{t} + V\ \mathbf{n}$, $\mathbf{t}$ and $\mathbf{n}$ denote the unit tangent and unit normal vectors to the axis of the beam respectively, and the (+) and (–) signs refer to the stress resultants acting on opposite sides of the same cross-section in beams. In 1742, in an unpublished note, Euler had calculated the stress vector $\mathbf{S}$ necessary to act at an imaginary cut in a bent beam to preserve its deformed configuration and discovered, like Parent had found in 1713 by purely statical considerations, that a transverse shear stress resultant V was required in addition to the axial stress resultant T:

$$\mathbf{S} = T\ \mathbf{t} + V\ \mathbf{n} \ .$$

In 1774, Euler studied the spatial bending of elastica as the inextensible axis of a beam with symmetric cross-section, in which the local orthogonal frame of reference $\{\mathbf{t}, \mathbf{n}, \mathbf{b}\}$ of Euler [also known as the Euler Triad] consisting of the tangential unit vector **t**, the normal unit vector **n**, and the binormal unit vector **b**, which was a new contribution in this paper. Euler calculated the radius of curvature $(1/r)$ of a bent skew elastica in space, and established various other equations. He derived his spatial bending equation of skew elastica as a vector-valued equation :

$$(B/r)\mathbf{b} = \mathbf{M},$$

where the bending moment vector is $\mathbf{M} = M\mathbf{b}$, **b** denotes the binormal, B is the bending stiffness of the spatial elastica, and $(1/r)\mathbf{b}$ is the change of curvature as rotation about **b** due to spatial bending.

Euler had already in 1736 established the tangential unit vector **t** and the normal unit vector **n** in his famous book on particle mechanics, the first such book published, in his vectorial expression of the velocity and the acceleration of a particle in intrinsic description, which in modern vector notation can be expressed in the form:

$$\mathbf{v}(t) = v\mathbf{t} ,$$
$$\mathbf{a}(t) = \frac{d\mathbf{v}}{dt} = \frac{dv}{dt}\mathbf{t} + \frac{v^2}{\rho}\mathbf{n} ,$$

where t is time and ρ denotes the radius of curvature of the path of motion $\mathbf{r}(t)$ of the particle. This book of Euler is also the first book published on vector analysis. Euler's vector analysis was written in indirect notation, since direct notation is a much later development of vector analysis. In it Euler assumed $d\mathbf{v}(t)$ to be an invariant vector-valued function of parameter t relative to different frames of reference. In particle dynamics a mobile local plane frame $\{\mathbf{t}, \mathbf{n}\}$ was sufficient to describe the motion as the expressions for $\mathbf{v}(t)$ and $\mathbf{a}(t)$ show. The vector **t** and **n** define what Leibniz called the 'osculating plane' of a spatial curve, here representing the path of motion. The binormal vector **b** was not required for the problem of particle dynamics because $\mathbf{v}(t)$ and $\mathbf{a}(t)$ have no binormal components for both are embedded in the osculating plane $\{\mathbf{t}, \mathbf{n}\}$. The bending problem of a beam with symmetric cross-section, however, required the introduction of the binormal vector **b** because both the bending moment **M** and the change of curvature $\boldsymbol{\kappa}$ are vectors directed along the binormal vector **b**. Euler derived the so-called 'Euler triad', the local orthogonal vector base $\{\mathbf{t}, \mathbf{n}, \mathbf{b}\}$ for the elastica bent in space, and gave the bending moment as a vector-valued couple moment:

$$\mathbf{M} = B\,\boldsymbol{\kappa},$$

where,

$$\boldsymbol{\kappa} = \kappa\,\mathbf{b} = [(d^2\mathbf{R}/ds^2) \times (d\mathbf{R}/ds)]/[(d\mathbf{R}/ds) \cdot (d\mathbf{R}/ds)]^{3/2},$$

represents the kinematically defined curvature vector of the bent elastica as a rotation $\kappa = \|\boldsymbol{\kappa}\|$ about the binormal **b**, and $\mathbf{R}(s)$ denotes the position vector of the bent elastica considered as a skew curve in space. In this brilliant work, Euler demonstrated his complete mastery of three-dimensional vector analysis, and his virtuosity in handling the spatial differential geometry.

In 1749, Euler gave the very first formulation of the general problem of celestial mechanics including the problem of three bodies by means of a system of differential equations. In this memoir is the first appearance of the so-called 'Newton's equations of motion':

$$m\,\mathbf{a} = \mathbf{F},$$

in their application to celestial mechanics, something that Newton did not give in his ***Principia***, but Euler did not yet declare that these equations are generally valid for all kinds of mechanical problems including solids and fluid media. Euler's differential equations in celestial mechanics are still being used to calculate the trajectories for contemporary astronauts.

Euler and the English mathematician Benjamin Robins (1707-1751) were responsible for the creation of the scientific theory of exterior ballistics and aerodynamics from 1742 to 1753.

In 1742, Robins invented the first reliable instrument for the experimental measurement of the velocity of the high-speed projectile, his ballistic pendulum. Robins discovered the enormous magnitude of the aerodynamic drag-force acting on the high-speed projectile from his ballistic pendulum experiments, which showed that the drag-force acting on a musket-ball projectile could be as high as 120 times its weight. For low speeds of the projectile, the ballistic pendulum proved relatively insensitive and, therefore, he invented another instrument for the measurement of aerodynamic drag-force of low-speed projectiles, the so-called 'whirling arm', which became the most widely used aerodynamic testing apparatus until the establishment of the windtunnel in the late nineteenth century. The English engineer John Smeaton (1724-1792) used the 'whirling arm' in 1759 in his windmill power experiments, the French naval engineer Charles Jean de Borda (1733-1799) used a redesigned 'whirling arm' to measure hydraulic resistance forces, and the English aviation pioneer George Cayley (1773-1857) used the 'whirling arm' to measure both the lift and the drag force acting upon airfoils.

Robins also discovered the so-called 'Robins effect' [usually called the 'Magnus effect' after the German chemist and physicist Gustav Heinrich Magnus (1802-1870) who investigated the effect of the medium upon the spinning projectile in 1850] caused by the spin of the projectile from a simple but ingenious experiment by means of which he was able to explain the lateral deviation in the trajectory of the flying projectile. In 1747, Robins explained why rifled guns which spin the projectile are more accurate than unrifled guns. Robins was the first to suggest that the motion of the projectile creates 'cavitation' in the atmosphere as an effect of the compressibility of air [which he regarded as a partial explanation for air resistance to projectile motion], that compressibility of air in the atmosphere increases resistance to the motion of the projectile, and that the assumption that the resistance of air to motion is proportional to the square of the speed of the projectile is only approximately valid for small changes about the given speed.

Robins carried out a simple yet fundamental thermodynamic analysis of the internal ballistics of a gun as an internal combustion engine of one cylinder, in which he made use of the isothermal gas law of Boyle-Towneley-Power, Daniel Bernoulli's analysis of internal ballistics in compressed-air guns, and a number of rather ingenious simplifying assumption of his own on combustion. His muzzle velocities obtained by this analysis were in surprisingly good agreement with his experimental measurements. Moreover, Robins found from his experiments that at the projectile velocities greater than 1,100 feet (335 m) per second, that is, near the speed of sound, the aerodynamic drag-force tripled, which represents the first recognition of the sudden change in the aerodynamic effect of air near the speed of sound, a discovery foreshadowing the modern concept of the sound-barrier. It was the first almost 'supersonic' aerodynamic experiment.

In 1742 Robins published his researches in ballistics in < New Principles of Gunnery >, a book which Euler not only translated into German language but also supplemented with extensive mathematical commentaries, corrections of analytical errors, and criticism of some assumptions of Robins. Euler also added the first mathematical analysis of supersonic aerodynamic drag-force, and his derivation of the ballistic trajectory. He simplified the nonlinear ballistic differential equation for low speeds, and showed that the launching angle for maximum range depended upon the aerodynamic drag-force. However, Euler was wrong when he denied the existence of the so-called 'Robins effect' in aerodynamics as the cause for the lateral deviation of projectiles, whereas his own explanation of it was wrong. Euler's annotated translation of Robin's book <New Principles of Artillery of Mr. Benjamin Robins translated from English and provided with many Commentaries> (***Neue Grundsätze der Artillerie aus dem Englischen des Herrn Benjamin Robins übersetzt und mit vielen Anmerkungen versehen***), Berlin, 1745, was the first scientific work on gunnery. 1753, Euler gave the first complete solution of the nonlinear differential equation of ballistics by using the experimental muzzle speed and the aerodynamic drag resistance obtained by Robins, and assuming the aerodynamic drag-force to be proportional to speed squared as first proposed by Christiaan Huygens. Using numerical integration of the differential equation of ballistics based on the trapezoidal rule, he calculated as an example the ballistic tables for particular families of trajectories, which gave the range, the altitude, the speed, and the time of impact of the trajectories. In this book Euler gave the first correct proof of the so-called 'd'Alembert paradox' in perfect fluid dynamics: 'A steady flow of fluid past an obstacle exerts no force on the obstacle'.

Euler is the actual founder of the mechanics of continuous media. He rejected the molecular theories of fluids, which were popular at the time, as 'absolutely sterile' for the establishment of a theoretical foundation of fluid mechanics. Euler incorporated into his hydrodynamics the first field theory in which each point of a region in space is characterised by some quantities of the physical theory that are functions of space coordinates and time as independent parameters. In the partial differential equations, which describe the properties of the field, these quantities represent dependent variables, whereas the space coordinates and the parameter time appear as independent variables. Euler was also the first to recognise that these equations can fail to be sufficient.

Euler established the basic axioms of motion for continuous space-filling bodies after almost a lifelong research of this topic. In 1750, he was the first to propose the so-called 'Newton's equations of motion' in Cartesian coordinates as the new general principle of linear momentum which in modern direct vector notation has the form:

$$\frac{d\left(\int_m dm\mathbf{v}\right)}{dt} = \int d\mathbf{F} \ ,$$

or

$$\frac{d(m\ \mathbf{v}_c)}{dt} = \mathbf{F} \ ,$$

where $m = \int dm$ is the total mass of the body, $\mathbf{v}_c$ is the instantaneous velocity of the mass center, and $\mathbf{F}$ is the resultant equipollent applied force acting at the mass center.

In 1750-1770, Euler employed the principle of linear momentum in the derivation of equations of motion for small vibrations of bars, hanging chains and flexible membranes, where he showed that the principle of small oscillations is a consequence of the principle of linear momentum. In many of these problems he proved Daniel Bernoulli's principle of superposition to be a consequence of the laws of motion. At this time Euler believed that the linear momentum principle is the only basic independent principle of mechanics. Introducing an additional hidden wrong assumption, the 'exclusion principle', and by applying the linear momentum principle to the infinitely many parts of a rigid body, Euler obtained the equations that govern the motion of a top with respect to a fixed point. But by using this method, Euler was unable to prove that every rigid body has an axis about which it can freely spin. In 1755 Johann Andreas [alias János András] Segner (1704-1777), professor of mathematics at the University of Göttingen in Germany, using Euler's work proved that every rigid body has at least three mutually orthogonal axes of free rotation which Euler himself managed to prove in 1758. From 1758 to 1765, Euler completed not only the distinction of mass from weight begun by Newton, but also separated inertia from mass that were often confused in older works. Euler also showed that Newton's second law applies appropriately only to infinitely small bodies or to the center of mass of finite bodies. Almost a quarter of a century later, from 1770 to 1775, Euler discovered that the principle of linear momentum does not suffice to recover the known and accepted theory of bent elastic bars, and he took recourse to the idea of Jacob Bernoulli by taking the principle of the balance of the moments of Jacob Bernoulli as his basis, and by adding to applied forces the reversed accelerations per unit of mass as inertial forces he arrived at the principle of rotational momentum [or moment of momentum] as the second independent principle of mechanics, expressed as a set of equations in Cartesian coordinates which can be expressed today as a matrix equation:

$$d\{H\}/dt = \{M\}\ ,$$

where $\{H\} = [I]\{\omega\}$, [I] denotes the moment of inertia tensor, {H} designates the rotational momentum vector, $\{\omega\}$ stands for the angular velocity vector of the rotating body, and {M} represents the resultant equipollent couple moment vector, all relative to the center of mass of the body. Expressed in terms of Gibbs' direct tensor [polyadic] analysis:

$$d\mathbf{H}/dt = \mathbf{M}\ ,$$

where rotational momentum tensor $\mathbf{H} = H_{ij}\,\mathbf{e}_i\,\mathbf{e}_j = \mathbf{I} \bullet \boldsymbol{\omega}$, moment of inertia tensor $\mathbf{I} = I_{ij}\,\mathbf{e}_i\,\mathbf{e}_j$, angular velocity vector $\boldsymbol{\omega} = \omega_k\,\mathbf{e}_k$, and resultant equipollent couple moment vector $\mathbf{M} = M_i\,\mathbf{e}_i$. Then,

$$\mathbf{H} = \mathbf{I} \bullet \boldsymbol{\omega} = (I_{ij}\,\mathbf{e}_i\,\mathbf{e}_j) \bullet (\omega_k\,\mathbf{e}_k) = I_{ij}\,\omega_k\,\mathbf{e}_i\,(\mathbf{e}_j \bullet \mathbf{e}_k) = I_{ij}\,\omega_j\,\mathbf{e}_i\ ,$$

since $\mathbf{e}_j \bullet \mathbf{e}_k = \delta_{jk}$ where $\delta_{jk} = 0$ for $j \neq k$ and $\delta_{kk} = 1$ for $j = k$, as i, j and k go over x, y, z, and $\mathbf{e}_x = \mathbf{i}$, $\mathbf{e}_y = \mathbf{j}$ and $\mathbf{e}_z = \mathbf{k}$ are the orthogonal unit base vectors associated with Cartesian orthogonal coordinates x, y and z in Gibbs' dot-product [his direct-product].

Euler's almost lifelong study of the distinction between mass and inertia finally resulted in his outstanding papers on the rotary inertia of a rigid body, and on the center of mass of a deformable body. The principle of rotational momentum made it possible for Euler to incorporate the theory of bent elastic bar within the general scheme of theoretical mechanics.

Euler recognised the principle of linear momentum and the principle of rotational momentum as the two fundamental independent axioms of mechanics which are applicable to every part of every body, and that the two principles together are sufficient to give directly the equations of motion of a spinning rigid body without the artificial 'exclusion principle' he had used earlier in their discovery. Euler also gave what is known as the tensorial law of transformation obtained by his extremum method to find the location of the three 'principal axes $\mathbf{e}_k$' of the moment of inertia tensor **I**, the principal moments of inertia I_{kk} of the principal moment of inertia tensor $\mathbf{I} = I_{kk}\,\mathbf{e}_k\,\mathbf{e}_k$, $k = 1,2,3$, in 1752, and more completely in 1765.

Already in 1744, Euler had first used the principle of linear momentum and the principle of rotational momentum as two independent laws of mechanics in setting up the equations of motion for a special mechanical system consisting of n linked bars moving in a plane, but he did not yet declare them generally applicable to all mechanical systems. It took him almost a quarter of a century to do so. The two principles together as fundamental independent axioms of mechanics sufficed to obtain his equations of 1750 for the motion of a spinning rigid body such as the top at once, and without the artificial extra assumption, the so-called 'exclusion principle', he had used to discover them.

In 1752, Euler derived the first potential equation [often erroneously called the equation of Pierre Simon Laplace (1749-1827)] for flow that is irrotational and volume-preserving motion of any material region:

$$\nabla\bullet \mathbf{v} = \nabla\bullet(-\nabla V) = -\nabla^2 V = \nabla^2 V = 0\,,$$

when he discovered the scalar function $V(x,y,z)$ as the velocity potential of the perfect fluid:

$$\mathbf{v} = -\nabla V\,,$$

where,

$$\nabla(-) \equiv \partial(-)/\partial\mathbf{r} \equiv [\partial(-)/\partial x]\mathbf{i} + [\partial(-)/\partial y]\mathbf{j} + [\partial(-)/\partial z]\mathbf{k}$$

and

$$\nabla\bullet\nabla(-) \equiv \nabla^2(-) \equiv [\partial^2(-)/\partial x^2] + [\partial^2(-)/\partial y^2] + [\partial^2(-)/\partial z^2]\,.$$

It was Euler who derived the modern form of the Bernoulli equation of fluid mechanics, and who gave in 1755 the general field equations of hydrodynamics in spatial description:

$$\rho\, d\mathbf{v}/dt = \rho\,[(\partial\mathbf{v}/\partial t) + \mathbf{v}\bullet\nabla\mathbf{v}] = (\partial\boldsymbol{\sigma}_x/\partial x) + (\partial\boldsymbol{\sigma}_y/\partial y) + (\partial\boldsymbol{\sigma}_z/\partial z) + \rho\,\mathbf{g}\ ,$$

expressed in Cartesian component form, where **v** denotes the velocity vector, $\boldsymbol{\sigma}_x$, $\boldsymbol{\sigma}_y$ and $\boldsymbol{\sigma}_z$ are the stress vectors in the Cartesian orthogonal frame {**i, j, k**}, **g** is the gravitational acceleration vector, and ρ the mass density. In spatial description attention is focussed on what is happening in a fixed region of space instead of in a material body as time t goes on. In 1759, he gave a general material description of motion in which attention is directly focussed on the material body in motion. The material derivative $d(-)/dt$ [that gives the time rate of change apparent to the observer following the material particle] is related to the spatial derivative $\partial(-)/\partial t$ [that gives the time rate of change apparent to the observer at the position **r** in space] by the relation: $d(-)/dt \equiv \partial(-)/\partial t + \mathbf{v}\bullet\nabla(-)$.

Euler also introduced the referential description of motion in which the motion of the material body is referred to its initial configuration at $t = 0$, which is mistakenly credited to the Italian mathematician of French stock, Joseph Louis Lagrange (1736-1813), who merely took it from Euler's work.

In 1759 Euler gave the partial differential equation for small vibration of taught membranes:

$$\partial^2 u/\partial t^2 = c^2\,\nabla^2(u)\,,$$

where $u(x,y)$ denotes the transverse displacement field of the membrane, and c is a constant, but he overlooked a few proper frequencies due to a trivial mistake. Euler also applied the linear wave equation:

$$\frac{\partial^2 y}{\partial t^2} = a^2\,\frac{\partial^2 y}{\partial x^2}\ , \text{(where } a \text{ is a constant)},$$

derived from the vibrating string problem, to sound propagation by applying the functional form,

$$y = \Phi(x + at) + \Psi(x - at)\,,$$

which satisfies the wave equation. But since the sound disturbance may contain discontinuities, Euler later used the functional form to represent the sound propagation rather than the wave equation, and gained from this assumption the foundation of his theory of sound with the minimum of physical assumptions as was his habit. Euler's mathematical models for hydrodynamics and wave motion made it possible to describe the transmission of action through fluid continua. The observation that beams of light pass through one another without interference justified Euler to use the linear field theory of acoustic waves to describe waves of light in luminiferous æther which he conceived to be a subtle fluid without shear resistance. The problem of transmission of action through an elastic continuum which can sustain shear stresses, Euler left unsolved, but this problem was solved in 1817 by the gifted French civil engineer and physicist Augustin Jean Fresnel (1788-1827) in his wave theory of light in which the disturbance of a light-wave was transmitted through a subtle linearly elastic æther. In 1766 Euler introduced, and explained, the tensorial components of the rate of deformation in mechanics of the perfect fluid where it is not required, but he did not apply it to elasticity where it is essential.

In 1761, d'Alembert introduced the stream function in 2-dimensional form, $Q(x, y)$, into hydrodynamics:

$$v_x = -\,\partial Q/\partial y\,,$$
$$v_y = \partial Q/\partial x\,,$$

where v_x is the velocity of the fluid in x-direction and v_y is the velocity in y-direction.

About 1740, Dr. Robert Barker had suggested a reaction-driven wheel device, popularly called the 'Barker Mill', which was similar to the hydraulic reaction machine of Philon of Byzantion, and worked like the modern rotative lawn sprinkler, as an experimental proof for Parent's optimal speed of waterwheels. An industrial version of the Barker Mill with 4 arms was designed by Segner as a power source. Using Daniel Bernoulli's reaction theory of water jets, Segner designed a 'reaction-wheel' and published in 1750 two proposals for such hydraulic power machines. In the same year Segner constructed such a 'reaction-wheel' which supplied power to machinery in a flour mill in Nörten, Germany. It inspired Euler to undertake a fundamental theoretical study of the hydraulic efflux turbine as a prime mover in a series of papers from 1750 to 1754 in which he compared its performance to the vertical waterwheel.

In 1754, Euler solved the mechanical theory of the reaction turbine successfully which gave his general relative motion equations by using both a fixed and a moving frame of reference:

$$\mathbf{v} = [\partial\mathbf{r}/\partial t] + [\boldsymbol{\omega} \times \mathbf{r}] + \mathbf{v}_o\,,$$
$$\mathbf{a} = [\partial^2\mathbf{r}/\partial t^2] + [\boldsymbol{\omega} \times (\partial\mathbf{r}/\partial t)] + [(d\boldsymbol{\omega}/dt) \times \mathbf{r}] + [\boldsymbol{\omega} \times (\boldsymbol{\omega} \times \mathbf{r})] + \mathbf{a}_o\,,$$

where $\boldsymbol{\omega}$ denotes the angular velocity of the moving frame, $\mathbf{v}_o$ the velocity of the origin of the moving frame, $\partial\mathbf{r}/\partial t$ and $\partial^2\mathbf{r}/\partial t^2$ the velocity and the acceleration relative to the moving frame, respectively, $\mathbf{a}_o$ the acceleration of the origin of the moving frame, and $\mathbf{r}$ the position vector relative to the moving frame. Euler's only mistake in his fundamental relative motion equations was that he had inadvertently dropped in his algebraic manipulations the factor *2* in the so-called 'Coriolis acceleration':

$$2\,[\boldsymbol{\omega} \times (\partial \mathbf{r}/\partial t)]\,.$$

The water-column efflux turbine studied by Euler is an appropriate power source where the stream of water falling several hundred feet would otherwise require the setting up of inefficient cascades of waterwheels. Euler demonstrated that very high speeds of the turbine are necessary for its efficient operation, and that the theoretical efficiency of the reaction-wheel was far above that of the vertical waterwheel. Euler, together with his eldest son Johann Albrecht Euler (1734-1800), prepared an engineering design for his hydraulic reaction turbine, which was of the efflux type, but it was not built owing to the war conditions which existed at the time in Prussia. However, in 1944 Euler's hydraulic efflux turbine was finally built in Switzerland on the occasion of an anniversary celebration of Euler, a native son of Switzerland, and its efficiency proved to be 71% which is comparable to some modern turbines with similar capacity and head that have efficiencies from 78% to 82 %. Moreover, in 1754 Euler also established the first correct hydraulic analysis of centrifugal and cylindrical pumps. He based his theoretical analysis of the action of the centrifugal pump on the concept of running his turbine backwards, an idea still used in the modern analysis of centrifugal pumps, by reversing the action in his theory of the efflux turbine.

Johann Euler was a competent mathematician and theoretical scientist who won a number of competitions set by scientific societies in Europe. One of his prize winning works was the memoir he wrote on the impulse-wheel, the gravity-wheel, and the horizontal reaction-wheel in 1754 for the competition set by the Royal Society of Göttingen in Germany. Johann Euler's paper was a work of rational mechanics which was based on the theoretical researches of Daniel Bernoulli and his father, Leonhard, but not on experimental results. Since Johann Euler measured the natural power of the stream by the product of the weight of water and its fall, he was able to prove analytically that overshot waterwheels operating under ideal conditions were *27/8* times as efficient as undershot waterwheels. Johann Euler's analysis of the superiority of the overshot waterwheel was a major advance in waterwheel analysis, although he did not completely clarify why this is the case. The final theoretical clarification of the superiority of the overshot waterwheel was given by the French naval engineer Jean Charles de Borda in 1767. Johann Euler published altogether 31 scientific memoirs many of which were written under the guidance of his father Leonhard Euler.

In 1754, Euler proposed the use of involute shapes for gears, but admitted that although the best shapes for gears were the cycloidal and involute curves, it was satisfactory to replace them for manufacturing purposes by arcs of circles as suitable approximations. It greatly simplified the technological production of gears, and remained an established practice for a long time.

It would be remiss not to mention briefly the enormous scope of Euler's scientific activity. He was the leader in the organisation of scientific work in the 18th century. His learned correspondence, on which he set a high value, stretched almost over the entire period of his working life, from 1726 to 1783. The correspondence not only concerned a wide range of mathematical, mechanical, astronomical, physical and optical problems of his time, but also dealt with questions in biology, geography [practical geography such as maps of Russia], engineering, philosophy and religion. Many of his letters are actually small memoirs presenting a theory together with deductions of theorems or indications of a course of proofs, statements of new problems, comparisons of various methods and viewpoints, and so on.

Euler's physical universe, which was 'continuous' to a degree but only piecewise smooth, remained the framework for classical and relativistic field theories without any revisions whatsoever. Euler's remarkable accomplishments in mechanics together with what he produced in optics, astronomy and molecular physics makes him unquestionably the greatest physicist of his era surpassing even Daniel Bernoulli. For instance, he was the first to derive an equation of state for a gas from the kinetic molecular theory. In geometric optics he invented the achromatic lens, his design for which required glasses of high, distinct and reproducible quality. He designed an apparatus for the measurement of the refractive index of a liquid, which was built by his son and remained in use over a century and a half. His published works include a classic treatise on harmony, a superb memoir of metaphysics, and reputable works on statistics, navigation, and geography.

Euler was an important philosopher, a subject in which he was totally independent of other philosophers. His major contribution to philosophy that was scoffed at by his contemporary French philosophists gaining respectable attention in modern times. It is not generally known that the German philosopher Immanuel Kant (1724-1804) derived his metaphysics from his study of Euler's metaphysical writings, but he was not an able enough mathematician to understand Euler's major metaphysical paper < Reflexions on Space and Time > to take advantage of it in his own researches on the subject. Kant's early philosophy was influenced by Euler's work on the subject. Euler, as a supreme mathematician, ranks with Eudoxos of Knidos and Archimedes of Syracuse. Contrary to common popular opinion, Euler was as scrupulous, precise and careful a mathematician as anyone before and after him be they Eudoxos of Knidos, Archimedes of Syracuse, Isaac Newton, Wilhelm Gottfried Leibniz, Johann Bernoulli, Joseph Louis Lagrange, Augustin Louis Cauchy, Carl Friedrich Gauss, Niels Henrik Abel (1802-1829), or Georg Friedrich Bernhard Riemann. He solved many outstanding problems which had bewildered his predecessors; invented new concepts and new disciplines; organised, unified, clarified, and simplified previously disparate theories which were regarded as intricate and difficult; and devised entirely new methods of numerical calculation which he applied to problems of natural science. Euler was the first mathematician to present the derivative as the limit of a difference quotient, to establish the differential calculus on the exact calculus of finite differences, and to show that differentials of higher order were superfluous in differential calculus. Euler gave a precise discussion of the convergence and divergence of geometric series in the sense of Cauchy, and at least one definition of the sum of a divergent series which is acceptable even today for a complex power series. He recognised that the definition of algebraic functions was in general inadequate, and gave a general definition which was reintroduced by the German mathematician Peter Gustav Lejeune Dirichlet (1805-1859) with unnecessary restrictions.

In 1739, Euler discovered mathematically the phenomenon of resonance that was an outstanding example of a purely mathematical discovery of a major physical phenomenon, a phenomenon which had been qualitatively explained by an Italian physician, Girolamo Fracastoro (1483-1553) in 1546, and more completely by Isaac Beeckman in 1618 which Marin Mersenne published in 1635. A few months later, Euler found the general exponential solution of linear differential equations with constant coefficients in his work on forced harmonic oscillators and on elastic rods in infinitesimal transverse motion. In his work on vibration of elastic bars, Euler discovered the wave propagation and the wave reflexion resulting from a partial differential equation. He was the first to publish a paper on partial differential equations, and to introduce the method of separation of variables for the solution of such equations.

Euler's book < Introduction to Infinitesimal Analysis > (***Introductio in analysin infinitorum***) published in 1748 is the most influential textbook of modern time since it made the function concept fundamental in mathematics. This book did for introductory analysis what < The Elements > (***Stoicheia***) of Eukleides had done for the geometry in antiquity. He popularised the definition of logarithms as exponents, and the definition of trigonometric functions as ratios. He distinguished between algebraic and transcendental functions as well as between elementary and higher functions. He developed the use of polar coordinates and parametric representation of curves, as well as the calculus of perturbations in celestial mechanics. He also wrote the first textbook on algebraic or coordinate geometry in 3 dimensions.

His textbooks < Principles of Differential Calculus > (***Institutiones calculi differentialis***) published in 1755, and 3 volumes of < Principles of Integral Calculus > (***Institutiones calculi integralis***) published from 1768 to 1774, contain our elementary differential and integral calculus, as well as our theory of differential equations, Taylor series, Euler's summation formula, Eulerian integrals, and the distinction between linear, exact and homogeneous differential equations still used in modern textbooks. The enormous prestige of Euler's textbooks settled many moot questions of notation in algebra and calculus, which all foremost mathematicians such as Lagrange, Laplace, and Gauss accepted in their works. Laplace called Euler : "...the master of us all."

Euler recreated the arithmetic theory of numbers, in which he discovered more theorems than all the mathematicians collectively had established before him. He discovered the law of quadratic reciprocity in number theory and the addition theory of elliptic functions. He created the analytic geometry as it is known today which was only superseded in the 1930's by the rise of modern linear algebra. He also established the key theorem in combinatorial topology, the so-called 'Euler Polyhedra Formula': 'In any simple polyhedron the number of vertices plus the number of faces is greater by 2 than the number of edges', which was proven later. Unbeknownst to everybody this theorem was buried in an unpublished manuscript of René Descartes.

Throughout his long productive life, Euler was physically handicapped. In 1735 he lost one eye and in 1771 he became totally blind from cataracts, yet his scientific production was not the least affected by this tragedy, since besides being irrepressibly high spirited he had a fabulous memory. The scientific fecundity of Euler was so immense that the volume of work of no other scientist or mathematician is even remotely comparable to that of Euler. Cauchy's mathematical works, the volume of which is impressive on its own account, is a distant second to such works of Euler.

The income from the positions Euler occupied in the scientific academies was high, and it was further enhanced by emoluments accruing from secondary stipends and rewards for particular mathematical works in addition to the first prizes Euler won 12 times in the competitions of the French Academy of Sciences with his research papers, about every 4th year of his active scientific life. In retrospect it seems that Euler, who knew how to invest his income profitably, earned more wealth from his mathematical researches than any other mathematician in history.

Euler dominated mechanics and mathematics in his time longer and more completely than any other scientist in history: every topic he worked on he transformed, clarified, refounded, generalised, and made more profound, thereby making all previous works obsolete. This statement gives the true measure of Euler's genius as a mathematician and man of science.

Postscriptum

The work on kinematics and dynamics by the 14th century Scholastics was the very breeding ground not only for the modern classical dynamics, but also for a number of other basic ideas of modern Western science despite the fact that mediæval dynamics was closer to Aristotelian viewpoint of the ancient Greek science in their emphasis on resistance rather than what is today called inertia in classical dynamics. The forerunners of modern ideas of inertia, momentum, and energy may be found in the theory of impetus proposed by Jean Buridan at Paris. Buridan rejected the Aristotelian theory of projectile motion in ancient Greek dynamics, and adopted the basic idea put forth by Philoponos of Alexandria about A.D. 517, which postulated that some incorporeal motive force is imparted by the projector to the projectile at the launching of the projectile. Buridan quantified this motive force called 'impetus' by defining it to be proportional to the matter and the speed of a body in motion, *mv*, a definition which came very close to the modern concept of linear momentum. Buridan assumed that impetus measures the tendency of a body to persevere in its motion, and that impetus would continue indefinitely if it were not reduced or annihilated by resistance, or by a contrary force. He thought that constant motion requires no force at all after the initial impulse. Buridan inferred from 'experience' with simple phenomena such as lances, ships and rotating millstones, that impetus would endure in a circle in celestial bodies, and in a straight line in terrestrial bodies. Between 1328 and 1350, William Heytesbury, Richard Swineshead, and John Dumbleton at Merton College in Oxford had discovered and proven the basic kinematical properties of uniformly accelerated motion by formulating a clear concept of instantaneous speed, thereby foreshadowing the concepts of the function and its derivative. They distinguished in their researches kinematics, *i.e.*, the theory of the geometry of motion, from dynamics, *i.e.*, the theory of the cause of motion. The Mertonian scholars developed their kinematical results by proven mathematical theorems, and illustrated them by examples from everyday life. They proved the Mertonian mean speed rule: 'The space traversed by a uniformly accelerated motion in a given time is the same as the space traversed in the same time by a uniform motion, the speed of which is the mean of the greatest and the least speed in the uniformly accelerated motion'. The Mertonian scholars replaced the qualities in ancient Greek kinematics by numerical quantities, a revolutionary disposition of the scientific mind of the West which has dominated Western science ever since. The works of Mertonian scholars spread quickly to France, Italy and the rest of Europe, where Giovanni di Casali and Nicole Oresme almost immediately found how to represent Mertonian results by geometrical graphs that connected the physical world to geometry, a scientific attitude which became a characteristic habit of Western scientific thought. Buridan took it upon himself to apply the Mertonian mathematical method to dynamics rather than to kinematics that had been the habit of Mertonian scholars. The concepts typical of the Western science of mechanics such as the function, its derivative, the inertia, and the assignable force, originated in the Mediæval Age and represent developments of mediæval ideas.